MELLOR'S MODERN INORGANIC CHEMISTRY

A COMPREHENSIVE TREATISE ON INORGANIC AND THEORETICAL CHEMISTRY

By J. W. MELLOR, D.Sc., F.R.S.

16 Vols.

A TEXT BOOK OF QUALITATIVE CHEMICAL ANALYSIS

by ARTHUR I. VOGEL, D.Sc., D.I.C., F.I.C.

A TEXT BOOK OF QUANTITATIVE INORGANIC ANALYSIS: THEORY AND PRACTICE

by ARTHUR I. VOGEL, D.Sc., D.I.C., F.I.C.

INTRODUCTION TO PRACTICAL ORGANIC CHEMISTRY

by F. G. MANN, Sc.D., D.Sc., F.I.C. and B. C. SAUNDERS, M.A., PH.D., B.Sc.

PRACTICAL ORGANIC CHEMISTRY

by F. G. MANN, Sc.D., D.Sc., F.I.C. and B. C. SAUNDERS, M.A., PH.D., B.Sc.

GENERAL AND INORGANIC CHEMISTRY

by P. J. DURRANT, M.A., PH.D.

A NEW DICTIONARY OF CHEMISTRY

EDITED by STEPHEN MIALL Editor of *Chemistry and Industry* with the help of well-known experts.

MELLOR'S MODERN INORGANIC CHEMISTRY

Revised and Edited by

G. D. PARKES, M.A., D.Phil.,
Fellow of Keble College, Oxford

in collaboration with

J. W. MELLOR, D.Sc.

With diagrams and illustrations

LONGMANS, GREEN AND CO.
LONDON · NEW YORK · TORONTO

546
m48m

24792

LONGMANS, GREEN AND CO.
55 FIFTH AVENUE, NEW YORK

Nov. 1948

LONGMANS, GREEN AND CO. Ltd.
OF PATERNOSTER ROW
43 ALBERT DRIVE, LONDON, S.W. 19
17 CHITTARANJAN AVENUE, CALCUTTA
NICOL ROAD, BOMBAY
36A MOUNT ROAD, MADRAS

LONGMANS, GREEN AND CO.
215 VICTORIA STREET, TORONTO

New Edition, Revised and Rewritten, 1939
Reprinted October, 1945
Reprinted June, 1946

PRINTED IN THE UNITED STATES OF AMERICA

PREFACE

THIS new edition of Mellor's *Modern Inorganic Chemistry* embodies extensive changes in comparison with the previous editions ; changes which have been indicated in part by criticisms of the older issues, and in part by the extensive development of the subject since the book was first written.

Mellor's *Modern Inorganic Chemistry* was first published in 1912 and very quickly achieved widespread popularity in many parts of the world. It had run to eight editions, several of which had been issued in more than one impression, when it became clear that in preparing a further edition the time had come for a drastic revision and re-arrangement of its contents. The present volume is the consequence. By the time that this decision had been made, Dr. Mellor was, unfortunately, in failing health, and this in conjunction with his very numerous commitments made it necessary for the work of revision to be undertaken jointly: Although Dr. Mellor passed away before it could be published, he had given a final revision to the whole of the joint work in manuscript form; so that the new edition is now issued with the confidence that it has his full authority.

The most obvious change which has been made is in the arrangement of the contents ; this is now so markedly different from that adopted in the older editions that the book has had to be almost entirely re-written. The plan now adopted begins with a series of chapters (I to XVI) covering all the necessary general and theoretical parts of the subject, starting from the properties of gases and proceeding by logical steps to the Atomic Theory, modern views of the Structure of Matter, the Electrolytic Dissociation Theory and so forth There then follows a group of seven chapters (XVII to XXIII) devoted to the elements hydrogen, oxygen, carbon, nitrogen, sulphur and the halogens, and their principal compounds. These elements, for the more part, do not fit very satisfactorily into a treatment strictly according to the Periodic Table, but they do comprise a large portion of the chemistry of any, more or less elementary, course. The remainder of the elements, and their compounds, are then discussed according to the order of the groups of the Periodic Table.

Another change in arrangement concerns the descriptions of salts. These are now given under the heading of the metal concerned ; their treatment under the acids in the earlier editions had given rise to considerable criticism. A standard order has also been adopted for the salts of each metal, so that rapid reference may be facilitated.

The principal further difference concerns the diagrams. A large proportion of these is new, and those which are not new have been redrawn. A number of new half-tone illustrations has also been included.

In carrying out the re-writing and revision I have attempted to preserve a proper balance between theories and the facts on which they are based. Dr. Mellor and I were both of the opinion that there is a tendency, at present, to give the former undue prominence and to treat the facts as of lesser importance Experience as examiners

has shown us that candidates for Scholarships and the like are frequently well versed in the latest theoretical developments and yet have,
at best, only a vague knowledge of the chemical behaviour, or the
preparation, of common substances. I hope that the treatment now
set forth will prove satisfactory in this respect.

Acknowledgments are due for permission to reproduce the following
diagrams and illustrations :—

The Chemical Society for Figs. 35, 200 ;

Edward Arnold and Co., Ltd., for Fig. 45 from Aston's *Isotopes*,
and for Figs. 120 and 185 from Morgan and Pratt's *British
Chemical Industry*;

The Director of the Natural History Museum, South Kensington,
for Figs. 59-65 ;

MacMillan and Co., Ltd., for Figs. 93, 120 and 173 from Partington's *Text Book of Inorganic Chemistry*;

The American Chemical Society for Fig. 180 ;

The Electrolux Co., Ltd., for Fig. 97 ;

Exclusive News Agency, for Fig. 98 ;

F. E. Becker and Co., Ltd., for Fig. 99 ;

Ozonair, Ltd., for Fig. 106 ;

Cornell University Press and Oxford University Press for Fig.
111 from Bragg's *Structure of Minerals* ;

The Times for Fig. 107 ;

Industrial Newspapers, Ltd., for Fig. 115 ;

Eyre and Spottiswoode, Ltd., for Figs. 116 and 117 from Meade's
New Modern Gasworks Practice;

MacMillan and Co., Ltd., for Fig. 118 from Lowry and Cavell's
Intermediate Chemistry ;

Technical Press, Ltd., for Fig. 172 from Martin's *Industrial
Chemistry*.

Thanks are also due to various authors and examining bodies for
permission to use quotations, and questions from examination papers.
The source of each of these is indicated where they occur in the text.
My own personal acknowledgments are due to many friends and
colleagues for valuable help and advice and in particular to Mr. J. M.
Harrison, M.A., Dr. H. Irving and Mr. A. Weston, M.Sc. I have to
thank Mr. Weston also for reading through the whole of the proofs.
My thanks are further due to Mr. N. Wilson for assistance with the
preparation of the index.

G. D. PARKES.

Keble College,
    Oxford.
  March, 1939.

A new impression being now required, the opportunity has been
taken to make corrections of misprints, etc., which had escaped previous detection. All data of physical constants have also been checked
and revised.   G.D.P.
  Aug. 1940

CONTENTS

CHAPTER I

INTRODUCTION

Let us remember, please, that the search for the constitution of the world is one of the greatest and noblest problems presented by nature.—G. GALILEI.

§ 1 Chemistry as a Branch of Science—The Aim and Meaning of Science

THE answer to the question, " What *is* chemistry ? " begins by saying that chemistry is a branch of natural science—or science, as it is more often called. What then is science, and what its meaning?

Science embraces the sum-total of human knowledge, and it ranges over the whole realm of nature. Science is not merely a mass of empirical knowledge gained by observation and experiment, but it is an organized body of facts which have been co-ordinated and generalized into a system. Science tacitly assumes that nature is a harmonious unity, and that rational order pervades the universe. Science seeks a complete knowledge of the multitude of inter-related parts of the universe which act and react on one another producing endless variety.

The edifice of science thus rests upon a foundation of reliable facts. Each of us in his or her daily life receives, through the senses of sight, touch, hearing, etc., many sensations, and through these sensations is made aware of many facts. These facts when stored in the memory constitute our individual stock of knowledge. Recorded, and their reliability ascertained, they comprise the accumulated knowledge of our civilization—but *they* are not science. This knowledge is sometimes known as empirical knowledge ; it describes facts. Science begins by comparing facts. Empirical facts, in consequence, can form a science only when they have been arranged, rearranged, grouped, or classified so as to emphasize the elements of similarity and identity in different phenomena. Accordingly Thomas Hobbes expressed the opinion that the main purpose of science is the tying of facts into bundles. This bundle-tying, indeed, forms no small or insignificant part in the development of science ; otherwise expressed, a significant advance has been made in the development of a science when the observed facts have been codified into a system so that a medley of empirical facts is systematically summarized under a small number of heads. The process of classification and correlation is one of the methods of scientific investigation. Knowledge so systematized is scientific knowledge.

§ 2 Experiment

In order that knowledge may be correlated, arranged and classified into a science, it is essential that the reliability of the facts concerned should be ascertained. Much of the so-called science of ancient times and of the Middle Ages is rendered worthless by neglect of this essential precaution. It is very likely true that few people in these periods really *believed* the more fanciful of the stories then current, but mere disbelief in itself is of little avail—truth is often stranger than fiction. What was lacking was the desire or inclination to *test* the truth of these statements. Stories were repeated by writer after writer without even the slightest attempt at verification.

In the modern period, such statements are submitted to the test of *experiment*. Experiment is the handmaid of science for it is really a method of *observation* which is employed either to test the validity of a recorded statement or when the facts are so masked by other conditions that they cannot be accurately observed unless the obscuring conditions are suppressed. The chemist would not make much progress if it were only possible to observe phenomena just as they occur in nature, and not possible to make observations under controlled conditions. By experiment, it is possible to make combinations of different forces, and different forms of matter which are not known to occur in nature ; to eliminate complex disturbing conditions ; and to observe phenomena under simplified conditions. An experiment has been well defined as *une observation provoquée*. Experiment is useful only when there are conditions which obscure direct observations. The most successful experiment does no more than make a fact which was previously obscure as patent as one that was open to direct observation from the first.

§ 3 Scientific Method—Hypotheses, Theories, Laws

As has been said, facts (whether collected by direct observation of nature or as the result of experiment) are not science, only knowledge. The method of science is to work upon these facts and upon them to found hypotheses ; that is, to put forward suggestions for (or guesses at) explanations or general principles which will serve to connect and correlate a certain body of facts.

It is a popular belief that the aim of science is to explain things ; as a matter of fact, the so-called explanations of science do not usually get much beyond describing the observed facts in the simplest possible terms so as to make their relations with one another clear and intelligible. The description may emphasize the history of a phenomenon, or the conditions under which the phenomenon occurs : in other words, science may explain a phenomenon by describing how one event is determined by an antecedent action—sometimes called a **cause** ; and how one particular set of conditions—the cause—can give rise to another set of conditions—the **effect**. Science explains a phenomenon (the effect) by showing that it is a necessary or rather a probable consequence of another phenomenon (the cause).

Although every effect may be traced to a previous event as its cause, in the physical world, phenomena follow one another as links in an unbroken chain of cause and effect. It is soon recognized that the cause of a phenomenon is an effect which itself needs explaining by some ulterior cause, so that causes can be traced backwards in a never-ending chain of events. Owing to the limited range of man's understanding in a world of infinite complexity, we are far, very far, from comprehending the true conditions, the true causes, or the true reasons for natural phenomena.

The mind cannot receive a long series of details without encircling and connecting them by a common bond which is a kind of *mental nexus* ; similarly, in the attempt to find the causes of many phenomena, man is compelled to build an imaginary model showing how a given set of conditions—the hypothesis or theory—is always followed by particular effects. A phenomenon is then explained by showing that it is bound to occur by the operation of the set of conditions postulated by the hypothesis. Consequently, hypotheses are essentially guesses at truth. The rational observer does not trust to random guesses, but he is guided by a more or less vague intuitive conjecture (hypothesis) as to the meaning of the phenomena under investigation, and experiments are devised accordingly, for

> Man's work must ever end in failure,
> Unless it bear the stamp of mind.
> The head must plan with care and thought,
> Before the hand can execute.—SCHILLER.

The next step is to test the hypothesis by using it to predict what ought to take place in a given set of conditions if it be true. These predictions are then submitted to the test of experiment. An hypothesis thus serves to prompt new experiments and to indicate the conditions under which the search for new facts is likely to be successful.

If, on the one hand, this testing by experiment fails to confirm its predictions, the hypothesis must be discarded and a new one framed and similarly tested. On the other hand, if experiment shows its predictions to be correct, it ultimately becomes a theory and thus an important part of science, for some of the facts which constitute knowledge have thus been co-ordinated and generalized into a system.

A theory must, however, still be submitted to the test of prediction and verification by experiment, and if, and when, new facts come to light which are inconsistent with the theory, it must, like an unsatisfactory hypothesis, be discarded or severely modified. But if every fresh testing serves to confirm the theory and to put its truth virtually beyond doubt it is then called a Law.

The process, therefore, of elevating an accumulation of facts into a science consists in the framing and testing of hypotheses, theories and laws. An hypothesis is a guess which, if true, will explain a given set of phenomena ; a theory is an hypothesis the truth of which, after testing, is apparently established ; and a law is a theory which has stood the test of new facts and of experiment so successfully that its truth is established beyond any reasonable doubt.

To sum up, *science* is *knowledge* organized, correlated and generalized into a system.   The *method* of science consists of the four stages :

(i) observation and experiment for the discovery of facts ;

(ii) classification and comparison of these facts ;

(iii) the framing of hypotheses to account for the facts ;

(iv) the testing and verification of hypotheses, resulting ultimately in the making of theories and laws.

§ 4 Branches of Science

Science, framed from the facts of nature as already described, is a coherent unity ; but the sum-total of human knowledge has now grown too vast to be comprehended in its entirety (even when classified and co-ordinated into a system) by any one man's mind.   The limitations of the human mind thus make it necessary to divide science artificially into departments, or branches, for the purposes of study and investigation.   These divisions are, of course, arbitrary ; for " the divisions of the sciences," as Francis Bacon has said, " are like the branches of a tree that join in one trunk "   Chemistry is such a branch of science—others are astronomy, physics, geology, biology and so forth.

The science of chemistry is concerned with the composition and properties of the different kinds of matter in the Universe ; with the ultimate constitution of matter and of the phenomena which occur when the different kinds of matter react with one another.

§ 5 The Early History of Chemistry

Chemistry as a *science* in the sense we have been using that word is of comparatively modern growth for no systematic study of the phenomena comprised within our definition of chemistry can be said to have been made until the seventeenth century.   But many of the familiar operations of experimental chemistry were practised in ancient times—in fact, chemistry as an *art* is very old.

It is impossible to say when the craft of chemistry originated ; its beginnings are lost in the mists of antiquity.   The extraction of the common metals from their ores—a crude kind of chemistry—is known to have been carried out for a very long period of time, and the preparation of active principles derived from plants for use as drugs, involving the use of many processes now associated with the practice of chemistry, has long been an important feature, even of primitive civilizations.

The great Greek philosophers were in no sense practical men ; they had no interest in the collection of facts by experiment nor in the practical verification of the results of their philosophical speculations ;

but at the same time it is in their writings that we find the first indications of anything approximating to a *science* of chemistry.

Thus Democritus (*ca.* 400 B.C.) suggested an atomic theory of the constitution of matter : it is true that it was vague and based on very little in the way of reliable fact ; but nevertheless it was an attempt to co-ordinate and explain what were believed to be facts about the behaviour of matter, and, in that very limited sense, it was a contribution to the beginnings of the *science* of chemistry.

The same is true of Aristotle's four-element theory : another attempt (based on a meagre foundation of fact and a large amount of philosophical theorizing) to explain the nature of matter. According to this theory, which was more or less current for 2,000 years, all matter consisted of a kind of primordial substance (which was really matter as we know it shorn of its " properties ") to which had been added varying amounts of the four " elements," earth, air, fire and water. The word element was clearly used in a sense different from that in which it is now employed in chemistry ; the modern conception of an element is really due to Robert Boyle (see page 44). To the follower of Aristotle, the term element implied a *quality* rather than a *kind* of matter. It is in this sense, perhaps, akin to the use of the word in the phrase " there is an *element* of truth in a given assertion." Thus, the element earth represented the qualities of coldness and dryness ; air, those of hotness and wetness ; fire, hotness and dryness ; and water, coldness and wetness. The long survival of theories of this type was due largely to the lack of any desire to test them ; but partly also to their very vagueness which, in the absence of the means for real quantitative work, would have rendered disproof difficult, even if it had been attempted.

That many essentially chemical operations and methods were known and practised in classical times is clear from many of the writings of the period which have come down to us. Thus, Pliny's famous treatise on " Natural History " contains, *inter alia*, many *facts* of chemistry, and also describes a great many chemical processes, such as the extraction of metals from their ores and the preparation in a state of purity of many common substances such as alum, white lead, and so forth. Many similar records are to be found in the writings of the classical period ; but they are collections of recipes for the making of useful substances and descriptions of technical arts and crafts of the time and in no sense do they contribute anything to the *science* of chemistry.

Similar accounts are found in the works of a number of writers of Alexandria and the northern portions of Egypt during the first few centuries of the Christian era, and here we find the first beginnings of the traditions of alchemy. It is here, too, that there occurs the first mention of the " Sacred and Divine Art " and the earliest use of the word " Chemeia " for it. The " School " of chemical craftsmen who lived at this period in Alexandria and surrounding districts of Northern

Egypt probably had its origin in a fusion of the philosophical speculation of Greece with the practical knowledge of the Egyptians. The
latter had a great tradition in the working of metals and glass and in
the dyeing of fabrics.

§ 6 The Alchemists

The Egyptian and Byzantine period may be considered to have
comprised the first six or seven centuries of the Christian era. Some
of the earlier writers such as Zosimus (*ca.* 250-300), Democritus (not
the Democritus referred to on page 5 as having propounded an
atomic theory, but another) and Mary the Jewess (who has been
credited with the invention of the water-bath, still known as " *bain-
marie* " in France) were evidently practical people with experience of
the laboratory and its problems ; but the later authors were either
content to write about alchemy without practising it, or else were too
obsessed with the idea of making gold to trouble about mentioning
anything which did not appear to have a bearing on this problem.

Egypt was conquered by the Arabs in A.D. 640 and so the Greek
writings on alchemy passed to Arabia and were soon translated into
Syriac or Arabic, possibly both.

The Arabs were a practical race and a good many discoveries of
chemical importance are no doubt due to them. Perhaps the most
important of the Arabian alchemists was Abu Musa Jabir ibn Hayyan
al Sufi, commonly called Geber (8th cent. A.D.). What purport
to be translations of his works into Latin appeared in the twelfth
century ; but there are conflicting views as to how far, if at all, these
Latin translations are really based on Geber's writings. It seems
likely, however, that at least a certain number of discoveries attributed
to Geber in the Latin " translation " are there wrongfully attributed
to him and were actually made at a much later date. Other notable
alchemists of the time were Rhazes (*ca.* 900) and Avicenna (*ca.* 980).

The knowledge acquired by the Arabs from Graeco-Egyptian and
Byzantine sources, and extended by themselves, gradually percolated
into Europe, and in the twelfth and thirteenth centuries translations
of Arabic works began to be made, especially in Spain, and the " pro-
fession " of alchemy soon rose to a position of considerable importance.
Among the great names of the period may be mentioned Albertus
Magnus (1193-1280), Roger Bacon (*c.* 1214-1294), usually considered
to have been the discoverer of gunpowder in the West, Raymond
Lully (1235-1315 ?), discoverer of the method of making pure alcohol,
and Arnold of Villanova (1234-1312).

This period saw the development of the idea of the three alchemical
elements, mercury, sulphur and salt, into the current thought of the
day. Geber (according to the Latin version) had taught that metals
are composed of mercury and sulphur from which they are generated
in the interior of the earth. Gold and silver were supposed to contain

a pure mercury and a " clean " sulphur ; while other metals contained an " unclean " sulphur. It was thus supposed that base metals could be converted into gold and silver by altering the proportions of mercury and sulphur in them, and by " cleansing " the sulphur. This was the theory underlying the traditional pursuit of alchemy, the finding of the philosopher's stone which would transmute the baser metals into gold or silver.

According to the three-element theory of the later alchemists, sulphur was the principle of combustibility, salt the " fixed part " left after calcination, while mercury was the principle of metallicness contained in all metals. The conception of an element implicit in these theories is still largely that of the Greeks and far removed from the modern meaning of the term.

§ 7 The Iatro Chemists

About 1525 there arose a new school of quasi-chemists usually known as the " Iatro-chemists " or " Medical Chemists." Their aim was to discover the " Elixir of Life " which would cure all diseases and confer the boon of perpetual youth. It was thought by some that the Elixir of Life and the Philosopher's Stone would turn out to be the same ; partly no doubt because of the idea that to change a base metal into gold involved a kind of healing.

The founder of Iatro-chemistry was Paracelsus (Philip Aureolus Theophrastus Bombast von Hohenheim) (1493-1541), whose chief distinction was that he demonstrated the value of many substances for use as medicines and so directed the minds of alchemists from the attempt to manufacture gold to other and more profitable ends.

The beliefs and writings of Paracelsus were, however, steeped in superstition, but among his successors were some, notably Libavius (1540-1616) and Van Helmont (1577-1644) who, though still credulous and superstitious, were yet men with something of the scientific spirit. Van Helmont is to be remembered particularly for the invention of the word " gas " and for being the discoverer of carbon-dioxide.

Some important works written under the *nom-de-plume* Basil Valentine, probably in the sixteenth or seventeenth century, were for a long time wrongly supposed to have been the work of a fifteenth-century Benedictine monk before Paracelsus. Anachronisms in the supposed writings of Basil Valentine show that these could not have been written so early as the fifteenth century and the imposition of Basil Valentine as a pre-Paracelsian writer has been called a " seventeenth-century hoax."

§ 8 The Birth of Modern Science

The course of European history during the sixteenth and seventeenth centuries was to a considerable extent determined by the birth of a new spirit of inquiry : that new attitude of mind and thought associated with that great movement which is called the " Renaissance." There arose at this time a spirit of inquiry which sought to understand the reasons for the beliefs men held, and a desire to seek after knowledge and the truth for its own sake. The infallibility of the past ceased to be a dogma, and the Renaissance, from which historians date the beginning of their modern period, was also the beginning of the period of modern knowledge and modern science.

Francis Bacon (1561-1626), who published in 1620 a work—*Novum Organum scientarum*—in which he sought to define the true method for obtaining knowledge, is sometimes called the " Father of Modern Science." He explained what he believed to be a new way of attacking scientific problems. In his method, the first stage is the accumulation of facts, to be obtained by direct observation and to be scrutinized critically in order to be free, so far as possible, both from errors of observation and from errors due to the predilections of the observer. The second stage is the survey of these facts and the search among them (without any attempt to make them fit in with a preconceived theory or philosophy) for those likenesses and differences from which the conceptions of the common properties and " laws " are to be formed. Bacon thus advocated the method of exclusion, or of deductive induction. This is Bacon's great contribution to science, and although his method of induction is only rarely consciously employed in scientific work, it nevertheless lies at the root of all scientific thinking ; in addition he is to be remembered for his insistence on the importance of careful observation, of the collection of facts and of the necessity for the utmost impartiality and open-mindedness in the correlation and co-ordination of observations.

If Bacon were the founder of modern science, Robert Boyle is usually thought of as the founder of the *science* of chemistry. He was probably the first to study it for its own sake and not for the sake of making gold or medicines (here we see the real spirit of the Renaissance in operation) ; he it was who introduced into chemistry a really rigorous experimental method for the testing of theories and for the ascertainment of the reliability of facts ; and to him is due that conception of an element with which we are familiar. He demonstrated the falsity of the Aristotelian and Alchemical doctrines of elements by showing that by no method available could these so-called elements be extracted from substances supposed to contain them ; and gave as a definition of an element " the practical limits of chemical analysis." That is to say, elements are substances incapable of further decomposition by any means available at a given time. He recognized that substances at one period regarded as elements might later, with the availability of new methods of attack, prove not to be so, but that until such a happening had occurred they must continue to be thought of as elements. Examples in modern times of the reality of this contingency can be quoted, as, for instance, the resolution by von Welsbach in 1885 of didymium into neodymium and praseodymium (see page 674). Boyle thus laid the foundations on which Lavoisier and Dalton were to build a century afterwards.

The intervening period was occupied with the rise and development of the Phlogiston Theory.

§ 9 The Phlogistonists

The Phlogiston Theory was due in the first place to Becher. Geber (about 776) had taught that all combustible substances burned because they contained the "principle of inflammability," and he identified this principle with sulphur. Becher (1667) pointed out that many combustible substances were known which did not contain sulphur and postulated instead the presence of another principle which he termed *terra pinguis*.

This idea was extended by Stahl (1660-1734) in whose hands the terra pinguis of Becher became phlogiston (from the Greek φλωγίστεω I set on fire). According to this theory the conversion of a metal into its calx* was due to escape of phlogiston or

$$\text{Metal} - \text{phlogiston} = \text{calx.}$$

Accordingly, in order to regenerate the metal it must be acted upon by a substance rich in phlogiston. Carbon, on account of its ready combustibility and the small amount of residue left on heating, was thought to be rich in phlogiston ; hence the reconversion of a calx into the metal by heating with carbon is readily explained. In a similar way a great many of the then known facts of chemistry could be explained and co-ordinated and, in fact, if we replace "presence of phlogiston" by absence of oxygen, the explanations of the phlogiston theory become true. The theory ultimately broke down when it was quantitatively tested—its final overthrow being due to Lavoisier (see Chapter XXI), but it had certain defects from the beginning. It failed really to account for the fact that air is necessary for combustion, although an attempt was made to obviate this difficulty by the suggestion that something was necessary to take up the escaping phlogiston. Also the fact which had been known to J. Rey in 1630, that a calx is heavier than the metal from which it is made, could only be explained by the phlogistonists by the improbable assumption that phlogiston possessed negative weight !

The phlogiston theory is sometimes held up to ridicule, but this is unfair both to the theory and to the men who upheld it. It represented the most perfect generalization known to the best intellects of its day and under its influence chemistry throve and multiplied its proportions. It served its purpose for a considerable period, for it afforded a means, lacking before, of correlating, classifying and explaining an otherwise disconnected series of chemical facts. In due course, when it became clear that it was no longer tenable, it was discarded ; but considerable achievements stand to its credit and it

* The process of heating a metal in air so as to convert it into a calx, is called *calcination*. The calces are generally equivalent to what the modern chemist calls "metallic oxides."

affords us an excellent example of the rise and ultimate fall of a theory due to the discovery (through its aid) of new facts inconsistent with it. It may well be that some of the theories of the present day which are regarded as firmly established may be thought of by posterity as the Phlogiston Theory is now thought of, and *our* inexplicable obtuseness and ignorance may well be a source of amazement to them. This need cause us no embarrassment.

A fallacious theory may be a valuable guide to experiment. Experiment and labour applied to the explication of the most extravagant hypothesis is not always lost. Guided by wrong hypotheses men have sought one thing and found another—Columbus sought the Indies, and discovered America.

§ 10 Chemistry at the End of the Eighteenth Century

The latter part of the eighteenth century was a period in which the number of chemical substances known was enormously extended. The pre-eminent worker of the time in this field was Scheele (1742-1786), an apothecary of Upsala and Köping in Sweden, who discovered a great many new substances of all types, among which may be mentioned chlorine, hydrofluoric acid, arsenic acid, lactic acid, oxalic acid, citric acid, tartaric acid, tungstic acid and many other substances. He is also entitled to priority by two years in the discovery of oxygen, although, owing to the slowness of publication and dissemination of such results in those days, Priestley may be credited with having discovered it independently.

Priestley (1733-1804) was an assiduous experimenter and a most capable investigator. He is noteworthy for the work on gases which he was able to carry out after perfecting and adding to the apparatus suggested by Stephen Hales (1677-1761) for the manipulation of gases. With the aid of the pneumatic trough and other apparatus which he invented, he discovered, or prepared in a pure state for the first time, many common gases such as oxygen (but see above *re* Scheele), nitric oxide, hydrogen chloride, sulphur dioxide, silicon tetrafluoride, ammonia and nitrous oxide. The discovery of oxygen, which he communicated to Lavoisier, was probably his most important contribution to chemistry, for in the hands of the latter it became the instrument for the final overthrow of the Phlogiston Theory. Priestley himself, however, remained a convinced phlogistonist to the last.

During the last quarter of the eighteenth century important chemical investigations of a quantitative nature were undertaken, notably by Black (1728-1799), Cavendish (1731-1810) and Lavoisier (1743-1794).

The work carried out by Black at Glasgow was instrumental in clearing up the inter-relationships of carbon dioxide, chalk and lime, magnesia and magnesium carbonate, and caustic soda and sodium carbonate ; and the completeness of the explanations was due to their being based on quantitative data obtained by him. This work is also of importance in that it attracted considerable attention at the time and was thus a means of spreading clearer ideas about the nature of chemical combination than had been current previously.

Cavendish is perhaps most often remembered for his celebrated investigations into the composition of water, which he established on a quantitative basis. The importance of his results in relation to the theory of phlogiston was not altogether realized by him for, like Priestley, he remained a believer in the Phlogiston Theory. His quantitative experimental work was marked by a degree of accuracy remarkable for the period.

A notable example of this is furnished by his experiments on the absorption of air by sparking with addition of oxygen, over a solution of caustic alkali, as a result of which he recorded that he could not bring about the absorption of the last bubble of air, being in amount $\frac{1}{120}$th of the whole. He may thus be regarded in one sense as the discoverer of the Inert Gases (see Chapter XXIV), and it is interesting to note that modern work places the proportion of these gases in the atmosphere at $\frac{1}{104}$th part of the whole.

To Lavoisier is due the credit of having demonstrated that the Phlogiston Theory was no longer tenable and of suggesting and establishing the true theory of combustion. This work is described in detail in Chapter XXI, and is important for its strictly quantitative character.

From the time of Lavoisier the science of chemistry has developed with remarkable rapidity and accuracy, and its subsequent history will be found interwoven in the chapters which now follow.

CHAPTER II

THE PROPERTIES OF GASES

The generality of men are so accustomed to judge of things by their senses that because air is invisible they ascribe but little to it, and think of it as but one remove from nothing.—R. BOYLE (1673).

§ 1 The Gaseous State of Matter

CHEMISTRY (page 4) is concerned with the composition and properties of the different kinds of *matter* in the Universe . . . and the study of matter has led to the recognition of three states of matter, viz., the solid, the liquid and the gaseous.

The third of these states of matter—the gaseous--was formally recognized by J. B. van Helmont, early in the seventeenth century, and it has been said that the discovery might have slipped back into oblivion had it not been emphasized by the invention of a name— **gas**—which he derived from the *chaos* of the ancients. Some, however, have sought to derive the word from the *geist* (spirit) of the German.

Of the three states of matter which are now recognized, the gaseous is that in which the simplest and most uniform behaviour is found when the external conditions, such as temperature and pressure, are changed, and this behaviour is to a considerable extent independent of the nature of the gas. A systematic account of the properties of matter may, therefore, conveniently begin with the consideration of the behaviour of gases.

§ 2 The Influence of Pressure on the Volumes of Gases—Boyle's Law

Robert Boyle having observed in the course of some experiments that a partially inflated lamb's bladder, placed under the receiver of an air pump, became distended when the air was exhausted from the receiver, was led to study the behaviour of air under different pressures.

He investigated the subject quantitatively by means of a U-tube of uniform bore (compare Fig. 1) having the shorter leg hermetically sealed at one end and the end of the longer leg open. He poured mercury into the longer leg so as to fill the bend and reach to the same height in both legs, thus confining a sample of air under a pressure equal to that of the atmosphere. He measured the length of the air space and then poured successive portions of mercury in the open end of the tube. After each addition of mercury he measured the length of the air space, and the difference between the levels of the mercury in the two limbs of the tube. In a tube of uniform bore, the length of the air space is proportional to the volume of the air contained in it, and Boyle was thus able to determine the relation between the volume of a given portion of air and the pressure to which it was subjected, as measured by the difference in level between the two mercury surfaces.

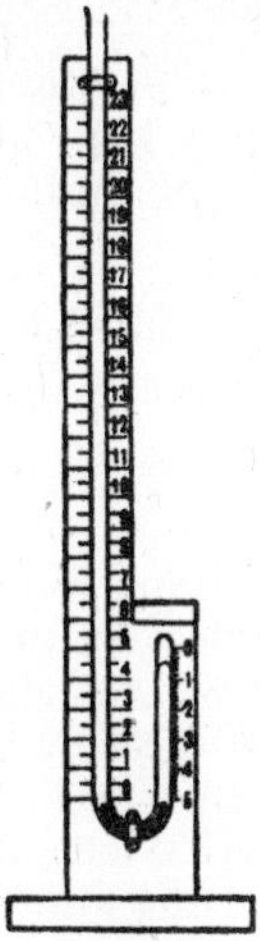

When Boyle had poured sufficient mercury in the longer leg to reduce the volume of the gas in the shorter leg one-half he said, " when we cast our eye on the longer leg, we observed, not without delight and satisfaction, that the quicksilver in the longer part was 29 inches higher than in the other." In other words, the volume was diminished one-half when the pressure was doubled by superposing on to the ordinary pressure of the atmosphere the pressure of a column of mercury 29 inches long and equal to the pressure of the atmosphere at the time of the experiment.

Boyle thus found (1661) " the pressures and expansions," as he expressed it, " to be in reciprocal proportions." In other words, **the volume of a fixed mass of gas kept at one uniform temperature varies inversely as the pressure.** This is **Boyle's Law.** E. Mariotte, fourteen years after Boyle's publication, followed along the same lines, and, on the Continent, the law is sometimes improperly ascribed to Mariotte.

FIG. 1.— Boyle's Law —High Pressures.

Boyle showed further by means of an arrangement similar to that illustrated in Fig. 2, that this same generalization holds good at pressures less than atmospheric. This may be illustrated as follows. Some mercury is poured into a narrow tube which is closed at one end and open at the other. The open end is closed by the thumb and inverted in the tall cylinder of mercury. The narrow tube is raised or lowered, and the volume of gas confined in the narrow tube, as well as the difference in the levels of the mercury in the narrow and in the wider tube, read at the same time. We can recognize the principle of the U-tube, Fig. 1, in this apparatus, Fig. 2. The pressure on the mercury in the wide cylinder is one atmosphere, and the pressure of the gas in the narrow tube is one atmosphere less the pressure of a column of mercury equal to the difference in the level of the mercury in the two tubes.

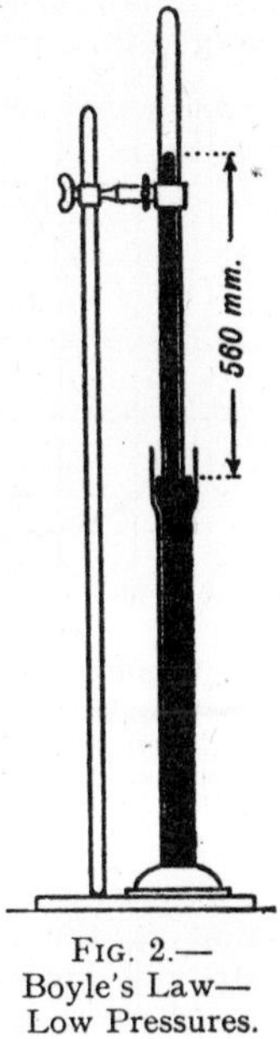

This important generalization may be illustrated by imagining 12 litres of gas at atmospheric pressure confined in such a way that pressures of 2, 3, 4 and 6 atmospheres can be imposed upon it. On measuring

FIG. 2.— Boyle's Law— Low Pressures.

the volume of the gas the following results would be obtained :—

Pressure . .	1,	2,	3,	4,	6 atmospheres
Volume . .	12,	6,	4,	3,	2 litres
Product-pv .	12,	12,	12,	12,	12

The law of Boyle can thus be stated in another way : **The product of the pressure and the volume of a fixed mass of gas kept at one uniform temperature is always the same.** Or, algebraically

$$pv = \text{Constant.}$$

Hence it follows that the behaviour of a gas which is represented by Boyle's Law is graphically expressed by a rectangular hyperbola (see Fig. 3—unbroken curve).

§ 3 Deviations from Boyle's Law

The pressures used by Boyle extended over a range varying from 3 cm. to 300 cm. of mercury. It is hazardous to infer that because the product pv is constant over a limited range of pressures, it will remain constant for pressures widely different from those actually measured. Many careful investigations have since been made, notably by Amagat, to find if the simple law of Boyle correctly describes the behaviour of gases at pressures far removed from the normal pressure of the atmosphere—76 cm. of mercury. The general results show that no two gases behave precisely in the same way. The deviations for many gases are insignificant. With most gases, the concentration increases more, that is the volume increases less than Boyle's law describes ; and at high pressures, the concentration increases less, that is the volume increases more than Boyle's law indicates. This is illustrated by plotting Boyle's law which, when graphed, furnishes the continuous curve shown in Fig. 3. This continuous curve is a rectangular hyperbola. The deviations of nitrogen from this ideal condition are indicated by the dotted line.

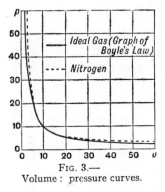

FIG. 3.—
Volume : pressure curves.

E. H. Amagat (1893), showed that while the product pv remains fairly constant at low pressures for many gases, the numerical value of pv changes in a remarkable manner as the pressures increase in magnitude. Amagat's measurements for carbon dioxide show that when

p	1,	50,	100,	125,	150,	200,	500,	1000 atms.
pv .	1,	0·92,	0·49,	0·31,	0·41,	0·50,	1·02,	1·81

that is, the product pv at first diminishes in magnitude and then steadily increases, as is brought out very clearly by plotting the numbers on a graph. If the products pv were constant for all values

of p, we should get the straight line, dotted, and marked "ideal gas line" in Fig. 4 ; with car-
bon dioxide, however, the curve descends below the line for an ideal gas, and then steadily rises, passing above the ideal gas line when the pressure is nearly 500 atmospheres.

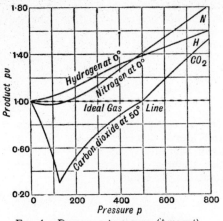

FIG. 4.—Pressure : pv curves (Amagat).

The curves for hydrogen and helium, at ordinary temperatures, do not descend below the ideal gas line, but take a path resembling the hydrogen line shown in Fig. 4. However, even these gases exhibit the same peculiar behaviour at lower temperatures. Thus, with hydrogen at −140°, the product pv reaches a minimum when the pressure is about 25 atmospheres ; at −195°, 45 atmospheres ; and at −213°, 51 atmospheres.

§ 4 Influence of Temperature on the Volume of Gases—Charles's Law

In 1790, Joseph Priestley concluded "from a very coarse experiment" that "fixed and common air expanded alike with the same degree of heat," and J. L. Gay-Lussac, in 1802, quoted some experiments in support of the broader view : **The same rise of temperature produces in equal volumes of all gases the same increase in volume, provided the pressure be kept constant.** This law is designated **Charles's law**, in honour of J. A. C. Charles, who, according to Gay-Lussac, made some crude experiments on the subject fifteen years before Gay-Lussac's publication. Some call this relation " Gay-Lussac's law."

The increase in volume which occurs when one litre of nitrogen at 0° is heated in a suitable vessel is shown in Table I (R. Chappius, 1888) :—

TABLE I—COEFFICIENTS OF THERMAL EXPANSION OF NITROGEN

Temperature θ°.	Volume v. litres.	Expansion per litre per degree.
0	1·0000000	
10	1·0367781	0·0036778
20	1·0735396	0·0036776
30	1·1102875	0·0036775
40	1·1470244	0·0036737

The numbers in the last column—called **the coefficients of thermal expansion**—mean that the volume v of a litre of nitrogen, measured at $0°$, when heated through $\theta°$, can be represented very closely by the expression : $v = (1 + 0.003676\,\theta)$ litres. In other words, nitrogen increases 0.003676, or very nearly $\frac{1}{273}$rd of its volume at $0°$ for every degree rise of temperature. More generally, if v_0 be used to denote the volume of a gas at $0°$, we have,

$$v = v_0 \left(1 + \frac{\theta}{273}\right)$$

This is very nearly true for most of the common gases, for while solids and liquids have their own characteristic coefficient of expansion, gases have nearly the same coefficient of thermal expansion. This is the meaning of Charles's law. The coefficients for the gases run something like this :—

Air	0.003665
Hydrogen.	0.003667
Carbon dioxide	0.003688

These numbers are close enough to "$\frac{1}{273}$" for most practical purposes. In general, the more easily a gas is liquefied, the greater the deviation from the constant 0.003665 found for air—witness carbon dioxide.

By plotting the above equation, we get a straight line which cuts the T axis at $-273°$ (see Fig. 5). If the temperature be less than

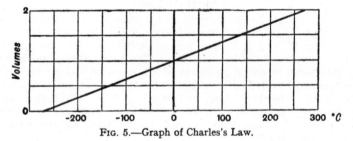

Fig. 5.—Graph of Charles's Law.

$-273°$, the gas would have a negative volume, that is a volume less than nothing ! If the temperature be $-273°$, the gas would occupy no volume ! It is impossible to imagine a substance occupying no space, but this seems to be a logical conclusion from Charles's Law. Where is the fallacy ? Charles's Law includes a simplifying assumption. The apparent volume of a gas may be resolved into at least two parts : (1) the " volume " occupied by the molecules of the gas ; and (2) the space between the molecules. Although, for the sake of simplicity, we assume v is employed to represent the *total volume* occupied by the gas, in reality v should refer only to the space between the molecules, and in that case, the conclusion that $v = 0$ when the temperature is $-273°$ involves no absurdity. Moreover the gas would liquefy before the temperature —273° was attained, and the simple gas law of Charles would not then be applicable.

The temperature —273° C. is consequently supposed to be a limiting temperature—the nadir or lowest possible temperature. Hence, it is sometimes called the **absolute zero** ; and temperatures reckoned from this zero are called **absolute temperatures.** Several other distinct lines of inquiry also converge to this same absolute zero. On the absolute scale of temperatures, 0° C. will be 273° abs. If T be employed to denote the temperature on the absolute scale, and θ the temperature on the centigrade scale, we have $T = 273 + \theta$. Hence, we see that if v be the volume of a gas when the absolute temperature is T, and v_1 the volume when the temperature is T_1, we get, from the preceding equation, another way of stating Charles's Law,

$$\frac{v}{T} = \frac{v_1}{T_1}$$

§ 5 Deviations from Charles's Law

We have already seen that the coefficients of thermal expansion of all gases are only approximately the same. The coefficients for the individual gases differ a little among themselves as indicated above. The variation in the coefficient of thermal expansion at temperatures and pressures not far removed from normal atmospheric temperatures and pressures is not very marked, and for regular gas calculations can be ignored. It remains to indicate the variation, if any, in the coefficient of thermal expansion with large variations of temperature and pressure.

1. *The influence of pressure.*—The coefficient of expansion of most gases is increased by augmenting the pressure of a gas until a maximum value is attained, after that, the coefficient diminishes with increased pressure. For instance, E. H. Amagat (1893) found that the coefficients of expansion of carbon dioxide at temperatures between 50° and 60° assumed the following values :—

Pressure	30,	60,	125,	200,	500,	1000 atm.
Coefficients	0·0069,	0·0085,	0·0410,	0·0085,	0·0033,	0·0018

Carbon dioxide thus shows a marked variation in the coefficient of thermal expansion at high pressures. The coefficient also diminishes as the pressure is reduced. The variation is not so marked with gases like nitrogen, oxygen, and hydrogen which are not easily condensed to the liquid condition. The value of p which furnishes the greatest coefficient of thermal expansion is that same value of p which gives the minimum product pv, p. 15. At ordinary temperatures, therefore, hydrogen and helium do not exhibit this variation in the value of their coefficients of expansion, and the coefficient of expansion steadily diminishes with increasing pressure.

2. *The influence of temperature.*—The maximum value for the coefficient of expansion with increasing pressure just indicated becomes

less and less as the temperature is raised and finally disappears. So does the minimum value of the product pv become less and less marked as the temperature is raised. The gradual "flattening" of the carbon dioxide curves as the temperature rises from 40° to 100° is brought out very clearly in Fig. 6. We have seen, p. 15, that all gases exhibit a minimum value for pv. The pressure required for the minimum depends on the temperature as well as on the nature of the gas. The minimum is most marked when the gas is near its critical temperature (p. 34). If the temperature is much

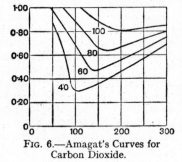

FIG. 6.—Amagat's Curves for Carbon Dioxide.

above the critical temperature, the minimum is very small—with hydrogen the minimum is inappreciable at 0°—Fig. 4. All other gases show a minimum at ordinary temperatures. Hence, Regnault, who discovered this phenomenon, was led to say that hydrogen is a "*gaz plus que parfait.*" But hydrogen also shows the minimum at reduced temperatures as indicated on p. 15.

§ 6 The General Gas Equation

Boyle's Law, expressed mathematically in the form $pv = $ Constant, and Charles's Law, which may similarly be expressed in the form $v/T = $ Constant, when combined into one equation give us a mathematical expression for the variation in the volume of a gas when temperature and pressure both vary. This combined equation is:

$$\frac{pv}{T} = \text{Constant.}$$

In this expression, when the quantity of gas concerned is a gram-molecule (see page 77), the constant is usually denoted by R and called the **gas constant,** so that the equation becomes

$$pv = RT,$$

when it is known as the **General Gas Equation.**

In the form

$$\frac{pv}{T} = \text{Constant,}$$

this equation is frequently employed in calculations involving variations in the volumes of gases due to changes in temperature and pressure. Thus, the volume is often determined at the temperature of the laboratory and at a pressure not equal to the standard pressure, whereas for chemical purposes it is usually necessary to know the volume at **standard (or normal) temperature and pressure,** that is, at 0° C. and 760 mm. pressure ; conditions which are often referred to by the abbreviations S.T.P. or N.T.P.

If p, v and T respectively denote the pressure, volume and absolute temperature of a given mass of gas under one set of conditions, and p_1, v_1 and T_1 tne pressure, volume and absolute temperature under another set of conditions, then from the above expression,

$$\frac{pv}{T} = \frac{p_1 v_1}{T_1}$$

Let us suppose that a gas measures 170 c.c. at a pressure of 735 mm. of mercury and at a temperature of 15° C., and that it is required to find its volume at normal temperature and pressure. We then have $p = 760$, $T = 273$, $T_1 = 288$, $v_1 = 170$ and $p_1 = 735$, while v is the volume required. Hence

$$\frac{760 \times v}{273} = \frac{735 \times 170}{288}$$

$$\therefore v = \frac{735 \times 170 \times 273}{288 \times 760} = 155 \cdot 8 \text{ c.c.}$$

§ 7 Dalton's Law of Partial Pressures

When two gases, which do not act chemically on one another, under the conditions of the experiment, are brought together, they mix intimately, by diffusion, so as to form an homogeneous mixture, and John Dalton (1802) found that in such a case each gas seemed to exert the same pressure as if it alone occupied the space ; the total pressure of the mixture of gases being the sum of the several pressures due to each gaseous component of the mixture. That is, if P be employed to denote the total pressure of the mixture, p_1 the partial pressure exerted by one of the gases, and p_2 the partial pressure exerted by the other gas, $P = p_1 + p_2$. In words, **in a mixture of gases which exert no physical or chemical action on one another, each gas exerts the same pressure as if it alone occupied the entire vessel, and the total pressure is the sum of the partial pressures due to each gas.** This is Dalton's law of partial pressures. It is independent of Boyle's Law, and can be extended to mixtures of any number of gases.

This law only holds strictly for perfect gases. The behaviour of actual gases deviates in greater or less degree from that indicated by Boyle's Law, and furthermore, it is highly probable that the molecules of nearly all gases exert some attractive influence on one another, and the gases will, in consequence of this *physical* action, " deviate " from Dalton's Law to an extent dependent upon the magnitude of the inter-molecular attraction. Many mixtures of gases show slight, but marked deviations from the law, e.g., carbon dioxide and sulphur dioxide ; hydrogen with air and with nitrogen, etc.

Thus, for example, when a given quantity of carbon dioxide at 760 mm. pressure is allowed to expand to twice its volume (at the ordinary temperature) its pressure does not fall quite to 380 mm. but becomes 381·1 mm. If, therefore, a mixture be made of equal volumes of hydrogen and carbon dioxide, both at afmospheric pressure, so that the final volume is twice that of either gas in the first place, the final pressure would be not 760 mm. but 761·1 mm.

A common application of Dalton's Law is the calculation at normal temperature and pressure of the volume of a gas measured when collected over water. At ordinary temperatures, water exerts a considerable vapour pressure, and the space occupied by the gas whose volume has been measured is also occupied by water vapour. Hence, by Dalton's Law, the total pressure exerted (and measured) is equal to the actual pressure of the gas in question plus the pressure of the water vapour present. It follows, therefore, that in carrying out the necessary calculation, the value to be used for the pressure of the gas must be the observed pressure minus the pressure of the water vapour present along with the gas. This value, which is the maximum pressure of water vapour at the temperature of the experiment, is taken from tables (see page 31).

§ 8 The Density of a Gas

The density of a gas or vapour can be expressed in two ways, viz.,

(i) the *normal* or *absolute density*, which is the weight in grams of 1 litre of the gas measured at 0° C. and 760 mm. pressure, the weights being corrected to sea-level at latitude 45° ;

(ii) the *relative density* which is the weight of a given volume of the gas divided by the weight of an equal volume of hydrogen, measured and weighed under identical conditions.

The implications of the first of these ways of expressing density are those which concern us here. Relative density and its importance will be discussed later (see page 69).

The determination of the absolute densities of gases with a high degree of accuracy requires experimental skill of a high order and calls for the use of delicate apparatus which includes many refinements.

Three methods are available :

(i) the Globe (or Regnault's) Method ;
(ii) the Volumeter Method ;
(iii) the Buoyancy (microbalance) Method.

The Globe Method

In this method, an evacuated globe is weighed, filled at a known pressure and temperature with the gas, and then re-weighed. The volume of the globe is then determined by filling it with water and weighing it again.

In order to obtain results of the highest order of accuracy many precautions have to be taken and corrections must be applied for those errors that cannot be entirely eliminated.

The following are the principal precautions and allowances which have to be made :—

(i) the globe must be *absolutely dry* ;

(ii) the gas in the globe should be as nearly as possible at *a temperature of 0° C. and a pressure of 760 mm. of mercury* ;

(iii) to avoid errors due to condensation of moisture on the outside of the glass globe and to allow for changes in the humidity, temperature and pressure of the air in the balance room, the globe is *counterbalanced against an exactly similar globe* and the two globes are always treated in the same manner ;

(iv) a correction must be applied for the *shrinkage* of the globe when evacuated ;

(v) the results must be corrected for the *latitude* and *height above sea-level* of the place where the observations are made.

In addition to the above errors may arise owing to adsorption (that is to say, the formation of a very thin, " condensed " layer) of the gas on the walls of the globe. This tends to make the results too high, but with the permanent gases the effect is very small.

The amount of the correction to be applied for the shrinkage of the globe on evacuation is determined as follows: The globe is mounted inside a closed vessel with its stem passing through one of two holes in the stopper of the vessel. A calibrated, vertical capillary tube is fixed into the other hole and the vessel is filled with water and immersed in a constant temperature bath. The globe is then evacuated and the extent of the fall of the water-level in the capillary tube is observed, from which the amount of the contraction of the globe can be calculated.

In order to correct for latitude and height above sea-level the value for the density calculated and corrected as above must be divided by

$$(1 - 0 \cdot 0026 \cos 2 \lambda - 0 \cdot 000000196 \ h)$$
where $\lambda =$ latitude of the place of observation
and $h =$ height of the place of observation
above sea-level (in metres).

Notable examples of the use of this method are furnished by the work of Lord Rayleigh on the densities of the common permanent gases (compare pp. 94, 538) and of Morley (1895) on the densities of hydrogen and oxygen.

The Volumeter Method

In this method, the weight of gas, whose volume, temperature and pressure have been measured, is determined either by releasing the gas from an apparatus which delivers only pure, dry gas (for example, hydrogen absorbed in palladium may be driven off by heating) or by absorbing the gas in a suitable absorbent and determining the increase in weight of the absorption apparatus. A convenient absorbent is charcoal, contained in a bulb immersed in liquid air.

The volumeter method permits the use of large quantities of gas, since the apparatus used for measuring the volume does not require to be weighed and therefore need not be portable, nor restricted to such dimensions as enable it to be attached to a balance.

This method was employed by Guye and Pintza for determining the density of nitrogen and may be understood from Fig. 7, which shows their apparatus in a simplified form.

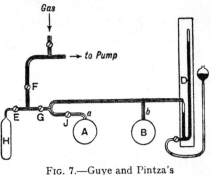

FIG. 7.—Guye and Pintza's Volumeter Method.

The apparatus consisted of two globes, A and B, attached to a manometer D, to a tube H containing coconut charcoal, to a pump and to a source of the gas under examination by means of tubing and suitably disposed glass taps. The volumes of A and B were determined by finding the weight of water filling them at 0°. The volume of the "dead-space" between "a" and "b" and the tap G and the zero of the manometer were also found. The tube H (actually attached to the apparatus by a ground joint) was evacuated and weighed. The whole apparatus was then evacuated and the gas whose density was to be found was allowed to enter slowly until the pressure in the apparatus was approximately that of the atmosphere. A and B were then immersed in melting ice, F and G were closed, the manometer adjusted to the zero mark and the pressure of the gas was then read. EFG was next evacuated, F was closed, E, G and J were opened, H was cooled in liquid air and so the gas was practically all absorbed in H. Taps E and G were then closed and the pressure of residual gas measured. The gas contained in the space EFG was pumped out and measured, while H was removed and re-weighed. The weight of gas absorbed was thus known, and from the difference in pressure before and after the experiment, and the amount of gas in the "dead-space," the volume of the gas absorbed could be calculated, and hence the density.

The Buoyancy Method

This method, which employs a microbalance, depends upon measurement of the pressure of the gas when buoying up a small quartz bulb immersed in the gas by a fixed amount.

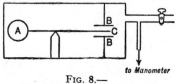

to Manometer

FIG. 8.—
Microbalance (diagrammatic).

The apparatus consists of a small quartz bulb A (Fig. 8) of about 0·5 c.c. capacity, evacuated and attached to a quartz beam resting on a knife edge. Excessive motion of the beam is prevented by the plates BB. The apparatus is evacuated and the gas is then allowed to enter until the end of the beam C is at the zero position on the scale of an observing telescope through which it is viewed.

The pressure of the gas is measured, and the process is exactly repeated with oxygen. It is then easy to see that the normal densities of the two gases ρ and ρ' are inversely proportional to the pressures observed (p and p'), i.e.,

$$\frac{\rho}{\rho'} = \frac{p'}{p}$$

whence the unknown density of the gas under examination can be calculated from the known density of oxygen.

The method is valuable since it is capable of great precision, it requires only a small amount of gas, and can be carried out relatively quickly. Low pressures are employed, for under these conditions Boyle's Law may be considered to express accurately the behaviour of the gases.

The determination of the densities of gases with a high degree of accuracy finds an important application in the evaluation of atomic weights : by furnishing a check on values obtained by purely chemical methods when these are possible ; by furnishing one of the few available physical means for determining these constants when, as in the case of the inert gases, chemical methods are not available. Further details of the method will be given later (see p. 103).

§ 9 The Diffusion of Gases—Graham's Law

If a jar of a light gas, such as hydrogen, be inverted over another jar containing a much heavier gas, like air, it might perhaps be expected that the samples of the two gases would maintain their relative positions, at any rate for some considerable time. In point of fact the two gases—hydrogen and air—will spread throughout the two vessels in a short time and in such a way that the two cylinders will enclose a homogeneous mixture of air and hydrogen. This phenomenon is known as **diffusion** and is closely related to the behaviour of a gas which, when confined in a vessel under a pressure, is allowed to escape through a small orifice. This latter process is called **effusion.**

Döbereiner observed in 1823 that hydrogen, collected over water in a cracked flask, escaped into the surrounding air and that the water rose in the neck of the flask. This observation indicates that gases diffuse at different rates and these facts may be demonstrated qualitatively by means of the following experiments.

Porous pots containing air are fixed to the ends of bent tubes as shown in Figs. 9 and 10. A cylinder of hydrogen is brought over the one porous pot, Fig. 9. Hydrogen diffuses through the walls of the pot faster than the air can diffuse outwards. Consequently, the pressure of the gas inside the porous pot will increase. This is shown by the motion of the coloured liquid in the U-tube away from the porous pot. Before the cylinder of hydrogen was placed over the porous pot, the air diffused inwards and outwards through the pot at the same rate. Repeating the experiment, Fig. 10, with a cylinder of carbon dioxide instead of hydrogen, the air moves outwards from the porous pot faster than the carbon dioxide can pass inwards. Conse-

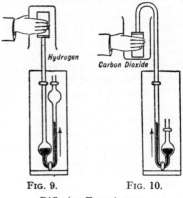

Fig. 9.   Fig. 10.

Diffusion Experiments.

quently, there is a reduction in the pressure of the gases in the porous pot. This is shown by the motion of the liquid in the U-tube towards the porous pot.

If the liquid in the leg of the U-tube be connected with a battery and electric bell, and if a wire be fused in the leg of the U-tube so that when the liquid rises electric contact is made, the bell will ring. A device based on this principle has been suggested as an alarm indicator for the escape of coal gas in rooms, or fire-damp in coal mines. These gases, like hydrogen, diffuse through the walls of porous pots faster than the air can escape. The experiments, Fig. 9, can be modified so that the liquid is sprayed from the tube like a miniature fountain.

The ready diffusion of gas through the walls of buildings plays a part in ventilation. Most building materials are porous, and permit the passage of gases through them in both directions. The diffusion does not take place so readily when the walls are saturated with moisture—e.g., new buildings, etc.

The quantitative aspect of diffusion was investigated by Thomas Graham (1832). His measurements were made in a series of experiments in which narrow tubes of from 6 to 12 inches in length were closed at one end by means of thin, porous plugs of plaster of Paris. (In some later experiments tubes with a bulb in the middle were employed.) These were filled with the gas under examination and confined over water (or other suitable liquid according to the nature of the gas being investigated) and diffusion allowed to take place. After the lapse of a given time, the gas remaining in the tube was analysed in order to determine the amount of gas remaining and the amount of air which had entered by diffusion. From the results of these experiments, Graham was able to show that the speed at which a gas can diffuse or travel through a thin porous membrane is related to the density of the gas.

For example, under similar conditions, hydrogen diffuses nearly four times as fast as oxygen ; the relative densities of hydrogen and oxygen are nearly as $1 : 16$; and the relative rates of diffusion of the two gases are nearly as $\sqrt{16} : \sqrt{1}$; i.e., as $4 : 1$. Thus we have **Graham's Law of diffusion : under comparable conditions the relative speeds of diffusion of gases are inversely proportional to the square roots of their relative densities.** Graham measured the speed of diffusion of gases through thin porous plates, and found the numbers indicated in the last column of the subjoined table recalculated to $H = 1$ instead of air = 1 (Table II). The preceding column represents the theoretical numbers calculated on the assumption that the speeds of diffusion are inversely as the relative densities. The observed numbers for the speeds of diffusion agree very closely with those obtained by calculation.

TABLE II—SPEEDS OF DIFFUSION OF SOME GASES AND GRAHAM'S LAW

Gas.	Relative density $H = 1$.	Calculated speed of diffusion from $\dfrac{1}{\sqrt{\text{relative density.}}}$	Observed speed of diffusion (Hydrogen = 1)
Hydrogen . . .	1	1	1
Methane (CH_4) . .	8	0·354	0·351
Carbon monoxide (CO) .	14	0·267	0·278
Nitrogen . . .	14	0·267	0·265
Oxygen . . .	16	0·250	0·248
Carbon dioxide (CO_2) .	22	0·213	0·212

A convenient form of apparatus for comparing the rates of diffusion of gases is illustrated in Fig. 11.

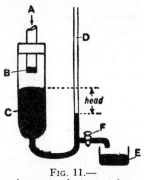

The gas under examination is admitted by way of the tube A which is closed at B by a porous plug. The vessel C and the gauge tube D contain mercury. When the tap F is turned, mercury runs out of the apparatus into the dish E, but the level of the mercury falls more rapidly in D than in C. As a consequence gas is drawn into the apparatus through B. When an experiment is in progress a constant " head " of mercury is maintained by adjusting the tap F, and the rate at which mercury collects in the weighed dish, E, then gives a measure of the velocity of diffusion of the given gas under the given

Fig. 11.—
Apparatus for comparing
Rates of Diffusion of Gases.

conditions. In order to compare the rates of diffusion of different gases it is necessary to arrange that the " head " of mercury, and other experimental conditions, e.g., temperature, are the same in each case.

§ 10 Applications of Graham's Law

Two practical applications of Graham's law have been made :
(1) for the separation of mixed gases ;
(2) for the determination of the density of gases.

If a slow current of a mixture of two gases of different densities be passed through a porous tube, the lighter gas will diffuse through the walls of the tube more rapidly than the heavier. Thus, for example, if a slow current of electrolytic gas, that is, the mixture of hydrogen and oxygen obtained by the electrolysis of water, be allowed to pass through the stem of a " church-warden " clay pipe, and the gas issuing from the pipe be collected in a gas trough, the gas thus collected will no longer explode when brought in contact with a flame. On the contrary, it will rekindle a glowing chip of wood, showing that oxygen is present. This phenomenon—the separation of one gas from another by diffusion—has been called, by Graham, **atmolysis**—$\dot{\alpha}\tau\mu\acute{o}s$ (atmos), vapour ; $\lambda\acute{v}\omega$ (lyo), I loosen.

This method has been successfully applied to the separation of the isotopes of neon (see page 134). The densities of these two isotopes are 10 and 11 respectively (compared to hydrogen), so that their rates

of diffusion are as $\dfrac{1}{\sqrt{10}} : \dfrac{1}{\sqrt{11}} = 1\cdot0 : 0\cdot953$. The separation is there-

fore only slight and it is necessary to repeat the process many times to obtain an appreciable separation.

The application of Graham's Law was made use of by Soret (1868) in determining the density of ozone (see page 317). Ladenburg later (1898) also employed the same method. He found that ozonized air required 367·4 seconds to diffuse under conditions where pure oxygen required 430 seconds : so that the density of the ozonized air is 1·3689, taking the density of oxygen as unity.

§ 11 The Kinetic Theory of Gases

The properties of gases and the laws describing their behaviour when the conditions to which they are subjected are altered have so far been discussed from the purely experimental standpoint, and the laws concerned have been arrived at mainly as a result of inductive reasoning based upon the facts provided by experiment. It is now necessary to consider what hypothesis or theory can be employed to bring these laws into relation with each other.

It is evident that matter must be either a discrete or a continuous medium. Our study of diffusion in solids, liquids and gases leads us to reject the hypothesis that matter is continuous, for how can two continuous media occupy the same space at the same time ? Our study of the compressibility of gases—Boyle's Law—leads to the same view. How can a continuous medium on rarefaction (that is, diminution of pressure) expand indefinitely ? How can compression diminish the volume of matter itself ? If matter be discrete, we can readily answer these queries. Compression involves a closer packing or a crowding together of the particles by diminishing the space between them.

Conversely, rarefaction involves an increase of the space between them, so that they become less closely packed and less crowded together. If matter be discrete we can also understand how one substance can diffuse into another—e.g., hydrogen into air.

A study of the physical and the chemical properties of matter has thus led to one conclusion : **Matter is discrete, not continuous ; and it is made up of minute particles called molecules.** This hypothesis is called the molecular theory of matter.

Are the molecules stationary or in motion ? Here again the phenomenon of diffusion has led us to assume that the molecules are in rapid motion. How could gases diffuse one into the other in such a remarkable way if the molecules were at rest ? Diffusion and the fact that a mixture of gases with different densities shows no signs of settling, compel us to assume that the molecules are in a state of incessant motion, and that they are travelling in all directions.

They seem to lead a more or less independent existence. They appear to be continually moving with a great velocity in sensibly straight lines in all directions. The molecules in their travels must be continually colliding with one another and bombarding the walls of the containing vessel. Thus the molecules continually change their speed and directions.

It is clear that an outward pressure must be exerted on the sides of the vessel every time a molecule strikes the boundary walls. The moving molecules must be perfectly elastic so that after each collision they rebound with the same velocity as before ; otherwise, their momentum would decrease with each collision, and the pressure of a gas would decrease with time, which it does not. Hence, it is inferred that the **molecules are in a state of perpetual motion.**

This description of the probable nature of gases is known as the *Kinetic Theory of Gases* and its principal assumptions may be summarized as follows :—

(i) the particles or molecules comprising a gas are in a state of perpetual motion ;

(ii) these molecules move in all directions in straight lines ;

(iii) the molecules are continually colliding with each other and with the walls of the vessel in which the gas is confined so that they are constantly changing their speed and direction ;

(iv) these collisions are perfectly elastic so that no energy is lost in these collisions.

§ 12 Deduction of the Gas Laws from the Kinetic Theory

On the basis of the above assumptions and two further ones, viz. :
  (a) that the molecules of a gas are of negligible size in comparison with the space they occupy,
and (b) that the molecules do not exert any attraction on each other ;
  it is possible to make some important deductions.

Suppose that we have confined in a cube whose sides are l cm. long, n molecules of gas, each of mass m, and let the mean velocity of the molecules be V.* The moving molecules will follow in fact a zig-zag path, but this irregular movement can be resolved into three component directions at right-angles. Since there is no tendency for the molecules to accumulate at any part of the cube, we assume that $\frac{1}{3}n$ molecules are travelling with a velocity V parallel to any particular edge, and therefore perpendicular to the two corresponding faces of the cube. One molecule moving with a velocity V will take l/V seconds to pass from side to side, and it will therefore strike a side $\frac{1}{2}V/l$ times per second. At each collision with the face of the cube, the velocity of the molecule is reversed in direction so that its momentum changes from mV to $-mV$; that is, its momentum changes $2mV$. The total change of momentum by $\frac{1}{3}n$ molecules striking a side $\frac{1}{2}V/l$ times per second will therefore be the product $\frac{1}{2}V/l \times 2mV \times \frac{1}{3}n$, or $\frac{1}{3}nmV^2/l$. This measures the total force exerted on one face of the cube. But the total surface of one face of the cube is l^2. Hence, the total pressure per unit area is $p = \frac{1}{3}nmV^2/l^3$. But l^3 represents the volume v of the cube. Hence

$$pv = \frac{1}{3}nmV^2 \ . \ . \ . \ . \ (1)$$
This may be written $pv = \frac{2}{3} \cdot \frac{1}{2} \cdot nmV^2 \ . \ . \ . \ (2)$

* Different molecules will, as mentioned previously, have different velocities, and the mean velocity to be employed is the *root mean square* velocity ; which means that if all the molecules were actually moving with this mean velocity the total kinetic energy would have the same value as the actual total kinetic energy.

But $\frac{1}{2}nmV^2$ is the total kinetic energy of the molecules, which will remain constant, provided that the temperature does not change. It follows, therefore, that at constant temperature,

$$pv = \text{Constant},$$

which agrees with *Boyle's Law*.

It has been shown (see p. 19) that gases which exert no chemical or physical action on one another and which are under the same conditions of temperature and pressure—can be mixed without change of temperature or pressure. Hence it is assumed that the molecules of equal volumes of two gases at the same temperature and pressure possess the same total kinetic energies.

From equation (2) above it is evident that the product pv is equal to $\frac{2}{3}$rds of the total kinetic energy of a gas. Hence, if the temperature be altered, pressure remaining constant, the kinetic energy (i.e., temperature) must alter to the same extent, and hence also the volume. Otherwise expressed, if the pressure remains constant, the same alteration of temperature will alter the volume to the same extent. This agrees with Charles's Law.

From what has been said we see that since equal volumes of two gases at the same temperature and pressure have the same value for the product pv, that is

$$n_1 m_1 V_1{}^2 = n_2 m_2 V_2{}^2,$$

and further, since the average kinetic energy per molecule in the two systems will be the same since the temperature is the same, that is

$$\tfrac{1}{2}m_1 V_1{}^2 = \tfrac{1}{2}m_2 V_2{}^2,$$

it follows that

$$n_1 = n_2$$

which agrees with *Avogadro's hypothesis* (p. 67).

It must be pointed out that this deduction of Avogadro's hypothesis depends upon the assumption that two gases are in thermal equilibrium when their kinetic energies are the same : which is an unverifiable assumption. This assumption can similarly be deduced from Avogadro's hypothesis. Hence the Kinetic Theory should not be quoted as *proof* of the truth of Avogadro's hypothesis.

Since $pv = \frac{1}{3}nmV^2$, the mean velocity

$$V = \sqrt{\frac{3\,pv}{mn}}$$

Now the density of a gas $(d) = \dfrac{\text{mass}}{\text{volume}} = \dfrac{mn}{v}$

Hence we have

$$V = \sqrt{\frac{3p}{d}}$$

or, in words, the mean velocity of a gas molecule is inversely proportional to the square root of its density. This is clearly in agreement with *Graham's Law* of Diffusion.

The Kinetic Theory not only correlates these previously discovered laws of the behaviour of gases, but also furnishes a means of calculating some molecular magnitudes.

Thus, since, as above, the mean velocity

$$V = \sqrt{\frac{3pv}{mn}}$$

For hydrogen at 0° C. and 760 mm. pressure we have

$$v = 1 \text{ c.c.}$$
$$p = 760 \text{ mm. of mercury} = 1{,}013{,}250 \text{ dynes per sq. cm.}$$
$$mn = \text{mass of 1 c.c. of hydrogen at 0° C. and 760 mm.} = \cdot00008988.$$

hence $v = \sqrt{\dfrac{3 \times 1{,}013{,}250 \times 1}{\cdot00008988}}$

$$= 184{,}000 \text{ cms. per sec. or 60 miles per min. nearly.}$$

§ 13 Application of the Kinetic Theory to Liquids

It is a familiar fact of observation that gases and vapours (see page 37), if cooled sufficiently and subjected to sufficiently high pressures, condense into liquids, and it is evident from its nature that in a liquid the particles or molecules comprising the substance are definitely exerting a force of attraction upon each other, whatever may be true of gases in this regard (see page 32).

The discussion of the implications of the Gas Laws and in particular of Charles's Law, has led (page 17) to a conception of an absolute scale of temperature, the absolute zero being taken to be −273° C. The Kinetic Theory gives a further meaning to the absolute zero, since, in terms of that theory, it is that temperature at which all molecular motion ceases.

Conversely, molecular motion only ceases entirely, according to the Kinetic Theory, at the absolute zero, and it follows, therefore, that in ordinary liquids, molecular motion must still occur, although, owing to the existence of molecular attractions of considerable magnitude, its extent will be much restricted when compared with gases. In liquids there will be practically no free path (as is believed to exist in gases) and the motion of the molecules is thought to be more in the nature of a gliding of particles over and amongst each other.

A molecule in the body of a liquid will experience attraction on all sides equally, whereas one in the surface will experience a resultant force directed towards the interior of the liquid due to the absence of any marked attraction exerted on it from outside the liquid itself.

This is illustrated in Fig. 12 and shows that there will be in the surface of a liquid a force acting inwards towards the bulk of the liquid. The effects of this force are observed in the phenomenon of *surface tension* which thus becomes a logical consequence of the Kinetic Theory.

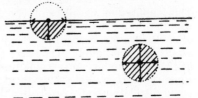

FIG. 12.—Molecular Forces in a liquid.

Although there can be practically no free path in liquids, nevertheless, the speeds with which individual molecules are moving will, at any instant, vary considerably. Thus there will be a few molecules possessing kinetic energy greater than the average of the molecules as a whole, and if such a molecule should approach the surface it may have sufficient energy to travel clean through the surface into the space outside the liquid. This effect is observed in the phenomenon termed *evaporation*. The removal of such molecules from the liquid will result in a reduction in the mean kinetic energy of the liquid which thus will become cooler, or, if the temperature is to remain unchanged, heat must be supplied from the surroundings. This is the *latent heat* of evaporation.

The molecules of the substance which have escaped from the liquid in this way constitute a *vapour** in the space above the liquid. These molecules of vapour behave like those of an ordinary gas, and so they will be moving with high speeds. Some of these molecules will approach the surface of the liquid where some of them will be attracted by the molecules in the surface of the liquid and so be dragged into the liquid again. These molecules will be accelerated as they enter the liquid, owing to the forces acting upon them, and their capture will result in an increase in the mean kinetic energy of the liquid, whose temperature will rise in consequence. Heat is therefore given out on condensation.

Suppose now that a liquid is evaporating in a closed vacuous space. The fleetest molecules accumulate as a gas or vapour in the space above the liquid. The concentration of the vapour in the space above the liquid will go on increasing, but a certain percentage will plunge back into the liquid. The number of molecules which return to the liquid from the space above per second increases as the concentration of the vapour increases, although the rate at which the molecules leave the liquid probably decreases as the concentration of the vapour increases. **When the number of molecules which return to the liquid in a given time is equal to the number of molecules which leave the liquid in the same time, the vapour is said to be saturated, and the system in equilibrium.** Thus,

$$\text{Water}_{\text{liquid}} \overset{100°}{\rightleftharpoons} \text{Water}_{\text{steam}}$$

This equilibrium, it will be observed, is not a static condition, that is, a state of rest ; both processes are active (kinetic). There is a shower of molecules streaming into the liquid, and an efflux of molecules away from the liquid. The effect of one is neutralized by the other ; neither can produce any visible result. Anything which disturbs this equality—e.g., a desiccating agent or a condenser in the space above (as in distillation), etc.—will alter the conditions.

If two glass tubes are taken, each about 80 cms. in length and sealed at one end, filled with dry mercury and inverted in dishes of mercury, the level of the mercury in each tube will sink somewhat but remain at such a height as represents the pressure of the atmosphere at the time of the experiment. The space above the mercury in such a tube is, to all intents and purposes, vacuous and is called a Torricellian vacuum (after Torricelli who, in 1643, first observed that mercury

---

* The distinction between " gas " and " vapour " is somewhat vague. If the " elastic fluid " be very far from its temperature of liquefaction, it is generally called a " gas " ; and " vapour " if it is near its temperature of liquefaction. E.g., oxygen, nitrogen, etc., at ordinary temperatures are gases ; whereas water or alcohol on evaporation would furnish vapours. Otherwise expressed, *a gas is an elastic fluid at a temperature above its critical temperature, and a vapour is an elastic fluid below its critical temperature, but not in a liquid state.*

would only stand at a height of about 30 inches in such a tube). If a few drops of water are introduced by means of a small pipette into one of the tubes, the level of the mercury will be depressed further, and this process will continue on introduction of more water until a thin layer of water is seen resting on the surface of the mercury. The pressure exerted by the water vapour is equal to that of a column of mercury whose height is the difference between the heights of the mercury in the two tubes. The value of this pressure when the space is *saturated*, that is, when the addition of more water merely increases the amount of the liquid water layer visible on the mercury, without causing any increase in pressure, is called the *maximum vapour pressure*.

Experiments of this kind have shown that, **at a given temperature, the vapour pressure of a liquid in contact with its own liquid is a constant quantity, and independent of the absolute amount of vapour and of liquid present in the system.** It is easy to see why this is so. If the surface of the liquid be doubled, it is true that twice as many molecules will leave the surface in a given time, but twice as many molecules will return.

If a barometer tube, such as was employed in the above experiments, be surrounded with a jacket through which warm water can be passed, and the maximum pressure of water (or other) vapour at various temperatures thus measured, we shall find that the higher the temperature, the greater the vapour pressure, provided all the liquid is not vaporized; but for any assigned temperature the vapour pressure of a given liquid always has one fixed and definite value.

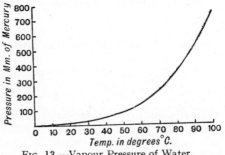

FIG. 13.—Vapour Pressure of Water.

It has been shown that evaporation is (according to the Kinetic Theory) the result of the escape of the fastest-moving molecules in a liquid through the surface of the liquid. Consequently, anything which increases the number of swiftly-moving molecules should assist the process of evaporation. Hence a current of air (through ether, for example) will remove these faster particles and lower the temperature in consequence. Supplying heat to the liquid so as to raise its temperature will also remove these fast-moving molecules, for we have seen that the mean speed of the molecules is increased by rise of temperature. When the temperature is high enough, the exposed surface of the liquid is not sufficient to allow the swift-moving molecules to escape fast enough, bubbles of vapour are accordingly formed *within* the liquid. Each bubble as it forms rises to the surface—increasing in size as it rises—and finally escapes into the atmosphere.

The process of vaporization by bubble formation is called **boiling** ; and the temperature at which boiling commences, the **boiling point** of the liquid. When the vapour pressure of the liquid is the same as the external pressure to which the liquid is subjected, the temperature does not rise any higher. Increasing the supply of heat only increases the rate at which the bubbles are formed so long as any liquid remains. Hence it is sometimes convenient to define : **The boiling point of a liquid is the temperature at which the vapour pressure of the liquid is equal to the external pressure exerted at any point on the liquid surface.** This external pressure may be exerted by the atmospheric air, by vapour and air, by other gases, etc. Hence a table of the vapour pressures of a liquid at different temperatures also shows the boiling points of that liquid under different pressures. Thus water at a pressure of 4·6 mm. of mercury boils at 0° C. Hence liquids which decompose at their boiling point under ordinary atmospheric pressure can frequently be distilled without decomposition at the lower boiling temperature obtained by reducing the pressure. This is the basis of the process of **distillation under reduced pressure,** or, as it is sometimes less accurately styled, **distillation in vacuo.**

§ 14 Deviations from the Gas Laws—Van der Waals' Equation

We have seen how the simple gas equation,

$$pv = RT,$$

was arrived at ; first, experimentally by the work of Boyle and Charles, and later, deduced theoretically by means of the Kinetic Theory. We have seen further that, while for many gases such as hydrogen, oxygen and nitrogen at temperatures and pressures not far removed from atmospheric, this equation is substantially true, yet for many other gases (viz., those which can easily be liquefied), even under these conditions, serious deviations from the simple gas laws occur, and even the so-called permanent gases also exhibit deviations at very high pressures.

In deducing the gas laws from the Kinetic Theory, two simplifying assumptions were made (see p. 27), viz. :

(i) that the molecules of a gas are of negligible size in comparison with the space they occupy, and

(ii) that the molecules do not exert any attraction on each other.

In a gas confined at high pressure these assumptions cease to be tenable, and account must be taken both of the actual size of the molecules of a gas and of the mutual attraction between them. One of the more important attempts to do this was due to Van der Waals, who reasoned somewhat as follows :

Let b denote the effective volume of a molecule as it moves to and fro between the boundary walls AB, Fig. 14. If this distance be halved to CD, Fig. 14, while the volume of the molecule remains constant, the molecule will have *less* than half its former distance to pass from one side to the other. It will therefore strike the walls more frequently than before. Hence the outward pressure of the molecule will increase more rapidly with decreasing volume than is described by Boyle's Law. Boyle's Law refers to the whole volume of the gas, but rather should it refer to the space in which the molecules move. We therefore write $v - b$ in place of v in Boyle's Law, and the result is :

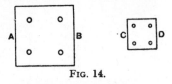

FIG. 14.

$$p(v - b) = RT$$

where b is called the " co-volume " or " vibratory volume " of the molecule.

It is evident-that a force of attraction does exist between the molecules since condensation to a liquid occurs when the temperature of a gas or vapour is lowered, and it is clear that the closer the molecules are to one another, the greater will be the effect of the attractive forces between them. This attractive force will tend to make the gas occupy a smaller volume. The effect is much the same as if the gas were subjected to the action of a greater external pressure than the observed or apparent pressure of the gas.

It has been assumed that these attractive forces in the case of two portions of gas are proportional to the product of their masses. Since these are proportional to their densities, which are in turn proportional to the volumes, we arrive at the conclusion that the attractive force is to be put as proportional to $\dfrac{1}{v^2}$ or equal to $\dfrac{a}{v^2}$

where a is a constant.* a/v^2 must therefore be added to the observed pressure of the gas in order to indicate the total pressure tending to compress the gas. On correcting the equation $pv = RT$ for the volume and the cohesion of the molecules, we obtain the so-called J. D. van der Waals' equation (1872) :

$$\left(p + \frac{a}{v^2}\right)\left(v - b\right) = RT$$

This amended equation agrees fairly well with a number of observations of gases under large pressures, and of gases which are near their points of liquefaction —e.g., ethylene, carbon dioxide, etc. It also describes many of the properties of liquids, and of the continuous passage of a gas to the liquid condition. The constants a and b must be evaluated from observations. The numerical values of the " constants " in van der Waals' equation are not always quite constant at different temperatures. Quite a number of attempts have been made to modify the gas equation still further so that it may describe the behaviour of gases under wide variations of pressure and temperature. J. D. van der Waals (1888) found that for carbon dioxide, $R = 0.00369$; $b = 0.0023$; and $a = 0.00874$. Let us find how van der Waals' equation describes the behaviour of carbon dioxide under variations of pressure. This gas is known to deviate considerably from the behaviour required by Boyle's law. On comparing the values of pv for carbon dioxide, calculated from the equation, at $20°$:

$$\left(p + \frac{0.00874}{v^2}\right)\left(v - 0.0023\right) = 1.08$$

with the numbers observed by E. H. Amagat (1893) at $20°$, we get:

* Mellor has shown that this correction implies a force whose magnitude varies inversely as the 4th power of the distance ; the force of gravity varies inversely as the square of the distance.

p atmospheres.	pv.	
	Observed.	Calculated.
1	1·000	1·000
50	0·680	0·678
75	0·180	0·179
100	0·228	0·226
200	0·419	0·411
500	0·938	0·936

The agreement between theory (van der Waals' equation) and fact (the observed data) is quite good. It will be remembered that if the gas behaves according to the equation $pv = RT$, pv would have the same value for all pressures. As has been shown (p. 15) the value of pv first decreases and then increases for all gases except hydrogen and helium. The two corrections act in opposite ways. At first the value of pv is decreased by the molecular attraction, and increased by the finite dimensions of the molecule. At low pressures, the correction for molecular attraction preponderates over that required for the volume of the molecule ; while the correction for the volume of the molecules is relatively large when the volume of the gas is compressed very small by a large pressure. (Cf. pp. 15, 18.) Several attempts have been made still further to improve the gas equation by the introduction of other terms, involving special constants which have to be evaluated from the experimental numbers, but they are therefore of very limited application.

§ 15 The Critical Phenomena of Gases and Liquids

In 1869 T. Andrews found that if carbon dioxide at ordinary temperature be gradually compressed in a vessel suitable for the observation, the volume diminishes more rapidly than would occur if Boyle's Law correctly described the behaviour of the gas ; and when the pressure attains a certain value, the gas begins to liquefy. A further decrease in the volume does not change the pressure, but only increases the quantity of gas liquefied. At length, when all the gas has liquefied, a large increase of pressure only causes a minute decrease in the volume of the liquid, since liquids in general undergo but a small change of volume on compression.

If the experiment be made with carbon dioxide at 0°, the gas commences to liquefy when the pressure has attained 35·4 atmospheres ; if at 13·1°, liquefaction commences at 48·9 atmospheres pressure ; if at 30°, at 70 atmospheres pressure ; while if the temperature exceeds 31°, no pressure, however great, will liquefy the gas. Other gases exhibit similar phenomena. **For each gas there is a particular temperature above which liquefaction is impossible, however great be the applied pressure.** Andrews called this the **critical temperature of the gas.** For instance, the critical temperature of :

Hydrogen.	.	− 240°	Nitrous oxide .	.	+ 36·5°
Nitrogen	.	− 147°	Ammonia .	.	+ 132°
Oxygen .	.	− 119°	Sulphur dioxide	.	+ 157°
Carbon dioxide	.	+ 31°	Water .	.	+ 374°

The least pressure which is sufficient to liquefy the gas at the critical temperature is called the **critical pressure** ; and the volume occupied by unit volume of gas at N.T.P. when the critical temperature and

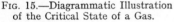

Critical Temperature

Below   At   Above

A   B   C   D

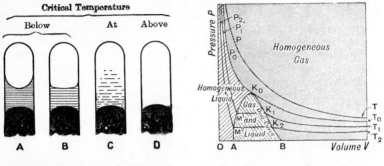

Fig. 15.—Diagrammatic Illustration of the Critical State of a Gas.

Fig. 16.—$p : v$—Curves for Carbon Dioxide.

pressure are attained is called the **critical volume**. It is interesting to notice the influence of temperature on carbon dioxide, partly liquid, partly gaseous. Fig. 15, A, represents the upper end of a glass tube in which the partly liquefied carbon dioxide is confined over mercury, at 18°. The surface of the liquid has a sharply defined curved meniscus. On raising the temperature, the meniscus of the liquid becomes flatter and flatter, Fig. 15, B, until, at 31°, Fig. 15, C, the surface seems to disappear. The sharp line of demarcation between the liquid and the gas vanishes. At 40°, the tube contains a homogeneous gas, Fig. 15, D. Liquid carbon dioxide cannot exist at this temperature, however great the pressure.

The relation between the pressure and the volume of, say, carbon dioxide, at different temperatures—T, T_0, T_1, T_2—is represented diagrammatically in Fig. 16. The portion of the curve K_2T_2, or K_1T_1, represents the behaviour of the gas when no liquid is present ; the portion K_2M_2, or K_1M_1, the behaviour of the gas in the presence of its own liquid ; and M_2P_2, or M_1P_1, the behaviour of the liquid when no gas is present. It will be observed that K_2M_2 or K_1M_1 is a straight line parallel with the v-axis. It illustrates in a graphic manner the law previously considered: At any fixed temperature, the pressure of a gas in the presence of its own liquid is always the same. The curve $T_0K_0P_0$ represents the relation between pressure and volume at the critical temperature ; and the curve T, the relation between p and v at a temperature when the gas does not liquefy. The line $K_0K_1K_2B$ represents the condition under which the gas, compressed at the stated temperatures T_0, T_1, T_2, begins to liquefy, and it is hence called the **dew curve,** because a gas under a gradually increasing pressure first shows signs of liquefaction under conditions represented by a point on this line; similarly, the line $K_0M_1M_2A$ is called the **boiling curve,** because a liquid, under a gradually diminishing pressure, first shows signs of vaporization under conditions represented by a point on this line. Note also that the lines K_0A, K_0B, and K_0P_0, divide the plane of the paper into three regions. Every point to the right of BK_0P_0 represents a homogeneous gas; every point in the region AK_0B represents a heterogeneous mixture of gas and liquid; and every point to the left of AK_0P_0, a homogeneous liquid. The gas in the region K_0BVT_0 is below its critical temperature, and is then said to be a vapour—*vide* p. 30. The diagram, Fig. 16, thus represents the conditions of equilibrium of a liquid or a gas under different conditions of temperature, pressure or volume.

It is possible to calculate the value of the critical constants from van der Waals' equation, as follows.

Van der Waals' equation may be written as a cubic in V :—

$$V^3 - \left(b + \frac{RT}{p}\right)V^2 + \frac{a}{p}\ V - \frac{ab}{p} = 0$$

This can have three roots. There may be only one real value of V which will satisfy the equation for a given temperature and pressure or there may be three such values. This latter case corresponds to curves such as $P_2M_2K_2T_2$ (Fig. 16). At the critical point (K_0—Fig. 16) the three roots become identical and equal to the critical volume (V_c). Hence at the critical point $(V - V_c)^3 = 0$. This equation must be identical with van der Waals' equation when the temperature is equal to the critical temperature (T_c) and the pressure is the critical pressure (p_c).

$$\therefore\ V^3 - 3V_cV^2 + 3V_c^2V - V_c^3 \equiv V^3 - \left(b + \frac{RT_c}{p_c}\right)V^2 + \frac{a}{p_c}\ V - \frac{ab}{p_c}$$

By equating coefficients of equal powers of V we have

$$3V_c = b + \frac{RT_c}{p}\ ;\quad 3V_c^2 = \frac{a}{p_c}\ ;\quad V_c^3 = \frac{ab}{p_c}.$$

$$\text{Whence } V_c = 3b\ ;\ p_c = \frac{a}{27b^2}\ ;\ T_c = \frac{8a}{27Rb}.$$

It is interesting to note historically that Caignard de la Tour, long before Andrews' experiment, noticed that when a liquid is heated in a sealed tube there is a definite temperature at which the surface of separation between the gas and liquid disappeared, and the whole contents of the tube become homogeneous. Caignard de la Tour's experiments thus demonstrate that the critical temperature is the upper limit to the liquid state; and Andrews' experiments prove that the critical temperature is the lower limit to the gaseous state. The passage from the one state to the other proceeds in a continuous manner. **The liquid and gaseous states are continuous, not abrupt.** The properties—density, surface tension, viscosity, refractive power, heat of vaporization, compressibility, etc.—of a liquid gradually lose their distinctive character as the temperature is raised, until, at the **critical temperature,** the properties of liquid and gas are the same.

§ 16 The Liquefaction of Gases

The familiar fact that a liquid such as water is converted by heat into a vapour (steam) and that the latter reverts to the liquid state on cooling makes it seem likely that many substances which ordinarily exist in the form of gases or vapours, such as ammonia or chlorine, would become liquid if cooled sufficiently. The difficulty of applying sufficient cooling, however, prevented an early verification of this surmise.

But the experiments of van Marum and of Northmore (1806), who succeeded in liquefying ammonia and chlorine respectively by the application of pressure, opened up a fruitful field of investigation.

In 1823 Faraday again succeeded in obtaining liquid chlorine, and in greater bulk than Northmore had done, by heating chlorine hydrate (p. 495) in one limb of a tube shaped as in Fig. 17, while the other limb was cooled in a freezing mixture. By a suitable choice of materials he was able to liquefy hydrogen sulphide, hydrogen chloride, carbon dioxide, nitrous oxide, cyanogen, ammonia, and a number of other gases, but he failed to liquefy nitrogen, oxygen or hydrogen. These gases for many years resisted all efforts to reduce them to the liquid state. These attempts relied largely on the application of very high pressures (thus Natterer used pressures up to 2790 atmospheres without success). In consequence of these failures, such gases as hydrogen, oxygen, nitrogen, methane and carbon monoxide were called *permanent gases*.

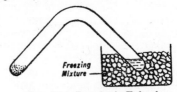

FIG. 17.—Faraday's Tube for liquefaction of Gases.

§ 17 The Liquefaction of the Permanent Gases

The clue to the difficulty experienced by the earlier workers when the liquefaction of the so-called permanent gases was attempted, was furnished by the work of Andrews who, as we have seen (p. 34), investigated thoroughly the critical phenomena of gases. It thus became evident that the obstacle to success in the experiments previously performed was insufficient cooling.

This incited experimenters to concentrate their attention on methods for the production of lower temperatures than those previously obtainable, and a number of the " permanent " gases were liquefied in small quantities by Pictet, who used liquid carbon dioxide, boiling under reduced pressure, as a cooling medium, and by Cailletet, who allowed the highly compressed gas to expand suddenly so that in having to do a certain amount of work against the pressure, heat corresponding to this work was taken from the gas itself, whose temperature fell in consequence.

W. Cullen (1755) seems to have been the first to notice that the temperature of air is decreased by rarefaction, and increased by compression ; and J. Dalton attempted to measure the effects. If a gas, whose molecules exert no attraction on one another, be confined in a suitable vessel, and compressed, the mechanical work employed in compressing the gas is equivalent to the product of the pressure into the change in volume. This energy is transformed into an equivalent amount of heat which raises the temperature of the gas. On the other hand, if the gas expands against atmospheric pressure, the gas will be cooled because the gas itself has done a certain amount of work equivalent to the product of the atmospheric pressure into the change in volume.

No heat is developed when an ideal gas expands into a vacuum because no external work is done by the gas. This was established experimentally by some early experiments by J. L. Gay-Lussac (1807), and by J. P. Joule (1845). Compressed air was allowed to expand into an evacuated vessel, and the result, as Joule expressed it, was as follows : " No change of temperature occurs when air is allowed to expand in such a way as not to develop mechanical power." Hence, it was also inferred that no work is performed under these conditions against inter-molecular attractions.

Our study of Boyle's and Charles's Laws has taught us that inter-molecular attractions occur with most gases. Hence, this latter deduction might be questioned. The experiments, however, were not sufficiently sensitive to detect the small change of temperature which occurs when a gas expands *in vacuo*, so that although no external work is done by the gas, internal work is done against molecular attraction. The molecules are torn apart, so to speak, against the (feeble) attractive force drawing them together. This involves an expenditure of energy —work must be done.

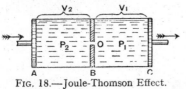

FIG. 18.—Joule-Thomson Effect.

Later, in a more delicate experiment, J. P. Joule and W. Thomson (Lord Kelvin)—1852-62 —forced a steady stream of gas under a pressure p_2 slowly along a tube, A, Fig. 18, in the direction of the arrows, through a small orifice, O, where it expanded against the pressure p_1. For the sake of simplicity, suppose the tube AB has unit sectional area, and that it is made of some material which does not conduct heat away from the gas. Two phenomena occur : (1) the gas is slightly heated by friction as it passes through the orifice O ; and (2) the gas is cooled as it passes through O against a pressure p_1.

Suppose a piston A, Fig. 18, moves from left to right so as to drive a volume of air v_2 at a pressure p_2 into the compartment BC. The work done *on* the gas is obviously p_2v_2. Similarly, the work done *by* the gas as it pushes the piston from, say, B to C through a distance v_1

will be p_1v_1. Hence, if the gas obeys Boyle's Law, we shall have $p_1v_1 = p_2v_2$, and there will be no variation of temperature of the gas on the side AB and BC. If, however, work be done against molecular attraction during the expansion of the gas, the work of expansion on the side BC will exceed the work of compression on the side AB. The extra work will absorb heat from the gas itself. Hence, the gas on the side BC will be cooled below the temperature of the gas on the side AB. In Joule and Thomson's experiments, the temperature of carbon dioxide, nitrogen, oxygen, and air fell about 1°, while the temperature of hydrogen gas rose about 0·039° above the temperature of the gas on the side AB. If, however, the experiment be conducted at a lower temperature, hydrogen gas behaves like the other gases, and is cooled. **The change of temperature which occurs when a gas is driven through a small orifice is called the Joule-Thomson effect.** The theoretical fall of temperature when the pressure falls from p_2 to p_1 is about $\frac{1}{4}$° per atm. difference $p_2 - p_1$ or more exactly, if T be the absolute temperature,

$$\text{Fall of temperature} = 75 \cdot 35(p_2 - p_1)/T.$$

If carbon dioxide at 4 atm. pressure at 0° in passing through a porous plug suffers a fall of pressure to one atm., the fall of temperature will be $75 \cdot 35 \times 3 \div 273$, or $0 \cdot 828°$.

The Joule-Thomson effect was applied in 1894-5 to the liquefaction of air on a large scale by Linde in Germany, and by Hampson in England. By this method all gases except helium had been liquefied (many such as hydrogen and fluorine by Déwar) by the end of the nineteenth century, and many had also been solidified. Helium, which was found to have a critical temperature as low as $- 267 \cdot 75°$, was finally liquefied by K. Onnes at Leyden in 1907 and solidified by Keesom in 1926, when a temperature of only $0 \cdot 89°$ abs. was reached.

The production of liquid air is now a process of commercial importance. The principle of the Linde-Hampson method will be understood after an examination of Fig. 19. The air to be liquefied—freed from carbon dioxide, moisture, organic matter, etc.— enters the inner tube of concentric or annular pipes, A, under a pressure of about 200 atmospheres. This tube is hundreds of yards long and coiled spirally to economize space. By regulating the valve C the compressed air suddenly expands in the chamber D. The air thus chilled passes back through the tube B which surrounds the tube A conveying the incoming air. The latter is thus cooled still more. The gas passes

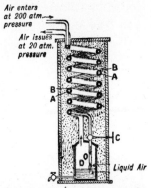

Fig. 19.—Linde's Apparatus for Liquefying Air (Diagrammatic).

along to the pumps where it is returned with more air to the inner tube. In this manner, the incoming air at 200 atmospheres pressure is cooled more and more as it issues from the jet *O*. Finally, when the temperature is reduced low enough, drops of liquid air issue from the jet. The tubes must all be packed in a non-conducting medium to protect them from the external heat.

It was suggested by Lord Rayleigh that the process could be made more efficient by allowing the expanding gas to do work in an expansion engine, whereby the heat equivalent to the work done by the engine is taken from the gas. This principle was applied by Claude in 1906 and is employed in modern liquid air plant, the expansion engine being used to drive a dynamo, and thus a portion of the energy used in compressing the air is recovered, and at the same time the cooling is more rapid.

The temperature of liquid air is about −190° C. and there is thus a far greater difference between its temperature and that of ordinary atmospheric air, than there is between the temperature of ice and boiling water. The preservation of liquid air is thus a far more difficult problem than would be involved in preventing cold water boiling away while surrounded by a steam jacket at 200°. James Dewar solved the problem by keeping the liquid air in a double (or triple) walled vessel with the space between the walls evacuated, Fig. 20. Glass is a poor conductor, and a vacuum is a non-conductor. Hence, the liquid in the inner vessel can receive heat only from above, and by radiation. The glass walls of the evacuated space are silvered to reduce the effects of radiant heat. Still air is a very bad conductor, so that the open end of the vessel is plugged lightly with cotton wool in order to reduce the ingress of heat from outside to a minimum. In this way, liquid air can be transported by rail, etc., with surprisingly little loss.

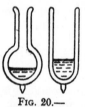

Fig. 20.—
Dewar Flasks.

§ 18 The Manufacture of Oxygen and Nitrogen from Liquid Air

The boiling point of liquid nitrogen is −195° C., and that of liquid oxygen is −182·5° C. There is thus a difference in boiling point of 12·5° C., which, though small, is sufficient to allow of their separation by the evaporation of liquid air which is a mixture of the two.

Whenever a mixture of two liquids, of different boiling points, is made to evaporate the vapour which first comes off contains a greater proportion of the substance of lower boiling point, and the residual liquid will therefore be richer in the constituent of higher boiling point. Unless the liquids comprising the mixture are immiscible, or of very widely different boiling point, a complete separation is not possible by a simple distillation. Separation can be effected, however, by the use of a fractionating (or rectifying) column.

A fractionating column consists of a vertical tube so arranged that a portion of the vapour condenses in it and so runs back into the vessel in which the liquid is being heated. The construction of the interior of the column is such that the rising vapour is brought into thorough contact with the descending liquid (see Fig. 21). The rising vapour will contain the more volatile constituent (in larger quantity)

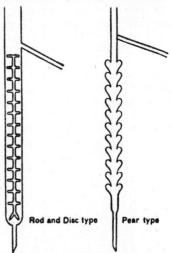

mixed with some of the less volatile one. The latter will condense more readily than the former so that a film of liquid will be found running down the tube, rich in the less volatile constituent. The rising vapour meeting this liquid, heats it and so evaporates off from it a vapour relatively rich in the more volatile part, while condensing more of the less volatile portion in so doing. Thus, the rising vapour becomes steadily richer in the more volatile constituent as it passes up the tube, while the descending portion becomes richer in the higher boiling part. In this way an almost complete separation can be effected if an efficient column be used.

This principle is applied to the manufacture of oxygen and nitrogen

Fig. 21.—Fractionating Columns.

from liquid air, oxygen being, as we have seen, the less volatile, and nitrogen the more volatile constituent.

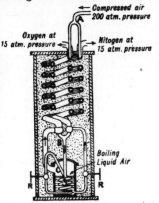

Fig. 22.—Linde's Apparatus for the manufacture of Oxygen from Liquid Air (Diagrammatic).

In Linde's process (1895), purified air is compressed to about 200 atmospheres, and driven along a pipe which divides at A, Fig. 22, into two streams and then passes down the interior tubes of a double set of annular or concentric pipes similar to the worm tube, Fig. 18. The two inner tubes finally unite into one single pipe, B. The air then passes through a spiral S, via the regulating valve R, and finally streams at C into the collecting vessel. The action is here similar to that described in the process for the liquefaction of air, Fig. 19. After a time, the air is liquefied in the collecting vessel, about the spiral S. The more volatile nitrogen boils off more rapidly than the oxygen. Hence, a gas rich in nitrogen passes up one of the two annular outer pipes as indicated on the left of Fig. 22. The liquid rich in oxygen is kept at a constant level by means of the valve, and thus the rate at which the liquid air in the collecting vessel is allowed to boil is also regulated. The oxygen passes from this tube on the right of Fig. 22 along the outer annular pipe, and finally emerges from the apparatus whence it is pumped into cylinders, etc., for use. If the valves are all properly regulated, the inrushing air is cooled by the counter currents of oxygen and nitrogen. The two latter gases pass along the tubes as indicated in the diagram. The tubes, etc., are all well insulated with non-conducting materials. By this process oxygen can be obtained as pure as is commercially desired, but the escaping nitrogen contains over 7 per cent of oxygen.

In 1906 Claude introduced an improved apparatus, involving two new principles as compared with Linde's method. As mentioned previously, he made use of an expansion engine for assisting in the rapid cooling of the air and for reducing the loss of power in the process ; he also liquefied the air in two stages, so obtaining two liquids, one rich in oxygen and the other in nitrogen. He employed a tall fractionating column and introduced the liquid rich in nitrogen near the top of this column, while the liquid rich in oxygen was passed in lower down the column at a point where the descending liquid had become, through the operation of the column, richer in oxygen and of about the same composition as the liquid being added.

A diagrammatic sketch of Claude's apparatus is shown in Fig. 23. The cooled

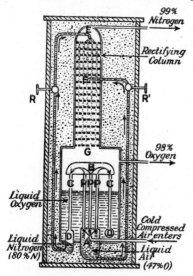

and purified air enters the lower part of the apparatus at a pressure of about 5 atm. and rises through a series of vertical pipes P surrounded by liquid oxygen, where it is partially liquefied. The liquid containing about 47 per cent. oxygen and 53 per cent. of nitrogen drains into the lower vessel A. The vapour which has survived condensation enters B and then descends through a ring of pipes C arranged concentrically about the set previously described. Here all is liquefied. The liquid which ultimately collects in this vessel D is very rich in nitrogen. The pressure of the vapour in the central receptacle forces the liquid nitrogen to enter the summit of the rectifying column E, and the liquid, containing 47 per cent. of oxygen, is likewise forced to enter the rectifying column at F lower down. The pressures and rates of flow are regulated by the cocks RR^1. The liquid nitrogen is 3° or 4° lower in temperature than the liquid rich in oxygen. Nitrogen evaporates from the down-streaming liquid, and oxygen condenses from the up-streaming gases. The heat supplied by the condensation of oxygen helps on the evaporation of nitrogen. Consequently, the descending liquid gets progressively richer and richer in oxygen, and the ascending gases richer in nitrogen. The liquid oxygen drains into the receptacle G, and is there evaporated by the latent heat of the gases condensing in the tubes. Finally, oxygen containing from 2 to 4 per cent. of nitrogen passes from the oxygen exit, and nitrogen containing 0·2 to 1 per cent. of oxygen escapes at the top of the rectifying column.

FIG. 23.—Claude's Apparatus for the separation of Oxygen from Liquid Air (Diagrammatic).

Most of the nitrogen and oxygen of commerce are now produced by processes such as these, whilst liquid air itself is a commercial product available in quantity.

CHAPTER III

CHEMICAL CHANGE

The common operations of chemistry give rise in almost every instance to products which bear no resemblance to the materials employed. Nothing can be so false as to expect that the qualities of the elements shall be still discoverable in an unaltered form in the compound.—W. WHEWELL.

Nature in her inscrutable wisdom has set limits which she never oversteps. —JEAN REY.

§ 1 Physical and Chemical Changes

IT is a commonplace of observation that changes are constantly taking place in all the substances which surround us ; changes which may or may not have been induced by our own intervention. These changes are classified for convenience into two types, physical and chemical, and although, as is frequently the case with our attempts at classification, there is no sharp dividing line between the two, the conception underlying this classification is of fundamental importance in chemistry. Broadly speaking, it may be said that a *physical change* involves only a few of the properties of the substance undergoing it and is of such a kind as to give us no reason to suppose that a new substance has been formed ; while on the other hand a *chemical change* is attended by so far-reaching and extensive an alteration of the properties of a substance that we are bound to conclude that a new substance has resulted.

In practice, three criteria are employed in distinguishing between physical and chemical changes. These are :

(i) Chemical changes are accompanied by a profound alteration in properties, while physical changes are partial in character ;

(ii) Chemical changes are usually permanent, while physical changes continue only so long as the exciting cause remains and can take place and be repeated as often as this cause is in operation ;

(iii) Chemical changes are usually attended with far greater energy changes than are physical.

When liquid water becomes ice or steam there is no change in the *chemical* nature of the substance, for the matter which makes steam and ice is the same in kind as that of liquid water. A substance can generally change its state, as when liquid water becomes steam or ice. The idea is further emphasized by the fact that in most cases a substance is called by the same name, whether it be in the solid, liquid, or gaseous state of aggregation, e.g., we speak of " liquid " oxygen, " liquid " air, " molten " silver chloride, etc. Again, matter may change its *volume* by expansion or contraction ; it may change its *texture*, as when a porous solid is compressed to a compact mass ; it may change its *form*, as when matter in bulk is ground to powder ; it may change its *magnetic qualities*, as when a piece of soft iron in contact

43

with a magnet attracts other pieces of iron, etc. It is conventionally agreed to say that in none of these cases of physical change is there any evidence of the formation of a new substance; and that the matter does not lose or change those properties which distinguish it from other forms of matter.

When magnesium metal is heated in air, a white powder is formed, and when mercuric oxide is similarly treated, mercury and oxygen are obtained. The action of heat in both cases furnishes forms of matter with very different specific properties from those forms of matter employed at the start.

When water is heated it turns into steam, and when the source of heat is removed the steam condenses to water again. In contrast, when magnesium is heated in air the white powder resulting remains as such when the source of heat is removed, and shows no tendency whatever to revert to magnesium metal. The former of these is a physical, and the latter a chemical change.

§ 2 Mixtures and Compounds

The investigation of samples of matter, whether as found naturally, or formed as the result of human intervention, soon reveals the fact that some samples are easily sorted into portions readily seen to be different, whereas others seem to be single substances. These last are sometimes called *pure substances*, and may be defined as single species of matter distinguished by exhibiting, under given conditions, characteristic and invariable properties. Samples of matter can thus be subdivided into mixtures and single (or pure) substances.

Pure substances may be of one or two kinds, viz., elements and compounds. Elements are substances which so far have not been resolved into any simpler form of matter; compounds are substances produced by the *chemical combination* of elements. The distinction between *elements* and *compounds* depends upon the possibility of separating from the given substance a form of matter simpler than itself. It is now necessary to consider the experimental tests necessary in order to distinguish a chemical compound from a mixture.

Summary.—The tests for distinguishing chemical compounds from mixtures involve answers to the following questions :—

1. Are the different constituents united in definite and constant proportions?

2. Is the substance homogeneous?

3. Can the constituents be separated by mechanical processes?

4. Are the properties of the substance additive?

5. Were thermal, actinic, or electrical phenomena developed when the substance was compounded?

1. The constituents of a compound are combined in definite proportions.—If a substance produced in different ways be not constant in composition, it is not considered to be a chemical compound, but rather a mixture. R. Bunsen (1846), for example, showed that the proportion of oxygen to nitrogen in atmospheric air is not constant, because the oxygen varies from 20·97 to 20·84 per cent. by volume, by methods of measurement with an error not exceeding 0·03 per cent. Hence, the oxygen and nitrogen in atmospheric air are said to be simply mixed together, and not combined chemically. We shall soon see, however, that substances with a definite composition are usually, but not always, chemical compounds.

2. Compounds are homogeneous, mixtures are usually heterogeneous.—It is comparatively easy to detect particles of sugar and sand in a mixture of the two ; and a simple inspection of a piece of Cornish granite will show that it is a mixture of at least four constituents— silvery flakes of mica ; black patches of schörl ; whitish crystals of felspar ; and clear glassy crystals of quartz. A photograph of a thin slice of this rock, as it appears under the microscope magnified about 50 diameters, is shown in Fig. 24. Although the particles of felspar, mica, schörl, and quartz differ from one another in size and shape, no essential difference can be detected in the composition and

FIG. 24.—Cornish Granite (× 50).

properties of different samples of pure quartz, pure felspar, mica, and schörl. Hence, it is inferred that the sample of granite is a mixture of schörl, felspar, quartz, and mica ; and that each of these minerals is a true chemical compound. Very frequently, the constituents of a mixture are too small to be distinguished by simple inspection, and the body appears homogeneous. A microscopic examination may reveal the heterogeneous character of the substance. Blood and milk, for instance, appear to be homogeneous fluids, but under the microscope the former appears as a colourless fluid with red corpuscles in suspension ; and milk appears as a transparent liquid containing innumerable white globules (fat). Naturally, too, the stronger the magnification, the greater the probability of detecting whether the body is homogeneous or not. Sometimes the microscope fails to detect non-homogeneity under conditions where other tests indicate hetero-geneity.*

Before constant composition can be accepted as a proof of chemical combination, it must also be shown that the substance is homogeneous. **A homogeneous substance is one in which every part of the substance has exactly the same composition and properties as every other part.** A substance may have a fixed and constant composition and yet not be homogeneous—e.g., cryohydrates and eutectic mixtures to be described later. A substance may be homogeneous, for all we can tell to the contrary, and yet not have a constant composition—e.g., atmospheric air; a solution of sugar in water, etc. This simply means that *all chemical compounds are homogeneous, but all homogeneous substances are not chemical compounds.* Indeed, it is sometimes quite impossible to tell by any single test whether a given substance is a mixture or a true chemical compound.

3. The constituents of a mixture can usually be separated by mechanical processes.—The properties of a mixture of finely powdered iron and sulphur have been used in chemical text-books since 1823 to illustrate the difference between mixtures and com-pounds. It would be difficult to find a better example. Rub together a mixture containing, say, 6 grams of iron and 4 grams of roll sulphur in a mortar, and note that : (1) the colour of the mixture is inter-mediate between the colour of the iron and of the sulphur ; (2) the particles of iron and sulphur can be readily distinguished under the microscope ; (3) some of the iron can be removed without difficulty by means of a magnet ; and (4) the two can be separated quite readily by washing the mixture on a dry filter paper by means of carbon disulphide. The sulphur dissolves in the carbon disulphide ; the solution can be collected in a dish placed below the filter paper ; and the sulphur can be recovered by allowing the carbon disulphide to evaporate from the dish. Sulphur remains behind as a crystalline residue. The metallic iron remains on the filter paper. Here then the constituents of the mixture have been separated by the mechanical processes—the attraction of a magnet and the action of solvents. It is not always possible to apply these tests. Solvents, as we shall find later, sometimes decompose a compound into its constituents, or conversely, " cause " the constituents of a mixture to combine.

Mechanical processes of separation.—The so-called mechanical processes of separation usually include : (1) Magneting, hand-picking, sieving, etc. ; (2) If some mixtures be placed in liquids of the right specific gravity, the lighter constituents will float and the heavier constituents will sink ; (3) Differences in the solubility of the con-stituents in suitable solvents ; (4) Distillation ; (5) Freezing ;

---

* See a later section on " Ultramicroscopic Particles." It may seem curious to refer a student to a later chapter. The reference, of course, is intended when the book is read a second time, not the first time. A text-book should be read forwards *and* backwards.

(6) Liquation ;   (7) Diffusion ;   (8) Elutriation ;   (9) Flotation, etc.
It may be useful again to emphasize the fact that the so-called "mechanical" processes of separation, involving solution, freezing, and distillation, are not always satisfactory tests for distinguishing chemical compounds from mechanical mixtures. It is generally stated that "a solution of sugar or of salt in water is a mechanical mixture because, though homogeneous, the salt or sugar can be recovered unchanged from the water by the mechanical process of evaporation." This is an unwarranted assumption. The salt and water may have combined, and the product of the chemical combination may be decomposed into salt and water during the process of evaporation.

4. A mixture usually possesses the common specific properties of its constituents ; the properties of a compound are usually characteristic of itself alone.—The properties of a mixture are nearly always additive, i.e., the resultant of the properties of the constituents of the mixture. For instance, a mixture of equal parts of a white and black powder will be grey. The specific gravity of a mixture of equal volumes of two substances of specific gravity* 3 and 5 will be 4, because if 1 c.c. of water weighs 1 gram, there will be a mixture of 0·5 c.c. weighing 1·5 gram of one substance ; 0·5 c.c. of the other substance weighing 2·5 grams ; and 1·5 + 2·5 = 4 grams per c.c. It must be added that such properties of compounds are additive, for they are the sum of the properties of their constituents.

EXAMPLES.—(1) What is the specific gravity of air containing a mixture of one volume of oxygen and four volumes of nitrogen when the specific gravity of oxygen is 16, and the specific gravity of nitrogen 14·01 ? One-fifth volume of oxygen weighs 3·2 units, and four-fifths volume of nitrogen weighs 11·2 units. Hence, one volume of the mixture will weigh 14·4 units when one volume of oxygen weighs 16 units.   .

(2) Ozonized air—a mixture of air and ozone—has a specific gravity 1·3698, and it contains 13·84 per cent. by weight of air, specific gravity unity, and 86·16 per cent. of ozone. What is the specific gravity of ozone ? Here 13·84 grams of air occupy 13·84 ÷ 1 volume ; and 86·16 grams of ozone occupy 86·16 ÷ x volumes, where x denotes the specific gravity of ozone. Hence, 100 grams of ozonized air occupy 100 ÷ 1·3698 = 73 volumes. Hence, 73·00 = 86·16 ÷ x + 13·84 ; or x = 1·456.

If a portion of the mixture of sulphur and iron indicated above be placed in a hard glass test-tube, and warmed over the bunsen flame,

---

* SPECIFIC GRAVITY.—The student is supposed to know that *specific gravity is a number which expresses how much heavier a given substance is than an equal volume of water taken at a standard temperature.* In the case of gases, it may be that air = unity, oxygen = 16, hydrogen = 1, or hydrogen = 2 is taken as standard ; and in the case of liquids and solids, water at + 4°, or at 0°, is taken as unity. The great value of specific gravity data lies in the fact that *specific gravity is a number which enables volume measurements to be converted into weights, and weight measurements to be converted into volumes.* Specific gravity may thus be regarded as the weight of unit volume if the standard water = 1 be taken, and the weights are reckoned in grams, and volumes in cubic centimetres. There is no need here to distinguish between density and specific gravity.

the contents of the tube begin to glow and a kind of combustion spreads throughout the whole mass. If when cold the test-tube is broken, it will be found that (1) the porous black mass formed during the action is quite different from the original mixture ; (2) under the microscope the powdered mass is homogeneous ; (3) it is not magnetic like iron,* and (4) it gives up no sulphur when digested with carbon disulphide. These facts lead to the assumption that there has been a chemical reaction between the sulphur and the iron. *When chemical combination occurs, the reacting constituents appear to lose their individuality or identity more or less completely, and each new substance which is formed has its own distinctive properties.*

5. Thermal, actinic (light), or electrical phenomena usually occur during chemical changes.—Attention must be directed to the fact that a great deal of heat was developed during the combination of the iron and sulphur. The heat required to start the reaction does not account for the amount of heat developed during the reaction. This point is perhaps better emphasized by placing an intimate mixture of powdered sulphur and zinc on a stone slab. After the flame of a bunsen burner has been allowed to play on a portion of the mixture for a short time to start the reaction, the zinc and sulphur combine with almost explosive violence. Large amounts of heat and light are developed during the reaction.

If a plate of commercial zinc be placed in dilute sulphuric acid, bubbles of gas are copiously evolved, and if a thermometer be placed in the vessel, the rise of temperature shows that heat is generated during the chemical action. If the zinc be pure, very little, if any, gas is liberated. It makes no difference if a plate of platinum be dipped in the same vessel as the zinc, provided the plates are not allowed to come into contact with one another. If the two plates are connected by a piece

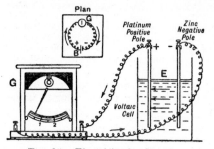

FIG. 25.—Electricity by Chemical Action—Voltaic Cell.

of copper wire, a rapid stream of gas bubbles arises from the surface of the platinum plate, and some gas also comes from the zinc plate. The platinum is not attacked by the acid in any way, but the zinc is rapidly dissolved. If a galvanometer or ammeter be interposed in the circuit between the two plates—Fig. 25—the deflection of the needle shows that an electric current " passes " from the platinum to the zinc, as represented by the arrows. The electric current is generated by the chemical reaction between the zinc and the acid, which

* This provided the iron was not in excess.

results in the formation of zinc sulphate and a gas. The action will continue until either all the acid or all the zinc is used up.

Nomenclature.—The junction of the wire with the zinc plate is conventionally called the **negative** or **— pole** ; and the junction of wire with the platinum plate is called the **positive** or **+ pole**. The vessel of acid with its two plates is called a **voltaic cell**, and this particular combination can be symbolized :—

Platinum | Dilute sulphuric acid | Zinc

The chemical reaction just indicated is far from being the most economical mode of generating electricity, but all the different forms of voltaic cell on the market agree in this : **Electricity is generated during chemical action.**

The development of heat, light, or electrification are common concomitants of chemical action. The absence of such phenomena when substances are simply mixed together is usually taken as one sign that chemical action has not taken place. When nitrogen and oxygen are mixed together in suitable proportions to make atmospheric air there is no sign of chemical action, and this fact is sometimes cited among the proofs that air is a mixture. The argument is not conclusive, because the condensation of water vapour and the freezing of liquid water are often cited as examples of physical change although heat is evolved in both transformations.

The above list does not exhaust the available tests, but in spite of what we know, there is sometimes a lingering doubt whether a particular substance is a mixture or a true chemical compound. This arises from the fact that some of the tests are impracticable, others are indecisive. As previously stated, owing to our ignorance, it is not always easy to state " the truth and nothing but the truth."

Suppose a substance is suspected to be a chemical compound because it appears to be homogeneous ; on investigation, we find that it has a fixed definite composition. This verifies our first suspicion, and the joint testimony gives a very much more probable conclusion than either alone. By piling up the evidence in this manner, for or against our suspicion, we can make a chain of circumstantial evidence which enables highly probable conclusions to be drawn. Each bit of evidence taken by itself is not of much value, but all the evidence taken collectively has tremendous weight. It is easy to see, too, that the probability that an hypothesis is valid becomes less as the number of unproved assumptions on which it is based becomes greater. On the other hand, plausible hypotheses neatly dovetailed may sometimes fit together so well as to strengthen rather than weaken one another ; but the truth of the hypotheses is not thereby established.

We can even get a numerical illustration. *If* the definite-compound test be right nine times out of ten, the probability that a given substance of definite composition is not a true compound is $\frac{1}{10}$; similarly, *if* the homogeneous test be right three times out of four, the probability that the given homogeneous substance is not a chemical compound is $\frac{1}{4}$; and the probability that the given homogeneous substance of definite composition is not a true compound is $\frac{1}{40}$. **Every bit of additional evidence in favour of a conclusion multiplies the probability of its being correct in an emphatic manner ; and evidence against a conclusion acts similarly in the converse way.** Huxley has stated that one of the tragedies in science is the slaughter of a beautiful hypothesis by one *incongruent fact* ; a conclusion based solely upon circumstantial evidence is always in danger of this Damoclean sword.

§ 3 The Law of Conservation of Mass

Lavoisier (1774) heated tin with air in a closed vessel and found that the weight of the whole system, before and after the calcination of the tin, was the same, thus showing that the whole system had neither gained nor lost in weight. This experiment demonstrated the fact that in spite of the most painstaking care, every time all the substances taking part in a chemical reaction are weighed before and after the change, there is no sign of any alteration in the quantity of matter. This fact is sometimes called the law of the indestructibility of matter and was tacitly assumed by many old investigators. A. L. Lavoisier is generally supposed to have first demonstrated the law in 1774 by experiments like that cited above, but the law was definitely enunciated in 1756 by M. W. Lomonossoff, and it must have been at the back of J. Black's mind when he worked on the alkaline earths in 1755.

The chemist's law of " the indestructibility of matter " really means that the total *weight* of the elements in any reacting system remains constant through all the physical and chemical changes it is made to undergo. The observed facts are better generalized as **the law of Conservation of Mass ; no change in the total weight of all the substances taking part in any chemical process has ever been observed.** If A and B represent respectively the weights of two elements which take part in a chemical reaction, producing the weights M and N of two other substances, the law of conservation of mass states that $A + B = M + N$ where " $+$ " means " together with," and " $=$ ", produces. If the weight of one of these four substances be unknown, it can be computed by solving the equation. Chemists constantly use this principle in their work ; for, as Lavoisier said : " Experiments can be rectified by calculations, and calculations by experiments. I have often taken advantage of this method in order to correct the first results of my experiments, and to direct me in repeating them with proper precautions."

When faith in magic was more prevalent than it is to-day, many believed that by some potent incantation or charm, matter could be called out of nothingness, or could be made non-existent.* Superficial observation might lead to the belief that a growing tree, the evaporation of water, and the burning of a candle prove the creation and the destruction of matter, but a careful study of these and innumerable other phenomena, has shown that the apparent destruction of matter is an illusion. Matter may change its state as when liquid water is vaporized, and when a candle is burnt. In the case of a growing tree, the nutrition the tree receives from the soil and from the air (carbon dioxide) is overlooked. Fig. 26 illustrates an instructive experiment which is commonly used to show that the apparent destruction of matter in the burning of a candle is illusory. A candle, A, is fixed on one pan of a balance below a cylinder B. A piece of coarse wire gauze,

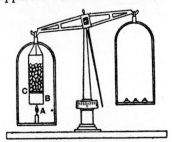

FIG. 26.—Apparent Increase in Weight during Combustion (after H. E. Roscoe and C. Schorlemmer).

C, is fixed in the lower part of the cylinder B. The wire gauze supports a few lumps of quicklime† on which rests a mixture of granulated soda lime and glass wool—the latter to prevent the soda lime clogging the tube. Weights are added to the right scale pan until the beam of the balance is horizontal. The candle is lighted. The gases rising from the flame pass through the cylinder B—and the products of combustion are absorbed by the soda lime. In three or four minutes the pan carrying the candle is depressed as illustrated in the diagram. The increase in weight is due to the fixation of the products of combustion by the soda lime. The products of combustion are formed by the combination of the carbon and hydrogen of the candle with the oxygen of the air. The oxygen of the air was not weighed in the first weighing.

Every time a chemical reaction takes place in a closed vessel, which permits neither the egress nor the ingress of matter, the total weight remains unchanged within the limits of experimental error. The more carefully the experiments are made, the more nearly do the values approach identity. Both A. Heydweiller (1901) and H. Landolt (1893) have tried to find if a loss in weight occurs during chemical action.

In 1900 the former reported the occurrence of small changes in weight when certain reactions were carried out in sealed vessels. Thus 80 gm. of copper sulphate dissolved in 150 c.c. of water and decomposed with

* H. Spencer considers that all the so-called experimental proofs by weighing tacitly assume the object being proved, since weighing implies that the matter forming the weights remains relatively unchanged in quantity; or, as H. S. Redgrove pointed out, weight measures matter because matter is indestructible, and matter is indestructible because weight measures matter.

† To prevent water dropping on to the flame.

15 gm. of metallic iron appeared to suffer a loss in weight of 0·217 mgm.

Landolt conducted a series of experiments beginning in 1893 and continuing until 1908 in order to discover whether these losses were real or could be traced to some source, or sources, of error in the experiment.

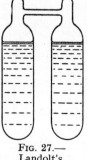

He placed in separate limbs of Jena glass tubes shaped as in Fig. 27, solutions of substances which react without the evolution of much heat (so that disturbances due to this cause might be eliminated so far as possible) and sealed off the tubes. Examples of the substances he employed are :

(i) silver nitrate and potassium chromate ;

(ii) slightly acidified potassium iodate and potassium iodide ;

Fig. 27.—
Landolt's
Experiment.

(iii) lead acetate and sodium sulphide ;

(iv) acidified potassium chromate and sodium sulphite.

The tubes were weighed, using exactly similar tubes as counterpoises, on a balance capable of detecting a change in weight of 1 part in 10,000,000 at its maximum load. One of the tubes was then tilted so as to cause reaction to take place and after cooling it was reweighed, when a very small change (usually a loss) in weight was noted. The counterpoise tube was then tilted and the processes repeated.

In the earlier experiments a slight change (maximum 0·167 mgm.) in weight was observed ; but it was later found, after a very long series of experiments, that the change observed was due to two causes :

(i) the slight evolution of heat caused the evaporation of traces of moisture condensed on the reaction vessel, and these traces did not recondense for a considerable time ;

(ii) the vessel suffered slight expansion owing to the heat evolution and did not recover its original volume until after the lapse of a long period.

By allowing the reaction vessels to stand for a long period after reaction had taken place before re-weighing, Landolt found that they recovered their original weight within the limits of experimental error —in this case 1 part in 10,000,000. Landolt thus concluded that " since there seems no prospect of pushing the precision of the experiments further than the degree of exactness attained, the experimental proof of the law may be regarded as established." The law of the Conservation of Mass can thus be stated : **A variation in the total weight of the substances taking part in chemical reactions, greater than the limits of experimental error, has never been detected.**

J. J. Manley in 1912, using a balance into which he had introduced many refinements, and applying corrections for, or taking precautions to avoid, certain possibilities of error in Landolt's experiments, was able to show that in the case of the reaction between barium chloride and sodium sulphate, any variation must be less than one part in 100,000,000.

§ 4 The Law of Constant Composition

Attention must now be directed to the singular observation made by Jean Rey (1630) that during the calcination of a metal in air, " the weight of the metal increased from the beginning to the end, but when the metal is saturated, it can take up no more air. Do not continue the calcination in this hope : you would lose your labour." Experiments have shown that one gram, and only one gram, of air is absorbed by definite amounts of given metals under the conditions of the experiment, and Lavoisier's work (see p. 425) proves that the *oxygen* of the air is alone absorbed. Accordingly, one part by weight of oxygen is equivalent to :

Oxygen.	Magnesium.	Zinc.	Aluminium.	Copper.	Tin.
1	1·52	4·09	1·12	3·97	3·71

Instead of taking the weight of oxygen unity, it will be more convenient, later on, and also more in accord with general usage, to make oxygen 8 instead of unity. Hence, multiplying the preceding numbers by 8, we obtain :

Oxygen.	Magnesium.	Zinc.	Aluminium.	Copper.	Tin.
8	12·16	32·72	8·96	31·76	29·68

When magnesium is calcined in the presence of oxygen, or air, the metal always unites with the oxygen in the proportion of one part of oxygen per 1·52 parts of magnesium, or 8 parts by weight of oxygen per 12·16 parts by weight of magnesium. The same principle obtains when magnesium oxide is made in several different ways ; and likewise with the other metallic oxides. Hence, as P. G. Hartog puts it : **two like portions of matter have the same composition.** The converse of this statement is not necessarily true.

The exact work of J. S. Stas and of T. W. Richards and many others has firmly established this deduction for the regular type of chemical compounds. J. S. Stas (1860), for example, studied among other things, the composition of silver chloride prepared by four different processes at different temperatures. He found that 100 parts of silver furnished 132·8425, 132·8475, 132·842, 132·848 parts of silver chloride ; and that neither the temperature nor the method of preparation had any influence on the composition of the chloride. The difference between the two extremes is less than 0·006 part per 100 parts of silver. This shows that the errors, incidental to all experimental work, are here remarkably small. Hence, Stas stated : " If the recognized constancy of stable chemical compounds needed further demonstration, I consider the almost absolute identity of my results has now completely proved it."

The student will take notice that *we are unable to prove the law of constant proportions with mathematical exactness.* *However skilful a chemist may be, it is impossible to make an exact measurement without committing an " error of observation " or an " error of experiment."* It is assumed that the small difference 0·005 per cent. between the two extreme results of Stas (1) is wholly due to the unavoidable errors of experiment, for we cannot expect an exact solution of the problem ; and (2) is not due to a very slight inexactitude in the law of constant proportions.

The composition of a definite chemical compound appears to be independent of its mode of formation, and therefore it is inferred that substances always combine in definite proportions. If an excess of one substance be present, the amount in excess is extraneous matter. This deduction from the observed facts is called **the law of definite proportions,** or **the law of constant composition : a particular chemical compound always contains the same elements united together in the same proportions by weight.** Probably no generalization in chemistry is more firmly established than this. It was not discovered by any particular man, but gradually grew among the doctrines of chemistry. The law was tacitly accepted by many before it was overtly enunciated—e.g., J. Rey (1630), I. Newton (1706), G. E. Stahl (1720), F. G. Rouelle (1764), C. F. Wenzel (1777), T. Bergman (1783), etc. So great is the faith of chemists in the truth of this generalization that a few accurate and careful experiments are considered sufficient to settle, once for all, the composition of a substance. For instance, if a substance possessing all the properties of magnesium oxide be given to a chemist, without taking any more trouble, he knows that it will contain 12·16 parts of magnesium for every 8 parts of oxygen.

Historical.—The validity of the law was the subject of an interesting controversy during the years between 1800 and 1808. J. L. Proust maintained that constant composition is the invariable rule ; C. L. Berthollet maintained that constant composition is the exception, variable composition the rule. Proust's words are worth quoting :

According to my view, a compound is a privileged product to which nature has assigned a fixed composition. Nature never produces a compound, even through the agency of man, other than balance in hand, *pondere et messura.* Between pole and pole compounds are identical in composition. Their appearance may vary owing to their manner of aggregation, but their properties never. No differences have yet been observed between the oxides of iron from the South, and those from the North ; the cinnabar of Japan has the same composition as the cinnabar of Spain silver chloride is identically the same whether obtained from Peru or from Siberia ; in all the world there is but one sodium chloride ; one saltpetre ; one calcium sulphate ; and one barium sulphate. Analysis confirms these facts at every step.

.It might be thought that positive assertions of this kind, backed by accurate experimental work, would leave no subject for disputation. But, surveying the battlefield in the light of the present-day knowledge, it seems that another quite different phenomenon was confused with the law of constant composition ; and the methods of analysis were not very precise. Some, probably from the unfounded belief that " Proust deservedly annihilated Berthollet," call the generalization discussed in this section " Proust's Law." In point of fact a phenomenon which Proust apparently did not clearly recognize prevented him from annihilating Berthollet.

§ 5 The Law of Multiple Proportions

The formation of chemical compounds is not a capricious and fortuitous process, but it proceeds in an orderly fashion. Chemical combination is restricted to certain fixed proportions of matter. These limitations appear to have been prescribed by nature as part of her scheme in building the material universe. This fact arrested the attention of J. Rey in 1630. Rey's conclusion that in the calcination of the metals " nature has set limits which she does not overstep," agrees with many facts ; but there are certain limitations. If one gram of lead be calcined for a long time at 500°, never more than 1·103 gram of a red powder—red lead—is obtained. Here, 64 grams of oxygen correspond with 621 grams of lead. If the lead be calcined at about 750°, one gram of lead will not take up more than 0·078 gram of oxygen to form a yellow powder—litharge ; otherwise expressed, 64 grams of oxygen correspond with 828 grams of lead. Here then nature has set *two* limits ; lead forms at least two definite oxides— a red oxide stable at a dull red heat, and a yellow oxide stable at a bright red heat. The relative proportions of lead and oxygen in the two oxides are as follows :

	Oxygen.	Lead:
Red oxide (red lead) . .	64	$621 = 207 \times 3$
Yellow oxide (litharge) . .	64	$828 = 207 \times 4$

This means that for a given weight of oxygen, the yellow oxide has four-thirds as much lead as the red oxide. Similarly, carbon forms two well-defined oxides called respectively carbon monoxide and carbon dioxide. In these we have :

	Oxygen.	Carbon.
Carbon dioxide . . .	8	$3 = 1 \times 3$
Carbon monoxide . . .	8	$6 = 2 \times 3$

At least five oxides of nitrogen are known. In these, the relative proportions of nitrogen and oxygen are as follows :

	Nitrogen.	Oxygen.
Nitrogen monoxide . . .	14	$8 = 1 \times 8$
Nitrogen dioxide . . .	14	$16 = 2 \times 8$
Nitrogen trioxide . . .	14	$24 = 3 \times 8$
Nitrogen tetroxide . . .	14	$32 = 4 \times 8$
Nitrogen pentoxide . . .	14	$40 = 5 \times 8$

These five compounds of the same elements united in different proportions form a series of substances so well marked and contra-distinguished that it is questionable if the most acute human intellect would ever have guessed that they contained the same constituents. Starting from the compound with the least oxygen, we see that for every 14 grams of nitrogen, the amount of oxygen increases by steps of 8 grams. Accordingly, in all five compounds of nitrogen and oxygen, the masses of nitrogen and oxygen are to one another as $m \times 14 : n \times 8$, where m and n are whole numbers. Hundreds of cases equally simple might be cited. Similar facts led J. Dalton (1802-4) to the generalization now called **the law of multiple proportions : when one element unites with another in more than one proportion, these different proportions bear a simple ratio to one another.**

There is no difficulty in tracing the " simple ratio " $m : n$ in the cases which precede, but it is not always easy to detect the *simplicity* of this ratio in perhaps the larger number of cases. For instance, the ratio $m : n$ for compounds of carbon and hydrogen passes from $1 : 4$ in methane, up to $60 : 122$ in dimyricyl, and still more complex cases are not uncommon. Still, the law is considered to be so well founded that it can be applied to predict the composition of compounds which have never been prepared. Thus, if an oxide of nitrogen containing rather more oxygen than nitrogen pentoxide be made, we may predict that it will contain $6 \times 8 = 48$ parts of oxygen for every 14 parts of nitrogen by weight. Again, if a substance be found to contain oxygen and nitrogen, not in the proportion $14 : 8$ or a multiple of 8, it is in all probability a mixture, not a true compound. Thus, air contains oxygen and nitrogen, but the proportions of nitrogen to oxygen is as $14 : 4.29$. This is usually given along with other circumstantial evidence to show the probability that air is a mixture and not a chemical compound.

§ 6 The Law of Reciprocal Proportions

Between 1810 to 1812, J. J. Berzelius published the results of a careful study of the quantitative relations of some of the elements. He found that 100 parts of iron, 230 parts of copper, and 381 parts of lead are equivalent, for they unite with 29·6 parts of oxygen, forming oxides, and with 58·73 parts of sulphur, forming sulphides. Hence, since 58·73 parts of sulphur and 29·6 parts of oxygen unite respectively with 381 parts of lead, then, if sulphur and oxygen unite chemically, 58·73 parts of sulphur will unite with 29·6 parts of oxygen, or, taking the law of multiple proportions into consideration, with some simple multiple or submultiple of 29·6 parts of oxygen. In confirmation, Berzelius found that in sulphur dioxide, 58·73 parts of sulphur are united with 57·45 parts of oxygen. The difference between $2 \times 29·6 = 59·2$ and 57·45 is rather great, but some of the methods of analysis were crude in the time of Berzelius, and very much closer approximations—very nearly 1 in 50,000—have been obtained in recent years.

J. B. Richter, some twenty years before Berzelius's work, proved that a similar relation held good for the combination of acids and alkalies. Berzelius extended Richter's Law* to combinations between the elements. The above relations are included in the generalization sometimes called the **law of reciprocal proportions. The weights —multiple or submultiple—of the various elements which react with a certain fixed weight of some other element, taken arbitrarily as a standard, also react with one another.** If two substances, A and B, each combine with a third substance C, then A and B can combine with each other only in those proportions in which they combine with C, or in some simple multiple of those proportions.

If a compound be formed by the union of two elements A and B, it is only necessary to find the proportion in which a third element C unites with one of the two elements, say A, to determine the proportions in which C unites with B. These numerical relations come out very clearly by comparing the proportions in which the different members of a series of elements, selected at random, combine with a constant weight of several other elements. Suppose the analysis of a substance shows that its ingredients are not in those proportions which we should expect from the known combinations of each of its components with another substance, we might safely infer that the substance analysed is a mixture, and not a single compound.

§ 7 Combining Weights, or Equivalent Weights

The following numbers represent the results obtained by the chemical analysis of a number of substances selected at random :

			Per cent.		Per cent.	
Silicon dioxide .	.	.	Silicon	46·93 ;	Oxygen	53·07
Hydrogen chloride	.	.	Hydrogen	2·76 ;	Chlorine	97·23
Magnesium chloride .	.	.	Magnesium	25·53 ;	Chlorine	74·47
Water .	.	.	Hydrogen	11·18 ;	Oxygen	88·81
Silver chloride .	.	.	Silver	75·26 ;	Chlorine	24·74
Silver fluoride .	.	.	Silver	70·05 ;	Fluorine	29·95

Taking any one of the elements as a standard, let us calculate what amount of each of the other elements will combine with a given quantity of the selected element. Let us take oxygen = 8 as the standard. Starting with silicon, 53·07 parts of oxygen are combined with 46·93 parts of silicon. Consequently, we have the proportion

$$53·07 : 8 = 46·93 : x ;\ \text{or,}\ x = 7·07$$

for silicon when oxygen = 8. Similarly, for water, hydrogen is 1·008 when oxygen is 8. Again, in hydrogen chloride, when hydrogen is 1·008, chlorine is 35·45 ; in silver chloride, silver is 107·88 when chlorine is 35·45 ; when silver is 107·88, fluorine is 19 ; and when

---

* C. F. Wenzel, 1777, is sometimes said to be the father of this generalization. This, however, appears to be an historical error.

chlorine is 35·45, magnesium is 12·16.   Collecting together the results
of these calculations, we get

Oxygen.	Silicon.	Hydrogen.	Chlorine.	Silver.	Fluorine.	Magnesium.
8	7·07	1·008	35·45	107·88	19	12·16

We have previously (p. 53) obtained a number of results for some
metals for the standard O = 8 by a different process, and the number
for magnesium obtained by an indirect process : Oxygen –≫ hydrogen
(water) –≫ chlorine (hydrogen chloride) –≫ magnesium (magnesium
chloride) gives the same result within the limits of experimental error
as was obtained by a totally different process.   Similar results are
obtained in all cases, subject, of course, to the greater risk of experimental error when a long chain of compounds is involved.

These numbers are known as the combining weights, or equivalent
weights of the respective elements for from them it is possible to
deduce the important generalization that **a number can be assigned
to each element which represents the number of parts by weight
of the given element which can enter into combination with 8
parts by weight of oxygen.**   All combining weights are relative
numbers, and they are conventionally referred to oxygen = 8.

The quantity of 8 parts by weight of oxygen had been adopted as
the standard for equivalent weights since oxygen forms a compound
with all the elements except the inert gases and the adoption of this
standard gives us a series of numbers, none of which is less than one,
and most of which are very close to whole numbers.

We thus arrive at the following definition :—

**The combining weight or chemical equivalent of an element
is the number of parts by weight of it which combine with, or
replace, 8 parts by weight of oxygen, or the combining weight
of any other element.**

§ 8 The Atomic Theory

The four laws of chemical combination : (1) the Conservation of
Mass ; (2) the law of constant composition ; (3) the law of multiple
proportions ; and (4) the law of reciprocal proportions, summarize
observed facts.   They exist quite independently of any hypothesis
we might devise about their inner meaning ; but we have an intuitive
feeling that there must be some peculiarity in the constitution of
matter which will account for the facts.

The ancient philosophers of the East—India, Greece, Italy, etc.—
made many quaint guesses at the constitution of matter.   Among
these guesses, we find one taught by Kanáda (the founder of a system
of Hindu philosophy) long prior to the rise of Grecian philosophy.
The same guess was made by Democritus, Leucippus, and Lucretius,
and their guess lives, more or less modified, in modern chemistry.
These philosophers seem to have taught : (1) matter is discrete ; (2)
all substances are formed of atoms which are separated from one

another by void space ; (3) the atoms are in constant motion ; and (4) motion is an inherent property of the atoms. The atoms were supposed to be too small to be perceived by the senses, and they were further supposed to be eternal, indestructible, and unchangeable. Atoms differed from each other in shape, size, and mode of arrangement, and the properties of all substances were supposed to depend upon the nature of the constituent atoms and the way the atoms were arranged. So far as the experimental evidence available to the Grecian philosophers in support of this particular guess is concerned, its long life—in the form of the chemist's atomic theory—can only be attributed to chance. The modern theory, unlike the old speculation, is based upon the observed laws of chemical change, and some physical properties of matter.

Many thinkers—Francis Bacon, Réné Descartes, Pierre Gassendi, Robert Boyle, Robert Hooke, John Mayow, etc.—were more or less partial to a theory of atoms. Isaac Newton (1675) tried to explain Boyle's Law on the assumption that gases were made up of mutually repulsive particles ; and he also referred chemical changes to different associations of the atoms. M. W. Lomonossoff, also, had a fairly clear concept of the atomic structure of matter in 1748 ; while Bryan Higgins (1776) and William Higgins (1789) explained the constant composition of salts, with more or less confidence, in terms of the atoms. Bryan Higgins appears to have held the view that two different atoms combine in the proportions of 1 : 1, and in that proportion only ; while William Higgins imagined a combination in multiple proportions, but believed that the combination 1 : 1 was the most stable.

Dalton's atomic hypothesis.—It is thus impossible to say who invented the atomic theory, because it has grown up with chemistry itself. In the work of William Higgins the hypothesis was little more than an inanimate doctrine. It remained for Dalton to quicken the dead dogma into a living hypothesis. John Dalton (1801) employed the atomic hypothesis to explain the diffusion of gases, and later (1803) based an hypothesis of the structure of matter and of chemical combination upon the following postulates, which may be regarded as a very brief statement of the so-called Dalton's atomic theory :

1. Atoms are real discrete particles of matter which cannot be subdivided by any known chemical process.

2. Atoms of the same element are similar to one another, and equal in weight.

3. Atoms of different elements have different properties—weight, affinity, etc.

4. Compounds are formed by the union of atoms of different elements in simple numerical proportions—1 : 1 ; 1 : 2 ; 2 : 1 ; 2 : 3 ; etc.

5. The combining weights of the elements represent the combining weights of the atoms.

The hypothesis of Dalton respecting atoms, and more particularly atomic weights, is not quite that which prevails in modern chemistry. John Dalton considered the atom to be indivisible, and this is expressed in his aphorism : " Thou knowest no man can split an atom." T. Graham defined the atom not as a thing which cannot be divided but as one which had not been divided. The modern idea is that while the atom is perdurable in chemical changes it may be and probably has been resolved into component parts. A formidable meta-chemistry has been elaborated, and is wholly based on the assumption that an atom is a complex system of sub-atoms or electrons.

§ 9 The Atomic Theory and the Fundamental Laws of Chemistry

It is necessary now to consider how far the Atomic Theory, as propounded by Dalton, agrees with the facts. The most important evidence for it which was available in Dalton's time was its explanation of the fundamental laws of chemistry, viz., the Laws of Constant Composition, of Multiple Proportions and of Reciprocal Proportions.

Since, according to the theory, the atoms are chemically indivisible and indestructible, chemical changes must consist of a rearrangement or interchange of these atoms. No change in weight is to be anticipated from a mere redistribution of portions of matter, the total amount of which remains constant. Hence the atomic theory is in accord with the Law of Conservation of Mass.

When two elements unite to form a compound they do so, according to the theory, because atoms of each element unite in simple numerical proportions, and in any one particular compound this proportion is fixed. Hence, since all the atoms of one element are alike (particularly in weight), the proportions by weight in which the two elements combine to form a given compound must always be the same. This is the Law of Constant Composition.

Suppose that two elements A and B can give rise to three different compounds and suppose that in these there are c atoms of A united with d atoms of B in the first, n of A and m of B in the second, and x of A with y of B in the third. Then the composition by weight of each compound will be :

(i) $ca : db$

(ii) $na : mb$

(iii) $xa : yb$

where a is the weight of an atom of A and b that of an atom of B.

Writing these slightly differently we have :

$$\text{(i)} \quad a : \frac{d}{c} \, b$$

$$\text{(ii)} \quad a : \frac{m}{n} \, b$$

$$\text{(iii)} \quad a : \frac{x}{y} \, b$$

The weights of element B combined with a fixed weight of element A will thus be in the proportion :

$$\frac{d}{c} : \frac{m}{n} : \frac{y}{x}$$

or clearing of fractions :

$$dnx : mcx : ycn.$$

Now all these several quantities are small whole numbers, by the theory, hence each of the products dnx, mcx, ycn will likewise be integers. That is, the proportions of B combining with a fixed weight of A in each of the three compounds is a small whole number. This is the Law of Multiple Proportions.

An exactly similar process of reasoning from the postulates of Dalton's Theory shows it to be in accord also with the Law of Reciprocal Proportions.

§ 10 The Atomic Theory and Atomic Weights

Dalton's Atomic Theory is thus able to give a basis for the fundamental laws of chemistry as deduced by experiment ; but there is one direction in which it proved to be incomplete.

According to the atomic theory : **an atom is the smallest particle of an element which can enter into or be expelled from chemical combination.*** How is the " smallest combining weight " of an atom to be fixed ? In carbon monoxide, for example, we have oxygen and carbon in the following proportions by weight :

Oxygen : Carbon = 8 : 6

and in carbon dioxide

Oxygen : Carbon = 8 : 3

What is the atomic weight of carbon if the atomic weight of oxygen is 8 ? Obviously, the evidence now before us would be consistent with many different views. Carbon monoxide may be a compound of one oxygen atom with two carbon atoms, each with a combining weight of 3 ; or a compound of one oxygen atom with one carbon atom with a combining weight of 6. In the latter case, carbon dioxide is a compound of one carbon atom combining weight 6 with two oxygen atoms,

---

* If we think of the derivation of the word *atom*—from the Greek ἀ, not τέμνω (temno), I cut—" that which cannot be subdivided," we must add "chemically." But our definition of the atom says nothing about subdivision ; nor about the ultimate nature of the atom. The term " atom " was once used to represent the " smallest interval of time," a " moment."

and the same combining weights would have been obtained if any number n of carbon atoms were combined with $2n$ oxygen atoms. Similar difficulties arise when we apply the idea of atoms so far developed to other combinations of the elements. There is, therefore, some confusion. The concept of the atom becomes more or less indistinct and vague when the attempt is made to develop a consistent system on the basis of the atomic hypothesis as propounded by Dalton. **Dalton's theory alone is thus not enough to fix the atomic weights of the different elements.**

The way out of the difficulty was ultimately found as a result of the work of Avogadro, and this must form the subject-matter of the next chapter.

§ 11 Chemical Symbols and Nomenclature

Naming the elements.—A great number of the elements have been christened with names derived from Greek roots. E.g., *iodine*—from its violet vapour ; *chlorine*—from its green colour ; *chromium*—from the colour of its compounds ; *rhodium*—from the rose colour of its salts ; *osmium*—from its smell ; *helium*—from its occurrence in the sun ; *argon*—from its indifference to chemical reagents, etc. Other elements have been named more or less capriciously ; thus some elements are named after particular localities—*strontium*, from Strontian (in Scotland) ; *ruthenium*, from Ruthenia (Russia) ; *yttrium, ytterbium, erbium,* and *terbium* are all derived from Ytterby (in Sweden) ; *palladium* is a name given in honour of the discovery of the planetoid Pallas ; *uranium* in honour of the discovery of the planet Uranus ; *beryllium* is derived from the name of the mineral beryl ; *zirconium*, from the mineral zircon ; *platinum*, from the Spanish " plata," silver ; *thorium*, from " Thor," the son of Odin, a god in Scandinavian mythology ; *vanadium*, from a Scandinavian goddess, Vanadis ; *tantalum*, from Tantalus in Grecian mythology ; and *niobium*, from Niobe, daughter of Tantalus.

Symbols.—The old alchemists used to represent different substances by symbols. For example, gold was represented by the symbol ⊙ or ★, for the sun ; silver, by ☾ the moon. Lavoisier used the symbol ▽ for water ; ⊕ for oxygen. Dalton made a step in advance by representing the atoms of the elements by symbols, and combining these symbols so as to show the elements present in a compound. Thus, ⊙ represented hydrogen ; ○ oxygen ; ● carbon. Water was represented by ⊙○ ; carbon monoxide by ○● ; carbon dioxide by ○●○ These symbols have all been abandoned. They are too cumbrous. To-day we follow J. J. Berzelius's method suggested in, 1811, and use one or two letters from the recognised name of the element to represent any particular element.* Thus, O represents

---

* Some elements have not yet been christened with a name recognized by all. Niobium—symbol Nb—and columbium—symbol Cb—are two different names for one element ; glucinum—symbol Gl—and beryllium—symbol Be—are two different names for another element.

an atom of oxygen ; H, of hydrogen ; C, of carbon ; N, of nitrogen ; etc. The names of ten elements start with C, and to prevent the possibility of confusion, a second leading letter is selected either from the name, or from the alternative Latin name of the element. Thus, C (carbon), Cb (columbium), Ca (calcium), Cd (cadmium), Ce (cerium), Cl (chlorine), Co (cobalt), Cr (chromium), Cs (cæsium), and Cu (cuprum, copper). The elements with alternative Latin names are symbolized : Sb for antimony (Lat. stibium) ; Cu for copper (Lat. cuprum) ; Au for gold (Lat. aurum) ; Fe for iron (Lat. ferrum) ; Pb for lead (Lat. plumbum) ; Hg for mercury (Lat. hydrargyrum) ; K for potassium (Lat. kalium) ; Na for sodium (Lat. natrium) ; and Sn for tin (Lat. stannum).

The evolution of chemical nomenclature.—Up to near the close of the eighteenth century, no systematic attempt had been made to name chemical substances in such a way as to indicate their composition. The names then in vogue were more or less arbitrary, for they were relics of alchemical terms—e.g., *crocus martis*—or derived from their discoverer—e.g., *Glauber's salt*—or based on some superficial resemblance furnishing what J. B. Dumas called the language of the kitchen. Thus, antimony trichloride was called *butter of antimony* because of its buttery appearance ; zinc chloride, *butter of zinc* ; and arsenic chloride, *butter of arsenic*. These three substances were classed together with butter from milk. Similarly with oil of vitriol, olive oil, etc. ; spirits of wine, spirits of salt, etc. T. Bergman and G. de Morveau simultaneously and independently attempted to devise a more complete system of naming chemical compounds. A. L. Lavoisier presented a report to the French Academy and terms like " ic " and " ate," " ous " and " ite " were employed. J. J. Berzelius followed up the subject, and inaugurated the system which is virtually that employed to-day.

Naming the compounds.—Each element forms with other elements a group of compounds which are said *to contain* the respective elements, because the elements in question can be obtained unchanged from the compounds. Consequently **every compound has an elementary or ultimate composition.** Compounds are symbolized by joining together the letters corresponding with the different elements in the compound. Thus, HgO represents a molecule of mercury oxide, a compound of mercury and oxygen. When only two elements are united to form a compound, the name of the second element is modified so that it ends in **ide.**

The symbol for the element also represents one of its atoms. If more than one atom is present in a compound, a small figure is appended to the bottom* right-hand corner of the symbol for an atom of the element, to indicate the number of atoms present. Thus " H_2O " represents a molecule of water, i.e., a compound containing two atoms of hydrogen and one of oxygen ; " CO " represents a molecule of

---

* In France, generally at the top.

carbon monoxide—a compound containing one atom of carbon and one atom of oxygen ; " Na_2CO_3 " represents a molecule of sodium carbonate—a compound containing two atoms of sodium, one atom of carbon, and three atoms of oxygen.   A number affixed in front of a group of symbols represents the number of times that group occurs in the given compound.   Thus crystallized sodium carbonate is symbolized : $Na_2CO_3.10H_2O$.   This means that this compound contains the equivalent of one Na_2CO_3, and ten equivalents of the group H_2O.

Compounds of one element with oxygen are called **oxides,** and the process of combination is called **oxidation.**   When an element forms more than one oxide, a Greek numerical suffix is often prefixed to the word **" oxide."**   Thus, SO_2 is, sulphur dioxide ; SO_3, sulphur trioxide ;   CO, carbon monoxide ; CO_2, carbon dioxide ;   PbO, lead monoxide ; PbO_2, lead dioxide or lead peroxide.

Sometimes the termination **-ic** is affixed to the name of the metal for that oxide which contains the greater proportion of oxygen, and **-ous** for the oxide containing the lesser proportion of oxygen.*   For instance, SnO is either stannous oxide, or tin monoxide ; FeO is ferrous oxide ;   and Fe_2O_3 ferric oxide.   The last-named method of naming the compounds is not always satisfactory when the elements form more than two compounds.   To get over the difficulty, a prefix **hypo-** (meaning " under," or " lesser ") is sometimes added to the compound containing the least, and **per-** (" beyond," " above ") is added to the one with the most oxygen.   Thus,

Persulphuric acid	.	. $H_2S_2O_8$	Perchloric acid	.	.	. $HClO_4$
Sulphuric acid	.	. H_2SO_4	Chloric acid	.	.	$HClO_3$
Sulphurous acid	.	. H_2SO_3	Chlorous acid	.	.	$HClO_2$
Hyposulphurous acid	.	. $H_2S_2O_4$	Hypochlorous acid	.	.	$HClO$

The five nitrogen oxides—nitrogen monoxide, dioxide, trioxide, tetroxide, and pentoxide—would be awkwardly named by this system. Oxides like alumina—Al_2O_3 ;   ferric oxide—Fe_2O_3, etc., are sometimes called *sesquioxides* (Latin, *sesqui*, one-half more).†

The nomenclature of inorganic chemistry is thus based upon the principle that the different compounds of an element with other elements can be named by a simple change in the beginning or termination of the word—witness ferric and ferrous oxides ; and also by the addition of a numerical suffix showing the relative number of atoms of the corresponding element in its compounds.

* For historical reasons, the names of some compounds do not conform to this system because the affix " ic " was assigned to the compound first discovered, and the compounds subsequently discovered were named accordingly.

† The oxides can be roughly divided into two classes.   Some oxides, with water, form acids, and others act as bases.   It is not very easy, at this stage of our work, to draw a sharp line of demarcation between the two.   The *acidic oxides* have a sour taste, and turn a solution of blue litmus red ;   the *basic oxides* turn a solution of red litmus blue, and have a soapy feel.

CHAPTER IV

AVOGADRO'S HYPOTHESIS AND MOLECULES

Avogadro's hypothesis affords a bridge by which we can pass from large volumes of gases, which we can handle, to the minuter molecules, which individually are invisible and intangible.—W. A. SHENSTONE.

Thou hast ordered all things in measure, and number, and weight.—WISDOM OF SOLOMON.

§ 1 Gay-Lussac's Law of Combining Volumes

NOT very long after Dalton had directed the attention of chemists to the relations existing between the weights of elements which combine in different proportions, Gay-Lussac established a similar correspondence between the volumes of combining gases. A. von Humboldt, the naturalist and explorer, collected samples of air from different parts of the world, and, with the aid of J. F. Gay-Lussac, analysed the different samples with the idea of finding if the composition of air was variable or constant. Gay-Lussac used Cavendish's process—explosion of a mixture of air and hydrogen gas. As a preliminary, Humboldt and Gay-Lussac investigated the proportion by volume in which hydrogen and oxygen combine, and found the ratio of hydrogen to oxygen, by volume, to be nearly as 2 : 1, provided that the measurements are made under comparable conditions of temperature and pressure. If either hydrogen or oxygen were in excess of these proportions, the excess remained, after the explosion, as a residual gas. Humboldt and Gay-Lussac (1805) found :

Vols. oxygen.	Vols. hydrogen.	Vols. residue.
100	300	101·1 hydrogen
200	200	101·7 oxygen

After making corrections for impurities, etc., in the gases, Gay-Lussac and Humboldt stated that " 100 volumes of oxygen required for complete saturation 199·89 volumes of hydrogen, for which 200 may be put without error."

Struck by the simplicity of the relation thus found, J. F. Gay-Lussac (1808) followed up the subject by numerous experiments with different gases. As a result, he concluded that " gases always combine in the simplest proportions by volume." For instance, under the same conditions of temperature and pressure, one volume of hydrogen combines with one volume of chlorine forming two volumes of hydrogen chloride ; this fact can be represented diagrammatically :

2 Volumes. 2 Volumes

Two volumes of hydrogen combine with one volume of oxygen forming two volumes of water vapour (which condenses to liquid water if the temperature be below 100°).

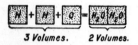

3 Volumes.   2 Volumes.

Three volumes of hydrogen and one volume of nitrogen form two volumes of ammonia. Thus :

4 Volumes.   2 Volumes.

Accordingly, we define **Guy-Lussac's Law : when gases react together, they do so in volumes which bear a simple ratio to one another, and to the volume of the gaseous product of the action.** It is essential, of course, that the initial and final products of the reaction are under the same conditions of temperature and pressure.

More recent investigations of the combining volumes of gases, carried out with many refinements in order to ensure a high degree of accuracy, have shown that the law is not exact. Thus A. Scott in 1893, using pure hydrogen prepared by passing steam over sodium, and oxygen obtained from silver oxide, and replacing the grease normally used for the lubrication of stopcocks by syrupy phosphoric acid (in order to eliminate the error which he found to be due to the carrying over of this grease into the explosion vessel) found that hydrogen and oxygen combine at S.T.P. in the ratio 2·00285 : 1.

More recently Burt and Edgar, in 1915, as a result of 59 determinations, concluded that the ratio is 2·00288, thus agreeing with Scott's value very closely. The special features of their work were :—(i) using very pure gases, prepared by special methods and subjected to rigorous purification and examination before use ; (ii) making all measurements actually at 0° C. and 760 mm. pressure in order to avoid all uncertainty due to deviation of the gases from Boyle's and Charles's Laws.

The gases were obtained by the electrolysis of barium hydroxide solution. The hydrogen was passed over caustic potash and phosphorus pentoxide to dry it, and further purified, either by the action of coconut charcoal at the temperature of liquid air, which readily absorbs nitrogen and oxygen, but which scarcely affects hydrogen, or by passing it over palladium black, which converts any oxygen present to water, followed by passage through the walls of an electrically-heated palladium tube, which is permeable only to hydrogen.

The oxygen was purified by liquefaction (by immersion in liquid air) and careful fractionation.

The purified gases were then passed into a special explosion apparatus where their volumes were accurately determined after three hours immersion in a bath of melting ice and at 760 mm. pressure. They were then exploded, the hydrogen being usually in excess. The water formed was frozen by means of a bath of solid carbon dioxide and acetone (giving a temperature of −78° (approximately). The residual hydrogen was then sucked off through a phosphorus pentoxide tube and its volume accurately measured (again at 0° C. and 760 mm. pressure).

Other gases which have been investigated and their composition by volume accurately determined have similarly yielded results very close to, but not exactly, those which would be expected from Gay-Lussac's Law. Thus Gray and Burt (1909) obtained 1·0079 volumes of hydrogen from 2 volumes of hydrogen chloride gas ; and Guye and Pintza found the combining ratio of nitrogen and hydrogen in ammonia to be 1 : 3·00172.

The deviations of these values from whole numbers are due to the circumstance already referred to that no gas exactly obeys the simple gas-laws, i.e., Boyle's Law and Charles's Law. Furthermore, the magnitudes of these deviations, even when small, are different for different gases. It follows, therefore, that whatever may be the underlying peculiarity of matter which reveals itself in the almost exact generalization of Gay-Lussac's Law, it will not hold with absolute exactness for an arbitrarily assigned pressure and temperature such as those of our Standard Temperature and Pressure must necessarily be ; but since Boyle's Law is more closely obeyed at low pressures, Gay-Lussac's Law will also be more nearly exact at very low pressures. The same reasoning which is held to account for the deviations of known gases from the simple gas laws (see Chapter II) may be taken, therefore, to be the explanation of the non-exactness of Gay-Lussac's Law of Volumes.

In the last chapter we traced the remarkable way in which elements combine by weight to a peculiarity in the constitution of matter ; so here, we are tempted to make a similar quest. It follows at once (1) if elements in a gaseous state unite in simple proportions by volume, and (2) if the elements also unite in simple proportions by atoms, then the number of atoms in equal volumes of the reacting gases must be simply related. J. Dalton concluded that Gay-Lussac's hypothesis required us to assume that equal volumes of the different gases under the same physical conditions contain an equal number—say n—of atoms. If this were so, when two volumes of hydrogen react with one volume of oxygen to form two volumes of steam, $2n$ atoms of hydrogen react with n atoms of oxygen to form $2n$ " compound atoms " of steam. Hence, two atoms of hydrogen react with one atom of oxygen to form two " compound atoms " of steam. In that case, every atom of oxygen must be split into half an atom to make two " compound atoms " of steam. This contradicts the fundamental postulate of the atomic theory, or Dalton's aphorism : " Thou knowest no man can split an atom," meaning, of course, that atoms are indivisible in chemical reactions. Similar contradictions are encountered in nearly every case of combination between gases, hence Dalton rightly claimed this guess to be an untenable assumption and it is clearly necessary we must try another.

§ 2 Avogadro's Hypothesis

A. Avogadro (1811) pointed out that the fallacy in Dalton's reasoning can be avoided if we distinguish clearly between elementary atoms and the small particles of a gas. Avogadro assumed that the small particles of a gas are aggregates of a definite number of atoms, and called these aggregates **molecules** in order to distinguish them from the ultimate atoms. The term " molecule " is the diminutive form of the Latin word *moles*, a mass. Each molecule of an elementary gas contains the same number and kind of atoms.

Hence, modifying Dalton's guess he suggested that **" equal volumes of all gases contain the same number of molecules."** To illustrate how this helps us to resolve the dilemma in which Dalton's suggestion places us, let us for the moment assume that each molecule of hydrogen gas is composed of two atoms of hydrogen, and let us make a similar assumption for oxygen.

Suppose that two volumes of hydrogen contain $2n$ molecules of hydrogen, then one volume of oxygen will contain n molecules. These react to form $2n$ *molecules* of steam—each molecule of steam contains two atoms of hydrogen and one atom of oxygen. Hence, as W. K. Clifford expressed it, although atoms cannot be split so that one atom of oxygen enters into the composition of two molecules of water, yet one molecule of oxygen can be divided between two molecules of water. You cannot put 50 living horses into 100 stables so that there will be the same amount of living horse in each stable, but you can divide 50 *pairs* of horses among 100 stables. The idea can be more clearly illustrated by means of the subjoined diagrams analogous to those used by A. Gaudin about 1832, in which each square represents one volume of a gas. Each volume contains n molecules. We do not know the numerical value of n, but, for the sake of simplicity, take $n = 4$. It makes no difference to the final conclusion what numerical value we assign to n. Then we have :

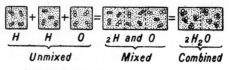

Again, with hydrogen and chlorine,

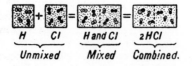

Avogadro thus modified the atomic hypothesis and introduced the conception of two orders of minute particles, (1) the atom as the unit of chemical exchange ; and (2) **the molecule or the smallest particle of an element or compound which exists free in a gas.** This definition of a molecule is usually extended into the less satisfactory definition : **A molecule is the smallest particle of an element or compound which exists in a free state** ; meaning that the specific properties of a substance depend on the component particles remaining intact. If the molecules be subdivided (or augmented) the substance will no longer have the same specific properties, because the nature of the component particles (molecules) is different.

Avogadro's hypothesis, that is to say, that *equal volumes of all gases at the same temperature and pressure contain the same number of molecules*, has proved to be one of the most suggestive and fruitful hypotheses in the development of chemistry. It has correlated what appeared to be antagonistic and contradictory ; it has harmonized what appeared to be discordant and confused, and made Dalton's atomic hypothesis a clear, intelligible and fertile theory. Nevertheless, although put forward as early as 1811, it was not until 1858, by which time confusion had become so serious as to threaten seriously the progress of chemistry as a *science*, that Cannizzaro succeeded in bringing Avogadro's hypothesis prominently before chemists ; until that time it had either been ignored or misunderstood.

§ 3 The Relative Weights of the Molecules

The absolute density of a gas has been defined (Ch. II) as the weight of a normal litre of the gas measured under standard conditions. Similarly the relative density of a gas may be defined as that number which represents how many times heavier any volume of the gas is than an equal volume of a standard gas measured at the same temperature and pressure. Hydrogen is usually taken as this standard gas since it is the lightest gas known, although air has been so used occasionally. Air is a poor standard on account of the variations in its composition which, though small, are yet appreciable in matters of this sort.

By Avogadro's hypothesis, equal volumes of gases contain the same number of molecules, consequently, **the relative density of a gas is proportional to its molecular weight.** For, let n represent the number of molecules in a volume v of each of two different gases at the same temperature and pressure (Avogadro's rule), and if the molecules of each gas are alike so that the molecular masses of the one gas can be represented by m_1, and of the other gas by m_2, then the mass of the one gas will be nm_1, and of the other, nm_2. Let the densities of the two gases be respectively D_1 and D_2, then, since density denotes the mass of unit volume, $D_1 : D_2 = nm_1/v : nm_2/v$; that is $D_1 : D_2 = m_1 : m_2$.

That is to say, the molecular weights of gases are proportional to their relative densities, so that we can determine the molecular weights of gases once we have established a standard for their densities, and hence the numerical relation between relative density and molecular weight. Further, since the molecular weight of a substance is equal to the sum of the atomic weights of all the atoms in the molecule (referred to the same standard as atomic weights), it follows that we have here a method which will help us to decide on the values of the atomic weights of elements, which, as we have seen (Ch. III), is not possible on the basis of Dalton's Theory alone.

Experimental methods for the determination of relative density thus assume considerable importance. Many substances which are solid or liquid at ordinary temperatures can be vaporized at higher temperatures, so that it is also possible to find the relative density of these substances, just as it is for those which are gaseous at ordinary temperatures. The relative density in these circumstances is known as the Vapour Density.

§ 4 Determination of Vapour Density

The relative density of a substance which is gaseous at the ordinary temperature may be determined from a knowledge of its absolute density together with that of hydrogen. The determination of these values is effected by the methods already described (see Ch. II).

In the case of substances which are solid or liquid at ordinary temperatures, but which can be vaporized without decomposition, these methods cannot be employed on account of the elevated temperatures required. For such substances three methods are available, viz. :

   (i) Dumas's method;
   (ii) Hofmann's method;
   (iii) Victor Meyer's method.

The decision as to which method is to be employed in any particular determination will depend upon the amount of substance available and its other properties, as will be seen from the descriptions of these methods which follow.

(i) Dumas's Method

This is an extension of the method used to determine the absolute densities of gases by the globe method, and the principle is therefore that of measuring the weight and volume of a vapour at a known temperature sufficiently high to vaporize the substance completely.

A light glass bulb, A, Fig. 28, between 100 and 200 c.c. capacity is weighed, and from 6 to 10 grams of the compound under investigation are introduced into the bulb. By means of a suitable clamp, D, the

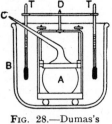

FIG. 28.—Dumas's Vapour Density Apparatus.

bulb is fixed in a suitable bath, B, at a constant temperature 20° to 30° above the boiling-point of the compound under investigation. The compound vaporizes, and when its vapour ceases to issue from the neck, C, of the bulb, the tube is sealed at C by means of a blowpipe with a small flame. The temperature of the bath at the time of sealing is the average between the two thermometers T; the barometric pressure is read at the same time. The bulb is then cooled, cleaned, and weighed. The volume of the bulb is now determined by breaking the tip, C, of the neck under water or mercury, and weighing the bulb when full of liquid.* The difference between the full and empty bulbs gives the amount of liquid in the bulb. The application of the data can be best illustrated by example.

---

* If the globe contains residual air, a correction must be made. The volume of the vapour will be equal to the volume of the globe, less the volume of the residual air ; and the weight of the vapour will be this difference plus the buoyancy of a quantity of air at t and p of the second weighing, equal to the volume of the vapour.

EXAMPLE.—The following data were obtained for vanadium tetrachloride, VCl₄ :

Weight of globe filled with air (9°, 760 mm.)	24·4722 grams
Weight of sealed globe (9°, 760 mm.)	25·0102 grams
Temperature of bath when sealing the globe.	215°
Barometer when sealing the globe	762 mm.
Weight of bulb full of water	194 grams

The globe held 194 less 24·4722 = 169·5 grams of water at 9°. This represents very nearly 169·5 c.c. of water, or the capacity of the globe is 169·5 c.c. The apparent weight of the substance at 9° is 25·0102 − 24·4722 = 0·538 gram. The empty globe was buoyed up, during weighing, by its own bulk of air at 9° and 762 mm., and since 1 c.c. of air at N.T.P. weighs 0·001293 gram, 169·5 c.c. of air at 9° and 762 mm. weigh, at N.T.P. (0·001293 × 169·5 × 273 × 762) ÷ (760 × 282) = 0·213 gram. This, added to 0·538 gram, gives 0·751 gram, the weight of the vapour in the globe at the time of sealing. The 0·751 gram of vapour occupied 169·5 c.c. at 215° and 762 mm. pressure, or 95·10 c.c. at 0° and 760 mm. pressure.

Then, since the weight of 1 c.c. of hydrogen at N.T.P. is 0·00009 grams, we have that the vapour density of vanadium tetrachloride

$$= \frac{0 \cdot 751}{95 \cdot 1 \times 0 \cdot 00009} = 88 \cdot 05$$

Since the vaporization is carried out at atmospheric pressure, it is also necessary to employ fairly high temperatures which makes the method inappropriate for substances which readily decompose ; but the vapour does not come in contact with mercury or any confining liquid and so this method can be used for substances, such as bromine, for which such contact must be avoided. By using porcelain or platinum vessels it can also be employed for substances which only volatilize at very high temperatures.

(ii) Hofmann's method.

This is a modification of an earlier method due to J. L. Gay-Lussac (1811). A known weight of the substance in a small stoppered glass bulb, shown on an enlarged scale at W, Fig. 29, is taken. The bulb is introduced below a barometer tube filled with mercury, and surrounded with a jacket through which the vapour of a liquid, which boils about 20° above the boiling-point of the compound under investigation, is passing. The bulb ascends to the upper level of the mercury, and the substance is thus vaporized under a reduced pressure. When everything is in equilibrium, the volume

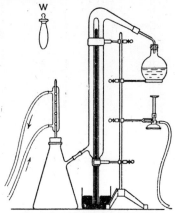

FIG. 29.—Hofmann's Vapour Density Apparatus.

of the vapour is read ; the height of the barometer, and the temperature of the apparatus are also read.

EXAMPLE.—The following data were obtained for carbon tetrachloride, CCl₄:

Weight of liquid in bulb	0·3380 grm.
Volume of vapour	109·8 c.c.
Temperature of vapour	99·5°
Barometer	746·9 mm.
Height of mercury in tube	283·4 mm.

The pressure of the vapour is the barometric height less the height of the column of mercury in the Hofmann's tube, that is, $746·9 - 283·4 = 463·5$ mm. Hence, 0·3380 gram of vapour at 99·5° and 463·5 mm. pressure occupy 109·8 c.c., and 49·09 c.c. at 0° and 760 mm.

So that the vapour density of carbon tetrachloride is

$$\frac{0·3380}{49·09 \times ·00009} = 76·8$$

This method is specially suitable for substances which decompose at or near their boiling-points at normal pressure.

(iii) Victor Meyer's Method.

In Victor Meyer's method, an elegant and simple method first described in 1877, the volume of *air* displaced by a known weight of vapour is determined. It can be carried out more easily and quickly than either of the preceding methods, and requires only small quantities of substance. It is therefore widely used.

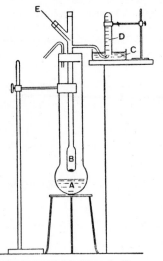

A bulb, *B*—about 200 c.c. capacity —has a long neck fitted with a side tube leading to a pneumatic trough, *C*, Fig. 30. At E is a side tube through which passes a glass rod so arranged that a small glass bottle—*W*, Fig. 29— will rest against it when introduced into the top of the apparatus. The bulb is surrounded as shown by an outer jacket, *A*, containing a liquid which boils at 20° to 30° above the boiling-point of the compound under investigation. To make a determination, a weighed quantity of the substance whose vapour density it is required to find, is introduced into the small stoppered bottle and placed in the apparatus resting against the glass rod *E*. The liquid in the outer jacket is boiled and when no more bubbles pass out through the side tube, a

FIG. 30.—Victor Meyer's Vapour Density Apparatus.

graduated tube, *D*, filled with water is inverted over the side tube. The glass rod, *E*, is partly pulled out so that the small bottle drops into the bulb *B* (which contains a little asbestos or glass wool to break its fall). The substance in the small bottle rapidly vaporizes and drives a stream of air bubbles into the graduated tube. When this stream of bubbles ceases, the tube is carefully transferred to a cylinder of water, and after a time the volume, temperature of the water, and barometric pressure are recorded.

EXAMPLE.—The vapour density of water was determined, and the following data were obtained. Xylene, boiling at about 138°, was used in the hot jacket :—

Weight of water in the stoppered tube W				.	.	0·0102 gram
Temperature of gas in burette			.	.	.	16·5°
Barometer	.	.	.	.	.	703·8 mm.
Volume of gas	.	.	.	.	.	16·6 c.c.

The 16·6 c.c. of vapour at 16·5° and 7˙˙8 mm. becomes 14·496 c.c. at 0° and 760 mm. This is the volume of 0·0102 gram of vapour.

Hence the vapour density of water is $\dfrac{0·0102}{14·496 \times ·00009} = 7·9$

§ 5 The Relation between Vapour Density and Molecular Weight

It was shown on page 69 that the molecular weights of gases are proportional to their relative densities, and that provided the appropriate numerical relationship can be established, the molecular weight of any given gas may be calculated from a knowledge of its vapour density.

The vapour density of a substance has already been defined as the ratio of the weight of a given volume of vapour, under given conditions, to the weight of the same volume of hydrogen under the same conditions. That is, the Vapour Density of a Substance

$$= \frac{\text{Wt. of a certain volume of substance at } t° \text{ C. and B mm. press.}}{\text{Wt. of same volume of hydrogen at } t° \text{ C. and B mm. press.}}$$

By Avogadro's hypothesis, both these volumes contain the same number (say " n ") of molecules. Hence, Vapour Density of Substance

$$= \frac{\text{Wt. of } n \text{ molecules of substance}}{\text{Wt. of } n \text{ molecules of hydrogen}}$$

$$= \frac{\text{Wt. of 1 molecule of substance}}{\text{Wt. of 1 molecule of hydrogen}}$$

Therefore, Molecular Weight of Substance

= Vapour Density of Substance
× Molecular Weight of hydrogen.

For the final solution of our problem it thus becomes necessary to know the molecular weight of hydrogen or, since that is what determines it, the number of atoms in the molecule of hydrogen.

We saw at the beginning of the present chapter that since hydrogen and chlorine combine in the proportion of 1 volume of hydrogen to 1 volume of chlorine to form two volumes of hydrogen chloride, the hydrogen molecule must contain *at least* two atoms of hydrogen. For by Avogadro's hypothesis n molecules of hydrogen furnish the hydrogen atoms required for $2n$ molecules of hydrogen chloride. If a single molecule of hydrogen chloride contains *one* atom of hydrogen only, then the molecule of hydrogen must consist of two atoms. If each molecule of hydrogen chloride contains more than one atom of hydrogen then the hydrogen molecule must consist of a multiple of two atoms.

It will be shown in a later chapter (see p. 504) that chemical evidence indicates that hydrogen chloride contains but one atom of hydrogen per molecule ; hence we conclude that the hydrogen molecule contains two atoms.

Evidence of an entirely different kind confirms this view, for it can be shown that the ratio of the two specific heats of a gas is related to the number of atoms in its molecule.

It will be remembered that " specific heat " is a term employed to represent the amount of heat required to raise the temperature of one gram of a substance 1° C. A gas can be heated by simple compression, its specific heat must then be zero ; but a certain amount of energy, equivalent to the specific heat, is needed for the work of compression. Again, a gas, if it be expanded, is cooled ; if the cooling effect of expansion just counter balances the heat added to the gas, the temperature remains constant ; and the specific heat appears to be indefinitely large. Here work, equivalent to the heat supplied, is performed by the expanding gas. These facts show that the condition of the gas must be stated before it is possible to define its specific heat. It is conventionally agreed that if the gas be allowed to expand during a change of temperature so that its pressure remains constant, the amount of heat required to raise the temperature of one gram of the gas 1° C. shall be called the **specific heat under constant pressure**, and symbolized by c_p. If the pressure be increased so that the volume remains constant when the gas is heated, the amount of heat required to raise the temperature 1° C. is likewise called the **specific heat under constant volume,** and symbolized c_v.

In the following discussion, it will be remembered that the Kinetic Theory assumes that the temperature is proportional to the average speed of translation of the moving molecules—an increase of the speed is accompanied by a rise of temperature, and conversely. The heat imparted to a gas is not spent merely in raising the temperature of the gas ; that is, in speeding up the motions of the molecules. Energy is spent in—

(1) *Augmenting the speed of the moving molcules.*—The heat required actually to increase the kinetic energy of the moving molecules so as to produce a rise of temperature is the same for all gases. Let a denote this quantity.

(2) *Performing external work.*—Heat energy is needed to overcome the pressure of the atmosphere when the gas is allowed to expand.

Call this quantity b. Since the coefficient of thermal expansion of all gases is the same (p. 15), this quantity is practically constant for equal volumes, or equimolecular weights.

(3) *Performing internal work.*—Heat energy is required to produce changes within the molecule which may alter the motions or orientation of the constituent atoms of the molecule, or raise the kinetic energy of the atoms moving within the molecule. Let c denote the energy spent within the molecule per degree rise of temperature. A certain amount of energy must also be spent in overcoming the effects of intermolecular attractions (p. 33). This can be neglected for the time being.

The ratio of the two specific heats may now be written :

$$\frac{C_p}{C_v} = \frac{a + b + c}{a + c}$$

The specific heat of a gas at constant volume.—We have seen, p. 27, that $pv = \frac{1}{3}MV^2$ where M denotes the mass, and V the average velocity of the molecules. But the kinetic energy of a body of mass M moving with a velocity V is $\frac{1}{2}MV^2$; hence $pv = \frac{2}{3} \times \frac{1}{2}MV^2$; or the kinetic energy of the molecular motions is $\frac{3}{2}pv$. But $pv = RT$, p. 18. Hence the kinetic energy of molecular motion is $\frac{3}{2}RT$. If one gram-molecule the kinetic energy becomes $\frac{3}{2}R(T + 1)$. Hence if the gas be heated 1° C. at constant volume, the thermal value of the increased kinetic energy is $\frac{3}{2}R(T + 1) - \frac{3}{2}RT = \frac{3}{2}R$ cals. This result represents the specific heat of the gas at constant volume ; or $C_v = \frac{3}{2}R$.

The external work done by an expanding gas.—Again, if a gram-molecule of gas expands against atmospheric pressure when its temperature is raised 1° C., the gas, in consequence, does work by pressing back the atmosphere, so to speak. The equivalent of this work must be supplied in the form of heat. This work is equivalent to the product of the pressure against the change in volume. Let x denote the change in volume when the gas is heated 1° C., under a constant pressure ; then, $p(v + x) = R(T + 1)$, and $pv = RT$, p. 18. By subtraction $px = R$. This means that when a gram-molecule of gas is heated 1° C., the resulting expansion against atmospheric pressure does work equivalent to R cals.

The specific heat at constant pressure.—Hence, R cals. must be added to the previous result to obtain the thermal equivalent of the energy supplied to one gram-molecule of gas in the form of heat when its temperature is raised 1°. That is, if one gram-molecule of gas be heated 1°, at constant pressure, an amount of heat equivalent to $\frac{3}{2}R + R = \frac{5}{2}R$ is required. This result represents the specific heat of the gas at constant pressure, or $C_p = \frac{5}{2}R$.

From these results we can evaluate the ratio of the two specific heats (usually denoted by the symbol γ) for

$$\gamma = \frac{C_p}{C_v} = \frac{\frac{5}{2}R + c}{\frac{3}{2}R + c}$$

The value of c will vary for different gases, for it is related to the molecular complexity of the gas, and for a monatomic gas it may be expected to be zero. When $c = 0$ we then have

$$\gamma = \tfrac{5}{3} = 1 \cdot 667.$$

Experimental determinations of the value of γ for various gases show that the maximum value so far found is $1 \cdot 667$ and that the remaining values fall into fairly well-defined groups, as can be seen from the following table :—

TABLE III—RATIO OF THE TWO SPECIFIC HEATS OF GASES.

Gas.	Mole-cule.	Atoms per mole-cule.	γ	Gas.	Mole-cule.	Atoms per mole-cule.	γ
Mercury	Hg	1	1·67	Carbon dioxide	CO_2	3	1·31
Argon	A	1	1·65	Nitrous oxide	N_2O	3	1·31
Hydrogen	H_2	2	1·41	Hydrogen sulphide	H_2S	3	1·31
Nitrogen	N_2	2	1·41	Ammonia	NH_3	4	1·30
Oxygen	O_2	2	1·40	Methane	CH_4	5	1·27
Carbon monoxide	CO	2	1·40	Ethylene	C_2H_4	6	1·24
Hydrogen chloride	HCl	2	1·39	Ethane	C_2H_6	8	1·18
Chlorine	Cl_2	2	1·32	Alcohol	C_2H_5OH	9	1·13
Bromine	Br_2	2	1·29	Benzene	C_6H_6	12	1·09
Iodine	I_2	2	1·29	Ether	$C_4H_{10}O$	15	1·06
Iodine chloride	ICl	2	1·31	Turpentine	$C_{10}H_{16}$	26	1·03

There is thus a group of gases for which γ is round about $1 \cdot 65$, another for which it is approximately $1 \cdot 4$ and so forth. There is no gas for which the value is much above $1 \cdot 4$ unless it is about $1 \cdot 65$, the theoretical value for a monatomic gas. It seems, therefore, reasonable to conclude that gases for which γ is $1 \cdot 4$ are diatomic, especially as when applied this conclusion is found to be in agreement with the chemical evidence.

Thus, the ratio of the two specific heats of hydrogen being $1 \cdot 41$ we have confirmation for the view that the hydrogen molecule contains two atoms.

Hence, resuming the discussion of the relation between vapour density and atomic weight, we have, as has been shown,

Mol. Wt. = Vap. Density × Mol. Wt. of hydrogen.

Since the atomic weight of hydrogen is 1 approximately (see p. 106), its molecular weight is therefore 2 and we have accordingly :

Molecular Weight of a Substance
                = 2 × Vapour Density.

§ 6 The Gram-Molecular Volume of a Gas at N.T.P.

We are now in a position to calculate another important constant, viz., the volume occupied at standard temperature and pressure by a gram-molecular weight (i.e., the number of grams numerically equal to the molecular weight) of any gas. Avogadro's Hypothesis shows us that this volume will be the same for all gases, so that if we calculate this value for one gas we shall, theoretically, know its value for all other gases.

The molecular weight of hydrogen has been shown to be twice its atomic weight. Hydrogen was formerly taken as the standard of atomic weights and hence its atomic weight was put at unity, and this is the value employed above. But, as will be explained in Chapter VI, it is now usual to take oxygen as the standard element with an atomic weight of 16. The atomic weight of hydrogen then becomes 1·008 and its molecular weight 2·016 in consequence.

Hence a gram-molecular weight of hydrogen = 2·016 grams.

The density of hydrogen is 0·09 grams per litre at N.T.P.

∴ 1 gram-molecular weight of hydrogen occupies $\dfrac{2·016}{0·09} = 22·4$

litres at N T.P.

Now consider another gas of molecular weight M.

$$\text{Since } M = \frac{\text{Weight of 1 molecule of substance}}{\text{Weight of 1 atom of hydrogen}}$$

Weight of 1 molecule of substance

$$= M \times \text{Weight of 1 atom of hydrogen}$$

1 gram-molecular weight of substance weighs M grams

∴ M grams of substance contain

$$\frac{M}{M \times \text{weight of 1 atom of hydrogen}} \text{ molecules}$$

$$= \frac{1}{\text{Weight of 1 atom of hydrogen}} \text{ molecules.}$$

That is to say, the gram-molecular weights of all gases contain the same number of molecules. Therefore, the gram-molecular weight of any gas at N.T.P. will occupy the same volume as 2·016 grams of hydrogen, that is, 22·4 litres.

This is a very important fact, and it can be used in calculating molecular weights, for if the weight of 22·4 litres of a gas of unknown molecular weight be determined, its gram-molecular weight, which is numerically equal to its molecular weight, is known. The results of the typical vapour density experiments given on pages 70-73 could have been used in this way to evaluate the molecular weights of the several substances.

§ 7 The Avogadro Number

It has just been shown that the number of molecules in a gram-molecular weight of any gas at N.T.P. is a constant. This constant is usually denoted by the symbol, N, and is called Avogadro's Constant or the Avogadro Number Its value has been found by several independent methods with results so concordant as to furnish very strong support indeed for the Molecular Theory. The accepted value is $6 \cdot 062 \times 10^{23}$.

The most direct method is that due to Rutherford and Geiger who counted the number of α-particles emitted from radium (see Ch. IX, p. 131 ; Ch. XXXVI, p. 849) in a given time, and collected the helium produced by a large quantity of radium in a long period. Since each α-particle becomes a helium atom, this gives a means of calculating the Avogadro Number.

Other methods which have been employed are based on the study of the Brownian movement (see Ch. XVI, p. 248) and the determination of the charge of the electron (see Ch. IX, p. 128).

CHAPTER V

EQUIVALENT WEIGHTS

Since it is already settled for us by custom that quantities of different substances are to be called equal when or because they are equivalent gravimetrically, we have no choice but also, from the chemical point of view, to call those quantities of substance equal which interact in single chemical changes.—E. DIVERS, 1902.

§ 1 Definition of Equivalent Weights of Substances

IN Chapter III (p. 57) it was shown that it is possible to assign to each element a number which represents the number of parts by weight of the given element which can enter into combination with eight parts by weight of oxygen, and that this number is known as the Combining Weight or the Equivalent Weight of the element. This quantity is defined as the number of parts by weight of an element which combine with, or replace, eight parts by weight of oxygen, or the combining weight of any other element.

Some such conception as that of the equivalent weight was in the minds of chemists quite early in the " modern " period of the subject. Thus Cavendish in 1766 called a given weight of potash the equivalent of another (different) weight of lime if both were able exactly to neutralize the same weight of an acid. In 1788 he demonstrated that the quantities of nitric and sulphuric acids which neutralized two identical weights of potash would also decompose identical weights of marble—different in weight, of course, from the potash. This seems to have been the first clear recognition of the principle of equivalents as understood chemically, and pre-dated Dalton's Atomic Theory (of which it is a logical consequence) by some fifteen years.

The generalization of these results is due to J. B. Richter who, in 1792, published a table of equivalent weights of acids and bases.

This early work serves to remind us that the conception of equivalents is not confined to elements, but applies also to compounds, that is to say, to any pure substance which is able to enter into a chemical reaction. This is an important matter in volumetric analysis which depends upon the use of solutions of known strength. The standard adopted for the strengths of such solutions is that known as a **normal** solution which is defined as **a solution which contains the gram-equivalent weight of a substance in a litre of solution.** The gram-equivalent weight is the number of grams of the substance numerically equal to the equivalent weight.

The equivalent weight of any pure substance is defined in the first instance as that weight of it which combines with, or replaces, the equivalent weight of hydrogen. Since the molecule of hydrogen consists of two atoms, its equivalent weight will· be half its molecular weight. Hence, since (p. 77) the gram-molecular weight of hydrogen

occupies 22·4 litres at N.T.P., the gram-equivalent weight of hydrogen
will occupy 11·2 litres at N.T.P.

Further, as a normal solution is one which contains a gram-equivalent weight in one litre of solution, one litre of the solution will react
with the gram-equivalent weight of any other substance with which it
is capable of entering into a reaction.

We thus arrive at the following comprehensive definition :—**The
gram-equivalent weight of a substance is that weight of it which
will combine with or displace 11·2 litres of hydrogen (measured
at N.T.P.) or 8 grams of oxygen, or the known equivalent of
any other element or react with 1 litre of any normal solution.**

In accordance with this definition the following definitions are sometimes employed in particular cases :—

(*a*) The equivalent weight of an **acid** is that weight of it which
contains one equivalent weight of replaceable hydrogen.

(*b*) The equivalent weight of an **oxidizing agent** is that weight of
it which contains one equivalent weight (i.e., 8 parts by weight) of
available oxygen.

§ 2 The Determination of Equivalent Weights

It is evident that the determination of the equivalent weights of
the elements is of fundamental importance, both on account of their
practical use in all quantitative, and particularly analytical, operations,
and also on account of their being, as will be seen in the next chapter,
the basis for the determination of Atomic Weights.

The different methods available for the determination of equivalent
weights may be summarized under the following heads :—

      (i) Hydrogen displacement.
     (ii) Oxide methods.
    (iii) Chloride methods.
    (iv) Replacement methods.
     (v) Electrolysis.
    (vi) Conversion methods.

§ 3 Equivalent Weight by Hydrogen Displacement

This method can be used for those metals which readily liberate
hydrogen from dilute solutions of mineral acids or of alkalies.   Thus
it can be employed to determine the equivalents of zinc, iron and
magnesium by the action of these metals with dilute hydrochloric acid ;
of aluminium, by its action with either dilute hydrochloric acid or
caustic soda solution.   The method can also be modified so as to apply
to sodium, by allowing it to react with alcohol, from which it displaces
hydrogen easily and smoothly.   It is evident, however, that the
method of hydrogen displacement can only be used for the determination of the equivalent weight of a limited number of metals.

The method may be explained by reference to Fig. 31.

The apparatus consists of a measuring-tube and a levelling tube containing water, connected by rubber tubing as shown. The flask contains dilute acid (or alkali or alcohol, as above) and a small tube is suspended in it containing a weighed quantity of the metal whose equivalent is to be determined. To perform the experiment the levelling-tube is raised until the surface of the water in the measuring tube is at zero, and on the same level as the water in the levelling tube, the flask being detached while this is being done. The flask is now attached to the apparatus; the levelling tube is raised or lowered until the water levels in both tubes are the same, and the position of the level in the measuring tube is read. The flask is then tilted

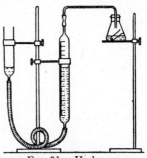

FIG. 31.—Hydrogen Displacement Method.

so that the metal comes in contact with the acid, and the levelling-tube is lowered at the same time. When all the metal has dissolved, and the apparatus has had time to cool to room temperature, the levels in the two tubes are again made the same. The position of the water level in the measuring tube is then read, thus giving the volume of hydrogen which has been liberated. The height of the barometer is then found, and the temperature of the room noted. The volume of hydrogen is then corrected to N.T.P., allowance being made for the pressure of aqueous vapour, since the moist gas has been measured (see pp. 20-31). We now have the volume of hydrogen at N.T.P. liberated by a known weight of metal, whence we can calculate the equivalent of the metal since 1 litre of hydrogen at N.T.P. weighs 0·09 grams ; or put in another way, since the equivalent of hydrogen occupies 11·2 litres at N.T.P.

§ 4 Oxide Methods

Methods for finding the equivalent weight of an element involving the use of the oxide may be subdivided thus :

(a) direct oxidation (direct synthesis) ;
(b) indirect oxidation (indirect synthesis) ;
(c) reduction of the oxide (analysis).

Direct Oxidation

The exact procedure to be followed depends upon the nature both of the element and of its oxide. Where a solid element burns reasonably slowly to a solid oxide, the conversion may be carried out in a crucible. If a gaseous oxide is formed, as in the case of carbon, a suitable means of discovering the weight of the oxide must be devised. For gaseous elements like hydrogen, a special technique has to be employed and much ingenuity has been expended in coping with this problem. (See Ch. VI for an account of the determination of the hydrogen-oxygen ratio.)

The method may be illustrated by experiments with calcium and with carbon.

The equivalent weight of calcium may be found by placing in a weighed crucible a known weight of calcium turnings and heating gently until the calcium burns, continuing the heating until all the action is over. The crucible is then allowed to cool and a few drops of water are added from a pipette,* the addition being made very carefully so as to avoid any loss due to the vigour of the reaction which takes place. The crucible is then heated again, at first gently, and then strongly, after which it is allowed to cool in a desiccator, and re-weighed. It is then repeatedly re-heated, cooled and re-weighed until a constant weight is attained.

From these weighings we know the weight of oxygen which has combined with a known weight of calcium. Hence the weight of calcium which would combine with eight grams of oxygen (i.e., the equivalent weight of calcium) can be calculated.

This method is sometimes recommended for the determination of the equivalent of magnesium, but it is not completely satisfactory for this metal for the following reasons. First, it is very difficult to prevent loss of magnesium oxide in the form of fumes; second, the magnesium attacks the lining of the crucible; and third, the weight of magnesium used is small and so relatively large errors are incurred in the still smaller weight of oxygen.

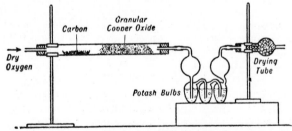

Fig. 32.—Equivalent Weight of Carbon.

The diagram (Fig. 32) illustrates, in simplified form, the apparatus employed by Stas to find the equivalent of carbon. A silica boat containing a weighed quantity of pure, dry carbon is heated in a current of pure dry oxygen and the carbon dioxide formed is absorbed

---

* Strictly speaking, in this case, the oxidation is partly direct and partly indirect. The calcium combines to some extent with the nitrogen of the air as well as with the oxygen, and water is added to convert the nitrogen compound so formed into the oxide. If the experiment were done in oxygen instead of air this would not be necessary.

in potash bulbs, containing a strong solution of caustic potash, which are weighed before and after the experiment. The drying tube is weighed along with the potash bulb, since its function is to prevent water vapour being carried out of the apparatus by the stream of oxygen passing through it. The tube in which the boat is heated is packed with dry, granular copper oxide, which is heated before the carbon in the boat is allowed to burn. This is done to ensure complete conversion to carbon dioxide, since any carbon monoxide formed would not be absorbed by the caustic potash solution ; should any carbon monoxide be formed it would be converted into carbon dioxide by the hot copper oxide (see Ch. XIX).

The loss in weight of the boat and contents in the experiment gives the weight of carbon burned, while the increase in weight of the potash bulbs gives the weight of carbon dioxide. Hence the equivalent can be calculated.

The equivalent weight of sulphur can be found in a similar manner, the use of copper oxide being unnecessary, however, in this case.

Indirect Oxidation

This method has to be employed when the required oxide is not formed by heating the element in air or oxygen. Examples of the application of this method are furnished by copper and tin.

With either of these metals conversion into the oxide can only be superficially effected by direct oxidation, but can easily be brought about indirectly by means of nitric acid. A weighed quantity of the metal is treated with a slight excess of somewhat diluted nitric acid and, after the first action has subsided somewhat, is warmed gently, and finally evaporated to dryness, care being taken to avoid loss. The dry residue is then heated strongly to constant weight. Copper, zinc, lead and magnesium are converted by this process, first, into their nitrates (see pp. 410, 619), and then by strong heating into the oxides. Tin does not form a nitrate, but an insoluble white compound, meta-stannic acid, results (see p. 696) which, when strongly heated, loses water, leaving stannic oxide.

Experiments such as these give the weight of oxide formed from a known weight of metal, from which the equivalent weight of the metal can be calculated.

Reduction of the Oxide

In this method the principle is the exact converse of the two preceding ones. In them a known weight of metal is converted, directly or indirectly, into the oxide whose weight is found. In the present method, a known weight of oxide is reduced to the metal. The method is applicable to those elements whose oxides are reduced at a moderate temperature by the action of hydrogen, or carbon monoxide (or coal-gas).

The process may be exemplified again by reference to copper, and is illustrated by Fig. 33.

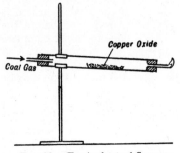

FIG. 33.—Equivalent of Copper.

A weighed quantity of dry copper oxide is placed in a porcelain or silica boat in a hard glass tube arranged as in the diagram. Hydrogen, or coal gas, is passed through the tube until all the air has been expelled and is then lighted at the jet as shown. The tube in the neighbourhood of the boat is then heated, at first gently and then more strongly until the reduction appears to be complete. The tube is then allowed to cool with the stream of gas still passing, the boat transferred to a desiccator and re-weighed. The process is repeated until a constant weight is obtained.

The calculation of the equivalent weight is carried out in the same way as in the two previous methods.

§ 5 Chloride Methods

The determination of equivalent weights by way of the chlorides of elements is one of the methods employed very widely in the most accurate atomic weight work (see Ch. VI, p. 96). It depends upon the fact that silver chloride is practically insoluble and that silver can be readily obtained in a high degree of purity. Also a very large number of elements form soluble chlorides which can be prepared in a high degree of purity. The equivalent weights of chlorine and silver are known very accurately and the extent of the very slight solubility of silver chloride is also known. Hence the method is one of wide application and capable of a high order of accuracy.

The procedure may be illustrated by the following simple experiment. A small quantity of pure, dry sodium chloride is weighed out on a small watch glass and then carefully transferred to a clean beaker, the last particles of salt being washed into the beaker by means of distilled water from a wash-bottle, and sufficient distilled water is added to dissolve all the salt completely. A little dilute nitric acid is also added. Silver nitrate solution is then added carefully, and a precipitate of silver chloride is formed. Silver nitrate solution is added until no further precipitate results on the addition of another drop of solution. The precipitate is then filtered off on a weighed filter paper or Gooch crucible (see below), care being taken to transfer every particle of precipitate to the paper and to wash thoroughly with distilled water until no soluble salts remain. The filter paper and precipitate are then dried in a steam oven and re-weighed.

The calculation of the equivalent weight from such an experiment is best illustrated by means of an example. In an experiment 0·6215 gms. of sodium chloride gave 1·5210 gms. of silver chloride. The equivalent weight of silver is 107·88 and that of chlorine 35·46. Hence if E is the equivalent of sodium we have

$(E + 35·46)$ gms. of sodium chloride give $(107·88 + 35·46)$ gms. of silver chloride

$$\therefore \frac{E + 35·46}{143·34} = \frac{0·6215}{1·5210}$$

$$\therefore E = 23·01.$$

The Gooch Crucible

This consists of a crucible of the shape shown in Fig. 34, having the base pierced by a number of fine holes. By pouring into the crucible a suspension of finely-ground, purified asbestos in distilled water, a thin pad of asbestos is formed over the bottom of the crucible. The crucible prepared in this way is then dried and weighed and is ready for the filtration of a precipitate. Filtration is effected by means of gentle suction, using the apparatus shown in Fig. 34.

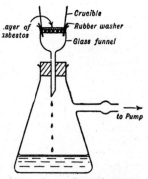

FIG. 34.—Gooch Crucible in use.

§ 6 Replacement Methods

This method depends upon the fact that some metals such as zinc, which are high in the electro-chemical series (see p. 204), will displace those lower in this series from solutions of their salts. A familiar example of this is the " plating " of the blade of a steel pen-knife with copper by dipping the blade into a solution of copper sulphate (see p. 586). The determination of equivalent weights by this method depends upon a knowledge of the equivalent weight of either the displacing or the displaced element, from which the equivalent weight of the other can be calculated from a knowledge of the weight of one element displaced by a known weight of the other.

The exact procedure to be followed will depend upon the particular element being displaced, but in general differs only in detail from the following.

A known weight of zinc foil is added to excess of copper sulphate solution contained in a porcelain dish, and the solution warmed slightly. The surface of the foil will be seen to become coated with copper, but by tapping it with a glass rod the copper can be made to flake off. In time all the zinc will have disappeared and a precipitate of copper will have been formed. This precipitate is very carefully transferred to a tared filter paper, great care being taken to remove all the particles of copper from the dish to the filter paper. The precipitate is then washed with distilled water until the washings no longer give a blue colour with ammonia solution (see p. 590), and then with a little alcohol. The precipitate is then dried in a steam oven to constant weight.

Theoretically, this method can also be employed with suitable modification for the determination of the equivalent weights of silver, lead, mercury and gold, all of which are displaced quantitatively from solutions of their salts, when treated with metallic zinc. In actual practice the method is not of wide application.

§ 7 Equivalent Weight Determination by Electrolysis

As a result of his experiments on the conduction of electricity through solutions of electrolytes, Faraday in 1834 was led to formulate two Laws of Electrolysis (see p. 191). The second of these laws, which states that " the same quantity of electricity passing through solutions of different electrolytes, liberates weights of elements which are proportional to their chemical equivalents," furnishes us with a method for finding the equivalent weights of some elements.

We shall see in Chapter XII that the passage of a current of electricity through slightly acidified water brings about the liberation of hydrogen at the cathode ; and similarly with a solution of copper sulphate, copper is deposited on the cathode. It is thus possible to use the process of electrolysis to find the equivalent weight of copper.

To do this an apparatus for the electrolysis of acidulated water is so arranged that the hydrogen evolved from the cathode may be collected and measured accurately, and is connected in series with an apparatus for the electrolysis of copper sulphate solution, and with a suitable variable resistance and a galvanometer. The plate forming the negative plate (or cathode) of the copper apparatus is cleaned and carefully weighed before and after the experiment. A current of about 0·01 amperes is used, a small value being necessary in order to ensure the formation of a compact deposit of copper. The current is allowed to pass until 50 to 100 c.cs. of gas have been collected. The increase in weight of the copper cathode is determined after washing and careful drying, and the volume of hydrogen liberated is measured and corrected to N.T.P. We thus know the quantities of hydrogen and of copper liberated by the same current, from which we can readily calculate the equivalent of copper.

§ 8 Conversion Methods

As we shall see in Chapter VI, the determination of the atomic weight of an element usually begins by an accurate determination of its equivalent weight, which latter quantity is generally found by some form of conversion method. The chloride method of finding equivalent weights considered on page 84 is an example of a conversion method and is one very frequently employed. Other examples would be the conversion of an oxide into its chloride, or other salt ; a chloride may be converted into a sulphate ; or a chlorate into a chloride. A definite weight of one compound is taken and the weight of the new compound into which it is converted is found. For the subsequent calculation of the equivalent weight, certain fundamental equivalent weights must be known, such as those of chlorine, silver, etc. The process of calculation is similar to that explained on page 85.

The experiments outlined in this chapter, illustrating the various methods available for finding equivalent weights, have been described in a relatively simple form in which they might be carried out by a careful student in any reasonably equipped laboratory. We shall see in the next chapter how these same methods, in the hands of the great masters of quantitative chemistry, have been made capable of yielding results of the highest accuracy, and so form the basis of our accepted values for the Atomic Weights of the elements.

CHAPTER VI

ATOMIC WEIGHTS

Every chemical element is regarded as having a distinct nature of its own, which nature, moreover, determines all its activities.—B. P. Browne.

§ 1 Atomic Weights and the Atomic Theory

WE have seen in Chapter III that the Atomic Theory as enunciated by Dalton suffered from one major defect, viz., that although it gives a definition of an atom as the smallest particle of an element which can enter into, or be expelled from, chemical combination, it does not help us to decide what the smallest combining weight is. The sort of difficulty which arises in attempting to fix the relative weights of the atoms was also pointed out in regard to the element carbon (see p. 61). As was then shown, the root of the difficulty is the uncertainty as to the number of atoms entering into combination.

Dalton himself had made the purely arbitrary assumption that when only one compound of two given elements was known, it was considered to be compounded of one atom of each. As was only to be expected, this unwarranted assumption soon led to confusion, and, coupled with the lack of any clear distinction between atoms and molecules, brought about a state of affairs in which, for the time being, almost all attempts to fix the relative weights of the actual atoms was abandoned, and attention was concentrated on combining weights or equivalent weights.

The solution of the problem was indicated by Avogadro in 1811, but it was not until 1858 when Cannizzaro showed how Avogadro's hypothesis could be applied to it that the confusion and difficulty was finally removed.

It is important to notice, before proceeding further, that what is termed the atomic weight of an element is a relative weight. The *absolute* weights of the atoms, although now known with a fair degree of accuracy, do not concern us here, but only the *relative* weights of the atoms of the different elements. For practical purposes this involves the fixing of an arbitrary standard, which was at one time based on hydrogen as unity; but is now taken from oxygen = 16 (p. 95).

§ 2 Atomic Weight from the Molecular Weight of Volatile Compounds by Cannizzaro's Method

Referring back to the difficulty in fixing the atomic weight of carbon from the ratio of the weights of carbon and oxygen in carbon dioxide, we saw that the problem is essentially to determine the number of atoms of each element contained in one molecule of the compound.

In Chapter IV it was shown that by means of vapour density measurements it is possible to find the molecular weights of volatile compounds. Furthermore, by way of ordinary chemical analysis the proportions in which the constituents are combined can be determined. Neither of these measurements implies *a priori* any views as to the number of atoms in the molecules of the compounds in question.

Now suppose, in the case of carbon, that by processes such as these, the composition of a number of volatile carbon compounds, their vapour densities and molecular weights have been found. Then, as in Table IV, the amount of carbon per molecule in each compound can be calculated.

TABLE IV.—MOLECULAR WEIGHTS OF SOME CARBON COMPOUNDS.

Volatile compound of carbon.	Composition by weight.	Molecular weight.	Amount of carbon per molecule.
Carbon monoxide .	Carbon 12 ; oxygen 16	28	12
Carbon dioxide .	Carbon 12 ; oxygen 32	44	12
Methane . . .	Carbon 12 ; hydrogen 4	16	12
Ethylene. . .	Carbon 24 ; hydrogen 4	28	$12 \times 2 = 24$
Propylene . .	Carbon 36 ; hydrogen 6	42	$12 \times 3 = 36$
Carbon disulphide .	Carbon 12 ; sulphur 64	76	12

The smallest weight of carbon in a molecule of any of its known compounds is 12, and consequently this number is assumed to be the atomic weight of carbon. The atomic weights of a great number of the elements have been determined in a similar manner.

The actual method used in finding the atomic weight of an element thus involves :

(1) An exact analysis of a compound containing the given element ; and consequently the compound investigated must be one which lends itself to exact analysis.

(2) The compound must be one which can be prepared in a highly purified condition.

(3) The compound must be volatile without decomposition, so that its vapour density can be determined.

(4) The compound must contain the smallest proportion of the element under investigation. This matter may need further amplification.

It is important to examine as large a number of volatile compounds as possible when fixing the atomic weight of an element. If only a small number of compounds be examined, there is always a possibility, and perhaps a probability, that the actual minimum weight does not occur amongst the set of compounds taken. It follows, therefore, that the **atomic weight of an element is the least amount of that element present in any molecule of all its known volatile com-**

pounds. The value so obtained is the maximum possible value ; the real value may afterwards prove to be a submultiple of this. The atomic weight must be a whole multiple or submultiple of its combining weight. Owing to the fact that the molecular weights of so many volatile compounds of carbon are known it is not very probable that the atomic weight of carbon is less than 12.

This method of fixing atomic weights is due to Cannizzaro (cf. Ch. IV).

§ 3 Dulong and Petit's Rule

P. L. Dulong and A. T. Petit (1819) in their study of the specific heats of different solid elements obtained a remarkable result. They found : **The product of the atomic weight, w, and the specific heat, C, of an element has nearly always the same numerical value—6·4, or say 6—Dulong and Petit's rule.** This means that the atomic heats or the thermal capacity of the atoms of the elements are approximately the same. The relation is usually expressed :

$$\text{Atomic heat} = Cw = 6\cdot4$$

In illustration, a few elements may be selected at random from a list containing nearly fifty elements for which data are available :

TABLE V.—ATOMIC HEAT OF ELEMENTS.

Element.	Specific heat.	Atomic weight.	Atomic heat.
Lithium . . .	0·9408	6·94	6·53
Silver. . . .	0·0559	107·88	6·03
Gold	0·0304	197·2	6·25
Copper . . .	0·0923	63·57	5·88
Bismuth . . .	0·0305	209·0	6·34
Lead	0·0315	207·21	6·52
Aluminium . .	0·2143	27·0	5·81
Iron	0·1098	55·85	6·12
Uranium . . .	0·0277	238·0	6·61

The atomic weights here range from 6·94 to 238·5, and yet, when multiplied by the respective specific heats, the products are nearly constant. Rigorous agreement cannot be expected. The divergencies are too large to be accounted for by the inevitable errors of observation involved in measuring the specific heats, but the very irregularity of the divergencies leads to the view that Dulong and Petit's Law approximates to a truth, and that the observed differences are due to disturbing effects which are not functions of the atomic weight—e.g., crystalline form ; different relations between the temperature at which the specific heats were determined and the critical fusion temperature ; etc.

This important generalization holds for a great many elements, though there are some important exceptions such as carbon, silicon, boron and beryllium. It can be applied to the computation of the approximate weight of any element whose specific heat is known, and therefore takes its place alongside vapour density measurements as one means by which atomic weights have been determined.

§ 4 Atomic Weight (exact) from Equivalent Weight and Approximate Atomic Weight

The value for the atomic weight obtained by the application of Dulong and Petit's Rule is clearly only approximate. Similarly, it is not as a rule possible to determine vapour densities and hence molecular weights very accurately. Hence although the percentage composition of a compound can be found with a high degree of accuracy, the atomic weight calculated by the method of § 2 may be only approximate. In contrast, the equivalent weight, like the percentage composition, can be found very accurately indeed. Thus if we can establish the relation between equivalent weight and atomic weight (for clearly they must be very closely related since the equivalent weight is a measure of the relative combining weight of the element and combination takes place between atoms), we shall be able to use our knowledge of the accurate value of the equivalent weight to correct the approximate value of the atomic weight found as above, and so find the atomic weight accurately.

Evidence of the kind referred to on pages 74, 504, makes it extremely probable that (with the exception of hydrazoic acid HN_3) one hydrogen atom rarely, if ever, combines with more than one atom of any other kind. Now consider the case of an element which combines with hydrogen. Let the equivalent weight of the element be e and its atomic weight a. Since, by definition, the equivalent weight of the element is the amount which combines with one part by weight of hydrogen, it follows that if the compound contains one atom of the element united with *one* atom of hydrogen $e = a$.

Similarly, if the compound contains the atom of the element combined with two atoms of hydrogen, then,

$$e = \frac{a}{2}$$

and, in general, if the hydrogen compound contains V atoms of hydrogen to one of the element,

$$e = \frac{a}{V}$$

Now since V is the number of hydrogen atoms, and an atom is indivisible (chemically) it follows that V must be a small whole number, whence,

atomic weight = equivalent weight
× small whole number.

This small whole number, which represents in the simplest case the number of hydrogen atoms with which an atom of another element can combine, is called the **valency** of the element and is defined as follows :—

The valency of an element is a number which expresses how many atoms of hydrogen, or of other atoms equivalent to hydrogen, can unite with one atom of the element in question.

We can now re-write the expression above in the form :

$$\text{Atomic weight} = \text{Equivalent Weight} \times \text{Valency}$$

or
$$\frac{\text{Atomic Weight}}{\text{Equivalent Weight}} = \text{Valency}$$

We have now established the relation which we set out to find at the beginning of this section by which to correct an approximate value for an atomic weight, found by means of vapour density or specific heat measurements. We now see that the accurate atomic weight must be an exact multiple of the equivalent weight, and we can use methods such as the above, or the others which follow, in order to determine the value of this multiple.

An example will serve to illustrate this conclusion and make the point quite clear.

When indium was first discovered the analysis of its chloride furnished indium 37·8 ; chlorine 35·5. The equivalent of indium is therefore 37·8. The valency of indium was thought to be 2 and the atomic weight was accordingly represented 75·6. The specific heat of the metal was found to be 0·057. Hence 6·4 ÷ 0·057 = 112·3. Now 112·3 ÷ 37·8 = 2·97. ∴ The valency of indium is 3 and the atomic weight will be 37·8 × 3 = 113·4, which is the number usually adopted for the atomic weight of this element.

It must be noted that some elements combine together in more than one proportion, so forming different compounds. The relation between the proportions in which the combining elements are present in the several compounds is of the kind given by the Law of Multiple Proportions (p. 55). It thus follows from our definition of the equivalent weight of an element that a given element may have more than one equivalent weight. Thus, for example, two oxides of copper are known, in one of which 31·78 grams of copper are combined with 8 grams of oxygen ; whilst in the other, 63·56 grams of copper are united to 8 grams of oxygen. Therefore, the equivalent weight of copper is 31·78 in the first case, and 63·56 in the second.

In a similar way an element may have three (or more) equivalents according to the number of different compounds which it can form with another given element. But any one element can only have one atomic weight, and accordingly from the relation,

$$\frac{\text{Atomic weight}}{\text{Equivalent weight}} = \text{Valency}$$

such elements as we have been discussing must have more than one value for the valency. Such elements are said to possess *variable valency*.

§ 5 Other Methods for Finding Atomic Weights

The discussion of the previous section reveals the importance of methods for finding the atomic weights of elements with a reasonable degree of accuracy, although a very high degree of exactness is not essential so long as the equivalent weight be known very exactly. Two such methods have already been described, viz.,

(*a*) from vapour density measurements;
(*b*) from Dulong and Petit's Rule.

Others which must now be referred to briefly are,

(*c*) from isomorphism;
(*d*) from the Periodic System (Ch. VIII).

Isomorphism and Atomic Weights

E. Mitscherlich in 1818 found that analogously constituted substances (that is substances having analogous formulae—Ch. VII) often crystallize in the same crystalline form. (Compare Ch. X, pp. 164-168.) This he expressed in the Law of Isomorphism (sometimes called Mitscherlich's Law), viz., "*the same number of atoms combined in the same manner produce the same crystalline form.*"

This law of isomorphism can be used as a control in deducing the chemical composition of a salt ; and also in atomic weight determinations for deciding between two numbers which are multiples of a common factor. The method is restricted to crystalline compounds ; and it is only applicable in conjunction with other methods of atomic weight determinations since at least one member of the isomorphous series must be known.

Thus Mitscherlich deduced the number 79 for the atomic weight of selenium by this method, and he also gave selenious and selenic acids formulae corresponding with sulphurous and sulphuric acids respectively, on account of the isomorphism of the sulphates and the selenates. The analyses of potassium sulphate and of potassium selenate gave :

	Potassium.	Oxygen.	Sulphur	Selenium.		Total.
Potassium sulphate .	44·83	36·78	18·39	—	—	100·00
Potassium selenate .	44·83	36·78	—	45·40	—	127·01

Assuming that the molecule of potassium sulphate contains one atom of sulphur ; that the molecule of potassium selenate contains the same number of atoms ; and that the atomic weight of sulphur found from the composition and densities of its volatile compounds, is 32, we have :

Atomic weight S : Atomic weight Se = 18·39 : 45·40

Hence,

32 : Atomic weight Se = 18·39 : 45·40
.. Atomic weight of selenium = 79·00

Atomic Weights and the Periodic System

In a later chapter (Ch. VIII), in which the classification of the elements is discussed, we shall see that the first satisfactory system was that due to Mendeléeff, and was based on the arrangement of the elements in the order of their atomic weights. Although modern developments have shown (compare Chs. VIII and IX) that the atomic weight itself, along with Mendeléeff's Periodic System, depends upon something still more fundamental, nevertheless the atomic weight is approximately proportional to this more fundamental property of the atom, viz., the atomic number (see p. 130). Accordingly, granted that the atomic weights of a sufficient number of elements are known to construct the table, we can use it to discover the correct value by which to multiply the equivalent weight in order to arrive at the atomic weight.

A good example is again furnished by the case of indium. According to C. L. Winkler, indium has the equivalent weight 37·8. The correct atomic weight must be some multiple of this, and for no special reason, the atomic weight was once taken to be 37·8 × 2 = 75·6. In that case indium would fall in a position in the periodic table where it would be quite mis-matched. Mendeléeff proposed to consider indium as tervalent, like aluminium, so that the atomic weight would be 37·8 × 3 = 113·4, and the element would fall in the table into a place where it fits very well. The subsequent determination of the specific heat of indium 0·0577 corroborates, as we have seen, the correction made by Mendeléeff in the atomic weight from 75·6 to 113·4.

§ 6 The Atomic Weights of the Inert Gases

The determination of the atomic weights of the inert gases (see Ch. XXIV) presents a problem which cannot be entirely solved by any of the methods so far described in this chapter, for, as their name implies, they form no compounds and hence no equivalent weight can be determined, for this latter quantity is essentially a *reacting* weight.

The densities of these gases have been determined with a high degree of accuracy by various workers (e.g., Rayleigh, Ramsay, Whytlaw Gray and others), but being elementary gases, it is necessary to know also their atomicity (i.e., the number of atoms in a molecule of the gas) in order that their atomic weights may be calculated from their densities, which will be, as we have seen, equal to one-half of their molecular weights. Whence it follows that, if the inert gases are monatomic, their densities (relative to hydrogen) will be one-half of their atomic weights ; if diatomic, the densities will be equal to the atomic weights, and so on.

The problem of the atomicity of the inert gases has been tackled in the same way as confirmation was sought for the view (deduced from chemical evidence) that the hydrogen atom is diatomic, that is to say, by determining the ratio of the two specific heats of a gas. The theoretical assumptions on which the method is based have been discussed already in Chapter IV (p. 74).

When applied to the inert gases experiments (e.g., measurements of the velocity of sound) show that γ for these substances is 1·66. Hence we conclude that the inert gases are monatomic, and that their atomic weights are twice their densities (relative to hydrogen). The values so obtained fit in the periodic table satisfactorily and are accordingly accepted as correct.

§ 7 Standard Atomic Weight

It has been emphasized above that the atomic weights of the elements as used by chemists are a series of numbers indicating the *relative* weights of the atoms of the different elements. For practical purposes, therefore, it is necessary to fix a standard for atomic weights, and this standard is now universally taken to be **oxygen = 16.**

This has not always been the case, however, for during the latter part of the nineteenth century, J. Dalton's (1803) standard, hydrogen = 1, was used for the atomic weights instead of oxygen = 16. Hydrogen was selected because it is the lightest element known. J. S. Stas (1860-5) pointed out that the determination of the atomic weight of an element should be connected with the standard as directly as possible. Very few compounds of the metals with hydrogen are suitable for an atomic weight determination, while nearly all the elements form stable compounds with oxygen. Hence, if hydrogen be the standard, it is necessary to find the exact relation between the given element and oxygen, and then calculate what that relation would be on the assumption that the relation between hydrogen and oxygen is known. Every improved determination of the relation between hydrogen and oxygen would then be followed by an alteration in the atomic weight of every other element whose value, with respect to hydrogen as a standard, has been determined by the indirect process just indicated. The determination of the exact relation between hydrogen and oxygen appears to be more difficult than many other determinations, and hence, the majority of chemists think it better to refer the atomic weights of the elements to oxygen = 16 as the standard instead of making the atomic weights depend on the more or less uncertain relation H : O. The standard oxygen = 16 is quite arbitrary. T. Thomson (1825) used oxygen = 1; W. H. Wollaston (1814), 10; J. S. Stas (1860-5), 16; and J. J. Berzelius (1830) used oxygen = 100 as standard. The latter number makes the atomic weights of many elements inconveniently large, and if the atomic weight of oxygen be any whole number less than 16, fractional atomic weights will be required. The use of the " oxygen-16 " unit involves the least change in the numbers which were in vogue when " hydrogen-unity " was the standard.

§ 8 Accurate Atomic Weight Work

The determination of atomic weights with the highest possible degree of accuracy requires an experimental technique of a very high order and so it is that there are only one or two men in each generation whose work in this field is of such a calibre that their results command universal acceptance.

Among such men the names of J. S. Stas (1813-91) and T. W. Richards (1868-1928) stand out as those of chemists whose work was thus accepted.

The determination of the equivalent weights, and hence of the atomic weights of a limited number of elements with the greatest possible accuracy was Stas's life work, and for a great many years his results were accepted as the most accurate values.   He it was who proposed oxygen as standard since, as he affirmed, the hydrogen : oxygen ratio was not known with complete certainty.

To this work Stas brought a degree of patience and skill hitherto unexampled, and he applied refinements in the methods to be used such as had never previously been attempted.   He made careful search for well-defined reactions and studied minutely the' conditions necessary for them to be complete ; he prepared and purified all his materials with meticulous care ; the balances employed were specially constructed and of the highest order of accuracy and sensitiveness available at the time ; and the practical details of manipulation were worked out with the greatest pains and ingenuity.

Although Stas's work on atomic weights was the most accurate that had then been performed, it only covered a limited range of elements, and he himself expressly disclaimed any finality for his results.   It was, therefore, natural that in due time this type of work should be taken up by another—and to T. W. Richards of Harvard it fell to continue and even to improve upon Stas's work.

Richards began with the intention of building upon the foundation laid by Stas in the sense of utilizing Stas's values, in particular his value for silver, and applying them to the determination of the atomic weights of other elements not investigated by Stas.   But his work soon revealed the existence of small but real discrepancies which at length he was reluctantly forced to conclude were due to systematic errors in Stas's work.

Stas had developed the use of silver as the basis for his work.   The element under examination was converted into its chloride, or bromide, which was then used, with silver nitrate solution, to precipitate silver chloride, or bromide. The results so obtained had been related to oxygen by Stas as follows.   He began by heating potassium chlorate and determining the loss of weight consequent upon the driving off of the oxygen (known to be six equivalents).   The potassium chloride was then precipitated with silver nitrate ; the value for silver itself being determined by burning pure silver in a current of chlorine.

Richards, in his earlier work, made use of Stas's values for silver and chlorine so obtained, but when discrepancies began to reveal themselves he was led to a critical examination of Stas's work, and thus to the discovery of the systematic errors in it.

The principal sources of these errors were found to be :

(i) even the most carefully purified potassium chlorate always contains chloride ;

(ii) silver chloride when precipitated by potassium chloride tends to carry down traces of the latter which cannot be removed by washing ;

(iii) Stas had at times carried out precipitation using *solid* chloride, thus aggravating the error of (ii) ;

(iv) Stas had worked with abnormally large quantities which had rendered the adequate washing of precipitates difficult ;

(v) there were slight inaccuracies in the end points of Stas's analyses owing to the slight solubilities of silver halides and the effect of excess of one or other of the reagents on them ;

(vi) Stas's silver had contained oxygen.

As a consequence Richards undertook the revision of these fundamental atomic weights of silver, chlorine and nitrogen.

§9 Richards's Determination of the Atomic Weights of Silver, Chlorine and Nitrogen

Richards and his co-workers attacked the problem of the atomic weights of silver, nitrogen and chlorine in the following way. They determined (i) the weight of silver in a given weight of silver chloride ; (ii) the weight of silver chloride obtained from a given weight of ammonium chloride ; and (iii) the weight of silver nitrate formed from a given weight of silver. From the results of these experiments, taking oxygen as 16·000 and using Morley's value (see below— § 11) for hydrogen (1·0076), the atomic weights of silver, nitrogen and chlorine can be calculated in terms of those of oxygen and hydrogen, independently of each other, or of any other determinations.

For this work pure silver was obtained by the reduction of silver nitrate, which had been fifteen times recrystallized, the silver being fused on lime in an atmosphere of hydrogen. The silver was dissolved in the purest nitric acid, the resulting solution diluted and silver chloride precipitated from it by a solution of very pure common salt. The determination was carried out in a red light and the end point of the reaction was accurately found by the use of the *nephelometer* (see below) specially developed by Richards for the purpose. The precipitate was filtered off, washed, dried and weighed with every possible precaution.

Two methods were employed for the preparation of pure ammonium chloride. In one, ammonium sulphate, treated with an acid solution of potassium permanganate to oxidize away all organic matter was made to yield ammonia by treatment with pure lime, and the resulting gas was absorbed in the purest hydrochloric acid. The solution was evaporated and the ammonium chloride sublimed. In the other method the ammonium sulphate used as a source of ammonia was obtained by the electrolytic reduction of pure nitric acid.

Ammonium chloride so prepared was weighed out with every possible precaution, dissolved in very pure distilled water and added to a solution of silver nitrate prepared as described above. The resulting precipitate was treated and weighed in an exactly similar manner.

Very pure silver nitrate was prepared by dissolving a weighed quantity of the purest silver, obtained as already described, in nitric acid repeatedly redistilled and diluted with very pure water. The experiment was carried out in a quartz flask and the solution was evaporated to dryness in a gentle current of air. The resulting silver nitrate was dried and weighed with great care and accuracy.

As a result of these three series of experiments the ratios of silver chloride to silver, ammonium chloride to silver chloride, and silver nitrate to silver were found with very great accuracy. These results connect the atomic weight of nitrogen with those of silver, chorine and hydrogen.

Representative results obtained by Richards are :

1·00000 gm. of silver gave 1·32867 gm. of silver chloride.

1·00000 gm. of silver chloride was precipitated by 0·373217 gm. of ammonium chloride.

1·00000 gm. of silver yielded 1·57497 gm. of silver nitrate.

The calculation of the atomic weights is then as follows :—

$$\text{Let the atomic weight of silver} = x$$
$$\text{Let the atomic weight of chlorine} = y$$
$$\text{Let the atomic weight of nitrogen} = z$$

Suppose that the ratios

$$\frac{\text{silver chloride}}{\text{silver}} = a \quad . \quad . \quad . \quad . \quad . \quad . \quad (1)$$

and

$$\frac{\text{ammonium chloride}}{\text{silver chloride}} = b \quad . \quad . \quad . \quad . \quad (2)$$

and

$$\frac{\text{silver nitrate}}{\text{silver}} = c \quad . \quad . \quad . \quad . \quad . \quad (3)$$

Taking oxygen $= 16$ and Morley's value ($1 \cdot 0076$) for hydrogen (see p. 102) we have, by substituting the values of the atomic weights in the values of the above ratios,

from (1) $x + y = ax$ . . . . (4)

from (2) $z + (4 \times 1 \cdot 0076) + y = b(x + y)$ . . . . (5)

and from (3) $x + z + 48 = cx$ . . . . . (6)

From (6) $z = x(c - 1) - 48$. Substituting this value in (5)

$$x(c - 1) - bx + y(1 - b) = 43 \cdot 9696$$

But by (4) $y = x(a - 1)$

$$\therefore x = \frac{43 \cdot 9696}{c - 1 - b + (1 - b)(a - 1)}$$

Substituting the experimental values obtained by Richards for a, b and c as given above, we find,

$$x = 107 \cdot 881 = \text{atomic weight of silver}$$
$$y = 35 \cdot 4574 = \text{atomic weight of chlorine}$$
$$\text{and } z = 14 \cdot 0085 = \text{atomic weight of nitrogen.}$$

§ 10 Richards's Methods in General

The above investigation into the atomic weights of silver, nitrogen and chlorine illustrates well the principles which guided Richards and his co-workers in this field. The nature of some of the practical details of the work, developed in order to ensure the highest possible accuracy, may be profitably considered further.

These principles are set forth in Richards's own essay on " Methods used in precise Chemical Investigation," and the following are some of the leading points to which reference is made :—

Of prime importance is the choice of a reaction to be used in the determination of an atomic weight. This in its turn is governed to a large extent by the choice of starting material, which is determined by considerations such as the following :

(i) the substance selected must be capable of preparation in a very pure condition ;

(ii) other elements contained in it (other than that whose atomic weight is being found) must be of known atomic weight ;

(iii) it must be capable of analysis or synthesis with exactness and under conditions where there can be no loss of material.

Of all the difficulties and problems which confront the atomic weight chemist that of purity is probably the greatest. Solids separating from solution, or even from a vapour, very frequently carry down with them some of the impurity present and from which the process is designed to free them. Richards was fully alive to this difficulty and devoted much time and care to its investigation and to methods for overcoming it.

He made a special study of *occlusion*, that is, the tendency of precipitates to entangle within themselves other substances present in the solution, and even to carry down with them portions of the solution itself. As a result he was led to a consideration of the superior suitability of certain precipitates by reason of the greater ease with which occluded impurities could be removed. Thus, in addition to the use of solutions of as high a dilution as practicable, a precipitate which has a sponge-like structure is better than a rigid crystalline one, since the innermost pores of a spongy precipitate are accessible, whereas those of a crystalline one are not. Hence, thorough washing is more likely to prove effective in the former case. It is fortunate that silver chloride is a precipitate of a spongy character.

Richards also developed the use of the centrifuge, or whirling machine, for the separation of solids from their mother liquor, a process which finds wide application in technical processes, but which has not been used by scientific investigators to anything like the same extent. There is little doubt that the extensive use of this process has contributed much to the success of Richards and his co-workers in this field.

Another improvement in technique due to Richards is the bottling apparatus : a device whereby substances can be heated for drying purposes, in any desired gas, or in a vacuum, under exactly reproducible conditions, and then weighed without exposure to the air at any stage.

The bottling apparatus is shown diagrammatically in Fig. 35.

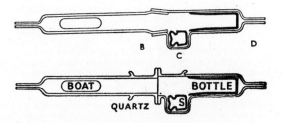

FIG. 35.—Richards's Bottling Apparatus.

It consists of a wide glass tube of quartz glass A fitted by means of a ground joint to a similar tube of soft glass which has a projection or pocket C in one side. The boat containing the substance to be dried is heated in the hard glass tube surrounded by an atmosphere of any desired gas, or gases. The weighing bottle is placed in the other end of the apparatus. After cooling these gases are displaced by pure dry air and the boat transferred to the weighing bottle by slightly tilting the apparatus, after which the stopper S is similarly inserted. The weighing bottle can then be transferred to a balance for weighing by opening the apparatus at the joint.

Another point to which Richards directed careful attention was the slight solubility of all so-called " insoluble " substances. Glass is not entirely unaffected by water, and in consequence the precipitates obtained by some previous workers were probably contaminated by traces of silica. Richards avoided this difficulty by the use, where possible, of platinum vessels ; otherwise quartz was used. Further, when the determination depends upon the precipitation of such a substance as silver chloride, which is ultimately weighed, its small but perceptible solubility in water must be allowed for, both in connection with the original precipitation and also in the subsequent washing of the precipitate. (Cf. p. 233 —solubility product.)

This problem was solved by Richards by means of a device which he called a nephelometer (= cloud-measurer). The construction of this apparatus is very simple. It consists of two test tubes, t, near together and slightly inclined to one another, arranged near a bright light from which they can be shaded, either wholly or partially, by means of sliding shades j. The tubes are observed from above by means of two prisms d of very small angle so that they can be observed

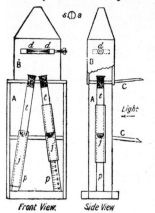

simultaneously and their brightness accurately compared. The arrangement is indicated by Fig. 36.

In estimating the amount of silver chloride carried away in the wash water, for example, the washings are treated with excess of a solution of silver nitrate which causes the precipitation of a small quantity of silver chloride (due to the common-ion effect, see Ch. XV, p. 235), so that the solution becomes faintly opalescent. This is done in one of the tubes of the nephelometer while a solution of a known amount is treated similarly in the other tube. Each precipitate reflects light so that the tubes appear faintly luminous. The shades are adjusted until the tubes appear to be equally bright. By comparing the lengths of the tubes then exposed to the light, the amount of precipitate in the " unknown " solution can be calculated.

Other precautions referred to by Richards may also be mentioned. Traces of solid are easily lost when solutions are evaporated to dryness ; and to avoid this, very carefully controlled conditions must be employed and the results checked by blank experiments. All substances must be rigorously protected from dust by the use of suitable hoods, and closed vessels. Heating by coal-gas tends to cause contamination by impurities from the gas ; this is avoided by the use of electrical heating.

Front View.   Side View

Fig. 36.—The Nephelometer.

To sum up we may quote Richards's own words :

" Every substance must be assumed to be impure, every reaction must be assumed to be incomplete, every method of measurement must be assumed to contain some constant error, until proof to the contrary can be obtained. As little as possible must be taken for granted."

§ 11 The Ratio of the Weights of Hydrogen and Oxygen in Water

The calculation of the atomic weights of silver, nitrogen and chlorine given in § 9 illustrates the fact that in this method at least the final result depends upon a knowledge of the atomic weight of hydrogen in terms of that of oxygen. This serves to illustrate the fundamental importance of this latter ratio, and an account of some representative determinations of it must now be given.

Two distinct methods are available : either the weight of hydrogen combining with a given weight of oxygen can be found, or the ratio in which these gases combine by volume can be determined, whence, from a knowledge of their densities, the ratio in which they combine by weight can be calculated.

The most accurate determinations of the oxygen : hydrogen ratio are those made by Morley (1895), who measured the ratio by weight, and by Burt and Edgar (1915), who measured the ratio by volume.

Morley's Determination of the Composition of Water by Weight

Historically, the most important measurement of the composition of water by weight had been made in 1842 by Dumas. He had synthesized water by passing purified hydrogen over red hot copper oxide and collecting the water so formed. Since the quantities are interdependent, he measured the weight of oxygen used and the weight of water formed, obtaining by difference the weight of hydrogen concerned. He was thus able to avoid the very difficult operation of weighing the hydrogen directly. (Compare Ch. XVII, p. 268.)

A notable feature of Morley's investigation was the fact that he weighed both the hydrogen and the oxygen used, *and* the water formed, whereas previous investigators had determined one of these quantities by difference. The accuracy of his work is indicated by the very close agreement among themselves of the values he found for these three quantities.

Morley prepared the oxygen used from potassium chlorate and purified it by passing it through a series of three wide tubes. The first contained glass beads moistened with strong caustic potash solution; the second, beads similarly moistened with sulphuric acid; and the third, phosphorus pentoxide and glass wool. After purification the gas was collected in large glass globes, previously evacuated.

Hydrogen was obtained by the electrolysis of dilute sulphuric acid, and purified by being passed successively through strong caustic potash solution, over red hot copper and then through three long drying tubes similar to those employed for the oxygen. There is always a difficulty in weighing hydrogen accurately on account of its very low density, which means that very small errors in the weighing of the containing vessel are magnified some 500 times relative to the weight of hydrogen deduced. Morley obviated this difficulty by absorbing his hydrogen in metallic palladium. Palladium is a metal (see p. 259) which possesses the property of absorbing some 800 times its own volume of hydrogen gas, and of giving up the gas again when heated to a dull red heat. By this means the magnification of errors in the weight of hydrogen can be avoided.

Both the globe containing the oxygen and the palladium tube containing the hydrogen were weighed with every possible precaution. (Compare Ch. II, p. 21.)

The globe containing oxygen was connected with C, Fig. 37. The oxygen passed through a layer of phosphorus pentoxide*, and thence into the glass chamber M via one of the jets, A; the globe containing

* The phosphorus pentoxide is not intended to dry the gases (they have already been dried) but to prevent loss of water at the later stage.

hydrogen was similarly connected with another tube, D, containing phosphorus pentoxide, and the hydrogen led into the chamber M via

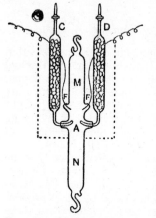

FIG. 37.—Morley's Experiment.—Synthesis of Water.

one of the jets A. The rates at which the gases enter the chamber were regulated by suitable stopcocks. The chamber M was previously evacuated and weighed. One of the gases, say oxygen, was allowed to enter M, and electric sparks were passed across the terminals F just over the jets A. Hydrogen was led into the apparatus and ignited by the sparks. The rates at which hydrogen and oxygen entered the chamber were regulated so that the formation of water was continuous. The water formed was condensed, and collected in the lower part of the chamber. To hasten the condensation, the apparatus was placed in a vessel of cold water—dotted in the diagram. When a sufficient amount of water was formed, the apparatus was placed in a freezing mixture. The

mixture of unconsumed oxygen and hydrogen remaining in the tube, was pumped away, and analysed. The weights of hydrogen and oxygen so obtained were added to the weights of unconsumed hydrogen and oxygen remaining in the globes. The phosphorus pentoxide tubes prevented the escape of water vapour. The amounts of hydrogen and oxygen used were determined from the weights of the corresponding globes before and after the experiment. The amount of water formed was determined from the increase in the weight of the above-described vessel before and after the combustion. Morley, as a mean of eleven experiments, found that :

Hydrogen used	.	.	.	3·7198 grams.
Oxygen used	.	.	.	29·5335 grams.
Water formed .	.	.	.	33·2530 grams.

Hence, taking oxygen $= 16$ as the unit for combining weight, it follows that 16 *parts by weight of oxygen combine with* 2·0152 *parts by weight of hydrogen to form* 18·0152 *parts of water*—within the limits of the small experimental error.

Burt and Edgar's Determination of the Composition of Water by Volume

Some account of Burt and Edgar's work on the volume composition of water has been given in Chapter IV (p. 66). As a result of fifty-nine determinations, they found the ratio 1 : 2·00288 for the combining volumes of oxygen and hydrogen in water. In conjunction with accurate values for the absolute densities of oxygen and hydrogen this result enables us to calculate a value for the ratio in which oxygen and hydrogen combine by weight. Morley (who determined this ratio by weight *directly*, with great accuracy, as described above) also made very careful measurements of the absolute densities of hydrogen and oxygen. His values are that the weights of one litre of hydrogen and oxygen at N.T.P. are 0·089873 gm. and 1·42900 gm. respectively. In conjunction with Burt and Edgar's value for the volume ratio, we then find the ratio for the atomic weights of oxygen and hydrogen to be 16 : 1·0077.

§ 12 Atomic Weight Determinations by Physical Methods

We have already seen (this chapter, § 6) that the atomic weights of the inert gases can only be determined by the application of physical principles, since they form no compounds and hence have no equivalent (or reacting weight). It is natural that for other elements confirmation of the chemical values should be sought from the results of purely physical measurements. An account of some representative work in this field must, therefore, now be given.'

Until recently, the most important of these methods was the so-called " limiting density " method. The great problem confronting attempts to determine atomic weights from values of gas densities arises from the fact that all gases show deviations from the gas laws in greater or less degree, and that the extent of these deviations varies from gas to gas. For this reason the ratio of the normal densities of two gases (as defined in Ch. II, p. 20) will not give the *exact* ratio of their molecular weights. For, if equal volumes of two given gases, measured at one particular pressure, did actually contain *exactly* the same number of molecules as required by Avogadro's hypothesis, it follows that at some other pressure, owing to the different compressibilities of the two gases, equal volumes would contain slightly different (although nearly the same) number of molecules.

It has been found that differences between various gases as regards their deviations from Boyle's Law, as well as the extent of the deviations, become very much smaller as the pressure is reduced, and hence it is reasonable to assume that at zero pressure these differences would vanish, and that the ratio of the densities of two gases at zero pressure (known as the **limiting densities**) would be an *accurate* value for the ratio of the molecular weights of the gases concerned.

The limiting density of a gas cannot be determined directly, but it can be evaluated from the density at N.T.P. if certain other factors can be found.

Suppose that a quantity of gas of mass m gm. occupies a volume of v litres at a temperature of $0°$ C. and a pressure of p atmospheres. If Boyle's Law were obeyed, the quantity m/pv would be the same at all pressures. Owing to deviations from Boyle's Law, it will, in fact, vary with the pressure. If $p = 1$, its value is that of the normal density as defined in Chapter II. As p approaches zero, its value approaches that of the limiting density. Now for any given gas, whose normal density (i.e., at N.T.P.) is D,

$$D = \frac{m}{p_1 v_1}$$

where $p_1 v_1$ is the value of pv when $p = 1$. Similarly, the limiting density is $\frac{m}{p_0 v_0}$, where $p_0 v_0$ is the limiting value of pv as p approaches zero.

$$\therefore \text{ limiting density} = D \times \frac{p_1 v_1}{p_0 v_0} .$$

The evaluation of the limiting density is thus a matter of determining the ratio p_1v_1/p_0v_0. This ratio, for any given mass of gas, can be found by either of two distinct methods. These are :—

(i) the extrapolation method ;
(ii) on the assumption that the deviation from Boyle's Law is proportional to the pressure, the measurement of pv at two low pressures enables p_0v_0 to be calculated. This is known as the **compressibility coefficient method.**

The extrapolation method

By making a number of determinations of pv at various pressures, a curve can be plotted which expresses the relation between pv and p. This curve can then be extrapolated back to $p = 0$, which enables the value of p_0v_0 to be found, and hence the ratio p_1v_1/p_0v_0.

The compressibility coefficient method

If the deviation of a gas from Boyle's Law is proportional to the pressure, we can then say the relative deviation,

$$\frac{p_0v_0 - pv}{pv} = \lambda p,$$

where λ is a constant called the **compressibility coefficient.** Two measurements of pv for different values of p (less than one atmosphere) will serve for the calculation of λ from this expression. Having found λ we see that

$$p_0v_0 = p_1v_1 \ (1 + \lambda) \quad \text{since } p = 1 ;$$

$$\text{whence limiting density} = \frac{\text{normal density}}{1 + \lambda}$$

For example, the following values have been obtained for oxygen and hydrogen :—

	Normal Density.	Compressibility.
Oxygen	1·42900	+ 0·000964
Hydrogen	0·089873	− 0·00054

$$\therefore \text{Limiting Density of Oxygen} \quad = \quad \frac{1·42900}{1·000964} = 1·42762 \text{ gms./litre.}$$

$$\text{and Limiting Density of Hydrogen} = \frac{0·089873}{·99946} = 0·089922 \text{ gms./litre.}$$

Since these are in the ratio of the molecular weights, and hence, being diatomic molecules, of the atomic weights, it follows that the hydrogen : oxygen ratio measured in this way is

$$16 : 1·0078$$

This value compares very well with those obtained by Morley (p. 102) and Burt and Edgar (p. 103).

Examples of the use of the limiting density method for finding atomic weights are Moles and Batuecas value for nitrogen, obtained from the limiting density of ammonia ; and Gray and Burt's value for chlorine, from that of hydrogen chloride.

As a result of their experiments with ammonia, Moles and Batuecas found the limiting density of ammonia to be 0·75990 gm. per litre. The limiting density of oxygen (determined similarly by Gray and Burt) is 1·42762 gm. per litre. The density of ammonia, referred to oxygen 16, is thus :—

$$\frac{0·75990}{1·42762} \times 16 = 8·516$$

Its molecular weight is therefore 17·032, which gives the value 14·0086 for the atomic weight of nitrogen, on the basis of hydrogen 1·0078.

In Gray and Burt's experiments with hydrogen chloride the following figures were obtained :—

$$\text{Normal density} = 1 \cdot 63915 \text{ gm. per litre}$$
$$p_1 v_1 = 54803$$
by extrapolation $\quad p_0 v_0 = 55213$

∴ Limiting density of hydrogen chloride

$$= \frac{1 \cdot 63915 \times 54803}{55213}$$
$$= 1 \cdot 62698 \text{ gm. per litre.}$$

As above, the limiting density of oxygen is $1 \cdot 42762$ gms./litre, ∴ Density of hydrogen chloride, referred to oxygen 16,

$$= \frac{1 \cdot 62698}{1 \cdot 42762} \times 16$$
$$= 18 \cdot 233.$$

The molecular weight of hydrogen chloride, therefore, is $36 \cdot 466$, which gives $35 \cdot 458$ as the value of the atomic weight of chlorine.

Values such as these are in excellent agreement with those found by chemical methods. It is therefore concluded that the limiting density method is capable of a degree of accuracy equal to that of the best chemical determinations.

During recent years, Aston has measured the atomic weights of many elements by means of the perfected forms of the mass-spectrograph, and a very high degree of accuracy has been attained. The description of this method of atomic weight determination must, however, be deferred until the far-reaching modern discoveries concerning the nature of matter have been described, for the theory of the method depends upon these modern results. An account will accordingly be found at the end of Chapter IX.

§ 13 International Atomic Weights

However great the care and ingenuity which may be expended in perfecting the methods to be used, and in eliminating errors from determinations of such quantities as atomic weights, it nevertheless remains true that all such measurements are affected by unavoidable errors of experiment, which, even though extremely small, are yet real. Hence it is that even the best available determinations of such a quantity as the atomic weight of an element differ among themselves within certain limits.

This being the case, it is convenient to select one representative value from the many different observations ranging between these limits. The majority of chemists have agreed to let the International Committee on Atomic Weights decide year by year what are the best representative values for the atomic weights of all the elements. Every time new and more refined methods of measurement are employed, a change—generally insignificantly small—may be necessary.

A careful consideration of all the available evidence considerably reduces the risk of error, and this method, adopted by the Committee, appears to be the most satisfactory solution of the problem.

The atomic weights of a few of the more important elements are indicated in Table VI. The numbers are those recommended by the International Committee on Atomic Weights. The full table appears inside the front cover of this book.

For ordinary calculations involving the use of atomic weights, all the atomic weights, excepting chlorine (35·5), copper (63·5), nickel (58·5), and zinc (65·5), are rounded off to the nearest whole numbers. The elements just named are then assigned the atomic weights indicated in the brackets. Some chemists—G. D. Hinrichs, for example—firmly believe that the rounded numbers are the best representative values of the atomic weights, and that the small deviations from the rounded numbers indicated in the "International Table" represent real, if unrecognized, errors of experiment. In view of the work on **isotopes,** to be discussed in a later chapter, this question has lost its significance until we have learned to interpret the fact that many of

TABLE VI.—INTERNATIONAL ATOMIC WEIGHTS.   O = 16.

Aluminium	.	.	Al	26·97	Iron .	.	.	.	Fe	55·85
Antimony .	.	.	Sb	121·76	Lead .	.	.	.	Pb	207·21
Arsenic	.	.	As	74·91	Magnesium	.	.	Mg	24·32
Barium	.	.	Ba	137·36	Manganese .	.	.	Mn	54·93
Bismuth	.	.	Bi	209·0	Mercury	.	.	.	Hg	200·61
Boron	.	.	B	10·82	Nickel	.	.	.	Ni	58·69
Bromine	.	.	Br	79·92	Nitrogen	.	.	.	N	14·01
Calcium	.	.	Ca	40·08	**Oxygen**	.	.	.	O	**16·00**
Carbon	.	.	C	12·01	Phosphorus.	.	.	P	30·98
Chlorine	.	.	Cl	35·46	Platinum	.	.	.	Pt	195·23
Chromium	.	.	Cr	52·01	Potassium	.	.	.	K	39·10
Cobalt	.	.	Co	58·94	Silicon	.	.	.	Si	28·06
Copper	.	.	Cu	63·57	Silver.	.	.	.	Ag	107·88
Fluorine	.	.	F	19·0	Sodium	.	.	.	Na	23·00
Gold .	.	.	Au	197·2	Sulphur	.	.	.	S	32·06
Hydrogen .	.	.	H	1·008	Tin .	.	.	.	Sn	118·7
Iodine	.	.	I	126·92	Zinc .	.	.	.	Zn	65·38

the atomic weights at present accepted are averages of mixtures of two or more different kinds of atoms which at present are given the same name, although they have slightly different atomic weights. So far as has yet been observed, these atoms cannot be distinguished from one another by any chemical process yet tried.

CHAPTER VII

FORMULAE AND EQUATIONS

However certain the facts of any science, however just the ideas derived from these facts, we can only communicate false or imperfect impressions to others if we want words by which these may be properly expressed.—A. L. LAVOISIER

In his calculations the chemist relies on the supposed chemical relations of the invisible, intangible, and immeasurable particles he calls atoms. These relations have been determined by others in whom he has confidence, and the accuracy of these constants has to be accepted on faith.—H. C. BOLTON.

§ 1 Symbols and Formulae

FOR convenience in recording and working on the facts of chemistry in so far as they concern the composition of substances, there has been developed a system of symbols and nomenclature, based upon the Atomic Theory (v. Ch. III, p. 62). To each element has been assigned a **symbol** consisting of one or two letters derived from the recognized name of the element (in some cases the Latin name, e.g., Hg for mercury from the Latin *hydrargyrum*). Compounds are similarly represented by joining together the symbols for the different elements present in the compound, with appropriate subscript numerals to indicate the number of atoms of each element present in one molecule of the compound. Familiar examples are H_2O and H_2SO_4 representing water and sulphuric acid respectively. Such a juxtaposition of symbols, representing a compound, is called a **formula**—the formula of the compound.

It is important to notice that these symbols and formulae do not merely represent the elements and their compounds in a qualitative or purely descriptive manner, but are quantitative. Thus the symbol of an element represents a definite *weight* of that element, numerically equal to the atomic weight, expressed in a convenient unit (e.g., grams or pounds). Similarly, the formula of a compound expresses a definite *weight* of the substance, being in fact the numerical sum of the atomic weights of the constituent atoms expressed in suitable units as before. Thus, for example, H_2SO_4 does not merely indicate sulphuric acid in a general and indefinite way, but indicates also 98 parts by weight of sulphuric acid. (The atomic weights of hydrogen, sulphur and oxygen being 1, 32 and 16 respectively, the formula weight of sulphuric acid is $1 \times 2 + 32 + 16 \times 4 = 98$.)

§ 2 Equations

The elements are represented by *symbols*, and compounds are indicated by combinations of symbols called *formulae*: the chemical changes which take place when elements or compounds react are similarly shown by means of **equations.**

When the initial and final products of a chemical reaction as well as the composition and proportions of the molecules concerned in the reaction are known, the facts can usually be symbolized in the form of a chemical equation.

Such an equation indicates the nature of the atoms and the supposed composition of the molecules concerned in the reaction ; as well as the proportions of the different molecules in the initial and final products of the reaction. For instance, when mercury is heated in air, and mercuric oxide, HgO, is formed, the reaction can be represented in symbols : $2Hg + O_2 = 2HgO$. We here ignore the nitrogen of the air because, so far as we can tell, it plays no direct part in the chemical reaction. Similarly, when mercuric oxide is heated to a high tempera- ture, it decomposes, forming metallic mercury and oxygen. In symbols, $2HgO = 2Hg + O_2$. The symbol " $=$ " is used instead of the words " produces " or " forms," and the symbol " $+$ " is used for " together with " on the right side of the " $=$ " sign, and for " reacts with " on the left side. The latter equation reads : " Two molecules of mercuric oxide, on decomposing, produce a molecule of oxygen and two molecules of monatomic mercury." The number and kind of the atoms of the two sides of the equation must always be the same (Law of Conservation of Matter).

In Chapter IV (p. 69) we saw that the molecular weight of an element or compound is the sum of the atomic weights of all the atoms contained within a molecule of that particular element or compound ; and as mentioned above, all symbols and formulae have a quantitative significance. Hence it follows that an equation indicates the propor- tions by weight of the substances concerned in the reaction. The atomic weight of mercury is 200, and the atomic weight of oxygen is 16, hence, the molecular weight of mercuric oxide is 216, and of oxygen 32. The latter equation can therefore be read : " 432 grams (ozs. or tons) of mercuric oxide, on decomposing, form 32 grams (ozs. or tons) of oxygen gas and 400 grams (ozs. or tons) of metallic mercury." Thus, the chemical equation can be employed in all kinds of arithmetical problems dealing with weights of substances formed or produced.

Further (Ch. IV, p. 77) the molecular weight in grams of any gas will occupy 22·4 litres at N.T.P. It follows, therefore, that **an equa- tion indicates the proportion by volume of the gases concerned in the reaction.** Consequently, we can express the idea conveyed by the equation $2HgO = O_2 + 2Hg$ in these words : " 432 grams of mercuric oxide will furnish 32 grams of oxygen, or 22·4 litres of oxygen gas at 0° C. and 760 mm., and 400 grams of mercury."

§ 3 Deduction of Formulae

1. From percentage composition

The formula of a compound, expressing the number and kind of atoms present in its molecule, is usually found from the results of experiment—the following four sets of data being required :—

(i) information as to the elements present in the compound ;
(ii) the percentage composition of the compound ;
(iii) the atomic weights of the elements present ;
(iv) the molecular weight of the compound.

(i) *the elements present*

The nature of the elements present is found by the processes or *qualitative* analysis, and as a rule no great difficulty is experienced in obtaining these necessary data.

(ii) *the percentage composition*

The percentage composition, or proportion by weight of each element present, is found by means of a *quantitative* analysis. The elements in a known weight of the compound are converted into some form in which they can be separated and weighed. Examples of this type of investigation have already been given in Chapters V and VI, and many others wil' be found in later chapters.

(iii) *the atomic weights*, found as described in Chapter VI, are derived, for purposes such as that now under consideration, from tables such as that printed on the inside of the front cover of this volume.

(iv) *the molecular weight* of the compound is discovered either by means of one of the methods described previously (Ch. IV) or by one of those referred to in Chapter XI.

The application of these data to the discovery of an actual formula is best explained by means of an example.

A volatile compound containing carbon and hydrogen only was found to have the following percentage composition : Carbon, 92·31 per cent., Hydrogen, 7·69 per cent. The density of the vapour of the substance (referred to hydrogen) was 39. Calculate its formula.

From the table on the inside of the front cover, we find that the atomic weights of carbon and hydrogen are approximately 12 and 1 respectively. In order to find the relative numbers of atoms of carbon and of hydrogen in the weights of these elements given in the percentage composition, we must divide these weights by the respective atomic weights.* We thus arrive at the following result :—

* Let the formula be $A_xB_yC_z$, and let the atomic weights of A, B and C be a, b and c respectively. Then

$$\text{percentage of } A = \frac{ax}{ax + by + cz}, \text{ i.e., } \frac{\text{percentage of } A}{a} = \frac{x}{ax + by + cz}$$

$$\text{percentage of } B = \frac{by}{ax + by + cz}, \text{ i.e., } \frac{\text{percentage of } B}{b} = \frac{y}{ax + by + cz}$$

$$\text{and percentage of } C = \frac{cz}{ax + by + cz}, \text{ i.e., } \frac{\text{percentage of } C}{c} = \frac{z}{ax + by + cz}$$

$$\therefore x : y : z = \frac{\text{percentage of } A}{a} : \frac{\text{percentage of } B}{b} : \frac{\text{percentage of } C}{c}$$

No. of carbon atoms : number of hydrogen atoms

$$= \frac{92 \cdot 31}{12} : \frac{7 \cdot 69}{1}$$

$$= 7 \cdot 69 : 7 \cdot 69.$$

By the atomic theory we cannot have fractions of atoms, hence dividing by $7 \cdot 69$ we have the ratio $1 : 1$ which leads to the formula CH. But compounds C_2H_2, C_3H_3, C_nH_n would clearly lead to the same result.

In the case under consideration, since the vapour density of the compound is 39, its molecular weight is 78. The molecular weight of C_nH_n is $13n$ whence $n = 6$. The formula of the compound is thus C_6H_6.

In calculating formulae for substances which cannot be vaporized, and to which one of the methods to be described later cannot be applied, it is usual to assume that the molecule has the simplest possible formula. In that case the formula is said to be *empirical*. Some prefer to use the term " formula weight " in place of " molecular weight " when the actual molecular weight has not been determined. The **formula weight**, like the molecular weight of a compound, is the sum of the atomic weights of the elements represented by the known, or assumed, formula of the compound.

2. From volume relationships

When gases are involved, either among the products or starting materials of a reaction, the tedious processes required for the weighing of gases may often be avoided and the formula calculated by the application of Gay-Lussac's Law of Volumes (p. 66) to the volume relationships of the reacting substances and their products.

The method can best be explained by means of an example.

5 c.c. of a gas containing only carbon and hydrogen were mixed with an excess of oxygen (30 c.c.) and the mixture exploded by means of an electric spark. After the explosion, the volume of the mixed gases remaining was 25 c.c. On adding a concentrated solution of potassium hydroxide, the volume further diminished to 15 c.c., the residual gas being pure oxygen. All volumes have been reduced to N.T.P. Calculate the formula of the hydrocarbon gas.

Let the formula of the gas be C_mN_n. Then the change, when it is exploded with excess oxygen, may be represented :

$$C_mH_n + \left(m + \frac{n}{4} \right) O_2 = mCO_2 + \frac{n}{2} H_2O.$$

That is, by Gay-Lussac's Law of Volumes (p. 66) and Avogadro's Hypothesis (p. 68),

1 volume of hydrocarbon needs $\left(m + \dfrac{n}{4} \right)$ volumes of oxygen to

produce m volumes of carbon dioxide and, if the experiment be performed at room temperature, a negligible volume of condensed, liquid water.

$$\therefore \text{Volume before explosion} = 1 + m + \frac{n}{4} + \text{un-needed oxygen}$$

$$\text{and volume after explosion} = m + \text{un-needed oxygen}$$

$$\therefore \text{Contraction on explosion} = 1 + \frac{n}{4}$$

The addition of potassium hydroxide removes the carbon dioxide; hence m volumes of carbon dioxide are removed in this way. Adjusting the numbers given in the example to correspond to 1 volume of hydrocarbon, we have :

Contraction on addition of potassium hydroxide

$$= m = \frac{10}{5} = 2 \quad \text{and}$$

$$\text{Contraction on explosion} = 1 + \frac{n}{4} = \frac{10}{5} = 2$$

$$\therefore n = 4$$

$\therefore$ The formula of the hydrocarbon is C_2H_4.

§ 4 Chemical Calculations

In view of the fact that the symbols and formulae which are employed in writing the equations which represent chemical reactions have a quantitative significance, they and these equations themselves can be made the basis for many chemical calculations. A few representative examples of these calculations follow.

1. *Calculate the percentage composition of potassium nitrate* KNO_3. ($K = 39$, $N = 14$, $O = 16$.)

Since the formula of a compound represents the number of atoms contained in its molecule, and the atomic weights are the relative weights of these atoms, we have

one atom of potassium $= 39$ parts by weight
and one atom of nitrogen $= 14$ parts by weight
and three atoms of oxygen $= 48$ parts by weight

are combined in one mole- $\left.\right\}$ $= 101$ parts by weight
cule of potassium nitrate

$\therefore$ in 100 parts by weight of potassium nitrate there are

$$\frac{39}{10} \times 100 = 38 \cdot 61 \text{ parts by weight of potassium}$$

$$\frac{14}{101} \times 100 = 13 \cdot 86 \text{ parts by weight of nitrogen}$$

$$\text{and} \quad \frac{48}{101} \times 100 = 47 \cdot 52 \text{ parts by weight of oxygen.}$$

That is to say, the percentage composition of potassium nitrate is :

potassium	. . .	38·61 per cent.
nitrogen	. . .	13·86 per cent.
oxygen	. . .	47·52 per cent.

2. *5 gms. of zinc are completely converted into crystallized zinc sulphate* $ZnSO_4.7H_2O$. *What weight of zinc sulphate is obtained?* ($Zn = 65\cdot5$, $S = 32, O = 16, H = 1$.)

One atom of zinc is present in one molecule of zinc sulphate.

∴ 65·5 parts by weight of zinc will yield

$$65\cdot5 + 32 + 4 \times 16 + 7(16 + 2) = 287\cdot5$$

parts by weight of crystallized zinc sulphate

$$\therefore 5 \text{ gms. of zinc will give } \frac{287\cdot5 \times 5}{65\cdot5}$$

$$= 21\cdot95 \text{ gms. of crystallized zinc sulphate.}$$

3. *What weight of iodine will be liberated by the action of the right amount of chlorine on a solution containing 2 gms. of potassium iodide, according to the equation* $2KI + Cl_2 = 2KCl + I_2$ *and what weight of chlorine will be needed?* ($K = 39, Cl = 35\cdot5, I = 127$.)

The equation shows that $2 \times (39 + 127)$ gms. of potassium iodide are acted upon by $2 \times 35\cdot5$ gms. of chlorine with the formation of 2×127 gms. of iodine.

∴ 2 gms. of potassium iodide will yield

$$\frac{2 \times 127 \times 2}{2 \times (39 + 127)} = \frac{2 \times 127}{166} = 1\cdot53 \text{ gms. of iodine.}$$

Similarly, the weight of chlorine required will be

$$\frac{2 \times 35\cdot5 \times 2}{2 \times (39 + 127)} = \frac{2 \times 35\cdot5}{166} = 0\cdot43 \text{ gms. of chlorine.}$$

4. *What weight of anhydrous sodium sulphate and what volume of carbon dioxide, measured at 15° C. and 735 mm. pressure, can be obtained by the action of excess of dilute sulphuric acid on 10 grams of washing soda crystals,* $Na_2CO_3.10H_2O$? ($Na = 23, C = 12, H = 1, O = 16$, $S = 32$.)

The equation for the reaction (compare Ch. XIX) is

$$Na_2CO_3.10H_2O + H_2SO_4 = Na_2SO_4 + CO_2 + 11H_2O$$

whence we see that :

286 grams of washing soda will yield 142 grams of sodium sulphate, and 22·4 litres of carbon dioxide at N.T.P.

∴ 10 grams of washing soda will produce

$$\frac{142 \times 10}{286} = 4\cdot96 \text{ grams of sodium sulphate}$$

and $\dfrac{22\cdot4 \times 10}{286}$ litres of carbon dioxide at N.T.P.

$$= \frac{22\cdot4 \times 10}{286} \times \frac{288}{273} \times \frac{760}{735} \text{ litres at } 15° \text{ C. and } 735 \text{ mm.}$$

$$= \cdot854 \text{ litres.}$$

5. *What weight of silver chloride would be precipitated if* 100 *c.c. of hydrogen chloride gas, measured at* 12° C. *and* 750 *mm. pressure were passed into excess of a solution of silver nitrate?* (H = 1, Cl = 35·5, Ag = 108.)

The equation for this reaction (compare Ch. XXVI) is :

$$AgNO_3 + HCl = AgCl + HNO_3$$

That is to say,

22,400 c.c. of hydrogen chloride at N.T.P. will precipitate
143·5 gms. of silver chloride.

Now 100 c.c. of hydrogen chloride at 12° C. and 750 mm.

$$= \frac{100 \times 273 \times 750}{285 \times 760} \text{ c.c. at N.T.P.}$$

Since 22,400 c.c. of hydrogen chloride at N.T.P. will precipitate 143·5 gms. of silver chloride

$$\therefore \quad \frac{100 \times 273 \times 750}{285 \times 760} \text{ c.c. at N.T.P. will precipitate}$$

$$\frac{143\cdot5 \times 100 \times 273 \times 750}{285 \times 760 \times 22,400} \text{ gm. of silver chloride} = 0\cdot6057 \text{ gm.}$$

Very many chemical calculations are variations of the above types.

CHAPTER VIII

THE CLASSIFICATION OF THE ELEMENTS

The primary object of classification is to arrange the facts so that we can acquire the greatest possible control over them with the least possible effort.

The periodic law has given to chemistry that prophetic power long regarded as the peculiar dignity of its sister science, astronomy. H. C. BOLTON.

§ 1 Early Attempts at Classification; Döbereiner's Triads—Newlands's Law of Octaves

IN any attempt at the classification of objects or things, the aim is to group together those which resemble each other in some respects, and to separate those which differ. Clearly, in any actual case, various criteria of likeness will be available : and according to that adopted as the basis for classification, the grouping may differ, so that things grouped together on account of similarity in one respect, may be separated if the classification be based on some other basis. The best classification will clearly be that which brings together things which resemble one another in the greatest number of ways. The classification of the elements has long been an attractive subject. The elements have been classed into metals and non-metals ; into acidic and basic, or, what amounts to the same thing, into electronegative and electropositive elements (see p. 191) and they have been classed according to their valency ; and also according to many other properties. In all these systems an element appeared in more than one class ; or elements with but few properties in common were grouped together. The properties of the elements used as the basis of classification may also vary with the conditions under which the properties are observed.

The method first referred to in the previous paragraph, viz., division into metals and non-metals, is often a convenient one ; though, as with most systems, exact subdivision is not practicable. As a general basis, however, metals and non-metals may be contrasted as indicated in the table on the next page.

To show how difficult it is to draw a hard-and-fast line of demarcation between metals and non-metals, the non-metals arsenic, antimony, and tellurium would be classed with the metals if we depended exclusively upon 6, 7, and 8 ; hence, some introduce a third division—the **metalloids**—to include the hybrids, or elements which have properties characteristic of both the metals and the non-metals. The metals lithium, sodium, potassium, magnesium, and aluminium have a low specific gravity. The non-metals carbon, boron, and silicon are less volatile than most metals. The non-metal hydrogen is a good conductor of heat ; and the non-metal graphitic carbon is a good conductor of heat and electricity. Hence the division of the elements into metal and non-metals is but a rough system of classification, arbitrarily adopted because it is convenient.

114

TABLE VII.—THE PROPERTIES OF THE METALS AND NON-METALS CONTRASTED

Metals.	Non-metals.
1. Form basic oxides.	1. Form acidic oxides.
2. Generally dissolve in mineral acids, giving off hydrogen.	2. Do not usually dissolve easily in mineral acids.
3. Either form no compounds with hydrogen, or form unstable compounds—usually non-volatile.	3. Form stable compounds with hydrogen — these are usually volatile.
4. Solid at ordinary temperature (excepting mercury).	4. Gases, liquids or solids at ordinary temperatures.
5. Usually volatilize only at high temperatures.	5. Excepting carbon, boron, and silicon, the non-metals are either gaseous or volatilize at low temperatures.
6. When in bulk the metals reflect light from polished or freshly cut surfaces.	6. Do not usually reflect light very well.
7. Specific gravity is generally high.	7. Specific gravity generally low.
8. Good conductors of heat and electricity. Electrical resistance usually increases with rise of temperature.	8. Bad conductors of heat and electricity. Electrical resistance usually decreases with rise of temperature.
9. More or less malleable and ductile.	9. Malleability and ductility are not well defined.
10. Molecules usually monatomic in vaporous state.	10. Molecules usually polyatomic in vaporous state.

In all chemical changes one property at least remains unaltered, and the more successful systems of classification were based, in the first instance, on this property, viz., the atomic weights of the elements. The early efforts in this direction were seriously hampered by the uncertainty in the numerical values of the atomic weights. But after chemists had cleared up the confusion associated with the atomic theory left by Dalton, and obtained a consistent system of atomic weights, the results were more promising.

Between 1816 and 1829, J. W. Döbereiner noticed some regularities in the atomic weights of certain related elements, for he found that most of the chemically related elements either exhibited almost the same atomic weight—e.g., iron, cobalt, and nickel—or else exhibited a constant difference when arranged in sets of three.

Thus, rounding off modern atomic weights :

	Calcium.		Strontium.		Barium.
Atomic Weight .	40		87		137
Difference .		47		50	

	Chlorine.		Bromine.		Iodine.
Atomic Weight .	35·5		80		127
Difference .		44·5		47	

	Sulphur.		Selenium.		Tellurium.
Atomic Weight .	32		79		128
Difference .		· 47		49	

These were called Döbereiner's Triads, but it was soon felt that his list was but a fragment of a more general law. Between 1863 and 1866, J. A. R. Newlands published a series of papers in which he arranged the elements in the ascending order of their atomic weights, and noticed that every succeeding eighth element was "a kind of repetition of the first." Thus,

H	Li	Be	B	C	N	O
F	Na	Mg	Al	Si	P	S
Cl	K	Ca	Cr	Ti	Mn	Fe
. . .		. . .		. . .		. . .

"In other words," said Newlands, "members of the same group of elements stand to each other in the same relation as the extremities of one or more octaves in music. This peculiar relationship I propose to provisionally term **the law of octaves**." Newlands noticed that elements belonging to the same group "usually" appeared in the same column, and he declared that all the numerical relations which had been observed among the atomic weights "including the well-known triads, are merely arithmetical results flowing from the existence of the law of octaves."

The "law of octaves" did not attract much attention, probably because faulty atomic weights seriously interfered with the arrangement.* Similar remarks apply to some papers by A. E. B. de Chancourtois in 1862, where also it was proposed to classify the elements by their atomic weights.

§ 2 The Periodic Law—D. I. Mendeléeff and L. Meyer

D. I. Mendeléeff and L. Meyer, quite independently and, so far as we can tell, quite in ignorance of Newlands's and Chancourtois's work, obtained a far clearer vision of the "law of octaves" about 1869. Mendeléeff said : "When I arranged the elements according to the magnitude of their atomic weights, beginning with the smallest, it became evident that there exists a kind of periodicity in their properties." Otherwise expressed, if the elements be arranged in the order of increasing atomic weights, their *properties* vary from member to member in a definite way, but return more or less nearly to the same value at fixed points in the series.. Mendeléeff continued : "I designate by the name ' periodic law ' the mutual relations between the properties of the elements and their atomic weights, these relations are

---

* When Mr. Newlands read a paper on "The Law of Octaves" at a meeting of the London Chemical Society in 1866, Prof. G. C. Foster said that any arrangement of the elements would present occasional coincidences, and inquired if Mr. Newlands had ever examined the elements according to their initial letters. Twenty-one years later the Royal Society awarded Newlands the Davy Medal for his discovery.

applicable to all the elements, and have the nature of a periodic* function." Expressed more concisely, we have **Mendeléeff's periodic law : The properties of the elements are a periodic function of their atomic weights.**

Consequently, Mendeléeff was able to construct a table in which the elements were arranged horizontally in order of their atomic weights and vertically according to their resemblances in properties. The early tables were very imperfect on account of the unreliability of many atomic weights, as then assigned, but they were afterwards amended and modified in the light of the more accurate data which became available. The table on page 118 shows Mendeléeff's scheme modified so as to conform with modern knowledge (Table VIII).

Mendeléeff's table was constructed on the basis of the atomic *weights* of the elements, the most fundamental property of the atom then known. It is now known, however, that the properties of the elements are in reality a periodic function of an even more fundamental number than the atomic weight, viz., the **Atomic Number.** This will be discussed fully in Chapter IX—for the present it may be defined as *the ordinal number of the element in the periodic table of Mendeléeff.* As we shall see in § 3, Mendeléeff reversed the order of certain pairs of elements, as indicated by the values of their atomic weights, in order to bring them into their proper places (as determined by their properties). This procedure has been abundantly justified, and the Periodic System as a whole placed on a firm, theoretical basis by recent discoveries concerning the structure of the atom, and the atomic number has been shown to possess a fundamental significance. Table VIII accordingly includes the values of the Atomic Numbers, as well as of the Atomic Weights.

§ 3 General Structure of the Periodic Table

Beginning with hydrogen, the element of lowest atomic weight, and writing down the elements in a horizontal row in the order of their atomic weights, we come to elements showing a recurrence of the properties of elements already written down, at intervals of 2, 8, 8, 18, 18 and 32 elements respectively. If we start a new line in the table at each of these recurrences, that is with the beginning of each new period, we shall find the elements arranged vertically in *families* or *groups* of like chemical properties. In the table the groups are numbered from I to VIII with the addition of Group O as shown. Groups VIII and O are unusual in that they are alternatives. The Periods are numbered 1, 2, etc., up to 7 ; the first three are known as *short* periods, the others as *long* periods. In the long periods the groups are sub-divided into two sub-groups, differentiated in the table by being placed to the left or right respectively in their appropriate columns. These are designated *A* and *B* respectively.

* A periodic function is one whose value repeats itself at regular intervals. The interval is called a " period."

Table VIII.—The Periodic Series of the Elements.

(Atomic numbers are given in brackets after the symbol of the element)

Periods	Group I. A	Group I. B	Group II. A	Group II. B	Group III. A	Group III. B	Group IV. A	Group IV. B	Group V. A	Group V. B	Group VI. A	Group VI. B	Group VIII. A	Group VIII. B	Group VII.			Group O.
I (short)	H(1) 1·0081													H(1) 1·081				He(2) 4·003
II (short)	Li(3) 6·94		Be(4) 9·02			B(5) 10·82		C(6) 12·01		N(7) 14·008		O(8) 16·00			F(9) 19·00				Ne(10) 20·183
III (short)	Na(11) 22·997		Mg(12) 24·32			Al(13) 26·97		Si(14) 28·06		P(15) 31·02		S(16) 32·06			Cl(17) 35·457				A(18) 39·944
IV (long)	K(19) 39·096	Cu(29) 63·57	Ca(20) 40·08	Zn(30) 65·38	Sc(21) 45·10	Ga(31) 69·72	Ti(22) 47·90	Ge(32) 72·60	V(23) 50·95	As(33) 74·91	Cr(24) 52·01	Se(34) 78·96	Mn(25) 54·93	Br(35) 79·916	Fe(26) 55·84	Co(27) 58·94	Ni(28) 58·69	Kr(36) 83·7
V (long)	Rb(37) 85·48	Ag(47) 107·88	Sr(38) 87·63	Cd(48) 112·41	Y(39) 88·92	In(49) 114·76	Ze(40) 91·22	Sn(50) 118·70	Nb(41) 92·91	Sb(51) 121·76	Mo(42) 95·95	Te(52) 127·61	Ma(43) —	I(53) 126·92	Ru(44) 101·7	Rh(45) 102·91	Pd(46) 106·7	Xe(54) 131·3
VI (long)	Cs(55)	Au(79) 197·2	Ba(56)	Hg(80) 200·61	La(57) 138·92	Tl(81) 204·39	Hf(72) 178·6	Pb(82) 207·21	Ta(73) 180·88	Bi(83) 209·00	W(74) 183·92	Po(84) —	Re(75) 186·92 / —(85)		Os(76) 190·2	Ir(77) 193·1	Pt(78) 195·23	Rn(86) 2·2?

Rare-earth series (Group III. A, Period VI):

La(57) 138·92
Ce(58) 140·13
Pr(59) 140·92
Nd(60) 144·27
I(61) —
Sm(62) 150·43
Eu(63) 152·0
Gd(64) 157·3
Tb(65) 159·2
Dy(66) 162·46
Ho(67) 163·5
Er(68) 167·2
Tm(69) 169·4
Yb(70) 173·04
Lu(71) 175·0

In periods 4 and 5 (the first of the long periods) it is necessary as we have seen to pass not 8 but 18 elements, before one of really similar properties is reached. Thus potassium is an alkali metal closely related to sodium, the first element of the second short period. The next alkali metal is rubidium. Of the elements which lie between potassium and rubidium (that is, the elements of the first long period) the ten elements scandium, titanium, vanadium, chromium, manganese, iron, cobalt, nickel, copper, zinc, are of a new type not hitherto met with. They may be regarded as related to the elements in the earlier periods in the groups into which they respectively fall, but as somewhat different in properties. They are placed, as we have seen, in separate sub-groups, and three of them, viz., iron, cobalt and nickel, are placed in a group by themselves (Group VIII) as they are clearly too closely related to be placed in separate groups. These elements are called *transition* elements and they are thus interposed between the eight elements typical of the groups as represented in the short periods. This is easily seen if we disregard these transition elements for the moment, for we then have the sequence,

K, Ca, Ga, Ge, As, Se, Br, Kr,

which closely resembles the previous short period which is,

Na, Mg, Al, Si, P, S, Cl, A.

A similar phenomenon is to be found in the second long period, but in the third long period a new feature is seen in the remarkable series of fourteen elements known as the rare earths ; a series which is interposed, as it were, between the typical elements and the transition elements. They constitute a series of distinct elements, having yet very similar properties, and are responsible for the expansion of this period from 18 to 32 elements.

These relationships between the groups, periods, transition elements and rare-earths are well brought out in the form of the Periodic Table shown in Table IX (p. 120). It emphasizes also the relationship, and yet the individuality of the sub-groups—the typical and transitional elements.

In three instances, as will be seen by reference to the Table on p. 118, the order assigned to the elements departs from that of the atomic weights. These are the three pairs of elements : argon and potassium, cobalt and nickel, tellurium and iodine. In each case the order, as determined by the atomic weights, is reversed so that these elements may fall into the places in the Periodic Table to which their properties rightly assign them.

This was done by Mendeléeff himself, who believed that subsequent determinations would show that the atomic weights then accepted were inaccurate, and that when known, the true values would fall into the order of the Periodic Table.

Many redeterminations of the atomic weights of these elements have been made in consequence ; but have failed to indicate that the atomic weights of these elements as usually accepted are seriously in error. Nevertheless, Mendeléeff's vision has been abundantly justified by more recent discoveries which have shown that the real property

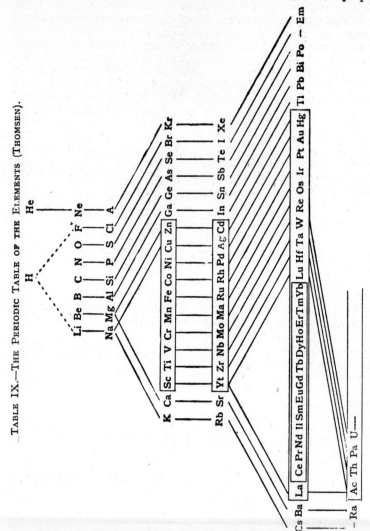

TABLE IX.—THE PERIODIC TABLE OF THE ELEMENTS (THOMSEN).

underlying the periodic classification is the *atomic number*, to which the atomic weight is approximately proportional. Recent work has also demonstrated the existence of isotopes; that is, atoms of slightly different mass, but identical properties and atomic number (see Ch. IX).

Most of the well-defined physical and chemical properties of the elements are periodic—valency, specific gravity, atomic volume, melting point, hardness, malleability, ductility, compressibility, co-efficient of expansion, thermal conductivity, latent heat of fusion, refraction equivalents for light, colour, electrical conductivity, magnetic power, etc. When the numerical values of these properties and the atomic weights of the elements are tabulated on squared paper, a curve is obtained which is broken up into periods.

This is particularly well illustrated by the curve showing the relationship between atomic volume and atomic weight, to which attention was first drawn by Lothar Meyer (Fig. 38). The atomic volume is the quotient obtained by dividing the atomic weight of an element by its specific gravity in the solid condition. When the atomic volumes of the elements are plotted against the atomic numbers, a periodic curve is obtained, as illustrated in Fig. 38. The atomic volume, for instance,

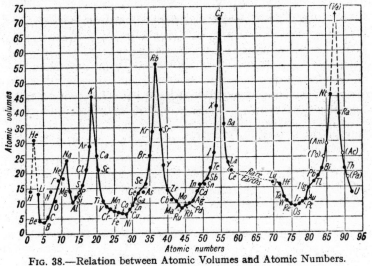

FIG. 38.—Relation between Atomic Volumes and Atomic Numbers.

decreases in passing from lithium to boron, after which it increases through carbon, oxygen, and fluorine to sodium, when it again decreases through magnesium down to aluminium, and thence increases to potassium.

The elements boron, aluminium, cobalt and nickel, rhodium, etc., occupy the troughs of the curve, while the alkali metals occupy the crests of the curve, thus corresponding with the fact that these elements have the largest atomic volumes, or the largest spaces between the atoms. Presumably, the spaces between the atoms of these solid elements are relatively large compared with the size of the atoms themselves. This is often taken to mean that the constituent particles of these elements approximate more nearly to the condition of the particles of a gas than other elements with small atomic volumes. According to D. I. Mendeléeff, the chemical activity of the alkali metals is due to this circumstance ; and this assumption is in agreement with the observed increase in the chemical activity of these elements in passing from lithium to caesium.

§ 4 The Gaps in Mendeléeff's Tables

Both Meyer and Mendeléeff considered it necessary to leave gaps in their tables for undiscovered elements, and more particularly in order to keep certain related elements in the same vertical column. Mendeléeff boldly prophesied that the **missing elements** would be discovered later, and in some cases even predicted their properties in considerable detail. For instance, when Mendeléeff announced the law, there were two blank spaces in group III, the missing elements were called **eka-aluminium** and **eka-boron** respectively ; and another space below titanium in group IV, the missing element in this case was called **eka-silicon**. The hypothetical character of these elements was considered to be an inherent weakness of the law, but the weakness was turned to strength when gallium, scandium, and germanium subsequently appeared duly clothed with those very properties which fitted closely with Mendeléeff's audacious prognostications. This hit attracted considerable attention, and served to strengthen the faith of chemists in the fundamental truth of the periodic law. In illustration, the case of eka-silicon and germanium is quoted side by side in Table X.

The confirmations of Mendeléeff's predictions of the properties of eka-aluminium (gallium) and of eka-boron (scandium) were equally striking.

§ 5 The Applications of the Periodic Law

Mendeléeff pointed out that the periodic law could be employed in : 1. The classification of the elements ; 2. The estimation of the atomic weights of elements not fully investigated ; 3. The prediction of the properties of hitherto unknown elements ; and 4. The correction of atomic weights.

1. The classification of the elements. The periodic system is undoubtedly superior to all the older methods of classification, for the law makes it possible to build up a system of the greatest possible completeness, free from much arbitrariness, and it furnishes strong circumstantial evidence of the correctness of the reasoning employed by Cannizzaro (p. 89) to deduce values for the atomic weights of the elements.

2. The estimation of the atomic weights of the elements. On account of practical difficulties, it is not always possible to fix the

TABLE X.—COMPARISON OF PREDICTED AND OBSERVED PROPERTIES OF GERMANIUM.

Eka-silicon, Es (predicted in 1871).	Germanium, Ge (discovered in 1886).
Atomic weight, 72.	Atomic weight, 72·6.
Specific gravity, 5·5.	Specific gravity, 5·47.
Atomic volume, 13.	Atomic volume, 13·2.
Element will be dirty grey, and on calcination will give a white powder of EsO_2.	The element is greyish-white and on ignition furnishes a white oxide GeO_2.
Element will decompose steam with difficulty.	The element does not decompose water.
Acids will have a slight action, alkalies no pronounced action.	The element is not attacked by hydrochloric acid, but it is attacked by aqua regia. Solution; of KOH have no action, but the element is oxidized by fused KOH.
The action of sodium on EsO_2 or on EsK_2F_6 will give the element.	Germanium is made by the reduction of GeO_2 with carbon, or of GeK_2F_6 with sodium.
The oxide EsO_2 will be refractory and have a sp.gr. 4·7. The basic properties of the oxide will be less marked than TiO_2 and SnO_2, but greater than SiO_2.	The oxide GeO_2 is refractory and has a sp.gr. 4·703. The basicity is very feeble.
Eka-silicon will form a hydroxide soluble in acids, and the solutions will readily decompose forming a metahydrate.	Acids do not precipitate the hydrate from dilute alkaline solutions, but from concentrated solutions, acids precipitate GeO_2 or a metahydrate.
The chloride $EsCl_4$ will be a liquid with a boiling point under 100° and a sp.gr. of 1·9 at 0°.	Germanium chloride, $GeCl_4$, boils at 86°, and has a sp.gr. at 18°, 1·887.
The fluoride EsF_4 will not be gaseous.	The fluoride $GeF_4.3H_2O$ is a white solid mass.
Eka-silicon will form a metallo-organic compound $Es(C_2H_5)_4$ boiling at 160°, and with a sp.gr. of 0·96.	Germanium forms $Ge(C_2H_5)_4$, which boils at 160°, and has a specific gravity slightly less than water.

atomic weights of some elements by vapour density determinations (Avogadro's rule), and by specific heat determinations (Dulong and Petit's rule), and the atomic weights of these elements were frequently assigned on somewhat uncertain grounds.

The application of the Periodic System to the alteration of the atomic weight of indium has already been mentioned (Ch. VI, p. 94). Other similar changes have been made analogously. Thus, beryllium, uranium, and a number of the rare earths at one time did not fit very well into the table, but Mendeléeff's alteration of the supposed atomic weights to make these elements fit the table was subsequently justified by vapour density determinations of the volatile chlorides, or by specific heat determinations.

3. The prediction of the properties of hitherto undiscovered elements. Some instances of Mendeléeff's predictions of the properties of undiscovered elements, and the subsequent verification of these predictions, have been given above.

In order to avoid introducing new names when speaking of unknown elements, Mendeleeff designated them by prefixing a Sanscrit numeral —eka (one), dwi (two), tri (three), etc.—to the names of the next lower analogous elements of the odd or even numbered series of the same group.

In addition to the prediction of germanium, gallium, and scandium already discussed, Mendeléeff foretold the possible discovery of eka- and dwi-caesium ; eka-niobium—En = 146 ; of eka-tantalum— Et = 235 ; of dwi-tellurium—Dt = 212 ; and of the analogues of manganese : eka-manganese—Em = 100 ; and tri-manganese—Tm = 190.

The case of the so-called **inert gases** is 'of more recent date.. The discovery of argon and helium could not have been predicted from Mendeleeff's periodic law, but after these elements had been discovered, accommodated in the periodic table between the strongly acid halogen family and the strongly basic alkali metals, the probable existence of other similar inert gases was indicated. When an exhaustive search was made, krypton. neon, and xenon were discovered with properties and atomic weights which could have been predicted from the arrangement made for argon and helium in Mendeléeff's table.

4. The correction of the values of atomic weights. If the atomic weight of an element does not fit with the regular course of, say, the atomic volume curve, Fig. 38, the atomic weight is probably in error. Thus, the atomic weights of platinum, iridium, and osmium at that time were probably too high, and subsequent determinations verified this inference. Thus the atomic weights of these elements were :

	Platinum.	Iridium.	Osmium.
In 1870 . . .	196·7	196·7	198·6
In 1940 . . .	195·23	193·1	190·2

Similar attempts to correct atomic weights such as those of iodine and tellurium have not been so successful as mentioned above, and as will be seen in the next chapter, the most recent investigations have indicated that in this respect, the applicability of the Periodic Law is not quite so wide as was thought by Mendeleeff.

§ 5 Some Defects in the Periodic Law

The **allocation of hydrogen** in the table has given rise to much discussion, because that element seemed to be without companions. It is univalent, and thus appears to fall either with the alkali metals (D. I. Mendeléeff), or with the halogens (O. Masson). In general hydrogen is electropositive like the alkali metals, but it is certainly not now considered to be a metal. It can be displaced by the halogens from organic compounds, and it forms hydrides with the metals not at all unlike the halogen salts. Indeed, *hydrogen appears to be a rogue element quite out of place in the general scheme*, and, as such, it occupies a unique position as the corner-stone, so to speak, of the structure, p. 120. Some have supposed that hydrogen is a member of a series of independent elements yet unknown.

There has been a difficulty in the **allocation of the rare earths.** Some of them are distributed in the table according to their atomic weights—Sc (21), **45·10** ; and Y (39), 88·92—and others are relegated to a class by themselves. B. Brauner made a special study of the rare earths, and he considered that they should be grouped together, like the asteroids of the planetary system—**the asteroid theory of the rare earths.** In accord with this view, the rare earths, with the exception of scandium and yttrium, were included in the 6th period of Table IX.

If the properties of the elements are dependent on their atomic weights the existence of two elements with different properties and approximately the same atomic weights should be impossible. Hence the difficulty with elements like cobalt and nickel ; ruthenium and rhodium, etc. The peculiarities of these elements would never have been suspected from the periodic law.

Some elements are allocated places in the table according to their atomic weights in opposition to their properties. For instance, copper, silver, and gold fall into one group with the alkali metals. The trivalency of gold appears to be unconformable with the valency of its companions, although in its present position the series : $PtCl_4$, $AuCl_3$, $HgCl_2$, and $TlCl$ is suggestive. Thallium is very like lead, but its sulphate and some other salts are quite different from lead salts.

Some elements which appear to be chemically similar are separated in the table. For example, copper and mercury ; silver and thallium ; barium and lead ; etc. The position of these elements in the table gives no hint of these characters. Still, it might be argued that these elements exhibit many essential differences. Thus the physical properties of mercury and copper, and the properties of the cupric and mercuric chlorides and sulphates show great contrasts. The stability of cuprous and mercurous chlorides is also very different. Lead and barium peroxides appear to have a different constitution. The unstable thallium sesquioxide, Tl_2O_3, corresponds with the other —more stable—sesquioxides in the group, but there are many important points of resemblance between thallium and the alkali metals, and between silver and lead.

CHAPTER IX

THE CONSTITUTION OF MATTER

The electron has conquered physics, and many worship the new idol rather blindly.—H. POINCARÉ (1907).

Even if we resolve all matter into one kind, that kind will need explaining, and so on for ever and ever deeper and deeper into the pit at whose bottom truth lies, without ever reaching it, for the pit is bottomless.—O. HEAVISIDE.

§ 1 General

FROM the earliest times men have hankered after some simplifying generalization which would co-ordinate the multitudinous variety of material substances by ascribing to them a common origin, or by building them up from some single form of matter or potential matter.

This tendency was marked among the earlier Greek philosophers and the suggestion arose of a *prima materia* (" potential matter ") which was supposed to consist of parts which, when grouped in different ways, produced the various kinds of matter considered by them to be elemental. This hypothesis is sometimes called the **unitary theory of matter**: all the different forms of matter in the universe are derived from one and the same primordial element.

Many suggestions have been made as to the nature of this primal element; at various times air, fire, earth, and water were so suggested. A more modern suggestion of this kind, which commanded considerable attention, was due to Prout (1816) and is known as Prout's hypothesis. This states that **the elements are different aggregates of the atoms of primordial hydrogen; that is, the different elements are polymers of hydrogen;** in consequence, within the limits of experimental error, the atomic weights of the different elements should be expressible by whole numbers when the atomic weight of hydrogen is unity.

Many writers, attracted by its apparent simplicity, gave unqualified support to Prout's hypothesis; but an impartial review of the facts, with very much more refined data than were available in Prout's day, led J. S. Stas (1860-1865) to state: " I have arrived at the absolute conviction, the complete certainty, so far as is possible for a human being to attain to certainty in such matters, that the law of Prout is nothing but an illusion, a mere speculation definitely contradicted by experience."

Although Prout's hypothesis in its original form did not survive the test of an impartial examination in the light of experimentally determined facts, the discovery of the Periodic Law by Mendeléeff, soon after the publication of this pronouncement by Stas, served to direct men's minds afresh to the problem presented by the circumstance that the clearly demonstrated *relationship* among elements might well imply a common origin, or common basis, for them all.

Other well-known facts pointed in the same direction. Thus, although it is true that a great many elements have atomic weights which are not even approximately whole numbers, nevertheless many of them, too many to be the result of chance, are very close to whole numbers. In the International Table of Atomic Weights for 1940, which contains eighty-six elements, forty-four have atomic weights which are whole numbers within one-tenth of a unit. Again, it is a significant fact that closely related elements are very often found associated together in nature, for they are often not widely distributed, nor do they as a rule have any marked chemical affinity for each other. Other evidence is also afforded by the regularities observable in the grouping of spectral lines, the results of the investigation of the discharge of electricity through rarefied gases and the study of radio-activity.

§ 2 Electric Discharge in Rarefied Gases

Under ordinary conditions, gases are such poor conductors of electricity that they are classed as good insulators. In order to get electricity to pass through air at ordinary atmospheric pressures, a voltage approaching 30,000 volts per cm. is required ; but as the pressure of the air is diminished the voltage required to produce a discharge diminishes in almost exactly the same proportion.

Experiments on the conduction of electricity through gases are carried out in suitable glass tubes, into the ends of which are sealed short wires (or electrodes) which can be connected to a source of a high potential difference such as an induction coil. The pressure in the tube is reduced by suitable means (air pump, mercury pump, etc.) according to the degree of exhaustion required.

At low pressures (0·03 mm.) the discharge takes the form of a blue glow proceeding from the cathode (or negative electrode) in a course perpendicular to the cathode, and independent of the exact position of the anode. When it strikes the glass a green fluorescence is produced. These " rays," proceeding from the cathode, were named **cathode rays** by Goldstein in 1876, but previously, Plücker (1858) had observed that they can be deflected from their course by a magnet (Fig. 41), showing that they are electrically charged. Also, W. Hittorf (1869) found that if a solid body—say a Maltese cross made of mica—be placed between the anode and cathode, as in Fig. 39, a true shadow appears on the glass ; the shape of the cross shows that *the cathode rays travel in straight lines normal to the surface of the cathode ; and they will cast a well-defined shadow if a solid object be placed between the cathode and the wall of the vacuum tube.* A wheel

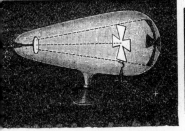

FIG. 39.—Shadows cast by
Cathode Rays.

FIG. 40.—Mechanical Motion by
Cathode Rays.

also, as was shown by Crookes in 1879, may be caused to rotate by allowing the cathode rays to strike against its vanes (Fig. 40), and a number of minerals glow, or phosphoresce, when acted upon by these cathode rays. Further, by the use of a concave cathode the rays may be brought to a focus and a substance such as a metal can be raised to incandescence, or even melted, by being placed there.

If the exhaustion of the tube in which the cathode rays are being produced is carried to the limit, the discharge ceases altogether and the current from the induction coil is no longer able to pass through the tube.

The fact that the tube when highly evacuated is non-conducting shows that *the electric current must somehow be carried from one electrode to the other by something.*

The fact already mentioned that the cathode rays can be deflected by a magnet indicates that they consist of charged particles of some sort. Perrin in 1895 was able to show that they are negatively charged by arranging a vacuum tube so that the cathode stream passed into a small metal cylinder inside the tube, and, by means of a wire, he connected the inner cylinder with an external electroscope. The electroscope acquired a gradually increasing negative charge, or a positively charged electroscope was discharged.

It is clear that particles of some kind are involved, and in 1879 Crookes had suggested that they were particles or molecules of a fourth state of matter—an ultra-gaseous state called radiant matter. Lenard was able to show in 1894 that

the cathode rays could pass through thin sheets of metal (but not through thick ones) and in August 1897 J. J. Thomson suggested the startling hypothesis that what Crookes called " radiant matter " or **the cathode rays, is a stream of negatively charged particles or corpuscles which have been formed by the disintegration of atoms of the gas in the vacuum tube.** The term **electron** had been applied by G. J. Stoney (1881) to designate the unit or atomic charge of electricity, and it is now used for the sub-atomic particles which stream from the negative electrode when a discharge is passing through an attenuated gas. No difference can be detected in the corpuscles derived from different gases, nor can any difference be detected in the properties of these electrons from whatever source they are obtained (they are now known to be emitted by heated metals, by the action of ultra-violet light on metals and by some chemical re-actions) and hence it is inferred that **the electrons are common constituents of all matter.**

FIG. 41.—Effect of a Magnet on Cathode Rays.

Thomson, by comparing and measuring the deflec-tions produced in the path of a stream of electrons by magnetic and by electric fields, was able to determine the ratio of the charge to the mass (usually represented by e/m) and found it to be 1.79×10^7 electro-magnetic units. This value was subsequently found to be substantially constant irrespective of the source of the electron, provided that its speed (which can vary over a very wide range, an average value being 20,000 miles per sec.) did not approach that of light when the " mass " of the electron increases with its velocity.

This value for the ratio e/m is about 1,840 times that of a hydrogen ion in electrolysis (see Ch. XII) from which it follows either (i) that the mass of the electron is $\frac{1}{1840}$th of that of the hydrogen atom, but carries the same charge as a hydrogen ion, or (ii) the masses are the same while the charge on the electron is 1,840 times that of a hydrogen ion. Experiment has decided in favour of the former alternative.

These results led naturally to the hypothesis that the constitution of matter is electronic in nature ; that is, that the atom has a structure involving, *inter alia*, electrons.

§ 3 X-rays or Röntgen Rays

When the exhaustion of a vacuum tube is such that the tube is on the verge of becoming electrically non-conducting, and the glass opposite the cathode is brilliantly fluorescent, rays proceed from the fluorescent glass, *outside the tube* ; these rays—called **X-rays** or **Röntgen rays**—have quite different properties from the cathode or Lenard rays, because they will pass through glass, and they are not deflected by a magnet.

Röntgen rays are produced by the destruction of the cathode rays and are formed when the cathode rays impinge on solid objects. Every substance when bombarded by electrons emits Röntgen rays—the glass walls of a vacuum tube, heavy metals like platinum or uranium, etc. These so-called X-rays are capable of penetrating freely through paper, wood, aluminium and flesh, but are absorbed by lead, platinum or bone. They can excite fluorescence on a paper screen coated with barium platinocyanide, $BaPt(CN)_4$, or calcium tungstate, $CaWO_4$; they can fog a photographic plate ; and make the air through which they pass a conductor of electricity, and have a remarkable power of penetrating substances opaque to ordinary light. Their penetrating powei varies according to the degree of exhaustion of the tube from which they are being produced. Thus Röntgen radiations with a low penetrative power, called *soft rays*, are emitted from a vacuum tube which has too much residual air. The supply of electrons is then plentiful ; their speed is comparatively slow ; and a current of comparatively low electromotive force is needed. Conversely, radiations with a high penetrative power, called *hard rays*, are emitted if the tube be too highly exhausted. The supply of electrons is then relatively small ; their speed is comparatively high ; and the necessary electromotive force is high.

These Röntgen rays consist of electro-magnetic waves in the aether similar to those of ordinary light, but of very much smaller wave-length, and may perhaps be thought of as the " aether-splash " which results when a stream of electrons is suddenly brought to rest.

For some time after their discovery it was not possible to detect, in the case of X-rays, one very characteristic property of a wave motion, in that it was not possible, on account of their extremely small wavelength, to obtain evidence of their diffraction by matter. This was at length accomplished by Laue, and by Friedrich and Knipping (1912), when they showed that X-rays suffer diffraction on passage through a crystal.

Before this time, crystallographers had come to the conclusion, from the study of the general properties of crystals themselves, that in a crystal the constituent particles are arranged at the points of different lattice structures, although they had not then decided the nature of the particles occupying the lattice points. (Compare Ch. X, p. 164 *et seq*.)

On the basis of this conception, it is possible to calculate from a knowledge of the density of a simple crystal such as rock-salt, the distances between the planes of particles in the crystal and the result of Laue's and of Friedrich and Knipping's experiments shows that these distances are commensurate with the wavelength of the X-rays employed. Their results also serve to confirm the space-lattice theory of crystal structure, and in the hands of W. H. and W. L. Bragg and others the correctness of this theory has been demonstrated and the structures of many crystals have been worked out. This aspect of the diffraction of X-rays is more fully treated in Chapter X—for the moment the important fact is, that as Bragg showed, they suffer reflection at definite angles of incidence in the same way as light from a diffraction grating ; thus providing a means for the analysis of X-rays themselves.

In this way it has been found that the rays emitted from an ordinary bulb are usually heterogeneous, mixed hard and soft, but C. G. Barkla (1906) showed that **if the existing stimulus be great enough, every substance can be made to emit a set of X-rays which can be regarded as homogeneous and characteristic,** in that the absorption coefficient, k, of the radiations from that substance, in some standard substance (say aluminium), is a constant, e.g. :

	Ca	Cr	Cu	Se	Ag	Ba
k	435·0,	136·0,	47·7,	18·9,	2·5,	0·8.

Substances with atomic weights between aluminium and silver, emit two sets of these homogeneous characteristic radiations, e.g., palladium emits two characteristic sets of homogeneous rays with wave-lengths respectively 0.58×10^{-8} and 0.51×10^{-8} cm., and nickel, 1.66×10^{-8} and 1.50×10^{-8} cm. respectively. H. G. J. Moseley (1913) further showed that when the increase in the atomic weight of the element is plotted with the corresponding decrease in wave-length, the curve does not run smoothly ; but if the logarithms of the wave-lengths or vibration frequencies be plotted against a series of natural numbers, the curve runs quite smoothly. This is illustrated by Fig. 42, in which the logarithm of wave-length $\times 10^8$ cm. is plotted against the numbers I3 to 30 ranging from aluminium to zinc for one of the homogeneous sets of rays. Analogous curves have been obtained for all the known elements. Indeed, the X-ray spectrum of every element from aluminium to gold is determined by an integer N called the **atomic number** ranging from 13 for aluminium to 79 for gold. There are some blanks corresponding with unknown elements. The order of the atomic numbers is the same as the order of the atomic weights, except where the latter disagrees with the order of the chemical properties, so that the atomic number in the periodic table is a more fundamental index of quality than the atomic weight. This shows that **the wave-length, or the vibration frequency, of the characteristic X-rays from different elements changes from element to element by regular jumps.**

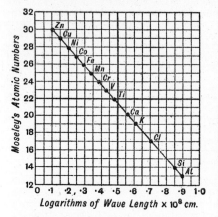

Fig. 42.—Relation between the Wave-length of the Characteristic X-ray of the Elements and the Atomic Number.

The wave-length of the characteristic X-rays of an element thus depends upon, and gives us a measure of, some fundamental property of the atom whose numerical value varies by one unit as we pass from atom to atom in the order of the Periodic table. This number (that is, the ordinal number indicating the position of an element in the Periodic table) is called the **Atomic Number.** The significance of this fundamental property and its relationship to the atomic number have been considerably elucidated from the study of the phenomena of radio-activity, which has furnished further striking confirmation of the view (resulting from the discovery of the electron) that the atom is complex.

§ 4 Radio-activity

This large subject cannot be completely discussed here and a fuller treatment will be found in Chapter XXXVI. But the following brief account will serve to explain the contribution its study has made to our knowledge of the structure of the atom.

Discovery of Radium

In 1896 Becquerel found that some substances, notably uranium minerals, and uranium salts in general, give out rays which are capable of affecting a photographic plate, even when the plate is protected with a layer of black paper. Thorium compounds were shown shortly afterwards to possess similar properties, and such substances have been termed **radio-active** from their property of emitting these radiations.

The examination of a number of uranium minerals by Madame Curie indicated that some of these minerals gave radiations of greater intensity than the purified uranium which they contained, and she was thus led to suspect the presence of a radio-active substance of much greater activity than uranium itself. Upon investigation she was able to isolate a salt of a new element, of a very much more active character than uranium, to which the name **radium** was given.

The Nature of the Radiations

Radio-active substances were found in general to be detectable in three ways, viz.,

(i) by the action on a photographic plate;

(ii) by the phosphorescence produced from certain minerals such as zinc blende;

(iii) by making the air in their neighbourhood capable of conducting electricity (thus causing, for example, the discharge of an electroscope).

Careful investigation shows that the rays emitted are of **three** kinds, which are known as α-rays, β-rays and γ-rays. By examining their behaviour when acted upon by powerful magnetic fields and when sheets of metal foil are interposed in their path, the nature of these rays has been shown to be as follows :—

(i) **α-rays.** These consist of positively charged particles, which are easily absorbed by thin sheets of metal foil and have a limited range in air.

(ii) **β-rays.** These are negatively charged particles, identical with the electron, emitted with a speed comparable with that of light, and able to penetrate thin sheets of aluminium.

(iii) **γ-rays.** These are unaffected by magnetic fields and consist of X-rays of very short wave-length. They are capable of penetrating a layer of lead several centimetres in thickness.

The α-rays, or α-particles, have further been found to have a mass of 4 units (compared with a hydrogen atom as unity) and have been shown by Rutherford to be atoms of helium, each carrying a positive charge equal in magnitude to *twice* the negative charge of an electron (see Ch. XXXVI, p. 850). These α-particles are projected at high velocities ($\frac{1}{15}$th to $\frac{1}{10}$th of that of light).

Careful investigation has revealed the fact that the emission of these radiations takes place at a rate which is entirely and absolutely independent of the external conditions. Thus, for example, the activity of radium is exactly the same at the temperature of liquid air as it is at a red heat. This is completely different from ordinary chemical change, the rate of which varies with temperature.

Another remarkable fact which soon became apparent is that the emission of these radiations is accompanied by the change of the element concerned into another element. Thus, for example, radium is undoubtedly an element ; it has a definite atomic weight and spectrum, and a definite place in the Periodic Table. It is constantly changing, however, at an absolutely characteristic (and so far as we are concerned) unalterable rate with the emission of an α-particle (as we have seen, a charged helium atom) and the formation of a radio-active gas known as niton, or **radon.** This gas, a typical inert gas, is, in the same sense as radium, an element. In its turn, radon, too, undergoes a radio-active transformation. Investigation has shown that radioactive changes take place in this way in series, the final non-radio-active product of these series being lead. At each stage the change may be accompanied by the emission of an α-particle or by the formation of a β-particle along with γ-rays. α-particles and β-particles are never emitted together in one single change.

The Disintegration Hypothesis

Radio-active changes are clearly atomic phenomena, since they are entirely unaffected either by reagents or the physical conditions, and are unchanged even by the formation of compounds of the element concerned. To account for these and other facts of radio-activity, Rutherford and Soddy in 1903 put forward the **theory of spontaneous disintegration.** According to this theory the atom of a radio-active element is a complex structure, potentially unstable, and spontaneous disintegration occurs at a rate dependent upon, and characteristic of, the nature of the element concerned, with the emission from the atom itself, either of an α-particle or a β-particle and the simultaneous formation of an atom of another element. This theory, which accounts satisfactorily for all the facts of radio-activity, presupposes the complexity of the atom, that is, that it has a structure.

§ 5 The Rutherford-Bohr Atom

The production of identical electrons from varying kinds of matter had revealed the complex nature of the atom and naturally led to attempts to evolve a picture of the structure of the atom. A noteworthy attempt of this kind was that of J. J. Thomson in 1898. It is clear that as the electron has a negative charge, and since the atom is electrically neutral, there must be, somewhere in the atom, a charge of positive electricity exactly equivalent to the charge of the constituent electrons. Thomson supposed that the electrons comprised the whole mass of the atom, and that they were " embedded " in a " sphere of positive electrification."

This theory was seen to be untenable when the results of Rutherford's experiments on the tracks of α-particles in matter became known. A typical diagram of such tracks is given in Fig. 43.

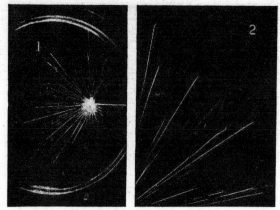

Fig. 43.—Tracks of α-particles.

It is thus seen that, in general, α-particles travel in straight lines without suffering any deflection, but that occasionally an α-particle is deflected through a very large angle, and at the same time a small spur can be seen, as of something moving in the other direction. It is clear that as a rule an α-particle must pass a great many gas molecules without there being any effect on its own track, but that on occasion it is deflected by collision with an atom of gas, the gas atom itself being caused to recoil with considerable velocity. It follows accordingly that the effective mass of the atoms of the gas must be concentrated in a **nucleus** which is extremely minute, even in comparison with the atom itself as a whole. Further, it is evident that this nucleus carries a large positive charge, since the α-particle itself is positively charged.

Rutherford was thus led to suggest that the atom consists of an extremely minute nucleus carrying a positive charge, surrounded by electrons, which are perhaps revolving in orbits round this nucleus and which are equal in number to the nuclear positive charge, thus making the atom as a whole electrically neutral. The mass of these electrons being extremely small, virtually the whole mass of the atom is considered to be concentrated in the nucleus.

As a result of his work on the X-ray spectra of the elements, Moseley (see p. 130) suggested that the atomic number, which clearly represents something fundamental in the atom, is in fact equal to the nett positive charge on the nucleus. This has been confirmed by Chadwick in 1920 by calculations based upon measurements of the scattering of α-particles passing through thin sheets of metal. He thus obtained values for the nuclear charge of elements such as platinum, silver and copper in good agreement with the values for their atomic numbers as found from their position in the Periodic table and from Moseley's experiments.

The atomic number is usually about half the atomic weight. Now hydrogen is the lightest atom known and hence has the lightest nucleus, and it is evident, since only one electron can be removed from the hydrogen atom (for hydrogen can only " take up " one positive charge), that the hydrogen nucleus of mass 1 carries also a positive charge of one unit. This is known as a proton. The nuclei of the other elements, if they consisted only of these positively charged units, would have weights approximately *equal* to their atomic numbers, whereas in fact their weights are roughly *twice* the atomic numbers. Hence the nuclei of the later elements must contain electrons approximately half in number as compared with the number of protons present. This conclusion, that the nucleus must contain electrons, is confirmed by the fact that some radio-active elements emit electrons which must come from the nucleus since radio-activity is clearly a nuclear phenomenon.* This conclusion is further supported by the fact that radio elements can lose electrons either as β-rays, or to form ions, but the latter change does not produce a new element.

Rutherford's conception of the atom is the basis of present-day views of atomic structure ; but modifications have been introduced by Bohr, so far as concerns the motions of the orbital electrons, in order to account for the observed phenomena of radiation as revealed in the spectra of the elements (see § 9). With these modifications this theory is able to correlate many observed phenomena in a very satisfactory way, and the " atom-model " employed is known as the Rutherford-Bohr atom.

§ 6 The Position of the Radio-Elements in the Periodic Table. Isotopes

It was natural that when the Disintegration Theory of radio-active change had established itself, investigation should have been begun into the chemical nature of the various elements comprising the radio-active series, with a view to their characterization and to the end that they might be assigned to their proper places in the Periodic table. As this work proceeded two important facts emerged. First, that these various elements are not all chemically distinct either from each other, or, in some cases, from previously known elements, although their radio-active properties are quite distinct ; and secondly, that their position in the Periodic table is closely connected with the nature of the change (whether α-ray or β-ray) by which they are produced.

At the beginning of 1913, several investigators stated that the expulsion of an α-particle by a radio-active element causes the residual product to shift its position two " places " in the Periodic table in the direction of diminishing mass, so that the residual product is not in the next family, but in the next but one. Similarly, when an element gives off a β-particle, the product shifts its position in the opposite direction one " place " in a direction opposite to that for an α-ray change. Hence two changes attended by the emission of β-particles, and one by an α-particle would bring the product back to its original position in Mendeléeff's table. This is the **displacement rule** : *whenever an α-particle is expelled by a radio-active element, the group in the table to which the resultant product belongs is either two units greater or two units less than that to which the parent belongs ; and when an element gives off a β-particle, with or without the accompaniment of X-rays, the resultant product shifts its position so that it is one unit greater or one unit less than that to which the parent belongs.* This is illustrated with the radium family by Fig. 44. Similar tables have been compiled for the actinium and thorium families. Further, when any number of radio-active elements occupy one place in the Periodic table, these elements cannot be separated from one another by any known chemical process. Thus, when mesothorium-I gives off two β-particles and one α-particle to form thorium-X, it is claimed that the two substances cannot be separated from one another in spite of the difference in their atomic weights ; and they are probably spectroscopically indistinguishable. These non-separable elements are what F. Soddy called **isotopic elements,**

* The conclusion that the nucleus consists of protons and electrons may require modification in view of the recently reported discovery of the neutron and the positron ; but at present too little is known of the way in which they enter into the constitution of the nucleus to admit of precise description.

or **isotopes,** e.g., ionium, thorium, and radio-thorium are isotopes, and meso-thorium is isotopic with radium (*vide supra*). The different forms of lead dis-covered by Soddy connected with radio-activity (1914) are also said to be isotopic, for they have the same atomic volumes and the same chemical properties.

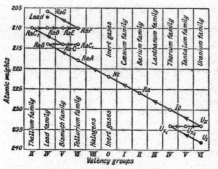

FIG. 44.—Arrangement of the Uranium -Radium Family in the Periodic Table.

These facts are readily ex-plained by the Rutherford-Bohr Theory of the atom, for as we have seen the chemical properties of an element and its position in the Periodic Table are determin-ed by the nett positive charge on the nucleus. It is evident that the expulsion of an α-particle (a charged atom of helium) will reduce the weight of an atom by four units and the positive charge on the nucleus by two units. Similarly, the loss of an electron (which, as has been said, must, in a radio-active change, come from the nucleus) will increase the nuclear charge by one unit without appreciable change in weight.

The discovery of isotopes among the radio-elements, along with the develop-ment of the theory of atomic structure which so successfully accounted for them, directed attention to the possibility of the existence of isotopes of the common elements. A very careful series of experiments by Richards (1914) on the atomic weight of lead derived from various sources showed that variations in this value undoubtedly exist ; a conclusion which has been confirmed by several later workers. Values as low as 205·927 and as high as 207·9 have been recorded for lead from radio-active minerals ; the value for common lead from galena being 207·21.

In the case of the radio-elements, the detection of isotopes is a relatively simple matter, since it depends upon radio-active data : no such method is available for the common elements. The only satisfactory criterion, a method of comparing the masses of *individual* atoms was, however, in process of development at the time when the possibility of the existence of these isotopes was being discussed. This was J. J. Thomson's parabola method of positive ray analysis. This has been developed by Aston, and by Dempster, into a very accurate method for the investigation of atomic masses. It depends primarily upon the observation of Goldstein (1886), who noticed that when a perforated cathode is employed in the vacuum tube used for producing cathode rays, luminous rays pass backwards through these perforations. These rays he called canal rays, and it was later shown that they consist of positively-charged particles of atomic size. Hence they are now usually known as **positive rays.**

The method consists essentially in subjecting the stream of positively-charged particles to the combined action of transverse electric and magnetic fields whereby the particles are made to follow parabolic courses, the size and shape of the parabola followed depending upon the mass of the particles concerned. These parabolas are focussed on a photographic plate and from the position of the trace so made the mass of the atoms concerned can be calculated.

J. J. Thomson's original experiments with apparatus of this kind were made before discoveries in the field of radio-activity had revealed the existence of isotopes, but he had made observations which could not be adequately explained until that later discovery cleared up the matter. In particular, Thomson had noticed, when investigating positive rays from neon, that there was evidence of a particle for which the ratio of the mass to the charge was 22. The suggestion that this was due to particles of carbon dioxide from the stop-cock grease, carrying *two* charges, was disproved by cooling the gas with liquid air, which removed the CO_2 particle with a single charge (44), but left the line at 22 unaffected.

After the existence of isotopes among the radio-elements had been discovered; and lead from different sources had been shown to have different atomic weights, the suggestion was made that Thomson's results were due to the presence of a second isotope in ordinary neon, of atomic weight 22 ; the gas being in fact a mixture of two or possibly more sorts of atoms of atomic weights 20 and 22, and perhaps others as well. This might be the explanation of the fractional atomic weight of neon (20·18) and similar considerations could be applied to other elements.

The investigation of this problem demanded an apparatus of greater accuracy than Thomson had used, and the subject was taken up by Aston who has developed the **mass-spectrograph,** as he termed it, to be capable of a high degree of accuracy.

§ 7 Isotopes of the Non-Radio-active Elements.   The Mass Spectrograph

A general idea of the construction and use of the mass-spectrograph is given by Fig. 45.   The radiations are produced by means of an X-ray bulb B, of which the anode, A and perforated cathode C are of aluminium.   The concentrated stream of electrons from the cathode falls on the silica bulb D.   This cuts down unwanted X-rays and protects the glass of the bulb.   A minute leak allows the entry of a trace of the vapour of a suitable volatile compound of the element under

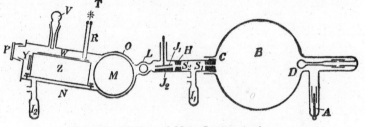

Fig. 45.—Section of Mass Spectrograph.

examination.   Positively-charged atoms result by the loss of electrons in the ionizing atmosphere and these pass through the perforated cathode, forming a beam of swift, positive particles.   This beam is passed through two very fine slits, S_1 and S_2, so forming a ribbon-beam of particles travelling in parallel directions.   The particles are then deflected by a powerful electrostatic field maintained by the plates J_1, J_2 ; it can be shown that this deflection is proportional to $\dfrac{e}{mv^2}$ where

$$e = \text{charge on a particle}$$
$$m = \text{mass of a particle}$$
$$\text{and } v = \text{velocity of a particle.}$$

After passage through a diaphragm, which selects a portion of this deflected beam, the particles are then acted upon by an intense magnetic field (produced by the electro-magnet M) so arranged as to cause deflection in the same plane, but in the opposite direction.   This deflection is proportional to $\dfrac{e}{mv}$, and so it is possible, by careful adjustment of the strengths of the two fields, to bring the

TABLE XI.—TABLE OF ISOTOPES.

Atomic Number.	Element.	Atomic Weight.	Isotopes (in order of abundance).
1	Hydrogen	1·008	1, 2, (3)
2	Helium	4·003	4
3	Lithium	6·940	7, 6
4	Beryllium	9·02	9 (8)
5	Boron	10·82	11, 10
6	Carbon	12·010	12, 13
7	Nitrogen	14·008	14, 15
8	Oxygen	16·0000	16, 18, 17
9	Fluorine	19·00	19
10	Neon	20·183	20, 22, 21
11	Sodium	22·997	23
12	Magnesium	24·32	24, 25, 26
13	Aluminium	26·97	27
14	Silicon	28·06	28, 29, 30
15	Phosphorus	30·98	31
16	Sulphur	32·06	32, 34, 33
17	Chlorine	35·457	35, 37
18	Argon	39·944	40, 36, 38
19	Potassium	39·096	39, 41, 40
20	Calcium	40·08	40, 44, 42, 43
21	Scandium	45·10	45
22	Titanium	47·90	48, 46, 50, 47, 49
23	Vanadium	50·95	51
24	Chromium	52·01	52, 53, 50, 54
25	Manganese	54·93	55
26	Iron	55·85	56, 54, 57, 58
27	Cobalt	58·94	59
28	Nickel	58·69	58, 60, 62, (61), 64
29	Copper	63·57	63, 65
30	Zinc	65·38	64, 66, 68, 67, 70
31	Gallium	69·72	69, 71
32	Germanium	72·60	74, 72, 70, 73, 76
33	Arsenic	74·91	75
34	Selenium	78·96	80, 78, 76, 82, 77, 74
35	Bromine	79·916	79, 81
36	Krypton	83·7	84, 86, 82, 83, 80, 78
37	Rubidium	85·48	85, 87
38	Strontium	87·63	88, 86, 87
39	Yttrium	88·92	89
40	Zirconium	91·22	90, 92, 94, 91, 96
41	Niobium (Columbium)	92·91	93
42	Molybdenum	95·95	98, 96, 95, 92, 94, 100, 97
43	Masurium	—	
44	Ruthenium	101·7	102, 101, 104, 100, 99, 96, (98)
45	Rhodium	102·91	103
46	Palladium	106·7	104, 105, 106, 108, 110, 102
47	Silver	107·880	107, 109
48	Cadmium	112·41	114, 112, 110, 111, 113, 116, 106, 108
49	Indium	114·76	115, 113
50	Tin	118·70	120, 118, 116, 119, 117, 124, 122, 112, 114, 115

TABLE XI.—TABLE OF ISOTOPES—*continued.*

Atomic Number.	Element.	Atomic Weight.	Isotopes (in order of abundance).
51	Antimony	121·76	121, 123
52	Tellurium	127·61	130, 128, 126, 125, 124, 122, 123
53	Iodine	126·92	127
54	Xenon	131·3	129, 132, 131, 134, 136, 130, 128, 126, 124
55	Caesium	132·91	133
56	Barium	137·36	138, 137, 136, 135
57	Lanthanum	138·92	139
58	Cerium	140·13	140, 142, 136, 138
59	Praseodymium	140·92	141
60	Neodymium	144·27	142, 144, 146
61	Illinium	—	
62	Samarium	150·43	152, 154, 147, 149, 148, 150, 144
63	Europium	152·0	151, 153
64	Gadolinium	156·9	156, 158, 155, 157, 160
65	Terbium	159·2	159
66	Dysprosium	162·46	164, 162, 163, 161
67	Holmium	163·5	165
68	Erbium	167·2	166, 168, 167, 170
69	Thulium	169·4	169
70	Ytterbium	173·04	174, 172, 173, 176, 171
71	Lutecium	174·99	175
72	Hafnium	178·6	180, 178, 177, 179, 176
73	Tantalum	180·88	181
74	Tungsten	183·92	184, 186, 182, 183
75	Rhenium	186·31	187, 185
76	Osmium	190·2	192, 190, 189, 188, 186, 187
77	Iridium	193·1	193, 191
78	Platinum	195·23	195, 196, 194, 198, 192
79	Gold	197·2	197
80	Mercury	200·61	202, 200, 199, 201, 198, 204, 196, (197), 203
81	Thallium	204·39	205, 203
82	Lead	207·21	208, 206, 207, 204, (203), (205), (209), (210)
83	Bismuth	209·00	209
84	Polonium	—	
85	—	—	
86	Radon (Niton)	222	
87	—	—	
88	Radium	226·05	
89	Actinium	—	
90	Thorium	232·12	232
91	Protoactinium	231	
92	Uranium	238·07	238, 235

" rays " to a focus at a position which then depends only upon $\dfrac{e}{m}$ and is independent of the speed. A photographic plate W is placed at this focus and so reveals, on development, a series of lines, each of which corresponds to a group of particles all of the same mass (strictly the same ratio $\dfrac{e}{m}$). This selective deviation of the particles from their original path is very similar to the dispersion of light by a prism. Consequently, the nomenclature of light is adopted : hence " mass-spectrograph " and " mass spectrum." This " spectrum " can be calibrated from the positions of the lines due to certain common elements always present, and so the masses of the particles producing the other lines can be calculated.

When it is desired to investigate an element from which no suitable volatile compound is available, a compound is fused on to the anode itself which is then heated electrically.

Several improvements and refinements have been introduced into this apparatus lately whereby its accuracy and precision have been greatly increased, but in fundamentals the method remains the same.

Dempster in America has also developed a mass spectrograph of rather different design in which the intensities of the spots (or lines) can be measured electrically.

As a result of this work, the great majority of the known elements have been found to have isotopes. Even hydrogen itself has an isotope of mass 2. 83 of the ninety-two elements have now been examined, 23 are simple, consisting of atoms of one mass only, the remainder consisting of two or more isotopes. Table XI gives a list of those discovered up to the time of writing (July 1938).

The results summarized in Table XI lead to certain remarkable and interesting conclusions. Thus, in view of the fact that so many elements consist of mixtures of two or more kinds of atoms, it is remarkable that their atomic weights, as determined by the ordinary chemical methods, are so constant. The only element for which, so far, differences in atomic weight have been detected in different samples (with the possible exception of boron) is lead ; and this we know from our study of radio-activity is derived from two different sources ; even meteoric samples have atomic weights indistinguishable from those of their terrestrial counterparts. For the non-radio-active elements we are forced to the conclusion either that since they were formed they have been so thoroughly mixed that the proportions of the various isotopes present has settled down to a fixed ratio which nothing has since succeeded in disturbing, or else that when they were first produced the process producing them did so in fixed proportions.

Another interesting conclusion to be drawn from the above table is that Prout's hypothesis is in a very real sense a true one, although not quite perhaps in the sense that he understood it. It is now clear that the masses of the individual *atoms* are whole numbers (though for a reason shortly to be discussed—§ 8—not exact multiples of that of a hydrogen atom), and they are built up of units of which the hydrogen nucleus is the chief.

It is curious to note that no odd-numbered element, with the possible exception of potassium and of the supposed isotope of hydrogen of mass 3, has more than two isotopes ; whereas the even elements frequently have a great many. The most complex element from this point of view, so far as present information goes, is tin, with eleven isotopes, ranging from 112 to 124, 113 and 123 being the only missing " numbers " in this range. Another remarkable fact which emerges is that a stable elementary atom is now known for almost every mass-number up to 210 ; some places are filled twice over, and a few three times, with **isobares** (atoms of the same weight but different chemical properties).

§ 8 Mass-Spectra and Atomic Weights

Quite soon after Aston had begun the search for isotopes of the non-radio-active elements, it became clear that the atoms comprising a great many elements had a mass expressible in terms of whole numbers in terms of oxygen $= 16$. But even with the first mass-spectrograph, whose "resolving power" was comparatively small by the side of the latest apparatus, Aston was able to show that hydrogen is not represented by an exact whole number on this scale.   The discrepancy is accounted for by the modern view that mass is electrical in origin, on the basis of which it can be shown that if two opposite charges are brought very close together a definite loss of mass results.   Now we have seen that, in general, the nucleus contains both protons and electrons.   These latter must clearly be in extremely close proximity to the positive charges and hence a loss of mass will have taken place when, in the remote past, the nucleus in question was formed from protons and electrons, an enormous amount of energy being liberated equivalent to this loss of mass.   Thus the total mass of this nucleus will not be equal to the combined masses of the protons and electrons which compose it, but something slightly less than this.   The hydrogen nucleus, which contains no electrons, will thus have a mass slightly greater than, for example, one-sixteenth of that of an oxygen atom (disregarding for the moment the isotopes of oxygen, concerning which see below).   This is known as the packing effect and with his latest apparatus Aston has shown that in many cases it differs slightly from atom to atom.   The magnitude of the divergence of the mass of any given atom from the whole number rule ($O = 16$) is known as the **packing fraction**.   These divergencies are, of course, very small, being of the order on the average of 10^{-4} : the departure of atomic weights, as determined by chemical methods, from whole numbers being due, as has been shown, to the existence of isotopes.

It is clear that if we know the packing-fraction of a given element, and the relative abundance of each isotope in the element, as ordinarily prepared, we can calculate the value of the chemical atomic weight.   It is only quite recently that it has been practicable to determine either of these quantities with sufficient accuracy for the purpose, but the refinements introduced into the apparatus by Aston, and by Dempster, have now enabled this to be done, and the atomic weights of many elements have now been determined by this method.   Where the result differed markedly from the accepted chemical value, redetermination of the latter has usually resulted in a change to a value very close to the result obtained from mass-spectrograph data.   It is noteworthy that two methods so essentially different in principle should give results so concordant, and it may be concluded that the theories underlying each have a substantial foundation of truth.

The discovery of isotopes has reduced somewhat the importance of atomic weights as physical constants, for it is now seen that the atomic weight is a statistical mean of the weights of the atoms present, and only when the element is simple does it represent the weight of any actual atom.   The important constants are now for any individual *atom* its mass-number, and atomic number, which respectively determine its weight and its chemical (and to a large extent physical) properties.   But the remarkable constancy of atomic weights, already referred to, indicates that their importance for ordinary chemical work and calculations, in particular those involved in quantitative analysis, remains unaltered.

In this connection the fact (recorded in Table XI) that oxygen consists of three isotopes has important consequences.   The existence of isotopes of oxygen of masses 17 and 18 was not at first detected by the mass spectrograph as the proportions in which they are present are too small to enable them to be identified with certainty by being distinguished from charged particles of OH, and OH_2 normally present in small quantities.   Their presence was revealed by a study of the infra-red absorption spectrum of oxygen, by which means they were shown to be present to the extent of 1 part in 10,000, and 1 part in 1,250 respectively. The chemical atomic weight of an element, referred to oxygen = 16, will thus differ slightly from the atomic weight calculated from mass spectrograph data alone which is referred to $O^{16} = 16$ (i.e., the abundant isotope) as standard. This difference is allowed for in comparing the results of the two methods, in the way previously described.

§ 9 The Structure of the Atom and the Spectra of the Elements

Rutherford's initial suggestion as to the structure of the atom postulated the existence of a central, positive nucleus surrounded by electrons equal in number to the nett nuclear charge, thus preserving the electrical neutrality of the atom (see p. 132). He also assumed that these extra-nuclear electrons rotate round the nucleus and thus are kept from falling into the nucleus by their centrifugal force. The difficulty then arises that on the basis of classical dynamics such rotating electrons would radiate energy continuously in the form of electromagnetic waves (light, etc.), and this energy being derived from that of the rotating electrons themselves, it would follow that their speed would gradually be reduced and they would eventually fall into the nucleus.

The way out of this difficulty was suggested in 1913 by N. Bohr who applied the principles of the **Quantum Theory** to the problem. For some years previously it had been clear that the principles of ordinary classical dynamics were not applicable to the problems of radiation in general, and in order to account for the observed results, M. Planck put forward the *Quantum Theory of Radiation*. According to this theory the energy of vibration is not radiated or absorbed continuously, but is given out, or taken in, in small, discrete portions called quanta, whose magnitude is not, however, universally constant for all radiation, but is proportional to the frequency of the particular radiation concerned, or, what is in reality the same thing, the frequency of the vibrating system producing the energy radiated. Thus where ν is the frequency of vibration the magnitude of the quantum of energy is given by $h\nu$ where h is an universal constant known as Planck's constant. Energy can only be radiated from a system whose vibration frequency is ν in amounts which are exact, integral multiples of the quantum for this system, that is, exact multiples of $h\nu$.

This theory has been very successful in accounting for many physical phenomena which could not be explained on the basis of classical mechanics and so is regarded as established.

In applying the quantum theory to the problem of atomic structure Bohr made the following assumptions :—

(i) of all the theoretically possible orbits (possible spatially, that is) of an electron rotating round the nucleus, only certain orbits are permissible—all others are forbidden. These orbits are known as *stationary states* ;

(ii) an electron radiates energy *only* when passing from one permissible orbit to another of lower energy ;

(iii) the positions of the permissible orbits are related in that an electron may possess 1, 2, 3 . . . n quanta of energy according to which of the n permissible orbits it is in. The energy of any given electron is thus given by $nh\nu$.

An electron passing from one orbit to the next will radiate (or absorb) one quantum of energy, that is if E_1, E_2 are the energies of two consecutive stationary states, the energy radiated has a frequency given by $E_1 - E_2 = h\nu$.

Bohr achieved a remarkable success with this theory of the atom when he applied it to the calculation of the spectrum of hydrogen. On classical theories, if radiation were emitted from rotating electrons, all frequencies should be represented in the spectrum, which should therefore be continuous. The spectrum of a glowing vapour is in fact a line spectrum, i.e., its radiation comprises a limited number of definite frequencies only. Assuming that hydrogen has a nucleus with one positive charge round which one electron rotates, Bohr was able to calculate the positions of all possible lines in the hydrogen spectrum, and his results are in exact agreement with the observed values. A similar success has been recorded in the case of ionized helium. The details of the spectra of the more complicated atoms are more difficult to calculate. but the results so far obtained are highly significant. The converse calculation has been employed for the deduction from observed spectra of the electronic structure of the more complex atoms, and the results show a very close correspondence with those required by the chemical properties as indicated, for example, in the Periodic Table.

§ 10 The Structure of the Atom and the Periodic Table

The conclusions we have so far arrived at for the structure of the atom may be summarized as follows :—

(i) Atoms are made up of positive and negative units of electricity—known as protons and electrons, respectively—whose charges are equal in magnitude, though opposite in sign ;

(ii) All the protons and (except in the case of hydrogen) some of the electrons constitute a nucleus in which is concentrated the mass of the atom, and which is of very small size in comparison with the atom as a whole ;

(iii) The remainder of the electrons revolve round the nucleus in orbits corresponding to 1, 2, 3 or more quanta of energy of radiation. this figure is known as the quantum number of a given electron ;

(iv) If W is the mass of a given atom and N is its atomic number the nucleus will contain W protons and $W - N$ electrons, while there will be N outer (or extranuclear) electrons.

The orbits of the extra-nuclear electrons may be circular, but will in general be elliptical. These elliptical orbits may have varying degrees of eccentricity and the value of the eccentricity is indicated by a second quantum number written as a subscript, e.g., 4_1, 4_2, 4_3, 4_4 (Fig. 46). These numbers refer to four orbits all corresponding to the possession by an electron travelling in them of four quanta of energy, but of differing degrees of eccentricity.

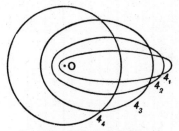

We can now consider the problem of the configuration of the electrons in the atoms of the different elements in their state of least energy, with all the electrons in their lowest orbits.

Fig. 46.—Elliptical Orbits of Quantum Number $n = 4$.

Conclusions in this field are based partly on data furnished by the investigation of the spectra of the elements, after the manner indicated above for hydrogen ; partly upon consideration of the chemical properties, particularly in so far as these are summarized in the Periodic Table.

It is clear in this latter connection, on the assumption that the outermost electrons are those which are concerned in ordinary chemical processes, that the inert gases must possess an extremely stable structure, which we interpret as meaning that in them the outermost group of electrons is complete and has reached its most stable size. Furthermore, the Periodic Table indicates that we find a reappearance of similar properties after passing 2, 8, 8, 18, 18, and 32 elements respectively. This fact must be reflected in the way in which we assume that the different levels are filled up, as we pass from atom to atom.

The conclusions derived both from physical and from chemical evidence are in good agreement, and have enabled us to assign structures to almost all the elements with a high degree of certainty. These conclusions are embodied in Table XII and may now be considered in slightly greater detail.

It is convenient for this purpose to assume that we can pass from element to element, adding each time one positive charge to the nucleus, and assigning them the consequent additional extra-nuclear electron to its appropriate place in the system.

TABLE XII.—ELECTR

Elements	At. No.	Number of Electrons in Orbits.																			
		1_1	2_1	2_2	3_1	3_2	3_3	4_1	4_2	4_3	4_4	5_1	5_2	5_3	5_4	5_5	6_1	6_2	6_3	6_4	6_5
H	1	1																			
He	2	2																			
Li	3	2	1																		
Be	4	2	2																		
B	5	2	2	1																	
C	6	2	2	2																	
N	7	2	2	3																	
O	8	2	2	4																	
F	9	2	2	5																	
Ne	10	2	2	6																	
Na	11	2	2	6	1																
Mg	12	2	2	6	2																
Al	13	2	2	6	2	1															
Si	14	2	2	6	2	2															
P	15	2	2	6	2	3															
S	16	2	2	6	2	4															
Cl	17	2	2	6	2	5															
A	18	2	2	6	2	6															
K	19	2	2	6	2	6	0	1													
Ca	20	2	2	6	2	6	0	2													
Sc	21	2	2	6	2	6	1	2													
Ti	22	2	2	6	2	6	2	2													
V	23	2	2	6	2	6	3	2													
Cr	24	2	2	6	2	6	5	1													
Mn	25	2	2	6	2	6	5	2													
Fe	26	2	2	6	2	6	6	2													
Co	27	2	2	6	2	6	7	2													
Ni	28	2	2	6	2	6	8	2													
Cu	29	2	2	6	2	6	10	1													
Zn	30	2	2	6	2	6	10	2													
Ga	31	2	2	6	2	6	10	2	1												
Ge	32	2	2	6	2	6	10	2	2												
As	33	2	2	6	2	6	10	2	3												
Se	34	2	2	6	2	6	10	2	4												
Br	35	2	2	6	2	6	10	2	5												
Kr	36	2	2	6	2	6	10	2	6												
Rb	37	2	2	6	2	6	10	2	6	0		1									
Sr	38	2	2	6	2	6	10	2	6	0		2									
Y	39	2	2	6	2	6	10	2	6	1		2									
Zr	40	2	2	6	2	6	10	2	6	2		2									
Nb	41	2	2	6	2	6	10	2	6	4		1									
Mo	42	2	2	6	2	6	10	2	6	5		1									
Ma	43	2	2	6	2	6	10	2	6	6		1									
Ru	44	2	2	6	2	6	10	2	6	7		1									
Rh	45	2	2	6	2	6	10	2	6	8		1									
Pd	46	2	2	6	2	6	10	2	6	10		0									

UCTURES OF THE ELEMENTS.

At. No.	Number of Electrons in Orbits.																					
	1_1	2_1	2_2	3_1	2	3_3	4_1	4_2	4_3	4_4	5_1	5_2	5_3	5_4	5_5	6_1	6_2	6_3	6_6	6_5	6_6	7_1
47	2	2	6	2	6	10	2	6	10		1												
48	2	2	6	2	6	10	2	6	10		2												
49	2	2	6	2	6	10	2	6	10		2	1											
50	2	2	6	2	6	10	2	6	10		2	2											
51	2	2	6	2	6	10	2	6	10		2	3											
52	2	2	6	2	6	10	2	6	10		2	4											
53	2	2	6	2	6	10	2	6	10		2	5											
54	2	2	6	2	6	10	2	6	10		2	6											
55	2	2	6	2	6	10	2	6	10	0	2	6				1							
56	2	2	6	2	6	10	2	6	10	0	2	6				2							
57	2	2	6	2	6	10	2	6	10	0	2	6	1			2							
58	2	2	6	2	6	10	2	6	10	1	2	6	1			2							
59	2	2	6	2	6	10	2	6	10	2	2	6	1			2							
60	2	2	6	2	6	10	2	6	10	3	2	6	1			2							
61	2	2	6	2	6	10	2	6	10	4	2	6	1			2							
62	2	2	6	2	6	10	2	6	10	5	2	6	1			2							
63	2	2	6	2	6	10	2	6	10	6	2	6	1			2							
64	2	2	6	2	6	10	2	6	10	7	2	6	1			2							
65	2	2	6	2	6	10	2	6	10	8	2	6	1			2							
66	2	2	6	2	6	10	2	6	10	9	2	6	1			2							
67	2	2	6	2	6	10	2	6	10	10	2	6	1			2							
68	2	2	6	2	6	10	2	6	10	11	2	6	1			2							
69	2	2	6	2	6	10	2	6	10	12	2	6	1			2							
70	2	2	6	2	6	10	2	6	10	13	2	6	1			2							
71	2	2	6	2	6	10	2	6	10	14	2	6	1			2							
72	2	2	6	2	6	10	2	6	10	14	2	6	2			2							
73	2	2	6	2	6	10	2	6	10	14	2	6	3			2							
74	2	2	6	2	6	10	2	6	10	14	2	6	4			2							
75	2	2	6	2	6	10	2	6	10	14	2	6	5			2							
76	2	2	6	2	6	10	2	6	10	14	2	6	6			2							
77	2	2	6	2	6	10	2	6	10	14	2	6	7			2							
78	2	2	6	2	6	10	2	6	10	14	2	6	8			2							
79	2	2	6	2	6	10	2	6	10	14	2	6	10			1							
80	2	2	6	2	6	10	2	6	10	14	2	6	10			2							
81	2	2	6	2	6	10	2	6	10	14	2	6	10			2	1						
82	2	2	6	2	6	10	2	6	10	14	2	6	10			2	2						
83	2	2	6	2	6	10	2	6	10	14	2	6	10			2	3						
84	2	2	6	2	6	10	2	6	10	14	2	6	10			2	4						
85	2	2	6	2	6	10	2	6	10	14	2	6	10			2	5						
86	2	2	6	2	6	10	2	6	10	14	2	6	10			2	6						
87	2	2	6	2	6	10	2	6	10	14	2	6	10			2	6						1
88	2	2	6	2	6	10	2	6	10	14	2	6	10			2	6						2
89	2	2	6	2	6	10	2	6	10	14	2	6	10			2	6	1					2
90	2	2	6	2	6	10	2	6	10	14	2	6	10			2	6	3					1
91	2	2	6	2	6	10	2	6	10	14	2	6	10			2	6	4					1
92	2	2	6	2	6	10	2	6	10	14	2	6	10			2	6	5					1

First Period of the Periodic Table

This period contains only hydrogen and helium. The work of Bohr, already referred to, has shown that hydrogen has one electron in 1_1 orbit, the nucleus being a single proton.

Helium, of atomic weight 4 and atomic number 2, must hence contain 4 protons and 2 electrons in its nucleus. The extra-nuclear electrons are both in 1_1 orbits. This inner pair of electrons in 1_1 orbits is believed to exist in all elements except hydrogen—that it represents a " completed " group is shown by the fact that helium is an inert gas.

Second Period

The element of atomic number 3 is lithium, and it appears that the introduction of a third electron into the 1_1 level would produce an unstable system on account of mutual repulsion ; two electrons in 1_1 orbits constituting a stable " complete " system for that level. Hence the third electron in lithium goes into a 2_1 orbit, and since it is situated further from the nucleus, it will be more readily removed than either of the others, and hence we find that lithium is an active element whereas helium is an inert one.

Passing along the first period successive electrons take up orbits represented by a quantum number 2—some are in 2_1 orbits, some in 2_2 orbits. The 2_2 orbits are believed to appear first in Boron. When the total number of electrons has reached 10 (2 in 1_1 orbits and 8 in 2_1 and 2_2 orbits) we have the inert gas neon. The second quantum group is now complete and the very stable configuration characteristic of an inert gas is produced.

Third Period

On the addition of an eleventh electron, since the second quantum group is now complete, it passes into a 3_1 orbit. The resulting system resembles lithium in that we have a solitary electron in the outermost level, with a complete group beneath it, hence the chemical analogy between sodium and lithium. Addition of further electrons, which pass into 3_1 and 3_2 orbits (3_2 orbits are first found in aluminium), causes the formation of elements which reproduce the general characteristics of the previous period and ends with argon when 8 have been added since neon. We then come once more to an outer group of 8 and the stability of an inert gas appears once more.

Fourth Period

The first element in this period is potassium, which has one electron in a 4_1 orbit ; the second, calcium, similarly has two electrons in 4_1 orbits. Thus an analogy exists between these elements and sodium and magnesium respectively. But with the addition of a further electron (i.e., in the element of atomic number 21, scandium) a new phenomenon appears. Scandium does not have three electrons in 4-quantum orbits, but only two, the additional electron passing into a deeper level in the atom and enlarging the 3-quantum group by taking up a 3_3 orbit. This process continues as we pass along the fourth period until all possible 3_3 orbits are filled, the number of 4 quantum electrons remaining unchanged, except in the case of chromium where one of these, too, drops into a 3_3 orbit, until there are 18 electrons in 3-quantum orbits. As soon as this has occurred, the later elements of the period each contain one additional 4-quantum electron until there are eight of these, when krypton results. We thus see that we have a series of " transition elements " in the middle of this period (compare Ch. VIII, p. 119) corresponding to the gradual enlargement of the 3-quantum group from eight to eighteen. These elements show variable valency, form coloured ions, and exhibit other characteristic properties, as well as having the marked " horizontal " relationships characteristic of this portion of the Periodic Table. The later elements of the period, viz., gallium to krypton, resemble the corresponding elements of the third period.

The Fifth Period closely resembles the fourth. It begins with two elements having respectively one and two electrons in 5_1 orbits, after which there follows a series of transition elements, during which the 4-quantum group is being enlarged from eight to eighteen, and ends with a normal series of elements analogous to those in the short periods.

The Sixth Period.

In this period we find an extension of the phenomenon first observed in the fourth period. The period begins normally with the addition of one, and two, electrons respectively in 6_1 orbits, forming caesium and barium respectively. With lanthanum, the next element, the transition group begins, the added electron passing into a 5_3 orbit, analogous to the corresponding phenomena in the fourth and fifth periods. But the sixth period contains 32 elements, and this expansion in the length of the period is caused by enlargement of the size of 4-quantum group from eighteen to thirty-two. This enlargement begins with cerium, the fourth element of the period, and continues uninterruptedly until the 4-quantum group has reached thirty-two. This results in the series of rare earths; elements which are remarkably alike on account of the fact that the difference from element to element occurs in a deep-down layer in the atom, which is shielded from normal chemical influences by two outer layers of electrons. After passing the rare earths, we have more transition elements corresponding to the filling up of the 5-quantum group, after which the period ends normally.

It is thus to be noted that in the sixth period the group of rare-earths is inserted into the transition elements, in the same way, and for an analogous reason, that the transition elements are inserted among the typical elements in the fourth and fifth periods.

§ 11 The Structure of the Atoms of the Groups of the Periodic Table

It is instructive to consider in the light of the atomic structures discussed in the previous section, the relations between those assigned to elements falling within the same group or family in the Periodic Table.

The probable structures of the elements in three such groups are given in Tables XIII, XIV and XV which are extracted from Table XII so as to bring together the elements of Groups O, Ia, and VIa.

Table XIII gives the structures of the inert gases, and from it we see that these are characterized by having an outer layer to which no more electrons can be added, viz., 8 (except in the case of helium).

TABLE XIII. GROUP O.

Element.	Number of Electrons in Orbits of Quantum Number					
	1	2	3	4	5	6
Helium	2					
Neon	2	8				
Argon	2	8	8			
Krypton	2	8	18	8		
Xenon	2	8	18	18	8	
Niton	2	8	18	32	18	8

TABLE XIV. GROUP Ia.

Element.	Number of Electrons in Orbits of Quantum Number					
	1	2	3	4	5	6
Lithium	2	1				
Sodium	2	8	1			
Potassium	2	8	8	1		
Rubidium	2	8	18	8	1	
Caesium	2	8	18	18	8	1

TABLE XV. GROUP VIA.

Element.	Number of Electrons in Orbits of Quantum Number.						
	1	2	3	4	5	6	7
Chromium	2	8	13	1			
Molybdenum	2	8	18	13	1		
Tungsten	2	8	18	32	12	2	
Uranium	2	8	18	32	18	13	1

In Table XIV, which depicts similarly the configurations of the alkali metals, we find in every case an outermost layer of but one electron, all the inner rings being complete. The outermost electron can be detached forming an ion, which will be monovalent. (See § 12 for the application of the electronic theory of the atom to valency.) We see that, as in the case of the inert gases, the outermost layer is the same for all the members of the group, and in addition it is seen the next layer of electrons is also the same.

Table XV gives the structures of a representative group from among the transitional portion of the Periodic Table. In each case these elements have fourteen electrons in the two outermost groups taken together ; sometimes divided as 13, 1 ; sometimes as 12, 2. The group of thirteen comprises (as may be seen by reference to Table XII) complete groups of eight 3_1 and 3_2, or 4_1 and 4_2, or 5_1 and 5_2, or 6_1 and 6_2 orbits, together with an incomplete $3_3, 4_3, 5_3$ or 6_3 group as the case may be. These incomplete groups and the single outer electron are easily removed so that six (or fewer) may be lost, resulting in the considerable variations in valency which we find among the members of this group.

§ 12 The Electronic Theory of Valency

The subject of valency has been mentioned briefly in Chapter VI, § 4 ; considerable elucidation of this matter is possible in the light of the results just described.

Compounds fall, in general, into one of two classes, viz., electrolytes (that is, substances whose aqueous solutions will conduct electricity—compare Ch. XII) and non-electrolytes. It is clear that the linking of the atoms which constitutes a non-ionizable valency must differ in some important respect from that involved in an ionizable valency.

G. N. Lewis and W. Kossel have succeeded in applying the results of the modern view of the atom to this problem, and that of the nature of valency in general, with considerable success. They both assumed that the arrangements of the outermost electrons which occur in the inert gases are the most stable structures and that combination between atoms occurs in such a way as to cause the attainment of these stable structures—this is, a group of two electrons in the case of helium, or of eight in all other cases. It is assumed all through that the outermost electrons are the valency electrons.

Electrovalent (or Ionizable) Linkages

Kossel's theory applies particularly to this type of linkage and is successful in explaining it. He considers that the inert gas type of structure is attained by the gain (or loss) of electrons, thus leaving the atom with the electronic configuration characteristic of the nearest inert gas, albeit the atom as a whole is changed i.e., it is an ion and not an uncharged or neutral atom. In his view, the ions are then held together in the solid compound by electrostatic attractions.

Thus, for example, sodium can readily lose one electron to form an ion with an electron grouping similar to that of neon, but, of course, carrying one positive charge. Magnesium similarly can form an ion with two positive charges (Fig. 47). In a corresponding manner, at the other end of the period, chlorine by gaining one electron would complete its outer group of 8, thus attaining to a structure comparable to that of argon, and forming an ion carrying one negative charge.   In

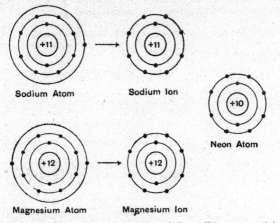

Sodium Atom   Sodium Ion

Neon Atom

Magnesium Atom   Magnesium Ion

FIG. 47.—Structures of Atoms and Ions (Diagrammatic).

solid sodium chloride the ions are held together by the electro-static attraction brought about by their being oppositely, but equally, charged.   When, however, the solid is placed in a solvent such as water, the electro-static forces are reduced owing to the high dielectric constant of the liquid and consequently the ions separate.   The process of combination is thus visualized as indicated in the following scheme :—

$$Na + Cl = Na^+ + Cl^-$$
$$(2.8.1)\ \ (2.8.7)\ \ \ (2.8)^+\ \ (2.8.8)^-$$
$$\text{neon}\quad \text{argon}$$
$$\text{type}\quad \text{type}$$
$$Na^+ + Cl^- = Na^+Cl^-$$

This theory is in accord with the known facts concerning the behaviour of electrolytes, and the relation between the valency of ions (equal to their charges) and the position of the element forming them, as explained in Chapter XII.   It is also in harmony with our knowledge of the crystal structure of polar (i.e., ionizable) compounds.   (See Ch. X.)

Covalent Linkages

The theory outlined above is clearly inapplicable to compounds such as SO_3 or O_2—there is, for example, no reason why one oxygen atom should lose two electrons in favour of the other, nor would the process result in the stable inert-gas configuration.   In general, this type of difficulty is experienced when attempting to deal with non-ionizable compounds, which are the great majority, since almost all carbon compounds fall in this category and they alone are more numerous than the compounds of all the other elements together.

G. N. Lewis propounded a theory in 1916 which obviates this difficulty.   He, like Kossel, assumes that combination occurs in such a way that the inert-gas configuration is achieved, that being the stable state.   The additional assumption which enabled Lewis to explain the formation of non-ionizable (or as they are now known, **co-valent**) compounds is the idea that such a link is formed by the *sharing* of *a pair* of electrons, this pair being able to contribute towards the stability of both the combining atoms. Thus, for example, atoms of oxygen and hydrogen may be indicated thus :

$$H\cdot \qquad\qquad :\overset{\cdot\cdot}{O}: \qquad\qquad H\cdot$$

(it is often convenient to represent linkages diagrammatically by showing the outer electrons only). On Lewis's assumption water is formed by the sharing of a pair of electrons by each hydrogen atom, with the oxygen atom, thus completing the stable group of eight (or octet) around the latter and the stable group of two (helium type) around the former. Water is hence represented :

$$H:\overset{\cdot\cdot}{\underset{\cdot\cdot}{O}}:H$$

In a similar way an oxygen molecule is formed by the sharing of *two pairs* of electrons between the two atoms ; thus each atom will be associated, in this sense, with eight electrons although there are only twelve altogether.

$$\overset{\cdot\quad\cdot}{\underset{\cdot\quad\cdot}{O:O}}$$

Or again, one atom of nitrogen has five electrons in the outer layer. In combining with three atoms of hydrogen to form a molecule of ammonia it shares three of these with the hydrogen along with the three contributed by the hydrogen atoms themselves, thus completing its octet. This can be understood from the following formula where the electrons originally belonging to hydrogen atoms are represented by a cross ($\times$) and those of the nitrogen atom by a dot ($\cdot$). Thus :

$$\begin{array}{c} H \\ \overset{\times\cdot}{} \\ H^{\cdot}_{\times} N: \\ \cdot\times \\ H \end{array}$$

Again, while the nitrogen has achieved the octet of electrons, thus making it conform to the neon-type, the hydrogen has similarly attained to the helium-type.

Co-ordinate Linkages

We have seen that according to Lewis's theory a non-ionizable linkage is due to the sharing of a pair of electrons, one being contributed in general, by each of the linking atoms. It is possible, however, for a co-valent link to be established even when both of the shared electrons are contributed by only one of the atoms. To this type of linkage the term *co-ordinate link* has been given, and it may be exemplified by the combination of sulphur and oxygen. The atom supplying the pair of electrons is called the *donor*, the other being known as the *acceptor*. Thus the atoms of sulphur and oxygen have each six electrons in the outer rings so that if the sulphur atom shares a pair of electrons with one oxygen atom, and donates a pair to another oxygen atom, a molecule of sulphur dioxide is formed, in which each atom has a completed octet. If sulphur trioxide is formed by the introduction of another atom of oxygen, each atom of the group also has a completed octet. Let the electrons of oxygen be represented by . , and those of sulphur by $\times$, then, the electronic structure can be represented by—

Sulphur Dioxide, SO₂.   Sulphur Trioxide, SO₃.

The molecule formed as a result of the sharing of two electrons from one atom in this way will exhibit a certain polarity,* for the sharing will cause the "donor" atom to be ome somewhat positive and the " acceptor " similarly will be negative. Accordingly this type of linkage is usually symbolized by $\rightarrow$ instead of by $-$. The arrow implies the presence of two electrons, and the head of the arrow is arranged to point away from the donor to the acceptor. Thus, sulphur dioxide has *two* covalent linkages, $=$, and one co-ordinate linkage, $\rightarrow$, whilst sulphur trioxide has two covalent linkages, and two co-ordinate linkages :

$$O=S\rightarrow O \qquad\qquad O=S\!\!\begin{array}{c}\nearrow O\\ \searrow O\end{array}$$

Sulphur Dioxide, SO_2.   Sulphur Trioxide, SO_3.

Further deductions from, and applications of, this theory, of great importance, are possible but cannot be fully discussed here. Its application to the Werner compounds is considered in Chapter XXXV.

§ 13 The Atomic Theory in the Light of Modern Developments

It is natural that the facts and theories discussed in the present chapter should cause us to pause and consider their effect on our conceptions of the atom, of an element and of the atomic theory in general as discussed in previous chapters.

As regards the fundamental postulate that all matter consists of atoms, we now have direct evidence for the truth of this, which was previously only an assumption. But we now know that the atoms of a given element are not all exactly alike in weight, nor is the atom the indivisible unit that it was formerly supposed to be.

As regards these two latter points, it has been said earlier (p. 136) that with the exception of lead from radio-active sources, the elements as we find them show a remarkable constancy in the proportions of the isotopes present, so that the *atomic weight* retains all its former significance in the field of *practical* chemistry. Furthermore, although the hypothesis that the atom of an element is an intricate bit of mechanism, a complex aggregate of parts liable to disruption when exposed to the right conditions, is now generally accepted, this does not affect the time-honoured definition of an atom. **The atom still remains a veritable unit indivisible in chemical transformation.** The facts, speculations, and theories discussed in this chapter do not alter our mode of presenting the facts of material chemistry.

* A molecule exhibiting polarity of this kind is said to have a *dipole moment*. This quantity, though small (of the order of 10^{-18} electrostatic units) is measurable, and its measurement can be used to demonstrate the existence of co-ordinate links in the molecules of particular compounds.

CHAPTER X

SOLUTION AND CRYSTALLIZATION

In the strictly scientific sense of the word insolubility does not exist, and even those substances characterized by the most obstinate resistance to the solvent action of water may properly be designated as extraordinarily difficult of solution, not as insoluble.—O. N. WITT.

§ 1 General Classification

THE behaviour of solids such as sugar or salt when brought into contact with water is a familiar fact of experience. The solid seems to disappear into the liquid, and we say that it has **dissolved,** while the resulting homogeneous mixture is termed a **solution.** The dissolved substance is often called the **solute** and the liquid in which it is dissolved, the **solvent.**

Solutions are thus a particular kind of mixture, but are not confined to mixtures of solids and liquids. Thus we can have:

Solutions of solids in solids
,,   ,,   ,,   ,, liquids
,,   ,,   ,,   ,, gases
,,   ,, liquids ,, solids
,,   ,,   ,,   ,, liquids
,,   ,, gases ,, solids
,,   ,,   ,,   ,, liquids
,,   ,,   ,,   ,, gases

The solution of a solid in a liquid is the most familiar type and hence serves best as a starting-point for the study of solutions.

§ 2 Solutions of Solids in Liquids

A mixture of a solid and a liquid may be one of three types, which shade off into each other almost imperceptibly. These types are: true solutions, colloidal solutions and suspensions.

If a small quantity of a salt, such as potassium iodide, be added to a fixed quantity of water and the mixture stirred, the solid seems to disappear. Further small quantities of potassium iodide can be added with the same result. A similar experiment with a coloured salt such as potassium dichromate, shows that the lump of coloured solid gradually disappears but the liquid becomes coloured. In all such cases there is found to be a limit beyond which (at a given temperature) no more solid will pass into the liquid. Within this limit the mixtures formed appear homogeneous to the ordinary sight and are called **simple, true solutions.** They are believed to contain either single molecules or parts of molecules. (Compare Ch. XII, p. 193.)

In such a solution the solid does not separate under gravity, and is not removed by ordinary filtration, but can be recovered on evaporation.

Suspensions consist of gross particles of a solid surrounded by the liquid. These gross particles settle out under gravity, are easily visible (often to the naked eye ; always under the microscope), and can be easily removed by ordinary filtration.

There exists also a class of solid-liquid mixtures in which the particles of solid are intermediate in size between the single molecules (or parts of molecules) of true solutions, and the gross particles present in suspensions. These are known as **colloidal solutions.** In them the particles of solid, which carry an electric charge, do not settle under gravity and are not easily removed by ordinary filtration. They consist of aggregates of relatively small numbers of molecules. The properties of these colloidal solutions are dealt with more fully in Chapter XVI.

In the absence of chemical combination, gases are miscible in all proportions and the properties of a gas mixture (or solution) are those of its constituents. (Compare Ch. II.) But, as mentioned already, there is, in general, a limit to the amount of a given solid which will dissolve in a fixed amount of a particular liquid at any particular temperature. For example, if potassium chloride be added to water kept at a constant temperature, the salt is gradually dissolved, and the process of solution continues until a definite amount has dissolved. The amount of solid remaining in excess of this will remain an indefinite time without further change, provided the temperature remains constant, and no solvent is lost by evaporation. The solid and solution are then in equilibrium. As in the analogous case of the vapour pressure of a liquid, see p. 30, the equilibrium between a saturated solution and a solid is dynamic, not static. The solution is said to be **saturated** with the salt at the temperature of experiment. **The weight of salt dissolved by 100 gms. of the solvent so as to make a saturated solution at any assigned temperature is called the solubility of the salt.*** Thus, 100 gms. of water at 20° will dissolve 35 grams of potassium chloride, and accordingly, 35 is the solubility of potassium chloride in water at 20°.

§ 3 Determination of the Solubility of a Solid in a Liquid

The amount of a given solid which will dissolve in a fixed quantity of any particular solvent is limited ; and further experiments such as those about to be described show that this limit is a constant for a given pair of substances, so long as the temperature remains constant. The determination of solubilities is, therefore, a matter of importance.

* Other modes of representing solubility are more convenient in special cases —e.g., in Fig. 50 the percentage amount of salt in a given weight of the solution is employed.

The usual method consists in the preparation of a saturated solution of the substance at the desired temperature, and the analysis of a known amount of the solution so obtained. This is carried out in an apparatus such as that shown diagrammatically in Fig. 48.

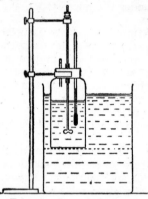

An excess of the finely-powdered solid is placed in a bottle, through the stopper of which there passes a thermo-meter, a mechanical stirrer and a stoppered tube by means of which a pipette may be inserted. Pure solvent (e.g., distilled water) is added, and the whole is immersed in a thermostat (i.e., a large bath of water automatically maintained at a previously determined temperature) whose temperature has been adjusted to that at which the solubility is to be determined. The mixture of solid and solvent is then vigorously stirred for some hours, or even days. At the end of a suitably long period the stirrer is stopped

FIG. 48.—Determination of the Solubility of a Solid.

and, after several hours during which time all undissolved solid has settled, a pipette, warmed to slightly above thermostat temperature and fitted with a filter, is inserted and a portion of the saturated solution is withdrawn by means of it. This solution is then transferred to a weighed vessel, and the weight of the solution deter-mined, after which it may either be analysed chemically, or very carefully evaporated to dryness if the compound concerned is such that it undergoes no change during evaporation. The weight of solid which has been dissolved in a known weight of solution can then be determined, and hence the weight of solid dissolved in 100 gms. of water may be found.

The calculations involved can be understood from the following example :—

In an experiment for the determination of the solubility of oxalic acid 16·37 grns. of solution saturated at 20° C. were diluted to 500 c.cs. Twenty-five cubic centimetres of this solution were titrated with a decinormal solution of barium hydroxide and were found to require 15·8 c.c. for neutralization. Calculate the solubility of oxalic acid at 20° C.

15·8 c.c. of decinormal barium hydroxide solution contain ·00158 equivalents of barium hydroxide.

∴ 25 c.c. of the dilute oxalic acid solution contain ·00158 equivalents of oxalic acid.

But the equivalent of oxalic acid is 45.   ∴ 500 c.c. of diluted oxalic acid solution contain $\dfrac{\cdot 00158 \times 500}{25}$ equivalents of oxalic acid

$$= \frac{\cdot 00158 \times 500 \times 45}{25} \text{ gms. of oxalic acid}$$

$$= 1 \cdot 422 \text{ gms. of oxalic acid}$$

∴ 16·37 gms. of saturated solution contain 1·422 gms. of oxalic acid,

∴ 16·37 − 1·422 gms. of water dissolve 1·422 gms. of oxalic acid,

i.e., 100 gms. of water dissolve $\dfrac{1 \cdot 422 \times 100}{14 \cdot 948}$ gms. of oxalic acid.

∴ The solubility of oxalic acid at 20° C. is 9·51 gms. per 100 gms. of water.

The solubility of a substance determined, as above, is found to vary, in general, with temperature, a rise in temperature usually causing an increase in solubility. When the solubility of a solid has been found for various temperatures, the relation between solubility and temperature can be plotted in the form of a graph. Such a graph is known as a solubility curve, and some typical solubility curves are shown in Fig. 49.

Curves such as these show that :

(i) solubility usually increases with increase of temperature ;

(ii) the effect of change of temperature on the solubility is different for different substances ;

(iii) the change is usually gradual, but sometimes (e.g., sodium

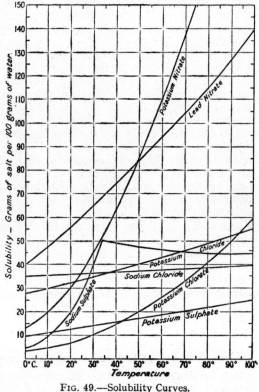

FIG. 49.—Solubility Curves.

sulphate, Fig. 50) the curves show sudden changes in direction (see below, p. 155).

§ 4 Purification by Crystallization

The considerable difference in the solubility of solids at different temperatures provides a convenient means for the purification of soluble substances.

If the impurity consists of a small quantity of an insoluble substance, the process consists in making a solution which is saturated or nearly saturated when hot, filtering it rapidly, and allowing the filtrate to cool, when the dissolved substance will crystallize out on cooling. This process is known as **recrystallization** and is of great importance in chemistry.

If the impurity which it is desired to remove is a soluble one, the process of recrystallization can often still be employed, particularly if one substance is present in only small proportion, or if the solubility curves of the two substances are sufficiently divergent.

In the former case the constituent present in small quantity will not, in general, be present in amount sufficient to saturate the solvent employed even at room temperature, and hence it remains in solution on cooling.

The principle involved in the latter case may be explained by an actual example. Suppose that it is desired to separate a mixture of equal quantities (say 30 gms.) of potassium chloride and potassium chlorate. Reference to Fig. 49 on p. 153 shows that at room temperature the solubilities of these are about 30 and 5 respectively, while at a temperature between 70° and 80° C. the solubilities are about 35 and 50 respectively. If, therefore, we dissolve our mixture in 100 c.c. of water at about 75° C. and allow the solution to cool, we shall find that potassium chlorate will separate at once, while potassium chloride (and a little potassium chlorate) will remain in solution, since the quantity of potassium chloride present barely reaches the amount required for a saturated solution even at room temperature. The chlorate will actually contain entangled traces of chloride which can be removed by a further recrystallization as described in the previous paragraph.

The solution from which the potassium chlorate has been removed will now contain approximately 30 grams of potassium chloride and 5 grams of potassium chlorate. If this solution be evaporated until it begins to crystallize, and then allowed to cool, potassium chloride will be deposited, contaminated with a trace of potassium chlorate. Again recrystallization will enable a pure specimen of potassium chloride to be obtained.

§ 5 Abnormal Solubility Curves

Usually solubility curves are smooth : there are no sudden breaks in them. Sometimes, however, the curve showing the relation between solubility and temperature, does exhibit sharp and sudden breaks or changes in direction.

An example of such a curve is that for sodium sulphate shown in Fig. 50.

On examining this graph we see that the solubility *increases* rapidly with rise of temperature, as shown by the slope of the curve *EO*, Fig. 50. There is an abrupt change in the direction of the solubility curve at 32·4° C. Above that temperature the solubility *decreases* with rise of temperature. The interpretation is that the solubility curve is really compounded of two solubility curves. Sodium sulphate is a *hydrated salt*, that is, it crystallizes with *water of crystallization* (p. 286) ; as ordinarily obtained, ten molecules of water are present along with one molecule of sodium sulphate. Thus in the diagram the curve of increasing solubility with rise of temperature below 32·4° represents the solubility curve of the decahydrate, $Na_2SO_4.10H_2O$; and the curve of decreasing solubility with rise of temperature represents the solubility curve of the anhydrous salt, Na_2SO_4, in rhombic crystals. The decahydrate, at 32·4°, is transformed into the anhydrous salt. The decahydrate is not stable above 32·4°; the anhydrous salt is not stable below 32·4°. This temperature is called the **transition temperature** or **transition point,** and the change is symbolized

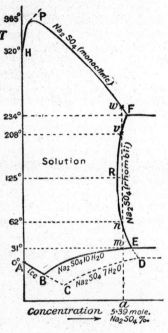

FIG. 50.—Solubility Curve of Sodium Sulphate.

$$\overset{32\cdot4°}{Na_2SO_4.10H_2O \rightleftharpoons Na_2SO_4 + 10H_2O}$$

The solubility curves, it will be observed, represent the condition of equilibrium between the solvent and salt.

It makes no difference whether we start with the anhydrous sulphate or the decahydrate. When in equilibrium, the solution in contact with the solid will contain the amounts of sodium sulphate—Na_2SO_4—indicated by the solubility curves. The saturated solutions, when in equilibrium, have the same concentration and are identical in every way. We cannot continue the observation of the solubility of the decahydrate beyond 32·4° because it *immediately* splits up either into the anhydrous form, or into some less hydrated form—e.g.,

$Na_2SO_4.7H_2O$; but since the transformation of the anhydrous salt into the hydrate takes an appreciable time, it is possible to measure the solubility of the anhydrous salt below 32·4. This is indicated by the dotted line in the diagram.

The solubilities of the two sodium sulphates—anhydrous and decahydrate—are quite different. At 32·4° the rhombic sodium sulphate passes into the monoclinic form with its own solubility curve. If the solid decahydrate were in contact with a saturated solution at 20°, and some of the anhydrous sulphate were added to the solution, some of the anhydrous sulphate would dissolve and be deposited later as the decahydrate. The final result would be a transformation, through the medium of the solution, of the anhydrous salt into the decahydrate.

Apparently abnormal solubility curves result also from the formation of double salts.

It is often found that if two simple salts are mixed in water and the mixed solution is then allowed to crystallize a salt is obtained which is a compound of both salts. For example, such a mixture of potassium sulphate and aluminium sulphate in solution will, when allowed to crystallize, deposit a compound of the formula $K_2SO_4.Al_2(SO_4)_3.24H_2O$ known as alum. Such a compound is called a **double salt.**

§ 6 The Freezing of Solutions

It has long been known, even as far back as Aristotle's day, that drinkable water could be obtained from frozen sea-water ; and that if an aqueous solution of salt be gradually cooled, comparatively pure ice first separates from the solution. The trace of salt generally found in ice which has separated from sea-water is mechanically entangled in the ice.

The curve OB, Fig. 51, represents the solubility of potassium chloride at temperatures ranging from −10·64° to +70°; the observation cannot be continued below −10·64° because the whole mass freezes ; the upward curve would probably stop only at the melting point of potassium chloride if it were not for the volatilization of the water.

The freezing temperature

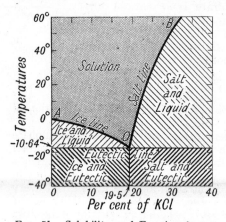

FIG. 51.—Solubility and Freezing Curves of Potassium Chloride-Water Solutions.

of a solution is generally lower than that of the pure solvent. More than a century ago, C. Blagden (1788) cited a number of observations which led him to the belief that the lowering of the freezing point is proportional to the amount of substance in solution. In Blagden's own words : **The effect of a salt is to depress the freezing point in the simple ratio of the proportion to water.** This generalization is sometimes called **Blagden's Law.** The freezing point of an aqueous solution of potassium chloride, that is, the temperature at which *ice* begins to separate, is gradually reduced by the continued addition of small quantities of potassium chloride, and reaches its lowest value, $-10.64°$, when the solution has nearly 19.5 per cent. of potassium chloride ; further additions of the salt raise the temperature at which solid separates. *Solid potassium chloride*, not ice, then separates from the solution.

Imagine a 5 per cent. solution of potassium chloride subjected to a gradually diminishing temperature. Start at 0°. When the temperature reaches, say, -4° ice separates from the solution. The mother liquid remaining has therefore more than 5 per cent. of salt in solution ; as the temperature falls, more ice separates. The further concentration of the mother liquid and the separation of ice continue until the mother liquid has about 19.5 per cent. of potassium chloride, when the whole remaining liquid freezes *en bloc* at $-10.64°$. Quite an analogous series of changes occurs if solutions containing more than 19.5 per cent. of potassium chloride be gradually cooled. This time, however, instead of pure ice, pure potassium chloride separates until the residual liquid has 19.5 per cent. of potassium chloride, when the whole solidifies *en masse* at $-10.64°$. If the cooling solution has just 19.5 per cent. of salt, neither ice nor salt separates until the temperature has fallen to $-10.64°$, when the whole freezes to a solid mass. No other mixture of water and potassium chloride freezes at a lower temperature than this. This solution containing 19.5 per cent. of potassium chloride is called a **eutectic mixture** ; and $-10.64°$ the **eutectic temperature.** F. Guthrie used to think that this mixture —water with 19.5 per cent. of potassium chloride—corresponded with the formation of a definite compound of potassium chloride and water, stable only at low temperatures. Hence his designation **cryohydrate** for the alleged compound. The term "eutectic mixture" is now preferred in place of cryohydrate for we now know that these cryohydrates are not compounds but only mechanical mixtures of ice and salt. The evidence for this conclusion may be summarized as follows :—(1) The heterogeneous structure is frequently apparent under the microscope. (2) Unlike true crystalline compounds, the cryohydrates are generally opaque and ill-defined. (3) Alcohol may dissolve the solvent, leaving behind a network of salt. (4) There are no special signs of chemical change during the formation of the cryohydrate. (5) The ratio of salt to solvent is not always in molecular proportions. The agreement in some cases is merely a coincidence.

(6) The composition of a cryohydrate is different when the solidification takes place under different pressures.

§ 7 Gibbs's Phase Rule

J. Willard Gibbs (1876-1878) discovered an important generalization which is known as the **Phase Rule,** and it has wide applications in the study of solubility and many other phenomena.

The Phase Rule deals with the behaviour of heterogeneous systems at equilibrium, and it employs three special terms, viz., phase, component and degree of freedom or variance.

A heterogeneous system is made up of different portions ; each of these is homogeneous in itself but is separated from the others by surfaces. Each of these portions is called a **phase.** Thus in the case of aqueous solutions of potassium chloride, the eutectic contained two phases—NaCl and H_2O. With an aqueous solution of sodium sulphate at the transition point, Fig. 50, we had to deal with four phases—Na_2SO_4 ; $Na_2SO_4.10H_2O$; the saturated solution ; and the vapour arising from the solution. With freezing water, we have the three phases : ice, water, and vapour. In homogeneous systems there can only be one phase, e.g., gaseous systems ; and in heterogeneous systems there are always two or more phases.

The conception of a **component** is rather more difficult to explain. The components of a system are taken to be the least number of independently variable constituents by means of which the composition of each phase can be expressed.

The components may be elements, or compounds which behave in a system, for the time being, *as if* they were elements. There is only one component in the system just considered, namely, water—H_2O ; the components in the system considered in the previous section—an aqueous solution of potassium chloride—are water (H_2O) and potassium chloride (KCl) ; and two components were involved in our study of the solubility of sodium sulphate namely, water (H_2O) and sodium sulphate (Na_2SO_4).

The **degree of freedom** of a system—sometimes called the **variance** of a system—is the number of independent variables which must be fixed before the state of the system can be defined without ambiguity.

Variance or degrees of freedom of a system.—It will be remembered that the condition of equilibrium of a gas with respect to temperature, pressure, and volume was defined (on p. 18) by the equation, $pv = RT$, for R is a numerical constant whose value depends upon the units of measurement (p. 18). If only one of these variables be fixed, say the volume, the state of the system will remain undefined, because the gas can retain one fixed volume, and yet have very different values for temperature and pressure. Two of the three variables must be known before the state of the system can be defined unequivocally, without ambiguity. If any two of the three variables be fixed, the third variable can only assume one definite value. The two fixed variables are said to be arbitrary or **independent variables** ; the third variable which can be calculated from the condition of equilibrium ($pv = RT$) when the two independent variables are known, is called the **dependent variable.** The gaseous system under consideration has two degrees of freedom.

With these terms clear in our minds we can now state the **Phase Rule** which is that **a system will be in equilibrium when its variance is equal to the number of components in the system less the number of phases, increased by two.** In symbols : $F = C - P + 2$ where C denotes the number of components, P the number of phases, and F the variance or degrees of freedom of the system.

Its application may be illustrated by consideration of the behaviour of water. Fig. 52 shows the relation between the vapour pressure of water and the temperature.

The system consisting of liquid water and vapour has two variables : vapour pressure and temperature. So long as liquid water is present, the pressure is determined solely by its temperature ; given either the pressure or the temperature, the other can be determined from the relation symbolized in the vapour pressure curve—Fig. 52. Hence the state of the system is defined by two variables—the one is dependent, the other independent. In other words, the system has one degree of freedom, that is, the system is **univariant** for $C = 1$ and $P = 2$ as there is only one component " water " in two phases, liquid and vapour.

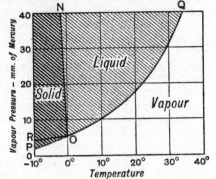

FIG. 52.—Vapour Pressure Curves of Water.

The three curves PO, OQ, and ON—Fig. 52—represent the conditions of equilibrium of three two-phase systems : solid-vapour, vapour-liquid, and solid liquid respectively. These three curves meet at the point O. Here three phases can coexist in equilibrium. Hence the point O is called a **triple point**. The co-ordinates of the triple point are : pressure, 4·57 mm. ; temperature, 0·0076° C If the pressure or temperature is altered ever so little, one of the phases—ice or liquid water—will disappear and a two-phase univariant system represented by a point on one of the curves OP, OQ, ON will appear. At the triple point the system is **invariant** for here $C = 1$ as before, and $P = 3$, as there are now three phases : solid, liquid and vapour.

If a system is such that it has two degrees of freedom—i.e., it is **bivariant**—it follows from the Phase Rule that $P = C$. Two variables must be known before the state of the system can be determined. A saturated solution in the presence of an excess of the solute is univariant, but bivariant if not saturated. In the former case there are two components and three phases—solid, solution, and vapour ; in the latter case there are two components and two phases. Hence in the one case, $F = 2 + 2 - 3$; and in the other, $F = 2 + 2 - 2$. Again, in the region PON, Fig. 52, the system will be bivariant, because there is only one phase and one component. Pressure and temperature may be altered without interfering with the state of the aggregation of the ice so long as the variations keep within the boundary lines PO and ON. The same remarks may be applied to the condition of the water represented by points in the regions NOQ and POQ.

The Phase Rule is therefore a method of grouping systems which behave in a similar manner into one class. It is essentially a system for the classification of states of equilibrium. Systems having the same variance behave in an analogous manner under the influence of variations in temperature, pressure, and volume or concentration. It makes no difference whether the changes be chemical or physical. As indicated above, the Phase Rule also tells us whether the phases of a heterogeneous system are those necessary for equilibrium.

§ 8 Solutions of Liquids in Liquids

In many ways mixtures of liquids exhibit a behaviour similar to that of mixtures of solids and liquids such as we have been discussing in the preceding sections. Thus some, such as mercury and water, are practically **immiscible** ; others, such as water and sulphuric acid are **completely miscible.** With some pairs of liquids, again, as for instance water and ether, each liquid dissolves to a limited extent in the other : they are **partially miscible.**

The immiscibility of mercury and water is analogous to the in-solubility of a solid (like sand) in water ; the partial miscibility of ether and water is analogous to the mixing of excess of salt with water—a solution of salt is formed and at the same time the solid salt is wet. Thus, if successive small quantities of ether are added to water, they dissolve completely at first ; but after a time a point is reached when, the water being saturated with ether, the addition of a further quantity causes the separation of a layer of ether which floats on the top of the aqueous solution. But this upper layer is not merely pure ether (in the sense that a solid in contact with its saturated solution is a pure substance) for the ether layer dissolves some water, as indeed can be easily seen by the addition of a little water to dry ether—the water dissolves completely. Thus, the two layers are respectively a saturated solution of ether in water, and a saturated solution of water in ether, and, provided the temperature is not altered, the percentage composition of both will remain constant even if more ether be added. This addition will cause, however, a change in the relative bulk of the layers, the ether layer (solution of water in ether) will gradually grow, and the water layer will gradually diminish until it finally disappears, when we have left a homogeneous solution of water in ether.

§ 9 Separation of Mixed Liquids

The separation of mixed liquids or the recovery of a solvent from a solution involves some form of **distillation.**

When a solution is being dealt with in which only the solvent is volatile, the process of simple distillation will serve for the recovery of the solvent in an almost pure state. If, however, the solution consists of a mixture of volatile liquids whose boiling points are not very far apart (say less than 60°) **fractional distillation** is necessary in order to separate them. This process has been described in Chapter II (p. 41).

§ 10 Solubility of Gases in Liquids

Gases, like solids and liquids, are found to vary enormously in the extent of their solubility in liquids such as water. Thus, for example, one volume of water, at normal temperature and pressure, will dissolve 1,200 volumes of ammonia, and but 0·021 volumes of hydrogen.

In this respect the solubility relations of gases stand in sharp contra-distinction to their behaviour in other circumstances for no " common " solubility has been observed, and we have no generalization of such wide applicability as Boyle's and Charles's Laws.

For a given gas, however, regularities are observed in the effect of pressure and temperature on solubility, particularly the former.

The influence of pressure on the solubility of gases which are not very soluble in water is summed up in **Henry's Law** which states that : **the amount of a gas dissolved by a given amount of a liquid at a given temperature is proportional to the pressure.** Since according to Boyle's Law the volume of a given mass of gas is inversely proportional to the pressure, the law may also be stated in the form : **the volume of a given gas dissolved by a given volume of a liquid is independent of the pressure.**

This law thus describes the behaviour of the less soluble gases very well—carbon monoxide, nitrogen, hydrogen, oxygen—but not the more soluble gases like ammonia, hydrogen chloride, sulphur dioxide. The deviation is not very great with carbon dioxide, though it is appreciable. Henry's Law refers (1) to gases which do not act chemically on the solvent. When carbon dioxide dissolves in water, one portion enters into combination to produce a new substance—carbonic acid—while the other portion dissolves in the physical sense as carbon dioxide. The latter portion alone comes within the province of Henry's Law. Henry's law also assumes (2) that the molecules of the dissolved gas are no heavier than the molecules of the gas itself. Hence it may be inferred that **if a gas " obeys " Henry's Law, it will have the same molecular weight in solution and in the gaseous condition.** Henry's Law is therefore to be regarded as a link connecting the molecular weights of gaseous and dissolved substances with one unit of measurement.

The Influence of Temperature

The solubility of a gas in a liquid is very sensitive to changes of temperature. The higher the temperature, the less the solubility of the gas.

This is illustrated by the curve (Fig. 53) which shows the solubility of chlorine at various temperatures. The solubility of gases always *diminishes* with temperature (which is the reverse of the behaviour of most solids).

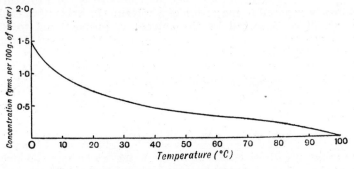

Fig. 53.—Solubility of Chlorine.

§ 11 Determination of the Solubility of a Gas in a Liquid

The solubility of gases in a liquid can be conveniently determined in the following apparatus, modified from that used by R. Heidenhain and L. Meyer

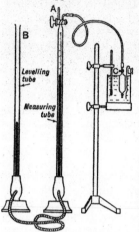

(1863). The pipette C (Fig. 54) is filled with a measured volume of the liquid under investigation. It is connected with a Hempel's burette by means of a piece of metal tubing of narrow bore. The gas under investigation is introduced into the measuring tube A, via the three-way cocks C and A, by first raising and then lowering the levelling tube B. A definite volume of liquid is then run from the pipette C by opening the lower cock and putting the pipette C in communication with the burette. A certain amount of gas enters the pipette. The contents of the pipette are then agitated, and when all is in equilibrium, and the liquid is saturated and the mercury in the burette and levelling tube are at a constant level, place the lower end of the absorption pipette beneath a vessel of mercury, and bring the liquid in the pipette to its former level. The diminution of the volume of gas in the burette represents the volume of gas absorbed by the volume of liquid in the pipette at the temperature and barometric pressure at the time of the experiment. To vary the temperature of absorption, the burette and pipette must be kept in a liquid or vapour bath at the desired temperature and the measurements made when everything is in equilibrium.

Fig. 54.—Determination of the Solubility of Gases.

The results are usually expressed as the number of volumes of gas reduced to N.T.P. absorbed by one volume of liquid. This has also been called by Bunsen the *absorption coefficient*.

§ 12 The Solubility of Mixed Gases

When a mixture of two gases is exposed to the action of a solvent, the quantity of each gas dissolved by the liquid depends upon the amount and the solubility of each gas present. The amount of each gas determines its partial pressure, and since the partial pressure of each gas is independent of the others, it follows that **when a mixture of gases is exposed to the action of a solvent, the amount of each gas which is dissolved by the solvent is proportional to its partial pressure.** Each gas behaves as if the others were absent. This is **Dalton's Law.** It is a simple extension of Henry's Law.

An interesting and important example of this principle is its application to the dissolving of atmospheric air in water. As we shall see in Chapter XXI, air consists of nitrogen, oxygen, water vapour, carbon dioxide and small quantities of inert gases. These last may be neglected for the moment.

When air containing, say, 79 volumes of nitrogen and 21 volumes of oxygen, and 0·04 volume of carbon dioxide, is shaken up with water, the amount of each gas absorbed by the water can be approximately computed in the following manner: The relative solubilities are:

nitrogen, 0·02 ; oxygen, 0·04 ; and carbon dioxide, 1·79.   The partial pressure of each gas is proportional to the relative amount of that gas present in a given volume of air.   If the pressure of air be just one atmosphere, the partial pressure of the nitrogen will be proportional to 0·79 × 1 ; of oxygen, 0·21 × 1 ; and of carbon dioxide, 0·0004 × 1. Hence the relative amounts of these gases absorbed by the water will be : nitrogen, 0·79 × 0·02 = 0·0158 ; oxygen, 0·21 × 0·04 = 0·0082 ; and carbon dioxide, 0·0004 × 1·79 = 0·00072.   Hence 1 c.c. of water dissolves 0·0158 c.c. of nitrogen ; 0·0082 c.c. of oxygen ; and 0·00072 c.c. of carbon dioxide.   The composition of the dissolved gases, if removed from the air by boiling, or exposure to a vacuum, will there-fore be : nitrogen, 63·9 per cent. ; oxygen, 33·2 per cent. ; carbon dioxide, 2·9 per cent.   The relatively large solubility of carbon dioxide is counterbalanced by its low partial pressure, otherwise we might expect a heavy rain storm to remove a great part of the carbon dioxide from the atmosphere.

§ 13 Solutions of Gases in Gases

Gases, as we have seen, are completely miscible in all proportions, providing there is no chemical action, and these mixtures may be considered to be solutions of one gas in another.   They correspond in one sense to the completely miscible liquids referred to in § 8.   The general behaviour of such mixtures has been considered in Chapter II, where it was seen (p. 19) that so long as there is no chemical action between them, each gas in a mixture behaves independently of the others present.   The behaviour of a mixture of gases towards a liquid solvent like water, which was considered in the preceding section, is an example of this.

An important part of the study of mixed gases concerns means for separating them.   Among these may be mentioned the methods depending upon :

(i) diffusion ;

(ii) liquefaction ;

(iii) solubility in liquids.

Separation of gases by diffusion has been mentioned in Chapter II (p. 25) and is referred to as a means of separating the isotopes of neon, and the separation of liquid air has been fully discussed (p. 40). Further applications of this method will be mentioned in describing the separation of the Inert Gases (Ch. XXIV).

The differential solubility of the gases of the atmosphere results in " air " which has been dissolved in water being richer in oxygen than ordinary air (see § 12 above).   Mallet proposed to separate oxygen from atmospheric air in this way.   If the carbon dioxide be removed by passing the air through an aqueous solution of sodium hydroxide, the oxygen and nitrogen in the remaining gases after the first absorption will be nearly in the proportion : nitrogen 65·7 per cent., and oxygen 34·3 per cent.   If this mixture be driven from the water by boiling, and the mixture again treated with air-free water, a gaseous mixture containing 49 per cent. of oxygen is obtained ; and after the eighth absorption, a gas containing 98 per cent. of oxygen results. The method is not practicable, though it is an interesting application of Henry's and Dalton's Laws.

§ 14 Crystals

A solid homogeneous substance may exist as an amorphous body or as a crystalline one, and in the great majority of cases solid substances are found to be made up of aggregates of **crystals.**

A crystal in this sense is a solid which has a definite geometrical shape, with flat faces and sharp edges.   A solid which has no definite shape and which cannot be obtained in the form of crystals is called amorphous, e.g., glass or flint.   Many substances, however, which were once thought to be amorphous, are now known to be made up of exceedingly small crystals.   **Every crystalline substance of definite chemical composition has a specific crystalline form characteristic of that substance.**   This is sometimes called **R. J. Haüy's Law.**   The faces of crystals of the same substance may vary in size and shape ; but if the crystals possess the same chemical composition, and are at the same temperature, the interfacial angles have the same numerical value.   In other words, **the angles between similar faces of crystals of the same substance are precisely the same, and are characteristic of that substance.**   This " law " was first announced by D. Guglielmimi (1688).   This means that the crystalline form of a substance is not determined by the absolute position nor by the sizes of the faces of the crystal, but rather by the dimensions of the interfacial angles.   The primary dominant faces, so to speak, may persist while the angles and edges of some of the crystals may be truncated and bevelled, giving rise to new facets.   In spite of these variations, the crystals of a given substance always retain its fundamental form. Different substances may have a similar chemical composition and different interfacial angles.

This is an essential property of crystals.

Another characteristic property of crystals is that of cleavage. Many crystals tend to split along certain definite directions or planes which are called cleavage planes.   These planes may be parallel to the faces of the original crystal, but sometimes they are not.   An interesting example of the application of this property of cleavage is in the " cutting " of diamonds.   Diamonds are intensely hard but can be split along the natural cleavage planes of the crystal.   This property of cleavage has had an important bearing on the development of our knowledge of crystal structure.

§ 15 The Classification of Crystals

The great variety of crystals formed by different substances, each substance having a characteristic crystalline form or forms (characterized by the interfacial angles) have been classified into *seven systems* and *thirty-two types*. The study of these is a special branch of science known as *crystallography*, and it is only possible here to indicate the general principles on which it is based.

Certain qualities are peculiar to the members of each of the seven systems into which the great variety of crystals can be arranged. For instance, the planes of symmetry of each class are characteristic. A **plane of symmetry** is an imaginary plane which divides the crystal into two parts such that one part is the exact but inverse counterpart of the other. In other words, the two parts bear to one another the same relation that the image in a mirror bears to its object. The mirror is the equivalent of a plane of symmetry. A crystal of sodium

Planes of Symmetry.

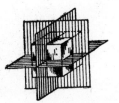

Fig. 55.—Sodium Chloride.

Fig. 56.—Gypsum.

chloride, for example, has nine planes of symmetry ; three are indicated in Fig. 55, and six others are obtained by taking planes diagonally through three faces of the cube. The crystal of gypsum, Fig. 56, has only one plane of symmetry ; and a crystal of zinc sulphate has three planes of symmetry, Fig. 57.

Then again, a crystal may be rotated about a definite axis through an angle, such that the faces, edges, and corners are brought into similar or symmetrical positions, and the aspect of the crystal is the same as

Fig. 57.—
Zinc Sulphate.

before rotation. The axes of rotation are then called axes of symmetry. Thus we speak of dyad, triad, tetrad, and hexad axes of symmetry according as there are 2, 3, 4, or 6 positions of symmetry during a complete rotation. Thus Fig. 58, *A*, represents a horizontal cross-section of a crystal with one hexad axis of symmetry, because during the rotation of the crystal about the axis *O*, there are six positions where the original aspect of the crystal is the same. Fig. 58, *B, C, D*, respectively, denote tetrad, triad, and dyad axes of symmetry.

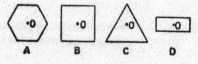

A   B   C   D

FIG. 58.—Axes of Symmetry.

The classification of crystals is thus determined by their symmetry and not by the particular external form of a given crystal. The names of the seven systems, together with some of their characteristics and the names of representative examples of each type are given below, and a series of photographs of real crystals of each type is given in Figs. 59 to 65.

I. Triclinic system.—Crystals of this system have no axes nor planes of symmetry. This system has also been designated the "anorthic," "clino-rhomboidal," "asymmetric," or the "double oblique" system.

EXAMPLES. — Potassium dichromate; copper sulphate—$CuSO_4.5H_2O$; calcium thiosulphate—$CaS_2O_3.6H_2O$; boric acid; potassium ferricyanide; anhydrous manganese sulphate; copper selenate; anorthite —lime felspar; cryolite; etc.

FIG. 59.—Copper Sulphate, Triclinic system.

II. Monoclinic system.—Members of this system have one plane of symmetry, or one dyad axis of symmetry, or both a plane and dyad axis. This system has also been styled the "monosymmetric," "clinorhombic," or the "oblique" system.

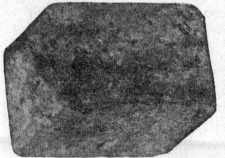

EXAMPLES. — Borax— $Na_2B_4O_7.10H_2O$; gypsum; ferrous sulphate— $FeSO_4.7H_2O$; sodium carbonate — $Na_2CO_3.10H_2O$; felspar — orthoclase; sodium sulphate — $Na_2SO_4.10H_2O$; ammonium magnesium sulphate — $(NH_4)_2SO_4.MgSO_4.6H_2O$; potassium chlorate; potassium tetrathionate—$K_2S_4O_6$; tartaric acid; sulphur—from fusion; cane sugar; arsenic disulphide—realgar; etc.

III. Rhombic system.

FIG. 60.—Orthoclose. Monoclinic system.

—Here the crystals may have three planes of symmetry, and three dyad axes of symmetry.

This system is sometimes called the "orthorhombic," "trimetric," or the "prismatic" system.

EXAMPLES.—Zinc sulphate —$ZnSO_4.7H_2O$; magnesium sulphate—$MgSO_4.7H_2O$; ammonium magnesium phosphate — $NH_4MgPO_4.6H_2O$; potassium sulphate; aragonite; anhydrous sodium or silver sulphate; sulphur from solution; barytes; sodium arsenate; sodium phosphate —$NaH_2PO_4.H_2O$; iodine; potassium nitrate; tartar emetic; potassium chlorate; potassium permanganate; topaz; marcasite; pyrrhotite; tin; tridymite; silver nitrate; lead carbonate; silver sulphide; ferrous sulphate — $FeSO_4.7H_2O$, etc.

FIG. 61.—Barytes. Rhombic system.

FIG. 62.—Zircon. Tetragonal system.

IV. Tetragonal system.—The members of this system may have five planes of symmetry, one tetrad, and maybe four dyad axes of symmetry. This system is sometimes called the "pyramidal," "quadratic," or the "quarternary" system.

EXAMPLES.—Rutile; cassiterite; zircon; mercurous chloride; potassium ferrocyanide; nickel sulphate; potassium hydrogen phosphate —KH_2PO_4; native lead molybdate—$PbMoO_4$; sodium meta-antimonite—$NaSbO_3$; potassium hydrogen arsenate—KH_2AsO_4; scheelite; tin; strychnine sulphate, etc.

V. Trigonal system.—The crystals of this system may have three planes of symmetry, one triad, and three dyad axes of symmetry This system is sometimes called the "rhombohedral" system, and it is sometimes regarded as a special development of the hexagonal system.

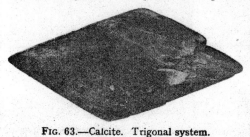

FIG. 63.—Calcite. Trigonal system.

EXAMPLES. — Sodium periodate — $NaIO_4.3H_2O$; quartz; tourmaline; antimony; bismuth; calcite; ice; graphite; sodium nitrate; arsenic; nickel sulphide—millerite; cinnabar; calcium chloride — $CaCl_2.6H_2O$; corundum; cadmium carbonate; bismuth iodide; ferrous carbonate; zinc carbonate; manganese carbonate; etc.

VI. Hexagonal system.—Here the crystals may have seven planes of symmetry, one hexad, and six dyad axes of symmetry.

EXAMPLES.—
Beryl; apatite; cadmium sulphide—greenockite; copper sulphide ; lead iodide ; magnesium ; beryllium ; zinc ; cadmium ; calcium ; pyrrhottite ; etc.

FIG. 64—Apatite. Hexagonal system.

VII. Cubic system.—The crystals in this system may have nine planes of symmetry, six dyad, three tetrad, and four triad axes of symmetry. This system has been variously styled the " isometric," " regular," " tesseral," " octahedral," or the " tessural " system.

EXAMPLES.—Diamond ; potassium chloride ; sodium chloride ; alum ; fluorspar ; iron pyrites ; lead nitrate ; magnetic oxide of iron ; barium nitrate ; arsenic trioxide ; galena ; garnet ; ammonium chloroplatinate ; silver chloride ; boracite ; iron ; platinum ; lead ; phosphorus ; gold ; copper ; silver ; arsenic ; etc.

§ 16 The Internal Structure of Crystals

Crystals are not only peculiar in the regularity of their external shape, but they also possess a definite internal structure. The properties of crystals are not always the same in different directions. The hardness, elasticity, crushing strength, rate of solution in acids, optical, thermal, and electrical properties are generally different in different directions. This means that the elasticity, refraction of light, thermal expansion, etc., of a crystal is usually different when measured in different directions. The external form of crystals is their most obtrusive characteristic, and it was naturally the first to arrest attention ; but

Pyrites.   Fluorspar.
FIG. 65.—**Fluorspar** and Pyrites. Cubic system.

the geometrical shape is by no means the most characteristic property of crystals, because the external geometrical form may be destroyed, and yet the fragments do not cease to be crystals. On the contrary, the most perfect glass model of a crystal is not a crystal, because it lacks the characteristic internal properties of crystals.*

It is clear, as has been long realized, that the structure of crystals can be explained on the supposition that a crystal is an aggregate of particles arranged in space in an orderly manner. But such a vague generalization does not take us very far. Haüy in 1784 showed that simple geometrically-shaped solids such as spheres or cubes could be piled up in such a way as to reproduce many crystal forms, thus showing that the regular piling of units could produce shapes analogous to those of actual crystals.

Bravais in 1848 modified and extended this idea by supposing that the solid " units " of Haüy's models were replaced by small particles situated at the

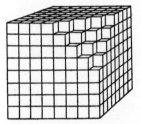

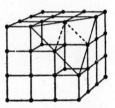

FIG. 66.—Haüy Model.   FIG. 67.—Space-Lattice.

centres of the geometrically-shaped solids. In this way there results an open structure of small particles arranged in a **lattice**—such an arrangement being called a **space-lattice**. We may further define a space-lattice as an arrangement of rows of points in three dimensions, in such a way as to form a series of cells, all consisting of parallelopipeds. A simple space-lattice, and the corresponding Haüy's model are illustrated in Figs. 59 and 60.

The work of Bravais and others has shown that 230 different space-lattices are theoretically possible, and that these will account for all the thirty-two classes (and seven systems) of crystals as ordinarily classified. It was further established that all the patterns of crystal faces found in actual substances could be explained on the assumption that all the crystals of any one system were constructed from space-lattices having the symmetry characteristic of that system.

§ 17 X-rays and Crystal Structure

The theory of crystal structure based on the idea of the space-lattice was worked out long before any means had been found for obtaining *direct* evidence for the internal structure of crystals. The application of X-rays to the problem by von Laue and by Friedrich and Knipping in 1912 was the first step towards the solution of this problem.

In Chapter IX (p. 129) it was pointed out that this work gave the first *direct*

* The shapes of gems cut and polished to accentuate the ornamental value of the gem must not be confounded with crystal structure. Similarly, the term " crystal " applied to cut glass has a different meaning from the special use of the word " crystal " in the text. Transparent glass is not crystalline ; some varieties of opaque glass are more or less crystalline.

evidence of the nature of X-rays; it also resulted in our being able to determine the internal structure of a great many crystalline substances.

The phenomenon of diffraction is dealt with fully in text-books of physics, in which it is shown that when a beam of light strikes a series of very fine lines ruled regularly on the surface of a metal or glass plate, each line acts as a fresh

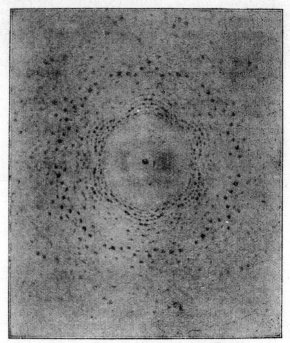

Fig. 68.—Laue Photograph of Zinc Blende.

centre from which a secondary train of light waves spreads out, or is, as we say diffracted. These diffracted rays "interfere" both with each other and with the original rays, causing enhancement of the light waves along certain definite directions. This principle is made use of in determining the wave-length of ordinary light by means of "diffraction gratings."

Now if the space-lattice theory of crystal structure be correct, the various planes of particles in the crystals should act in an analogous way upon light of sufficiently short wave-length. This was shown to be the case by the experiments of Laue, Friedrich and Knipping, who passed a pencil of X-rays through a suitable crystal and then allowed it to fall on a photographic plate.

Fig. 68 illustrates the result of one such experiment; the black central spot due to the undeviated beam of X-rays being surrounded by a pattern of spots which were easily shown to be characteristic of the type of crystal being used.

This process was modified by W. H. and W. L. Bragg, by using the crystal as a reflection grating instead of passing the beam of X-rays through the crystal.

Fig. 69 illustrates the principle of the Bragg method. PA and PA' represent incident and "reflected" rays from a point in the topmost lattice plane CD

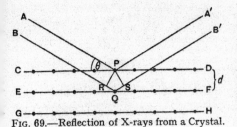

FIG. 69.—Reflection of X-rays from a Crystal.

of a crystal. EF and GH are two similar planes lower down in the crystal, the distance between successive planes being d. QB and QB' are incident and " reflected " rays which have been diffracted in the second lattice plane. It can easily be seen that the difference in the lengths of the paths traversed by APA' and BQB' is $RQ + QS = 2PQ$ $sin\ \theta = 2d\ sin\ \theta$. These two rays will interfere and reinforce each other when this difference in path is equal to an integral number of half wave-lengths; i.e., when

$$n\lambda = 2d\ sin\ \theta$$

where $\lambda =$ wave-length of the X-rays used and n is a small integer. By this means, therefore, the distances between the planes in crystals can be compared and measured.

For a full discussion of the way in which the results of experiments based on these principles have been used for the elucidation of the details of crystal structures suitable works on physical chemistry or on the X-ray analysis of crystals must be consulted ; but a summary of some of the conclusions is given below.

In the first place, the mathematically-deduced space-lattice theory has been completely confirmed ; and, in addition, a great deal of information has been obtained as to the mode of combination of many compounds.

In the case of rock salt, for example, it soon became clear that the units from which the lattice is built up are not actual molecules of sodium chloride, but atoms (or more probably ions—see Ch. XII, p. 191) of sodium and chlorine. This result followed from evidence which showed that in certain directions in the crystal the planes (actually the octahedral plane) of the space-lattice consisted of particles all of the same kind in a given plane, but alternately of different kinds as we pass from plane to plane. To sum up, the rock-salt crystal was shown to have the structure represented in Fig. 70.

The remarkable conclusion is thus forced on us that in such a crystal a given sodium atom is not united to any particular chlorine atom—the identity of a particular molecule is lost.

Similar results attended the investigation of other crystals ; but in such a substance as calcium carbonate it was found that calcium ions and CO_3 groups constituted the units from which the crystal lattice is built up.

Crystals of salts (which are electrolytes —compare Ch. XII) usually have lattices made up of individual ions, as in the case of rock salt or calcium carbonate. These are substances which are held together by electro-valent links, as explained in the preceding chapter. Compounds whose atoms are united by covalent links are found to have a different type of unit making up the lattice. Two types have been distinguished, viz., that in which the unit is the molecule, and that in which the crystal is a kind of giant molecule.

The first is the most usual type, and since a molecule whose atoms are, of course, covalently linked, would not be expected to show very great attraction

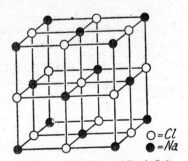

$\bigcirc = Cl$
$\bullet = Na$

FIG. 70.—Structure of Rock-Salt Crystal.

for similar molecules, we should expect the crystals to be much softer and more readily fusible than those of salts where the units are held together by powerful electrostatic forces.   This is, in fact, the case : crystals of covalent compounds such as benzene and sulphur are much softer and melt at a much lower temperature than those of salts like sodium chloride.

In the giant molecule type of crystal every atom is chemically combined by a covalent linkage to the next. Examples of this type are the diamond (the internal structure of which is illustrated in Fig. 110, p. 332) and aluminium oxide after ignition. It would be expected that crystals built up on this kind of plan would be hard and very difficult to fuse, and the examples quoted confirm this expectation

CHAPTER XI

PROPERTIES OF DILUTE SOLUTIONS

The act of dissolution is probably not due to chemical combination in the first place, but is probably analogous to the sublimation of a solid into a gas, and proceeds from the detachment of molecules from the surface of the solid, and their intermixture with those of the surrounding liquid. This is doubtless due to the impact of the moving molecules of the liquid.—W. G. TILDEN.

The substitution of analogy for fact is the bane of chemical philosophy ; the legitimate use of analogy is to connect facts together and to guide to new experiments.—H. DAVY.

Vague similarities in certain properties are never sufficient to determine a person who earnestly seeks for the truth and is not shackled by hypotheses.— J. BERGMAN.

§ 1 Diffusion in Liquids

LET a large crystal of a coloured salt—say copper sulphate—be placed at the bottom of a tall glass cylinder, and the remainder of the jar be filled with water. The coloured salt is chosen because the movements of the resulting solution can be readily seen. Let the jar stand where it will not be disturbed by evaporation, agitation, etc. The surface of separation between the solid and solvent will be gradually obliterated ; in time, the coloured salt will diffuse uniformly throughout the whole body of liquid. The diffusion of the salt in the solvent seems to be analogous with the process of diffusion in gases, and so it is inferred that the molecules of the liquid are in perpetual motion in all directions ; and that the protracted time occupied by the diffusion of the molecules of the dissolved salt in the liquid is due to the close packing of the molecules of the liquid.

Just as the molecules of a gas in a closed vessel are disseminated in a relatively large space, so are the molecules of a solid in solution scattered in a relatively large volume of solvent. It is true that the molecules of the salt in solution could not occupy the space if the solvent were absent, otherwise the analogy between a substance dissolved in a solvent and a gas scattered in space would be very close.

If the diffusion of gases be resisted by placing a permeable partition between two gases, a pressure will be exerted upon the partition (see p. 23). It is easy to show that the particles of a dissolved substance exert a similar pressure when a partition is placed between the solution and solvent so that the partition offers no obstacle to the free circulation of the molecules of the solvent, but resists the free passage of the molecules of the dissolved substances.

A piece of the thinnest grade of commercial cellophane, about 10 cms. square, is folded over the end of a wide glass tube and bound tightly with string. The cellophane and the string are then immersed in water, when the cellophane softens and the string contracts, so making a water-tight joint. A quantity of a concentrated solution of cane sugar is placed in the tube and the whole is immersed in a vessel of water as in Fig. 71. The level of the solution in the tube is marked with gummed paper and the apparatus is allowed to stand overnight. In the morning the liquid in the tube will have risen by several centimetres. Water has obviously passed through the membrane into the sugar solution.

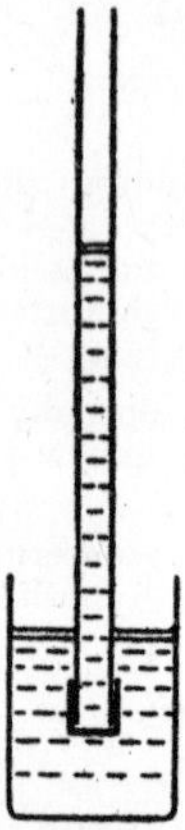

The passage of water through a membrane in this manner is called **osmosis**—from the Greek ὠσμός (osmos), a push. The membrane permeable to the solvent, impermeable to the dissolved substance, is called a **semipermeable membrane.** The extra pressure exerted upon the membrane by the sugar solution was styled, by W. Pfeffer (1877), "the **osmotic pressure** of the sugar solution." Solutions with the same osmotic pressure are said to be *isosmotic* or **isotonic.**

§ 2 The Measurement of Osmotic Pressure

Fig. 71.
Illustration of
Osmotic Pressure.

A cellophane membrane is unsatisfactory when exact measurements are required because, to a certain extent, the results depend upon the nature of the membrane ; the membrane is not strong enough to withstand the great pressures developed by osmosis ; and, most serious of all, the membrane is not truly semipermeable, an appreciable amount of, say, sugar does actually pass through the membrane. It would therefore be as profitable to measure the pressure of a gas in a leaking vessel as to try to measure the osmotic pressure of a solution with a membrane which allows part of the dissolved substance to pass through. We therefore fall back on artificially prepared membranes. No artificial membrane has been so successful as a film of copper ferrocyanide deposited between the inner and outer walls of a " porous pot," and illustrated by the sketch of a broken pot, A, Fig. 72. The porous pot with its semipermeable membrane A is fitted with a suitable manometer (Fig. 73) to indicate the pressure. W. Pfeffer made some measurements with cells made in this manner, in 1877. The apparatus was immersed in a large bath of water to maintain the temperature constant during the experiment.

Manometer→

By means of apparatus such as this, Pfeffer obtained results which, although not of the order of accuracy now obtainable, were yet sufficiently accurate to enable Van't Hoff in 1887 to develop a theory of dilute solutions which has been, and is, of the highest importance (see § 3 on next page).

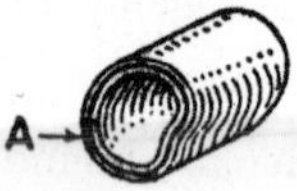

Fig. 72.
Semipermeable
Membrane.

Fig. 73.
Measurement of
Osmotic Pressure.

The technique of the measurement of osmotic pressure with a high degree of accuracy and in concentrated solutions has been developed more recently by Morse and Frazer and their collaborators in America, and by Berkeley and Hartley in England.

Morse and Frazer employed in essence Pfeffer's method, using the most elaborate precautions to obtain porous pots of uniform texture, and to produce very perfect membranes. For very high pressures they utilized the apparatus shown in Fig. 74. In Pfeffer's experiments, and in their own earlier work, the solution was placed in the porous pot which was surrounded by solvent. The pressure thus developed inside the pot and was so directed outwards. It can easily be realized that the membrane would be able to withstand a higher pressure in the reverse direction, for here the principle of the arch is involved.

The apparatus shown in Fig. 74 makes use of this principle. The porous pot, M, is firmly clamped inside the bronze cylinder, J, into which the manometer, A, was securely fixed. The solution was placed outside the porous pot (in the walls of which the membrane was deposited) and the pot was kept full of water. By means of this apparatus pressures as high as 273 atmospheres were successfully measured.

The method employed by Berkeley and Hartley was essentially different in that instead of measuring the pressure developed in the cell by the passage of the solvent into it, they applied a gradually increasing hydrostatic pressure to the solution until the direction of flow of the solvent was reversed. The value of the pressure at the turning point, that is, of the pressure which is just sufficient to prevent the inward flow of solvent, is taken as the osmotic pressure.

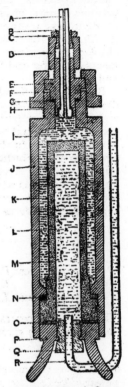

FIG. 74.—Morse's Osmotic Pressure Apparatus.

§ 3 Van't Hoff's Theory of Dilute Solutions

In § 1 of this chapter reference was made to the analogy which seems to exist between the behaviour of gases and the behaviour of substances in solution. After Pfeffer had published the results of his experiments on the determination of osmotic pressure, J. H. van't Hoff developed this analogy very considerably.

Pfeffer's results had shown clearly that the osmotic pressure of a solution is proportional to its concentration, and that it increases, for a given concentration, with rise of temperature. Van't Hoff pointed out that if we regard a dissolved substance as analogous to a gas, and the osmotic pressure as similar to gas pressure (on the assumption that it is produced by the bombardment of the semi-permeable membrane by the solute molecules) the proportionality of osmotic pressure and concentration is analogous to the relationship between pressure and volume expressed in Boyle's Law (p. 13). He was able, further, to justify the analogy on theoretical grounds based upon the Laws of Thermodynamics, and further deduced that the proportionality between osmotic pressure and temperature should be the same as that between gas pressure and temperature as expressed in Charles's Law (p. 15). In other words, the pressure should be proportional to the absolute temperature. This deduction was borne out by the experiments of Pfeffer and has been further confirmed by the work of Morse and Frazer.

But Van't Hoff did not stop even here. With the aid of thermodynamics and the conception of the semipermeable membrane he arrived at the important conclusion that **the osmotic pressure of a solution is equal to the pressure which the dissolved substance would exercise in the gaseous state if it then occupied a volume equal to the volume of the solution.** Expressed in another way, this means that Avogadro's Hypothesis applies to dilute solutions. This conclusion is also confirmed by experiment. The relationship between osmotic pressure, concentration and temperature can be expressed in the form :

$$\frac{P}{C} = KT$$

where P = osmotic pressure of the solution
C = concentration of the solution
and T = absolute temperature

Since the concentration is inversely proportional to the volume of the solution for a given mass of solute, this may be re-written :

$$PV = KT$$

where V = volume of solution in which a given amount of solute is dissolved.

If now in this expression we substitute the values for P and V, obtained by experiment at a given temperature (V being now expressed as the volume of solution containing one gram-molecular weight of solute), we can find the value of K. Using the results obtained, for example, by Berkeley and Hartley, this gives a value for K equal to within 1 per cent. of the value of the gas constant R, calculated from the gas equation $PV = RT$ for the case of a gas (compare p. 18). We are thus justified in writing the equation for a dilute solution in the same form as for a gas : in the case of n gram-molecules of solute as

$$PV = nRT$$

An important deduction from this result is that since $P = \dfrac{nRT}{V}$ the osmotic pressure is proportional to the number of gram-molecular weights of solute dissolved in a given bulk of solution, or in other words, **equimolecular solutions of all substances have the same osmotic pressure.*** Osmotic pressure is thus what is called a **colligative** property, that is, a property which depends on the number of particles present and not on the kind of particles. It will thus furnish us with a method for the determination of molecular weights, and although the manipulative difficulties involved in the accurate measurement of osmotic pressures cause the method to be but rarely used, it provides the theoretical basis, nevertheless, for some of the most important and widely used methods for the determination of molecular weights in solution (see below §§ 5, 6, 7, 8).

It is, however, important to notice that just as the equation $PV = RT$ is the equation for a *perfect* gas, to the behaviour of which actual gases conform with different degrees of closeness, none being absolutely exact, so in the application of the corresponding equation to solutions the equation expresses the behaviour of an *ideal* solution to which actual solutions conform more or less. The deviations which occur are probably to be accounted for in a manner similar to that of gases, viz.,

(i) attraction between the molecules of the solute ;

(ii) attraction between molecules of the solute and solvent ;

(iii) the volume of molecules themselves.

As in the case of gases, the divergence is wider at high concentration (i.e., high pressure and small volume), and the simple Van't Hoff theory is in reality only applicable to *dilute* solutions and within a moderate range of temperature. Also as already indicated, it requires modification when applied to solutions of electrolytes. (Compare Ch. XII, p. 194.)

§ 4 Mechanism of Osmotic Pressure and Membrane Action

The close analogy between the behaviour of dilute solutions and gases demonstrated by Van't Hoff led naturally to the view that osmotic pressure and gas pressure are due to similar causes, i.e., to bombardment by the molecules of the solute or gas of the semipermeable membrane or the walls of the containing vessel respectively. At the same time it was natural to assume that the action of the semipermeable membrane is that of an atomic sieve whose pores, while large enough to permit the passage of solvent molecules, are too small to allow of solute molecules passing through them.

These explanations are not now felt to be completely satisfactory as they stand, particularly as it has been shown that the actual pore-diameter of a copper-ferrocyanide membrane is too large to block the passage of even a sugar molecule. This has led to various modifications in the theory, such as the suggestion that the pores are hydrated (or solvated) to an extent sufficient to prevent the passage of solute molecules.

Callendar's Theory

Callendar's vapour pressure hypothesis (1909) is one of the most successful of the purely physical explanations of osmotic pressure.

Experiment shows that the maximum vapour pressure of a solution can be altered in three ways : (1) by altering the temperature (p. 31) ; (2) by varying

---

* This statement is only true for solutions of non-electrolytes. The corresponding behaviour of electrolytes is discussed in Chapter XII.

the concentration of the solution ; and (3) by altering the pressure under which the liquid itself is confined.

The relation between vapour pressure and osmotic pressure.—It has been proved experimentally that the maximum vapour pressure of a solution under very great pressures is rather greater than the maximum vapour pressure of the same solution under atmospheric pressures. Again, the vapour pressure of a solution is *less* than the vapour pressure of the pure solvent, Fig. 52. Consequently, if the pressure on a solution be sufficiently augmented, the pressure of its vapour can be made equal to the vapour pressure of the pure solvent under atmospheric pressure. This is the condition necessary in order that solution and solvent can exist side by side in equilibrium. If the vapour pressure of the solution were less than that of the pure solvent, the system would not be in equilibrium, because vapour would distil from the solvent into the solution until the vapour pressure of both were the same. Conversely, when a solution under its own osmotic pressure and the pure solvent are in equilibrium, it follows that their vapour pressures must be equal. Hence, according to Callendar : **The osmotic pressure of a solution represents the external pressure which must be applied in order to make its vapour pressure equal to that of the pure solvent.** With this hypothesis, Callendar has calculated the osmotic pressures of sugar solutions of different concentration from published vapour pressure data, and the results are in close agreement with observation :

Concentration . . .	180,	300,	420,	540 grams per litre.
Observed osmotic pressure .	14·6,	26·8,	44·0,	67·5 atmospheres.
Calculated osmotic pressure	14·1,	26·8,	43·7,	67·6 atmospheres.

Hence it is inferred that **osmotic equilibrium depends upon the equality of the vapour pressure of the solution and of the pure solvent.**

A semipermeable membrane may be likened to a partition pierced by a large number of minute capillary tubes ; suppose that the capillary tubes are not wetted by either the solvent or solution, then neither the liquid solvent nor the solution can enter the capillaries, although vapour can diffuse through the capillary tubes. But the vapour pressure of the solution on one side of one of the capillary tubes is less than the vapour pressure of the solvent on the other side ; consequently, vapour will pass through the capillary and distil from the solvent to the solution. Hence the volume of the solution will increase, and if the solution be confined in a closed vessel, the pressure must rise and continue rising until the vapour pressure of the solvent and solute are the same. This increase in the pressure is the so-called " osmotic pressure of the solution."

§ 5 Molecular Weight of Dissolved Substances

Van't Hoff's Theory of Solution gives, in theory, a means of measuring molecular weights in solution by finding the osmotic pressure of a solution of known concentration, but as explained in § 3, this method is not practicable in most cases. However, a close relation does exist between the osmotic pressure of a solution and the lowering of the vapour pressure as compared with that of the pure solvent, and between this lowering of the vapour pressure and the depression of the freezing point, and the elevation of the boiling point, of a solution. These latter changes provide important and widely-used methods for the determination of molecular weights.

§ 6 Relation of Osmotic Pressure to the Vapour Pressure of a Solution

M. Faraday knew, in 1822, that the vapour pressure of a solution is lower than the vapour pressure of the pure solvent; but A. Wüllner discovered the important fact experimentally, in 1858, that **the lowering of the vapour pressure of a solution is proportional to the quantity of substance in solution provided that the dissolved substance is non-volatile.** This is sometimes called **Wüllner's law.**

Suppose a solution A, Fig. 75, confined in a long-stemmed tube, as illustrated in the diagram, to be separated by a semipermeable membrane M from the pure solvent. Let all be confined in a closed vessel. Osmotic pressure will force the solution to rise in the narrow tube to a height h, when the whole system is in equilibrium. Let p_s denote the vapour pressure of the solution in the narrow tube, and p the vapour pressure of the solvent in the outer vessel. The vapour pressure of the solution at the surface in the narrow tube must be equal to the vapour pressure of the solvent at the same level, otherwise distillation would take place either to or from the surface of the liquid in the narrow tube and there would be a constant flow of liquid respectively to or from the vessel A through the semipermeable membrane in order that h may have a constant value. Hence the vapour pressure of solution and solvent at the upper level of the solution in the narrow tube must be the same. The vapour pressure of the solvent at the level a will be equal to the vapour pressure of the solvent

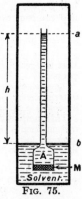

Fig. 75.

at the lower level b less the pressure of a column of the height h or $p = p_s + w$. Since the height h is determined by the osmotic pressure, which in turn is determined by the concentration of the solution, there must be a **simple proportionality between the osmotic pressure or concentration of the solution and the lowering of the vapour pressure.**

This relation is calculated as follows. We have seen that

$$p - p_s = h \times \text{density of vapour}$$
$$= h\rho \text{ (say).}$$

Now, if the vapour be assumed to obey the gas laws, then one gram-molecule of the vapour at a pressure p and absolute temperature T will occupy a volume v given by:

$$v = \frac{RT}{p}$$

$$\therefore \rho = \frac{M}{v} = \frac{Mp}{RT}$$

where M is the molecular weight of the solvent in the vapour state.

Substituting this value of ρ in the equation above, we have:

$$p - p_s = h \cdot \frac{Mp}{RT}$$

Now the osmotic pressure of the solution is equal to the hydrostatic pressure of the column of liquid of height h, so that $P = hs$, where s is the density of the solution, which for a *dilute* solution may be taken to be the same as that of the solvent.

Substituting the value for $h = \dfrac{P}{s}$ in the preceding equation, we now have:

$$p - p_s = \frac{PMp}{RTs}$$

$$\text{or} \quad \frac{p - p_s}{p} = \frac{PM}{RTs}$$

which gives us the relation between the relative lowering of the vapour pressure and the osmotic pressure of a solution.

For a given solvent, at a particular temperature, $\dfrac{M}{RTs}$ will be a constant, so that the relative lowering of the vapour pressure is proportional to the osmotic pressure.

This relation clearly furnishes, at least in theory, a means for molecular weight determination since the osmotic pressure of a solution of given concentration is inversely proportional to the molecular weight of the solute as we have seen.

This method for determining the molecular weight of a substance from direct measurements of the lowering of the vapour pressure is of great theoretical interest, but in practice the method is seldom employed, because some of the related properties of solutions are more amenable to accurate measurement.

§ 7 Relation of Lowering of Vapour Pressure to the Boiling Point and Freezing Point of a Solution

In the previous chapter (p. 157) it was pointed out that Blagden more than a century ago detected a relationship between the freezing point of a solution, and its concentration. This observation was extended by Raoult (1883-4), who investigated both the depression of the freezing point and the elevation of the boiling point of a solvent owing to the presence of a dissolved substance. As a result of his experiments, he concluded that for solutions of non-electrolytes **the depression of the freezing point (or the rise in the boiling point) of a solvent is proportional to the number of molecules of the dissolved substance, and inversely proportional to the total number of molecules present.** This important generalization was deduced empirically by Raoult, but can now be seen to have a theoretical basis For the elevation of the boiling point, or lowering of the freezing point, are clearly related to the relative lowering of the vapour pressure of the solution, and from this Raoult's Law can readily be deduced.

The relative lowering of the vapour pressure of a solution is proportional to the osmotic pressure and hence, as we have seen, inversely proportional to the molecular weight of the solute. The boiling point of a liquid is the temperature at which the vapour pressure becomes equal to the pressure of the atmosphere ; while the freezing point of a solution is that temperature at which the vapour pressure of the solid solvent and liquid solvent are equal. Hence it follows that the elevation of the boiling point, and depression of the freezing point, of a solution of given strength are inversely proportional to the molecular weight of the dissolved substance.

Expressed in another way, we may say that, if $T°$ is the boiling point or freezing point of a pure solvent, and that $T_1°$ is that of a solution of given concentration, then:

$$T \backsim T_1 \text{ varies as } \frac{1}{M}$$

i.e., $T \backsim T_1 = \frac{K}{M}$, where M is the molecular weight of the dissolved

substance and K is a constant. Extending to a solution of concentration w gms. in W gms. we have:

$$T \backsim T_1 = \frac{cw}{WM}$$

$$\text{or } M = \frac{cw}{W \triangle}$$

where c is a constant known as the freezing point (or boiling point) constant of the solvent and $\triangle = T \backsim T_1$. c can be shown, on theoretical grounds, to be given by the expression:

$$c = \frac{2T^2}{L}$$

where T is the freezing (or boiling) point on the absolute scale and L is respectively the latent heat either of fusion or vaporization of the solvent.

If c be known, either from the results of direct experiment, or from calculation as above, M can be found by measuring the change in freezing (or boiling point) of a solution of known concentration. (c is also sometimes called the molecular depression, or elevation.)

§ 8 Practical Methods for Finding Molecular Weights

Several methods for the determination of the molecular weights of substances have been given in earlier chapters, while a group of methods dependent, as has just been explained, upon the osmotic properties of dilute solutions must now be described. This is therefore a convenient place to summarize and classify the methods available, describing in detail those which have not been dealt with already.

The different ways in which the molecular weight may be found differ in their applicability, and this serves as a convenient basis for classification, so that we may divide the available methods as follows :—

Methods available for

(1) Permanent Gases — e.g., Regnault's Method with extension to evaluation of limiting densities.

(2) Substances which vaporize at ordinary pressures, without decomposition — e.g., Dumas's and Victor Meyer's Methods.

(3) Substances which decompose if vaporized at ordinary pressure — e.g., Hofmann's Method.

(4) Non-volatile substances which are soluble — e.g., Osmotic Pressure, Lowering of Vapour Pressure, Elevation of Boiling Point, Depression of Freezing Point.

(5) Bases — e.g., titration, thermal decomposition of chloroplatinates.

(6) Acids — e.g., titration, thermal decomposition of silver salts.

Regnault's method has been described on page 20, Chapter II, along with the Volumeter and Buoyancy methods, and the extension of the principle of molecular and atomic weight determination with a high degree of accuracy is discussed on page 103, Chapter VI.

The methods originated by **Dumas, Victor Meyer and Hofmann** are described on pages 70-73, Chapter IV.

Osmotic Methods

The methods named under heading (4) of our classification are all based either directly or indirectly upon the osmotic pressure of a solution, and the theoretical connection between them has been given.

The actual determination of the osmotic pressure of a solution is a matter of considerable practical difficulty, and so is rarely used for molecular weight determinations in practice. Almost the only case of its use is in the determination of the so-called molecular weights of colloids. Methods employed for finding the osmotic pressures of solutions of substances like cane sugar have been described in § 2 of the present chapter.

The measurement of the **relative lowering of the vapour pressure** of a solution is also beset with practical difficulties if attempted directly, and although it has been employed with a certain measure of success in the hands of Dieterici and Frazer, it has not found wide application. Apart from this work, in so far as vapour pressure methods have been used, an indirect method known as the **air-saturation method** has usually been employed.

The principle of the method depends upon the fact that if dry air be passed over or through a solution it will take up vapour to an extent proportional to the vapour pressure of the solution ; and if this air stream be now passed over, or through, a sample of the pure solvent it will take up a further quantity of vapour, proportional in amount to the difference between the vapour pressure of the solvent and that of the solution. If the vessels containing the solution and the solvent be weighed before and after the experiment, the loss in weight in each case will be a measure of the amount of vapour taken up by the air stream, so that (with the notation of § 6 of this chapter) we have

$$\frac{p_s}{p - p_s} = \frac{\text{loss of weight of solution}}{\text{loss of weight of solvent}}$$

By far the most important and widely used of osmotic methods are those dependent upon the elevation of the boiling point or depression of the freezing point.

The first really practicable method for evaluating the **elevation of the boiling point** of a solution was due to Beckmann and consisted in measuring as accurately as possible the boiling point of the pure solvent and afterwards of the solution formed by adding a known weight of solute. Precautions were taken to avoid error, but in spite of these it is not easy to avoid errors due to the inherent difficulties of the method, such as superheating, fluctuations due to radiation, etc. Other ways of carrying out the experiment have accordingly been adopted.

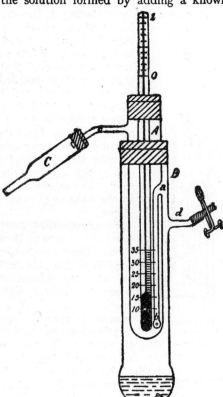

When the solution of non-volatile solute boils, the vapour of the solvent and solute are in equilibrium; this condition can be established by leading the vapour of the boiling solvent into the solution. When the solution is at its boiling point, the vapour will pass through the system without condensation, and if the solution is below this temperature some vapour will condense, and the latent heat of condensation will continue heating the solution until the boiling point is reached. There is virtually no danger of superheating the solution.

FIG. 76.—McCoy's Apparatus for Boiling-Point Determinations.

This principle has been employed successfully in measuring the boiling points of solutions in molecular weight determinations.

Among the various forms of apparatus which have been devised in order to apply this method, one of the most convenient is that due to H. N. McCoy. This is illustrated diagrammatically in Fig. 69. The apparatus consists of a tube, B, inside which is fitted a narrower tube, A, graduated in cubic centimetres as shown. Sealed into the wall at a point near the bottom of A is the narrow tube, ab. The graduated tube, A, is fitted with a cork carrying a Beckmann thermometer* graduated in $\frac{1}{100}$ths of a degree, while the side tube is attached to a condenser, C, as shown.

To perform a determination, pure solvent is placed in B, and 10-15 c.c. also is placed in A, and B is heated. When the solvent in B boils, the vapour rises and, surrounding A, thereby heats it. When the vapour has risen far enough, it forces its way through ab into the liquid in A and so raises this liquid to the boiling point. When a steady state is reached, the temperature (being that of the boiling point of the pure solvent) is recorded. The clip on the side tube d is then opened and the heating stopped for the moment. A weighed quantity of the substance whose molecular weight is to be determined is then introduced into A and the boiling point of this solution determined as above. This time, however, after opening the clip the thermometer is carefully raised out of the solution, the volume of which is then read. The experiment can then be repeated if desired by the addition of successive further quantities of substance.

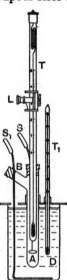

FIG. 77.

Beckmann's Apparatus for Freezing-point Determinations

Freezing-point depressions are usually determined by means of Beckmann's apparatus, which is shown diagrammatically in Fig. 77. The tube A, Fig. 77, with a side neck, B, is weighed, and about 15 c.c. of the solvent are added, and the tube is weighed again. The Beckmann thermometer, reading to the $\frac{1}{100}$ of a degree, and set so that the mercury is near the top of the scale when set for the freezing point of the solvent, has a reading lens. The thermometer T and a stirrer S are placed in the solvent, and the whole arrangement is placed in a glass tube A which serves as an air jacket. This is surrounded by a vessel, D, of water or some liquid at a temperature about 5° below the freezing point of the solvent. This vessel is fitted with a thermometer, T_1 and stirrer, S_1. The temperature recorded by the

* This thermometer has a reservoir of mercury at the top so that it can be set for use at any desired temperature as indicated in text-books of laboratory processes. In this way, an inconveniently long, or an inconveniently large number of thermometers are not needed. The thermometer is always tapped before a reading to make sure the mercury is not lagging behind.

thermometer slowly falls until the solvent begins to freeze ; it usually falls from 0·2° to 0·3° below the freezing point of the solvent, and then begins to rise to the freezing point proper. The thermometer should always be tapped before a reading is taken to make sure the mercury is not lagging behind. The highest point reached by the mercury in the thermometer is taken to be the freezing point of the solvent. Owing to under-cooling, it is sometimes difficult to start the freezing of the solution. In that case, a few pieces of platinum foil, or a minute fragment of the frozen solvent, will start the freezing. Each determination should be repeated two or three times and the successive observations should agree within 0·002° to 0·003°. When the freezing point of the solvent has been determined, add a sufficient amount of the substance under investigation to give a depression of 0·3° to 0·5°. After the freezing point has been determined again, find the freezing point after adding a second and then a third portion of the substance under investigation.

The determination of the **molecular weights of acids** by either of the methods mentioned on page 182 depends upon a knowledge of the *basicity* of the acid concerned. The basicity of an acid (see p. 307) may be defined as the number of hydrogen atoms which it contains which are replaceable by a metal. If this number is known (see p. 307 for methods of discovering it) we can find the molecular weight of the acid either, by estimating the amount of it which will react with a gram-molecular weight of a standard alkali by means of a titration of the kind common in volumetric analysis, or by finding the amount of metal in one of its normal salts. The latter method is particularly useful in the case of organic acids which are usually weak acids and therefore not always satisfactory in a titration.

The metal usually employed in this process is silver, since the silver salts are usually *normal* salts (compare p. 307), they are only sparingly soluble in most cases and hence readily prepared by precipitation, and are decomposed by heat, leaving a residue of metallic silver. The process consists then in the preparation of a pure, dry sample of the silver salt, a weighed portion of which is ignited and the metallic silver residue is weighed. The equivalent weight of the acid is then : weight of salt containing 1 equivalent of silver − 108 + 1, and hence

Molecular weight of acid = equivalent weight × basicity.

The **molecular weights of bases** can be evaluated by processes analogous to the foregoing provided that the *acidity* (i.e., the number of equivalents of an acid which are neutralized by one molecular weight) of the base is known. As with acids, the titration method is more applicable to inorganic bases ; for organic bases use is made of the fact that they form like ammonia (compare p. 840), crystalline chloro-platinates with platinic chloride of the general formula $B_2H_2PtCl_6$ where B is a molecule of a mono-acid organic base. These chloro-platinates decompose on heating, leaving metallic platinum, the weight of metal contained in a known weight of chloroplatinate being thus determined. Then, the atomic weight of platinum is contained in one molecular weight of the salt, and therefore

Molecular weight of base

$$= \frac{\text{Molecular weight of salt} - \text{molecular weight of } H_2PtCl_6}{2}$$

Examples

The following examples illustrate the methods of molecular weight determination discussed in this section.

Examples of the application o the limiting density method arc given in Chapter VI (p. 104) and o vapour density methods in Chapter IV (pp. 71-73).

(1) *An aqueous solution of 1·0047 gm. of orthoboric acid per litre has an osmotic pressure of 28·8 cm. of mercury at 15°. What is the molecular weight of the acid ?*

Since 1 gm.-molecule of a substance in 22·4 litres of solution will exert an osmotic pressure of 1 atm. at 0°, we have to discover what weight of boric acid dissolved in 22·4 litres at this temperature will have this osmotic pressure.

Since 1·0047 gm. in 1 litre has an osmotic pressure, 288 mm. at 15°

$$\frac{1 \cdot 0047 \times 22 \cdot 4 \times 760 \times 288}{288 \times 273}$$ gm. in 22·4 litres will have an osmotic

pressure 760 mm. at 0°

$$= 62 \cdot 63 \text{ gms.}$$

$$\therefore 62 \cdot 63 = \text{molecular weight of boric acid.}$$

(2) *When 108·24 gm. of mannitol were dissolved in 1000 gm. of water, the vapour pressure of the solution was found to be 17·354 mm., at 20°. At the same temperature the vapour pressure of water is 17·54 mm. What is the molecular weight of mannitol ?*

It was shown on page 180 that $\frac{p - p_s}{p} = \frac{PM}{RTs}$. From this Raoult's Law can be deduced, viz. :

$$\frac{p - p_s}{p} = \frac{n}{N + n}, \text{ where}$$

n = number of molecules of solute
N = number of molecules of solvent.

For very dilute solutions this may be written :

$$\frac{p - p_s}{p} = \frac{n}{N}$$

Then if w = weight of solute
W = weight of solvent
m = molecular weight of solute
M = molecular weight of solvent

we have :

$$\frac{p - p_s}{p} = \frac{\dfrac{w}{m}}{\dfrac{W}{M}}$$

whence, $m = \dfrac{wMp}{W(p - p_s)}$

Substituting in this expression the values given, we have :

$$m = \frac{108 \cdot 24 \times 18 \times 17 \cdot 54}{1000 \times 0 \cdot 186}$$

$$= 183 \cdot 7$$

$$= \text{molecular weight of mannitol.}$$

(3) *The boiling point of a solution of 0·1050 gm. of a substance in 15·84 gm. of ether was found to be 0·100° higher than that of pure ether. What is the molecular weight of the substance ? (Molecular elevation for ether per 100 gm. = 21·6.)*

We have seen (p. 181) that the molecular weight is given by :

$$M = \frac{cw}{W \triangle} , \qquad c \text{ being the constant for 1 gm.}$$

In this case, therefore :

$$M = \frac{21 \cdot 6 \times 100 \times 0 \cdot 1050}{15 \cdot 84 \times 0 \cdot 100}$$

$$= 143 \cdot 2.$$

(4) *The solution of 0·622 gm. of a substance in 40 gms. of water froze at −0·51°. What is the molecular weight of the substance ? (Freezing point constant for water = 18·58, for 100 gms.)*

As before, the molecular weight is given by

$$M = \frac{cw}{W \triangle}$$

$\triangle$ this time being the depression of the freezing point, whereas in the preceding example it represents the elevation of the boiling point.

So that we have

$$M = \frac{18 \cdot 58 \times 100 \times 0 \cdot 622}{0 \cdot 51 \times 40}$$

$$= 56 \cdot 7.$$

(5) *On heating 0·3652 gm. of the silver salt of an organic acid until no further loss of weight occurred, there remained 0·172 gm. of silver. If the basicity of the acid is 1, what is its molecular weight?*

0·172 gm. of silver is contained in 0·3652 gm. of salt

∴ 108 gm. of silver is contained in $\dfrac{0·3652 \times 108}{0·172}$ gm. of salt

= 229·3 gm.

= molecular weight of the salt since the acid is monobastic.

Therefore, if M = molecular weight of the acid, we have, M = 229·3 − 108 + 1 = 122·3, for M will be the molecular weight of the salt less the atomic weight of silver, plus that of hydrogen.

(6) *0·7010 gm. of the chloroplatinate of a monoacid organic base gave 0·2303 gm. of platinum on heating. Calculate the molecular weight of the base.*

Since 0·2303 gm. of platinum are contained in 0·7010 gm. of chloroplatinate

195 gms. of platinum are contained in $\dfrac{0·7010 \times 195}{·2303}$ gm. of chloroplatinate

= 594·2 gms.

This is the molecular weight of the salt $B_2H_2PtCl_6$

∴ The molecular weight of B

$$= \frac{594·2 - 409·9}{2}$$

$$= 92·15$$

409·9 being the molecular weight of H_2PtCl_6.

§ 9 Abnormal Molecular Weights

It will be evident from an inspection of the list of methods for measuring molecular weights given on page 182 that in many cases two or more methods can be employed for the same substance. Thus, for example, the molecular weight of iodine can be found either by one of the vapour density methods, or by the raising of the boiling point or depression of the freezing point of its solution in a suitable solvent, e.g., ether.

In many instances the results obtained by different methods show a satisfactory agreement; but there are a number of cases where the value for the molecular weight comes out either very much higher or very much lower than would have been expected. Such molecular weights are called **abnormal molecular weights.**

Thus, for example, the vapour density of acetic acid at a temperature well above its boiling point indicates a molecular weight of 60, which is in agreement with the formula which has been assigned to it on chemical grounds. But investigation of the effect of acetic acid on the freezing point of benzene leads to a value for the molecular weight very near to 120. That is to say, the observed depression of the freezing point, and hence the osmotic pressure of the solution, is only about half of what would be expected. Therefore the number of molecules present in the solution must be approximately half of what was anticipated.

This result is explained on the assumption that acetic acid, and substances exhibiting a like behaviour, undergo **association**; that is to say, two or more molecules have combined to form a larger molecule. On this assumption, the depression of the freezing point (or other similar phenomenon) can be used in order to calculate the *degree of association*.

Abnormally great osmotic pressures (and hence elevations of the boiling point or depressions of the freezing point) are observed principally in the case of solutions of acids, alkalis and salts. All acids and alkalis, except very weak ones (compare p. 194), and practically all salts, are found to have an abnormally high osmotic pressure in solution in water, whereas in most other solvents the value is about what is to be expected from the chemical evidence, vapour density data and so forth. For example, hydrochloric acid gas has a density as determined from absolute density measurements, or from effusion experiments, corresponding to a molecular weight of about 36.5; whereas as calculated from the freezing point of its solutions in water its molecular weight is close to 19. Clearly something akin to the converse of association is taking place—the development of this theme however, belongs to the next chapter.

CHAPTER XII

ELECTROLYSIS AND THE ELECTROLYTIC DISSOCIATION THEORY

The electricity which decomposes, and that which is evolved by the decomposition of a certain quantity of matter are the same.—M. FARADAY.

In framing hypotheses we must see that they agree with facts ; in other respects they may be as inconceivable (not self-contradictory) as any fairy tale.—M. M. P. MUIR.

§ 1 The Conduction of Electricity in Liquids

THE fact that a current of electricity will pass through materials such as copper wire has become a commonplace of everyday life, and further it is well known that, whereas some substances such as copper (or, in fact, metals generally) will allow such a current to flow, others, as for example glass or rubber, will not do so. The former are called **conductors** : the latter **insulators** or **non-conductors**.

In a similar way, when we come to investigate the behaviour of solutions, we find that some will conduct a current, while some will not do so. Substances whose solutions are conductors are called **electrolytes** ; those whose solutions are non-conductors are termed **non-electrolytes.**

Investigation of the phenomena associated with the passage of electricity through solutions of electrolytes shows that they differ markedly from the corresponding behaviour of metallic conductors. Thus metallic conductors do not appear to undergo any chemical change due to the passage of a current, whereas a solution of an electrolyte shows evidence of chemical action, for gases are often liberated and other chemical changes can be observed.

For example, if a source of electricity such as an accumulator be connected to two platinum plates which are immersed in a solution of copper sulphate, we see, as soon as the circuit is complete, that bubbles of gas appear on one of the platinum plates, viz., that which is connected to the positive pole of the accumulator. The other plate begins to turn pink, owing to the deposition of a thin film upon it. Investigation shows that the gas is oxygen and the pink film is copper. If the current is allowed to pass for a sufficient length of time, the blue colour of the solution will fade gradually and a solution of sulphuric acid will be left. If the plate from which the oxygen is being liberated be immersed, at the beginning of the experiment, in copper sulphate solution contained in a porous pot, the pot itself being immersed in copper sulphate solution into which the other plate also dips, we shall find that the sulphuric acid is formed round this plate. Clearly, considerable chemical changes are taking place, but the process differs from ordinary cases of chemical change in that a current of electricity is necessary in order to bring them about, and the products of the change make their appearance at points which may be separated by a considerable distance. This process of the passage of a current through a solution of an electrolyte with its resulting chemical change is called **electrolysis,** and the plates or other conductors dipping into the solution by means of which the current enters and leaves it are known as **electrodes.** The electrode by which the current *enters* the solution is termed the **anode** : that by which it leaves, the **cathode.** The anode is thus the *positive* electrode, and the cathode the *negative* electrode.

Phenomena akin to those just described occur only with liquids ; these liquids being either solutions of acids, alkalis, and salts, or fused compounds, such as alkalis and salts.

It is noticeable that such compounds all consist of two portions, an acidic radical and a basic radical (see p. 305), and the process of electrolysis appears to separate these two halves and cause them to appear at the electrodes. The acidic radical appears to be liberated at the anode, and the basic radical at the cathode. These two parts of the substance were termed **ions** by Faraday, those which appear at the anode being called **anions,** and those which are liberated at the cathode, **cations.**

§ 2 Faraday's Laws of Electrolysis

It has been known for a very considerable period that an electric current will decompose an electrolyte ; and application was made of this fact by Davy early in the nineteenth century, for it was by this means, for example, that he first isolated sodium.

The first thorough quantitative study of electrolysis was made by Faraday in 1834 and he thereby discovered two laws of fundamental importance which are known as **Faraday's Laws of Electrolysis.** These are :

(1) **the mass of substance decomposed is directly proportional to the quantity of electricity passing through the solution ;**

(2) **when the same current is passed through several electrolytes in series, the masses of each substance liberated are proportional to their chemical equivalents.**

Faraday measured carefully the amount of substance liberated by one coulomb (i.e., the unit quantity of electricity) and hence the quantity of electricity required to liberate the chemical equivalent of any substance is known. One coulomb will deposit 0·001118 gm. of silver ; and hence 107·88 gm. of silver (i.e., the equivalent of silver) will be deposited by 96,494 coulombs of electricity. Thus it follows that Faraday's Laws can be summed up in the statement that **one gram-equivalent of any substance is liberated by the passage of 96,494 coulombs of electricity.** This quantity of electricity is known as a **Faraday** (not to be confused with the farad, the unit of *capacity*).

§ 3 The Mechanism of Electrolysis

The first attempt to explain the phenomena of electrolysis was due to **Grotthus** who, in 1805, put forward his chain theory.   He supposed that the passage of the current through the solution and the chemical

FIG. 78.—Grotthus's Theory.

decomposition accompanying it are brought about by the successive decomposition and recombination of the particles of the dissolved substance.   This is illustrated in Fig. 78, where ⒶⒷ represents a molecule of the electrolyte; Ⓐ and Ⓑ being oppositely charged "halves" of it.   According to this theory, as soon as the electrodes are connected up to a source of electricity the molecules are turned so as to arrange themselves as shown in line 1 (Fig. 78).   Owing to the polarity of the electrodes, Ⓐ and Ⓑ are supposed to be attracted.   Consider the attraction of Ⓐ to its electrode.   This splits it off from the part Ⓑ to which it was attached, and the part Ⓑ, finding itself free, attacks the molecule next to it, depriving it of its Ⓐ portion.   This process goes on all along the line, a part Ⓑ being similarly attracted to the other electrode.   This is illustrated in line II (Fig. 78).   The parts Ⓐ and Ⓑ attracted to the electrodes are liberated and the state represented by line II (Fig. 78) results, the position being the same as at the beginning except that the molecules are all the opposite way round.   The attraction of the electrodes will, therefore, cause them to turn over and the sequence of changes described will be repeated (line III).

This theory of Grotthus had to be given up as soon as it had been shown that Ohm's law applies to electrolytes.   This means that all the energy of the current is utilized in overcoming the resistance of the solution and none in the splitting of the molecules, as would be required by Grotthus's theory.

After the Grotthus theory had been disproved, the next real attempt to explain electrolysis was due to **Clausius** who, in 1857, suggested that in solution an electrolyte is split up into ions whether a potential difference was applied to it or no, and that at all times there is in the solution an equilibrium between these ions and the whole molecules of the electrolyte. These ions were supposed to be charged and, therefore, would travel towards one or other electrode when these are placed in the solution, there to be discharged and liberated as the ordinary products of electrolysis. Clausius, however, supposed that only a very minute proportion of the electrolyte was split up into ions.

This theory of Clausius was satisfactory up to a point ; but it made no real attempt at a quantitative explanation. The extension of Clausius's theory in this way is due to Arrhenius.

The Theory of Electrolytic Dissociation, or the Ionic Theory as it is often called, as put forward by **Arrhenius** in 1887, supposes that all electrolytes are dissociated in greater or less degree in solution, the products of this dissociation being ions. These ions consist of atoms, or groups of atoms (the acidic or basic radicals of the dissolved substance), carrying charges numerically equal to the valency of the radical in question. The total charge on the ions at any time will thus be algebraically equal to zero. The formation of these ions is considered to be a partial and reversible process which is most nearly complete in very dilute solutions.

The facts of electrolysis are readily accounted for by this theory, and Faraday's Laws also. For the presence of the ions in the solution, quite apart from the insertion of electrodes, accounts for the fact that the solution obeys Ohm's Law, on the assumption that the current is carried by the movement of the ions to the electrodes. The appearance of the products of electrolysis at widely separate points (i.e., at the electrodes) is also explained.

If we assume that any univalent ion carries a charge of magnitude e, since the current passes by the discharge of ions, the quantity of electricity which passes through the solution will depend upon the number of ions discharged. As each ion of the same valency carries the same charge, the current will be proportional to the number of ions discharged, and hence to the mass of substance liberated. This is Faraday's First Law of Electrolysis.

A quantity of electricity e will be carried through the solution by one ion carrying this charge and will involve the liberation of that one ion. If the ion carries a charge $2e$ (i.e., if it be a bivalent ion) twice the quantity of electricity will be involved in the discharge of the ion. Hence we see that, since the charge of an ion is equal to e multiplied by the valency of the ion, the quantity of substance liberated by the passage of a current corresponding to e units will be equal to the weight of the ion divided by its valency ; that is, to one equivalent of the ion. This is Faraday's Second Law in another form.

The further quantitative verification of the Ionic Theory by Arrhenius depended upon two distinct phenomena, viz.: (1) the abnormal molecular weights of electrolytes as revealed by the osmotic properties of their solutions, and (2) measurements of the conductivity of solutions at different dilutions.

§ 4 The Ionic Theory and Osmotic Phenomena

Mention has been made in the preceding chapter (p. 189) of the fact that solutions of acids, alkalis and salts show an abnormally high osmotic pressure, and hence give abnormally low values for the molecular weights of the dissolved substances. It is found that these abnormal values are a specific property of electrolytes, and Van't Hoff in developing his theory of solution introduced a factor i (known as the Van't Hoff Factor) into the equation $PV = RT$ when this was to be applied to solutions of electrolytes so that it then read (for one gram-molecule of solute)

$$PV = iRT.$$

The value of i as determined from freezing point measurements is found to vary with the dilution of the solution, and also with the nature of the solute, in a regular way. Thus, for sodium chloride and similar uni-univalent salts it has a value $1 \cdot 8$ approximately in moderately strong solutions, but increases with dilution to a value close to $2 \cdot 0$ at high dilution. Sodium sulphate gives a value for i which similarly varies from $2 \cdot 2$ to approximately $3 \cdot 0$.

This behaviour resembles that of certain gases whose vapour density is anomalously low in comparison with the value which would be anticipated from other evidence. Ammonium chloride vapour is a case in point (see p. 398). This result has been shown to be due to the dissociation of the ammonium chloride when in the vapour state into ammonia and hydrogen chloride. As the osmotic phenomena of solutions are seen to be, in general, analogous to the behaviour of gases, and in particular are colligative properties, Arrhenius suggested that the Van't Hoff factor i represented the extent to which the molecules of electrolyte had become dissociated into ions in any particular case. Thus, in a sodium chloride solution, for which $i = 1 \cdot 85$, this would be accounted for on the assumption that the salt is 85 per cent. dissociated at this particular dilution.

Arrhenius confirmed this view by a comparison of the values obtained for i in various solutions with those for the electrical conductivity of similar solutions. For, according to him, the conductivity of a solution is determined by the number of ions present, and so should show a close correspondence with the value of the factor i.

§ 5 Measurement of the Conductivity of Solutions

The problem of a suitable experimental technique for finding the conductivity of solutions was solved by Kohlrausch in 1869 and following years, and most of the important work in this field has been based on his methods.

When a metallic conductor is included in an electrical circuit, it opposes a certain resistance to the passage of the current, which resistance depends upon the length and cross-section of the conductor as well as upon the material of which it is made. The latter actor is defined by the *specific resistance* of the material, which is the resistance (usually measured in ohms*) of a cube of the substance whose edges are 1 cm. long. The reciprocal of this quantity is called the **specific conductivity** and is measured in *reciprocal ohms* or **mhos.** Calculations involving metallic conductors usually employ the *resistance* of the conductor; for solutions it has proved more convenient to employ the *conductivity*.

Another distinction between solutions and metallic conductors is that the conductivity of the former does not depend upon the whole of the material between the electrodes but only upon the ions present. Hence, the comparison of the conductivity of two solutions should be made with solutions containing equivalent amounts of solute, and the quantity most commonly employed in the investigation of solutions is the **equivalent conductivity,** which may be defined as **the conducting power of one gram-equivalent of the substance dissolved in the solvent and placed in a cell whose opposite walls, one centimetre apart, form the electrodes.** Otherwise expressed, the equivalent conductivity represents the conducting power of a layer of the solution 1 cm. thick and containing 1 gram-equivalent of the substance in solution. This quantity, the equivalent conductivity, is usually represented by the symbol λ and can easily be seen to be equal to the specific conductivity multiplied by the volume of solution which contains 1 gram-equivalent.

The term **molecular conductivity** is sometimes employed and represents similarly the conductivity of a solution containing one gram-molecule of the solute.

The determination of the equivalent conductivity of a solution thus depends, primarily, upon finding the resistance of a portion of solution of known strength, between electrodes of known area and fixed distance apart. It is here that the principal difficulties arise, for if the measurement be carried out in the same way as for a metallic conductor, using a direct current, electrolysis occurs with the liberation of gases which cause the setting up in the solution of a back electromotive force (or polarization E.M F.) which completely masks the resistance due to the solution alone. This difficulty was surmounted by Kohlrausch who used an alternating current from an induction coil, in conjunction with the ordinary Wheatstone Bridge arrangement for the measurement of resistance, the arrangement employed being shown diagrammatically in Fig. 79.

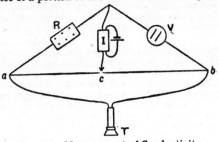

FIG. 79.—Measurement of Conductivity of Electrolytes.

The terminals of the secondary coil of the induction coil, *I*, are connected as shown; *ab* is the bridge wire (which is usually one metre long and lies along a

* The international standard ohm is the resistance at 0° C. of a column of mercury 106·3 cm. long and weighing 14·4521 gms.

metre-scale). R is a resistance-box and V is a conductivity vessel containing the solution under examination. On account of the use of alternating current, the null point on the wire ab cannot be found by using a galvanometer as detecting instrument as in the ordinary Wheatstone Bridge arrangement ; a telephone is therefore used as detecting instrument, the slide c being moved until there is a minimum of sound in the telephone. When this point has been found :

$$\frac{R}{V} = \frac{ac}{cb} \text{ or } V = R. \frac{cb}{ac}$$

where V = resistance of the solution
and R = resistance in the resistance-box.

Various forms of cell are employed in work of this kind. These consist of small cylindrical glass vessels with parallel platinized platinum electrodes. These are rigidly sealed into glass tubes and connection is made to them by means of mercury. The electrodes are electrolytically coated before use with a layer of platinum black, the sharpness of the minimum in the telephone being thereby much improved. The glass tubes are fixed in position by means of an ebonite lid, and during a determination the whole cell is immersed in a thermostat, since the conductivity of a solution is markedly affected by changes of temperature.

The specific conductivity of a solution is, as we have seen, the conductivity of a centimetre cube of the solution. But, in general, the electrodes of a conductivity cell will not be exactly 1 sq. cm. in area, nor exactly 1 cm. apart so that the value determined by experiment for the conductivity will have to be multiplied by a factor to give the specific conductivity. Since this factor evidently depends only upon the dimensions of the cell it is usually determined by finding the conductivity in the cell of a solution of known conductivity, whence this factor, known as the **cell constant,** can be calculated and used in subsequent measurements. For this purpose use is generally made of Kohlrausch's values for the conductivity of potassium chloride solutions.

Conductivity Water

In exact measurements of conductivity, and particularly at high dilutions, it is necessary that the water used for making the solutions should be as pure as possible. It has been found that ordinary distilled water still has a considerable conductivity (due to the presence of traces of dissolved electrolytes and of gases such as carbon dioxide) and for conductivity work of a high order of accuracy a much purer water is required. The purest possible water still has a very slight conductivity due to the fact that water is itself very slightly ionized :

$$H_2O \rightleftharpoons H\cdot + OH'$$

The conductivity of this ultra-pure water is about $0\cdot0384 \times 10^{-6}$ mho. at 18° C., while that of ordinary distilled water is usually in the neighbourhood of 3 to 6 $\times 10^{-6}$ mho. at 18° C.

For conductivity work, a water having a conductivity of about 0·9 mho is employed. This is known as **conductivity water** and is obtained by careful redistillation of ordinary distilled water over acidified potassium permanganate, then from a little barium hydroxide, and then finally into a block tin condenser in a stream of carbon dioxide—free air. This water must not be allowed to come into contact with ordinary glass vessels, or with the air, for it would dissolve sufficient impurity to raise its conductivity considerably.

§ 6 Equivalent Conductivity and Concentration—Kohlrausch's Law

Kohlrausch found, on examining the values he had obtained for the equivalent conductivities of solutions of different concentration, that the equivalent conductivity of all electrolytic solutions increases with dilution ; and further, that with increasing dilution the equivalent conductivity tends towards a maximum, usually referred to as the equivalent conductivity at infinite dilution.

Another generalization put forward by Kohlrausch is that *the equivalent conductivity at infinite dilution is the sum of two values, one depending on the cation and one on the anion.* This is known as Kohlrausch's Law, and has an important application in the quantitative development of the Ionic Theory by Arrhenius.

According to the electrolytic dissociation theory of Arrhenius, the equivalent conductivity of a solution depends upon the number of ions present and the increase in equivalent conductivity with dilution is interpreted to mean that the proportion of the solute molecules which have become dissociated into ions is increasing, the limit being reached when complete dissociation has occurred. That being so, the **degree of ionization**—represented by α—at any given dilution will be given by the ratio of the equivalent conductivity of a solution of that degree of dilution (λ_v) to the equivalent conductivity of the same solute at infinite dilution (λ_∞) or

$$\alpha = \frac{\lambda_v}{\lambda_\infty}$$

This ratio is often expressed in practice as a percentage.

TABLE XVI.—DEGREE OF DISSOCIATION FROM FREEZING POINT AND CONDUCTIVITY MEASUREMENTS.

Substance.	Volume in litres, containing 1 gm.-mol.	i	α-from freezing point.	α-from conductivity.
Potassium Chloride	200	1·96	0·96	0·97
	20	1·88	0·88	0·90
Potassium Nitrate	200	1·96	0·96	0·95
	20	1·85	0·85	0·87
Hydrochloric Acid	200	1·99	0·99	0·98
	10	1·91	0·91	0·92
Nitric Acid	200	1·97	0·97	0·98
	5	1·87	0·87	0·92
Sodium Hydroxide	200	1·99	0·99	0·96
	20	1·83	0·83	0·91
Calcium Nitrate	20	2·41	0·70	0·73
	10	2·41	0·70	0·68
Potassium Ferrocyanide	40	3·32	0·58	0·54
	10	2·79	0·45	0·46

The value of the equivalent conductivity at infinite dilution can be obtained easily by extrapolation in the case of substances which show high equivalent conductivity at moderate dilutions (the so-called strong electrolytes) ; in the case of so-called weak electrolytes Kohlrausch's Law is made use of, the component of the total conductivity due to each ion being determined from the equivalent conductivities of strong electrolytes derived from these ions.

The results obtained by Arrhenius for the degree of ionization of various electrolytes at different degrees of dilution from calculations thus based on conductivity measurements agreed extremely well with the values deduced from the Van't Hoff factor in the investigation of the osmotic properties of solutions (see § 4 above).

§ 7 Statement of the Electrolytic Dissociation Theory

We are now in a position to summarize the principal points in the theory of electrolytic dissociation as put forward by Arrhenius. According to him, when an electrolyte is dissolved in water its molecules undergo to a greater or less degree, dissociation into positive and negative ions. These ions behave as independent entities, having their own specific properties and reactions. To them are due the electrical properties of the solution, the abnormal osmotic properties, and the characteristic behaviour of all the salts of a given metal or a given acid.

Evidence in Support of the Ionic Theory

(1) It provides a satisfactory explanation of the phenomena of electrolysis ; both quantitatively and qualitatively (see § 3) ; and also enables the behaviour of voltaic cells in the production of electricity to be explained (§ 10).

(2) It explains the increase in equivalent conductivity of solutions with increasing dilution, and also the difference in the equivalent conductivity of solutions of different electrolytes (§ 6).

(3) Solutions of electrolytes show additive properties. Thus, for instance, all copper salts give blue solutions (the same blue) ; the colour of permanganate solutions is similarly independent of the nature of the cation ; all sulphates which are soluble in water give characteristic reactions. These facts are readily explained by the existence in the solution of the respective ions, free and uncombined.

(4) The " abnormal " osmotic phenomena exhibited by electrolytes (high osmotic pressure, large depression of the freezing point) can be accounted for, and are in quantitative agreement with the results of conductivity measurements.

(5) The equivalent heat of neutralization (i.e., the heat evolved when 1 gram-equivalent of an acid reacts with 1 gram-equivalent of an alkali) is the same for all strong acids and bases. This follows from the ionic theory, according to which (since the salt produced is itself an electrolyte) the process consists in the formation of water (which is

only very slightly ionized since when pure it has a very low conductivity). Thus :

$$HCl \rightleftharpoons H^{\cdot} + Cl'$$
$$NaOH \rightleftharpoons Na^{\cdot} + OH'$$
$$H^{\cdot} + Cl' + Na^{\cdot} + OH' = H_2O + Na^{\cdot} + Cl'$$
$$\text{i.e., } H^{\cdot} + OH' = H_2O.$$

(6) Reactions between electrolytes are very rapid, while those of non-electrolytes are usually slow.

(7) Evidence in favour of the existence of ions has also been furnished by modern work on the structure of the atom and the nature of valency (see p. 146) ; and also by the results of the recent investigation of the structure of crystals.

Evidence against the Ionic Theory

Many objections have been levelled against the Ionic Theory ; a natural enough circumstance in view of its startling nature, when first suggested. The following are some of the principal criticisms which have been urged against it :—

(1) The ions produced would be, in many cases, substances which would react with water, e.g., sodium.

(2) The affinity between the different parts of the molecule (e.g., sodium and chlorine in sodium chloride) is very great ; how can mere solution in water serve to separate them ?

(3) If free ions are present in the solution as definite entities, it ought to be possible to separate them by diffusion or some other mechanical process.

(4) Compounds like mercurous chloride, very prone to thermal dissociation (see Ch. XXVIII, p. 651) are not readily ionized ; while compounds like calcium chloride, which resist thermal dissociation, are readily ionized. Would not the Ionic Theory predict the opposite ?

(5) Why do not the ions which carry large charges recombine, being then held by the normal attraction between oppositely-charged bodies ?

These objections have been met to a large extent, the more so since some of them rest upon a confusion between the nature of an ion and an uncharged atom.

Thus it was held from the start that a charged atom of sodium (i.e., a sodium ion) is very different from an uncharged sodium atom, and hence it does not react with water. The same answer was made to the objection that the affinity, for example, between the sodium and chlorine in sodium chloride was so great that mere solution would not separate them ; since the separation required by the theory is into *ions* and not into the original atoms.

This explanation is now felt to have even greater weight than was understood when it was first put forward, for according to modern views (Ch. IX, p. 146) the sodium atom very readily parts with an electron to form a sodium ion which has the same electronic configuration as the very stable neon atom. Similarly, the chlorine atom very easily takes up an electron to reproduce the stable electronic configuration of an argon atom. Furthermore, it has also been shown, as was suggested by Ostwald, that a large amount of energy is evolved in this process ; that is, in the formation of an ion from an uncharged atom.

We now know also, that even in the crystal, substances like common salt exist in the form of ions, being held together by purely electrostatic forces. The influence of these forces is weakened when exerted in a medium of high dielectric constant, for the work done in separating two opposite electrical charges is inversely proportional to this constant. Hence, the degree of ionization of a given substance should vary with the dielectric constant, and to a large extent this has been shown by experiment to be the case. This answers objections (2) and (5) as water has a very high dielectric constant. This effect is, however, masked in some instances by the property of the ions of combining with the solvent to an extent sufficient to give it the preponderating influence, thus accounting for the variations which have been observed from strict proportionality between dielectric constant and degree of ionization.

The criticism that separation ought to be practicable has been met by pointing out that the electrical charges would tend to cause the ions to arrange themselves in the solution in a quasi-pattern which would make separation difficult, though not impossible. In fact, such a separation is believed to have been effected by Tolman (1911) by centrifuging solutions of sodium, potassium and hydrogen iodides, when the ends of the tubes acquired charges of an opposite kind, presumably through the heavy iodide ions having been accumulated at one end. This evidence has been questioned by some, who have attributed the production of the charges to the same cause as other electrical effects which can be produced by rapid motion in the air.

The lack of direct proportionality between thermal and electrolytic dissociation must also be ascribed to the difference in the nature of these processes. Thermal dissociation produces uncharged atoms or molecules, presumably on account of the increase in molecular agitation at higher temperatures as postulated by the Kinetic Theory. But ionization is brought about, as already mentioned (pp. 146, 200, Ch. IX and this), by the placing of the substance in a medium of high dielectric constant, thus weakening the magnitude of the purely electrostatic forces which previously held the ions together.

In consequence of the objections mentioned, and others of a like nature, attempts have been made, from time to time, to work out other theories to explain the observed phenomena of electrolytes, and the behaviour of solutions of electrolytes in general. These have usually been based upon the assumption of the formation of complexes by reactions between molecules of the solvent of different degrees of complexity, and hence of differing constitution, with the molecules of the solute. Notable among these theories is that of H. E. Armstrong, but so far the Electrolytic Dissociation Theory holds the field since, in spite of difficulties, it affords the most consistent explanation of the fundamental facts which has so far been put forward.

§ 8 Modern Developments and the Ionic Theory

In certain directions the theory as put forward by Arrhenius has undergone modification in recent years ; principally at the hands of Debye and Hückel. These modifications have been suggested in the attempt to meet two difficulties, viz., first the fact that modern knowledge of the structure of the atom and the nature of crystals (Ch. IX ; Ch. X, p. 171) has shown that a crystal of an electrolyte consists already of ions held together only by electrostatic forces ; and secondly, the apparent failure of the Law of Mass Action (Ch. XV, p. 232) to account for the behaviour of strong electrolytes.

The former of these points to the view which is now put forward by Debye and Hückel of a **theory of complete ionization,** according to which it is concluded that solution of a salt in water involves merely the separation of the groups of pre-existent ions. The latter difficulty is also to some extent explicable by this hypothesis. The Law of Mass Action which, as will appear (Ch. XIV), affords a quantitative explanation of many diverse chemical equilibria, when applied to electrolytes satisfactorily agrees with the results of experiment only for weak electrolytes ; that is, electrolytes whose equivalent conductivity is but small at considerable dilutions. For strong electrolytes there is no semblance of agreement between the experiment and theory based upon the Arrhenius view of Electrolytic Dissociation.

The Debye-Hückel Theory attempts to meet both these difficulties by postulating, in the case of strong electrolytes, complete ionization at all dilutions. Increase in the value of the Van't Hoff factor i, i.e., in the osmotic activity of the solution, or of the equivalent conductivity, is ascribed not to increase in the number of the ions, but to an increase in what is termed the ionic **activity.** The mass law is based on the assumption that the various kinds of molecules concerned in a reaction are subject to no attractive or repulsive forces and that molecular collisions are due to chance. This assumption cannot be valid when the " molecules " in solution are charged particles. Hence, when the Law of Mass Action is applied to ions, the observed concentration, c, of a given ion must be corrected to allow for the electrical and other effects of the ions on one another. The correction factor, f, is termed the *activity coefficient*, and the corrected concentration, the *activity*, a, for a given ion, so that $a = cf$. The activity is thus an *effective* concentration, the true " active mass " of the mass law.

Debye and Hückel examined the effect of electrical restraints on the conductivity due to ions in a solution. They supposed, as already stated, that there is complete ionization for strong electrolytes and that the mobility of the ions is affected mainly by two kinds of electrical restraints.

The attractions between positive and negative ions will result in there being an excess of negative ions round each positive ion, and vice versa, providing what they term an *ionic atmosphere* round each ion. (The arrangement thus suggested would be similar to that obtaining in a sodium chloride crystal—p. 172.) When an ion begins to move under the influence of an applied potential difference, this ionic atmosphere has to be renewed in front of the moving ion, while that behind it dies away. It is supposed that the formation of the new atmosphere lags behind the decay of the old, the time interval being known as the *relaxation time*. There will thus always be an excess of ions of opposite sign to the moving ion behind it, which will cause its movement to be retarded. In addition, the applied potential difference will tend to move the ionic atmosphere itself in a direction opposite to that of the moving ion, which will cause further retardation of the latter. These effects will be larger the greater the concentration, and so with increasing dilution, the speed of a given ion, under a given potential gradient, will increase and with it the equivalent conductivity, reaching a maximum at infinite dilution.

As a result of their mathematical analysis of these effects, Debye and Hückel showed that the effect of the retardations mentioned should be proportional to the square root of the concentration, i.e.,

$$\lambda = \lambda_\infty - a\sqrt{c}$$

where λ = conductivity at concentration c and a is a constant.

This theory has met with a certain measure of success when applied to dilute solutions, but its range of applicability is very limited and it is evident that the theory is far from complete. It is now recognized that there is an element of truth in the original electrolytic theory, and that as our knowledge grows, attempts to apply that theory to the facts will approach closer and closer to a more complete explanation of those facts.

The Hydration of the Hydrogen Ion

Another modification of the details of the Electrolytic Theory, as put forward by Arrhenius, in consequence of the results of later work, is due to the fact that ions are usually hydrated, i.e., they carry with them a certain amount of water. The existence of this hydration has been shown by measuring the change in concentration of a non-electrolyte, present in the solution, which occurs as a result of electrolysis. Evidence has accumulated to show that, for instance, in a solution of an acid it is not hydrogen ions themselves which are present, but ions of the formula $[H_3O]^\cdot$, known as hydroxonium ions. One of the important consequences of this fact is referred to in Chapter XV (p. 239) in connection with the strengths of acids.

§ 9 Voltaic Cells

It has long been known that if plates of two dissimilar metals are connected by a wire and immersed in a solution of an electrolyte, a current will flow along the wire. If plates of zinc and copper are taken and immersed in dilute sulphuric acid the arrangement is known as a **simple cell.** If the cell is allowed to work for a little time it will be found that zinc is dissolving in the acid and that bubbles of hydrogen appear on the copper plate, which is not otherwise affected. If the strength of the current passing through the wire be investigated, it will be found that by the time the copper plate has become covered with hydrogen the current has dropped almost to zero. On brushing away the bubbles from the copper plate the current will rise again to its former value.

In normal electrical terms, it is found that a current is flowing along the wire from the copper to the zinc ; although, in fact, it is now known that a stream of electrons is passing along the wire from the zinc to the copper. Zinc is going into solution, forming a solution of zinc sulphate ; or, in terms of the ionic theory, zinc ions $Zn^{\cdot\cdot}$, that is, atoms of zinc carrying double positive charges. The formation of a zinc ion, which has thus two electrons fewer than the atom from which it is derived, will thus leave the zinc plate with these two electrons, which are conducted through the wire to the copper plate. In the solution there are hydrogen ions, caused by the dissociation of the acid (see Ch. XV). When the copper plate receives the two electrons, by way of the connecting wire, it becomes negatively charged and hence attracts hydrogen ions (i.e., hydrogen atoms each having lost one electron) which are positively charged, and these take up electrons from the copper plate, so becoming hydrogen atoms again and being liberated as hydrogen gas. The production of the current is thus seen to depend upon the tendency of the zinc atoms to become zinc ions, concerning which more is said in the next section.

The simple cell is not a useful cell on account of the tendency for its activity to be stopped by the accumulation of hydrogen on the copper plate, a phenomenon which is known as **polarization**. In consequence, various other forms of cell have been devised in order to avoid this difficulty. The usual method for avoiding it is to replace the copper by carbon and to surround this with an oxidizing agent which oxidizes the hydrogen to water as soon as it is formed. Some cells, however, employ two liquids, as for example, the Daniell cell, which consists of a plate of zinc immersed in dilute sulphuric acid contained in a porous pot, the whole standing in a solution of copper sulphate in which there is also a copper plate. In this the zinc dissolves as before, but the copper plate, when negatively charged, attracts not hydrogen ions but copper ions which, when discharged, are deposited on the copper plate as metallic copper. Thus no change in the working of the cell occurs.

The most important form of cell at the present time is the Leclanché cell, particularly in the form of the so-called dry cell, the manufacture of which for use in wireless receivers and for similar purposes has become an important industry.

The ordinary Leclanché cell consists of a carbon rod in a porous pot surrounded by a mixture of powdered carbon and manganese dioxide. The whole stands in a vessel of ammonium chloride solution in which is also a zinc rod. The zinc dissolves as before, forming zinc ions, while the ammonium ions are discharged at the carbon pole. After discharge they break up into am-

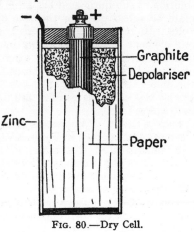

FIG. 80.—Dry Cell.

monia and hydrogen, the former remaining dissolved while the latter is oxidized to water by the manganese dioxide. This oxidation is slow so that the cell may polarize if too big a load is put on it ; but it will recover if allowed to rest, and also it will yield a small current for an almost indefinite period.

The modification of the Leclanché cell known as the dry cell is illustrated diagrammatically in Fig. 80.

A cylinder of zinc, A, serves both as the negative pole of the cell and as a container. Inside this is a layer of soft cardboard, or similar absorbent material, B, saturated with ammonium chloride solution. Within this is a bag containing a moist mixture C, of carbon, manganese dioxide, ammonium chloride and zinc chloride surrounding a central carbon rod. The action of this cell is exactly similar to that of the preceding cell.

§ 10 Electromotive Force and Chemical Affinity, the Electro-chemical Series of the Elements

In the preceding section, the production of the current in a simple cell was seen to be due to the tendency of zinc in the atomic state to go into solution as zinc ions. In order that a current may be driven round a circuit, there must be a difference of potential between the poles of the cell. Even when no current is flowing, a difference of potential is found to exist and in these circumstances it is called the **electromotive force** or E.M.F. of the cell. Experiment has shown that the value of the E.M.F. of a cell depends upon the nature of the substances forming its poles and, to a lesser extent, on the concentration of the solution in which they are immersed. Thus, for example, a cell consisting of zinc and copper plates immersed in a decinormal solution of sulphuric acid has an E.M.F. of about 1·1 volts ; if an iron plate be substituted for the zinc one the E.M.F. falls to about 0·67 volts. By measurements of this kind we can draw up a table in which any element A which is higher in the series than an element B will give a greater E.M.F. than B when used in a voltaic cell with a plate of some other standard substance C. That is to say, a cell of which the plates are composed of A and C will have a higher E.M.F. than a similar cell using plates of B and C, the electrolyte being the same in both cases.

Such a table is known as the **electro-chemical series** of the elements and is given in Table XVII.

Examination of this table, in the light of the known chemical behaviour of the elements, shows that it corresponds closely with this chemical behaviour, and affords us some measure of the **chemical affinity** of two substances, that is of their tendency to react.

This quantity is not very easy to evaluate. It may be taken to be proportional to the energy change which takes place when two substances react. Thus, for example, the difference between the energy latent in a mass of sodium and a mass of chlorine on the one hand, and in the mass of sodium chloride formed by their combination, on the other hand, is a measure of the affinity of sodium for chlorine. But it is not easy to be certain of the value of this difference. It is often *approximately* equal to the heat given out in the process, and was at one time thought to be equal to this heat change ; but this is now recognized as being not necessarily true since the internal energy of the compound must be taken into account. Nevertheless, the heat change does give

TABLE XVII.—ELECTRO-CHEMICAL SERIES OF THE ELEMENTS.

Electro-positive

"Metals"	"Non-Metals"
Caesium	
Rubidium	
Potassium	
Sodium	
Lithium	
Barium	
Strontium	
Calcium	
Magnesium	Silicon
Aluminium	Carbon
Chromium	Boron
Manganese	Nitrogen
Zinc	Selenium
Cadmium	Phosphorus
Iron	Sulphur
Cobalt	Iodine
Nickel	Bromine
Tin	Chlorine
Lead	Oxygen
Hydrogen	Fluorine
Antimony	
Bismuth	
Arsenic	
Copper	**Electro-negative**
Mercury	
Silver	
Palladium	
Platinum	
Gold	
Iridium	
Rhodium	
Osmium	

a rough measure of the relative affinities of substances, and the results of such investigations are in quite good accord very often with what would be anticipated from a consideration of the electro-chemical series.

It is found also that metals will displace each other from solution in a certain order. The displacement of copper by iron (as, for instance, by immersing a penknife blade in copper sulphate solution) is a very familiar fact. Zinc will similarly displace iron, and magnesium will displace zinc (see p. 619). The affinity of magnesium might reasonably be thought to be greater than that of zinc which is in its turn greater than that of iron. Care has to be taken when interpreting the results of displacement experiments to make certain that other factors than the affinities of the elements concerned are not interfering with the results (for example, by causing the evolution of a gas which is removed from the system, etc.). These other disturbing factors will be dealt with more fully in Chapter XIV, but when taken into account, a displacement series of the elements can be drawn up, the order of which is virtually the same as that of the electro-chemical series.

There is thus a good experimental basis for considering that the electro-chemical series gives the relative affinities of the elements and this conclusion can also be justified on theoretical grounds.

When a voltaic cell is in operation producing electrical energy a chemical change is taking place, and the energy liberated in this chemical change is the source of the electrical energy produced. The *quantity* of electricity resulting will depend on the total number of atoms of the material of the plate going into solution which is converted into its compound (strictly speaking, into its *ion*), but the *potential* at which the electrical energy is produced will be determined by the work given out in building up the compound (in the form of its ions) from its elements.

Suppose Q faradays of electricity are produced when m grams of compound are formed in the cell (in the form of ions).

Then by Faraday's first law

$$Q = \frac{m}{e}$$

where e = electro-chemical equivalent.

The work done by the current will be EQ

Where E = potential difference produced.

Let W = work given out in building 1 gm. of the compound from its elements

Then W is a measure of the affinity. Since the work given out is the source of the electrical energy, we have :

$$mW = EQ$$

but $$Q = \frac{m}{e}$$

$$\therefore \quad We = E$$

that is, is proportional to the affinity per gram equivalent of compound formed.

Hence it is justifiable to assume that the E.M.F. produced when an element goes into solution forming a compound is a measure of chemical affinity ; and the order of the electro-chemical series is thus an order of chemical affinities.

CHAPTER XIII

THERMO-CHEMISTRY

Sine igni nihil operamur.—C. Glaser.

Heat and cold are Nature's two hands by which she chiefly worketh.—F. Bacon.

Each element as well as each compound embodies a distinct and invariable amount of energy as well as a distinct and invariable quantity of matter, and thus energy is as constitutive and essential as a part of the existence of such element or compound.—J. B. Stello.

§ 1 Chemical Energy

In the discussion of the criteria of chemical change (Ch. III, p. 48) we saw that such changes are in general associated with changes of energy in the form of heat, light or electricity. These energy changes are most often noticed in the form of the *heat evolution* or *heat absorption* accompanying a reaction, but on occasion other forms of energy are liberated.

The study of the heat changes accompanying chemical action is often referred to as the study of **thermo-chemistry.**

All chemical substances are associated with a certain amount of intrinsic energy, which is liberated, usually as we have seen in the form of heat, to a greater or less degree when it undergoes a chemical reaction. Any chemical system, whether comprising a single substance or a group of substances, contains a definite amount of energy depending upon the mass, chemical nature and physical conditions of the system. This remains constant so long as the system remains unaltered, but when a reaction takes place the products of the reaction will constitute a new chemical system of different intrinsic energy. What these intrinsic energies (i.e., the absolute value of the total energies) are we do not know, but the *change* in total energy when the initial system passes into a new system can be determined, and if no external work is done the decrease in intrinsic energy will be equal to the heat evolved, or vice versa.

§ 2 Heat of Reaction

Experiment shows that the heat effect associated with any given chemical change has a constant value for a given quantity of the reactants. When this value is expressed as the quantity of heat liberated (or absorbed) during the reaction of the gram-molecular quantities of the reacting substances as indicated by the equation for the reaction, it is known as the **Heat of Reaction.** The amount of heat is usually expressed in Kilogram-Calories (represented by Cals) ; a Kilogram-Calorie being the amount of heat required to raise the temperature of one kilogram of water by 1° C. The heat of reaction is often included in the equation, as, for instance :

$$C + O_2 = CO_2 + 94{\cdot}3 \text{ Cals.}$$

which indicates that 12 grams of carbon combine with 32 grams of oxygen with the formation of 44 grams of carbon dioxide and with the liberation of 94·3 Calories of heat.

The heat of reaction will, of course, depend upon the physical state of the reacting substances and of the products of reaction, and, unless there is no possibility of doubt, this ought to be indicated when giving the value of the heat of reaction.   In practice, it is usual to quote heats of reaction calculated on the assumption that all the substances concerned are in that physical state characteristic of them at normal temperature and pressure.

Allowance must be made in calculating the heat of reaction as defined above from observed values when gases are liberated (or absorbed) for the external work thus done, which will be equivalent to some of the heat evolved by the reaction.   When a gas is formed under atmospheric pressure, the external work done per gram-molecule of gas is given by $PV = RT$.   Since R in this case has the value 1·988 gram-calories, it follows that for each gram-molecule of a gas formed in a reaction under atmospheric pressure there must be added to the measured heat of reaction 1·998 T gram-calories (T being expressed on the absolute scale).   Thus, to quote an example mentioned by Findlay, the reaction $Zn + H_2SO_4 aq = ZnSO_4 aq + H_2$ gives out a *measured* quantity of heat equal to 34·2 Cals. at 16°.   For this temperature, $RT = 575$ gm.-cals., or ·575 Cals., so that the real heat of reaction is $34{\cdot}2 +{'} {\cdot}575 = 34{\cdot}775$ Cals.   Conversely, if gases are absorbed during a reaction, a quantity 1·998 T. gm.-cals. must be subtracted from the measured value to give the true heat of reaction.

§ 3 Hess's Law

As stated in the previous section, a certain definite heat change is associated with each particular chemical change.   That the value found for this heat of reaction is independent of the way in which the reaction is carried out was further shown by G. M. Hess who, in 1840, measured the heat developed during the formation of a compound made in several different ways and came to the conclusion that **the amount of heat evolved during the formation of a given compound is the same whether the compound is formed directly all at once or slowly in a series of intermediate stages.**   This is called **Hess's Law.**   The principle may be illustrated by making calcium chloride by the action of quicklime on dilute hydrochloric acid.   It is found that :

$$CaO + 2HCl aq = CaCl_2 aq + H_2O + 46 \text{ Cals.}$$

Instead of this, first slake the quicklime, and

$$CaO + H_2O = Ca(OH)_2 + 15 \text{ Cals.}$$

Dissolve the calcium hydroxide in water, and

$$Ca(OH)_2 + Aq = Ca(OH)_2 aq + 3 \text{ Cals.}$$

Mix the lime water with dilute hydrochloric acid, and

$$Ca(OH)_2 aq + 2HCl aq = CaCl_2 aq + H_2O + 28 \text{ Cals.}$$

These three steps in the formation of the solution of calcium chloride give a total $28 + 3 + 15 = 46$ Cals. as the heat of formation. The same result was obtained by the direct action of the dilute acid on quicklime. A number of experiments made on similar lines have shown that (1) **The heat of formation of a compound is independent of its mode of formation** ; and (2) **the thermal value of a reaction is independent of the time occupied by the change.**

It follows from Hess's Law that if the heat of formation of carbon dioxide be : $C + 2O = CO_2 + 94.3$ Cals. ; and $CO + O = CO_2 + 68$ Cals., we have

$$(C + 2O) - (CO + O) = 94.3 - 68 \text{ Cals.}$$

Consequently, the heat of formation of carbon monoxide is : $C + O = CO + 26.3$ Cals. This illustrates the fact that **the thermal value of a reaction is the sum of the heats of formation of the final products of the reaction less the heats of formation of the initial products of the reaction.** This corollary to Hess's Law is valuable because it enables the heat of formation of a compound from its elements to be computed when a direct determination is either impracticable or very difficult. Similarly the thermal value of a reaction can be deduced when the heats of formation of the different substances which take part in the reaction are known.

Thus, if we know that

$$C + O = CO + 26.3 \text{ Cals.}$$
$$Pb + O = PbO + 50.3 \text{ Cals.}$$
$$\text{and } C + O_2 = CO_2 + 94.3 \text{ Cals.}$$

it follows that the heat of. the reaction :

$$PbO + CO = CO_2 + Pb$$

is given by $94.3 - (26.3 + 50.3) = 17.7$ Cals.

It is to be noted that heats of reaction calculated indirectly in this way may involve considerable error, for although the percentage error in the various experimental values may be quite small, that in their difference may be large.

§ 4 Measurement of Heats of Reaction

The measurement of the heat of reaction for a given chemical change may be either direct or, making use of Hess's Law as explained above, indirect. But in either case we are dependent finally on actual measurements of the heat change inherent in some reaction or reactions, so that methods of determining these are of importance.

The value of the heat of reaction for a change which takes place in solution can be found by ordinary calorimetric methods. Thus, to determine, for example, the heat of neutralization of a dilute solution of hydrochloric acid and sodium hydroxide a known volume of sodium hydroxide solution of definite concentration is placed in a calorimeter. An equivalent quantity of hydrochloric acid solution is contained in a separate vessel and both solutions are brought to the same temperature. This temperature is noted, and the acid is then added rapidly to the alkali and the mixture well stirred. The rise in temperature is measured by means of a delicate thermometer.

Suppose that $\frac{1}{n}$ th normal solutions were used and that v c.c. of each were used while the rise in temperature was $t°$. Let w be the water equivalent of the calorimeter. Assuming that the solutions were sufficiently dilute for the specific heats and densities to be taken as unity without serious error, we have :

Heat produced in the reaction $= (w + 2v)t$. cals.

Now 1 gram-molecule of each substance is contained in n litres. Therefore, the heat produced on mixing n litres of each solution would be

$$\frac{(w + 2v)t \times 2000n}{2v} \text{ Cals.} = \frac{(w + 2v)tn}{v} \text{ Cals.}$$

$$= \text{ heat of neutralization.}$$

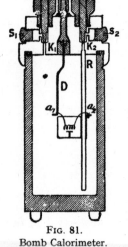

FIG. 81.
Bomb Calorimeter.

When the heat evolved in a reaction under investigation is very large, or where large quantities of gaseous products result, special methods have to be used.

As an example of these the use of the bomb calorimeter may be cited, this being particularly suitable for the measurement of *heat of combustion*, i.e., the heat produced when a combustible substance, as, for example, carbon, combines with oxygen. This process consists in burning a known weight of the substance in compressed oxygen in a closed steel vessel known as the *bomb*.

The bomb used is illustrated diagrammatically in Fig. 81.

It consists of a steel vessel with a tight-fitting lid which is screwed down on to a lead washer. The substance to be burned is weighed and placed in the crucible, T, and the bomb is filled with oxygen by way of the channel K_2 and the tube R until the pressure is about 20-25 atmospheres. The bomb is then immersed in a known weight of water contained in a calorimeter. The combustion is started by connecting the spiral of wire (made of platinum or iron) $a_1 \, a_2$ to a source of electricity, thereby raising it to incandescence. The temperature of the water in the calorimeter is then taken every minute so that a cooling correction may be applied to the maximum temperature recorded. The heat of combustion of the substance, at constant volume, can then be calculated, the water equivalent of the bomb being known.

§5 Endothermic and Exothermic Compounds

We are apt to think of the formation of a compound from its elements as being accompanied by the *evolution* of heat, because many familiar instances where this is true present themselves to our minds. But it is by no means always the case, and many substances are known which, if they are formed by combination of their constituent elements, *absorb* heat. A common example of this class of substance is the gas acetylene. Compounds which are formed with evolution of heat are called **exothermic** compounds ; while those which are formed with absorption of heat are known as **endothermic.** Reactions are referred to similarly as exothermic or endothermic reactions, according as they are attended with evolution or with absorption of heat.

The knowledge as to whether a given compound is exothermic or endothermic is of considerable importance, for it enables us to predict its stability under different temperature conditions. An endothermic compound will contain more energy than the elements from which it is made, and it follows from Le Chatelier's Principle (see p. 219), as shown in the next chapter, that such a compound will require a high temperature for its formation and will be stable at high temperatures rather than low ones. Conversely, endothermic compounds are stable at low temperatures, but not at high temperatures.

Familiar examples of endothermic compounds are acetylene, oxides of nitrogen and ozone. Common exothermic substances are carbon monoxide and carbon dioxide, and water.

§ 6 Heats of Linkages

It was pointed out earlier in the present chapter that we have no means of determining the total intrinsic energy either of reacting substances or of the product of a reaction, but only the difference between them. In stating the heats of reaction and of formation of compounds, we have accordingly taken as our datum line the elements themselves.

In certain cases, however, this will lead to errors and discrepancies for the molecular condition of different elements is very different. Thus, carbon in the form of a diamond is a complicated structure (cf. p. 332) of atoms joined together by certain bonds, and when this is burnt to carbon dioxide these bonds will have to be severed and energy will be used up in the process. This supposition is confirmed by the fact that the heat of combustion of amorphous carbon is greater than that of diamond.

Similarly in any combustion the oxygen molecule has to be broken down into its atoms before combination can take place, and again energy will be required. Modern research in thermo-chemistry has accordingly been directed to the determination of the heat changes involved in the formation of various linkages and these are now known with a fair degree of accuracy.

CHAPTER XIV

CHEMICAL EQUILIBRIUM AND THE VELOCITY OF REACTIONS

I often say that if you can measure that of which you speak, and can express it by a number, you know something of your subject ; but if you cannot measure it, your knowledge is meagre and unsatisfactory.—LORD KELVIN.

" . . . The streaming atoms
Fly on to clash together again and make
Another and another state of things
For ever. . . ."

Rejected Addresses.

§ 1 The Extent to which Reactions Proceed

IT is well known that reactions do not all proceed instantaneously or to completion, although many do both. Thus, for example, if we mix aqueous solutions of sodium chloride and silver nitrate of equivalent concentration, we immediately see the formation of a precipitate of silver chloride, and almost the whole of the silver and of the chlorine are removed from the solution, the slight trace of either remaining in solution being due to the slight, though measurable, solubility of silver chloride.

There are, however, reactions which proceed relatively slowly, and often these do not proceed to completion. Thus, for example, when a mixture of equal volumes of iodine vapour and hydrogen is passed through a red-hot tube, or better, over finely-divided platinum or platinized asbestos, or charcoal, some hydrogen iodide, HI, is formed. If hydrogen iodide gas be treated in a similar way, some iodine and hydrogen are produced. In either case, if the temperature of the tube be 440°, we have approximately 80 per cent. of hydrogen iodide, and 20 per cent. of a mixture of equal volumes of iodine and hydrogen. The only apparent effect of the catalytic agent—platinized asbestos, etc.—is to accelerate the reaction, and if these agents be absent, the time required to make 80 per cent. of hydrogen iodide from the mixture of hydrogen and iodine is much longer. Once this proportion of hydrogen iodide has been formed, the composition of the exit gases remains unchanged, however long the mixture may be heated at 440°, with or without the catalytic agents. This is due to the fact that although at this temperature hydrogen and iodine will combine together to form hydrogen iodide, this hydrogen iodide, when formed, has in its turn a tendency to decompose into hydrogen and iodine. So that, in fact, we have two reactions occurring simultaneously, which may be represented thus:

$$H_2 + I_2 \rightarrow 2HI$$

$$\text{and } 2HI \rightarrow H_2 + I_2$$

212

This reaction is therefore spoken of as a **balanced** or **reversible reaction** and is usually represented by replacing the equality sign in the equation by two arrows, thus :

$$H_2 + I_2 \rightleftharpoons 2HI.$$

When, as in the above example, the gases have been maintained in contact for a sufficient length of time, a state of *equilibrium* is set up between the hydrogen and iodine on the one hand and the hydrogen iodide on the other.

§ 2 The Law of Mass Action

The condition of equilibrium, under given conditions (in particular at a given temperature) in the case of a balanced reaction can be deduced by the application of the **Law of Mass Action** which was first enunciated clearly by Guldberg and Waage in 1867, in consequence of which it is sometimes known as Guldberg and Waage's Law. This states that *the rate of a chemical reaction is proportional to the products of the active masses of the reacting substances.* The phrase " active mass " is perhaps strange to our ears ; by it, Guldberg and Waage meant what we term the concentration of a substance.

We can apply this law to determine the condition of equilibrium in a homogeneous reaction in the following way. Consider the reaction :

$$A + B \rightleftharpoons M + N$$

and let C_A and C_B respectively denote the concentrations of the substances A and B, expressed in gram-molecules per litre. Similarly, let C_M and C_N respectively denote the concentrations of M and N. We have previously found that the speed of the reaction is proportional to the concentrations of the reacting substances, that is, the velocity of the reaction $A + B$ is equal to $kC_A C_B$. Similarly, the velocity of the reaction in the opposite direction will be proportional to $C_M C_N$ or equal to $k'C_M C_N$. In these expressions k and k' are constants, sometimes called *velocity constants* (see § 7 below). When the conditions are such that the velocities of these two reactions are identical, a state of equilibrium results. We then have :

$$kC_A C_B = k'C_M C_N$$

i.e., $$\frac{C_M C_N}{C_A C_B} = \frac{k}{k'} = K \text{ (another constant).}$$

So that at equilibrium we conclude that the product of the concentrations of the substances on the right-hand side of the equation, divided by the product of the concentrations of the substances on the left-hand side of the equation, is a constant at a given temperature. This constant is known as the *equilibrium constant* for the reaction at this temperature.

Some examples of the application of these conclusions to actual reactions may now be given. The simplest cases are those which occur in gaseous systems, and the hydrogen—iodine—hydrogeniodide equilibrium already referred to is a good example of this type. The reaction is represented, as we have seen, by the equation :

$$2HI \rightleftharpoons H_2 + I_2$$

from which we conclude that the condition of equilibrium at a given temperature will be given by

$$\frac{C_H C_I}{C_{HI}.C_{HI}} = \frac{C_H C_I}{C^2_{HI}} = K$$

Suppose that a gram-molecules of hydrogen and b gram-molecules of iodine are heated together, the total volume being v litres. Let the amount of hydrogen iodide present at equilibrium be $2x$ gram-molecules, x gram-molecules of hydrogen and x gram-molecules of iodine having combined. Then we have, at equilibrium :

$$C_H = \frac{a - x}{v}, \ C_I = \frac{b - x}{v} \ \text{ and } \ C_{HI} = \frac{2x}{v}$$

$$\therefore K = \frac{\left(\dfrac{a - x}{v}\right)\left(\dfrac{b - x}{v}\right)}{\left(\dfrac{2x}{v}\right)^2} = \frac{(a - x)(b - x)}{4x^2}$$

The volume term v is thus seen to cancel out in this expression, from which it follows that the equilibrium in this case is not affected by change of volume, and consequently change of pressure is also without effect.

This equilibrium has been extensively investigated by Bodenstein (1897) and his results confirm these conclusions. In addition, he showed that the same equilibrium is set up whether we begin with hydrogen and iodine, or with hydrogen iodide.

Another interesting and instructive example of equilibrium in the gaseous state is afforded by nitrogen peroxide. This gas undergoes dissociation at moderate temperatures, as indicated by the equation :

$$N_2O_4 \rightleftharpoons 2NO_2$$

(compare p. 421). If we apply the law of mass action here we have :

$$\frac{C^2_{NO_2}}{C_{N_2O_4}} = K$$

Now supposing we have a gram-molecules of N_2O_4 in a volume of v litres, and that x gram-molecules have dissociated, thus forming $2x$ gram-molecules of NO_2. Then,

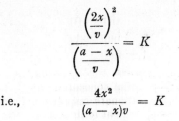

$$\frac{\left(\dfrac{2x}{v}\right)^2}{\left(\dfrac{a-x}{v}\right)} = K$$

i.e.,
$$\frac{4x^2}{(a-x)v} = K$$

Here v the volume appears in the expression for the equilibrium constant, and hence the concentrations of the two types of molecule at equilibrium are dependent upon the volume, and consequently upon the pressure. Further, since v appears in the denominator, it follows that if we increase the volume (or decrease the pressure) of the system there will be an increase in the proportion of NO_2 molecules present, and vice versa. These conclusions are borne out by the results of experimental investigations of this equilibrium.

Generalizing from the two examples so far discussed, we see that where a reaction in the gaseous state takes place without change of volume, pressure is without influence on the equilibrium ; conversely, reactions which involve a change in volume have the equilibrium altered by changes in pressure.

Homogeneous reversible reactions are not confined to the gaseous phase, but may take place in solution. Since almost all reactions in solution between inorganic substances are ionic in nature, the equilibria involved are largely bound up with those of the ions themselves. This application of the Law of Mass Action to electrolytes is discussed in the next chapter. The most familiar examples of balanced reactions in solution are, therefore, those of organic compounds and consequently fall outside the scope of a text-book of inorganic chemistry.

§ 3 The Law of Mass Action and Heterogeneous Systems

So far we have considered only balanced reactions which take place in one phase, that is, homogeneous reactions. There are, of course, a great many reactions which take place between substances in different phases, and these are known as heterogeneous reactions. Numerous reversible, heterogeneous reactions are known, and it is necessary now to consider how far the Law of Mass Action can be applied to such cases.

Let us consider the familiar reaction of the decomposition of calcium carbonate by heat—a well-known example of a reversible reaction (compare p. 626) which may be represented by the equation :

$$CaCO_3 \rightleftharpoons CaO + CO_2.$$

If all three substances were in the form of vapour we could apply the

Law of Mass Action to the equilibrium and should have the result :

$$\frac{C_{CaO} \times C_{CO_2}}{C_{CaCO_3}} = K$$

where C_{CaO}, C_{CO_2} and C_{CaCO_3} are the concentrations of calcium oxide, carbon dioxide, and calcium carbonate respectively. Now, although under the conditions of the experiment both calcium oxide and calcium carbonate are solids, we may legitimately assume that they have a real, though very small, vapour pressure. Now we can express the concentrations of substances in the vapour phase in terms of their partial pressures, since these are proportional to the concentrations. The expression for the equilibrium constant then becomes :

$$\frac{p_{CaO} \times p_{CO_2}}{p_{CaCO_3}} = K$$

where p_{CaO}, p_{CO_2} and p_{CaCO_3} are the partial pressures of calcium oxide, carbon dioxide and calcium carbonate respectively. The vapour pressures of the solids will be constant, at a given temperature, so long as these solids are present ; hence in the present instance p_{CaO} and p_{CaCO_3} are constants, so that we have :

$$p_{CO_2} = K$$

The system, therefore, is at equilibrium at a given temperature when the partial pressure of the carbon dioxide present has the required fixed value. This result is confirmed by experiment which shows that there is a certain fixed **dissociation pressure** of carbon dioxide for each temperature. The same conclusion can be deduced from the application of the phase rule (see p. 158). We have two components existing in three phases ; hence $F = 2 - 3 + 2 = 1$, or the system possesses one degree of freedom.

We may thus legitimately conclude that the assumption made in applying the Law of Mass Action to a heterogeneous system is justified, and hence conclude that in such systems *the active mass of a solid is constant.*

Another common example to which the same considerations apply is that of the action of steam on red-hot iron, which is represented by the equation :

$$3Fe + 4H_2O \rightleftharpoons Fe_3O_4 + 4H_2$$

Assuming that the active masses of the solids are constant, we have, as before :

$$\frac{(p_{H_2})^4}{(p_{H_2O})^4} = K$$

i.e.,
$$\frac{p_{H_2}}{p_{H_2O}} = K'$$

Again, this result is borne out by experiment, so that the assumptions on which it is based seem to be justified.

§ 4 Dissociation of Salt Hydrates

Similar considerations apply to the dehydration of salts which contain water of crystallization.

Consider the case, for example, of hydrated copper sulphate—$CuSO_4.5H_2O$. When this is heated it passes, first, into $CuSO_4.3H_2O$, then into $CuSO_4.H_2O$, and finally into anhydrous copper sulphate. The first of these stages may be represented by the equation :

$$CuSO_4.5H_2O \rightleftharpoons CuSO_4.3H_2O + 2H_2O.$$

Applying the principles employed in the preceding section, we have :

$$\frac{p_2 \times p_3^2}{p_1} = K$$

when p_1, p_2 and p_2 are the partial pressures of the pentahydrate, the trihydrate and of water vapour respectively. But, as we have said, so long as the solids remain, their vapour pressures will be constant, so that p_1 and p_2 are constant ; hence the expression for the equilibrium becomes :

$$p_3^2 = K$$
i.e., $$p_3 = \sqrt{K} = K'$$

Again, we see that at a given temperature a particular pressure of the water vapour present is necessary for equilibrium. This result again is deducible from Phase Rule considerations.

When one of the hydrates has disappeared, a new equilibrium will be set up, and the partial pressure of water vapour will have a different value, but will again remain constant so long as the same two hydrates are present.

These conclusions are upheld by experimental results which show that in the dehydration of copper sulphate the pressure remains constant at the value for the dissociation pressure of the pentahydrate for some time, and then drops *suddenly* to that of the next hydrate. The graph in Fig. 82 shows the variation in vapour pressure of copper sulphate in a dehydration experiment.

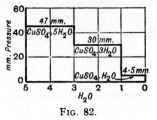

FIG. 82.

Vapour Pressure Curves of the Hydrates of Copper Sulphate.

Consideration of these results enables us further to account for the phenomena of **efflorescence** and **deliquescence.** Thus, if the partial pressure of the water vapour present in the air at a given time is *less* than the dissociation pressure of a particular salt hydrate, the latter will give up water vapour, thus losing part (or all) of its water of crystallization. This is the phenomenon known as **efflorescence**. If the partial pressure of water vapour is *greater* than that of the hydrate, the salt will absorb moisture from the atmosphere. This is what is known as **deliquescence**.

These conclusions are illustrated by Table XVIII. The partial

TABLE XVIII.—VAPOUR PRESSURES OF HYDRATES.

Salt.	Vapour pressure. mm.	Property.
$CaCl_2.6H_2O$	3·2	Deliquescent
$FeCl_3.6H_2O$	6·0	Deliquescent
$Na_2SO_4.10H_2O$	27·8	Efflorescent
$Na_2CO_3.10H_2O$	24·2	Efflorescent

pressure of water vapour in the atmosphere is normally in the region of 10 mm. of mercury, and rarely exceeds 15 mm.

§ 5 The Effect of Pressure and Temperature on Equilibria— Le Chatelier's Principle

The application of the Law of Mass Action to homogeneous systems in equilibrium leads to the conclusion that the equilibrium will be unaffected by pressure if the reactions occurring take place without change of volume (see § 2, p. 215). Also, where change of volume does take place, increase of pressure will cause the equilibrium to shift in that direction, which is attended with a decrease in volume, and vice versa. These conclusions, further, have been verified by experiment and hence it may be said that in general, *when a system is in a state of physical or chemical equilibrium, an increase of pressure favours the system formed with a decrease in volume ; a reduction of pressure favours the system formed with an increase in volume ; and a change of pressure has no effect on a system formed without a change in volume*—**G. Robin's Law** (1879). Thus we have a qualitative generalization giving the effect of *pressure* on equilibria.

Similar considerations apply to the influence of temperature, but we cannot get any direct guidance from the Law of Mass Action in this case. Experience shows that most reactions proceed at an increased speed with increase of temperature, but that no two reactions are affected to the same extent. In consequence, it follows, that since equilibrium is established when the speeds of the forward and back reactions are equal, if these speeds are changed by rise in temperature to a different extent, then the position of the equilibrium will be moved. How can we predict in which direction it will move ?

By analogy with the effect of pressure which we have correlated with the change in volume in the reaction, it might be expected that the effect of temperature could be related to the heat change which

(Ch. XIII) accompanies all reactions. By analogy also, a rise in temperature would be expected to promote those reactions which proceed with the absorption of heat, and vice versa. Experiment bears out this supposition and so, generalizing, it may be said that : *When a system is in physical or chemical equilibrium, a rise of temperature promotes the formation of those products which are formed with an absorption of heat ; a rise of temperature resists the formation of those products formed with an evolution of heat ; and a change of temperature has no effect on the equilibrium of reactions thermally neutral.*—**J. H. van't Hoff's equilibrium law** (1884).

These two generalizations are combined in that made by Le Chatelier (1888) and known as **Le Chatelier's Principle,** which states that : *if a system in physical or chemical equilibrium be subjected to a stress involving a change of temperature, pressure, concentration, etc., the state of the system will automatically tend to alter so as to undo the effect of the stress.*

This important principle enables us qualitatively to predict the influence of external conditions upon equilibria, and its application to some important cases may now be discussed.

As an example of an equilibrium unaffected by pressure, in which the effect of temperature alone can, therefore, be studied, we may take the synthesis of nitric oxide from its elements, a reaction of considerable technical importance (see p. 406). This reaction may be represented :

$$N_2 + O_2 \rightleftharpoons 2NO - 43\cdot2 \text{ Cals.}$$

so that the formation of nitric oxide, while involving no change in volume, is attended with the *absorption* of a large quantity of heat. The amount of nitric oxide present at equilibrium will thus, according to the Principle of Le Chatelier, be unaffected by changes of pressure, whereas increase of temperature should cause the formation of a larger proportion of nitric oxide. These conclusions were confirmed by the work of Nernst, and the following figures indicate the kind of result obtained :

Temperature . . .	1811°	2033°	2195°	3000°	3200°
Percentage of NO at equili-brium . . .	0·37	0·64	0·997	4·5	5·0

The Birkeland-Eyde process for the Fixation of Nitrogen is based upon these facts (see p. 406).

It is not possible to find a reaction for discussion in which the pressure effect can be isolated, because reactions always involve heat changes ; but the combined influence of temperature and pressure can be studied in the important reaction between nitrogen and hydrogen used in the synthesis of ammonia by the Haber Process (see p. 390).

This reaction is represented :

$$N_2 + 3H_2 \rightleftharpoons 2NH_3 + 22\cdot4 \text{ Cals.,}$$

which indicates that the formation of ammonia from its elements is attended by a large reduction in volume (the volume is halved) ; and the evolution of a considerable quantity of heat. Consequently, increase of pressure will favour, and increase of temperature will hinder the production of ammonia. This is borne out by Table XIX, which shows the percentage of ammonia at equilibrium under different conditions, as determined by Larson and Dodge (1923).

TABLE XIX.—EQUILIBRIUM BETWEEN NITROGEN, HYDROGEN AND AMMONIA.
Percentage of Ammonia.

$t°$ C.	Pressure in Atmospheres.					
	10	30	50	100	300	600
350°	7·35	17·80	25·11			
400°	3·85	10·09	15·11	24·91		
450°	2·04	5·80	9·17	16·35	35·5	53·6
500°	1·20	3·48	5·58	10·40	26·2	42·1

The effect of temperature and pressure are both clearly shown by these figures and are in accordance with anticipations. The application of these results to the commercial synthesis of ammonia is discussed in Chapter XX.

§ 6 The Velocity of Reactions

So far we have considered the conditions for the attainment of equilibrium in balanced (or reversible) reactions, and, although we assumed that these were dependent upon the speeds of the opposing reactions, we have not yet discussed these reaction velocities themselves.

The Law of Mass Action, stated on page 213, is primarily a generalization concerning the *velocity* of chemical reactions, although so far we have only applied it to the case of equilibria (recognizing that these equilibria are kinetic in nature). But it is important to consider its application to reaction velocities themselves and the methods by which they may be investigated experimentally, especially as the law does not tell us anything about the *absolute* velocity of any given reaction, although it gives us valuable information about the way in which the velocity is altered by changes in the proportions of the reacting substances.

Although our knowledge is steadily increasing, we are still somewhat uncertain as to the *exact mechanism* of chemical change, but the Kinetic Theory affords a useful picture of the sort of considerations involved. According to the Kinetic Theory, we imagine that a gas consists principally of empty space in which the molecules are continuously moving, colliding with each other and the walls of the vessel, and rebounding. A liquid we conceive as a collection of molecules, also in motion, colliding and rebounding with each other, but having very little free space between them; held together by molecular attraction and only prevented from close and continuous contact by their motion. A solid we believe to be composed of atoms or molecules in ceaseless *vibration*.

It is a reasonable assumption that, for a chemical reaction to occur between two substances, the reacting molecules should come into contact, or at least approach each other very closely, so that it would be expected that reactions between two solids would be very rare; while reactions involving liquids and gases, either with other liquids or gases, or with solids, should occur frequently. This is, of course, what is found experimentally; non-volatile solids react with each other as a rule only if subjected to very heavy pressure.

The older chemists did not believe that solids could react chemically, but W. Spring claims to have formed sulphides and arsenides of metals, by the alternate compression and filing of intimate mixtures of the metals with sulphur and arsenic respectively. Other reactions brought about, according to Spring, by pressure, are those between sodium carbonate and barium sulphate; potassium nitrate and sodium acetate; mercuric chloride and potassium iodide, etc. There is no reason to doubt that combination did occur in these cases, even if it did not go to completion; and this fact shows that the molecules of solids can be brought close enough for chemical union.

On this assumption, that chemical reaction involves a close approach between the reacting molecules, we should expect that any condition tending to increase the number of collisions between molecules would also increase the rate of reaction. The number of these collisions can clearly be increased in two ways (assuming, for the moment, a constant temperature). These are :

(1) the average distance between the molecules can be decreased by increasing the pressure upon the system;

(2) the number of molecules of each kind present can be increased.

If two molecules are to react they must (on our assumption) collide The chances of *each* molecule doing so are doubled if the total volume of the system is halved; hence the chances for *both* are multiplied by four, i.e., as the square of the pressure. Similarly, in a reaction involving n molecules, the chances of the appropriate juxtaposition of molecules will vary as the nth power of the pressure. The rate of reaction will thus vary also according to the nth power of the pressure.

Similarly, if we require two molecules of different kinds to meet (and react) the chance of a particular molecule being at a particular spot is proportional to the number of molecules of that kind within reach. So also with the second molecule, and so with n molecules. Hence, there is a logical reason for the dependence of reaction velocity upon concentration.

These considerations are summed up in the Law of Mass Action which, as given on page 213, states that *the rate of a chemical reaction is proportional to the products of the active masses of the reacting substances.*

For a long period before the Law of Mass Action had been enunciated by Guldberg and Waage it was known that the progress of a reaction is affected by the amount of reacting substances present. Thus, Wenzel in 1777 investigated the solution of zinc and copper in acids and recognized the relationship in this case between the rate of reaction and concentration. He found that if an acid of a given concentration reacts with one unit of metal per hour, an acid of half that concentration will take two hours. Similarly, Wilhelmy in 1850 investigated the inversion of cane sugar and expressed his results in a mathematical relation between the rate of inversion and the concentration, and a more general investigation, along similar lines, was undertaken by Harcourt and Esson, 1866, just before Guldberg and Waage published their conclusions embodied in the Law of Mass Action as we have it.

Influence of Temperature

In general, almost all chemical reactions proceed at a faster rate when the temperature is raised ; sometimes this increase in velocity is very great and on the average it is found that the reaction velocity is doubled by a rise in temperature of 10° C. This effect is *qualitatively* in harmony with what would be expected on the basis of the Kinetic Theory, for according to this theory (compare Ch. II, § 11) a rise in temperature causes an increase in the velocity of the molecules, and hence of the number of collisions between them. This increase can readily be calculated, but comes out at a figure which rarely exceeds one-fifth of that which is found by experiment, and is usually only one-tenth or less.

The explanation of this discrepancy is believed to be the fact that not all the collisions between molecules are fruitful collisions in the sense of bringing about reaction. Thus Bodenstein, in the course of his investigations on hydrogen iodide, found that at 283°, at a concentration of 1 gram-molecule per litre, the number of molecules which react per second is only $2 \cdot 1 \times 10^{17}$, whereas it is calculated that the number of collisions is 6×10^{34}. Some other factor than mere collision is thus involved.

§ 7 The Order of Reactions

The Law of Mass Action states that the rate at which a given chemical reaction proceeds is proportional to the concentrations of the reacting substances. Clearly, therefore, a reaction which involves the interaction of *two* molecules (whether alike or different) will proceed at a rate, the mathematical expression of which will involve *two* factors, and which will therefore have different characteristics as compared with a reaction which involves only the decomposition of a single molecule, or with one in which more than two molecules are essentially involved.

It is convenient to classify reactions on this basis. Reactions which involve only one molecule are termed *unimolecular* reactions or reactions of the *first order* ; those which involve two molecules are called *bimolecular* or second order reactions, and so on. Expressed mathematically we may say that in the reaction :

$$lA + mB + nC + \ldots \rightarrow aX + bY + cZ \ldots \ldots$$

the speed is given by :

$$V = kC_A^l C_B^m C_C^n \ldots$$

and the order of the reaction is the sum of the indices $l + m + n \ldots$ It is to be observed that the order of a reversible reaction is often different in the reverse direction as compared with the forward direction.

The characteristics of each type of reaction may be discovered from the mathematical expression of the Law of Mass Action.

Thus a **unimolecular reaction** proceeds at a speed proportional to the concentration of the reacting substance. Consider such a reaction as may be represented by the equation :

$$A \rightarrow B + C + \ldots \ldots$$

Suppose that at the beginning of the reaction there are a gram-molecules of A present per litre, and that after a time t has elapsed x gram-molecules of A have undergone change so that there are now $a - x$ gram-molecules of A remaining. Then, using the notation of the calculus, we have from the Law of Mass Action :

$$v = \frac{dx}{dt} = k(a - x)$$

i.e.,

$$\frac{dx}{a - x} = kdt$$

which on integration gives us :

$$- \log_e (a - x) = kt + C$$

where C is a constant which can be evaluated from the fact that when $t = 0$, $x = 0$. We then have :

$$- \log_e a = C$$

$$\therefore k = \frac{1}{t} \log_e \frac{a}{a - x}$$

k is, of course, a constant known as the *velocity constant* of the reaction. This equation is characteristic of the behaviour of all unimolecular reactions.

A simliar reasoning applies to **bimolecular reactions.** Let us consider the reaction

$$A + B \rightarrow C + D + E \ldots \ldots$$

Suppose that, as before, the initial concentration of A is a gram-molecules, and for simplification let the initial concentration of B be the same. Let x gram-molecules of each have reacted after time t. Then, by the Law of Mass Action we have :

$$v = \frac{dx}{dt} = k(a - x)^2$$

which on integrating gives

$$k = \frac{1}{t} \cdot \frac{x}{a(a - x)}$$

When the initial concentrations of the reacting substances are different the calculation is more complicated, but need not be considered for the present.

Reactions of **higher orders** than the second can be dealt with in a similar manner, but their treatment lies outside the scope of the present work. For their discussion reference should be made to books on physical chemistry.

§ 8 Some Typical Reactions of the First and Second Orders

The investigation experimentally of the velocity with which reactions proceed, with a view to the determination of their *order*, is a matter of considerable importance since it enables us to elucidate the mechanisms of many such reactions. The experimental methods available may be summarized as follows :—

(i) Comparison of the experimental data with the formulae deduced as in § 7 to discover which they fit ;

(ii) determination of how the time required for the completion of a given fraction of the change depends upon the concentration of the reacting substances (actually a modification of (i) which has much practical convenience) ;

(iii) determination of the order as in (i) having each reactant separately in excess, in turn, when the sum of the orders so found is the order of the reaction.

Unimolecular Reactions

Experiment has shown that truly unimolecular reactions are unexpectedly rare. The best known case of such a reaction is the decomposition of nitrogen pentoxide. This reaction is usually represented by the equation :

$$2N_2O_5 \rightarrow 2N_2O_4 + O_2$$

which would lead us to conclude that it is bimolecular. It was investigated by measuring the pressure after various intervals, and also, since it takes place in solution, by measuring the volume of oxygen evolved when it was allowed to decompose when dissolved in carbon tetrachloride.

Many reactions appear to be unimolecular when investigated under given conditions, though they are not actually so, and are termed

pseudo-unimolecular reactions. Many of these are gas reactions which only take place at the surface of a catalyst. (See § 9 for discussion of the phenomena of catalysis.) The walls of the vessel often behave as such a catalyst, in which case the reaction is called *a wall-reaction*, and measurements then frequently indicate a unimolecular reaction where, in fact, the reaction is of another order. (This is further explained in § 9.) In the case of nitrogen pentoxide this point has been investigated and it has been shown that a wall-reaction is not involved.

The fact that the decomposition of nitrogen pentoxide is unimolecular, whereas our equation for the reaction would show it to be of the second order raises an interesting point. It is evident that two consecutive reactions are involved, one of which is much slower than the other. Whenever we make measurements of reaction velocity in cases where a series of reactions is involved, it is clear that the actual speed observed will be that of the slowest of the reactions occurring. In the case of nitrogen pentoxide, it is likely that the reaction measured is: $N_2O_5 \rightarrow N_2O_4 + O$, which is followed by the very much faster reaction

$$O + O \rightarrow O_2$$

This is an example of the way in which measurements of reaction velocity assist in the elucidation of the mechanism of reactions.

Pseudo-unimolecular reactions have been referred to above, and one type, viz., wall-reactions, mentioned. Another important type of pseudo-unimolecular reaction is that in which one of the reacting substances is present in a concentration relatively so large that its concentration does not change appreciably during the course of the reaction. A case in point, which has been much investigated and which may be mentioned, although it belongs strictly to the study of organic chemistry, is the hydrolysis of esters such as methyl acetate. This reaction is represented by the equation :

$$CH_3COOCH_3 + H_2O \rightleftharpoons CH_3COOH + CH_3OH.$$

When carried out in dilute solution this reaction appears to obey the unimolecular law since the amount of water present is too large to have its concentration appreciably affected by the reaction. This, incidentally is the principle underlying method (iii) mentioned above for determining the order of a reaction.

Bimolecular Reactions

Bimolecular reactions are found to be by far the most common type —reactions of a higher order than 2 are found to be rare.

The decomposition of ozone into oxygen is an example of a bimolecular reaction ; and the reaction between hydrogen and iodine vapour, like the reverse reaction, is a straightforward bimolecular change, as would be expected from the equation :

$$H_2 + I_2 \rightleftharpoons 2HI.$$

This reaction was extensively investigated by Bodenstein, whose results indicated that both reactions are indeed bimolecular. The calculations involved are rather more complicated than those given in § 7 since the reaction is a reversible one so that the velocities in both directions must be taken into consideration. It can be shown, however, that the velocity constant for the decomposition of hydrogen iodide, at a given temperature, can be calculated from a knowledge of the amount of hydrogen iodide decomposed in a given time, and the amount decomposed at equilibrium. Similar considerations apply also to the combination of hydrogen and iodine.

The hydrolysis of organic esters (e.g., ethyl acetate) by sodium hydroxide is an example of a straightforward, irreversible bimolecular reaction. The equation for it is :

$$CH_3COOC_2H_5 + NaOH = CH_3COONa + C_2H_5OH.$$

As the reaction proceeds, caustic soda is used up and so, by determining how much of it remains at stated intervals, the rate of reaction can be measured. For this purpose a dilute solution of ethyl acetate is mixed with an equivalent quantity of sodium hydroxide solution (so that the simplified form of the equation for the velocity of the reaction may be employed) and kept at constant temperature in a thermostat. Measured volumes of the mixture are withdrawn at stated intervals, mixed immediately with excess of standard acid (to stop the reaction) and then titrated back with standard alkali. The amount of alkali used is thus known, and hence the quantity of ester decomposed can be calculated.

Some results obtained in an experiment of this kind are given in Table XX, which shows clearly that the bimolecular equation is being obeyed and not the unimolecular.

TABLE XX.—HYDROLYSIS OF ETHYL ACETATE.

Time (in minutes).	x	$\frac{1}{t} \log_e \frac{a}{a-x}$ (unimolecular).	$\frac{1}{at} \cdot \frac{x}{a-x}$ (bimolecular).
5	5·76	0·0893	0·0070
15	9·87	0·0640	0·0067
25	11·68	0·0524	0·0069
35	12·59	0·0442	0·0066
55	13·69	0·0352	0·0067

$a = 16·00$ gm.-mols.

§ 9 Catalysis

We have seen that the speed at which a chemical reaction proceeds depends upon the physical conditions (i.e., temperature and pressure) under which it takes place, and also upon the concentration of the reacting substances. It is also affected, sometimes to a large extent, by the presence of small quantities of foreign substances ; that is to say, of substances which do not appear in the equation for the reaction, and which can be recovered unchanged chemically after the reaction is over. Such substances are called **catalysts** or **catalytic agents** and the general phenomenon of the alteration of the speed of reactions by the presence of catalytic agents is termed **catalysis.** A **catalyst** may thus be defined as **a substance which, when present in comparatively small amount, influences the speed of a chemical reaction without itself undergoing any permanent change in quantity or chemical composition.** Catalysis is generally taken to include the retardation of a reaction, as well as its acceleration, though the more familiar and more practically important cases of catalysis concern the increase in speed.

The usually accepted criteria of catalysis are due to Ostwald and are :—

(i) The catalyst must remain unchanged in amount and in chemical composition at the end of the reaction ;

(ii) only a small amount of catalyst is necessary to produce a measurable effect ;

(iii) the catalyst cannot start a reaction, but only alters the speed of the reaction ; it does not alter the final state of equilibrium in a reversible reaction ;

(iv) in a reversible reaction, the catalyst alters the speeds of the forward and back reactions to the same extent.

(The considerations discussed in the earlier sections of this chapter indicate that (iv) is a necessary consequence of (iii).)

These criteria are sometimes true only with certain restrictions or reservations. Thus the requirement that the catalyst should remain unchanged only applies to the chemical composition ; in many cases it manifestly does not apply to the *physical* condition. Thus, for example, if in the preparation of oxygen from potassium chlorate using manganese dioxide as a catalyst (see p. 297) the manganese dioxide is in the form of small lumps to begin with, it will be found to have become disintegrated to a fine powder in the course of the reaction. Similarly, in the oxidation of ammonia to nitric acid, using platinum as catalyst (see p. 407) a smooth platinum surface is found to have become roughened.

The criterion that only a small quantity of catalyst is necessary is usually sound. In fact, the minute quantity of catalyst which will on occasion produce a marked effect is one of the most striking characteristics of catalytic phenomena. Thus, in the absence of catalysts, the oxidation of solutions of sodium sulphite by oxygen takes place only slowly (see p. 568). But in the presence of minute traces of copper the speed of the reaction is noticeably increased. Thus, for example, a concentration of copper ions of only 0·0000000636 gm. per litre can be readily detected, and even allowing the water from which the sodium sulphite solution is made up to stand in contact with a copper vessel for 45 seconds, is sufficient to produce a measurable increase in the rate of oxidation.

There has been a good deal of controversy as to whether a catalyst can or cannot initiate a reaction. Many reactions, so far as we can judge, do in fact seem to be started by a catalyst, as, for example, some of the observations of Baker on the catalytic influence of water mentioned on page 284. This work seems to show that many reactions cannot take place at all in the absence of water. This objection has been answered by the assumption that such reactions are in fact proceeding, but infinitely slowly. The distinction, however, between a reaction which is proceeding infinitely slowly, and one which is not going at all, is clearly of theoretical interest only, and for purely practical purposes may be ignored. Or as P. Duhem has said : " it comes to the same thing experimentally whether we say that the velocity of a reaction is absolutely null, or that it is so small that there is no way of detecting it."

Again, there are cases where reactions give different products with different catalysts. Thus, alcohol, in presence of nickel decomposes into acetaldehyde and hydrogen ; whereas in contact with alumina ethylene and water are formed. Similarly, carbon monoxide and hydrogen in presence of copper give formaldehyde ; with chromic oxide, methyl alcohol ; while in presence of nickel, methane and water result. Thus it appears that catalytic agents can not only start, accelerate or retard the speed of chemical reactions, but they can also in some cases direct or determine the course of a reaction.

The phenomena of catalysis are usually considered under two main headings, viz., homogeneous catalysis, and heterogeneous catalysis.

Cases of homogeneous catalysis are those in which the catalyst is not separated from the reacting mixture by a surface. Thus, the commonest examples of this type are those of the catalysis of reactions in solution where the catalysts are also soluble. A typical example is the acceleration of the hydrolysis of ethyl acetate by the presence of a small quantity of a strong acid such as hydrochloric acid. The addition of the acid causes a very large increase in the rate of hydrolysis. As an example of homogeneous catalysis in the vapour phase, mention may be made of the fact that carbon monoxide and oxygen will not combine unless a trace of water vapour is present. (Compare p. 284.)

In heterogeneous catalysis, the catalyst is separated from the reacting mixture by boundary surfaces. Important examples are the manufacture of sulphur trioxide from sulphur dioxide and oxygen in the presence of platinum (see p. 466) ; and the production of ammonia by the combination of nitrogen and hydrogen in presence of ferric oxide and traces of molybdenum (see p. 390).

§ 10 Types of Catalyst

It is probable that almost all reactions are capable of being catalyzed, and that almost all substances can act as catalysts for some reaction or other. There are, however, certain types of substances which exhibit catalytic power to a greater degree. These may be classified as follows :—

(i) Substances readily oxidizable and then easily converted back to their original condition ;

(ii) Hydrogen ions ;

(iii) Water ;

(iv) Metals : in particular those of Group VIII of the Periodic Table.

The mechanism of these actions probably varies from case to case, but, in the main, it seems as though the action is to be ascribed to one or other of two main classes, viz. :

(i) The formation of unstable intermediate compounds ;

(ii) the formation of a " condensed " layer of high concentration of reacting substances on the surface of the catalyst.

Considering now the types of catalyst mentioned above in the light of these ideas, we can attempt to find an explanation of the action in individual cases.

(i) Readily oxidizable compounds probably owe their effectiveness to the formation of intermediate compounds. An example of this type of catalysis is the decomposition of solutions of hypochlorites in the presence of cobalt oxide, whereby oxygen is evolved (see p. 509). The equation for this reaction is simply (in the case of sodium hypochlorite) :

$$2NaOCl = 2NaCl + O_2,$$

but it is probable that the cobaltous hydroxide which is present in the mixture is oxidized to cobaltic hydroxide by the hypochlorite, and this being unstable readily loses oxygen, so reverting to the cobaltous condition, when the process is repeated :

$$2Co(OH)_2 + NaOCl + H_2O = 2Co(OH)_3 + NaCl$$
$$2Co(OH)_3 = 2Co(OH)_2 + O + H_2O$$
$$O + O = O_2$$

Another example of this type of catalysis, and one of great industrial importance, is found in the manufacture of sulphuric acid by the chamber process in which the oxidation of the sulphur dioxide is catalyzed by the presence of oxides of nitrogen (see p. 463).

(ii) Hydrogen ion is a most efficient catalyst in many reactions. The acceleration of the hydrolysis of ethyl acetate by the addition of hydrochloric acid mentioned above is an example of this, since all acids behave similarly and the common constituent of these is (on the Ionization Theory) the hydrogen ion. The precise mechanism of this action is not known with certainty, though Brønsted and his collaborators have met with a certain measure of success in the correlation of the catalytic effect of ions in general with modern views of valency. The subject is too advanced, however, for discussion here.

(iii) Water is apparently almost, if not quite, the universal catalyst. The majority of reactions appear to be retarded enormously, if not prevented altogether by the intensive drying of the reacting substances. Very numerous examples of this effect are now known, chiefly through the work of H. B. Baker, and the whole subject is discussed in some detail in Chapter XVIII (p. 284) in the section on Water.

(iv) Metals. Whatever may be the explanation of the catalytic activity of the substances referred to in (i), (ii) and (iii) above (and it is quite possible that in many cases intermediate compounds are formed) the large group of catalysts comprised under the heading of metals can hardly be thought to act in this way. Certain metals, such as platinum, nickel, and iron are very effective catalysts, especially where hydrogen is concerned, and many of the examples of catalysis involving their use are of great technical importance.

The most probable explanation of this behaviour is thought to be connected with the fact that these metals have the power of absorbing or adsorbing* large volumes of gases. It is believed that the gases contained in a reacting mixture are condensed on the surface of the metal in a layer one molecule thick ; the local concentrations of the reacting substances being thus greatly increased and hence the rate of reaction.

That this is the *basis* of the effect seems highly probable, but that it is not the whole explanation seems equally certain. Thus, the acceleration of some reactions is too great to be accounted for in this way, although the fact that the greater the *surface* area of the catalyst, the greater the effect, shows that this is important.

Again, the fact that different catalysts can bring about the formation of different products from the same reacting substances seems very difficult to explain.

The observation that the occurrence of wall-reactions causes reactions of higher order than one to appear unimolecular (pseudo-unimolecular reactions) referred to in § 8 can now be understood. For, if the reaction is only taking place on the surface of the walls of the vessel or other catalyst, the active mass of the reacting substance is that in the layer adsorbed on the surface of the catalyst. When all the adsorbing area is covered, the rate of reaction will not be proportional to the pressure of the gas, and hence the true order of the reaction is obscured. Below a certain value of the pressure, of course, the rate of reaction will be such as to indicate truly the order of the reaction ; for all the adsorbing surface will not be covered. But in general this condition is not observed.

---

* An increase in the concentration or condensation of matter on a surface is called *adsorption*.

Among important examples of catalysis by metals, may be mentioned the following :—

(i) combination of hydrogen and oxygen in presence of platinum (see p. 258) ;

(ii) combination of sulphur dioxide and oxygen to form sulphur trioxide in presence of platinum. (Contact Process for sulphuric acid, p. 466);

(iii) combination of nitrogen and hydrogen to form ammonia in presence of iron. (Haber process, p. 390) ;

(iv) oxidation of ammonia to nitric acid in presence of platinum (p. 407) ;

(v) the hardening of oils by hydrogenation in presence of finely divided nickel ; used in the margarine and soap industries.

The last four are of great technical importance, being the basis of large industries, and the industrial applications of catalysis are constantly being increased. Several of these are referred to again in later chapters.

Promoters

It has been found that in some cases of catalysis, the addition of yet another substance, which of itself has no catalytic activity, causes an increase in the effectiveness of a catalyst already present. The effect might be called " the catalysis of a catalyst." A case in point is the addition of various oxides to the iron used as catalyst in the Haber process for the synthesis of ammonia (see p. 391). This effect is usually found in the case of solid catalysts, and the added substance is known as a **promoter**. The way in which promoters act is uncertain, though the effect may be partly due to an increase in the adsorption of the reacting substances ; but the effect cannot be wholly explained in this way.

Catalysis in general must be regarded as a term which covers a group of phenomena of many and various kinds, having only in common the fact that the speed of a reaction has been changed by the presence of " foreign " substances. It is unlikely, therefore, that any single explanation can be found for so many diverse effects.

CHAPTER XV

THE APPLICATION OF THE LAW OF MASS ACTION TO ELECTROLYTES

The evidence is so unambiguous and convincing that ions and some molecules combine with more or less of the solvent, that it seems that it can now be accepted as a fact of science.—H. C. JONES.

§ 1 Ostwald's Dilution Law

ACCORDING to the Electrolytic Dissociation Theory of Arrhenius an electrolyte in solution at moderate dilutions consists of a system in equilibrium, viz., the undissociated substance and its ions. As such, its behaviour should be in conformity to the Law of Mass Action.

Thus suppose we have the substance AB undergoing ionization in solution, we have, according to Arrhenius, the equilibrium

$$AB \rightleftharpoons A^{\cdot} + B'$$

and if we apply the Law of Mass Action it follows (using the same notation as previously) that :

$$\frac{C_A. \times C_{B'}}{C_{AB}} = k$$

The constant k is then known as the *ionization constant*.

Suppose that we have 1 gram-molecule of electrolyte in v litres of solution, and that the degree of dissociation (compare Ch. XII, § 6) is a. Then, at equilibrium, the amount of non-ionized electrolyte will be $(1 — a)$ gram-molecules and of each of the ions a gram-molecules. Substituting in the above expression we then have

$$\frac{\frac{a}{v} \cdot \frac{a}{v}}{\frac{1 — a}{v}} = k$$

That is,

$$\frac{a^2}{(1 — a)v} = k$$

The application of the Law of Mass Action in this way was first suggested by Ostwald and the expression so deduced is the mathematical form of what is known as **Ostwald's Dilution Law.**

The experimental testing of this expression was at once undertaken, and a large number of organic acids was investigated from this point of view by Ostwald himself, while Bredig examined a number of bases. As a result, the law was found to hold excellently for *slightly ionized* (or *weak*) electrolytes, but to be very wide of the mark for *highly ionized* (or *strong*) electrolytes.

This failure of the Law of Mass Action in this form to apply to any but weak electrolytes has caused much attention to be directed to the revision of the Ionic Theory, since the consistent success of the Law of Mass Action in every other field in which it has been tested makes it very improbable that it is at fault. This matter has been referred to in Chapter XII, § 9, where an outline of the attempts to surmount the difficulty has been given.

§ 2 Solubility Product

Although the exact quantitative application of the Law of Mass Action to electrolytes in solution is somewhat limited in scope, we are able, nevertheless, to use the law in the elucidation of many of the phenomena connected with precipitation, and the behaviour of mixed electrolytes.

Let us consider first the state of affairs existing in a *saturated* solution of an electrolyte AB which ionizes thus :

$$AB \rightleftharpoons A^{\cdot} + B'$$

The solution is now in equilibrium both with the solid and with the ions formed, i.e.,

$$AB \rightleftharpoons AB \rightleftharpoons A^{\cdot} + B'$$
$$\text{solid} \quad \text{saturated} \atop \text{solution}$$

Now the Law of Mass Action applied to the ions gives the expression :

$$\frac{C_A . C_{B'}}{C_{AB}} = k$$

Now, in a solution, if by any means the concentration of either ion be increased, the equilibrium is disturbed and the concentration of un-dissociated salt will be increased also ; when, as in the case under discussion, the solution is already saturated, this means that the solution will tend to become over-saturated, and hence some solid will be precipitated. This is in agreement with experiment, for it is found that the solubility of a salt is usually diminished in the presence of another compound with a common ion. Further, in a saturated solution, at a given temperature, the concentration of undissociated salt is constant, hence the expression given above may be rewritten

$$C_A . C_{B'} = k \, C_{AB}$$
$$= S$$

where S is a new constant which is called the **Solubility Product** of the substance. We see, too, that a condition for saturation of a solution is that the product of the concentrations of the ions should be equal to the solubility product.

Familiar examples of this phenomenon are the precipitation of sodium or potassium chlorides from saturated solutions by passing hydrogen chloride through the solutions, or by adding a concentrated aqueous solution of the acid. The phenomenon is quite general. Barium chloride may be substituted for sodium chloride; again, nitric acid will precipitate barium nitrate from concentrated aqueous solutions; a nearly saturated solution of silver bromate will give a precipitate of silver bromate, if either silver nitrate or sodium bromate be added to the solution; sodium chlorate added to a saturated solution of potassium chlorate will lead to the precipitation of the last-named salt.

§ 3 Application to Qualitative Analysis. Precipitation

These conclusions enable us to understand the reasons for many of the operations of ordinary qualitative analysis, in which identification and separation of the different substances present depends to a large extent on their solubility (or precipitation) relationships.

A substance is precipitated from solution when that solution tends to become supersaturated; or, in the light of the preceding section, when the product of the concentration of its ions tends to exceed the solubility product.

Now suppose we have a normal solution of silver nitrate and add to it an equal amount of a normal solution of hydrochloric acid. There will be an immediate formation of a precipitate of silver chloride. The reason for this is now clear. The silver nitrate and the hydrochloric acid are both highly ionized substances and so there will be, in their respective solutions, concentrations of silver ion and of chloride ion of something approximating to one gram-ion per litre. The mixed solutions would therefore contain about 0·5 gram-ion per litre of each. The product of these concentrations thus is:

$$C_{Ag}.C_{Cl'} = 0.25,$$

whereas the solubility product of silver chloride is only $1·7 \times 10^{-16}$. Hence the immediate, and virtually complete precipitation of silver chloride.

The separation of the metals into groups in qualitative analysis depends upon the different solubilities of their sulphides in different circumstances. Thus, one group comprises metals whose sulphides are precipitated in acid solution (e.g., copper and cadmium), whereas others (e.g., zinc and manganese) are only precipitated as sulphides in alkaline solution. The reason for this behaviour can be understood in the light of the foregoing.

In a saturated solution of hydrogen sulphide, there will be a certain concentration of sulphide and of hydrogen ions related according to the expression:

$$\frac{C_{H}^{2}.\ C_{S''}}{C_{H_2}} = k,$$

the actual concentrations of the ions being small since hydrogen sulphide is only feebly ionized in solution (cf. § 4 below). The addition of hydrochloric acid to this solution will cause a large increase in hydrogen ion concentration, since hydrochloric acid is highly ionized in solution. In order to maintain the equilibrium, therefore, the concentration of sulphide ions must be diminished, that is to say, the ionization of the hydrogen sulphide is driven back. In fact, the concentration of sulphide ions in a saturated solution of hydrogen sulphide is approximately 10^{-8} gram-ion per litre in absence of hydrochloric acid ; whereas in the presence of twice normal hydrochloric acid it is only 10^{-20} gram-ion per litre.

Now suppose we have a solution containing soluble salts of copper, cadmium, and manganese, each of about "normal" concentration. The solubility products of the sulphides of these metals are, approximately :

Copper sulphide	$8 \cdot 5 \times 10^{-45}$
Cadmium sulphide	$3 \cdot 6 \times 10^{-29}$
Manganese sulphide	$1 \cdot 4 \times 10^{-15}$

The concentration of copper ion in a normal solution will be slightly less than 1 gram-ion per litre since the copper salt will not be completely dissociated at this concentration. The concentration of sulphide ion in presence of hydrochloric acid is, as we have seen, approximately 10^{-20} gram-ion per litre. So that, if we add hydrochloric acid to the solution of the copper salt and then saturate the solution with hydrogen sulphide, we have

$$C_{Cu^{..}} \times C_{S''} = 10^{-20}$$

a number many times larger than the solubility product of copper sulphide, which is therefore precipitated.

A similar value would result for the product of the concentrations of the metal ions and sulphides in the case of solutions of salts of the other metals named. In the case of cadmium sulphide the solubility product is exceeded and so it is precipitated ; but the solubility product of the sulphide of manganese is not reached so that it is not precipitated.

Similar considerations explain why the hydroxides of iron, chromium and aluminium are precipitated by the addition of a solution of ammonia to solutions of salts of these metals to which ammonium chloride solution has been added, whereas the hydroxides of manganese, cobalt, nickel, zinc, calcium, etc., are not precipitated.

The common-ion effect which is involved in the above explanations also applies in the reverse way in the solution of precipitates in some cases. For example, just as in the equilibrium,

$$\underset{\text{solid}}{AB} \rightleftharpoons \underset{\substack{\text{saturated} \\ \text{solution}}}{AB} \rightleftharpoons A^{\cdot} + B'$$

the addition of a solution of a substance giving the ions $A^{\cdot}$ or B' will cause precipitation, the addition of any solution causing removal of

$A^{.}$ or B' by forming non-ionized, but soluble, salts will bring about solution of some of the solid AB.

As an example, we may take the case of a solution of a magnesium salt. The addition of ammonia solution will cause the precipitation of magnesium hydroxide. If now we add excess of a strong solution of ammonium chloride, the large increase in the concentration of ammonium ions which results (ammonium chloride being largely dissociated at moderate dilutions) drives back the dissociation of the ammonium hydroxide, and hence, reduces the concentration of hydroxyl ions to a very small value. The equilibrium :

$$Mg(OH)_2 \rightleftharpoons Mg(OH)_2 \rightleftharpoons Mg^{..} + OH' + OH'$$
$$\text{solid} \qquad \text{saturated}$$
$$\text{solution}$$

is thereby upset and some, if not all, the magnesium hydroxide will dissolve again.

Another related phenomenon is the solution of precipitates by the addition of a soluble substance which can form a *complex ion* with ions derived from the precipitate. A familiar example is the solution of a silver chloride precipitate in aqueous ammonia. This is due to the fact that silver ions will combine with ammonia to form a complex ion $[Ag(NH_3)_2]^{.}$ and the equilibrium

$$Ag^{.} + 2NH_3 \rightleftharpoons [Ag(NH_3)_2]^{.}$$

lies far over to the right-hand side ; that is to say, at equilibrium there are very few silver ions ($Ag^{.}$) left in the solution. A precipitate of silver chloride in contact with water maintains the equilibrium

$$AgCl \rightleftharpoons AgCl \rightleftharpoons Ag^{.} + Cl'$$
$$\text{solid} \quad \text{saturated}$$
$$\text{solution}$$

and although, owing to its very low solubility product, the concentration of silver ions is low, it is yet much greater than that at equilibrium with argentammonium ion, so that addition of ammonia causes silver chloride to go into solution again.

A similar fact is made use of sometimes in separating copper from cadmium in qualitative analysis, by addition of excess of potassium cyanide solution. Complex ions are formed which are in equilibrium with only small concentrations of the simple metal ions ; but whereas the complex ion formed from copper is in equilibrium with only a very small concentration of copper ions, that from cadmium requires a considerable concentration of cadmium ion for equilibrium. The result is that the concentration of copper ion is so low that on passing hydrogen sulphide into the solution, the very small solubility product of copper sulphide is not exceeded and so no precipitation results. In the case of cadmium, however, the cadmium ion is present in sufficiently high concentration for the solubility product of cadmium sulphide to be exceeded and so it is precipitated.

§ 4 Strengths of Acids and Bases

Many definitions of an acid have been given (see for example Ch. XVIII, § 9) but from the point of view of the Ionic Theory an **acid** is defined as **a substance which when dissolved in water** (or an ionizing solvent) **furnishes hydrogen ions as the only positive ion.** A **base** similarly, in terms of the Ionic Theory, is **a substance which yields hydroxyl ions as the only negative ion, when dissolved in an ionizing solvent (usually water).** The general and characteristic properties of acids are thus those of hydrogen ions, and those of bases are the properties due to hydroxyl ions.

These conceptions give us a means of investigating the problem of the *strengths* of acids and bases. We say that sulphuric acid, for example, is a strong acid, and that acetic acid is a weak one, since the former will attack more substances (particularly metals) with greater vigour than the latter. But this criterion is vague, arbitrary and often misleading. As shown below, the Ionic Theory (in conjunction with the Law of Mass Action) furnishes us with a criterion applicable to a great many cases, and giving results in harmony with other methods.

The action of sulphuric acid on sodium chloride (p. 499), which results in the formation of hydrochloric acid, seems to prove that sulphuric acid is stronger than hydrochloric acid ; but when hydrochloric acid is added to a solution of silver sulphate, silver chloride is precipitated. The hydrochloric acid expels the sulphuric acid from its combination with silver :·

$$Ag_2SO_4 + 2HCl = 2AgCl + H_2SO_4,$$

and it seems as if hydrochloric acid is stronger than sulphuric acid. These two conclusions are contradictory and there must therefore be a fallacy in our reasoning. We have wrongly assumed that the two acids were competing for sodium and for silver under similar conditions. This is not the case. When hydrochloric and sulphuric acids compete for the sodium, the hydrochloric acid, being volatile, escapes from the system as fast as it is formed ; while the non-volatile sulphuric acid alone remains behind. Again, when sulphuric and hydrochloric acids are competing for silver, the hydrochloric acid carries the silver away from the sulphuric acid as an insoluble precipitate of silver chloride.

To compare the relative strengths of the acids, and, *mutatis mutandis*, of the bases, it is necessary that the comparison be made under conditions where the reacting acids and the products of the reaction are in the same physical condition —say, all in solution. Thus, if an equivalent of a solution of sodium hydroxide be mixed with an equivalent of a solution of sulphuric and of hydrochloric acids, the two acids can compete for the one base under the same conditions, and hence the stronger acid will be able to unite with more sodium than the weaker acid. In 1803, C. L. Berthollet pointed out that when a neutral salt is dissolved and an acid is added to the solution, the free acid enters into competition with the combined acid, and they both act on the alkali base in the ratio of their respective concentrations as though no combination had existed. It cannot therefore be said that if all the conditions remain equal, one acid displaces another from the base with which it had been united, but the base is shared between the two acids. The proportion in which it is so shared depends upon the concentrations of the respective acids as well as their strengths in the sense in which that word is used in this section.

It is found experimentally that the same result is obtained when equivalent quantities of sodium hydroxide, sulphuric acid, and hydrochloric acid are mixed together, as when equivalent quantities of sodium sulphate and hydrochloric acid, or equivalent quantities of sodium chloride and sulphuric acid, are mixed, provided, of course, the whole of the system has been allowed to stand long enough for equilibrium.

The proportions of a base shared between two acids, or of an acid between two bases, cannot be determined by the ordinary methods of chemical analysis without disturbing the equilibrium of the mixture. The distribution of an acid between two bases, or of a base between two acids, must be determined by physical processes which do not interfere with the solution. In illustration, the equivalent heat of neutralization of sodium hydroxide by sulphuric acid is 15·69 Cals. ; and by hydrochloric acid, 13·74 Cals. If, therefore, on mixing hydrochloric acid with sodium sulphate, all the sulphuric acid were displaced by the hydrochloric acid, the thermal effect resulting from the decomposition of the sodium sulphide, and the formation of the sodium chloride would be 13·74 — 15·69 = — 1·95 Cals. After making a small allowance for secondary reactions between sodium sulphate and sulphuric acid, J. Thomsen found that the thermal value of the reaction was —1·3 Cals. Hence it follows that — 1·3 ÷ — 1·95 or about two-thirds of the hydrochloric acid combines with about two-thirds of the base to form sodium chloride ; and about one-third of the sulphuric acid combines with the other third of the base to form sodium sulphate. A similar result was obtained with a mixture of sodium chloride and sulphuric acid as with sodium sulphate and hydrochloric acid. Consequently, in the competition of sulphuric and hydrochloric acids for sodium under comparable conditions, the hydrochloric acid can hold twice as much of the base as the sulphuric acid; and consequently, hydrochloric acid is nearly twice as strong as sulphuric acid.

Similar results have been obtained by measuring the specific gravity, index of refraction, absorption of light, etc. The relative strengths of the different acids have also been determined by measuring the effects of the different acids on the speed of hydrolysis of cane sugar, methyl acetate, etc.

From the point of view of the Ionic Theory, the strength of an acid is related to the extent to which it furnishes hydrogen ions in stated circumstances, that is to the concentration of hydrogen ions in solution. The concentration of hydrogen ions depends upon the degree of ionization of the different acids. Hence the relative strengths of the acids can presumably be expressed in terms of the electrical conductivity of equivalent solutions. The speed of a reaction dependent upon an acid is thus connected with the concentration of the $H^{\cdot}$ ions. In hydrochloric acid, a greater number of hydrogen ions are ready to react with the metal than with acetic acid, and consequently the available hydrogen in hydrochloric acid is more rapidly exhausted than with acetic acid, where but few ions are in a condition to react with the metal at any moment, and consequently the reaction progresses slowly for a long time.

Hence hydrochloric acid is a stronger acid than acetic. On the assumption that the order of strength of acids is the same as that of the conductivities at corresponding dilution, we find that hydrochloric and nitric acids are of approximately equal strength and are both stronger than sulphuric acid. This is indicated in the last column of Table XXI, which table shows the order of strengths of acids as deduced by several independent methods.

TABLE XXI.—RELATIVE STRENGTHS OF ACIDS.

	Thomsen's Thermal Method.	Specific Gravity Method.	Ester Hydrolysis Method.	Conductivity Method.
Hydrochloric Acid .	100	100	100	100
Nitric Acid . .	100	100	91·5	99·6
Hydrobromic Acid .	89	97	—	100
Sulphuric Acid .	49	68	54·7	65·1
Phosphoric Acid .	13	—	—	7·3
Acetic Acid . .	3	1·25	0·35	0·4

Hydrochloric acid has been taken as the standard of reference in this table and its strength arbitrarily called 100. The figures for the other acids thus express their strengths as percentages of that of hydrochloric acid.

This table shows that the results obtained by the different methods, although not in exact quantitative agreement, are yet sufficiently close to show that the order of strengths is consistent and that the relative strengths of these acids are very close to the values derived from any of these criteria. The discrepancies between them may be due to differences in the conditions under which the different determinations were made.

Similar results have been obtained from investigations on bases, from which it has been found that sodium hydroxide and potassium hydroxide are strong bases, whereas ammonium hydroxide is a weak base whose strength is not much more than 10 per cent. of that of potassium hydroxide.

The Hydroxonium ion.—The correlation in the way just described of the strength of an acid with the concentration of hydrogen ions in the solution requires some modification in the light of the modern view that the ion which is really concerned is the hydroxonium ion $H_3O^{\cdot}$ as discussed on page 202.

One of the difficulties of the simple ionic theory of acids is that, on modern theory, for a substance to ionize it must be an electrovalent compound, whereas many acids when quite pure do not conduct electricity and hence must be presumed to be covalent compounds. Consequently, the fact that they give conducting solutions requires some further explanation.

This explanation is furnished by the conception that the ion formed is not $H^{\cdot}$, but $H_3O^{\cdot}$. For water is capable of co-ordination (Ch. IX) and can act as a donor by virtue of the lone pairs of the oxygen atom. Considering the case of hydrogen chloride, assumed to be a covalent compound (when pure it is a non-conductor), the oxygen of a water molecule can co-ordinate on to the hydrogen chloride molecule giving a " molecule " which can now ionize, one of the ions being the $H_3O^{\cdot}$ ion. This may be illustrated by the scheme :

$$
\begin{array}{c} H \\ \cdot\cdot \\ :\!\ddot{O}\!: \\ \cdot\cdot \\ H \end{array}
\;+\;
\begin{array}{c} H \\ \cdot\cdot \\ H:\!\ddot{C}l\!: \\ \cdot\cdot \end{array}
\;\rightarrow\;
\begin{array}{c} H \\ \cdot\cdot \\ :\!\ddot{O}\!:H:\!\ddot{C}l\!: \\ \cdot\cdot \quad \cdot\cdot \\ H \end{array}
\;\rightarrow\;
\left[\begin{array}{c} H \\ \cdot\cdot \\ :\!\ddot{O}:H \\ H \end{array}\right]^{\cdot}
\;+\;
\left[\begin{array}{c} \cdot\cdot \\ :\!\ddot{C}l\!: \\ \cdot\cdot \end{array}\right]'
$$

In general, therefore, the solution and ionization of a strong acid in water is to be represented by the equilibrium

$$ HA + H_2O \rightleftharpoons H_3O^{\cdot} + A' $$

and the phrase " hydrogen ion concentration " must be taken to refer to the $H_3O^{\cdot}$ or hydroxonium ion.

§ 5 Salt Hydrolysis

It might be expected that solutions of salts made by the combination of equivalent quantities of acid and base would show a neutral reaction (compare p. 242), but this is found in many cases not to be true. Thus, for example, although solutions of sodium chloride are neutral, as would be expected, solutions of potassium cyanide are alkaline, while those of ferric chloride are acid.

The nature of this effect depends upon the relative strengths of the acid and base from which the salt is made. Thus, sodium chloride is the salt of a strong acid and a strong base and is therefore neutral. On the other hand, hydrocyanic acid is a very weak acid and hence its potassium salt (potassium hydroxide being a strong base) is alkaline in solution. Similarly, ferric hydroxide being a weak base, its salt with the strong acid hydrochloric acid is acid in aqueous solution.

This behaviour of salts, known as salt hydrolysis, is due to the fact already noted in Chapter XII (p. 196) that water itself is very slightly dissociated into hydrogen and hydroxyl ions :

$$ H_2O \rightleftharpoons H^{\cdot} + OH' $$

the product of the concentrations of these ions being approximately 10^{-14}, i.e.,

$$ C_{H^{\cdot}} \times C_{OH'} = 10^{-14} $$

Now suppose that we have in solution a salt AB, being the salt resulting from the combination of the acid HA and the base BOH :

$$HA + BOH = AB + H_2O$$

Now the salt in solution will be largely ionized

$$AB \rightleftharpoons A\cdot + B'$$

so that the solution will contain a high concentration of $A\cdot$ ions and B' ions and a slight concentration of $H\cdot$ and OH' ions due to the ionization of the water. If the acid HA and the base BOH are both strong, nothing particular will happen for the equilibria :

$$HA \rightleftharpoons H\cdot + A'$$
$$BOH \rightleftharpoons B\cdot + OH'$$

will be such that large concentrations of ions are in equilibrium with very small concentrations of acid or base. But suppose that the acid HA is a weak acid, that is to say, it only dissociates to a very slight extent in solution. The circumstances resulting from the solution of a salt of such an acid will then momentarily involve the co-existence in the solution of $H\cdot$ ions along with a high concentration of A' ions, so the product of the two concentrations will largely exceed that required by the equilibrium relations of the acid, as defined by its dissociation constant, i.e.,

$$\frac{C_{H\cdot} \times C_{A'}}{C_{HA}} = \text{ionization constant (small for a weak acid)}$$

Accordingly hydrogen ions and A' ions will combine to form undissociated HA ; the equilibrium between the $H\cdot$ and OH' ions from the water is thereby upset, and more hydroxyl ions will be formed from the water to restore the equilibrium between the water and its ions. Hydroxyl ions will thus accumulate in the solution, which will therefore be alkaline.

A similar reasoning, *mutatis mutandis*, will show that the salt of a weak base with a strong acid will give an acid solution.

Neutralization (see p. 305), which may be represented by the equation :

$$HA + BOH = BA + H_2O$$

is, in one sense, the formation of a salt and water from an acid and a base. Hydrolysis is thus, in one sense, the formation of an acid and a base by the action of water on a salt :—

$$BA + H_2O = HA + BOH$$

and so is the reverse of neutralization. These facts may be conveniently summed up by combining these two equations into one :

$$\overset{\text{neutralization}}{HA + BOH \underset{\text{hydrolysis}}{\rightleftharpoons} BA + H_2O}$$

§ 6 Indicators

The action of acids and alkalis in changing the colour of litmus solutions is one of the familiar facts of elementary chemistry. Substances such as litmus, which change colour in this way, are known as *Indicators* and have been used to distinguish between these two groups of compounds at least since the time of Boyle.

Many natural colouring matters can be used for this purpose, the most important of which are **litmus,** obtained from certain lichens, and **turmeric** which is obtained from the root of an Indian plant (the same as is used in making curry). Litmus is turned red by acids and blue by alkalis, while turmeric is yellow in acid, and brown in alkaline solution.

Many synthetic organic dyes are now used as indicators; the most important of these are **methyl orange** (red with acids, yellow with alkalis) and **phenolphthalein** (colourless with acids, red with alkalis).

Indicators are largely employed, not only for distinguishing between acids and alkalis, but also for determining the neutral point when neutralizing acids with alkalis either for the preparation of salts, or in the quantitative operations of acidimetry and alkalimetry in volumetric analysis.

Theory of Indicators

According to Ostwald's theory of indicators these substances are weak acids, or weak bases, whose colour is different according as they are in the ionized or non-ionized condition. Thus according to Ostwald the behaviour of phenolphthalein which is a weak acid is to be represented:

$$\underset{\text{colourless}}{\text{HA}} \rightleftharpoons \underset{\underset{\text{red}}{\underbrace{\qquad\qquad}}}{\text{H}^{\cdot} + \text{A}'}$$

The addition of an acid will increase the concentration of hydrogen ions, so driving back the dissociation of the indicator which becomes colourless. Addition of an alkali reverses this process by removal of hydrogen ions. Similar considerations serve to explain the behaviour of an indicator, such as methyl orange, which is a weak base:

$$\underset{\text{yellow}}{\text{XOH}} \rightleftharpoons \underset{\underset{\text{red}}{\underbrace{\qquad\qquad}}}{\text{X}^{\cdot} + \text{OH}'}$$

It is now generally believed that this is not the whole story, since marked change of colour in organic chemistry betokens a change of structure. This difficulty is met by the assumption, now well justified, that in addition to the equilibrium between undissociated indicator and its ions, there is another equilibrium between two forms of the indicator itself. This is represented in the following scheme:

$$\underset{\text{yellow}}{\text{XHO}} \rightleftharpoons \underset{\text{red}}{\text{XOH}} \rightleftharpoons \underset{\underset{\text{red}}{\underbrace{\qquad\qquad}}}{\text{X}^{\cdot} + \text{OH}'}$$

applicable to methyl orange. The same principles, however, still serve to explain the effect of acid or alkali in causing the change of colour of an indicator as the two equilibria are inter-related and inter-dependent.

Choice of Indicator

Experiment has shown that an indicator changes colour when the hydrogen, or hydroxyl, ion concentration of the solution which contains it has reached a certain value, and that this value is different for different indicators. A knowledge of the value of the hydrogen ion concentration at which the colour change takes place is thus important, as it determines the choice of indicator for a particular operation.

This choice depends also upon the way in which the hydrogen ion concentration changes with the relative proportions of acid and alkali, and we must now consider this in typical cases.

Neutralization as we have seen is, according to the Ionic Theory, primarily the combination of hydrogen and hydroxyl ions to form water

$$HA \rightleftharpoons H^{\cdot} + A'$$
$$BOH \rightleftharpoons B^{\cdot} + OH'$$
$$H^{\cdot} + A' + B^{\cdot} + OH' = H_2O + B^{\cdot} + OH'$$

i.e.,
$$H^{\cdot} + OH' = H_2O$$

Strict neutrality is, therefore, achieved when the hydrogen and hydroxyl ion concentrations are equal (and equal accordingly to their values in pure water).

Now the value of the ionic product for water is constant in all aqueous solutions, at a given temperature, and approximately equal, as we have seen, to 10^{-14}:

$$C_{H^{\cdot}} \times C_{OH'} = 10^{-14}$$

At the neutral point, the $H^{\cdot}$ and OH' concentrations are equal:

i.e.,
$$C_{H^{\cdot}} = C_{OH'} = \sqrt{10^{-14}} = 10^{-7}$$

If the $H^{\cdot}$ concentration is greater than 10^{-7} the solution is acid; if it is less than 10^{-7} it is alkaline.

This important quantity, the concentration of hydrogen ions, is sometimes represented by the number in the index of the value of the concentration and is then described as the pH value. Thus a neutral solution (concentration of $H^{\cdot} = 10^{-7}$) has a $pH = 7$, and so on.

It might be thought from this that the indicator required for any titration or neutralization was one which changes colour when the pH value of the solution is 7. But a little consideration will show that this is not always the case. In the preceding section we saw that many salts are hydrolyzed in solution and that their solutions in consequence are not strictly neutral, but acid or alkaline according as the acid or base from which the salt was made was the stronger. Conversely, it follows that although chemically exactly equivalent quantities of an acid and a base have been mixed, the solution will only be neutral (i.e., have a pH value of 7) if acid and base were both equally strong. So that it follows that the choice of indicator for any particular titration is determined by the hydrogen ion concentration of the solution when chemically equivalent quantities of acid and base are present.

The concentration of $H^{\cdot}$ ions at which the common indicators mentioned above change colour are approximately as follows :—

litmus : 10^{-7}
methyl red : 10^{-5}
methyl orange : 10^{-4}
phenolphthalein : $10^{-8.5}$

From these figures we can derive the general rules indicated in Table XXII as to the choice of indicator for a particular titration :

TABLE XXII.—CHOICE OF INDICATORS.

For the titration of	Use, as indicator
Strong base and strong acid	Litmus
Weak base and strong acid	Methyl orange or methyl red
Strong base and weak acid	Phenolphthalein
Weak base and weak acid	None satisfactory

The fact given in the last line of the table is easily explained when it is remembered that the salt of a weak base and a weak acid is almost completely hydrolyzed in solution ; and that as the acid and base are both weak, at no point during such a titration will the hydrogen ion concentration be far removed from that corresponding to neutrality (i.e., 10^{-7}). Accordingly there is no sharp change in H· ion concentration, so that no indicator will show when equivalent quantities of acid and base are present, in these circumstances. The titration of a weak acid by a weak base is consequently a process to be avoided.

The conclusions summarized in Table XXII are also supported by investigations into the way in which the hydrogen ion concentration of a solution changes with the relative amounts of acid and base present in the neighbourhood of the equivalent point. The results of these investigations are summarized in the diagrams Figs. 83, 84, 85 and 86, which show the changes in pH value with the relative amount of acid and base for some typical cases.

The curve of Fig. 83 shows this relation for the titration of a strong base by a strong acid (as, for example, sodium hydroxide and hydrochloric acid). The long straight portion indicates that, in the neighbourhood of the equivalent

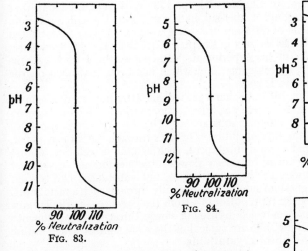

FIG. 83.

FIG. 84.

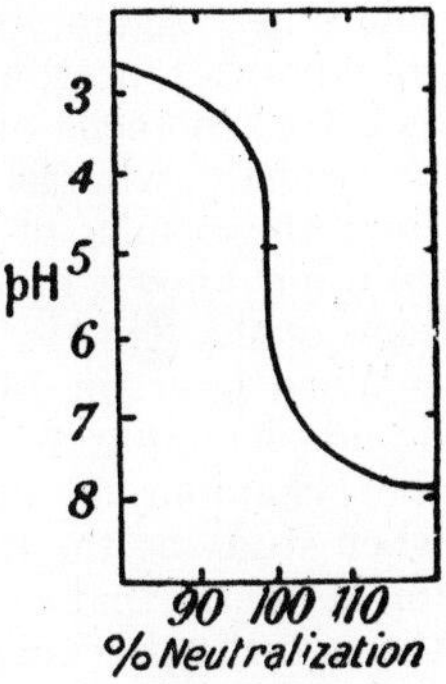

FIG. 85.

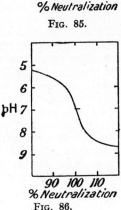

FIG. 86.

point, a very small excess of one or other reagent produces a very large change in the hydrogen ion concentration. Consequently, a suitable indicator will change colour very sharply, and as the straight portion of the curve extends over a wide range of pH values several indicators are available.

Fig. 84 shows the similar relation for the titration of a weak acid (such as acetic acid) with a strong base; and Fig. 85 that for the converse operation (strong acid, e.g., HCl and weak base, e.g., NH_4OH). In these the curve still has a considerable straight portion, but it is shorter than in Fig. 83. Also, the middle of the straight part (corresponding to equivalence) is displaced from a pH value of 7, and so an indicator whose colour change occurs at a pH different (in the appropriate sense) from 7 is required.

Fig. 86 shows the curve for a weak acid and a weak base, and the absence of a straight portion shows that no indicator will mark the end-point of this process. Titration of a weak acid by a weak base is thus to be avoided.

CHAPTER XVI

THE COLLOIDAL STATE

§ 1 Graham's Experiments

It has already been mentioned (Ch. X, p. 151) that intermediately between true solutions of solids in liquids and coarse suspensions, there exists a class of solid-liquid mixtures which are known as colloidal solutions. Again, in Chapter XI (p. 173) it was pointed out that soluble substances, like copper sulphate, can *diffuse* through a solution.

The phenomena of diffusion in general were extensively investigated by Graham, who, as we saw in Chapter II (p. 24), was able to deduce, from the results of his experiments with gases, the law of gaseous diffusion known by his name, and which has been confirmed on the basis of the Kinetic Theory.

When later (in 1861) Graham turned his attention to diffusion in liquids, he found that there was often a very marked difference between the behaviour of different substances. This he noticed particularly when studying the rate of diffusion of salts through parchment paper, for he found that certain substances, such as glue or gelatine, diffuse through the parchment only very slowly : the membrane* was almost entirely impervious to these substances, but substances like sodium chloride, or magnesium sulphate pass readily through such a membrane. Graham applied the term **colloids**—from the Greek κολλα (kolla) glue —to those substances which diffuse but slowly through the parchment ; and since crystalline salts are typical of those substances which diffuse rapidly, he called them **crystalloids.**

Subsequent experience has not upheld Graham's distinction between crystalloids and colloids as representing different kinds of substances ; for many substances can exist in either condition according to circumstances. In consequence, it is now usual to consider these as *states*, rather than as *types* of matter, and accordingly we speak of substances whose behaviour is that which Graham associated with colloidal substances, as being in the **colloidal state.** It is now known that, at any rate, in a great many cases, the determining factor is the size of the particles concerned.

§ 2 Suspensoids and Emulsoids

Colloidal solutions fall into one or other of two definite classes, each of which exhibits certain definite characteristics. These two categories are known as **suspensoids** and **emulsoids.**

* The membrane used in these experiments must be distinguished carefully from the semipermeable membranes used in osmotic pressure investigations, and which are impervious to dissolved solids of all kinds, allowing only the passage of solvent.

Colloidal solutions consist of particles of the substance in the colloidal state (intermediate in size between the molecules of the solute in true solutions and the particles of coarse suspensions which settle out rapidly when allowed to stand) dispersed in a liquid medium, usually water.   When the particles partake of the nature of solids, the solution is that of a **suspensoid** ; if the dispersed particles are droplets of liquid an **emulsoid** is formed.   Examples of suspensoids are arsenious sulphide, ferric oxide and gold ; and of emulsoids are gelatine and albumin.   In regard to viscosity and surface tension, colloidal solutions of suspensoids differ little if anything from water.   Their stability is due to their motion (the Brownian movement, see p. 248) and particularly to the fact that the particles are electrically charged (see § 4 below).   In the case of emulsoids, the viscosity is usually much greater than that of water, the surface tension lower, and the medium in which they are dispersed is taken up to a greater or less extent by the colloidal particles.   The stability of these solutions, therefore, depends to a considerable extent upon the nature of the medium in which they are dispersed and not so greatly upon the electrical charge on the particles as in the case of suspensoids.

§ 3 Preparation of Colloidal Solutions

Since many colloidal solutions are unstable in presence of electrolytes (being precipitated or coagulated thereby—see § 4 below) it is necessary, in their preparation, to remove electrolytes as far as possible, also to use very pure materials and clean apparatus.

The principal methods available are :

(i) Chemical precipitation, followed sometimes by *dialysis* (see below for explanation of this term).

(ii) Electrical dispersion, e.g., Bredig's arc method.

(iii) Mechanical dispersion.

Examples of the use of each of these methods will now be given.

Chemical Precipitation

When a very sparingly soluble substance is precipitated from a very dilute solution, in circumstances such that the solution is practically free from ions, a colloidal solution frequently results.   Thus, for example, if a cold, dilute solution of arsenic trioxide in water is saturated with hydrogen sulphide, and then filtered to remove such coarse particles as have been formed, a colloidal solution of arsenic sulphide is obtained.

$$As_2O_3 + 3H_2S = As_2S_3 + 3H_2O$$

Similarly, if very dilute solutions of salts of silver or gold are reduced by certain substances (as, for example, phosphorus in ether, or formaldehyde) the metal is not precipitated but remains suspended in a colloidal solution, which is usually highly coloured, due to scattering of the light by the minute particles of the metal.

In some cases, owing to the presence of ions, chemical precipitation gives the colloidal substance in a more or less coagulated condition, from which a colloidal solution can be obtained by removing the electrolyte present.   This is effected by the process known as **dialysis,** and which was proposed by Graham.   It makes use of the fact already referred to that substances in the colloidal state do not readily pass through parchment membranes. The operation is carried out in a piece of apparatus called a dialyser, and is illustrated in Fig. 87.

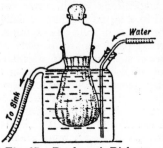

It consists of a parchment bag, containing the solution to be treated, immersed in a vessel through which a constant stream of water is kept running. Any non-colloidal substance (such as salt, or other electrolyte) will pass through the parchment and is carried away by the running water, while the colloidal substance remains.

The use of this method is exemplified by the preparation of a colloidal solution of ferric hydroxide, sometimes called " dialysed iron." A few drops of ammonia are added to a solution of ferric chloride, and a reddish-brown precipitate of ferric hydroxide is formed. This redissolves in the unchanged ferric chloride. When the solution of ferric

FIG. 87.—Proskauer's Dialyser.

chloride is saturated with the ferric hydroxide, any further addition of ammonia will give a permanent precipitate of ferric hydroxide. A few drops of hydrochloric acid are now added to dissolve the precipitated ferric hydroxide, and the solution is diluted with water so that it contains about 5 per cent. of solid in solution. This solution is poured into the dialyser, the soluble ferric chloride and ammonium chloride pass into the outer vessel, and a dark red liquid remains in the inner vessel. This dark red liquid is the colloidal solution of ferric hydroxide.

A colloidal solution of silicic acid can be prepared similarly (see p. 684).

Bredig's Arc Method

When it is desired to obtain a colloidal solution of a metal by this method, an arc is struck beneath the surface of the liquid, using poles of the required metal and keeping the liquid cold by means of ice.

This method is particularly applicable to the production of dilute colloidal solutions of silver or platinum in water. It is believed that the metal is first torn off the poles in the form of vapour and that the sudden condensation by the water causes it to remain in the colloidal state.

Mechanical Dispersion

Colloidal solutions can sometimes be made by fine grinding of the solid concerned. For example, indian ink is a rather coarse colloidal solution of " carbon " made by grinding lamp black with water and a little gum.

This principle has been extended recently in the use of the so-called " colloid mill." The substance which it is desired to get into colloidal solution is suspended as a coarse precipitate in water (or whatever liquid is to be used as the medium for the solution) and the whole is passed between two plates kept very close together and rotating in opposite directions at a speed of about 7,000 revolutions per minute. By this process, only a proportion of the solid is ground sufficiently fine to form a stable colloidal solution, so that, in time, the large particles settle out ; but a proportion is nevertheless reduced to particles of colloidal diameter.

§ 4 Properties of Colloidal Solutions

Colloidal solutions exhibit certain properties which are different in many respects from those of true solutions.

For example, colloidal solutions are not homogeneous, for a beam of light passed through such a solution is marked by a visibly luminous track, whereas a similar beam passing through water, or a true solution, is not as a rule visible in this way. This phenomenon is known as the

Tyndall effect. Furthermore the light coming from this track is polarized, so that it is evident that there are present in the system particles which are sufficiently large to cause the scattering of light, although they are too small to be seen directly, even with the aid of a powerful microscope. The ability of the particles of a colloidal solution to scatter light can be applied, however, to the problem of determining both their number and their size, as is described in § 5 below.

A remarkable fact about colloidal solutions is that their particles are electrically charged ; not that, as in the case of solutions of electrolytes, there are in a given solution equal numbers of particles of each electrical sign, but all the particles in a given solution are charged in the same sense. Also in some colloidal solutions the particles are always charged positively (for example, colloidal solutions of ferric hydroxide), whereas in others they are negatively charged (arsenic sulphide, for example). The existence of these charges is shown by the fact that if two electrodes, connected to a source of potential difference, are placed in a colloidal solution, the particles are found to move slowly towards one pole or the other, and by observing in which direction they move, the nature of the charge can be determined.

It is the existence of this charge which, to a large extent, keeps the particles of a colloidal solution dispersed through the medium with which they form a colloidal solution. For since all the particles in a given solution carry the same charge, they are prevented by the natural repulsion between like charges from coalescing and so forming larger particles which would " settle-out." Granted that the particles are of sufficiently small size, and that they are prevented from coalescing, they will be kept dispersed through the medium by the molecular motion of the medium—the phenomenon known as the **Brownian Movement** (see below).

As a consequence of the fact that the particles of a colloidal solution are prevented from coalescing by the electrical charges which they carry, it follows that any disturbance of the system which tends to neutralize these charges will cause coalescence, and hence precipitation. This accounts for the fact that addition of electrolytes to colloidal solutions frequently causes precipitation ; for the electrolyte furnishes ions of both signs, one or other kind of which, being opposite in sign to the charge on the colloid particles, will discharge them and hence cause precipitation. It is also in accord with this observation that *the efficiency of an ion as a coagulating agent is roughly proportional to its valency*, that is, to the number of charges it carries. This is known as the *Hardy-Schulze Law* and is illustrated by the following figures which give the concentration of typical electrolytes having monovalent, divalent and trivalent cations required to precipitate arsenious sulphide (Table XXIII).

TABLE XXIII.—PRECIPITATION OF ARSENIOUS SULPHIDE.

Electrolyte.	Concentration required (in gm.-mols. per litre × 10^{-3}).
NaCl	51·0
KCl	50·0
MgCl$_2$	◦0·72
BaCl$_2$	0·67
AlCl$_3$	0·093

It is to be noted that, as the particles in a colloidal solution of arsenious sulphide are negatively charged, it is the *cation* which is effective in causing coagulation and precipitation. In the case of a positively charged colloid, such as ferric hydroxide the efficiency of an electrolyte as precipitant depends upon the valency of the *anion*.

A further consequence of the differing sign of the charge on different colloidal particles is the fact that two colloidal solutions whose particles are oppositely charged will, when mixed, cause mutual precipitation. This is well illustrated by the action which takes place if suitable quantities of colloidal solutions of ferric hydroxide and arsenious sulphide are mixed. Both these solutions are coloured, but on allowing the mixture to stand the supernatant liquid becomes quite colourless if the proportions of the two solutions were correctly adjusted.

The Brownian Movement

If very fine particles of an insoluble solid are suspended in a liquid they are found, on examination, to be in a state of motion which is quite continuous. This phenomenon is known as the **Brownian Movement**, after R. Brown, the botanist, who first observed it in 1827. It can be observed with particles of microscopic size, such as those of gamboge or lycopodium, and the smaller the size of the particles, the brisker the motion becomes. The Kinetic Theory of molecular motion seems to furnish the only admissible explanation of the phenomenon. According to this theory, the perpetual movements of the molecules of the liquid result in these molecules continually striking the suspended particles, thus driving them irregularly to and fro in the liquid It would be expected, on this assumption, that, as is found to be the case, the movements become more and more vigorous as the size of the particles is diminished. Since colloidal particles are much too small, as a rule, to be seen directly under the microscope (see § 5), their motion, due to the Brownian movement, will be vigorous, and hence they show no tendency to settle out so long as they are prevented from coalescing into larger aggregates.

It is interesting to note that, using the assumptions of the Kinetic Theory, Einstein was able to calculate a relation between the m tion of a particle undergoing the Brownian movement and the Avogadro Number (the number of molecules in a gram-molecule—p. 78). This relation was used in the experiments of Perrin, and gave a value for

N in good agreement with that obtained by very different methods.

Gels

A concentrated colloidal solution will often set to a jelly when cooled, and pass back into a solution again on warming. A familiar example is afforded by a gelatine solution or a soap solution, and the process of forming a jelly and re-liquefaction by alternate cooling and warming can be repeated an indefinite number of times. A jelly of this kind is found to have a heterogeneous structure, often of a honeycomb type, the cells being occupied by viscous liquid, and is known as a **Gel**.

Gels are also obtainable, at times, by coagulation. Thus, for example, if a colloidal solution of ferric hydroxide, prepared as described on p. 246, be allowed to stand for some weeks in a glass vessel, a gelatinous solid is precipitated. Similar gels are obtained from silicic acid, and aluminium hydroxide, and like all gels they retain water very tenaciously, but when dried by the action of heat often exhibit the power of absorbing large quantities of water again. Some gels, such as silica-gel, differ from that of gelatine, for example, in that they do not liquefy again on warming, but otherwise the resemblance between the two types is close.

Colloids find many applications in industrial processes. Large quantities of silica-gel are manufactured for use as absorbents for gases, for which it is found to be as effective in many cases as charcoal. Its ability to absorb large quantities of water has been made use of, for example, for the purpose of drying the blast used in the smelting of iron (see p. 804). It also possesses the power of absorbing many substances from solution and has been applied to the removal of sulphur compounds from petroleum. It is almost certain also that dyeing is a colloidal process—certainly most dyes form colloidal solutions. Plastic clay becomes an easily pourable " slip " in the presence of a small percentage of alkali, a principle which is extensively used in the shaping of clay wares by casting. This is a very beautiful process and gives excellent results. The treatment of sewage is also a colloidal problem since a large proportion of the impurities are present in colloidal solution. The use of alum in precipitating sewage is explained by the efficiency of cations of high valency in bringing about the coagulation of negatively charged colloids. Other industrial processes involving colloids are the manufacture of paints and tanning ; while they are intimately concerned in such diverse matters as the study of the soil, biological processes in general, and the formation of deltas at the mouths of rivers, but the discussion of these topics is outside the scope of the present work.

§ 5 The Size of Colloidal Particles and its Measurement

It has been noted above that the particles of a colloidal solution are too small to be seen directly, even with a powerful microscope. But the scattering of light which they are capable of causing, and which makes the track of a beam of light passing through the solution visible (a phenomenon known as the Tyndall effect), can be made use of in order to detect their presence, and hence to count them.

The way in which this is done is by means of the **ultramicroscope**, a device due to Zsigmondy. An intense beam of light—arc light, or better, a beam of bright sunlight—is focused into the liquid under examination, so that the light enters the liquid at right-angles to the direction in which it is viewed under the microscope. In one of the earliest experimental methods (1903) of ultra-microscopy a beam of sunlight was reflected from a mirror, M, Fig. 88, through a lens, L, and focused in the trough of liquid under examination in the field of a microscope. The latter forms of the instrument are more complicated than this, though the principle is the same.

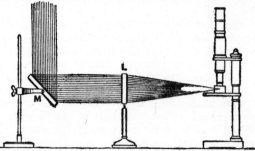

FIG. 88,—Early Form of Apparatus for Ultramicroscopy.

While the opalescence of the Tyndall effect merely shows that a solution contains a number of distinct individual particles in suspension, the ultra-microscope enables the *individual* particles to be detected. The ultramicros-copic particles appear as glittering discs of light with a dim or dark background.

By means of the ultramicroscope, it is possible to count the particles in a minute, but known, quantity of a colloidal solution. If then the total weight of the particles present in a larger (but also known) volume of the solution is deter-mined, it is possible to calculate their average size.

Other methods of determining the size of colloid particles are based upon the rate at which the particles settle (if they are large enough to do so); ultrafiltration ; and the colour of the solution.

The first of these methods is only applicable to fairly large particles, as other-wise settlement is not sufficiently fast, even if it takes place at all. The calcula-tion involves the use of an expression known as Stokes's Law, which gives a relation between the rate of settlement under gravity and the radius of the particle, the viscosity and density of the medium and the density of the particle being known.

Membranes can be prepared of different degrees of porosity so that colloid particles of different sizes may be separated by passing the solution containing them through such a membrane. Such membranes are known as **ultrafilters**, and can be prepared by impregnating filter paper with gelatine hardened with formaldehyde, or with collodion. By using solutions of different concentration, membranes of different porosity can be obtained and can be used to estimate the size of the particles of a given colloidal solution.

The relation between the size of colloid particles and the colour of their solu-tions depends upon the effect of small particles in causing the scattering of light, as mentioned above in connection with the Tyndall effect and the ultramicroscope. The scattering effect is greater for long waves than for short, and is also more marked the smaller the particles. On the assumption that these are spherical in shape, it is possible to calculate the size of particle necessary to give a certain (observed) colour. This has been tried experimentally and found to give results in satisfactory agreement with those of other methods.

CHAPTER XVII

HYDROGEN AND WATER

Inflammable air is undoubtedly charged with abundance of the principle of inflammability.—T. BERGMANN (1779).

Water is absolutely indispensable to both animal and vegetable life; it is the cause of many of the most striking phenomena in nature; and it is employed for countless purposes by man.—P. F. FRANKLAND.

§ 1 History and Occurrence

History

It has been known for a very long time that an air or gas is produced when iron is dissolved in dilute sulphuric acid. T. B. Paracelsus, in the sixteenth century, described the action somewhat quaintly. He said that when the acid acts on iron " an air arises which bursts forth like the wind." J. B. van Helmont (c. 1609) described this gas as a peculiar variety of air which was combustible and a non-supporter of combustion, but his ideas were somewhat hazy, for he confused hydrogen with other gases, like methane and carbon dioxide, which do not support combustion. Priestley, and writers generally up to about 1783, used " *inflammable air* " as a general term to include this gas, as well as the hydrocarbons, hydrogen sulphide, carbon monoxide, and other combustible gases. H. Cavendish (1766) showed that the inflammable air produced by the action of dilute sulphuric or hydrochloric acid on metals like iron, zinc, and tin was a distinct and definite substance, and A. L. Lavoisier (1783) called the gas " hydrogen."

Occurrence

The element hydrogen occurs free in nature in comparatively small quantities. The atmosphere is said to contain about one volume of hydrogen per 15,000 to 20,000 volumes of air. The proportion of hydrogen in the atmosphere increases when higher altitudes are attained. Hydrogen is also present in volcanic gases; in the gases from the Stassfurt salt beds; and in some meteorites. The presence of hydrogen in natural gas from the oil fields has been denied, although many published analyses of these gases include " hydrogen." The sun's chromosphere shows what appear to be stupendous flames of incandescent hydrogen, in some cases towering over 300,000 miles (M. Fényi, 1892) into space, and 100,000 miles in width (C. A. Young, 1872)—thousands of times larger than the earth on which we live. Spectroscopic observations also show that hydrogen is present in nebulae and certain stars.

Combined hydrogen is common. Water contains one-ninth of its weight of hydrogen. Hydrogen, together with oxygen, is one of the chief constituents of animal and vegetable tissue. Hydrogen also is present in nearly all organic compounds, and in many gases—methane, the hydro-carbons, hydrogen sulphide, etc.

§ 2 Formation of Hydrogen

The methods available for the formation or preparation of hydrogen fall into three main groups :—

(i) The electrolysis of aqueous solutions ;

(ii) the displacement of hydrogen from its compounds by other elements ;

(iii) decomposition by heat of compounds containing hydrogen.

Electrolysis

Pure water is ionized to such a very slight degree (see p. 196) that it is almost a non-conductor and hence cannot be electrolyzed. But the electrolysis of aqueous solutions of substances, whose decomposition products react with water with the formation of hydrogen, is often a convenient means of obtaining the element. Solutions of acids, bases or salts can be used according to the circumstances.

When such solutions are electrolyzed, the positively charged ion will move to the cathode, and there be discharged and liberated. In solutions of acids the cation is a hydrogen ion, which, on reaching the cathode, is discharged and liberated as hydrogen gas. In solutions of bases or salts the cation is a metal ion which, after being discharged at the electrode, will, if a more electro-positive element than hydrogen (compare Table XVII, p. 205) displace the latter from the water. If less electro-positive than hydrogen, the metal will be deposited as such on the electrode. Consequently hydrogen can be obtained by the electrolysis of solutions of acids and of compounds of metals more electro-positive than hydrogen.

Displacement of Hydrogen

Hydrogen may be displaced by suitable means, either from water itself, or from solutions of acids and alkalis.

Displacement from Water

The more active metals, such as sodium, potassium and calcium, will displace hydrogen from cold water ; others, such as iron, zinc, and magnesium, will, when heated, decompose steam. The liberation from steam can also be brought about by the action of red-hot carbon, which produces a mixture of equal volumes of carbon monoxide and hydrogen, known commercially as water gas (see p. 362). The hydrogen can be separated from the mixture by methods such as are described below.

Displacement from Acids

Acids are substances which contain hydrogen replaceable by a metal (see p. 306). Many metals can replace this hydrogen directly, though, in the case of weak acids (compare p. 238), the action is only very slow. Also these metals which are below hydrogen in the electro-chemical series (Table XVII, p. 205) will not displace hydrogen directly, and acids which are also oxidizing agents, as, for example, nitric acid, enter into secondary reactions which often result in the hydrogen being oxidized (see Ch. XX, p. 409) to water. The action of diluted solutions of the common mineral acids, hydrochloric acid and sulphuric acid upon zinc, iron or tin, furnishes a convenient method for the production of hydrogen.

Displacement from Alkalis

A number of elements will react with concentrated solutions of alkalis, such as sodium hydroxide, with the liberation of hydrogen. Such are aluminium, zinc, tin and silicon, all of which displace hydrogen from a hot concentrated solution of caustic soda. The action may be represented in the case of zinc by the equation :

$$Zn + 2NaOH, = Na_2ZnO_2 + H_2$$

from which it is seen that in the other product besides hydrogen, viz., sodium zincate, the zinc is found in the electro-negative (or acidic) radical, whereas when it is dissolved in hydrochloric acid it is the electro-positive radical in the product (zinc chloride).

Decomposition of Hydrogen Compounds by Heat

Hydrogen results from the action of heat on substances such as sodium formate, which is thereby converted into sodium oxalate with evolution of hydrogen

$$2H.CO_2Na = (CO_2Na)_2 + H_2 ;$$

and on certain hydrides such as that of copper,

$$2CuH = 2Cu + H_2$$

These methods, however, are of theoretical interest only.

§ 3 Preparation and Manufacture of Hydrogen

1. *Preparation of Hydrogen in the Laboratory*

For general laboratory work, hydrogen is prepared by the action of dilute hydrochloric acid or sulphuric acid on granulated zinc.

Granulated zinc is placed in a two-necked Woulfe's bottle,* A, Fig. 89. One neck is closed air-tight by a one-hole rubber stopper fitted with a thistle funnel, B, extending nearly to the bottom of the bottle ; the other neck is fitted with a glass tube, C—**delivery tube**—bent as shown in the diagram. The delivery tube dips under the

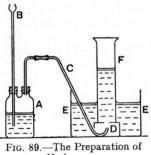

FIG. 89.—The Preparation of Hydrogen.

* The tubulated bottles for washing gases appear to have been first described by Peter Woulfe in 1784, hence the term **Woulfe's bottles**, not " Woulff's bottles."

beehive, D, placed in a basin of water, E. The vessels D and E form a **collecting, gas, or pneumatic trough.***

Some water is poured through the thistle funnel until the zinc is well covered, having made sure that all the joints are air-tight, and that no escape of gas is possible other than through the delivery tube. Concentrated sulphuric acid is then added, a little at a time, through the thistle funnel until the gas begins to come off vigorously. The mixture of air and hydrogen gas first issuing from the delivery tube is very explosive. It is therefore necessary to make sure that all the air has been expelled before the hydrogen is collected in the gas cylinders, or **gas jars,** F. Hence, a test-tube full of water is inverted over the hole in the upper floor of the " beehive." When the tube is full of gas, a lighted taper is applied to the mouth of the test tube. If the gas detonates, the trial must be repeated until the gas burns quietly. Then a gas jar full of water, covered with a greased glass plate, G, is turned upside down, and the plate removed while the mouth of the gas jar is below the surface of the water in the gas trough. The mouth of the jar is placed over the hole in the floor of the " beehive." When the jar is full of gas, the mouth of the jar is covered with the glass plate and the jar removed from the collecting trough.

The reaction which is taking place may be represented by one of the equations :

$$Zn + 2HCl \quad = ZnCl_2 + H_2$$
$$Zn + H_2SO_4 \quad = ZnSO_4 + H_2$$

If very pure zinc is used in this process the reaction may be very slow, but it can then be accelerated by the addition of a little copper sulphate solution. Iron filings or turnings can be substituted for zinc, but the gas is then very much more impure and has an unpleasant smell due to the presence of hydrocarbons (i.e., compounds of carbon and hydrogen) formed by the action of the acid on iron carbides in the iron. A purer gas can be obtained by the use of magnesium, or by the action of a solution of mercuric chloride, slightly acidified with hydrochloric acid, on aluminium turnings. In this reaction mercury is deposited on the aluminium and establishes a small electrolytic couple which prevents the formation of a protective film of oxide or hydroxide on the aluminium. The equation for the reaction proper is :

$$2Al + 6H_2O = 2Al(OH)_3 + 3H_2$$

When a steady current of hydrogen is needed for some time, or when variable quantities of gas are required intermittently, the apparatus described above may with advantage be replaced by a **Kipp's apparatus.** One form of Kipp's apparatus is illustrated in Fig. 90. If it is to be used for the preparation of hydrogen, zinc is placed in the middle bulb, and dilute sulphuric acid (1 volume of the concentrated acid to

* The discovery of the water pneumatic trough is often attributed to Stephen Hales, about 1730; J. Priestley afterwards used mercury in place of water, and this enabled him to manipulate gases soluble in water.

8 volumes of water) or hydrochloric acid poured into the upper bulb, A, and so to the lowest vessel, C. On opening the tap T, so that the acid may displace the air in the apparatus, the acid rises into the bulb B, where it reacts with the zinc, generating hydrogen. When the tap is closed the evolution of gas continues for a time and the pressure so developed forces the acid into the upper bulb, A, and so away from the zinc, thereby bringing the reaction to an end until the tap T is opened again.

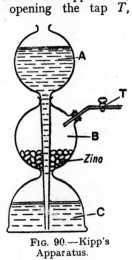

Fig. 90.—Kipp's Apparatus.

For very accurate work, such as that involved in the determination of the combining ratio of hydrogen and oxygen (compare Ch. VII, p. 100), very pure hydrogen is required. Various methods have been employed for this purpose, but the most usual now is the electrolysis of a warm solution of recrystallized baryta contained in a hard glass tube, using nickel electrodes. This gives a relatively pure gas, but the last traces of impurity are removed by passing it over a hot platinum gauze where any trace of oxygen present is burned to water, then through tubes of caustic potash and phosphorus pentoxide to dry it ; after which it is passed into an exhausted bulb containing warm metallic palladium foil which possesses the property of absorbing 600 times its volume of hydrogen. Under these conditions only hydrogen is absorbed and so, by re-evacuating the bulb after cooling, all traces of gaseous impurities can be removed. On heating the palladium foil to a dull red heat, pure hydrogen is evolved.

2. *Manufacture of Hydrogen Industrially*

The uses of hydrogen in the industries are increasing in number and variety, as mentioned in § 8 below, and so the production of hydrogen cheaply, and in quantity, is a matter of prime importance. The most important industrial methods for making hydrogen are by extraction from water gas and by electrolysis.

Water gas is the name given to that mixture of hydrogen and carbon monoxide and a trace of carbon dioxide, which is formed when steam is passed over red-hot coke (see p. 362).

$$H_2O + C = H_2 + CO$$

Two methods are in common use for applying water gas to the production of hydrogen.

In the **Bosch process** the water gas is mixed with more steam and passed over a catalyst, consisting usually of heated ferric oxide mixed with a trace of chromic oxide which stimulates the catalyst (see p. 231, promoters). The steam and carbon monoxide react with the production of hydrogen and carbon dioxide :

$$H_2O + CO = H_2 + CO_2$$

The carbon dioxide is removed by washing the gas with water under a pressure of about 25 atmospheres. Traces of unchanged carbon monoxide are then removed by means of a hot solution of sodium formate under very high pressures.

In the **Lane** (or iron) **process** water gas is only indirectly the source of the hydrogen. Steam is passed over iron heated to about 700° in vertical retorts when hydrogen is formed and an oxide of iron (ferrosic oxide) remains (compare pp. 216, 812) :

$$3Fe + 4H_2O \rightleftharpoons Fe_3O_4 + 4H_2$$

(as mentioned in Ch. XIV, this is a reversible reaction, but as the current of steam is maintained, the reaction proceeds to completion from left to right). When the iron is all oxidized, the steam supply is cut off and the oxide is reduced to iron again by passing over it a stream of water gas, both constituents of which will reduce ferrosic oxide to iron at a red heat :

$$Fe_3O_4 + 4H_2 \rightleftharpoons 3Fe + 4H_2O$$
$$Fe_3O_4 + 4CO \rightleftharpoons 3Fe + 4CO_2$$

By alternately passing the steam and water gas over the iron, hydrogen can thus be made in large quantities, using only a limited amount of iron.

Very large quantities of hydrogen result as a by-product of the manufacture of caustic soda (see p. 494), and also of metallic sodium. In the former process, aqueous solutions of common salt are electrolyzed. Sodium is thus liberated at the cathode and reacts at once with the water present to form caustic soda and hydrogen :

$$2Na + 2H_2O = 2NaOH + H_2$$

This is probably the most important source of hydrogen in commerce.

The use of hydrogen in airships has led to the devising of several chemical mixtures which can be readily transported and used for the production of hydrogen for military purposes. These mixtures are rather expensive. Calcium hydride is used under the name of **hydrolith**. In contact with water hydrogen is evolved, one gram of hydrolith yielding over a litre of gas :

$$CaH_2 + 2H_2O = Ca(OH)_2 + 2H_2$$

Hydrogenite is a mixture of 25 parts of silicon, 60 parts of caustic soda and 20 parts of slaked lime. This mixture, when heated, burns, and it then evolves hydrogen ; between 270 and 370 litres being obtained from a kilogram of hydrogenite. In the **silicol** method, an alloy of silicon and iron is acted upon by a strong solution of caustic soda

$$Si + 2NaOH + H_2O = Na_2SiO_3 + 2H_2$$

§ 4 Properties of Hydrogen

Hydrogen is a colourless gas without taste or smell, though as ordinarily prepared it may contain traces of impurities (hydrocarbons or arsine) which give it an unpleasant smell. The gas is combustible, for on plunging a lighted taper into a jar of the gas held mouth downwards, it burns with a scarcely visible blue flame at the mouth of the jar, but the taper is extinguished, thus showing that hydrogen is a non-supporter of combustion. Its specific gravity is very low in comparison with air, being only 0·069, and its normal density is 0·08987 gm. per litre. Its lightness is well illustrated by the experiment indicated in Fig. 91, which shows that the gas can be poured upwards from one jar to another. It can be proved that the gas has actually been transferred by testing the contents of each jar with a lighted taper.

Fig. 91.—Pouring Hydrogen upwards.

Hydrogen is not very soluble in water—100 volumes of water at 0° absorb about 2·15 volumes of gas, and at 20°, 1·84 volumes of gas. Hydrogen was once used as the standard for the atomic weights because it is the lightest element known, but this was later abandoned in favour of the oxygen standard, for the reasons explained in Chapter VI (p. 95).

Hydrogen is not poisonous, but animals placed in hydrogen are suffocated for the want of oxygen. When hydrogen is inhaled, the voice becomes shrill—approaching falsetto. The pitch of organ pipes and other wind instruments is raised if a blast of hydrogen be used in place of air. This is in agreement with the fact that the frequency of a note is inversely as the square root of the density of the gas.

The critical temperature of hydrogen (p. 34) is very low, being, in fact —239·9°, so that it is much more difficult to liquefy than air, or most other gases. Furthermore, when hydrogen under pressure is allowed to expand through a small orifice, unlike most other gases which are cooled by this process, hydrogen gets hotter, unless the temperature of the gas, before expansion, is below — 205° C. Below this temperature, hydrogen behaves like air and is cooled when allowed to expand suddenly through an orifice.

Just below the critical temperature, a pressure of about 20 atmospheres will liquefy the gas. The liquid is clear and colourless, resembling water, but it has a specific gravity 0·07, and boils at —252·7°. Hydrogen solidifies when the liquid is evaporated in a partial vacuum. The white solid is crystalline, melts at — 259·14°, and has a specific gravity 0·08. The data concerning the change of state of hydrogen can be symbolized :

$$\text{Hydrogen}_{\text{solid}} \overset{- 259\cdot14°}{\rightleftharpoons} \text{Hydrogen}_{\text{liquid}} \overset{- 252\cdot78°}{\rightleftharpoons} \text{Hydrogen}_{\text{gas}}$$

The spectrum of hydrogen, usually obtained by an electrical discharge in a vacuum tube, is simpler than that of most elements. As long ago as 1885, Balmer showed that a series of prominent lines which it contained (usually known as the Balmer series) could be expressed by the formula $R\left(\dfrac{1}{2^2} - \dfrac{1}{n^2}\right)$ where R is a constant, and n is a small whole number. In addition to the Balmer series, the spectrum is interspersed with fine lines, and, as mentioned in Chapter IX (p. 140), Bohr, on the basis of his theory of the structure and behaviour of the atom, was able to account for this expression, and also, by making allowance on relativity principles for the variation in the mass of the electrons with their velocity, was able to explain the fine-line structure to a great extent.

Hydrogen, as has been mentioned, is a combustible gas ; the product of the burning of hydrogen in air is water :

$$2H_2 + O_2 = 2H_2O$$

The recognition of this fact constituted one of the landmarks in the progress of chemistry and is more fully discussed below. If instead of allowing the hydrogen to burn at a jet it is mixed with air or oxygen, the mixture on ignition explodes with great violence. This can be illustrated by mixing two volumes of hydrogen gas with either one volume of oxygen or five volumes of air in a soda-water bottle. A lighted taper applied to the mouth of the bottle causes the gas to detonate violently. The combustion of the whole mass is almost instantaneous. The explosion is so violent that N. Lemery believed thunder to be due to the " fulminations of hydrogen."

Hydrogen and oxygen, so far as can be detected, do not react at room temperature in the absence of catalysts ; though some maintain that the gases do react, though very, very slowly (compare p. 228) Reaction under normal conditions is perceptible at 180° and explosive at 550°. But in the presence of certain catalysts, such as palladium black, or platinum black, combination will take place at room temperature, and the heat evolved is sufficient to cause the gases to ignite (see p. 258).

Although the combustibility of hydrogen is one of its most characteristic properties, perfectly dry hydrogen ignites with difficulty, if at all, when mixed with perfectly dry oxygen, even at 900°. Similarly many other combustible substances, if perfectly dried, do not burn when moisture is rigorously excluded. This phenomenon is discussed more fully on page 284.

Hydrogen combines with a good many non-metals, but as a rule does not react with metals. Examples of the former are its behaviour with the halogens (hydrogen combines, for example, with fluorine with explosion even in the dark), sulphur and nitrogen. A very few metallic hydrides are known, the principal ones being sodium hydride, NaH, and calcium hydride, CaH_2. It is interesting to note that in the case of the metallic hydrides, when electrolysis is possible (e.g., fused lithium hydride) the hydrogen is liberated at the *anode*, whereas in the electrolysis of water and acids (in fact, in almost all other cases) the hydrogen appears at the *cathode*.

Occlusion of Hydrogen

Although hydrogen combines chemically with but few metals, there are some metals—particularly platinum and palladium—which under certain conditions can absorb relatively large volumes of hydrogen. According to Thomas Graham (1867-9), palladium will absorb 935 times its own volume of hydrogen in cooling from a red heat, and at ordinary temperatures, 276 times its volume. The actual amount absorbed depends upon the physical condition of the metal. According to G. Neumann and F. Streintz (1892), one volume of the following finely divided metals will absorb the following volumes of hydrogen :—

Palladium black	.	. 502·3	Nickel	.	.	15·6
Platinum sponge	.	. 49·3	Copper	.	.	4·5
Gold.	. .	. 46·3	Aluminium	.	.	2·7
Iron	. .	. 19·2	Lead	.	.	0·1

The hydrogen is given off when the metal is heated, particularly under reduced pressure, and this property of palladium furnishes a useful means of weighing hydrogen gas. It was used by Morley in his work on the combining weights of oxygen and hydrogen (p. 101).

Palladium increases in volume during the absorption, but its general appearance and properties are not much altered, although a considerable amount of heat is evolved during the absorption. Graham called the phenomenon **occlusion** (from *occludo*, I shut up). The gas is said to be occluded by the metal. The phenomenon is now generally called **adsorption**, meaning that the gas *ad*heres in some unknown way to the metal. It was formerly believed that a chemical compound was formed, but it is now thought almost certain that this is not so, although in the occluded form hydrogen is more active than ordinary hydrogen. This effect may be due to the hydrogen and the metal constituting a voltaic cell, for as Table XVII shows, hydrogen is strongly electro-positive to such metals as platinum and palladium. The effect may also be due to the high concentration of hydrogen present, for the amount of hydrogen present in a given volume corresponds to its compression to anything up to 800 atmospheres or so, and we know that molecular hydrogen under pressure will reduce, say, copper sulphate under high pressure. A third possibility is that the hydrogen is occluded in the atomic state. Whatever be the explanation of its activity, the exact relation between the occluded hydrogen and the metal is not clear.

Reducing Action of Hydrogen

The readiness with which hydrogen will combine with oxygen and certain other non-metals makes it able very often to remove oxygen and chlorine from their compounds with the other elements. Thus, when hydrogen is passed over hot ferric oxide, lead oxide, nickel oxide, copper oxide, etc., the hydrogen combines with the oxygen of the oxide and leaves behind the metal. In these experiments, the hydrogen is said to be *oxidized* ; and the metallic oxide, *reduced*, or deoxidized. (See Ch. XVIII, p. 310, for a fuller discussion of the terms " oxidation " and " reduction.") Direct reduction with ordinary hydrogen in this way usually requires a high temperature, which limits the usefulness of the method, but hydrogen generated in the body of the liquid to be reduced will often bring about reduction where ordinary hydrogen bubbled through the solution will not. (See below —nascent hydrogen.) Also numerous reductions can be effected by passing a mixture of hydrogen and the vapour of the substance to be reduced over finely-divided metals such as nickel (see pp. 231, 830).

Nascent Hydrogen

Hydrogen at the moment of its formation is more chemically active than ordinary hydrogen. For instance, ordinary hydrogen can be passed into an acidified solution of ferric chloride without producing any appreciable change, but if metallic zinc be placed in the solution, the brisk evolution of hydrogen is soon attended with the reduction of the ferric chloride to ferrous chloride.

$$FeCl_3 + H = FeCl_2 + HCl$$

Chlorates can be reduced to chlorides similarly :

$$KClO_3 + 6H = KCl + 3H_2O$$

Hydrogen prepared and acting in this way has been termed nascent hydrogen, i.e., hydrogen at the moment of birth.

It was at first suggested that the activity of nascent hydrogen is due to the fact that at the moment of liberation it exists as single atoms, whereas in ordinary hydrogen the atoms have combined to form molecules H_2. The latter molecules will require work to be done on them to separate them into single atoms before they can react, while the single atoms of nascent hydrogen are ready at once and require no further work to be done on them before reaction can take place.

This theory is very attractive at first sight, but does not account for all the facts ; in particular, the different degrees of reactivity of nascent hydrogen made from different reagents. Thus, for example, chlorates are reduced to chlorides by the nascent hydrogen made from zinc and dilute sulphuric acid, but not by that which results when the action of sodium amalgam on water is used. Similar differences have been observed in the reducing power of the hydrogen evolved by electrolysis when using different metals as cathode, which suggests that these phenomena may be connected and so be capable of a single explanation.

It has been shown that in electrolysis those metals whose use as cathode require the highest voltages in order to bring about liberation of hydrogen yield hydrogen of the greatest activity. Thus, to obtain hydrogen by the electrolysis of dilute sulphuric acid with a lead cathode requires a voltage 0·49 volts higher than that required with a silver cathode, and, in general, the higher the " over-voltage," the greater the activity of the hydrogen formed. It seems, therefore, as though some of the extra energy supplied has become associated with the hydrogen, thus enhancing its chemical activity.

Similarly, it may be that the difference between nascent hydrogen formed in different reactions is due to the difference in the energy changes involved in these reactions. Energy is liberated as a result of the reaction producing the hydrogen, but this may not always all appear as heat, but may become associated with the hydrogen being formed which is thus more reactive than ordinary hydrogen.

Another suggested explanation of the behaviour of nascent hydrogen is that at the moment of production the gas will be in the form of very minute bubbles, the internal pressure of which will be very great on account of their small size. Now it has been shown by Ipatiev that by the application of great pressure the activity of ordinary hydrogen can be increased and it may well be that this is connected with the behaviour of nascent hydrogen.

It is not possible in the present state of our knowledge to decide definitely between these theories except to say that the simple atomic-hydrogen hypothesis is not so much favoured as formerly.

§ 5 Formula and Atomic Weight of Hydrogen

The atomic weight of hydrogen and its formula have been discussed in detail in Chapter IV (p. 74) and Chapter VI (p. 101). The combining weight has been determined by various investigators by measurements with the most elaborate precautions, of the composition of water, both by weight and (in conjunction with the known densities of the gases) by volume. The number of atoms in the molecule has been inferred from observations on the combination of hydrogen and chlorine (pp. 68, 504) and from measurements of the specific heats of hydrogen.

The accepted value for the atomic weight of hydrogen at present is 1·008 and its formula is H_2.

§ 6 Forms of Hydrogen

Ortho- and Para-Hydrogen

According to the latest conclusions about the structure of the atom (see Ch. IX, p. 133), the hydrogen atom consists of a nucleus of mass 1 carrying a unit positive charge (i.e., a proton) and one electron. Consequently, the hydrogen molecule, which as mentioned in § 5 comprises two atoms of hydrogen, contains two protons and two electrons. It has been shown theoretically that such a molecule should be capable of existing in two forms, differing in the relation between the spins of the two nuclei. In one form the spins are in the same sense, and in the other in opposite senses (Fig. 92). These forms were named ortho- and para-hydrogen respectively and their existence has been confirmed by the partial separation of hydrogen into two forms.

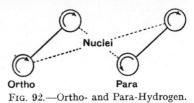

FIG. 92.—Ortho- and Para-Hydrogen.

Ordinary hydrogen is an equilibrium mixture of ortho- and para-forms (containing about 75 per cent. of ortho-hydrogen at ordinary temperatures). Theoretical considerations show that there will be a relatively large amount of heat evolved when the ortho-form is converted into the para-form, and hence it follows, from Le Chatelier's principle (p. 219), that the equilibrium proportion of the latter will be greatest at low temperatures. By the application of these facts, Bonhoeffer and Harteck (1929) were able to prepare almost pure para-hydrogen by keeping hydrogen at liquid air temperature and 350 atmospheres pressure for a week. Practically pure para-hydrogen can also be obtained by the adsorption of hydrogen on charcoal at the temperature of liquid air. Ortho-hydrogen has not yet been obtained pure.

These two forms of hydrogen differ in certain physical properties, e.g., specific heat. Also the melting-point of para-hydrogen is given as − 259·17° C., whereas that of ordinary hydrogen is − 258·9° C.

Active Hydrogen

By subjecting hydrogen at ordinary temperatures to the action of a silent electric discharge, at an electrical pressure exceeding 30,000 volts (compare formation of ozone, p. 313) an active variety of hydrogen is obtained. It is marked by considerable chemical activity ; thus, for example, it will combine directly, at ordinary temperatures, with lead or sulphur, forming hydrides, and will reduce cupric and ferric oxides in the cold.

It has been suggested that this " active hydrogen " consists of molecules H_3, or of single atoms, but neither of these explanations has been widely accepted, and it is generally regarded as an active form of ordinary hydrogen H_2 (see active nitrogen, p. 386).

Atomic Hydrogen

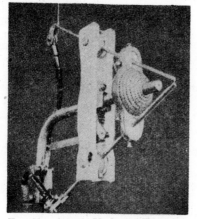

FIG. 93.—Atomic Hydrogen Blowpipe.

Atomic hydrogen can, however, be produced by subjecting hydrogen to very high temperatures such as that of the electric arc; as was shown by Langmuir (1912). He also showed that this dissociation is brought about when hydrogen is in contact with a heated tungsten wire. The combination of two hydrogen atoms to form a hydrogen molecule is attended with the evolution of a very large amount of heat. Consequently the heat produced by the combustion of atomic hydrogen is very great, for the total heat evolved by the combustion of atomic hydrogen will be equal to the normal heat of combustion of molecular hydrogen *plus* the heat energy of formation of a molecule of hydrogen from its atoms. This fact is made use of in the atomic hydrogen blowpipe (see below; p. 265).

§ 7 Isotopes of Hydrogen

It has been mentioned in Chapter IX (p. 134) that isotopes of an element have identical nuclear charges, but different atomic masses. The ordinary hydrogen atom consists of a nucleus with unit mass and unit charge, with one electron rotating round it. The simplest isotope of this atom would have a nucleus of mass 2, charge 1, and 1 electron as before. Whereas in general the isotopes of one element differ very slightly indeed in their ordinary properties, since a difference of one or two units represents only a small fraction of the total weight of the atom, in the case of hydrogen the differences to be expected are considerable in view of the relatively large difference in the weights of the atoms of the two isotopes.

The discovery of the heavy isotope of hydrogen, now known as **Deuterium** and represented by the symbol D, was the result in the first place of a discrepancy between the value of the atomic weight of hydrogen—as determined by physical and chemical means. The value obtained by the improved mass-spectrograph method of Aston was 1·0078, taking oxygen = 16·00 as standard. The best chemical value was also 1·0078, and as at this time oxygen was thought to be a " pure " element (i.e., to have no isotopes), the agreement between the two methods left nothing to be desired. The discovery in 1929 that ordinary oxygen contains two isotopes of mass 17 and 18 respectively showed that this agreement was more apparent than real, and the view was soon put forward that it must be due to the presence of a small quantity of a heavy isotope in hydrogen also. Consequently a search for it was begun, and before long its existence was confirmed.

A spectroscopic examination of the residues remaining after the evaporation of large quantities of liquid hydrogen revealed faint lines corresponding to an isotope of hydrogen of mass 2 (Urey, 1932). About the same time Washburn and Urey examined the water from some commercial electrolytic cells which had been in operation for a number of years and found that it contained a larger proportion of " heavy " hydrogen than ordinary water. This observation gave the clue to a method of preparing " heavy " water and hence " heavy " hydrogen in quantity.

The method was applied by G. N. Lewis to the preparation of almost pure " heavy " water. He started with 20 litres of water in which the heavy-water content had already been somewhat increased by electrolysis, and continued the electrolysis of this until only 1·5 c.c. of liquid remained. This sample then contained approximately 66 per cent. of heavy water. By combining the products of several such electrolyses and continuing the process, there finally resulted about 1·3 c.c. of almost pure D_2O.

Heavy water can also be obtained by fractionation, quite a large separation resulting when water is distilled, using a long fractionating column and working at a reduced pressure.

From the almost pure heavy water, heavy hydrogen itself can be obtained and finally purified by diffusion.

Heavy water differs markedly from ordinary water in physical properties. A comparison of some of these properties is given in Table XXIV. In addition to these properties the solubilities of some substances is considerably less in heavy water than it is in ordinary water.

The chemical differences between H_2O and D_2O and between H_2 and D_2 are only just beginning to be investigated. One of the most interesting facts which has so far emerged is the ready interchange of hydrogen atoms which it indicates. Thus, for example, a solution of

TABLE XXIV.—PROPERTIES OF WATER.

	Ordinary Water.	Heavy Water.
Melting Point . . .	0°	3·8°
Boiling Point . . .	100°	101·42°
Specific Gravity. .	1·0	1·056
Temperature of Max. Density	4°	11·6°
Surface Tension (at 20°) .	72·75 dynes	67·8 dynes
Refractive Index . .	1·3329	1·3281
Viscosity	10·9	12·6
Dielectric Constant . .	82·0	80·5

ammonium chloride in heavy water, on evaporation yields a solid containing the same proportion of heavy hydrogen as was present in the water used. Again, if sugar is dissolved in heavy water *half* the hydrogen atoms of the sugar are exchanged for heavy hydrogen.

A similar phenomenon is observed when heavy hydrogen is kept over water for some weeks. The volume of the gas remains unchanged although all but about 5 per cent. of it is replaced by ordinary hydrogen.

The existence of a third isotope of hydrogen of mass 3 has also been reported. The abundance of this third isotope (to which the name Tritium has been given) in ordinary water is estimated as 7 parts in 10^{12}.

§ 8 Uses of Hydrogen

Hydrogen finds increasing employment in modern industrial operations, but the most important uses at present are in the manufacture of synthetic ammonia (see page 390) and for the hydrogenation of oils (page 231). It is becoming increasingly important for the production of " oil from coal " by hydrogenation of the coal, in presence of a catalyst such as ferric oxide, mixed with alumina and a little titanium oxide. Large quantities are also used for the filling of balloons and airships ; since it is the lightest known gas and its lifting power is considerable.

The lifting power is readily calculated, for, by the principle of Archimedes, it will be equal to the difference between the weight of that volume of air displaced by the hydrogen, and that of the hydrogen itself. Now the weight of a litre of hydrogen at 0° C. is 0·09 gms. and that of 1 litre of air at the same temperature is 14·4 times this. Therefore the lifting power at 0° of 1 litre of hydrogen is : $(14·4 - 1)0·09$ gms. $= 1·203$ gms. The lifting power at a higher temperature will be less than this on account of the expansion of the gases, and can be calculated according to Charles's Law.   For a litre of hydrogen at, say, 15° will weigh ·09 $\times \dfrac{273}{288}$ gms. and the weight of 1 litre of air will be 14·4 times this, so that the lifting power becomes :

$$(14\cdot4 - 1) \times 0\cdot09 \times \frac{273}{288} = 1\cdot13 \text{ gms.}$$

Hydrogen burns readily and when used in the oxy-hydrogen blow-pipe gives a very hot flame (about 2800°).   This instrument was once widely used, but it has now been largely replaced by the oxy-acetylene blowpipe (see page 340).   But it is still employed for fusing quartz and silica (e.g., for the manufacture of mercury vapour lamps), and for melting platinum.   It is also used (sometimes as an *air*-hydrogen blowpipe) for the autogenous soldering of lead, for use in situations (such as the lead chambers used in sulphuric acid manufacture, p. 461) where ordinarily soldered joints would be readily corroded.   The edges of the pieces of lead to be joined are welded by melting the edges together by means of the air- (or oxy-) hydrogen blowpipe.   The flame is very suitable for this purpose since it is hot and yet reducing in character.

Another form of blowpipe known as the **atomic hydrogen blow-pipe** has also found employment in certain welding operations.   As mentioned above (p. 262) atomic hydrogen is formed when an arc struck between tungsten electrodes is allowed to burn in an atmosphere of hydrogen.   By blowing a jet of ordinary hydrogen across such an arc, the intensely hot flame, which results on account of the formation of atomic hydrogen, can be directed on to any suitable spot.   This flame is capable of melting tungsten (which requires a temperature of 3400°), and a feature of its use is the great rapidity with which a surface can be heated—an important factor in welding operations.   Owing to the reducing character of the flame, iron ore alloys can be melted without fear of oxidation, and contamination with other elements, such as carbon (which sometimes occurs with the oxy-acetylene flame) is readily avoided.

§ 9 The Position of Hydrogen in the Periodic System

The position to be assigned to hydrogen in the Periodic System is not easily decided.   As was pointed out in Chapter VIII (p. 124), it does not easily fit into the general scheme.   It has sometimes been placed at the head of Group I of the Table (the alkali metals), and though in view of its electro-positive nature it is better classified with these elements than with any other group, this position is not entirely satisfactory.   For although like them it has a powerful affinity for non-metals, and little or none for metals, and in its compounds with the former often forms electrolytes (acids) which bear resemblances to the corresponding salts of the alkali metals, it nevertheless is certainly not to be thought of as a metal.   On the other hand, as mentioned on page 258, when fused lithium hydride is electrolyzed, hydrogen is liberated at the anode, just as chlorine is in the electrolysis of fused chlorides.   To this extent, hydrogen resembles the halogens, though it is scarcely to be thought of as a halogen.   In fact, the atomic structure of hydrogen (a nucleus carrying one positive charge and one electron) differs so markedly from that of any other element that it is justifiable to accord to it a special place in the Periodic Table and not to associate it with any particular group.   This is what is done in the form of the table given on page 120.

§ 10 Water. Composition

The older chemists considered water to be an element.   They were quite right so far as their knowledge went, because they did not know how to decompose it into simpler substances.

Priestley has told us that in 1776 his friend, J. Warltire, noticed that when a flame of hydrogen is allowed to burn in air confined under a bell-jar, the whole of the receiver appeared to be filled with a white powdery substance, and when the flame goes out, the air left in the jar was perfectly noxious.   In the same year P. J. Macquer inquired whether the flame of hydrogen evolves soot or smoke, and he thus described his experiment :

By placing a saucer of white porcelain in a jet of inflammable gas burning tranquilly at an orifice, I found that the part of the saucer which the flame licked was moistened by small drops of liquid as clear as water, and which, in fact, appeared to be nothing but pure water.

It is probable that J. Warltire's white cloud was nothing but condensed steam.   In the spring of 1781, J. Priestley made what he called " a random experiment " to " entertain a few philosophical friends," in which a mixture of " inflammable air " with oxygen or atmospheric air was exploded in a closed vessel by means of an electric spark.   The sides of the glass vessel were found " bedewed " with moisture after the explosion, but Priestley paid no particular attention to the phenomenon.   H. C. Cavendish looked upon the deposition of the dew as a fact " well worth examining more closely," and immediately followed up the subject, in 1781, by exploding a mixture of " one measure of oxygen with two measures of inflammable air (hydrogen) " in a closed vessel.   No gas remained in the globe after the explosion, but the hydrogen and oxygen lost their gaseous form, and produced a certain weight of water.   The vessel and its contents underwent no change in weight, or parted with anything ponderable during the explosion, whilst a certain volume of gas was replaced by a certain weight of water.   Hence, Cavendish deduced that **liquid water consists, weight for weight, of the hydrogen and oxygen gases lost in its production.**   He thus established the fact that water consists of hydrogen and oxygen only, united in the proportions of two to one by volume approximately.

Cavendish's experiment has been repeated from time to time, with the introduction of all possible refinements in order to secure an accurate figure for the volume composition of water. Notable examples are the work of Scott, and of Burt and Edgar which have been described already (p. 66).

Experiments of this kind serve to establish the composition of water *synthetically*; corresponding *analytical* evidence was forthcoming soon after the time of Cavendish's experiment.

W. Nicholson and A. Carlisle, May 2, 1800, happened to put a drop of water in contact with two wires from an electric battery and noticed the formation of small bubbles of gas about the tips of the wires when the tips of the wires were not in contact. They then immersed the two wires in a glass of water, and found that gases were formed about both wires. They found the gas collected at one wire to be hydrogen, and at the other wire, oxygen. Two volumes of hydrogen were collected for every volume of oxygen. The gases were mixed and exploded. The result was water.

Nicholson and Carlisle's experiment is often repeated in the following modified form. The apparatus employed is illustrated in Fig. 94 and is sometimes called a **water voltameter.** It consists of two glass tubes, *A* and *B*, terminated at the top by stopcocks, and connected near the bottom by a horizontal tube, to which is also attached a third vertical tube, *C*, which ends in a funnel, *D*. The electrodes *E*, *E*, consist of pieces of platinum foil. Pure water is a very poor conductor, and so the experiment is carried out by filling the apparatus with water to which a little sulphuric acid has been added. A current is passed through the solution by connecting the electrodes to an accumulator

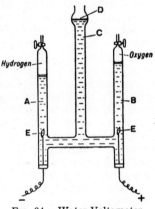

FIG. 94.—Water Voltameter.

or a primary battery. During the passing of the electric current, bubbles of gas from about the metal plates rise into the glass tubes. More gas is given off at one plate than the other. The gas in each tube can be examined by means of a lighted taper or otherwise. In the one tube, the taper burns with the " blinding brilliance " characteristic of oxygen ; and the gas in the other tube burns with the blue flame characteristic of hydrogen. Some of the water has disappeared, but no change can be detected in the amount of sulphuric acid mixed with the water. Hence it is inferred that the water, not the acid, has been decomposed. The experiment succeeds equally well if a very dilute solution of sodium or potassium hydroxide be used with nickel or iron electrodes.   Here again the water, not the alkali, is decomposed.

A mixture of one volume of oxygen and two volumes of hydrogen, called **electrolytic gas** or **detonating gas,** is often wanted in gas analysis, etc.   This is easily provided by placing both electrodes under one receiver.   Electrolytic oxygen contains a little ozone and hydrogen peroxide if prepared by the electrolysis of acidulated water, but not if a solution of barium hydroxide be electrolyzed.

The information derived from these experiments did not, by itself, establish the formula of water for, as explained in Chapter IV, no relation between the combining volumes of gases and the number of atoms uniting was then known.

Crude attempts were made to discover the *weights* of hydrogen and oxygen combining together to form water, by multiplying the volumes found by Cavendish, by the densities of the gases.   But with the comparatively primitive types of apparatus then available the results were very inaccurate.

A determination of a different kind was made by Dumas in 1843, Although its accuracy is inferior to that of more modern experiments. it was far superior to any which preceded it and it was the forerunner of accurate atomic-weight determinations.   The experiment illustrates some important principles, and it is therefore here described in outline.

It depends upon the fact, already noted (p. 259), that when the oxides of such metals as iron, copper or lead are heated in a current of hydrogen, water is formed and the oxide is reduced to the metal.

If a known amount of copper oxide be employed, and the water formed be collected and weighed, the weight of the reduced copper oxide will show how much oxygen has been used in forming a definite amount of water.   This was done by J. B. A. Dumas in 1843.   The hydrogen was prepared by the action of zinc on sulphuric acid.   It might be thought that pure zinc and pure sulphuric acid should be used.   Experiment shows, curiously enough, that the action is so very, very slow, that it is often stated that " absolutely pure sulphuric acid, even when diluted with pure water, has no action on perfectly pure zinc."   Moreover, it is exceedingly difficult to prepare pure zinc and pure sulphuric acid.   Hence, pure reagents were not used for the preparation of the hydrogen.   Accordingly, the gas may contain nitrogen and oxygen derived from the air ;   sulphur dioxide and hydrogen sulphide derived from the reduction of the sulphuric acid by the hydrogen, carbon dioxide, arsenic hydride (if the acid or the zinc contained arsenic) ;   hydrogen phosphide (if the zinc or the acid contained phosphorus) ;   nitrogen oxides (if the acid contained nitrogen oxides) ;   and water vapour.   Accordingly, Dumas used sulphuric acid, which had been well boiled to get rid of dissolved air, and then passed the hydrogen through a series of U-tubes—Fig. 95—containing :   (1) pieces of glass moistened with lead nitrate to remove hydrogen sulphide ;   (2) solution of silver sulphate to remove arsenic and phosphorus compounds ; (3) solid potassium hydroxide to remove sulphur dioxide, carbon dioxide, and nitrogen oxides ;* and (4) phos-

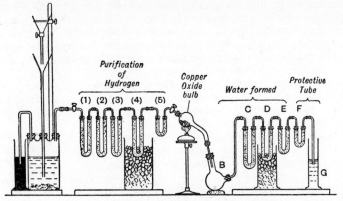

FIG. 95.—Dumas's Experiment (abbreviated).

phorus pentoxide to remove moisture† not absorbed by the solid potassium hydroxide. The phosphorus pentoxide tubes were placed in a freezing mixture. The tube marked (5) in the diagram contained phosphorus pentoxide. It was weighed before and after the experiment. If no change in weight occurred, it was assumed that the hydrogen passing through was quite dry.

The experiment.—The purified hydrogen was passed through a weighed bulb, *A*, containing copper oxide, and heated by the spirit lamp underneath. Most of the water condensed in the bulb *B*, and the remainder was absorbed in the U-tube, *C*, containing solid potassium hydroxide, and in *D* and *E* containing phosphorus pentoxide. The phosphorus pentoxide tube *D* was kept cool by a freezing mixture. The three tubes, *C*, *D* and *E*, and the bulb *B*, were weighed before and after the experiment. The last U-tube, *F*, containing phosphorus pentoxide, was followed by a cylinder, *G*, of sulphuric acid through which hydrogen escaped. The vessels *F* and *G* were not weighed ; they served to protect the other tubes from the external atmosphere.

The results.—The average of nineteen experiments by Dumas gave :

Copper oxide lost in weight	. .	44·22 grams.
Water produced	. . . .	49·76 grams.
Hydrogen (by difference)	.	5·54 grams.

Hence, every 16 parts by weight of oxygen combined with 2·004 parts by weight of hydrogen to form water. The latter determination of Morley (see p. 102) gave 16 : 2·0152. There is a curious error in Dumas's

* Dumas used three potassium hydroxide tubes, and two phosphorus pentoxide tubes. Only one of each is shown in the diagram.
† Ibid.

experiment which, if not corrected, makes the result a little high. The reduced copper retains some hydrogen very tenaciously (see occlusion of hydrogen by the metals, p. 259). Other objections to Dumas's experiment have been made : (1) The expulsion of the air from the large apparatus is difficult ; (2) The air absorbed by the sulphuric acid is slowly evolved along with the hydrogen when the acid acts on zinc ; (3) The copper oxide is contaminated with nitrogen absorbed from the air ; (4) The slight reduction of sulphuric acid by hydrogen, forming gaseous sulphur dioxide ; and (5) The complete drying of the hydrogen is very difficult. In approximate work we may take it that 2 parts by weight of hydrogen combine with 16 parts by weight of oxygen to form 18 parts of water.

Dumas himself believed that the true value of this ratio should be 1 : 8 ; in fact, as is now known, his value was itself too high. The generally accepted value, based on Morley's work (see pp. 101-2), is 1 : 7·94.

Up to about 1860 it was assumed that the formula for water was HO and hence, the atomic weight of hydrogen being unity, that of oxygen is 8 approximately. This gave satisfactory results in many respects for the formulae of other substances and the equations for reactions correctly indicated the proportions by weight of the elements in molecules of compounds and the weights of materials taking part in reactions.

But this formula for water, and the consequential formulae and atomic weights of other compounds and elements, rendered difficult of explanation the volume relationships between reacting gases. Avogadro's hypothesis gave the clue to the solution of the problem, but it was not until 1857 that, in the hands of Cannizzaro, it was properly applied and then very quickly accepted. It was then recognized that the molecules of hydrogen and oxygen must each contain two atoms, and that the formula of water is H_2O. The difficulties which had existed in any attempt to correlate the results of experiments on the combining volumes of gases with their densities and molecular weights disappeared ; and observations such as that just described in the electrolysis of water, whereby two volumes of hydrogen result for one of oxygen, became easily explicable. This matter has already been discussed in some detail in Chapter IV.

An experiment performed by Gay-Lussac in 1808, and repeated by Hofmann in 1865, and which showed clearly the volumetric composition of steam, helped also to confirm the formula H_2O for water.

This experiment can be illustrated in the following manner. A graduated eudiometer or explosion tube (a stout glass tube fitted with electrodes for firing gases by passing a spark) is surrounded by a hot vapour jacket through which can be passed the vapour of a liquid which boils at a temperature above 100°.

The experiment is illustrated in Fig. 96. The upper end of the glass jacket surrounding the explosion tube is connected with a flask, *M,* containing toluene, boiling at about 110°, or amyl alcohol, boiling at about 130°. The lower end of the jacket is connected with a flask and condenser N, so that the amyl alcohol can be recovered. The explosion tube is filled with mercury by adjusting the levelling tube B and the stopcock C. A mixture containing one volume of oxygen and two volumes of hydrogen is introduced into the explosion tube via the stopcock C by depressing the levelling tube. When the explosion tube is about half or three-fourths filled, the volume of its contents is read by bringing the mercury to the same level in both levelling tube and explosion tube. Then the levelling tube is lowered so that the mercury falls nearly to the bottom of the explosion tube. When the amyl alcohol is steadily boiling, and the explosion tube has been filled, the gases are sparked. In

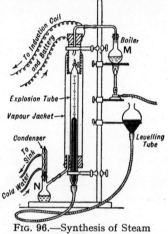

FIG. 96.—Synthesis of Steam by Volume.

a few minutes, when the temperature has had time to adjust itself, bring the levelling tube in position for a reading. It will be found that the steam occupies just two-thirds the original volume of the mixed gases. Otherwise expressed,

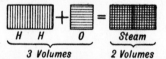

$$H \quad H \qquad O \qquad Steam$$
$$3 \text{ Volumes} \qquad 2 \text{ Volumes}$$

Hence, it is inferred that **when water is synthesized at a temperature above the point of condensation—100°—two volumes of hydrogen react with one volume of oxygen to form two volumes of steam.**

If we adopt Avogadro's Hypothesis, it follows that two molecules of hydrogen and one molecule of oxygen form two molecules of water (or steam). Hence, if hydrogen is H_2 and oxygen O_2 (see p. 68), H_2O is the only possible formula for steam, i.e.,

$$2H_2 + O_2 = 2H_2O$$

§ 11 Occurrence of Water

It has been estimated that three-fourths of the surface materials on the crust of the earth is water. Animals and plants contain a large proportion of combined water—e.g., fish contains the equivalent of about 80 per cent. ; beef, 60-62 per cent. ; the human body, 70 per cent. ; aquatic plants between 95 and 99 per cent. ; and ordinary land plants, 50-75 per cent. A great many rocks contain water—combined and absorbed. Clay, for example, contains up to 14 per cent. of combined water.

The circulation of water in nature—the water cycle.—Water is widely distributed in its three states of aggregation—steam or aqueous vapour, liquid water, and solid ice and snow. All the water on the earth passes through a remarkable cycle of changes. The heat of the sun leads to the evaporation of water from the seas, etc. ; water vapour is only 0·62 times as heavy as an equal volume of air, and consequently it rises into the upper regions of the atmosphere, as well as diffusing into and mixing with atmospheric air. The temperature of the ascending vapour gradually decreases, and consequently a plane must be reached where the air is saturated with moisture. The vapour will then condense in the form of fine drops of water—mist or clouds. The fine drops coalesce into larger drops. Ultimately, the condensed water must descend again to the earth as rain, snow, or hail. The wind distributes the vapour. The heat given up during the condensation of the vapour is distributed or carried from the hotter regions—where evaporation is fastest—to the colder regions—where the vapour is condensed—thus helping to " stretch " the temperate regions nearer to the poles. The water which is sprayed, as rain, etc., on the surface of the globe, does a certain amount of physical and chemical work. On the chemical side, water helps in the decomposition and weathering of rocks ; and on the physical side, it transports matter in suspension from the higher to the lower levels. The soluble matters ultimately collect in the seas.

Thus the water cycle involves : (1) evaporation from the oceans, seas, lakes, etc. ; (2) condensation in the upper regions of the atmosphere as a fine mist of distilled water where it collects as clouds ; (3) further condensation is followed by rain ; (4) the rain-water percolates through the soil and collects on an impervious bed of rock to be again forced to the surface, as spring water, by the pressure of the superincumbent layers ; and (5) this is collected by the streams and rivers. The rivers return whence they came—to the sea, and commence anew the never-ending cycle. It must be added that a relatively small proportion of the water which finds its way into the ground falls out of the cycle since it is fixed by reaction with certain silicates and rocks forming hydrated silicates, hydrated alumino silicates, etc.

Rain-water

" No water," said T. Bergman, " is ever found on the surface of the earth in a state of purity." Rain, in its journey through the air, dissolves oxygen, carbon dioxide, and nitrogen, as well as ammonia and ammonium nitrate. It also carries down dust—

organic and inorganic. Rain-water, particularly if collected near the sea in high winds, contains sodium chloride ; and if collected near towns, sulphur compounds—sulphur dioxide and sulphuric acid—derived from the products of combustion of coal. When evaporated to dryness, 10,000 parts by weight of rain-water will give about 0·34 part of solid matter, most of this consisting of sodium chloride and organic matter. Rain-water contains in solution about 0·013 per cent. of dissolved nitrogen, 0·0064 per cent. oxygen, and 0·0013 per cent. carbon dioxide. The rain which falls at the end of a shower is more pure than that which falls at the beginning, because the atmosphere is washed, so to speak, during the earlier part of the shower.

Spring and Mineral Water

Directly the rain-water strikes the ground, it begins to attack and dissolve various rocks, decaying organic tissue (humic compounds), etc., forming *surface and ground water*. It is estimated that between 25 and 40 per cent. of the rainfall, in temperate regions, soaks into the ground. In its journey underground—*underground water*—the percolating water loses most of its organic matter and dissolves more or less mineral matters—compounds of calcium, magnesium, and sodium—and also dissolves carbon dioxide, etc. The greater the depth to which the water sinks the greater the amount of solid matter it can dissolve. Water under great pressure is a powerful solvent. Sooner or later the water which has percolated underground will be forced to the surface as *spring water*. If the spring water holds an unusual amount of some particular constituent in solution which gives it a marked taste, or some specific property, the term *mineral water* is applied. Mineral waters do not necessarily contain a large excess of mineral matters in solution. The water from mineral springs is often named according to some special constituent dissolved in the water, or from the locality of the spring. " Fresh water " is a vague term applied to a natural water which does not contain much dissolved impurity.

River-water

Spring water collects in rivers and streams. It has been estimated that the rivers of the world discharge some 6524 cubic miles of water into the ocean per annum. Rivers contain not only the solid matter furnished by spring waters, but also organic matter derived from plants growing on the sides and bottom of the river, and also from the drainage of villages and towns through which the river passes. The river, in virtue of its greater volume and force, carries along a considerable amount of suspended solids. River water also contains in solution matter from the country which it drains. Thus the water of the Dee (Scotland), draining slate and sandstone rocks, contains about 0·0056 per cent. of solid matter, about one-fourth of this being calcium salts ; the Thames, draining chalk rocks, contains about 0·03 per cent. of solid matter, two-thirds of which is calcium salts.

Sea-water

Just as spring water flows into the rivers, the rivers flow into the sea carrying their dissolved salts, and suspended matters which have not been deposited in transit. The vapour which rises from the sea by evaporation is almost pure water ; hence, unless the dissolved matters are continuously removed, sea-water must be gradually getting more and more " salty." Sea-water contains a relatively large proportion of soluble salts *—about 3·5 per cent. of solids in solution. Where the evaporation is greatest we naturally expect to find the greatest proportion of salts in solution. Thus the Mediterranean contains about 3·4 per cent. of solids in solution ; whereas the Baltic, with its numerous tributaries, and less evaporation, contains between 0·3 and 0·8 per cent. of solids in solution. Salts accumulate in land-locked seas and lakes much faster than in the sea. In illustration, the Dead Sea contains 22·8 per cent. of solids in solution ; the Great Salt Lake (Utah), 23 per cent. ; and the Elton Lake (Russia), 27 per cent. These masses of water behave as if they were exposed in a large evaporating basin, for the salts accumulate in the water and are deposited in crystalline masses on the shores of the lakes as the water evaporates.

§ 12 Purification of Water for Town Supply

Potable water, that is, water which is fit for human consumption, is obtained principally from rivers and lakes, and also from wells— artesian and otherwise. The inorganic or mineral matters usually found in solution in natural water are not directly injurious to health. The purification of water for towns and cities is a very important practical problem for the chemist. The best solution can only follow after a careful study of the local conditions. Water should be free from pathogenic (disease-producing) bacteria, and from suspended impurities. This is generally done by filtration through large filter beds made from layers of sand and gravel, extending in some cases over an acre of ground. Most of the bacteria which may be present in the raw water are removed in this way ; but for safety, especially where the supply is drawn from a river which, as for example, in the Thames valley may suffer contamination from inhabited areas higher up the valley, sterilization by means of chlorine is often utilised. Three parts of chlorine per million is usually sufficient to destroy all bacteria in a short period of time.

To maintain the purity of the water supply up to the proper standard, it is necessary to make (1) a periodical critical examination of the source from which the water is obtained ; (2) regular bacteriological

* For instance, an average type contains about 96·5 per cent. of water ; 2·7 per cent. of sodium salts ; 0·07 per cent. of potassium salts ; 0·14 per cent. of calcium salts ; 0·59 per cent. of magnesium salts, as well as dissolved gases ; 0·012 per cent. of nitrogen ; 0·006 per cent. of oxygen ; and 0·017 per cent. of carbon dioxide.

examinations for pathogenic germs ; and (3) chemical examinations for nitrogenous organic matter—albumenoids, etc.—upon which bacteria feed, and for the products of bacterial life—free ammonia, ammonium nitrate and nitrite. The presence of these substances in water throws it under suspicion.

§ 13 Hard Water

Water which will only with difficulty give a lather with soap is called **hard** water. The difficulty of obtaining a lather is due to the presence in the water of substances which react with the soap and form an insoluble precipitate. Water containing in solution salts of calcium or magnesium or of any metal other than the alkali metals or ammonium, behaves in this way.

The commonest cause of hardness is the presence of calcium salts, usually the bicarbonate or sulphate, or both ; but the corresponding magnesium salts also occur.

It is a familiar fact of chemistry that the action of carbon dioxide turns lime water milky. Lime water is a solution of slaked lime in water, and although slaked lime is only sparingly soluble in water it yet has a measurable solubility. The action of carbon dioxide on the lime water is to convert the slaked lime (or calcium hydroxide) which it contains into calcium carbonate which may be reckoned to be insoluble :

$$Ca(OH)_2 + CO_2 = CaCO_3 + H_2O$$

If, after the lime water has thus been rendered turbid through the precipitation of calcium carbonate, more carbon dioxide is passed, the solution will go clear again. This is due to the formation of calcium bicarbonate which is a soluble salt.

$$CaCO_3 + CO_2 + H_2O = Ca(HCO_3)_2$$

This experiment gives the clue to the formation of one kind of hard water—that whose hardness is due to the presence of calcium (or magnesium) bicarbonate (magnesium carbonate behaves similarly). Rain-water absorbs carbon dioxide both from the air through which it falls and from decaying vegetation on the ground, and this water, thus charged with carbon dioxide, can dissolve calcium carbonate or magnesium carbonate if it flows over rocks composed of these substances, owing to the formation of calcium or magnesium bicarbonate.

These bicarbonates are easily decomposed by heat with the re-formation of the normal carbonate. This process is complete at the boiling point of water, so that a sample of hard water, whose hardness is due to the presence of these bicarbonates, has the hardness removed by boiling. Such water is said to exhibit **temporary** hardness. Hardness which is due to substances such as calcium sulphate is not removed by boiling and is known as **permanent** hardness.

Hard water is then so called on account of the difficulty of getting a lather with it with soap. Soap is a compound of sodium with a fatty acid. The soap is decomposed by magnesium or calcium salts. The fatty acid unites with the latter to form an insoluble curdy precipitate. This action continues until all the calcium and magnesium salts have been precipitated. Any further addition of soap at once produces a lather, and the soap can then be used as a cleansing agent. If a solution of soap of definite strength and a definite volume of water be employed—and this can be made by finding what volume of a given soap solution is required to produce a permanent lather with a solution of calcium chloride of known concentration—say equivalent to one gram of calcium carbonate per litre—the hardness of a given sample of water can be represented in terms of the amount of soap required to produce a lather—**T. Clark's soap test.** The hardness of water thus refers to the " soap-destroying power " of the water, and it is expressed in degrees. *Each degree, of hardness corresponds with one grain of calcium carbonate, or its equivalent in other calcium or magnesium salts, per gallon of water.* Hardness is also expressed in parts of calcium carbonate, or its equivalent, per 100,000 parts of water.

EXAMPLE.—6 c.c. of a standard soap solution (1 c.c. = 0·001 grm. $CaCO_3$) were required in titrating 50 c.c. of water in order to produce a lather which persisted for 5 minutes after the bottle containing lather and soap solution had been wel shaken. Hence, the water had 12 parts of calcium and magnesium salts—bicarbonates , sulphates, nitrates and chlorides—equivalent to 6·4 grams of calcium carbonate by weight per 100,000 c.c. of water. To convert this number into grains per gallon, multiply by 0·7. The result 8·4, represents the number of grains of calcium carbonate per gallon of water. The hardness of the water on Clark's scale is therefore 8·4.

Waters containing but small quantities of calcium and magnesium salts lather freely with soap and they are accordingly called **soft waters.** A water less than 5° hardness may be called " soft," and a water between 18° and 20° hardness is " moderately hard," and if over 30° hardness, " very hard." Very soft waters are liable to attack metals like lead, zinc, and iron, and so to introduce soluble salts of these metals into the water, which, if used for drinking purposes, is liable over a period of time to produce cumulative poisoning. Where this is so it is usual for the water-supply undertakings to harden the water artificially, as it then forms a coating on the surface of the lead which prevents further action.

Hardness in water is a cause of considerable waste and inconvenience. For washing purposes it induces great waste of soap, since no lather can be obtained until the calcium or other metal present has been removed by the soap. When temporarily hard water is boiled, the calcium and magnesium carbonates are deposited, often as a crust on the containing vessel. This is the cause of the formation of " fur " in kettles, and of scale in boilers. Methods for the removal of the hardness of water are thus of primary importance in all industrial work.

§ 14 The Softening of Water

The process of removing lime salts from hard water is called **softening the water.** In the case cited above, soap is the softening agent. If the hardness of the water be due to the presence of acid carbonates of calcium or magnesium, mere boiling will soften the water because, as indicated already, the acid carbonates are then decomposed, and the normal carbonates are precipitated. In **T. Clark's process for softening water** (1841), the necessary amount of milk of lime or lime-water is added to convert all the acid carbonates of lime and magnesium into the normal carbonate. We have here the curious paradox—" add lime to remove lime." This process depends upon the fact that the slaked lime reacts with the carbon dioxide present in the solution to form calcium carbonate, which is precipitated. The carbon dioxide is thus removed from the bicarbonate present, calcium carbonate again being precipitated. These facts are expressed in the equation :

$$Ca(HCO_3)_2 + Ca(OH)_2 = 2CaCO_3 + 2H_2O$$

It is important to avoid adding excess of slaked lime as some of this will then dissolve, forming lime water which is a permanently hard water and may well be very much harder indeed than the water which is being softened.

Water, any part of whose hardness is temporary, may be softened by boiling. If the water also possesses permanent hardness, it may be dealt with as follows.

After removing the temporary hardness, if present, by boiling or by Clark's lime process, the permanent hardness may be removed by the addition of sodium carbonate. The boiling as well as the alkali carbonate processes of softening water were known towards the middle of the eighteenth century and were described by T. Bergman (1778). The sodium carbonate precipitates the calcium and magnesium as insoluble carbonates : $CaSO_4 + Na_2CO_3 = CaCO_3 + Na_2SO_4$. The water still contains sodium sulphate and sodium chloride, but the presence of a small quantity of these

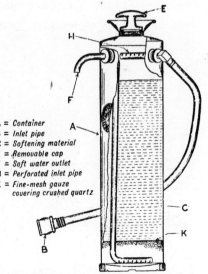

A = *Container*
B = *Inlet pipe*
C = *Softening material*
E = *Removable cap*
F = *Soft water outlet*
H = *Perforated inlet pipe*
K = *Fine-mesh gauze covering crushed quartz*

FIG. 97.—Permutit Type of Water Softener.

salts is not usually objectionable. Sodium carbonate will remove temporary as well as permanent hardness.

A process of water softening which is becoming increasingly important is the **permutit** or **base-exchange** process. In this process the water is passed through a layer of powdered zeolite, either natural or artificial—called commercially *permutit*—made by fusing a mixture of quartz sand, china clay, and soda ash. The calcium and magnesium salts in the water react with the zeolite forming insoluble calcium and magnesium zeolite, and a soluble sodium salt. This removes both temporary and permanent hardness. Iron and manganese salts are also removed by this process. The "exhausted" zeolite is revived by passing a concentrated solution of sodium chloride through it. The calcium and magnesium zeolite reforms sodium zeolite.

The reactions taking place may be represented by the equations :

$$Ca(HCO_3)_2 + Na_2Al_2Si_2O_8.xH_2O = CaAl_2Si_2O_8.xH_2O + 2NaHCO_3$$

when softening is taking place, and

$$CaAl_2Si_2O_8.xH_2O + 2NaCl = Na_2Al_2Si_2O_8.xH_2O + CaCl_2$$

when the exhausted permutit is being regenerated.

Hard water in nature.

Rain-water percolating through limestone rocks becomes highly charged with dissolved calcium bicarbonate ; such water in dripping

FIG. 98.—Stalactites and Stalagmites in the Jenolan Caves, N.S.W.
Photo: *Exclusive News Agency.*

through the roof of a cave or subterranean cavern will be exposed to the air ; as a result, some carbon dioxide escapes from the solution, and a certain amount of calcium carbonate is deposited. Each drop of water adds its own little share of calcium carbonate. The deposit grows—maybe on the roof, when it is called a **stalactite** ; maybe on the floor, when it is called a **stalagmite**. All depends upon the time occupied by each drop in gathering and dropping, how fast the carbonate is deposited. Measurements of a stalactite in the Ingleborough Cavern (Yorkshire), made in 1839 and 1873, show that it grew at the rate of 0·3 inch per annum. The San Filippo spring (Tuscany) is said to deposit "lime" at the rate of 12 inches a month, and the spring has formed a bed of limestone rock 250 feet thick, $1\frac{1}{4}$ miles long, and $\frac{1}{3}$ mile wide. The stalagmite grows upwards from the ground, and the stalactite grows downwards, like an icicle, from the roof. In time, the two may meet and form a pillar. Fig. 98 conveys but little idea of the beauty of some limestone caverns in which stalactites and stalagmites have been growing. The photograph shows stalactites, stalagmites, and pillars which have no doubt been formed in this manner. There are some very fine grottos, caves, or

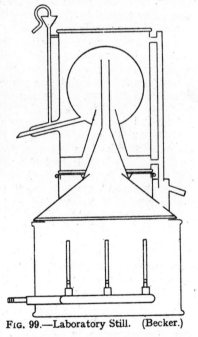

FIG. 99.—Laboratory Still. (Becker.)

caverns in Castleton and other parts of Derbyshire, at Cheddar in Somerset, in the Isle of Skye, Antiparos (Archipelago), in the Hartz (Germany), Auxille (France), New South Wales, Auckland, United States, and numerous other limestone districts. The building stone called *travertine* (Tiberstone) is probably a limestone deposited from a mineral spring. The Colosseum and much of ancient and modern Rome were built with this stone.

§ 15 Purification of Water for Scientific Purposes

The water supply of a town is watched, as has been said above, to ensure its fitness for drinking ; but it is still far from being "chemically pure," and so for many scientific purposes it is unsuitable. Two grades of water are ordinarily distinguished for laboratory work, viz.,

   (i) Distilled water ;
   (ii) Conductivity water.

Distilled water can be made by means of an apparatus comprising a distilling flask and Liebig condenser, but partly on account of the slight solvent action of water on the glass, and partly because of the considerable quantities required in the average laboratory, some form of water-still designed for the purpose is usually employed. One form out of the many which have been devised for such work is illustrated in Fig. 99. Such a still is usually made of copper plated with tin, and the principle involved in its use is identical with that of the simple distillation apparatus using a Liebig's condenser and distilling flask.

Distilled water prepared in this way is pure enough for most chemical work, but for the investigation of matters such as the conductivity of solutions, it is still not pure enough. The yet purer water required for these purposes is known as conductivity water, and its preparation has already been described (p. 196).

§ 16 Properties of Water

Physical Properties

At ordinary temperatures, pure water is a tasteless and odourless liquid ; it is colourless in moderately thin layers, but appears greenish-blue when viewed in thick layers. According to J. Aitken, the blue colour of large bodies of water—e.g., in china clay settling pits, in tanks in which water is being softened by the addition of milk of lime, etc.—is an optical effect due to the action of the fine particles suspended in the liquid, on the light.

Liquids are but slightly compressible. If 1000 c.c. of water be subjected to a pressure of two atmospheres the volume will be reduced 0·05 c.c. According to P. G. Tait, this very small compressibility means that if sea-water were quite incompressible, the average level of the sea would be raised 116 feet higher than it is to-day, and 4 per cent. of the present land surface would be submerged.

Non-metallic liquids are bad conductors of heat ; water is one of the best of liquids for conducting heat (mercury excepted), but even then, the thermal conductivity is small. Witness a piece of weighted ice at the bottom of a test-tube of cold water. If the test-tube be held obliquely, and heated by a bunsen burner near the surface, the water at the surface will boil, but the ice at the bottom will remain unmelted.

Water boils at 100° under 760 mm. pressure. The greater the pressure, the higher the boiling point ; and conversely, the less the pressure,* the lower the boiling point. These phenomena occur with liquids generally, and it is therefore necessary to state the pressure when giving the boiling point of a liquid. If no pressure is stated " 760 mm." is understood. Thus at Quito (9350 feet above sea-level), with the barometer at an average height, 525·4 mm., water boils at 90·1° ; and on the top of Mount Everest (29,002 feet), barometer at

---

* Roughly about $\frac{1}{27}$° C. per mm. for a few degrees above and below 100°.

255·3 mm., water would boil at 72°. Steam or water vapour is an invisible, colourless gas which condenses to a visible cloud of small particles when it comes in contact with the atmosphere. This is readily shown by boiling water in a flask; inside the flask, the vapour is invisible, and a cloud of minute water particles—condensed steam —appears where the steam comes in contact with the cold air.

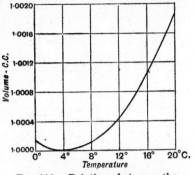

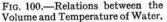

FIG. 100.—Relations between the Volume and Temperature of Water.

Liquid water freezes at 0° into crystalline ice. Water vapour freezes into hoar frost and snow. The crystals of ice are extremely rare and difficult to measure. The crystals can often be seen when a piece of ice is examined with a lens while a beam of bright light is passed through it. Snow crystals are common. They appear in the form of an hexagonal (six-sided) nucleus or six-rayed star with the rays developed in bewildering complexity. The crystals are of inimitable delicacy and beauty. No two seem alike; but all are fashioned after one definite type—the six-rayed star. Ice appears to be colourless or white when pure, but it is pale blue when seen in large masses.

By plotting the volume of a given mass of water at different temperatures, we get a curve similar to that illustrated in Fig. 100. This curve shows that, at temperatures above 4°, water, like most liquids, expands when heated and contracts when cooled down to 4°; but the curve below 4° is abnormal. It shows that water expands when cooled below, and contracts when heated up to 4°. If the specific gravity of water at 4° be taken as unity, it follows that water becomes specifically lighter when the temperature is raised or lowered beyond this point. The expansion of water when cooled from 4° to 0° is very small, but that minute quantity has a very important bearing in nature. When the water on the surface of, say, a lake is cooled, it contracts. The heavier cold water sinks, and the warm water rises. This circulation cools the temperature of the whole body of water down to 4°; any further cooling results in the formation of specifically lighter water. Accordingly, this remains on the surface, and circulation ceases. Finally, as a result of this remarkable and abnormal property, when the temperature of the atmosphere falls to 0°, a surface film of ice is formed.* If the water did not expand in this way, as the temperature fell to 0°, the whole body of water would freeze from below upwards and produce profound climatic changes, since the larger amount of ice

* " Ground ice " or " anchor ice " is formed at the bottom of rapidly moving streams when the water is thoroughly mixed and does not settle in layers.

formed in winter would materially affect the temperature for the rest of the year. These remarks do not apply to sea-water which contracts as the temperature is lowered down to the freezing point. In the act of freezing water expands so that 100 c.c. of liquid water at 0° gives approximately 110 c.c. of ice at the same temperature. The specific gravity of ice at 0° varies with its mode of formation from 0·9159 to 0·9182 ; the specific gravity of water at 0° is 0·999867. Accordingly, ice floats on the surface of water. The expansion of water during freezing is an important factor. The expansion may burst the inter-cellular tissue of plants by freezing the cell-sap ; the expansion may disrupt the fibres of flesh, so that frozen meat appears rather more " pulpy " than ordinary meat. If water freezes in pipes, the expansion of water in the act of freezing may burst the pipe, and water will " leak " when the ice " thaws " ; water freezing in the surface crevices of rocks splits and widens the fissures so that the surface crust of the rock appears to disintegrate during a " thaw." The debris collects as " talus " at the foot of the rocks, ready to be transported by water to lower levels. Hence this simple force plays an important part in the weathering and decay of rocks, building stones, etc., in countries exposed to alternate frost and thaw ; and J. Tyndall adds : " The records of geology are mainly the history of the work of water."

The electrical properties of water have already been mentioned in Chapter XII (p. 196). It is a poor conductor of electricity, having a specific conductivity at 25° C. of only $0·04 \times 10^{-6}$ mhos. It is, how-ever, notable in being a good *ionizing* solvent, that is to say, compounds like common salt and hydrochloric acid, i.e., polar compounds or compounds containing an electro-valency, dissolve in it, giving con-ducting solutions in which the solute has become largely dissociated into ions. Water is not the only ionizing solvent known, but it is about the best.

It has been observed that solvents whose dielectric constant (or specific induc-tive capacity) are highest are the best ionizing solvents, and this is in agreement with what would be expected on the basis of the electronic theory of valency, according to which polar compounds, such as sodium chloride, are united by the electrical forces between the ions.

Chemical Properties.

The chemical properties of water can be classified broadly under three main headings, viz., (i) reactions in which water undergoes decomposition ; (ii) reactions in which water acts as a catalyst ; (iii) reactions in which water forms addition compounds.

Decomposition Reactions

The combination of hydrogen and oxygen to form water is attended with the evolution of a large quantity of heat, as indicated by the equation :

$$2H_2 + O_2 = 2H_2O + 116·2 \text{ Cals.,}$$

the water formed remaining as steam. It therefore follows, by the application of the principle of Le Chatelier, that if the reaction is to any extent reversible, the dissociation of the steam into hydrogen and oxygen will occur most at high temperatures. Investigation shows that dissociation does in fact take place, but it is difficult to carry out such an experiment since the decomposition only takes place at high temperatures, and recombination occurs very rapidly when the temperature is lowered, so that the formation of oxygen and hydrogen is not easily detected. Table XXV gives some values of the dissociation at various temperatures.

TABLE XXV.—DISSOCIATION OF WATER.

Temperature	Degree of Dissociation (per cent.).
1124°	0·0073
1288°	0·034
1984°	0·77
2369°	4·3
2488°	8·6
2656°	11·1

Many elements which are higher in the electro-chemical series than hydrogen will, as pointed out on page 252, decompose water at a suitable temperature. The alkali metals (sodium, potassium, etc.) attack water readily at the ordinary temperature :

$$2Na + 2H_2O = 2NaOH + H_2,$$

and the alkaline earth metals (calcium, strontium, etc.) behave similarly :

$$Ca + 2H_2O = Ca(OH)_2 + H_2$$

Magnesium, however, is only slightly affected by cold water, but reacts fairly readily with hot water. Magnesium, zinc and iron readily react with steam. Aluminium does not react with water in ordinary circumstances, since it is protected by a surface film of oxide, but if it is removed and some means adopted for preventing its re-formation, aluminium will decompose water in the cold. This can be effected by amalgamation with mercury (compare preparation of hydrogen, p. 254).

Non-metals for the most part do not react with water ; the exceptions being carbon and silicon, and fluorine and chlorine. Carbon at a red heat decomposes steam, forming water-gas (see pp. 362-4) and silicon reacts similarly, but much more slowly :

$$C + H_2O = CO + H_2$$
$$Si + 2H_2O = SiO_2 + 2H_2$$

Chlorine, when passed into water, first dissolves forming a green solution, but, on standing, reacts forming hydrochloric and hypochlorous acids :

$$Cl_2 + H_2O = HCl + HOCl,$$

but in sunlight the latter acid breaks up with the formation of oxygen :

$$2HOCl = 2HCl + O_2$$

Fluorine acts somewhat similarly, but no intermediate stage can be detected, and hydrofluoric acid and oxygen (mixed with ozone) are obtained in all circumstances :

$$2F_2 + 2H_2O = 2H_2F_2 + O_2.$$

Reactions involving water, but in which hydrogen is not evolved are, of course, very numerous, and plentiful examples occur in later chapters. Among these mention might now be made of **hydrolytic** reactions, that is to say, the decomposition of a compound by means of water. Examples are the hydrolysis of the halides of non-metals, such as the phosphorus halides :

$$PCl_3 + 3H_2O \rightleftharpoons P(OH)_3 + 3HCl,$$

in which the halogen is removed as its hydracid and the corresponding hydroxy derivative of the non-metal is formed. A similar reaction occurs with substances such as sulphuryl chloride (which may be regarded as the chloride of the " group " SO_2—a group possessing non-metallic properties) :

$$SO_2Cl_2 + 2H_2O = SO_2(OH)_2 + 2HCl$$

$SO_2(OH)_2$ otherwise H_2SO_4 is, of course, sulphuric acid.

Salts which are derived from acids and bases of markedly different strengths are generally hydrolyzed in aqueous solution (see Ch. XV). In some cases a basic salt is formed, for example bismuth trichloride is hydrolyzed to bismuth oxychloride,

$$BiCl_3 + H_2O = BiOCl + 2HCl$$

§ 17 Water as a Catalyst

The remarkable catalytic activity of water has been alluded to in Chapter XIV (p. 228), but calls for more extended consideration here.

Isolated experiments, going back to the latter half of the eighteenth century, had shown that some chemical reactions proceed more readily in the presence of water than in its absence, but real knowledge of the subject begins with the observation of Dixon in 1880 that a mixture of carbon monoxide and oxygen which had been dried for some time over sulphuric acid did not explode on passage of a spark, although after the addition of the merest trace of water to the mixture a violent explosion occurred when a spark was passed.

Further investigations along the same lines, by H. B. Baker, revealed several other reactions, normally taking place with explosion, or at least with the liberation of a great deal of energy, which are inhibited by the intensive drying of the reactants ; and later, and perhaps yet more remarkable, he showed that intensive drying has in many cases a pronounced effect on the physical properties of substances.

Baker's investigations have shown that the *complete* drying of any substance or substances is a difficult task, particularly as minute traces of water are retained by surfaces such as those of the glass vessels in which the experiments are carried out. In order to remove these traces, it is necessary to heat them in a stream of perfectly dry air. The intensive drying demanded in order to achieve Baker's results is effected by prolonged exposure of the gases, or liquids, concerned to phosphorus pentoxide.by sealing them up in tubes for a period of some months or even years.

Among the reactions which are inhibited or slowed down enormously by complete drying, the following may be mentioned. Carbon only combines with oxygen very slowly on heating ; ammonia and hydrogen chloride do not combine on mixing ; sulphur, and phosphorus, may be distilled in perfectly dry oxygen. Hydrogen and chlorine, and hydrogen and oxygen will not explode when perfectly dry.

As regards this last reaction, Baker made the remarkable observation that perfectly dry hydrogen and oxygen, when mixed and heated almost to the melting point of silver, do not combine ; but that a spark will cause combination to take place to some extent but *without* explosion. Further, although after the passage of a spark the sides of the tube can be seen to be covered with dew, still no explosion can be brought about. It has been suggested that the water formed is too pure to catalyze the reaction.

Ammonium chloride, which dissociates when heated in the ordinary way, was reported by Baker to be capable of vaporization without dissociation if intensively dried. Much controversy has taken place concerning the theoretical implications of this result ; but recently (1929) Rodebusch and Michalek have claimed that Baker's conclusion was due to a faulty method of density measurement.

As regards the effect of moisture on the physical properties of substances Baker found that, after several years drying with phosphorus pentoxide, many liquids had their vapour pressure reduced and their boiling point and surface tension increased. The melting points of solids such as iodine and sulphur were similarly found to be raised.

These results have been disputed in some quarters and the question is still *sub judice*, but for the moment it is necessary to accept the accuracy of Baker's work although it is very difficult to explain its results.

§ 18 Addition Compounds of Water

Water exhibits a marked tendency to form additive compounds with other substances of the kind known as **molecular compounds.** This property is believed to be due to the electronic structure of the water molecule, which may be represented :

$$H : \overset{..}{\underset{..}{O}} : H$$

and which thus contains two " lone-pairs " of electrons which can form co-ordinate linkages (see Ch. IX, p. 148).

The most important of these compounds are the hydrates—particularly salt hydrates. Very many salts, when crystallized from water, yield crystals which contain water combined in simple molecular proportions. Familiar examples are washing soda, $Na_2CO_3.10H_2O$, and ordinary blue copper sulphate, $CuSO_4.5H_2O$. These compounds lose their water (often known as **water of crystallization**) on heating, but the different molecules of water are often held with greater or less tenacity. Thus, for example, copper sulphate crystals lose four molecules of water at a temperature very little above $100°$, whereas a temperature in excess of $200°$ is required to drive off the fifth. (Compare Fig. 82, p. 217.)

It is thought by some that the water molecules are attached to the ions of the salt by co-ordinate valencies, and that in the case of copper sulphate one molecule is attached to the sulphate ion, whereas the other four are attached to the copper ion, thus accounting for the difference in the strength of attachment. This may be so, but we really know very little beyond the simple facts that : (1) Water is a product of the dissociation of the hydrates ; (2) water is usually given off at comparatively low temperatures ; (3) water is not an essential part of the reacting unit in its most characteristic transformations ; and (4) water is not generally necessary for the formation of the salt since water of crystallization can generally be removed by suitable means leaving the salt anhydrous. Several zeolites may lose their combined water and take it up again without losing their crystalline form.

If the term " water of crystallization " be carelessly employed, it may suggest that crystallization is somehow dependent on the presence of water, and this the more, as efflorescent salts " appear " to lose their crystalline character when water is lost. Crystals of gypsum—$CaSO_4.2H_2O$—form a white chalky powder when the water is driven off ; crystalline sodium carbonate, and also Glauber's salts, likewise produce white powders when their combined water is expelled. The powdered dehydrated substances are all crystalline. In fact, practically all chemical compounds can be crystallized. Crystallization is not dependent upon the presence of water. Sulphur, common salt, iodine, potassium chlorate, potassium sulphate, and numerous other crystalline substances do not contain the elements of water. Again, crystalline calcspar does not contain the elements of water, and yet when calcined it gives a white powder. The calcspar has lost carbon dioxide, not water.

Related to this property of water of forming additive compounds is the fact that, in ordinary circumstances, liquid water is *associated*, that is, its molecules are probably more complex than is indicated by the formula H_2O. Water is so frequently represented by this formula that it is easy to forget that in all probability it does not accurately represent liquid water. The evidence for these statements may be summarized as follows :—

(i) Steam has a vapour density just above its boiling point, which is higher than that corresponding to H_2O ;

(ii) water boils at 100°, whereas hydrogen sulphide its analogue (p. 446), which would be expected to have a higher b.p. than water, boils, in fact, at $-61°$;

(iii) many of its physical properties such as its high surface tension, high dielectric constant, show departure from the values to be anticipated if it were not associated.

This behaviour has been ascribed to the possibility of co-ordination between water molecules, the oxygen of one molecule acting as donor and the hydrogen of another as acceptor (Ch. IX, § 148). This is indicated in such formulae as $H - O - H \leftarrow O - H$
$$| $$
$$H$$

§ 19 Hydrogen Peroxide.   Formation and Preparation

Hydrogen peroxide is a remarkable compound which was discovered by L. J. Thenard in 1818. It is formed in small quantities in a variety of reactions. For example, it is formed when oxygen is bubbled about the electrode from which hydrogen is being evolved during the electrolysis of dilute acid, and also at the anode during the electrolysis of dilute sulphuric acid by a current of high density. Water confined in a quartz vessel is decomposed by exposure to ultra-violet light rays —from a mercury lamp, sunlight, etc.—and hydrogen peroxide and hydrogen are formed :

$$2H_2O = H_2O_2 + H_2.$$

Hydrogen peroxide is produced during the combustion of hydrogen in air. For instance, when a jet of burning hydrogen impinges on the surface of cold water in which ice is floating, or on ice itself, hydrogen peroxide can be detected in the water; and is formed when moist ether is exposed to sunlight ; and when ozonized oxygen or air is passed through water on the surface of which a little ether floats.

Like ozone, q.v., hydrogen peroxide can be formed at a high temperature by passing a current of moist oxygen through a tube at about 2000° and rapidly chilling the issuing gases. It is often formed when a substance is oxidized in the presence of moisture. For instance, when zinc, copper, or lead is shaken up with air and dilute sulphuric acid (1 : 55), the reaction symbolized :

$$Zn + 2H_2O + O_2 = Zn(OH)_2 + H_2O_2 ;$$

and

$$Zn(OH)_2 + H_2SO_4 = ZnSO_4 + 2H_2O$$

occurs.

Hydrogen peroxide is ordinarily made by the action of acids on certain peroxides, such as sodium peroxide (p. 553) or barium peroxide (p. 637).

By treating a cold aqueous solution of sodium peroxide with dilute and cold hydrochloric acid, a solution of hydrogen peroxide mixed with sodium chloride is obtained :

$$Na_2O_2 + 2HCl = 2NaCl + H_2O_2.$$

A variation of this process is the employment of phosphoric acid, when the sodium hydrogen phosphate formed crystallizes out with 10 molecules of water of crystallization, thus effecting a considerable concentration of the solution :

$$Na_2O_2 + H_3PO_4 = Na_2HPO_4 + H_2O_2.$$

This is convenient on account of the ease with which hydrogen peroxide decomposes when heated.

It is, however, not easy to separate hydrogen peroxide from soluble salts formed in its preparation ; and so barium peroxide is the usual starting point as the barium can be precipitated as carbonate or sulphate.

Barium peroxide is added slowly to ice-cold water through which a stream of carbon dioxide is passing. The insoluble barium carbonate is precipitated, and a dilute aqueous solution of hydrogen peroxide remains :

$$BaO_2 + CO_2 + H_2O = BaCO_3 + H_2O_2.$$

If an excess of carbon dioxide be used, the yield of hydrogen peroxide is low and an insoluble barium percarbonate, $BaCO_4$, is precipitated. Or barium peroxide, mixed with a little ice-cold water, is gradually added to ice-cold dilute hydrochloric, sulphuric, silico-fluoric, or phosphoric acid. A barium salt—chloride, sulphate, silico-fluoride or phosphate—and hydrogen peroxide are formed. In the first case, the barium chloride is soluble. It can be removed by adding just sufficient silver sulphate to precipitate insoluble barium sulphate and silver chloride :

$$BaCl_2 + Ag_2SO_4 = BaSO_4 + 2AgCl.$$

This method is of historical interest because J. Thénard employed a similar process when he discovered hydrogen peroxide in 1818. The sulphuric acid process is more commonly used. In this, insoluble barium sulphate is precipitated. If concentrated sulphuric acid be allowed to react with barium dioxide, ozonized oxygen is evolved ; a more dilute acid gives oxygen ; and a very dilute acid gives hydrogen peroxide. It is important in this preparation to avoid the presence of excess of barium peroxide for this reacts with hydrogen peroxide.

Hydrogen peroxide is also made technically either by distilling the solution of persulphuric acid obtained by the electrolysis of sulphuric acid (p. 473) or by distilling potassium persulphate with dilute sulphuric acid.

Concentration of Solutions of Hydrogen Peroxide

A dilute solution of hydrogen peroxide can be concentrated in several ways. If it is evaporated on a water bath at about 70° in a smooth platinum or porcelain basin until signs of effervescence appear, the strength of the solution is raised to about 45 per cent. If a dilute solution of hydrogen peroxide is frozen, ice separates and the remaining liquid is richer in hydrogen peroxide.

A solution of hydrogen peroxide decomposes rapidly when heated to 100°—even if the solution be dilute—hence, for a long time, the concentration of an aqueous solution of hydrogen peroxide by fractional distillation was thought to be impossible ; but R. Wolffenstein (1902) discovered that the hydrogen peroxide can be distilled under reduced pressure without undue decomposition. This can be done in an apparatus such as that shown in Fig. 101. The concentrated solution

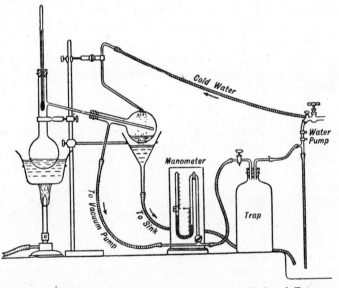

FIG. 101.—Distillation of Hydrogen Peroxide under Reduced Pressure.

of hydrogen peroxide obtained by evaporation at ordinary pressure is placed in the flask and heated to 35-40° C., the pressure being reduced to 15 mm. The liquid which then distils is mainly water, and distillation can be continued until the temperature of the liquid in the flask reaches about 70°. The liquid then remaining in the flask contains only a very small proportion of water.

Further concentration is best effected by placing a beaker containing some of the hydrogen peroxide solution in a mixture of solid carbon dioxide and ether. The whole mass freezes. A little of the frozen solid is dropped into a portion of the concentrated hydrogen peroxide solution. At between − 8° to − 10° small needle-shaped crystals separate and the mother liquid is drained away from the crystals.

In this way, it is possible to prepare 100 per cent. hydrogen peroxide.

The solution remaining in the distilling flask will serve for most experiments where concentrated solutions of hydrogen peroxide are required. This solution can also be further concentrated by evaporation over concentrated sulphuric acid *in vacuo.* This operation is conducted as follows : The dish containing the mixture rests on the perforated shelf of a desiccator, Fig. 102. The desiccator has a layer of concentrated

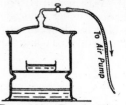

sulphuric acid below the perforated shelf. The lid of the desiccator, well greased, is placed in position. The desiccator is then exhausted by connecting the stoppered tube to a pump. Any water vapour given off by the solution in the dish is gradually absorbed by the concentrated acid.

FIG. 102.—Evaporation under Reduced Pressure.

§ 20 Occurrence and Properties of Hydrogen Peroxide

Occurrence

There is uncertainty about the alleged occurrence of hydrogen peroxide in rain, snow, dew, and air as is indicated (p. 318) in connection with the occurrence of ozone in air. Much of the published work does not clearly discriminate hydrogen peroxide from other oxidizing substances.

Properties

Pure hydrogen peroxide is a viscid liquid ; colourless, when viewed in thin layers, but with a bluish tinge when viewed in thick layers. The liquid has no smell. Dilute aqueous solutions have a peculiar bitter metallic taste. When a drop of liquid peroxide comes in contact with the skin, it forms a white blister. If concentrated sulphuric acid be mixed with hydrogen peroxide at a low enough temperature to prevent heating, oxygen rich in ozone is evolved. The liquid decomposes rapidly when heated at ordinary atmospheric pressures, but under reduced pressure it can be readily distilled. It boils between 68° and 69° under a pressure of about 26 mm., and at 84°-85° under a pressure of 68 mm. The liquid crystallizes in needle-like prisms at $-2°$. The liquid is soluble in water in all proportions.

Pure hydrogen peroxide is fairly stable. Dilute aqueous solutions keep fairly well—particularly if acid—a 3 per cent. solution suffered no appreciable change when kept a year. Alkaline solutions do not keep very well. Impurities like silica, iron, manganese, and alumina lead to a more rapid decomposition. If alcohol or ether be present, the aqueous solutions are more stable. The strength of aqueous solutions is represented commercially by the number of volumes of oxygen which 1 c.c. of the solution will furnish on decomposition. Thus 1 c.c. of a " 10-volume solution " will give 10 c.c. of oxygen when decomposed. A 3 per cent. solution of hydrogen peroxide is very nearly a "10-volume solution"; a 6 per cent. hydrogen peroxide solution is nearly of "20-volume" strength, and so on. The most concentrated solution on the market is called **perhydrol**, and it contains about 30 per cent. of hydrogen peroxide, corresponding with a "100-volume" strength.

Decomposition by contact action

Pure hydrogen peroxide is decomposed very rapidly if any dust be present. A little platinum black causes an explosion. Finely divided gold, silver, and similar metals, as well as powdered manganese dioxide, behave similarly. The action appears to be catalytic; a small trace of colloidal platinum, gold, etc., can accelerate the decomposition of large amounts of hydrogen peroxide. The action has been compared with that of yeast on a solution of sugar, and these "colloidal" metals have been given the name *inorganic ferments*.

A few drops of liquid hydrogen peroxide on a piece of cotton wool will make the cotton inflame. Similar results are obtained with aqueous solutions of hydrogen peroxide, but the action is much less vigorous. Rough surfaces have a disturbing effect on the stability of hydrogen peroxide—a concentrated solution is decomposed when poured on to a ground-glass surface. The presence of small quantities of some substance—e.g., manganese silicate—make the solutions more stable; these agents have been called *anticatalysts*, *negative catalysts*, or *retarders*. Acetanilide is particularly useful in preserving hydrogen peroxide solutions.

Oxidizing Properties

Hydrogen peroxide, as will be seen, resembles ozone in its strong oxidizing qualities. It liberates iodine from solutions of potassium iodide (p. 315). The reaction is accelerated by acetic and mineral acids, and particularly by ferrous sulphate. According to Schönbein, one part of hydrogen peroxide in the presence of 25,000,000 parts of water can be detected by a mixture of potassium iodide and ferrous sulphate. It converts lead sulphide into lead sulphate, as is also the case with ozone. Hence the use of hydrogen peroxide for cleaning oil paintings which have been darkened by the action of hydrogen sulphide—sometimes present in the air of towns—upon the lead compounds in the paint.

Dilute solutions of hydrogen peroxide are used for bleaching silk, feathers, straw, hair, ivory, teeth, etc., where more violent bleaching agents would injure the material. Instead of hydrogen peroxide an acidified solution of sodium peroxide is sometimes employed. The actions are similar. Since the products of the decomposition of hydrogen peroxide—water and oxygen—are harmless, it is also used medicinally and surgically as an antiseptic. Hydrogen peroxide is also used in analytical work for the oxidation of sulphites to sulphates; arsenites to arsenates; chromic salts to chromates; ferrous to ferric salts; nitrites to nitrates, etc. H. B. Baker and L. H. Parker showed that if hydrogen peroxide be removed from synthetic water, the water attacks sodium amalgam much more slowly than water containing, say, 1 part of the peroxide in 100,000.

Peroxidizing Properties

Hydrogen peroxide forms peroxides of the alkalis and alkaline earths when treated with the corresponding hydroxides. For instance, with barium hydroxide :

$$Ba(OH)_2 + H_2O_2 = BaO_2 + 2H_2O.$$

W. Spring (1895) pointed out that hydrogen peroxide behaves in these reactions like an acid (p. 306). In confirmation, if sodium carbonate be added to hydrogen peroxide the corresponding alkaline peroxide is formed and carbon dioxide is evolved :

$$H_2O_2 + Na_2CO_3 = Na_2O_2 + CO_2 + H_2O ;$$

on the contrary, if the hydrogen peroxide be added to the solution of the carbonate, oxygen is evolved :

$$2H_2O_2 + Na_2CO_3 = Na_2CO_3 + 2H_2O + O_2.$$

The sodium carbonate acts as a catalytic agent in the latter case. It is not at all uncommon to find reactions progressing differently according to the way the substances are mixed together.

With titanium salts, hydrogen peroxide gives an orange-yellow coloration supposed to be due to the formation of pertitanic acid :

$$TiO_2 + H_2O_2 = H_2O + TiO_3.$$

The particular tint depends upon the amount of titanium present, and hence the reaction is used for the determination of the amount of titanium in various materials.

The reaction is also used as a test for hydrogen peroxide. It is said that one part of titanium in 1800 parts of water gives a deep yellow coloration, and one part in 180,000 a light yellow coloration. Cerium and vanadium salts give brick-red coloration, and uranium a bluish coloration, but these reactions are not so sensitive as with titanium salts.

With chromic acid, H_2CrO_4, hydrogen peroxide forms a blue solution which begins to decompose immediately with the evolution of oxygen. Some consider the oxide formed to be a compound of perchromic acid, $HCrO_4$, with hydrogen peroxide, say, $HCrO_5$ (q.v.). This is pure hypothesis ; no such compound has been isolated. The blue-coloured peroxide, whatever it be, is much more soluble in ether than in water, so that if a mixture of chromic acid and hydrogen peroxide in a test-tube be shaken with ether, a blue ethereal solution of the peroxide will float on the surface of the aqueous layer. The compound decomposes when the ether is evaporated. This reaction is used for the detection of chromates. It is said that this method will indicate one part of hydrogen peroxide in 80,000 parts of water.

Reducing Properties

Hydrogen peroxide appears to act as a reducing as well as an oxidizing agent. With ozone it forms oxygen and water :

$$O_3 + H_2O_2 = H_2O + 2O_2 ;$$

with silver oxide, metallic silver and oxygen :

$$Ag_2O + H_2O_2 = 2Ag + H_2O + O_2.$$

Similarly with gold oxide :

$$Au_2O_3 + 3H_2O_2 = 2Au + 3H_2O + 3O_2 ;$$

and lead dioxide,

$$PbO_2 + H_2O_2 = PbO + H_2O + O_2.$$

Curiously enough, in these reactions, the reducing agent is itself reduced—usually the reducing agent is oxidized during the reduction. The lead dioxide obtained when red lead is digested with dilute nitric acid dissolves very slowly, but if a few drops of hydrogen peroxide be added, all the lead dioxide dissolves in a few moments. The lead dioxide is reduced to lead monoxide by the hydrogen peroxide, and the product dissolves immediately in the dilute acid. This method is generally employed to hasten the solution of red lead in dilute acid prior to analysis. Hydrogen peroxide in alkaline solutions oxidizes manganese oxide, MnO, to manganese dioxide, MnO_2 ; but in acid solutions it reduces manganese dioxide to manganous oxide :

$$MnO_2 + H_2SO_4 + H_2O_2 = MnSO_4 + 2H_2O + O_2.$$

The reducing action of the hydrogen peroxide is only apparent. According to B. Brodie (1872) the oxides of silver, manganese, etc., have an atom of oxygen which is readily disengaged from its combination. Similarly, hydrogen peroxide readily parts with its odd atom of oxygen. Consequently, the atom of oxygen in hydrogen peroxide is supposed to *oxidize* the odd oxygen atom in the metallic peroxide.

A solution of potassium permanganate—$KMnO_4$—acidified with sulphuric acid is rapidly reduced by hydrogen peroxide :

$$5H_2O_2 + 2KMnO_4 + 3H_2SO_4 = K_2SO_4 + 2MnSO_4 + 8H_2O + 5O_2.$$

Consequently, if an aqueous solution, containing a known amount of potassium permanganate, be run from a burette into a known volume of hydrogen peroxide until the pink colour of the permanganate is no longer discharged, the amount of hydrogen peroxide present can be calculated. This is a convenient method for the determination of hydrogen peroxide.

Detection of Hydrogen Peroxide

A number of the reactions of hydrogen peroxide are similar to those of other oxidizing agents—particularly ozone (*q.v.*). It is necessary, in consequence, to be able to distinguish hydrogen peroxide from these other substances and also to be able to detect it in their presence. The actions of hydrogen peroxide on titanium sulphate and on chromic acid are distinctive and hydrogen peroxide is also the only substance which will liberate iodine from potassium iodide in presence of ferrous sulphate. A table of distinguishing tests for ozone and hydrogen peroxide will be found on page 317 (Table XXVI).

§ 21 Composition and Constitution of Hydrogen Peroxide

The composition of hydrogen peroxide was determined by Thénard, who introduced a weighed quantity into a graduated cylinder over mercury. He then decomposed it either by heat, or by adding manganese dioxide and obtained about 8 parts by weight of oxygen and 9 parts of water from 17 of hydrogen peroxide. The empirical formula of hydrogen peroxide is thus HO.

The molecular weight of hydrogen peroxide has been found, from its vapour density (which is 17 at 90°), and from the freezing points of its solutions, which also indicates 34 as its molecular weight. Hence the molecular formula is H_2O_2.

There is still doubt as to the constitutional formula to be assigned to hydrogen peroxide. It was at first suggested that it is H - O - O - H which is supported by the fact that hydrogen peroxide is formed in reactions involving the reduction of oxygen and not by the oxidation of water. But in order to account for the instability of one oxygen atom, Kingzett (1884) suggested the formula

$$\begin{array}{c} H \\ H \end{array}\!\!\Big\rangle O = O$$

In terms of the modern electronic theory of valency, the maximum covalency of oxygen is three and so this would become $\begin{array}{c} H \\ H \end{array}\!\!\Big\rangle O \to O$,

otherwise written $H : \overset{..}{O} : \overset{..}{\underset{H}{O}} :$, or $\left[H : \overset{..}{O} : \overset{..}{O} : \right]^- H^+$ which latter formula

is in agreement with the fact already noted, that in some cases hydrogen peroxide behaves as a weak acid. Against this view, however, must be set the evidence of Baeyer and Villiger (1900) from organic reactions with hydrogen peroxide which clearly points to the di-hydroxyl formula; but it is unsafe to attach too much importance to the structure of organic derivatives as evidence of that of the corresponding hydrogen compound. The reported discovery of a new variety of hydrogen peroxide formed by the action of atomic hydrogen on oxygen at liquid air temperature (Geib and Harteck, 1932) suggests the existence of molecules of both types.

CHAPTER XVIII

OXYGEN

" On the first of August, 1774, I endeavoured to extract air from *mercurius calcinatus per se* * and I presently found that . . . air was expelled from it very readily. Having got about three or four times as much as the bulk of my materials, I admitted water to it and found that it was not imbibed by it. But what surprised me more than I can well express was that a candle burned in this air with a remarkable brilliant flame."—J. PRIESTLEY.

§ 1 History and Occurrence

THE discovery of oxygen must be accounted one of the most important advances in the history of chemistry, ranking along with the discovery of the composition of water. As has been said (p. 5) air was for long considered to be an element, and it was not until the end of the eighteenth century that it was recognized to be essentially a mixture, the active constituent of which we now call oxygen.

Oxygen was discovered independently by Scheele some time between 1771 and 1773, and by Priestley in 1774. Scheele called the gas " fire-air " and " vital air," and made it by heating red oxide of mercury ; sulphuric acid and manganese dioxide ; nitre ; and some other substances. Scheele did not publish an account of his work until 1777. Meanwhile Joseph Priestley independently prepared the same gas, which he called " dephlogisticated air," while examining the effect of heat upon a great variety of substances confined in a cylinder (*A*, Fig. 103) along with mercury, and inverted in a trough of mercury, somewhat as in Fig. 103. Priestley focused the sun's rays upon the different substances by means of a " burning lens of 12 inches diameter, and 20 inches focal distance." Priestley announced his discovery of oxygen in the words quoted at the head of this chapter.

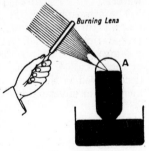

FIG. 103.—
Priestley's Experiment.

Many erring steps have stumbled on the threshold of the discovery of oxygen ; for instance, Eck de Sultzbach, in 1489, knew that red oxide of mercury gave off a " spirit " when heated ; had he named and isolated the " spirit " he would have been credited with the discovery of oxygen. In 1678, O. Borch prepared the gas by heating saltpetre ; in 1727, S. Hales collected the gas obtained by heating saltpetre ; P. Payen obtained it in 1774 ; and J. Priestley himself obtained it the same year. These are not usually considered to have been discoveries

* That is, mercuric oxide, or red oxide of mercury.

of the gas because no attempt was made to determine the specific properties of the product. There are also indications in old books that the Greeks knew about oxygen in the fourth century ; and that the Chinese were acquainted with the gas long before Priestley's and Scheele's experiments.

The real importance of this discovery escaped both Scheele and Priestley on account of their adherence to the doctrine of phlogiston, and it fell to Lavoisier to show that combustion, calcination of metals and respiration are related phenomena and are processes of combination with oxygen. The account of Lavoisier's work in this field belongs properly to the history of the elucidation of the nature of the atmosphere and is given elsewhere (Ch. XXI)

Occurrence

Oxygen is the most widely distributed and commonest of all the elements.

About one-fourth of the atmospheric air, by weight, consists of free oxygen, and water contains nearly 89 per cent. of combined oxygen. Oxygen also forms a material part of rocks. Thus calcium carbonate, which occurs as chalk, limestone, marble, etc., contains 48 per cent. of oxygen ; and silica, which is found in flint, quartz, etc., contains over 53 per cent. of oxygen by weight.

§ 2 Preparation and Manufacture of Oxygen

Oxygen is obtained either from the atmosphere, or by the decomposition of oxygen-containing compounds, such as oxides and salts of oxy-acids. It is also formed along with hydrogen in the electrolysis of water.

The atmosphere is the only source of oxygen which is used for its manufacture (see below), but other methods are employed for its preparation in the laboratory.

Many oxides are not decomposed by heat, but some, notably those of the so-called " noble " metals (e.g., mercury, gold and silver), are decomposed in this way. Priestley's method of making oxygen from mercuric or silver oxide exemplifies this fact :

$$2HgO = 2Hg + O_2$$
$$2Ag_2O = 4Ag + O_2,$$

but this method is not of great practical importance. The higher oxides of some other metals lose oxygen on heating and a lower oxide remains. Examples are manganese dioxide, lead dioxide, red lead, barium dioxide,

$$3MnO_2 = Mn_3O_4 + O_2$$
$$2PbO_2 = 2PbO + O_2$$
$$2Pb_3O_4 = 6PbO + O_2$$
$$2BaO_2 = 2BaO + O_2.$$

Barium dioxide has been utilized for the commercial preparation of oxygen since it can be readily obtained by heating barium oxide in the air. (See Brin's process—below, p. 299.)

The peroxides of the alkali metals give off oxygen when brought in contact with cold water, and oxygen is sometimes prepared in this way :

$$2Na_2O_2 + 2H_2O = 4NaOH + O_2.$$

Oxone is a commercial preparation consisting of sodium peroxide mixed with a little catalytic agent like colloidal manganese dioxide, and is used for the making of oxygen on a small scale. The salts of some oxy-acids such as chlorates, permanganates and nitrates decompose when heated, yielding oxygen, and this is the basis of the ordinary laboratory method of preparing oxygen, potassium chlorate being the most convenient salt to use.

Preparation of Oxygen from Potassium Chlorate

Potassium chlorate is a white crystalline solid which melts to a clear liquid when heated to about 340°. At about 10° higher the melted chlorate appears to boil, because bubbles of oxygen gas are copiously evolved. The potassium chlorate is decomposing. When the bubbling ceases, the molten mass begins to " thicken " or solidify. The potassium chlorate has decomposed into potassium perchlorate, potassium chloride, and oxygen. If the temperature be raised still further—over 600°—the mass again melts to a clear liquid and the potassium perchlorate decomposes, giving off more oxygen. The final products of decomposition are potassium chloride and oxygen. The reactions which take place may be represented :

$$2KClO_3 = 2KCl + 3O_2$$
$$4KClO_3 = KCl + 3KClO_4$$
$$KClO_4 = KCl + 2O_2$$

The temperature required to drive off the whole of the oxygen is rather higher than is convenient for ordinary work, but the salt may be completely decomposed, at a much lower temperature, if it has been mixed with manganese dioxide.

After the action, manganese dioxide still remains, but the potassium chlorate has decomposed into potassium chloride and oxygen. Manganese dioxide can be recovered from the residue by lixiviating the mass with water. The water dissolves the potassium chloride, and leaves the manganese dioxide as a residue. Cobalt and nickel oxides, like manganese oxide, accelerate the decomposition of potassium chlorate. Accordingly, for regular experimental work, oxygen is prepared by heating a mixture of potassium chlorate (not powdered) with its own bulk of manganese dioxide*—oxygen mixture—in a wide-

* If the manganese dioxide contains carbonaceous matters, an explosion may occur. Hence the manganese dioxide should be tested by heating a little with potassium chlorate before a large quantity is heated.

necked Florence flask, or a retort, or a special copper " oxygen tube," fitted with a wide delivery tube, because the gas is liable to come off rapidly in rushes. The tube is best clamped while tilted slightly downward towards the mouth, as indicated in Fig. 104, because a considerable amount of moisture is usually discharged from the mixture, and there is a risk of the moisture trickling back and cracking the glass. The gas is collected over water as in the case of hydrogen. The oxygen obtained by this process sometimes contains traces of carbon dioxide and chlorine. These can be removed by passing the gas through a soda-lime tube as shown in Fig. 104.

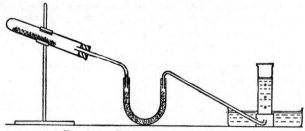

Fig. 104.—Preparation of Oxygen.

The action of the manganese dioxide in this experiment is curious. It was first observed by Döbereiner in 1820 and has been referred to already in Chapter XIV as an example of " catalytic agent," i.e., a substance which can accelerate (or retard) a reaction, without itself undergoing any permanent chemical change in the process. In the decomposition of potassium chlorate many other oxides act similarly, but not quite so vigorously—e.g., ferric, copper, cobalt or nickel oxide may be used in place of manganese dioxide.

The exact way in which the manganese dioxide acts is still uncertain. One plausible idea is that potassium permanganate is alternately formed and decomposed as indicated in the following equations :—

$$2MnO_2 + 2KClO_3 = 2KMnO_4 + Cl_2 + O_2$$
$$2KMnO_4 = K_2MnO_4 + MnO_2 + O_2$$
$$K_2MnO_4 + Cl_2 = 2KCl + MnO_2 + O_2$$

This view is supported by the fact that a trace of chlorine is often found in the gas prepared in this way and the potassium chloride left is often coloured pink.

Other suggestions have been alternate formation and decomposition of a higher oxide of manganese, e.g.,

$$2MnO_2 + KClO_3 = Mn_2O_7 + KCl$$
$$2Mn_2O_7 = 4MnO_2 + 3O_2$$

and that the manganese dioxide provides nuclei which prevent the supersaturation of the chlorate with oxygen.

Many other methods are available for the preparation of oxygen, as, for example, by heating sulphuric acid with manganese dioxide, chromic acid, potassium dichromate, potassium permanganate, or other salts rich in oxygen. A 10 per cent. solution of hydrogen pe oxide and a concentrated solution of potassium permanganate gives off oxygen when acidified with sulphuric acid. Potassium permanganate, when heated alone, also gives off some oxygen, and bleaching powder solution readily decomposes in presence of a cobalt salt (as a catalytic agent) yielding oxygen (compare p. 297).

Manufacture of Oxygen

For the industrial preparation of oxygen the atmosphere is the only practicable source, the governing consideration, as in all technical production, being that of cost. Oxygen was formerly made on a manufacturing scale by Brin's process (1881). This depends upon a very interesting reaction. When barium oxide—BaO—is heated in air to about 500°, it is rapidly oxidized to barium dioxide :

$$2BaO + O_2 = 2BaO_2.$$

If the barium dioxide be heated to a still higher temperature, 800°, the oxygen is given off and barium oxide remains as a residue :

$$2BaO_2 = 2BaO + O_2.$$

The barium oxide can be reoxidized and used over and over again, provided the air be freed from carbon dioxide, organic matter, dust, and any substance which forms a compound with barium oxide which is not decomposed under the given conditions. The regulation of the temperature offered practical difficulties which were overcome by keeping the temperature constant in the vicinity of 700°. Barium oxide is then transformed into the dioxide if the pressure of the atmosphere be about 2 kilos per square cm.* The peroxide is decomposed into the oxide and oxygen at the same temperature under a reduced pressure—about 0·05 kilogram per square cm. The gas pumped off under these conditions contained about 90 to 96 per cent. of oxygen, and 4 to 10 per cent. of nitrogen.

Brin's process is now obsolete since it cannot compete successfully with the extraction of oxygen from liquid air, by which practically the whole of the oxygen of commerce is now manufactured. The fractionation of liquid air has been described on pages 40-42.

§ 3 Properties of Oxygen

Oxygen is, at ordinary temperatures, a colourless, tasteless, and odourless gas. It is a little heavier than air. Oxygen is appreciably soluble in water—100 volumes of water, at 0°, can dissolve nearly 5 volumes of oxygen under a normal pressure of 760 mm., and at 20° about 3 volumes of the gas are dissolved. Fish are dependent upon the air dissolved in water for the oxygen they need for respiration. Animals are dependent upon the oxygen in air for respiration. Air normally contains 21 per cent. of oxygen, and if the proportion falls to 17 per cent. no known deleterious effects have been observed.

* Normally the atmospheric pressure is 1·033 kilograms per square cm.

Indians living in the upper reaches of the Andes breathe air which has oxygen equivalent to air with 12 per cent. of oxygen at ordinary atmospheric pressure. When the proportion of oxygen falls below this value the air is getting dangerous, and although air with less than 7 per cent. of oxygen can be breathed with impunity for a short time, life will soon be extinguished. A candle is extinguished in air with less than 17 per cent. of oxygen. A mouse soon dies if placed in an atmosphere deprived of oxygen. Pure oxygen can be breathed for a short time without harm, and oxygen is used medicinally for the resuscitation of persons who have been suffocated, or suffering from carbon monoxide poisoning, etc., where, owing to the enfeebled action of the lungs, the blood is not sufficiently aerated; and where it is necessary to stimulate a person with an internal injury—e.g., a broken rib—which would prevent artificial respiration. The prolonged inhalation of oxygen soon raises the temperature of the body dangerously high. An animal placed in ordinary or in compressed oxygen soon dies.

Metallic silver, gold, platinum, and palladium absorb oxygen at about 500°. Molten silver dissolves about ten times its volume of oxygen, and gives it up again on cooling. In cooling, a solid crust forms on the exterior surface; as the interior cools the gas bursts through the solid crust driving out a spurt of the still fluid metal—the phenomenon is called the "spitting" of silver. Molten platinum behaves in a somewhat similar way.

Oxygen has been condensed to a bluish-coloured mobile liquid which boils at −183°, at 760 mm. The liquid has a specific gravity of 1·14. Liquid oxygen can be frozen to a pale bluish-white solid not unlike snow in appearance. The solid melts at −219°, and has a specific gravity 1·43. The critical temperature of oxygen is −119° and the critical pressure 50 atmospheres.

Liquid oxygen is strongly attracted by a magnet, so that if a little liquid oxygen is placed in a cup beneath the poles of an electromagnet, it leaps up to the poles and remains permanently attached until all is evaporated. Mixtures of liquid oxygen and petroleum are violently explosive. It is said that a lighted candle falling into a bucket of liquid oxygen sent G. Claude to the hospital "in a very pitiable condition." Lamp-black soaked in liquid oxygen burns slowly when ignited, but explodes violently when detonated by a fulminate primer.

The great chemical activity of oxygen is well typified by Priestley's quaint observation, indicated on p. 295. A glowing splint of wood ("cedar splints") when plunged into oxygen bursts into flame, the carbon of the wood being oxidized to carbon dioxide (CO_2). The inflammation of a glowing splint is often used as a test for oxygen. A mixture of air and oxygen with less than 28–29 per cent. of oxygen does not re-ignite a glowing splint, and if the air has less than 16 per cent. of oxygen the glowing splint will be extinguished. Oxygen alone has no action on clear lime water, but after a splint has burnt in the gas, the clear lime water becomes turbid. Oxygen combines directly with most other elements, particularly at elevated temperatures, forming **oxides.** Iodine, bromine, fluorine, gold, platinum, and argon and its companions do not combine directly with oxygen ; but oxygen combines indirectly with all elements excepting the argon group of elements, and possibly bromine. If the metals be arranged in the order of their avidity or readiness to combine with oxygen, caesium, potassium, and sodium will be found at one end of the series, while platinum and the argon family will be found at the other end.

The direct combination of oxygen with some of the elements can be illustrated by placing small dry pieces of carbon, sulphur, phosphorus in deflagrating spoons, heating them until combustion begins, and then plunging each into a jar of oxygen. The glowing piece of **charcoal** burns very brightly and forms a gaseous oxide—carbon dioxide, CO_2. **Sulphur** burns with a lavender-blue flame, forming gaseous sulphur dioxide—SO_2—which has the peculiar odour characteristic of burning sulphur. **Phosphorus** burns in oxygen vigorously and brilliantly, forming a white cloud of phosphorus pentoxide—P_2O_5. The phosphorus pentoxide dissolves in cold water, forming metaphosphoric acid, HPO_3. These reactions will be studied in more detail when the elements in question are treated individually.

To show the combustion of **iron** in oxygen gas, tie a tuft of " steel wool " to the end of a stout iron wire by means of a piece of steel wire. Heat the end of the wool in a Bunsen's flame until incipient combustion begins, and quickly plunge it into a jar of oxygen on the bottom of which a layer of water, sand, or asbestos paper has been placed. The wool burns with dazzling scintillations, the product of the reaction— iron oxide—falls to the bottom of the jar in fused globules. When cold, the oxide of iron resembles a blacksmith's hammer scale. It is called black or magnetic oxide of iron—Fe_3O_4. The reaction is usually written :

$$3Fe + 2O_2 = Fe_3O_4.$$

The subject of oxidation and combustion will be considered later (pp. 310, 372).

§ 4 Formula and Atomic Weight of Oxygen

As mentioned in Chapter VI (p. 95), the atomic weight of oxygen at 16·000 is taken as the International Standard for chemical atomic weights. The physical standard is that of the isotope of oxygen of mass 16, and since there are, in ordinary oxygen, traces of two other isotopes (see § 5 below) the two standards differ slightly—in fact by about 1 part in 10,000.

The formula of oxygen is taken to be O_2. The evidence for this is of the same kind as led to H_2 as the formula of hydrogen (see pp. 68, and 261). Experiment shows that from one volume of oxygen there are formed two volumes of steam, or of carbon monoxide or of nitric oxide. From which it follows that one molecule of oxygen must contain *at least* two atoms. That it does not contain more than two atoms is shown by the fact that the ratio of its specific heats is 1·4 (compare p. 76).

§ 5 Isotopes of Oxygen

Before 1929 it was believed that oxygen was a " pure " element, that is, consisting of atoms of one mass only. In that year, however, it was shown by Giauque and Johnston that the analysis of the spectra of atmospheric absorption bands indicated the existence of an isotope of mass 18, and a little later a still rarer isotope of mass 17 was reported. The ratio of the abundance of these isotopes has proved difficult to determine, but the figures at present accepted are 0·20 per cent. of the isotope of mass 18, and 0·04 per cent. of that of mass 17.

Attempts have been made to concentrate the heavier isotopes of oxygen by the electrolysis of aqueous solutions, and by the fractionation of liquid oxygen, but so far the effects observed have been very slight. It is also proposed to attempt it by diffusion.

The bearing of the discovery of isotopes of oxygen and the discovery of heavy hydrogen on the evaluation of atomic weights, have already been discussed (pp. 139, 263).

§ 6 Uses of Oxygen

Oxygen is used in medical practice as already mentioned (p. 300) and in cases of artificial respiration it is sometimes employed mixed with carbon dioxide or with helium.

Oxygen is used in conjunction with hydrogen for the oxy-hydrogen flame (*q.v.*), and with acetylene for the oxy-acetylene flame used in welding. Thick steel plates can be cut with ease by playing a fine stream of oxygen on the red-hot metal. Advantages are claimed for enriching with oxygen the air-blast of a blast furnace, etc. Oxygen is used in bleaching, in the oxidation and thickening of oils to be used in making varnishes, linoleum, etc.

Liquid air, or rather liquid air enriched with oxygen, furnishes the explosive *oxyliquite* when mixed with charcoal ; 3 cm. cartridges charged with one part carbon, one part petroleum, and eight parts of liquid oxygen were tried experimentally when cutting the Simplon tunnel. The cartridges are exploded by an electric fuse and a mercury fulminate cap. The chief objection is that the cartridges must be used within three minutes after charging, or the oxygen will evaporate. This objection might be an advantage under some circumstances, since a mis-fired shot is harmless in a short time.

§ 7 Oxides

The compounds of the elements with oxygen are called **oxides** and are important substances. They can be classified, broadly speaking, into six main groups. These are :

(i) Neutral oxides

(ii) Acidic oxides

(iii) Basic oxides

(iv) Amphoteric oxides

(v) Peroxides

(vi) Compound oxides

Neutral oxides

These are oxides which do not exhibit any tendency to form salts either with acids or bases, and nitrous oxide is an example of a neutral oxide.

Acidic Oxides

are oxides which combine with bases to form salts. An example of such an oxide is carbon dioxide, which will react, for example, with sodium hydroxide solution, forming sodium carbonate :

$$2NaOH + CO_2 = Na_2CO_3 + H_2O.$$

It often happens that such oxides will react with water, forming acids. A good example is furnished by sulphur trioxide which combines readily with water forming sulphuric acid, a reaction which can be employed for the manufacture of this acid :

$$H_2O + SO_3 = H_2SO_4$$

Oxides such as sulphur trioxide and phosphorus pentoxide, which form acids with water, are also called **anhydrides** or " acid anhydrides," from the Greek $α$, without ; ὕδωρ (hydor), water. Thus SO_2 is not only called sulphur dioxide, but also sulphurous anhydride ; and P_2O_5 is not only phosphorus pentoxide, but phosphoric anhydride. An anhydride can be regarded as the residue left when the elements of water are removed from an oxy-acid. Thus sulphuric acid, less water, gives sulphuric anhydride, SO_3, also called sulphur trioxide ; sulphurous acid, less water, gives sulphurous anhydride, SO_2. Other important acid anhydrides, or acid-oxides, are silica, carbon dioxide, nitrogen trioxide and pentoxide and the oxides of the halogens. From this it appears that the oxides of non-metals are usually acidic oxides.

Basic Oxides

Many oxides are found to combine with acids to form salts and water. Such oxides are called basic oxides, and, if they are soluble in water, that is, if they form soluble hydroxides, they are known as **alkalis.** Sodium monoxide, which combines with water to form sodium hydroxide, in solution if excess of water be used, is an example of this,

$$Na_2O + H_2O = 2NaOH.$$

Important examples of basic oxides are the oxides of calcium, copper and iron. Basic oxides are always the oxides of metals.

Amphoteric Oxides

It is found that there are a number of oxides which can behave either as acidic or as basic oxides according to circumstances. Thus, aluminium trioxide will combine with hydrochloric acid, forming a solution of aluminium chloride—thus behaving as a basic oxide when in acid solutions ; and it will also combine with concentrated sodium hydroxide solution forming sodium aluminate;

$$Al_2O_3 + 6HCl = 2AlCl_3 + 3H_2O$$
$$Al_2O_3 + 2NaOH = 2NaAlO_2 + H_2O$$

—thus behaving as an acidic oxide when in alkaline solutions. Such oxides are called amphoteric oxides. Other examples are the oxides of zinc, arsenic, and antimony, stannous oxide and lead monoxide.

Peroxides

A true peroxide is an oxide which, when treated with dilute acids, yields hydrogen peroxide. An example of such an oxide is barium dioxide :

$$BaO_2 + H_2SO_4 = BaSO_4 + H_2O_2.$$

Peroxides may be thus thought of as salts of hydrogen peroxide, which in turn is then considered to be a weak acid.

The term peroxide is often loosely applied to higher oxides such as PbO_2 and MnO_2. These, however, do not yield hydrogen peroxide with dilute acids, but give the salts of the lower oxides and free oxygen (or if hydrochloric acid is used, chlorine). They probably differ, therefore, in structure from true peroxides. In order to distinguish between these two kinds it has been proposed to call those which yield hydrogen peroxide **superoxides** or true peroxides, and those which give oxygen **polyoxides.**

Compound Oxides

are oxides which behave as though they are compounds of two oxides ; though it is not certain that they are all compounds. A familiar example is red lead, Pb_3O_4, which behaves like a compound of PbO and PbO_2, for, when treated with nitric acid, lead nitrate is formed and lead dioxide is deposited :

$$Pb_3O_4 + 4HNO_3 = 2Pb(NO_3)_2 + PbO_2 + 2H_2O.$$

Red lead here seems to be a lead salt of the weak acid corresponding to PbO_2. Other examples of this type of oxide are ferrosic oxide (triferric tetroxide), Fe_3O_4 and the similar oxide of manganese Mn_3O_4.

The oxides of the elements are among the most important of their compounds, and their properties are of importance in relation to the classification of the elements (compare Ch. VIII). Thus, boron, carbon, nitrogen, phosphorus, sulphur, selenium, tellurium, chlorine, bromine and iodine form *only acidic oxides* ; whilst sodium, potassium, calcium, strontium, barium, copper, silver, cadmium, mercury, cobalt, nickel and platinum have oxides with *basic* properties only. Again, zinc, aluminium, tin, lead and gold yield *amphoteric oxides.*

§ 8 Preparation of Oxides

The methods of preparing the oxides of the several elements are described in the chapters on the elements themselves, but the subject is one of sufficient importance to warrant collecting together here, in summary form, the principal methods available. These are :

Burning element in air (or oxygen), e.g., CO_2, P_4O_{10}, MgO ; burning element in steam, e.g., MgO ; action of steam on element at red heat, e.g., Fe_3O_4, CO ; heating in air, sometimes under specific conditions, e.g., PbO, Pb_3O_4 ; decomposition of hydroxide by heat, e.g., CuO ; decomposition of carbonate by heat, e.g., CaO ; decomposition of nitrate by heat, e.g., CaO, ZnO ; oxidation by nitric acid, e.g., SnO_2 ; reduction of higher oxide, e.g., CO ; decomposition of compound oxide, e.g., PbO_2 from Pb_3O_4.

§ 9 Acids, Bases and Salts

The classification of oxides, given in § 7, depends to a large extent upon their behaviour towards acids and bases. Some detailed consideration of what is meant by these terms is therefore necessary.

The early chemists appear to have learned gradually to arrange certain substances into two groups according as these substances possessed certain qualities in common with vinegar or with wood ashes. The former were called **acids** (from the Latin, *acidus*, sour) ; and the latter, **alkalis** (from the Arabian, *alkali*, ashes of a plant), because the alkalis were generally obtained by calcining various materials and reducing them to ashes. Towards the end of the seventeenth century, Robert Boyle summarized the properties of acids as substances which (1) have a sour taste ; (2) dissolve many substances (corrosive) ; (3) precipitate sulphur from alkaline solutions of sulphur ; (4) change many vegetable blue colours (e.g., blue litmus) red ; and (5) lose their acid characteristics when brought into contact with the alkalis. The alkalis were considered to be substances which (1) possessed detergent and soapy properties ; (2) dissolved oils and sulphur ; (3) restored vegetable colours reddened by acids ; and (4) had the power of reacting with acids to produce indifferent substances.

The properties of acids and alkalis were thus opposed to one another ; for, when mixed together, the one neutralized the other. **Salts** were considered to be products of the interaction of acids and alkalis. It was soon found that some substances with alkaline qualities did not melt nor change when heated, and were almost insoluble in water—these substances were called *earths*. In 1744 G. F. Rouelle employed the word *base* to include the earths, alkalis, metallic oxides (" calces "), and all substances which produce salts by reacting with the acids.

Acids

In his study of the properties of oxygen, Lavoisier noticed that when certain elements were burnt in oxygen, the resulting oxide forms an acid with water—e.g., carbon, sulphur, and phosphorus. Hence Lavoisier concluded (1777) that " oxygen is an element common to all acids, and the presence of oxygen constitutes or produces their acidity." Lavoisier considered oxygen to be the essential constituent of all acids. The very name *oxygen*, given to this element, was derived from Greek words signifying " the generative principle of acids "— ὀξύς (oxus), sour, and γεννάω (gennao), I produce.

With increasing knowledge, it was found that **Lavoisier's oxygen theory of acids** led to confusion and error, and it was gradually abandoned by chemists when it was recognized that :

1. *Some oxides form alkalis, not acids, with water.*—E.g., sodium, potassium, and calcium oxides.

2. *Some acids do not contain oxygen.*—C. L. Berthollet showed, in 1787, that hydrocyanic (prussic) acid is a compound of carbon, nitrogen, and hydrogen, but contains no oxygen ; and he also came to a similar conclusion with regard to hydro-sulphuric—hydrogen sulphide. But for some time Lavoisier's reputation had more weight than Berthollet's facts: In 1810-11 Humphry Davy proved that hydrochloric acid is a compound of hydrogen and chlorine, and that no oxygen could be detected in the compound. In 1813 Davy also proved that hydriodic acid contained hydrogen and iodine, but no oxygen. Hence, added Davy, " acidity is not connected with the presence of any one element."

In 1815 Davy suggested the possibility that hydrogen, not oxygen, gives the acid characters to the acids ; but he did not rush to the other extreme and say that all hydrogen compounds are necessarily acids. There is no one property which we can use as an absolute criterion or decisive test of acidity. In a crude sort of way, it can be said that *acids usually have a sour taste, are usually corrosive, redden the blue colour of vegetable substances (e.g. litmus), and contain hydrogen, part or all of which can be replaced when the acid is treated with a metal, metallic oxide, hydroxide, or carbonate.* Acids are known with a sweet taste, and which are not corrosive. Alum does not contain replaceable hydrogen, and it would not therefore be classed as an acid, although it is sour, corrosive, and colours blue litmus red. But we are far from a satisfactory definition of acids, although, as has been said in Chapter XV, a very fair definition can be framed in terms of the Ionic Theory.

Salts

In modern chemistry the word **salt** is a descriptive term applied to a distinct family of substances and not to any particular individual. In the kitchen, " salt " is colloquially applied to one specific individual, sodium chloride. A salt is produced by replacing all or part of the hydrogen of an acid by a metal or basic radical. For instance, zinc displaces the hydrogen, of sulphuric acid :

$$Zn + H_2SO_4 = ZnSO_4 + H_2$$

forming zinc sulphate as indicated on p. 253. Hence C. Gerhardt (1843) defined acids to be " salts of hydrogen."

In **normal salts** all the displaceable hydrogen of the acid is replaced by the base. For instance, sodium sulphate—Na_2SO_4—is a normal salt because all the replaceable hydrogen of sulphuric acid is displaced by sodium. In **acid salts** only part of the replaceable hydrogen has been displaced by a base, and the salt still contains replaceable hydrogen. For instance, acid sodium sulphate—$NaHSO_4$—contains half the replaceable hydrogen of sulphuric acid, and half as many equivalents of sodium as normal sodium sulphate. If an acid contains two or more replaceable hydrogen atoms, it does not follow that all need be displaced by the same element. Thus, for example :

H_2SO_4—sulphuric acid.
$NaHSO_4$—sodium hydrogen sulphate.
Na_2SO_4—sodium·sulphate.
$NaKSO_4$—sodium potassium sulphate.

Sometimes the term " hydrogen " is used in place of " acid " for the acid salts, and sometimes the prefix " bi- " or " di- " is appended to the term for the acid in the salt. Thus " acid sodium sulphate " is also called, as above, " sodium hydrogen sulphate," " sodium bisulphate," as well as " mono-sodium sulphate," etc. The normal salts are sometimes called " neutral salts " in the sense that all the hydrogen has been· " neutralized " or displaced from the acid. These salts, however, are not necessarily neutral to litmus—thus normal zinc or copper sulphates react towards litmus as if they were acids ; borax, sodium nitrite, and normal sodium carbonate react as if they were alkalies.

It is sometimes necessary to use the prefixes mono-, di-, tri-, . . . to discriminate between the different salts of one acid. Thus with phosphoric acid—phosphorus quinquevalent—

H_3PO_4—phosphoric acid.
NaH_2PO_4—monosodium phosphate.
Na_2HPO_4—disodium phosphate.
Na_3PO_4—normal, or tri-sodium phosphate.

It would be a mistake to assume that all the hydrogen of an acid is replaceable by a base. Thus, so far as we know, hypophosphorous acid—H_3PO_2—has only one of its three hydrogen atoms replaceable by a metal. No one has ever prepared Na_2HPO_2, or Na_3PO_2. Similarly, acetic acid—$C_2H_4O_2$ or $CH_3.CO_2H$—has only one hydrogen atom replaceable in this way. **The number of atoms of hydrogen in one molecule of an acid which are replaceable by a metal, or a radical, is termed the basicity of the acid.** Thus hydrochloric acid—HCl—is monobasic because each molecule of hydrochloric acid contains one replaceable hydrogen atom ; sulphuric acid—H_2SO_4—is dibasic ; phosphoric acid—H_3PO_4—is tribasic ; and silicic acid—H_4SiO_4—is tetrabasic. Hypophosphorous acid—H_3PO_2—and acetic acid—$C_2H_4O_2$—are monobasic.

Bases

A base—Greek βάσις (basis), a base—is a substance which reacts with an acid to produce a salt and water. For instance, zinc oxide reacts with sulphuric acid to produce zinc sulphate and water :

$$ZnO + H_2SO_4 = H_2O + ZnSO_4.$$

Sodium hydroxide reacts with sulphuric acid to produce sodium sulphate and water :

$$2NaOH + H_2SO_4 = 2H_2O + Na_2SO_4.$$

The bases include the oxides and the hydroxides of the metals, and certain groups of elements equivalent to a metal. For convenience, certain groups of elements like ammonia—NH_3, hydroxylamine—NH_2OH, hydrogen phosphide—PH_3, etc., are called bases, although they form salts by direct addition or combination without the separation of water. Thus ammonia and hydrogen chloride form ammonium chloride :

$$NH_3 + HCl = NH_4Cl.$$

This definition is not entirely satisfactory because it depends upon the definition of an acid, which, as stated on p. 306, is not easily framed unequivocally ; but it works fairly well on the whole ; and the difficulties are, to a considerable extent, overcome by the application of the Ionic Theory (see § 10, below).

The term base was originally intended to express the idea that the metal or metal oxide was the more important constituent, the foundation or base, so to speak, of a salt. This idea was dropped when it was recognized that the acidic constituent of a salt is just as important as the basic constituent.

It is necessary to avoid any confusion between the terms alkali and base, for they are not synonymous. Most alkalis are bases but not every base is an alkali. The distinction between the two has already been referred to (p. 305) ; what it amounts to is that the soluble bases are alkalis.

The hydroxides of sodium, lead and bismuth have a composition represented by the formulae :

$$NaOH \qquad Pb(OH)_2 \qquad Bi(OH)_3$$

and inspection of these reveals an analogy with the formulae of acids such as hydrochloric, sulphuric and phosphoric in that the hydroxides contain one, two and three hydroxyl groups respectively, whereas the acids have one, two and three hydrogen atoms respectively. It is natural, therefore, to inquire if salts can be formed by replacement of one or more of these hydroxyl groups by acids, just as the hydrogen of phosphoric or sulphuric acids can be replaced one by one by bases. If this is so, it would be anticipated that **basic salts** should exist, corresponding to the acid salts already discussed.

Such salts do, in fact, éxist so that there can be obtained :

$Pb(OH)_2$—lead hydroxide

$Pb(OH)NO_3$—basic lead nitrate

$Pb(NO_3)_2$—lead nitrate,

a series corresponding, *mutatis mutandis*, to that given on page 307. A corresponding nomenclature is also employed—a hydroxide such as lead hydroxide is termed a di-acid base, and in general, **the number of hydroxyl groups replaceable by acid which a base contains is termed the acidity of the base.**

§ 10 Acids, Bases and Salts according to the Ionic Theory

In Chapter XII it was stated that certain chemical compounds are marked off from others in that their solutions in water are capable of conducting an electric current, and also exhibit other characteristic properties. In Chapter IX these were distinguished also as being what is termed electrovalent compounds. An examination of compounds exhibiting this behaviour shows that they are all substances which, apart from these characteristics, would be included in the groups of substances which are called acids, bases or salts. So far no attempt has been made in the present chapter to define these substances in terms of the theory—the theory of electrolytic dissociation or the ionic theory—which is believed to explain these phenomena.

According to the Ionic Theory, an Acid is an electrovalent substance which in solution in water yields hydrogen ions. This is represented by the equation :

$$HA \rightleftharpoons H^{\cdot} + A'$$

Similarly, an alkali or a base may be defined as a substance which will yield hydroxyl ions ; which may be expressed by the equation :

$$BOH \rightleftharpoons B^{\cdot} + OH'$$

A base, however, may well be given the wider definition of a substance which will combine with hydrogen ion. Such a definition will include not only alkalis for which the action may be represented :

$$BOH = B^{\cdot} + OH'$$
$$OH' + H^{\cdot} \rightleftharpoons H_2O,$$

but also basic oxides such as litharge :

$$PbO + 2H^{\cdot} = Pb^{\cdot\cdot} + H_2O$$

and such substances as ammonia :

$$NH_3 + H^{\cdot} = NH_4^{\cdot}$$

Salts, according to the ionic theory, are substances which give conducting solutions in which hydrogen ions are not the only positive ions present, and hydroxyl ions are not the only negative ions formed. This definition is able to cover normal, acid and basic salts, e.g.,

$$NaCl \rightleftharpoons Na^{\cdot} + Cl'$$
$$NaHSO_4 \rightleftharpoons Na^{\cdot} + HSO_4' \rightleftharpoons Na^{\cdot} + H^{\cdot} + SO_4''$$

§ 11 Oxidation and Reduction

The terms oxidation and reduction have been used several times already, and now call for more extended treatment.

The conversion of an element into its oxide by direct combination with oxygen is the simplest case of oxidation. For example, when calcium is heated in air it is *oxidized* to calcium oxide. Similarly, any process which will convert an element into its oxide is an oxidation. An analogous process may involve the combination of a compound already containing some oxygen with still more oxygen, as for example when barium oxide is heated in air to a suitable temperature and thereby converted into barium dioxide

$$2BaO + O_2 = 2BaO_2$$

This again is clearly an oxidation. Oxidation, in the simplest case, is thus a process which adds oxygen to an element or compound.

The reverse of this process, that is, the removal of oxygen from a compound containing it, is known as reduction. Thus, for example, when copper oxide is converted into copper by passing hydrogen over the heated oxide, the copper oxide is said to be *reduced* to copper. This is the original idea underlying the terms oxidation and reduction, and is the simplest use.

It soon became evident, however, that the process of removing hydrogen from a compound containing that element involves something closely akin to oxidation as indicated above, and, similarly, the addition of hydrogen closely resembles reduction as previously understood. The same reagents will often bring about both addition of oxygen and removal of hydrogen, or vice versa, and the changes brought about in the state of combination of an element are similar. Hence, the idea of oxidation and reduction was extended to cover these cases.

As chemistry developed, it was realized that some processes which do not directly involve hydrogen and oxygen at all are in principle so closely related to oxidation and reduction, as understood when referred simply to changes in the oxygen or hydrogen content of a compound, that the idea has been still further extended.

For example, ferrous oxide, FeO, is a base which gives rise to a series of salts called the ferrous salts. Ferrous oxide can be oxidized, for example, by the oxygen of the air, to ferric oxide, Fe_2O_3. Ferric oxide in its turn is a base which with acids forms ferric salts. Ferrous and ferric salts thus stand in the same relationship to each other as ferrous and ferric oxides. Now a solution of a soluble ferrous salt, on exposure to air, will slowly turn to the ferric salt—clearly oxidation has occurred. For example, ferrous chloride is converted partly into ferric chloride and partly into ferric hydroxide :

$$12FeCl_2 + 6H_2O + 3O_2 = 8FeCl_3 + 4Fe(OH)_3$$

But ferrous chloride can be converted very simply into ferric chloride by the action of chlorine :

$$2FeCl_2 + Cl_2 = 2FeCl_3,$$

which must be reckoned to be an oxidation since it is agreed that the conversion of ferrous chloride into ferric chloride is an oxidation. But no oxygen has taken part in the process. Hence the term oxidation must be extended to cover this process.

Conversely, reduction must also be similarly extended. Similar reasoning to the above indicates that the conversion of mercuric chloride, $HgCl_2$, into mercurous chloride, Hg_2Cl_2, is a process of reduction. This can be brought about by means of stannous chloride, for example, without the intervention of hydrogen at all :

$$2HgCl_2 + SnCl_2 = Hg_2Cl_2 + SnCl_4.$$

This last example illustrates one very important fact. Mercuric chloride is reduced to mercurous chloride in this reaction, but the stannous chloride by means of which this result is brought about is changed into stannic chloride ; in other words, it has been oxidized. In general, oxidation and reduction are reciprocal processes, one substance is oxidized while the other is reduced.

It is thus necessary to extend the definition of oxidation and reduction so as to include all these types of reaction. The term **oxidation** is applied to **any process which involves the passage of a compound representing a lower stage of combination with oxygen to a substance equivalent to a higher stage of combination with oxygen, by the addition of oxygen or of an electro-negative atom or radical, or by the removal of hydrogen or an electro-positive atom or radical. Reduction** is the **converse** of oxidation.

In terms of the Ionic Theory, oxidation and reduction are seen to involve merely the transference of electrical charges. Thus the conversion of ferrous chloride into ferric chloride written in terms of ions becomes :

$$2Fe^{..} + 4Cl' + Cl_2 = 2Fe^{...} + 6Cl'$$

or eliminating the terms common to both sides of this equation :

$$2Fe^{..} + Cl_2 = 2Fe^{...} + 2Cl'.$$

That is to say, the ferrous ion loses one negative charge (or electron) and thus becomes a ferric ion, while each atom of the chlorine molecule gains one negative charge (or electron).

The reduction of mercuric chloride can be represented in terms of ions by the equation :

$$2Hg^{..} + Sn^{..} = Hg_2^{..} + Sn^{....}.$$

Reduction is thus a matter of making smaller the number of positive charges on an ion, and oxidation of increasing them.

An oxidizing agent is a substance which can bring about oxidation as defined above, and a reducing agent conversely.

Among the **available oxidizing agents** are : oxygen, ozone, the peroxides, and the higher oxides as well as the unstable basic oxides of silver, gold, etc. ; the oxy-acids (nitric, nitrous, chromic, chloric, and the other oxy-acids of the halogens) and their salts ; the halogens (chlorine, bromine, iodine) ; permanganic acid and its salts ; potassium ferricyanide, etc.

Among the **available reducing agents** or **deoxidizers** are : hydrogen, unstable hydrides (hydrogen sulphide, hydrogen iodide, phosphine, arsine, stibine, etc.) ; carbon, carbon monoxide, sulphur dioxide, and the sulphites ; phosphorous acid and the phosphites ; hypophosphorous acid and the hypophosphites ; potassium cyanide ; potassium formate ; ferrous, stannous, and chromous salts ; the metals sodium, potassium, magnesium, aluminium, etc.

§ 12 Ozone

Historical

Van Marum observed the peculiar smell (now known to be that of ozone) when an electrical discharge takes place in air ; and this was attributed to a new gas, and given the name ozone (from the Greek ὄζω, ozo, I smell) by Schönbein in 1840.

Formation

Ozone is produced by the action of the ultra-violet rays and radium radiations on oxygen. It is said to be formed by the violent mechanical disturbance of air as when grinding wheels are being tested for bursting speed ; but the effect may here be due to the electrification of the air. Ozone can generally be detected in the oxygen gas obtained during the electrolysis of acidulated water. By the electrolysis of sulphuric acid (between 1·075 and 1·1 specific gravity), with an anode made by embedding platinum foil in glass and grinding away the edge so that a line of platinum, 0·1 mm. broad, is exposed, oxygen containing 17 to 23 per cent. of ozone has been obtained. The yield increases with increasing current density.

The oxygen liberated by many reactions also contains ozone. For instance, manganese dioxide and sulphuric acid ; barium dioxide and sulphuric acid ; potassium permanganate and sulphuric acid, per-sulphuric acid, persulphates, etc. Purified potassium chlorate gives oxygen free from ozone, but if traces of some indifferent substances be present, ozone may be formed. When fluorine decomposes water forming hydrogen fluoride and oxygen, from 13 to 14 per cent. of the " oxygen gas " is ozone.

Ozone is formed during the slow oxidation of many substances. Ozone can be detected in the atmosphere of a flask containing a couple of sticks of clean phosphorus.

Ozone is also said to be formed when turpentine, several hydro-carbons, coal tar, and many essential oils are oxidized. J. K. Bocke thinks that the effect is due to the formation of nitrogen oxide. Ozone is said to be formed during the combustion of ether as well as during the combustion of hydrogen compounds generally.

The formation of ozone by the evaporation of water or dew is said to account for the bleaching of linen spread on lawns.

Much atmospheric ozone seems to be formed by the action of solar ultra-violet light in the upper regions of the atmosphere. Ozone is here present in relatively greater proportions ; thus, on the Alps at an altitude of 20 kilometres the air had 5 parts of ozone per million (volumes) ; and at an altitude of 2·1 kilometres, half this proportion. Electrical discharges in the atmosphere also produce ozone. Homer in several passages referred to the odour which attended the " thunderbolts " or flashes of lightning.

Preparation of Ozone

The most usual method of making ozone, or rather of preparing ozonized air and ozonized oxygen is to expose dry air or oxygen to a silent discharge of electricity. Quite a number of instruments are available. That illustrated in Fig. 105, is virtually the one devised by W. von Siemens (1858). It consists of two concentric tubes. The inner tube is coated on its inner surface with tinfoil in metallic contact with the terminal A ; and the outer tube is coated on its outer surface with tinfoil in metallic contact with the terminal B. The two terminals are connected with an induction coil. A slow stream of dry oxygen is led through the annular space between the concentric tubes, and is there exposed to the action of a silent discharge of electricity. The

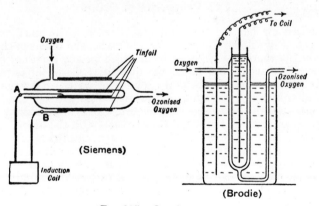

FIG. 105.—Ozonizers.

gas issuing from the ozonizer is charged with 3 to 8 per cent. of ozone. In *Brodie's or Berthelot's ozone tube* the tinfoil coatings are replaced with sulphuric acid (Fig. 105). If air be used in place of oxygen, some nitrogen oxides are said to be formed at the same time. The presence of moisture reduces the yield of ozone,* although no difference has been detected in the amount of decomposition of the dry and moist gas when heated for some time at 100°.

When required to be produced commercially, ozone is also obtained by means of a silent discharge, but a modified type of apparatus is employed such as that shown in Fig. 106.

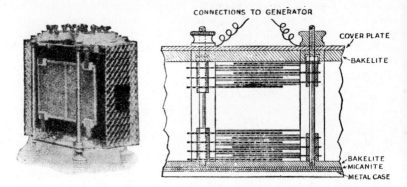

FIG. 106.—Commercial Ozonizer.

§ 13 Properties of Ozone

Ozonized air has a strong unpleasant smell. The smell reminds some people of sulphur dioxide, others of garlic, and others of chlorine. If air highly charged with ozone be breathed for any length of time, it produces headache ; but in minute quantities the odour is pleasing and refreshing. Ozone is slightly soluble in water—100 volumes of water at ordinary temperatures and pressure dissolve about one volume of ozone—and the water smells of the ozone and exhibits many of the properties of ozone. The water slowly reacts with the ozone.

Ozone is dissolved by essential oils such as turpentine, cinnamon oil, etc. This is because these oils contain what in organic chemistry are known as unsaturated compounds, that is, the molecules of these compounds contain one or more pairs of carbon atoms united by a " double bond." Such compounds readily form addition products with bromine or with ozone.

Unlike oxygen, ozone liberates iodine from neutral potassium iodide. This can be shown by dipping paper in a solution of potassium iodide and holding it at the exit tube of the ozonizer. The paper

* Ozone is decomposed by cork and indiarubber. In consequence, these materials should not be used for any part of the ozonizer in contact with the gas.

turns brown owing to the liberation of iodine. If a little starch be mixed with the potassium iodide, the paper will appear blue. The reaction is usually represented :

$$O_3 + 2KI + H_2O = O_2 + I_2 + 2KOH$$

Ozone.   Oxygen.   Potassium hydroxide.

Ozone is a very powerful oxidizing agent. Organic matter—cork, rubber, etc.—is rapidly corroded by ozone. Paper coloured by a solution of indigo sulphate or a solution of litmus is bleached. If a globule of mercury is placed in a small flask and ozonized air passed in, the mercury loses its lustre, and spreads a film over the walls of the flask. Ozone is said to cause mercury to " tail." The globule of mercury is restored when the film is shaken up with water. If a piece of silver foil, cleaned with silver sand, be heated in a bunsen burner for a moment, and while still warm, held in a stream of ozonized air, the silver is blackened, owing, it is said, to the formation of silver peroxide. Silver perfectly free from the oxide does not show the reaction at ordinary temperatures unless the metal be contaminated with some substance like oxide of silver, cobalt, nickel, etc., which acts as a catalytic agent. A trace of oxide is supposed to be formed when the silver is heated in the bunsen burner. The reaction is characteristic of ozone, but it is not very sensitive. Ozone converts dark brown coloured lead sulphide into white coloured lead sulphate :

$$PbS + 4O_3 = PbSO_4 + 4O_2.$$

Many other sulphides—copper, antimony, zinc, cadmium—behave in a similar manner. Nickel and cobalt sulphides form peroxides and sulphuric acid. A solution of manganese sulphate used as an invisible ink is browned by exposure to ozone.

Ozone decomposes in the presence of finely divided platinum, lead dioxide, manganese dioxide, silver and copper oxides. The ozone is converted into ordinary oxygen without decomposing the oxides. Hence the reactions are grouped among catalytic reactions.

When ozone is brought into contact with sodium peroxide, the two substances mutually decompose and oxygen is liberated :

$$O_3 + Na_2O_2 + H_2O = 2NaOH + 2O_2.$$

Ozone seems to be fairly stable at ordinary temperatures, although it gradually decomposes on standing. It also appears to be fairly stable at high temperatures, while at intermediate temperatures it is unstable.

By passing ozonized oxygen through a tube cooled by immersion in boiling liquid oxygen, or by ozonizing oxygen in a tube kept at this temperature, a solution of ozone in liquid oxygen is obtained. By allowing the liquid to boil, most of the oxygen is removed. In this manner a deep indigo blue liquid is obtained which is opaque in layers 2 mm. thick. The liquid is said to be explosive. By allowing the blue liquid to vaporize, A. Ladenburg (1898) obtained a gas containing about 86 per cent. of ozone.

§ 14 Formula of Ozone

The determination of the formula of ozone presented many difficulties, since pure ozone cannot be obtained.

The question whether ozone is elementary in nature or not caused considerable controversy, and for some time it was uncertain whether it should be regarded as an allotropic form of oxygen or as an " oxidized " form of water. It was proved in 1860, by Andrews and Tait, that ozone is a condensed form of oxygen. This they did by exposing pure, dry oxygen to a silent discharge in a sealed tube, attached to a manometer, when a contraction in volume was observed. On heating the ozonized oxygen so formed, expansion to the original volume took place. Further, when a small sealed tube containing potassium iodide was placed in the larger tube of oxygen and broken after a silent discharge had been passed and a contraction in volume had occurred, iodine was liberated without change of volume. The residual gas, on heating, now showed no increase in volume. Hence, ozone is a form of oxygen. This conclusion was also confirmed by Soret in 1863. He took thoroughly dried ozone, decomposed it by heating, and showed that no trace of any compound of hydrogen (such as water) could be detected.

These experiments served to show that ozone contains only oxygen, but do not indicate how many atoms there are in a molecule of ozone. This was first demonstrated by Soret in 1866.

He took advantage of the fact that essential oils absorb ozone without decomposition. Hence, if ozonized oxygen be shaken with, say, cinnamon oil, the ozone will be removed from the mixture. On treating one portion of a sample of ozonized oxygen with cinnamon oil, Soret found that a contraction corresponding with about 2 c.c. was obtained. On heating another portion of the same sample so as to convert the ozone into ordinary oxygen, Soret found an expansion corresponding with 1 c.c. Hence it was inferred that **three volumes of oxygen produce two volumes of ozone.**

Now if the formula of ozone is O_n we have, when it is decomposed:

$$2O_n = nO_2$$

that is to say, according to Avogadro's hypothesis, 2 volumes of ozone are formed from n volumes of oxygen. Soret's experiment showed that 3 volumes of oxygen produce 2 volumes of ozone. Therefore, $n = 3$ and the formula for ozone is O_3.

Soret's work was rather crude, but B. Brodie (1872) repeated the **experiments with cinnamon oil, turpentine, stannous** chloride, in such a way that the above conclusion was the only possible interpretation of the experiments.

This formula has been confirmed by diffusion experiments as mentioned on page 26.

§ 15 Detection and Determination of Ozone

The detection of ozone is complicated by the fact that many of the most obvious of its reactions are similar to those of other oxidizing agents.

Ozone may be detected by its action on mercury, or by its action on clean silver foil, which is blackened by ozone. It liberates iodine from potassium iodide in common with many other oxidizing agents, but may be distinguished from others, except hydrogen peroxide, in that it will not liberate iodine after passage through a hot tube.

The real difficulty arises in distinguishing ozone from hydrogen peroxide. This may be done by means of potassium permanganate solution which is decolorized by hydrogen peroxide but not by ozone Alternatively, C. Arnold and C. Mentzel (1902) propose the use of test-papers soaked in an alcoholic solution of " tetramethyl base." These are not affected by hydrogen peroxide, but are turned violet with ozone ; blue, with chlorine and bromine ; and straw yellow, with nitric oxide. C. Engler and W. Wild (1896) state that if a mixture of ozone and hydrogen peroxide be passed through a concentrated solution of chromic acid, the hydrogen peroxide is alone decomposed, the ozone is not affected. The same investigators say that paper steeped in a concentrated aqueous solution of manganous chloride is turned brown by ozone, but not by hydrogen peroxide.

Some reactions of ozone, hydrogen peroxide, chlorine, and nitrogen peroxide are compared in Table XXVI.

TABLE XXVI.—DISTINGUISHING TESTS FOR OZONE AND HYDROGEN PEROXIDE.

Reagent.	Ozone.	Hydrogen peroxide.	Chlorine.	Nitrogen peroxide.
KI and starch .	Blue	Blue	Blue	Blue
Indigo solution .	Bleached	Bleached	Bleached	Bleached
Litmus solution .	Bleached	Bleached	Bleached	Bleached
Clean silver foil .	Blackened	Nil	White film	No change
Mercury bead .	Trail on glass	Nil	White	No change
CrO$_3$ and ether .	Nil	Blue	Nil	Nil
Titanic acid . .	Nil	Yellow	Nil	Nil
Tetramethyl base .	Violet	Nil	Blue	Yellow to brown
KMnO$_4$ solution .	Unchanged	Decolorized	Decolorized	Decolorized
Benzidine .	Brown	No change	Red	Blue

The method used for the determination of ozone in air, etc., is based upon the reaction symbolized on p. 315. A known volume of air is drawn through a neutral solution of potassium iodide, and the liberated iodine is determined by acidifying the solution, and titrating the liberated iodine with a standard solution of sodium thiosulphate, as will be indicated later. The standard method for estimating ozone in, say, the atmosphere is to expose ozone test papers* for a definite time to the air and compare the resulting tint with a standard scale of colours obtained with air containing known quantities of ozone. Since other oxidizing substances, likely to be present in air, produce a similar reaction, it is a moot question whether the large number of "ozone determinations" which have been made really represent ozone, or hydrogen peroxide, nitrogen oxides, chlorine, etc. Rather does the result of the test represent the presence of "oxidizing substances."

§ 16 Uses of Ozone

Ozone is used for the purification of water in special cases, but is rather expensive. Its function is to oxidize the organic matter, and sterilize the water. Ozonized air is also used in ventilation, for bleaching oxidizing oil in the manufacture of linoleum, etc. It has also been employed as a bleaching agent for wax and certain other materials.

* Papers steeped in an emulsion of starch containing a small proportion of potassium iodide are called ozone test papers.

CHAPTER XIX

CARBON

Modern civilization is the daughter of coal, for coal is to-day the greatest source of energy and wealth.—G. GAMACIAN (1913).

The manufacture of coal gas for purposes of illumination is one of the most striking instances of science enlisted in the divine cause of civilization. Once a luxury or convenience, it is now almost a necessity.—ANON.

§ 1 Unique Character of Carbon

CARBON is an element which is characterized by the enormous number of compounds which it is able to form ; the number of known carbon compounds is already far in excess of the number of known compounds of all the other elements taken together, and there are no signs as yet of any limit being reached. This fact has resulted in the study of the compounds of this element being made into a separate branch of chemistry known as **Organic Chemistry,** which is thus, strictly speaking, the chemistry of the compounds of carbon.

At the same time, the properties of the element itself, and of a few of its compounds which are most closely related to those of the other elements, are properly included in any scheme of Inorganic Chemistry also.

The enormous number and variety of carbon compounds are the outcome of the fact that carbon atoms can form remarkably strong chemical linkages with each other. Thus whereas chains of atoms of other elements, for example, of sulphur, are usually very unstable, chains of carbon atoms of great length and complexity are perfectly stable. In addition, carbon also forms stable linkages with a great many other elements, and in particular with hydrogen, nitrogen, oxygen, sulphur and the halogens, and so it follows that an enormous variety of stable compounds is possible.

§ 2 Allotropy and Varieties of Carbon

Carbon exists in more than one form, that is to say, it exhibits allotropy. Until recently, it has been usual to distinguish three allotropic forms, but it is now believed that there are two only, viz., **diamond** and **graphite.** The third so-called form, **amorphous carbon,** is held to include the different varieties of vegetable and animal charcoals—lampblack, charcoal, soot, gas carbon, and coal. These are more or less impure forms of carbon.

Modern work has shown that these varieties probably do not differ from graphite except in purity, porosity, and in the size and shape of the actual particles. Examination by X-ray methods has shown that all these materials possess the same internal crystalline structure as graphite. The peculiar properties of amorphous carbon, in so far as they differ from those of diamond or graphite, are apparently due to their relatively large surfaces in proportion to their mass or the presence of impurities. For it has been observed that charcoal usually contains combined hydrogen, and that the more thoroughly this is removed, the closer are the properties of the resultant material to those of graphite. Also, the only forms of carbon having definite properties, which can be accurately defined, are diamond and graphite.

It is clear, however, that there are many varieties of carbon, the following being usually distinguished in addition to the two pure allotropic forms, viz., lampblack, charcoal (including wood charcoal and bone or animal charcoal), coal, coke and gas carbon.

§ 3 Lampblack and Charcoal

Lampblack is made by burning substances rich in carbon in a limited supply of air so that the maximum amount of smoke is developed—for example, turpentine, petroleum, tar, acetylene, etc. The smoke is passed into large chambers in which coarse " blankets " are suspended. The " soot " collects on the blankets. Lampblack is also made from natural gas.

The lampblack falls into a hopper and is conveyed by elaborate machinery to be ground to the finest powder, sifted, and weighed into sacks. Lampblack is used for making printer's ink, stove and shoe polish, paints, and in fact nearly everything in which a black pigment for colouring matter is required. It is also employed as a filler in the manufacture of rubber tyres.

Lampblack is one of the purest varieties of amorphous carbon. The analysis of a sample of acetylene " soot " furnishes 1·4 per cent. of hydrogen and 98·6 per cent. of carbon.

Most of the hydrocarbon impurities can be removed by heating in a current of chlorine.

Charcoal

There are two main varieties of charcoal—wood and bone. Wood charcoal is made by burning wood with a limited supply of air in a charcoal pit or kiln ; or by heating wood in closed vessels so that air is excluded.

In outline the industrial preparation is as follows : Small logs or billets of wood are loosely piled into vertical heaps and covered with sods and turf to prevent the free access of air. There are several systems of piling the sticks—one is illustrated in Fig. 107. A " shaft " is left in the middle of the pile to act as a central chimney or flue ; and smaller holes are left round the bottom to admit the air. The pile so prepared is called a " charcoal pit " or a *Meiler* (German). The wood is lighted by brushwood at the centre, and just sufficient air to allow the wood to smoulder is passed through the pile. The volatile matter escapes, and in about fifteen days the fire dies out. Between 80 and 90 per cent. of the weight of the wood, on the average, is lost by combustion, and the remaining 10 to 20 per cent. is wood charcoal.

Some valuable gaseous and liquid products are lost in making pit charcoal. In modern processes, the wood is heated in ovens, kilns, or retorts, sealed from the outside air. The operation may be conducted simply for charcoal without recovering the by-products, or the operation may be conducted somewhat similarly to the process used for the manufacture of coal gas. The products of the dry distillation of wood include : solid charcoal in the retort ; liquids—wood tar (*Stockholm tar* from pine wood) ; water containing wood spirit ; *pyroligneous (acetic) acid* ; acetone and fatty oils ; and gaseous wood gas—containing hydrogen, carbon dioxide, carbon monoxide, methane, acetylene, etc.

Times Photo

Fig. 107.—Meiler in course of Construction.

Bone or Animal Charcoal

This is made by heating bones, blood, etc., in closed retorts. The bones may or may not have been subjected to a preliminary extraction with naphtha or benzene to remove the fat—degreased bones ; or with superheated steam or water to remove gelatine (glue)—degelatinized bones. The products of the distillation include : solid bone charcoal in the retort ; liquids—a number of ammonium salts, bone oil, bone pitch, pyridine, etc. ; and gases of various kinds. Bone charcoal contains about 10 per cent. of carbon, so that it is questionable if it ought to be included with the varieties of carbon at all. However, the carbon is very finely divided and disseminated through a porous mass of about 80 per cent. of calcium and magnesium phosphates, and it seems to have specially valuable qualities. Bones furnish *boneblack* —sometimes called ivory black—the term *ivory black* is usually applied to the product obtained by digesting bone black with hydrochloric acid to remove the calcium phosphates. Blood furnishes *blood charcoal*. For the uses of bone black and animal charcoal, see below ; ivory black is used as a pigment ; in the manufacture of blacking, etc.

§ 4 Properties of Amorphous Carbon

Charcoal is a black porous substance of very low *apparent* specific gravity, due to the presence of a considerable volume of air entangled in the pores.

On account of its porosity charcoal possesses a very large surface in proportion to its weight so that it exhibits what are known as *surface effects* to a high degree. All solids retain a thin film of gas upon their surfaces, and on account of its large surface area charcoal can absorb large quantities of many gases.

The phenomenon is sometimes styled **adsorption,** meaning that the gas adheres in some unknown way to the surface of the charcoal. One volume of coco-nut charcoal absorbs (Hunter) at 760 mm. pressure :

	Volumes at 0°.	Vols. at − 185°.
Ammonia	171	—
Ethylene	75	—
Carbon dioxide	68	—
Carbon monoxide	21	190
Oxygen	18	230
Nitrogen	15	155
Hydrogen	17	135
Helium	2	15
Argon	12	175

The gases are evolved again on heating, but when cooled in liquid air the amount of gas absorbed becomes very much greater. Thus a piece of charcoal which will absorb eighteen times its volume of oxygen at 0°C., will absorb two hundred and thirty times its own volume at the temperature of liquid air (− 185° C.).

This property affords a means of producing high vacua, and also of separating gases which are not readily absorbed (helium, neon, p. 540) from those which are readily absorbed (air, etc.).

It appears as if the gases which are absorbed in greatest quantity by the charcoal are approximately those most easily condensed to the liquid state ; and, rightly or wrongly, it is sometimes stated that the gases are actually liquefied on the surface of the charcoal. In any case, the " condensed " gas is usually more chemically active than the gas in the ordinary condition. Thus if charcoal be allowed to absorb chlorine, and then be brought in contact with dry hydrogen, the hydrogen and chlorine combine to form hydrogen chloride under conditions where they would not otherwise react.

Charcoal also absorbs solids and liquids in a similar way. A solution of litmus (indigo, tea, vinegar, etc.) passes through filter paper without any noticeable change in the colour of the solution ; but if the solution be filtered through charcoal, or if some recently ignited animal charcoal —say 10-20 grams—be shaken up with 50 c.c. of litmus solution and filtered, the filtrate is colourless.

Advantage is taken of this property of animal charcoal or bone black to remove the colouring matter from many products manufactured industrially. E.g., coloured solutions of brown sugar are " bleached " on boiling with animal charcoal. The charcoal removes the brown resinous colouring matter, and the evaporated syrup furnishes white sugar ; fusel oil can be removed from whisky by filtration through animal charcoal before the whisky is rectified. Charcoal filters are used for removing organic matter, etc., from drinking water.

Charcoal is, chemically, the most reactive of the forms of carbon, again probably on account of its large surface. It burns readily in excess of air or oxygen to carbon dioxide :

$$C + O_2 = CO_2,$$

but some carbon monoxide is also formed if the supply of air or oxygen is restricted.

Charcoal reacts with many oxidizing agents as, for example, nitric acid and sulphuric acid, the reactions being represented by the equations :

$$C + 4HNO_3 = 2H_2O + 4NO_2 + CO_2$$
$$C + 2H_2SO_4 = CO_2 + 2H_2O + 2SO_2$$

These are, of course, examples of the power of charcoal to act as a reducing agent, due to its great "affinity" for oxygen. Hence, in metallurgical industries, carbon is often used as a reducing agent (compare manufacture of iron, p. 801, zinc, p. 641, copper, p. 589, and lead, p. 702, etc.). When a mixture of carbon with the oxide of one of these metals (litharge, for example) is heated in a crucible, either carbon monoxide or carbon dioxide is evolved and the metal remains behind :

$$PbO + C = Pb + CO$$
$$2PbO + C = Pb + CO_2$$

§ 5 Coal

Coal is a complex carbonaceous material, resulting from a series of decompositions which have taken place in a restricted supply of air. High pressure also is believed to have played an important part in the process.

Geologists have potent reasons for believing that coal is of vegetable origin. The softer varieties of coal are often changed so little that their vegetable origin is easily seen. Fossil plants can be recognized and photographs of thin slices under the microscope show clearly the vegetable character of the coal. In some of the harder varieties, the vegetable origin can only be demonstrated by analogy and comparison with varieties less modified. There is a closely graded series ranging between peat at one end, and the anthracite coals, or maybe graphite, at the other. It is convenient, however, to pick out certain members of the series as types. We thus obtain peat, lignite, bituminous, and anthracitic coals. There are no hard-and-fast lines between these different types ; the one merges into the other by insensible gradations.

The chemistry of the process of coal formation appears to be somewhat as follows :—

When vegetable tissue is exposed to the air, it oxidizes and decays comparatively quickly ; the gaseous products of the oxidation diffuse into the atmosphere ; and the mineral constituents remain behind. If the oxidation takes place in a limited supply of air, e.g., while submerged in a swamp or bog, the process of decomposition is rather different. Some of the carbon is oxidized to carbon dioxide, and some of the hydrogen is oxidized to water, and probably some is transformed into methane—marsh gas—etc. As a result an increasing proportion of carbon remains behind. The total weight of the organic matter decreases ; and, although the total amount of mineral matter—ash—remains constant, the *percentage* amount increases.

While it is probable that the early stages of the metamorphosis are brought about by bacteria and oxidation in a limited supply of air, it is also probable that the *pressure* of the superincumbent deposits of sand, mud, etc., extending over long periods of time, are needed for the later transformations. The gases—carbon dioxide, methane, water, etc.—formed during the earlier stages of the process of conversion of vegetable tissue to coal, can escape ; later, when the air is shut off, methane, etc., may be imprisoned in the coal to be released as " firedamp," p. 333, when the pressure is relieved during the mining of the coal. In some cases, the coal appears to have been *heated under pressure*. The nature of the final product, as now mined, must depend on the character of the original deposits and on the particular conditions which prevailed at the different stages of the process of transformation. The vegetable matter may have been deposited in fresh or salt water, in lakes, lagoons, seas ; in marine swamps ; etc. The original vegetable tissue may have been algae deposits in sargossa seas, peat bogs, vegetable accumulations on the soil in luxuriant forests, delta and drift deposits, etc. The pressure may have been comparatively small, extended over a long period of time, and applied comparatively early in the process of transformation ; the pressure may have been very great and applied late in the process of conversion ; etc. An " old " coal geologically, might be " young " chemically, and conversely.

Geologists can sometimes form a good idea what has happened ; in other cases, they confess complete ignorance.

Coals of many different types can thus be distinguished ; the following are the principal ones.

Lignite or **Brown Coal** is intermediate in type between peat and coal proper. It contains much moisture, and although it ignites easily, its calorific power is low. It usually disintegrates on exposure to the air. Extensive deposits of lignite exist on the Continent and in the U.S.A., but not in England.

Bituminous Coal is the commonest variety. It is black, hard and brittle and gives off large quantities of gas when heated (compare § 15, p. 341).

Cannel Coal, although resembling bituminous coal in many ways, appears to have been formed differently. Some specimens yield fragments which ignite so readily that they burn like a candle (hence the name). Cannel coal is used almost exclusively for gas making (see p. 341).

Anthracite is very hard, dense, black and brittle and exhibits little or no trace of vegetable origin in its structure. It ignites with difficulty but its calorific power is very high.

Table XXVII gives averages from a number of published analyses of different varieties of coal.

TABLE XXVII.—AVERAGE COMPOSITION OF DIFFERENT TYPES OF COAL, ETC.

	Ash.	Fixed Carbon.	Volatile Matter.	Moisture.
Wood . . .	1·5	25·0	53·5	20·0
Peat . . .	1·2	29·2	51·5	18·1
Lignite . . .	8·0	43·1	42·7	6·2
Bituminous Coal .	6·3	63·5	29·2	4·0
Cannel Coal . .	1·5-5	30-50	50-70	3·0
Anthracite . .	5·4	86·5	6·1	2·0

Coal was formerly regarded as a variety of carbon, but it is now known that it contains only a small proportion of uncombined carbon. This is shown to be the case since a considerable proportion of coal is soluble in pyridine (pure carbon being quite insoluble), and also since a large proportion of volatile matter is driven off on heating, comprising a large variety of carbon compounds.

§ 6 Coke

Coke is the more important solid product of the action of heat upon coal in absence of air. The whole subject of this action of heat upon coal is discussed in §§ 15-17, pp. 341-350, and so the manufacturing processes, etc., need not be dealt with here.

Coke is a more or less impure form of carbon, containing from 85 to 90 per cent. of that element. It is used in the manufacture of iron and steel, and in a great many metallurgical operations where its comparative freedom from sulphur and certain other impurities render it more suitable than coal.

The properties of coke depend upon the nature of the coal from which it is obtained, and upon the way the coal is " coked." The two main varieties are *soft coke*—porous, black, brittle, ignites with difficulty, and is used for smith's forges, etc. ; *hard coke*—dark grey in colour, bright lustre, compact, metallic ring when struck, bears great pressure without crushing, used for furnace work and metallurgical operations generally.

§ 7 Graphite

Prior to 1779, molybdenum sulphide and graphite were confused together and thought to be the same substance. In that year K. W. Scheele showed that the former mineral gave a solid " acid " when burnt in air (see p. 780) and evolved sulphur dioxide, whereas the behaviour of graphite in these circumstances was quite different. There was also confusion with the native sulphides of many other elements such as antimony, manganese and lead. This is still reflected in the use of names such as plumbago and black lead for graphite.

Graphite was for a time believed to be a carbide of iron. Scheele noticed that it is deposited from molten iron in blast furnaces, and native graphite usually leaves a residue of oxide of iron when burned. This idea was not altogether given up until Brodie in 1855 prepared pure graphite, after which it was recognized as an allotropic form of carbon.

Graphite is widely distributed in different parts of the world. Large deposits occur in Ceylon and other parts of India, Eastern Siberia, United States, Canada, Bavaria, Bohemia, Moravia, Pinerola (Italy), etc., and formerly there were extensive deposits at Borrowdale in Cumberland, but the mines there are now worked out. Graphite also occurs in the form of fine crystals in many meteorites.

Graphite is manufactured artificially by subjecting amorphous carbon to a very high temperature by means of the electric furnace. This is carried out at Niagara and the process can be understood from the diagram—Fig. 108.

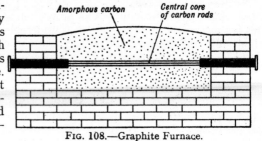

FIG. 108.—Graphite Furnace.

A rectangular firebrick furnace is packed with a ground-up mixture of petroleum coke with coal tar or molasses, and silica or iron oxide, moulded to any desired shape. Carbon rods lead a current through the mass, which is thus heated to a very high temperature for a period of twenty-four to thirty hours. It is thought that silicon carbide (carborundum) is first formed and then decomposed, the temperature being high enough to volatilize off the silicon :

$$SiO_2 + 3C = SiC + 2CO$$
$$SiC = Si + C \text{ (graphite)}$$

Graphite is a dark grey substance with a well-known and characteristic greasy feel ; it has a lustre somewhat resembling that of a metal. It crystallizes in hexagonal plates, but as usually found it has a structure similar to that of mica, composed of a series of easily separated sheets.

Graphite varies in specific gravity from 2 to 3. Hard graphite and soft diamonds have nearly the same specific gravity.

Chemically graphite is rather inactive, though not to the same extent as the diamond (q.v. § 8).

Graphite when heated in air or oxygen burns to carbon dioxide, but it undergoes no change when heated in the absence of air or oxygen. It is rather difficult to ignite.

Pure graphite is not attacked by heating it in a current of chlorine ; nor by fusion with potassium or sodium hydroxide ; some varieties are attacked by fused nitre. Chromic acid or a mixture of sulphuric acid and potassium dichromate oxidize it to carbon dioxide. Neither dilute nitric nor dilute sulphuric acid attacks graphite, although some varieties swell up into worm-like structures—sometimes 12 cm. long —when the finely granulated (not powdered) graphite is moistened with nitric acid (specific gravity 1·52-1·54) in a platinum dish, and then heated. W. Luzi (1891) calls those varieties which are indifferent to the nitric acid treatment—**graphitites** ; and those which swell up— **graphites.** It is generally believed that the phenomenon is a physical effect due to the absorption of acid in the capillary pores and subsequent expansion through the development of gas under the influence of heat.

The action of nitric acid on graphite is characteristic and distinguishes graphite from amorphous carbon, even though the different varieties of graphite differ considerably among themselves. Finely powdered graphite is intimately mixed with three parts of potassium chlorate and sufficient concentrated nitric acid to give a liquid mass. After heating three or four days on a water bath, the solid residue is washed with water, and dried. The treatment with nitric acid, etc., is repeated four or five times until no further change occurs. Finally, a yellow substance is obtained which retains the form of the original graphite. It is called **graphitic acid** (B. Brodie, 1859). The composition of graphitic acid is not quite clear. Diamonds are not attacked by the treatment and ordinary charcoal gives a brown mass soluble in water.

Graphite when rubbed on paper leaves a black mark—hence the term graphite—from γράφειν (graphein), to write. It is therefore used for making *lead pencils*. For this purpose the natural graphite is purified by grinding and washing so as to remove the grit. The purified graphite is mixed with a little washed clay and forced by hydraulic pressure through dies of the necessary shape. It is then stoved and cased in wood (red cedar for preference). Scaly graphite has been largely used, on account of its refractory qualities and high heat conductivity for the manufacture of *plumbago crucibles*. The graphite is mixed with different proportions of clay and sand—e.g., 75 parts of plastic clay, 25 of sand, and 100 of graphite. The crucibles are moulded by machinery or by hand, dried, and baked at a red heat. Other refractory goods are also made from graphite. Graphite is also used as a lubricant for machinery, a coating for iron to prevent rusting, coating for goods—say plaster of Paris—to be later electrotyped, preventative for boiler scale, stove polish, polishing powder, for gunpowder, etc. Graphite is also used largely in making electric furnaces either alone or mixed with carborundum—thus *kryptol* is a mixture of graphite, carborundum, and clay. The resistance offered by this material to the passage of the electric current raises the temperature of the mass. If the mixture be suitably enclosed very little graphite is lost by combustion. Graphite conducts electricity very well, and electrodes of graphite are used in the electro-chemical industries—e.g., as anodes in the manufacture of chlorine by electrolysis of sodium chloride. Graphite is also used for battery plates, electric light carbons, etc. *Colloidal graphite* obtained by deflocculating graphite with an aqueous solution of tannin and also with oil, is used as a lubricant, etc., under the commercial names *aquadag* and *oildag*.

§ 8 Diamond

For long ages diamonds have been prized as ornaments on account of their beauty, rarity, and permanence. As a gem, the diamond is altogether unique, for it is separated from all other gem-stones by peculiar and distinct properties—physical and chemical.

Diamonds occur in their natural state as more or less rounded rough-looking pebbles not unlike pieces of gum arabic in appearance. The natural diamond must be cut and polished to bring out its lustre and sparkle. The diamond-cutting industry is developed chiefly in Amsterdam and Antwerp. The shape of the crystal as it leaves the diamond cutter has no relation to the natural crystalline shape. About half the diamond is lost during the cutting.

The *Cullinan* is the largest known diamond. It was found near Pretoria (South Africa), January, 1905, and weighed over $1\frac{1}{4}$ lbs. ;

after cutting, it weighed about 800 carats,* and was valued at £100,000. It was presented to the King of England by Cape Colony in 1909.

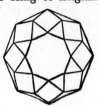 

The *Regent* or *Pitt diamond* owned by the Treasury of the French Crown is the purest and finest known. It weighs 136½ carats, and is valued at F.480,000. Stones over an ounce in weight are comparatively rare.

Occurrence

Diamonds are sparsely distributed in different parts of the world. The chief localities are South Africa, Brazil, Ural,

Fig. 109.—. Diagram of Diamond— Crystal and Cut.

India, Borneo and Australia. They have been found in meteorites —e.g., the Canyon Diablo meteorite (Arizona, U.S.A.) contained both black and transparent diamonds.

The chief source of diamonds at the present day is in what are known as the diamond-pipes of South Africa. These " pipes " are thought to be the shafts of extinct volcanoes, and are found to be filled with a curious type of rock called *blue-ground*. When first mined, this substance is hard, but when exposed to the weather it falls to powder and diamonds are found in the disintegrated mass.

Diamonds have proved surprisingly difficult to make artificially. In general, it is possible to obtain an element crystalline either by deposition from solution (compare sulphur, Ch. XXII) or by very slow cooling of the molten element, or by sublimation. It is only recently that carbon has been melted, and it has been found to solidify to pure graphite. It volatilizes at ordinary pressures at about 3600° without melting, but the vapour condenses to amorphous carbon and not to diamond. Carbon does not dissolve in any ordinary solvent but does so to an appreciable extent in molten iron. The occurrence of diamonds in supposedly volcanic shafts suggest that pressure is an essential condition for their formation. Hence, that if carbon could

* Diamonds are sold by the " carat." The carat represents the Roman *siliqua* or Greek κεράτιον. It was $\frac{1}{24}$th of the golden solidus of Constantine, which was $\frac{1}{6}$th oz. It is now a measure of weight used for diamonds and other precious stones, and was originally $\frac{1}{142}$th oz. or 3½ grains, but it is now nearer 0·207 gram, $\frac{1}{150}$th oz. troy, or 3⅛ grains troy. The value of the international carat is 0·2 grm., or 3·08647 grains troy. The term " carat " is derived from the carob bean, formerly used as a small weight by the diamond merchants of India. Its exact value has varied in time, and it varies in different countries. The carat is also a proportional measure of $\frac{1}{24}$th and is used in stating the fineness of gold.

be deposited from molten iron, under the right conditions of temperature and pressure, it seemed likely that diamonds would result.   Moissan was for many years believed to have proved this.   He packed a piece of iron, as pure as practicable, in a carbon crucible with sugar charcoal.   The crucible was heated between the poles of an electric arc furnace.   Under these conditions the iron melted and dissolved much carbon.   When the temperature had reached 4000°, and the iron was volatilizing in clouds, Moissan plunged the crucible in molten lead. The sudden cooling solidified the outer layer of iron.   The compression which the inner liquid core underwent on solidifying must have produced an enormous pressure.   Hence, the carbon separated from the iron under a very great pressure.   After dissolving away the iron, etc., some of the carbon which remained was believed to be in the form of transparent diamonds—microscopic, it is true.   More recently some workers have concluded that Moissan could not have obtained diamonds in this way, and that the artificial production of diamonds has yet to be achieved.   (Cf. Desch, 1928.)

Varieties

Diamonds are usually tinged slightly yellow.   The clearest and most nearly colourless diamonds without flaw are most prized as " diamonds of the first water."   Diamonds are also occasionally coloured blue, pink, red, and green owing to the presence of traces of foreign metals.   Some diamonds are dark grey and even black ; they exhibit a more or less imperfect crystalline structure, and are known as *black diamonds*—boart or bort, and carbonado.   *Boart* is an imperfectly crystallized black diamond which has various colours, but no clear portions, and is therefore useless as a gem ; boart is used in the drilling of rocks, and in cutting and polishing other stones.   *Carbonado* is the Brazilian term for a still less perfectly crystallized black diamond. It is as hard as boart, and has similar uses.   Boart and carbonado are usually regarded as intermediate forms between diamonds and graphite.

Properties

The diamond is rather brittle.   It is the hardest substance known. Crystalline boron comes next ; it is nearly as hard as the diamond. The hardness, refracting power, and other properties vary with different diamonds ; and, indeed, in different parts of one diamond.   The specific gravity varies from 3·514 to 3·518 ;   carbonado, 3·50 ;   boart, 3·47 to 3·49.   Amorphous graphite has a specific gravity of 2·5 ;   hard gas carbon, 2·356 ;   and amorphous carbon, 1·45 to 1·70.   The diamond is transparent to Röntgen's rays, whereas glass, used in imitation of the diamond, is nearly opaque to these rays.   This furnishes a ready means of distinguishing imitation diamonds from the true gems.

The refractive index, about 2·4, is considerably higher than that of any other solid.

Chemically the diamond is not very active. It is insoluble in all liquids. Fused potassium hydrofluoride mixed with 5 per cent. of nitre attacks the diamond slightly; a mixture of potassium dichromate and sulphuric acid oxidizes the diamond to carbon dioxide at about 200°. Unlike graphite and amorphous carbon, diamonds are scarcely attacked by a mixture of potassium chlorate and nitric acid.

Diamonds will burn in air or oxygen, but only with difficulty, the temperature of ignition, which varies from 700° to 900°, depending upon the hardness, etc., of the particular specimen.

It is rather difficult to burn the diamond unless the temperature be maintained by, say, placing the diamond on a piece of platinum foil heated red hot by an electric current.

When burnt in air or oxygen, carbon dioxide is formed and only a trace of ash (chiefly silica and oxide of iron) is left. The combustibility of the diamond was predicted by Newton who, in 1675, arguing from the high refractory power of camphor, olive oil, amber, etc., " which are fat, sulphureous, unctuous bodies," inferred that " a diamond is probably an unctuous substance coagulated," although he was anticipated by A. Boetius de Boot in 1609.

In 1694, Averani and Targioni of the Academy of Amento first burnt the diamond by exposing it in the focus of a large " sun glass." Lavoisier in 1775, and H. Davy in 1814, showed that the diamond forms carbon dioxide when burnt, and unlike graphite and charcoal, it gives no aqueous vapour, showing that it is free from hydrogen and water. Hence it was inferred that *the diamond is crystallized carbon.*

Uses

Apart from its use as a gem stone, the diamond is used industrially, particularly for making rock-drills, since it is the hardest substance known. It also finds application for glass-cutting, gem-engraving and so on.

§ 9 Internal Structure of the Forms of Carbon

The examination of the forms of carbon by means of X-rays, by the methods described in Chapter X, has yielded results of great interest and importance.

It has been shown that, in the diamond, the atoms are arranged in such a way that each is at the centre of a regular tetrahedron, and is joined to four other atoms which lie at the corners of the tetrahedron. The arrangement is indicated in Fig. 110. The diamond thus consists of a series of interlacing hexagons (a conclusion in harmony with the theories of organic chemistry), each atom being covalently linked to four others. These facts account for the difficulty of chemical attack, and for the nearness of the atoms and hence the high density.

Examination of graphite by X-rays has shown that it consists of planes of covalently-linked carbon atoms, but that there is no chemical union between those in different planes. This structure accounts for the readiness with which graphite can be cleaved along these planes, as well as its softness and lubricating power. The arrangement is shown in Fig. 111.

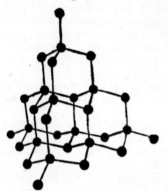

Fig. 110.—Structure of Diamond.　　　Fig. 111.—Structure of Graphite.

Charcoal and amorphous forms of carbon in general are found to possess a graphite-like structure, but the planes are much smaller and arranged in an irregular manner. This accounts for the greater reactivity, but also lends support to the view that amorphous carbon is not a distinct allotropic form.

§ 10　Atomic Weight of Carbon

Many determinations of the atomic weight of carbon have been made by the gravimetric synthesis of carbon dioxide by burning a known weight of diamond in a current of pure oxygen, and weighing the carbon dioxide formed by absorption in potash solution (see p. 353). (For atomic weight work it is necessary to apply a correction for the expansion of the potash solution after absorption of carbon dioxide, since this alters the air displacement.)

Richards and Hoover in 1915 neutralized a known weight of very pure sodium carbonate with hydrobromic acid, thus forming sodium bromide, which was precipitated and estimated in the usual manner of the Harvard determinations (see Ch. VI, pp. 97-100). In this way they obtained the value 12·003.

Physical determinations, by the method of limiting density, have been made using carbon monoxide, and methane. Gray and Woodhead in 1933 obtained a value very close to 12·01 from the limiting density of carbon monoxide. Similar experiments by Cawood and Patterson (1936) with carbon dioxide, ethylene and carbon tetrafluoride led to the value of 12·011.

Owing to the existence of the isotope C^{13}, it is believed (using the best available data for the abundance ratio of the isotopes) that the true chemical value lies close to 12·01.

The " International " Value at present (1940) stands at 12·010.

The *equivalent* of carbon is approximately **3** ; but it is known that the atomic weight is .four times this value, viz., **12** approximately, since this is the smallest weight of carbon found in any of the very numerous volatile organic compounds whose vapour density (and hence molecular weight) have been determined.

§ 11 Hydrocarbons. Methane

Several hundred compounds of carbon and hydrogen are known, and their study belongs to Organic Chemistry.   They can be arranged in a few series, the members of which have many properties in common, and it is convenient to consider the first members of three of these series in Inorganic Chemistry.   These three hydrocarbons are :

Methane	CH_4
Ethylene .	C_2H_4
Acetylene	C_2H_2

Methane, CH_4

Occurrence

This gas, methane, occurs naturally as " *natural gas* " and *firedamp* ; and it is also evolved from decomposing vegetation in ponds and marshes.   Hence it is sometimes known as **marsh gas.**

Natural gas is found associated with oil, or petroleum, which is a complex mixture of hydrocarbons, the simpler constituents being gaseous at ordinary pressures.   These gaseous constituents are known as natural gas, and contain a large proportion of methane.

The chemical processes believed to take place in the formation of coal have been discussed on p. 323, where it was mentioned that methane is formed and often imprisoned in the coal, sometimes under considerable pressure.   When the coal is mined, this gas naturally escapes and, since it forms an explosive mixture with air, it is a source of danger and has given rise to many serious explosions.   Among miners the gas is known as *firedamp*.

Methane appears to be a product of the gradual decay of vegetable matter in a very limited supply of air, and escapes in bubbles when the marshy bottoms of stagnant pools are disturbed.   The gas can be collected and identified as methane.

Methane is also an important constituent of coal gas, comprising from 25 to 40 per cent. of the gas which results from the destructive distillation of coal.

Preparation of Methane

Carbon and hydrogen unite slowly at a dull red heat with the formation of methane, but the amount of methane formed is too small for this to be a practicable method of preparation.

Methane is usually prepared in the laboratory by the following process. A quantity of fused (anhydrous) sodium acetate is intimately mixed with about three times its weight of soda lime in a mortar ; and the mixture transferred to a copper tube (or flask), A (Fig. 112). The tube (or flask) is connected to an empty bottle, B, arranged as shown so as to prevent water being sucked back into A during the course of

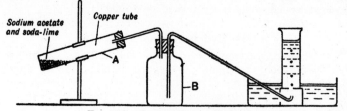

Sodium acetate and soda-lime

Copper tube

A

B

FIG. 112.—Preparation of Methane.

the experiment. The gas formed when A is strongly heated is collected over water as shown. The reaction may be represented by the equation :

$$CH_3.COONa + NaOH = Na_2CO_3 + CH_4.$$

Sodium hydroxide itself is not used on account of its fusibility.

The gas prepared by this process is not very pure and contains about 90 per cent. of methane, but the mode of preparation is useful for ordinary purposes. For instance, this gas burns with a luminous flame, whereas pure methane burns with a non-luminous flame. A fairly pure gas—mixed with a little ammonia and acetylene—is formed by the action of water on commercial aluminium carbide :

$$Al_4C_3 + 12H_2O \rightarrow 4Al(OH)_3 + 3CH_4.$$

The gas can be washed free from acetylene by means of an ammoniacal solution of cuprous chloride. When pure methane is required, methyl iodide, CH_3I, is reduced by nascent hydrogen formed by the action of a mercury : aluminium couple, or a copper : zinc couple on water or alcohol, thus :

$$CH_3I + 2H = CH_4 + HI$$

This method of preparation is discussed in works on organic chemistry.

Methane is now being manufactured from water gas (see p. 367).

Properties

Pure methane is free from colour, and is without smell. The gas prepared by the ordinary process usually has a slight smell, but this is due to the presence of impurities. Methane is lighter than air. 100 volumes of water at 0° dissolve $5\frac{1}{2}$ volumes of the gas ; and at 20°, $3\frac{1}{2}$ volumes. Methane is father more soluble in alcohol. It liquefies at 0° under a pressure of 140 atmospheres. The liquid boils at $-160°$, and solidifies at $-184°$. Methane has no well-defined physiological action on the system other than diluting the oxygen and so inducing suffocation.

Pure methane burns with a pale blue, almost non-luminous flame, forming carbon dioxide and water :

$$CH_4 + 2O_2 = CO_2 + 2H_2O.$$

It is a non-supporter of combustion, as is shown by plunging a lighted taper into a jar of the gas (held mouth downwards). The taper is extinguished, while the gas burns at the mouth of the jar.

Methane forms explosive mixtures with air, even when present only to the extent of 5 or 6 per cent.

Apart from its combustibility methane is chemically very stable and attacked by but few reagents. It is attacked by chlorine, the nature of the products depending upon the conditions. A mixture of methane with excess of chlorine explodes when exposed to direct sunlight, carbon being deposited :

$$CH_4 + 2Cl_2 = C + 4HCl.$$

When a mixture of equal volumes of chlorine and methane is exposed to *diffused daylight*, they gradually react forming methyl chloride, CH_3Cl. If more chlorine be present it gradually replaces all the hydrogen :

$$CH_4 + Cl_2 = CH_3Cl + HCl$$
methyl chloride

$$CH_3Cl + Cl_2 = CH_2Cl_2 + HCl$$
methylene chloride

$$CH_2Cl_2 + Cl_2 = CHCl_3 + HCl$$
chloroform

$$CHCl_3 + Cl_2 = CCl_4 + HCl$$
carbon tetrachloride

This process of replacing one or more atoms in a molecule by equivalent atoms is called **substitution**. The formation of these should be contrasted with the **addition** compounds of ethylene (see p. 338). Methane is unattacked by other chemical reagents.

§ 12 Formula of Methane

The formula of methane, and of other gaseous hydrocarbons can be found from the results of exploding a measured volume of the gas with excess of oxygen in an eudiometer. The water formed condenses and causes a contraction on cooling which determines the amount of hydrogen present since it is equal to the volume of the steam formed. The carbon dioxide also formed can then be absorbed by potassium hydroxide solution and the resulting contraction measured. The calculation of the formula from the data so obtained is illustrated by the following example :—

In an experiment 10 *c.c. of methane were exploded with* 40 *c.c. of oxygen. After cooling the volume of the mixture was* 30 *c.c. After absorbing the carbon dioxide by means of potash solution the volume of unused oxygen remaining was* 20 *c.c.   What is the formula of methane?* (All volumes have been reduced to N.T.P.)

The results of the experiment show that one volume of methane reacts with three volumes of oxygen, and that one volume of carbon dioxide is formed.

Hence, if the formula of methane be C_xH_y, we have (Ch. VII, p. 110) :

$$x = 1 \text{ and } x + \frac{y}{4} = 2$$

$$\therefore y = 4$$

so that the formula of methane is CH_4.

§ 13 Ethylene, C_2H_4

Occurrence and Preparation

Ethylene was discovered by J. J. Becher about 1669, and its properties were distinguished from ordinary inflammable air by the Dutch chemists, J. P. Deimann, A. P. van Troostwijk, N. Bondt, and A. Lauwerenburgh (1795). These chemists also showed that the gas contained carbon and hydrogen. It was clearly distinguished from methane in 1805 by W. Henry.

Ethylene occurs in natural gas (p. 333). Some analyses of " pit gases " show that up to 6 per cent. of this gas may occur in the air in coal pits. This gas is also obtained when coal or wood is heated in closed vessels, and coal gas contains from 4 to 10 per cent. of ethylene.

Ethylene is usually prepared by the action of concentrated sulphuric acid on alcohol. This is an interesting reaction since, according to the conditions, either ethylene or ether may be formed. This latter substance is studied in organic chemistry.

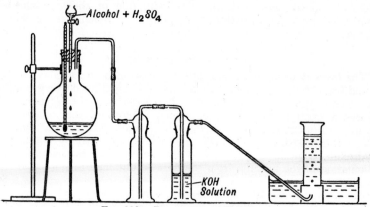

FIG. 113.—Preparation of Ethylene.

For the preparation of ethylene 30 c.c. of alcohol are mixed with 80 c.c. of concentrated sulphuric acid in a large flask, through the neck of which passes a tap-funnel and a thermometer (with its bulb *in* the liquid) as well as a delivery tube. The mixture is heated to 160° on a sand bath, when ethylene is formed along with sulphur dioxide, carbon dioxide, a little ether, etc. The gas is washed by passing it through a bottle containing strong caustic potash solution and collected over water (see Fig. 113). The supply of gas can be maintained by adding slowly a mixture of equal volumes of alcohol and concentrated sulphuric acid through the tap-funnel.

The reactions which take place may be represented by the equations :

$$C_2H_5OH + H_2SO_4 = C_2H_5HSO_4 + H_2O$$

alcohol   ethyl hydrogen
                     sulphate

$$C_2H_5HSO_4 = C_2H_4 + H_2SO_4.$$

The former reaction takes place at ordinary temperatures, but the ethyl hydrogen sulphate formed breaks up into ethylene and sulphuric acid at temperatures above 150°. Summarizing the two equations, we have :

$$C_2H_5OH = C_2H_4 + H_2O,$$

and so the process is sometimes thought of as a dehydration of alcohol.

Syrupy phosphoric acid can be used in this experiment instead of sulphuric acid, but a temperature of 200-220° is then required.

Properties

Ethylene is a colourless gas with a peculiar ethereal odour. It has nearly the same density as air. 100 volumes of water at 0° dissolve 25·7 volumes of the gas, and at 20°, 15 volumes ; the gas is nearly 13 times as soluble in alcohol. Ethylene liquefies at 0° under a pressure of 43 atmospheres ; the liquid boils at −104°, and solidifies at −169°. The gas behaves like methane towards a lighted taper, but it burns with a luminous smoky flame unless it be diluted with hydrogen or methane. Ethylene is decomposed at a high temperature. This is illustrated by passing the gas through a bulb-tube of hard glass. When all the air has been expelled, heat the bulb in the blowpipe flame. By rotating the bulb, a mirror-like deposit of carbon can be formed in the interior of the bulb.

Ethylene forms an explosive mixture with air and the explosion is even more violent than with methane.

If a mixture of hydrogen and ethylene be passed over reduced copper, between 180° and 300°, the ethylene, C_2H_4, is reduced to **ethane,** C_2H_6, a gas resembling methane in many of its properties. Finely divided nickel can also be used as a catalyst.

The formula for the gas can be determined in the same way as that of methane (q.v.). In this way it is found to be C_2H_4, which is confirmed by vapour density measurements which show that the molecular weight is 28.

The graphic formula for ethylene with carbon quadrivalent and hydrogen univalent is not possible if all the valencies have to be saturated or "satisfied." Hence the graphic formula involves two sleeping or unsaturated valencies. On joining the carbon atoms by a double bond, we get :

$$\begin{matrix} H \\ H \end{matrix}\Big> C = C \Big< \begin{matrix} H \\ H \end{matrix}$$

Most of the evidence for this type of linkage (sometimes called a **double bond**) belongs to the realm of organic chemistry. It appears to involve a state of strain in the molecule, and hence a compound possessing a linkage of this kind is reactive and forms addition **products.**

Thus, one molecule of ethylene readily combines with a molecule of chlorine when equal volumes of the two gases are mixed, forming an oily liquid known as **ethylene dichloride,** the formula of which is $C_2H_4Cl_2$:

$$C_2H_4 + Cl_2 = C_2H_4Cl_2.$$

One of the earliest properties of ethylene to be observed was the formation of this oil which gave rise to the name *olefiant* (= oil forming) *gas* for ethylene.

Ethylene will react similarly with hydrobromic and hydriodic acids :

$$C_2H_4 + HBr = C_2H_5Br.$$

It is also readily oxidized by oxidizing agents, such as potassium permanganate :

$$C_2H_4 + H_2O + O = C_2H_4(OH)_2$$

and is absorbed by very strong or fuming sulphuric acid forming ethyl hydrogen sulphate :

$$C_2H_4 + H_2SO_4 = C_2H_5.HSO_4$$

Ethylene is thus a very reactive substance and forms, as a rule, **addition** products. In this respect its behaviour is in marked contrast with that of methane which is chemically inert and, when it reacts at all, forms substitution products.

§ 14 Acetylene, C_2H_2

This gas was discovered by E. Davy in 1836. He obtained it by the action of water on the black mass formed as a by-product in the manufacture of potassium.

Preparation

Acetylene is formed in small quantities by sparking carbon electrodes in an atmosphere of hydrogen. It is also found in small quantities in the gases issuing from a bunsen burner which has " struck back."

The most convenient and usual method for preparing acetylene is by the action of water on calcium carbide (p. 625). The reaction may be represented by the equation :

$$CaC_2 + 2H_2O = Ca(OH)_2 + C_2H_2.$$

In the laboratory the reaction can be conveniently carried out in an apparatus such as is indicated in Fig. 114.

When prepared in this way the gas contains small traces of sulphur and phosphorus compounds ammonia, etc., but it is usually pure enough for experimental work. The gas can be purified from the most objectionable impurities in the following manner. First pass the gas through a wash-bottle containing a solution of copper sulphate acidified with sulphuric acid. This

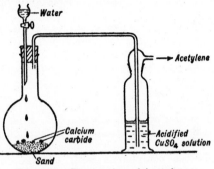

FIG. 114.—Preparation of Acetylene.

removes ammonia, phosphorus, and sulphur compounds. The gas then passes through a tower fitted with perforated shelves on which rest " chloride of lime," this removes the phosphorus compounds.

The formula for acetylene, determined in the same way as that of methane, is C_2H_2, and the graphic formula is written

$$H - C \equiv C - H$$

since it exhibits the unsaturated behaviour of ethylene in a double degree.

Properties

Acetylene is a colourless gas, which, when pure, has an ethereal odour which is not unpleasant. As usually prepared and purified the gas has traces of impurities which impart to the gas an offensive smell reminding one of garlic. Acetylene is rather lighter than air. 100 volumes of water at 0° dissolve 173 volumes of acetylene ; and at 20°, 103 volumes of the gas. Alcohol dissolves about six times its own volume at ordinary temperatures ; and the gas is absorbed by fuming sulphuric acid. Acetylene can be hydrogenized (reduced) to ethylene, C_2H_4, and to ethane, C_2H_6, if it be mixed with hydrogen, and passed over finely-divided nickel. Acetylene is poisonous and soon induces headache. It melts at $-84°$ and boils at 82°.

Acetylene burns with a luminous smoky flame, but, like the other hydrocarbon gases, it extinguishes a lighted taper plunged into the gas. If acetylene be burned from a jet with a very fine aperture the flame is not smoky, but it is exceedingly luminous. In most acetylene burners the gas issues as two small jets so arranged that they strike

against one another and produce a flat flame. Other holes are located
so that air is drawn in and mixed with the gas as it rushes through the
nozzle—e.g., the gas jet of an ordinary acetylene bicycle lamp. The
great luminosity of the acetylene flame, coupled with the easy preparation of the gas from " carbide," has led to the extensive use of acetylene
for bicycle lamps, houses, etc., where coal gas is not convenient ;
acetylene is also used to increase the luminosity of other inflammable
gases.

Acetylene is violently explosive when mixed with $2\frac{1}{2}$ times its volume
of oxygen. The gas cannot be safely stored under a greater pressure
than 2 atmospheres—30 lbs. per square inch—because it is then
liable to explode violently by mere shock. One method of storing
acetylene under pressure is to employ a solution of the gas in acetone,
which, under a pressure of 12 atmospheres, dissolves 300 times its
volume at ordinary temperatures. It is stored and transported thus
in steel cylinders, when required for industrial operations such as
welding, cutting steel, etc., as mentioned below.

Acetylene resembles ethylene in the readiness with which it forms
additive compounds with chlorine, oxidizing agents, etc. When
mixed with chlorine, it inflames spontaneously and carbon and hydrogen chloride are formed ; but under regulated conditions acetylene
tetrachloride results.

$$C_2H_2 + 2Cl_2 = C_2H_2Cl_4.$$

Acetylene tetrachloride is now manufactured by passing chlorine
and acetylene into chambers filled with kieselguhr (infusorial earth,
p. 682) and is sold under the name *westron*.

Acetylene reacts with solutions of some metallic salts with the
formation of explosive compounds known as acetylides. The most
familiar of these is cuprous acetylide, which is formed as a red precipitate when a current of acetylene is passed through an ammoniacal
solution of cuprous chloride. This precipitate has the formula
$Cu_2C_2.H_2O$ and, when dried, forms the acetylide Cu_2C_2. Similar
acetylides are formed by silver and mercury. The action of dilute
acids on these compounds produces pure acetylene.

Uses

The use of acetylene as an illuminant has already been mentioned.
Oxy-acetylene blowpipes are used for welding pieces of iron and steel
together under conditions where forge welding is impracticable. The
flame is produced by burning a mixture of the two gases delivered into
special blowpipes under pressure (the acetylene from an acetone
solution of acetylene under pressure). The flame at the apex of the
small central white cone has a temperature of about 3000°. At that
point, the flame is almost entirely carbon monoxide surrounded by a
jacket of hydrogen. The temperature at the apex of the flame is too
high to allow the hydrogen to combine with the oxygen. The flame is
therefore hot enough to melt iron and steel, and yet sufficiently

reducing to protect the fused metal from oxidation while the welding is in progress.

It is also used, particularly at Niagara Falls and at Visp in Switzerland, as the starting point for the manufacture of acetic acid and a large range of other organic chemicals.

§ 15 Coal Gas

Coal gas consists of a mixture, in varying proportions, of hydrogen, carbon monoxide, methane and other hydrocarbons, and is the gas which results from the distillation of coal out of contact with the air. The formation of such a gas is referred to by writers as early as the seventeenth century, but its use as an illuminant was not developed until the end of the eighteenth century. Its use was introduced by William Murdoch in 1792, and in 1798 he installed a plant for the lighting of Boulton and Watt's engineering works at Soho, Birmingham, by gas.

When coal is heated in closed vessels to about 400°, it is carbonized, and a comparatively small quantity of gaseous, and a relatively large quantity of liquid, products are obtained. If the temperature of distillation be raised, the quantity of liquid products decreases, and the quantity of gaseous products increases. In other words, more gas and less tar is obtained. The gas obtained by the high temperature distillation has less illuminating power, when burned at a jet such as the flat-flame or fish-tail burner. In modern practice, there is a tendency to raise the temperature of distillation, thus sacrificing illuminating power for quantity (cubic feet of gas per ton of coal). Since nowadays it is the heating value of the gas which is important (for even when used for lighting it is in conjunction with incandescent mantles), the lower illuminating power of the gas is not a disadvantage.

Experiments are now being conducted, however, with low-temperature distillation (i.e., at a temperature of 300-400° C.) because of the improved yield of volatile liquid products (benzene, etc.) which are then produced and which are valuable for use as motor spirit, etc. In ordinary gas-works practice, however, a temperature of about 700-1000° C. is employed.

When coal is heated in this way there is formed :

(i) A mixture of gases, consisting mainly of hydrogen, methane and ethylene.

(ii) A liquid portion. This separates into two layers, viz.,

    (a) an aqueous layer containing ammonia, ammonium sulphide, phenol (carbolic acid), pyridine and small quantities of other organic compounds ;

    (b) a layer of " tar " insoluble in water consisting of a large number of hydrocarbons (e.g., benzene, toluene, naphthalene) and related organic compounds of great technical importance.

(iii) A non-volatile residue of coke.

(iv) A hard greyish-black form of carbon known as **gas-carbon** adhering to the walls of the retort.

The approximate amounts of the various products obtained from one ton of coal are :

Coal gas	...	10,000-12,000 cu. ft.
Tar ...	...	115 lbs.
Ammonia	...	7 lbs.
Coke ...	...	1,550 lbs.

FIG. 115.   *Industrial Newspapers Ltd*

§ 16 Coal Gas Manufacture

The details of the plant in use at various gas works differ consider ably, in particular in the arrangement of the retorts, but the chemistry of the process is essentially the same in all. Different types of retort are illustrated by Figs. 115, 116 and 117, and the general layout by Fig. 118.

1. The Retorts

The coal is distilled in fireclay retorts, which may be set horizontally or in an inclined position, or vertically. When horizontal, or inclined the retorts are ⌂-shaped in section and uniform throughout their length ; when vertical they are rectangular and usually taper somewhat towards the top.

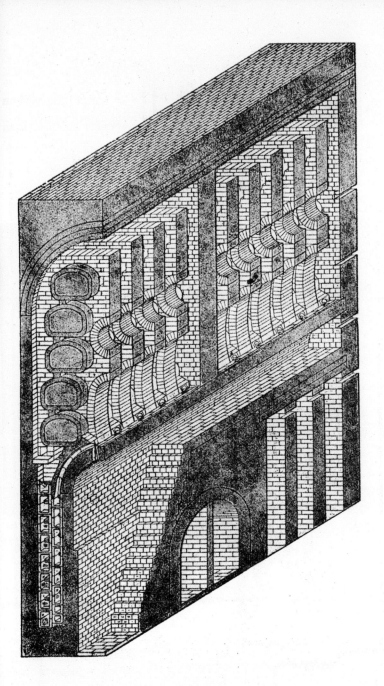

Fig. 116.

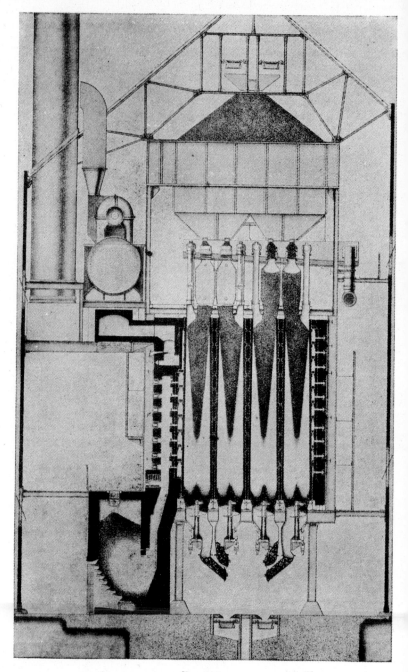

Fig. 117.

When horizontal retorts are used they are fixed to an iron furnace front, each fitted with a door and connected with a vertical exit pipe —*the ascension pipe*—for the escape of volatile products. The retorts are arranged in banks of five or more, heated by a single furnace.

Each group of retorts is heated by **producer gas** formed by passing air through a bed of hot coke in a special furnace underneath. (See p. 360 for a fuller account of producer gas which is essentially a mixture of carbon monoxide and nitrogen.)

The volatile products pass from the retort into the *hydraulic main* which contains condensed coal tar and water. This main runs horizontally over the front of the bench of retorts, and all the retorts discharge into it. The gas is here partly cooled, and some tar and water are condensed from the hot gas. The pipe leading the gas from the retort dips into the liquid in the hydraulic main, and so prevents the gas from passing back when the retorts are recharged. The liquid in the hydraulic main is kept at a constant level by leading the excess into the *tar well*. In from four to six hours, the distillation will be complete. The coke is pushed or raked from the retort, and quenched with water to prevent further combustion. Another charge of coal is quickly introduced into the retort.

The arrangement of horizontal retort settings is illustrated by Figs. 115 and 116.

When vertical retorts are employed they are arranged in a manner which may be understood from Fig. 117. In these the coal enters at the top from a special hopper in a slow continuous stream, while the coke is similarly removed from the bottom. The advantages of vertical retorts are continuous operation, and the by-products include a more fluid tar and a larger proportion of ammonia. Also steam can be introduced into the retorts if desired ; this steaming produces a proportion of water gas at the same time as the coal is distilled. (Compare also p. 362.) Vertical retorts are heated by producer gas in a similar manner to the horizontal type.

2. The Condensers

The hot impure gases pass from the hydraulic main into a series of iron pipes, several hundred feet long—the condensers—connected so that the gas must pass through the entire length of the pipe. The gas is here cooled still further, and more tar is condensed and run to the tar well. The condensed liquid in the tar well separates into two layers—the lower layer is *gas tar* ; and the upper aqueous solution containing ammonia and ammonium salts is the *gas liquor*. The gas is drawn from the hydraulic main through the condensers by means of an *exhaust pump* which reduces the pressure in the retort, and also regulates the pressure of the gas sent along to be still further purified.

3. The Scrubbers

In modern works all the tar is removed from the gas in the condensing plant, but the gas still contains sulphur compounds, carbon

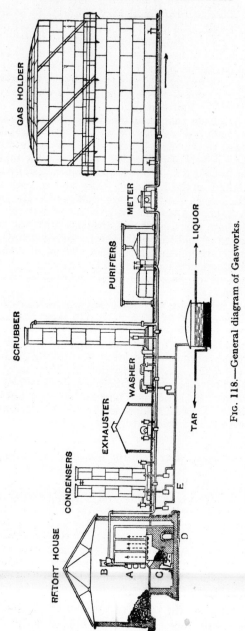

FIG. 118.—General diagram of Gasworks.

From Lowry & Cavell's " Intermediate Chemistry," by permission of Messrs. Macmillan & Co. Ltd.

dioxide and some ammonia.   In one form of scrubber, a tower is filled
with trays charged with coke or pebbles.   The tower has a partition
so that the gas flows down one side of the tower and up the other.
A spray of water trickles down the coke.   The gas in passing through
the coke is broken up into small bubbles and washed free from
ammonium compounds by the water.
    Another form of scrubber is illustrated by Fig. 119.   This consists
of a horizontal cylindrical vessel, divided internally into compartments

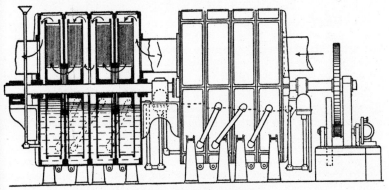

FIG. 119.—Rotary Scrubber.

by vertical plates having suitably-placed openings for the passage of
the gas.   A central revolving shaft carries, in each compartment, a
disc to which are attached bundles of thin wooden boards.   The gas
passes over the surfaces of the wood, which is kept wetted by revolving
through the liquor at the bottom of each compartment.   Rotary
scrubbers are more efficient and occupy less room than the older types.
    The water from the scrubbers is drawn off from time to time and
mixed with the gas liquor from the tar well.

4. The Purifiers

    Some of the hydrogen sulphide and carbon dioxide in the gas combine
with the ammonia and are removed in the scrubbers.   The gas still
contains sulphur compounds.   If these were not removed, the burning
gas would form sulphur dioxide which is objectionable.   The gas
leaving the scrubbers is directed into a series of low rectangular iron
tanks—the purifiers—fitted with horizontal shelves or grids.   The
shelves are loosely packed with a layer of slightly damped slaked
lime—say, six inches deep.   The lime removes hydrogen sulphide and
carbon dioxide.   A mixture of calcium sulphide—CaSH.OH, or
$Ca(SH)_2$—and calcium carbonate is formed.   The calcium sulphide
may absorb some carbon disulphide :

$$2Ca{<}^{SH}_{OH}\ C+ CS_2 = Ca(OH)_2aCS_3 + H_2S.$$

When the lime is spent or fouled it is called *gas lime*, or *spent lime*. To make sure that all the sulphur compounds are removed, the gas is generally passed through another purifier containing ferric hydroxide (" bog iron ore ")—$Fe_2O_3.H_2O$. The ferric hydroxide forms ferric sulphide :

$$Fe_2O_3H_2O + 3H_2S = Fe_2S_3 + 4H_2O ;$$

or ferrous sulphide and free sulphur :

$$Fe_2O_3H_2O + 3H_2S = 2FeS + S + 4H_2O.$$

When the mixture is fouled it is placed in a heap for about twenty-four hours and then spread out in layers twelve inches deep. The layers are turned over repeatedly to expose fresh surfaces to the action of the air. The black iron sulphides are oxidized by exposure to the air, and free sulphur separates :

$$2Fe_2S_3 + 3O_2 = 2Fe_2O_3 + 6S ; 4FeS + 3O_2 = 2Fe_2O_3 + 4S;$$

the net result is that the hydrogen sulphide of the gas is converted into free sulphur, and the ferric oxide is revived ready to be used again. This alternate fouling and oxidizing of the " iron " is repeated about sixteen times when so much sulphur accumulates—55 per cent.—that it is no longer economical to use the oxide again. The *spent oxide* is sold to the manufacturer of sulphuric acid, and used as a source of sulphur. Recently it has also been used as a source of iron, being worked up after a preliminary treatment for blast furnace use.

5. The Gas Holder

The purified gas next passes through a large meter which records its volume and then into the familiar gas holder. This is usually an enormous cylindrical iron tank which floats in a cistern of water and rises, or falls, as gas enters, or leaves. The use of waterless gas holders in which the gas is confined in an iron tower under a large " piston " sealed by flowing tar has been developed of late years. From the gas holder the gas passes to the *governor*, where its pressure is regulated, and then to the supply mains for use.

The gas so obtained has approximately the following composition :—

Hydrogen	...	...	45 per cent
Methane...	...	...	35 ,, ,,
Ethylene	...	...	4 ,, ,,
Carbon Monoxide	...	8 ,, ,,
Carbon Dioxide...	...	2 ,, ,,
Nitrogen...	...	...	$5\frac{1}{2}$,, ,,
Oxygen ...	...	...	$\frac{1}{2}$,, ,,

Before being supplied to the public a proportion of water gas sometimes enriched or carburetted (pp. 362-4) is very generally added. This has the effect of increasing the percentage of carbon monoxide and decreasing that of methane, etc. The gas supplied to the public thus has, as a rule, only a basis of coal gas proper and contains a much higher percentage of carbon monoxide (usually between 15 and 20). On account of the very poisonous nature of carbon monoxide, modern town gas is more dangerous if allowed to escape than true coal gas, and so the very greatest care is necessary to prevent leakage in confined spaces.

§ 17 By-products of Gas Manufacture

As stated above (p. 341), coal gas is only one of the numerous products of the operations described in the preceding section. Along with it are produced numerous valuable by-products. Among these may be mentioned gas carbon, gas lime, tar, ammonia, cyanides and coke.

Gas Carbon is a hard dense deposit of almost pure carbon which gradually collects on the inside of the retort. It is a good conductor of electricity, and is used for the manufacture of carbon rods for arc lamps and searchlights, and of plates for galvanic batteries. *Gas lime* is used for agricultural purposes. *Tar*—gas tar, coal tar—is a black viscid foul-smelling liquid used as a protective paint for preserving timber ; making tarred paper, waterproofing masonry, etc. Tar is a mixture of many " organic substances " which are separated by distillation at different temperatures. It furnishes carbolic and creosotic oils, benzene, naphthalene, anthracene, etc. Benzene is a most. interesting compound discovered by M. Faraday ; as A. W. Hofmann has said, its history and uses would fill a volume. It is capable of undergoing an endless number of Proteus-like transformations, and it has given rise to new and important branches of industry. It is used in the manufacture of aniline dyestuffs, flavouring essences, perfumes, oils, etc. The residue in the retort is " pitch." Artificial asphalt* is a solution of pitch in heavy tar oils, and is used in making hard pavements, varnish, etc. *Ammonia*—the ammoniacal liquid is boiled with milk of lime and the expelled ammonia is mixed with sulphuric acid. The tarry matters are separated, and the solution of ammonium sulphate is evaporated and crystallized for the market. This subject is further referred to in Chapter XX. *Cyanides*, which are of value, are usually removed by passing the crude gas through a washer containing an alkaline solution of ferrous sulphate, so that ferrocyanides are formed. The recovery and utilization of these substances is discussed on p. 570.

Coke, as explained in § 6 of this chapter, is a valuable fuel and is in great demand for metallurgical and other industrial operations (see also producer gas, p. 360, and water gas, p. 362). As a consequence, large quantities of coal are carbonized for the direct production of coke in order to supplement the gas works supply. This is carried out in plant known as coke ovens.

* This must be distinguished from the natural asphalt obtained from the famous pitch lakes in Trinidad.

Coke ovens are of two main types : the older being known as **Beehive ovens** on account of their shape, and the more modern as **Recovery** (e.g., Simon-Carves) **ovens.**

The **Beehive oven** consists of a covered mound of brickwork in which the coal is partly burned in a limited supply of air (compare charcoal burning, p. 320). It produces an excellent coke, but all the volatile products are lost and it is wasteful.

Recovery ovens, such as the Simon-Carves and Becker ovens, make use of fireclay retorts not unlike those used in coal-gas manufacture. Fig. 120 is a diagram of a section of such an oven. The coal is heated

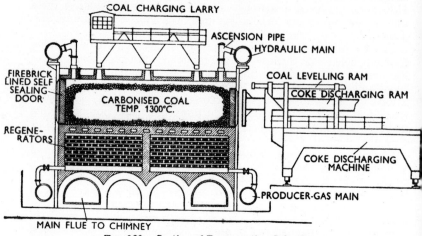

FIG. 120.—Section of Regenerative Coke Oven.

in these retorts and gives off a mixture of products as in gas manufacture. Part of the gas evolved is used for heating the retorts, being mixed for this purpose with pre-heated air. This air derives its heat from the hot gases from the furnace by way of a heat-exchanger. The gas evolved from the retorts is cooled to separate the tar, and scrubbed to remove ammonia, etc., before being burned. Because of the value of the numerous by-products, recovery ovens are displacing the beehive type. Recently, there has been established in the neighbourhood of Sheffield, where there are numerous coke ovens in operation, a gas-grid linking up the various plants and making a very cheap supply of gas available for use in the nearby towns.

§ 18 Oxides of Carbon. Carbon Dioxide

Three oxides of carbon, all of which are gaseous at ordinary temperatures, are definitely known, carbon dioxide (CO_2), carbon monoxide (CO), and carbon suboxide (C_3O_2). Other oxides such as C_4O_3, C_5O_2, $C_{12}O_9$ and C_8O_3 have been reported.

Carbon Dioxide, CO$_2$

History and Occurrence

Carbon dioxide has been known for a long time, but the early writers confused it with " air." J. B. van Helmont called it *gas sylvestre* to distinguish it from common air. He prepared it by the action of acids on alkalis and calcareous substances ; he showed that it was formed during the combustion of charcoal, during the fermentation and the decay of organic matter, and he recognized it in the " mineral water " at Spa (Belgium) ; in the Grotta del Cane (Naples), and other localities. He also knew that the gas extinguished flame, and suffocated animals. but he confused it with other gases which do not support combustion. J. Black (1755), however, proved the gas to be a peculiar constituent of carbonated alkalis, being " fixed " there in the solid state. Hence Black called the gas *fixed air* ; and T. Bergman (1774), *aerial acid*. The chemical nature of carbon dioxide was clearly explained by Lavoisier who showed it to be an oxide of carbon.

Carbon dioxide is present in the atmosphere to the extent of about 3 parts in 10,000 (0·03 per cent.) by volume. This is a fact of the utmost importance and significance, for upon the presence of this carbon dioxide depends the continued existence of life as we know it. Both plants and animals consist essentially of carbon compounds ; and the source of the carbon contained in them is ultimately the carbon dioxide in the atmosphere. Plants in sunlight are able to bring about what is known as *photosynthesis*, that is, can build up sugars, starches, and other organic compounds from the carbon dioxide of the atmosphere and water. The carbon compounds contained in animals are derived either from plants eaten by the animals, or from eating other animals which in their turn have consumed plants as food.

The carbon thus absorbed by animals is ultimately partly returned to the atmosphere in the form of carbon dioxide exhaled by the lungs ; while the decomposition of the dead bodies of plants and animals also liberates carbon dioxide. There is thus maintained a balance between plant and animal life which results in the maintenance of the propor-

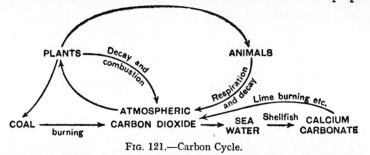

FIG. 121.—Carbon Cycle.

tion of carbon dioxide in the atmosphere at a remarkably steady value. Carbon dioxide is appreciably soluble in water and a certain amount of carbon dioxide has been more or less permanently removed from the air through the formation by aquatic animals of shells composed of calcium carbonate. This is the origin of the enormous beds of limestone and chalk which exist in various parts of the world, and it is quite probable that this process is still going on. Against this may be set the fact that man is busily engaged in converting enormous quantities of coal and oil into carbon dioxide by burning them. These various changes are indicated diagrammatically by Fig. 121.

Carbon dioxide is found to issue from the ground in many places both as a gas and in aqueous solution (mineral water). J. B. Boussingault (1844) estimated that Cotopaxi emitted more carbon dioxide per annum than was generated by life and combustion in a city like Paris. Owing to the fact that carbon dioxide is nearly one and a half times as heavy as air, this gas is inclined to collect as a gas in old deep wells, in valleys, and in depressions in the ground near lime kilns ; and in certain neighbourhoods where carbon dioxide is evolved from volcanoes and fissures in the ground—e.g., the Valley of Death (Lake of Laach, Java), where one traveller says the whole of the bottom is strewn with the skeletons of human beings, animals, and birds which have been asphyxiated in an atmosphere overloaded with carbon dioxide. In the Grotta del Cane (Pozzuoli, Naples) there is said to be a constant depth of about 18 inches of carbon dioxide on the floor so that dogs entering the cave are suffocated while men are safe.

Carbon dioxide is also evolved in the Death Gulch in the Yellowstone Park and the skeletons of dead animals which have been suffocated by it are to be seen there.

Preparation of Carbon Dioxide

Carbon dioxide is formed whenever carbon, or carbon compounds, are burned in excess of air, but this is not as a rule a convenient source of the gas. It can be made :

(i) by the action of heat on carbonates (except those of the alkali metals) ;

(ii) by the action of acids on carbonates ;

(iii) by fermentation.

The first and third are common industrial sources of the gas, while the usual laboratory preparation is an example of the second.

Preparation of Carbon Dioxide in the Laboratory

Carbon dioxide is generally made in the laboratory by the action of dilute hydrochloric acid upon calcium carbonate—marble, limestone or chalk. The operation may be carried out in a Woulfe's bottle or Kipp's apparatus (compare Figs. 122 and 90, pp. 353 and 255). Fragments of marble are placed in the Woulfe's bottle and covered with water. Concentrated hydrochloric acid is added by way of the thistle funnel. The reaction is represented by the equation :

$$CaCO_3 + 2HCl = CaCl_2 + CO_2 + H_2O.$$

The gas is somewhat soluble in water and so it is usually collected by downward delivery as in Fig. 122.

The gas can be dried by means of calcium chloride, or concentrated sulphuric acid, or phosphorus pentoxide.

It is not advisable to use sulphuric acid in the preparation since the lumps of marble or limestone soon become covered with the very sparingly soluble calcium sulphate which then stops further action.

Industrially, large quantities of carbon dioxide are obtained in the course of the manufacture of quicklime, which is made by the action of heat on limestone (see p. 626).

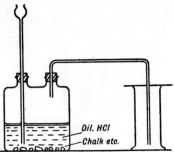

Fig. 122.
Preparation of Carbon Dioxide.

Dil. HCl
Chalk etc.

In the course of this operation, carbon dioxide is given off, and utilized :

$$CaCO_3 = CaO + CO_2.$$

This is the source of the carbon dioxide used in the Solvay process for the manufacture of sodium carbonate (see p. 558).

In the brewing industry, large quantities of carbon dioxide are evolved as a result of the fermentation of sugars or substances containing sugars, by yeast. The main reaction involved in the alcoholic fermentation of sugar may be represented by the equation :

$$C_6H_{12}O_6 = 2C_2H_5OH + 2CO_2,$$

but small quantities of several other substances are formed at the same time, so that there are probably a number of side reactions taking place also.

§ 19 Formula and Properties of Carbon Dioxide

Formula

The composition of carbon dioxide can be determined directly both by weight and by volume. The composition by weight is found by burning a weighed amount of carbon—diamond, graphite, or sugar charcoal—at a red heat in a stream of oxygen, in an apparatus such as that indicated in Fig. 123.

The carbon is weighed into a platinum or porcelain boat, A, and placed in the hard glass tube C, one half of which is packed with granular copper oxide, F. The tube is heated by means of a combustion furnace, and a slow stream of pure, dry oxygen is passed through the apparatus. The carbon burns in the oxygen, and any traces of carbon monoxide which may be formed are completely oxidized to carbon dioxide by passage through the hot copper oxide, F.

The carbon dioxide is absorbed in the weighed potash bulbs, D. The calcium chloride tube, E, is weighed along with the potash bulbs as

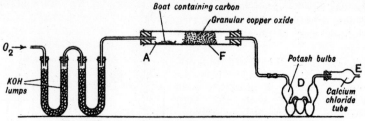

Boat containing carbon

Granular copper oxide

$O_2 \rightarrow$

A   F

Potash bulbs

E

KOH lumps

D

Calcium chloride tube

FIG. 123.—Gravimetric Composition of Carbon Dioxide.

its purpose is to prevent loss of water vapour from D by being carried along by the stream of excess oxygen.

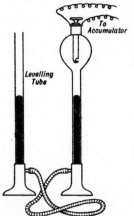

To Accumulator

Levelling Tube

FIG. 124.—Composition of Carbon Dioxide by Volume.

Experiments of this kind show that 8 parts by weight of oxygen, combine with 3 parts by weight of carbon; that is, the equivalent of carbon in this gas is 3. Since the vapour density of the gas is 22, its molecular weight is 44 and it follows that the weight of carbon in the molecular weight is $\frac{3}{11}$ of 44; that is 12 units of weight which corresponds to one atom of carbon. Similarly the weight of oxygen is $\frac{8}{11}$ of 44, that is 32, which corresponds to two atoms of oxygen. Therefore the formula of the gas is CO_2.

The volumetric composition of carbon dioxide may be found in an apparatus such as that indicated in Fig. 124.

The bulb of the right tube, Fig. 124, is charged with oxygen; and the stopper which carries a bone-ash crucible containing a chip of charcoal, is lowered into the position illustrated in the diagram. A slip of gummed paper is placed on the right tube indicating the position of the mercury when that liquid is at the same level in both tubes. The platinum wires are connected with an accumulator or battery. The small loop of platinum wire in contact with the carbon is thus heated red hot. This ignites the carbon which burns to carbon dioxide. The heat of the combustion expands the gas, but in a short time, when the apparatus has cooled, the level of the mercury is the same as before the experiment. Hence the gas formed by burning carbon in excess of oxygen contains its own volume of oxygen.

The fact that carbon dioxide contains its own volume of oxygen indicates that its formula is C_nO_2 for, by Avogadro's Law, it shows that one molecule of the gas contains one molecule of oxygen. Since the vapour density ($H_2 = 1$) is found to be 22, its molecular weight is 44, and since it contains one molecule of oxygen, i.e., 32 units of weight, the amount of carbon is $(44 - 32) = 12$ units of weight which corresponds to one atomic weight of carbon. The formula of the gas is therefore CO_2, which accounts for the name carbon dioxide.

Properties

Carbon dioxide is a colourless gas with a faint taste and smell. It is believed that it is not poisonous, and that its harmful effects are mainly due to suffocation (absence of oxygen), and to the physical disturbance of delicate equilibria. Small increases in the amount of carbon dioxide in air—say 2 or 3 per cent.—do no perceptible harm ; 5-6 per cent. induces a rise of pulse and marked panting ; 10 per cent. violent panting ; above this the gas exerts a narcotic effect, and with 25 per cent. death will occur in a few hours ; air with 50 per cent. carbon dioxide can be breathed a short time without fatal results. The ill-effects which attend breathing in a badly ventilated room are probably due to the increase of moisture and temperature.

Water dissolves about 1¾ times its volume of the gas at 0° and 760 mm. pressure ; and about its own volume at 15°, 760 mm. In the manufacture of " soda water " the gas is dissolved by the water under pressure—60-150 lbs. per square inch. The solution effervesces and froths when the pressure is withdrawn, owing to the escape of the carbon dioxide.

All natural waters contain dissolved carbon dioxide, and the existence and growth of aquatic plants depends upon its presence. The reaction of such waters with calceolareous rocks has been referred to on page 352.

Carbon dioxide is comparatively easily liquefied, and it was first obtained in this state by Faraday in 1823 (p. 37).

Liquid carbon dioxide is now manufactured as a commercial article by pumping the gas into steel cylinders (bombs) by powerful compression pumps. Liquid carbon dioxide is also utilized for making " home-made " soda water, the " sparklet " bulbs sold for this purpose being filled with it.

At −5°, carbon dioxide requires a pressure of 30·8 atmospheres for liquefaction ; at +5°, 40·4 atms. ; and at +15°, 52·1 atms. ; and over 32° it cannot be liquefied by any known pressure. Liquid carbon dioxide is a colourless mobile liquid. It floats on water without mixing with it. It boils at −78·2° at atmospheric pressure.

If liquid carbon dioxide be allowed to escape into the air from the nozzle of the bomb, the absorption of heat which attends the rapid evaporation causes a portion of the liquid to solidify. The solid is collected by tying a small canvas bag over the nozzle and inverting the bomb. By opening the nozzle for a few minutes, quite a lot of solid carbon dioxide can be collected. The solid can be shaken from the bag into a cardboard box for examination. It crystallizes in the cubic system.

Properties of Solid Carbon Dioxide

Solid carbon dioxide is a soft, white snow-like substance—" carbonic acid snow." It evaporates in air without melting, but under a pressure of 5 atms. it can be melted to a liquid. It can be handled safely provided no pressure is applied. The effect of pressure is to break the film of gas between the solid and the warm hand and cause a severe burn, or rather, a blister, resembling the blister produced by a burn. A horn spoon can be used for handling the material.

Carbon dioxide " snow " dissolves in ether, and as the ether evaporates, a temperature approaching $-110°$ can be obtained in air, and $-140°$ under reduced pressure. The solution is a good conductor for heat, and serves as an excellent freezing mixture. A great many gases can be liquefied by passing them through tubes immersed in this mixture.

Solid carbon dioxide is now a commercial product and is used as a refrigerant under the name of " *Drikold.*" It is convenient for this purpose since it leaves no residue.

Chemically, carbon dioxide is a rather stable substance and it is not easily decomposed. It is heavier than air, and extinguishes the flame of most burning bodies. It is non-combustible. Certain very active metals, e.g., sodium, potassium and magnesium will, however, burn in carbon dioxide, carbon being deposited in black specks :

$$CO_2 + 2Mg = C + 2MgO.$$

This behaviour is possibly due to the high temperature causing slight dissociation of the carbon dioxide.

Carbon dioxide is fairly stable at high temperatures. When heated under atmospheric pressure, at $1300°$, only $0·004$ per cent. is decomposed ; at $1400°$, $0·14$ per cent. ; and at $1478°$, $0·32$ per cent.

The solution of carbon dioxide in water exhibits feeble acid properties and is therefore believed to contain the acid **carbonic acid,** H_2CO_3, carbon dioxide being consequently known as **carbonic anhydride.** Neither liquid nor dry gaseous carbon dioxide affects dry blue litmus paper, but if the paper be moistened it is coloured port-wine red. There can be little doubt, therefore, that in solution some of the gas forms carbonic acid by combination with the water :

$$H_2O + CO_2 \rightleftharpoons H_2CO_3.$$

Carbonic acid is, however, unstable and has never been isolated ; further, only a very small quantity of the acid is formed as is evident from the low solubility of the gas in water. The system is in equilibrium when but a small proportion of the dissolved gas has produced H_2CO_3. If a base be present, it will react with the carbonic acid and form a carbonate. More H_2O and CO_2 unite, and the resulting H_2CO_3 is removed by the base as fast as it is formed, until all the carbon dioxide in solution has been converted into carbonate.

Orthocarbonic acid corresponding with $C(OH)_4$, or H_4CO_4, is not known, although some **orthocarbonates,** e.g., ethyl orthocarbonate,

$C(OC_2H_5)_4$, are familiar to the student of organic chemistry. The ordinary " carbonates," now to be considered, are really **meta-carbonates** derived from **metacarbonic acid,** $CO(OH)_2$.

Carbonic acid is a di-basic acid (p. 307) so that it forms two series of salts, **normal carbonates** and acid or **bi-carbonates.** Thus, by the action of carbon dioxide on a solution of sodium hydroxide, there is first formed normal sodium carbonate :

$$2NaOH + CO_2 = Na_2CO_3 + H_2O,$$

but if excess of the gas be passed through the solution, sodium bi-carbonate results :

$$Na_2CO_3 + H_2O + CO_2 = 2NaHCO_3.$$

The analogous behaviour of slaked lime with carbon dioxide, which is of great importance in the study of hard water, has been discussed on page 275.

Solutions of caustic alkalis and lime are thus excellent absorbers of carbon dioxide. In practice, potassium hydroxide is a better absorbent than sodium hydroxide since the sodium carbonate is less soluble than potassium carbonate and is liable to crystallize out and block the tubes of a wash-bottle or absorption apparatus.

Detection and Determination

The action of the gas on lime water is the standard method for detecting carbon dioxide. Slaked lime (p. 627) is only rather sparingly soluble, but calcium carbonate is virtually insoluble. If, therefore, a sample of lime water is brought into contact with carbon dioxide, calcium carbonate is precipitated, or, as it is commonly said, the lime water is " turned milky."

$$Ca(OH)_2 + CO_2 = CaCO_3 + H_2O.$$

The action of excess of carbon dioxide causes the lime water to go clear again owing to the formation of the soluble bicarbonate (compare p. 275).

$$CaCO_3 + H_2O + CO_2 = Ca(HCO_3)_2.$$

Carbon dioxide is determined by its action on baryta water (a solution of barium hydroxide—p. 637). A known volume of the gas containing the carbon dioxide to be determined (e.g., air) is shaken up with, or aspirated through, a known volume of baryta water of known strength (usually about N/50). Barium carbonate is precipitated and the excess of barium hydroxide is determined by titration with a standard solution of oxalic acid, using phenolphthalein as indicator. The determination in this way of the amount of carbon dioxide in the atmosphere is sometimes described as Pettenkofer's method.

§ 20 Uses of Carbon Dioxide

Carbon dioxide is employed in a variety of ways in industry. A familiar use, for which large quantities are required, is the making of soda water and aerated drinks. It is employed in fire extinguishers on account of its property of extinguishing flames. In some forms, these contain an acid contained in a glass bottle, and a bicarbonate (usually sulphuric acid and sodium bicarbonate). The extinguisher is brought into operation by a blow on a plunger so placed as to break the bottle. When the two substances mix, carbon dioxide is evolved and may be used to project a stream of water highly charged with carbon dioxide on to the fire. The foam type of fire-extinguisher depends upon the formation of a stable foam of carbon dioxide bubbles, by mixing the water with a substance such as glue or alum which reduces its surface tension considerably.

The use of liquid carbon dioxide in the steel industry for hardening steel has been tried, particularly by the firm of Krupp. If liquid carbon dioxide is allowed to come into contact with molten steel in strong gas-tight chambers, a very high pressure of gas results which frees the casting from bubbles. Carbon dioxide is also used for precipitating lime in the manufacture of sugar; in the Solvay process for the manufacture of sodium carbonate (p. 558); and directly or indirectly in the production of white lead. There has also been much work done recently on the preservation of fruit in an atmosphere of carbon dioxide. This is being applied particularly to the storage of apples. It has also found application in the destruction of insects in grain silos. The use of solid carbon dioxide as a refrigerant has been mentioned earlier.

§ 21 Carbonates

Most metals form carbonates and a great many of these are found native. The only important metals which do not form carbonates are those whose hydroxides are very weak bases, for example, chromium.

Metallic carbonates are usually insoluble; those of the alkali metals being the only important exceptions. They can usually be prepared, therefore, by precipitation by the action of a solution of sodium carbonate on a solution of a soluble salt of the metal, e.g.,

$$CuSO_4 + Na_2CO_3 = CuCO_3 \downarrow + Na_2SO_4.$$

All carbonates, except those of the alkali metals, decompose on heating with evolution of carbon dioxide and formation of the oxide of the metal, e.g., "lime-burning," page 626.

$$CaCO_3 = CaO + CO_2.$$

Carbonates are decomposed by acids with evolution of carbon dioxide. The action of excess of carbon dioxide on carbonates results in the formation of bicarbonates, but with the exception of those of the alkali metals they cannot, as a rule, be isolated.

Many basic carbonates are known, some of which are of importance, as, for example, white lead which is usually given the formula $2PbCO_3.Pb(OH)_2$, although it is not certain that it is a definite compound. (Cf. p. 707.)

§ 22 Carbon Monoxide, CO

Occurrence

Carbon monoxide seldom occurs free in nature, and then only in small quantities. Minute traces have been detected in air, in volcanic gases, occluded in coal, and in meteorites. It is found in tobacco smoke, in chimney gases where the air is not in a sufficiently large excess, in the gases from blast and other furnaces, and in the exhaust gases of internal combustion engines. It is an important constituent of fuel gases such as coal gas (p. 348), producer gas (p. 360) and water gas (p. 362).

Preparation

Industrially, carbon monoxide is made in large quantities in the form of producer gas, and water gas as described below (pp. 360-362). It can be prepared in the laboratory by the action of concentrated sulphuric acid either on formic acid or oxalic acid (whereby the elements of water are removed) ; or on ferrocyanides. Carbon monoxide is also formed by passing carbon dioxide over strongly heated carbon, but the process is not easy to carry out in the laboratory.

$$CO_2 + C = 2CO.$$

The method usually employed in the laboratory is the action of concentrated sulphuric acid on oxalic acid.

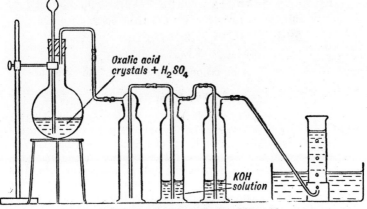

Oxalic acid crystals + H_2SO_4

KOH solution

Fig. 125.—Preparation of Carbon Monoxide.

A suitable quantity (say 30 gms.) of oxalic acid crystals is placed in a 500 c.c. flask, fitted with a thistle funnel and delivery tube as in Fig.

125. The crystals are covered with concentrated sulphuric acid, added by way of the thistle funnel. On heating the mixture, carbon monoxide and carbon dioxide are evolved in equal volumes ; so that the gases must be passed through wash-bottles containing strong potassium hydroxide solution in order to remove carbon dioxide. Carbon monoxide is not soluble in water, so that it can be collected over it. It can be dried by means of the usual drying agents as, for example, calcium chloride, concentrated sulphuric acid or phosphorus pentoxide. The reaction taking place is the withdrawal of the elements of water by the sulphuric acid :

$$H_2C_2O_4 + H_2SO_4 = CO + CO_2 + H_2SO_4.H_2O.$$

If desired, sodium formate can be substituted for the oxalic acid, in which case washing with caustic potash solution is unnecessary :

$$H.CO_2Na + H_2SO_4 = H.CO_2H + NaHSO_4$$
$$H.CO_2H + H_2SO_4 = CO + H_2SO_4.H_2O.$$

Carbon monoxide is also sometimes prepared by heating potassium ferrocyanide (p. 821) with 10-20 times its weight of concentrated sulphuric acid, but a rather high temperature is required. The reaction is usually represented by the equation :

$$K_4Fe(CN)_6 + 8H_2SO_4 + 6H_2O =$$
$$3(NH_4)_2SO_4 + 4KHSO_4 + FeSO_4 + 6CO,$$

but it is probable that it takes place in stages. Hydrocyanic acid is thought to be first formed, and then hydrolyzed to formic acid and ammonia. The former is then dehydrated by the sulphuric acid as above :

$$K_4Fe(CN)_6 + 5H_2SO_4 = 6HCN + 4KHSO_4 + FeSO_4$$
$$6HCN + 12H_2O = 6H.CO_2H + 6NH_3$$
$$6NH_3 + 3H_2SO_4 = 3(NH_4)_2SO_4$$
$$6H.CO_2H = 6CO + 6H_2O.$$

Summarized, these four equations reduce to the one given above.

§ 23 Producer Gas

Producer gas consists of a mixture of carbon monoxide and nitrogen, formed when air is blown through incandescent coke. Producer gas thus obtained is cheap, but since its calorific value is not very high, distribution would be uneconomic. It is usually made, therefore, *in situ*, as when required for heating the retorts in gas works (p. 345).

The apparatus in which this gas is made is called a **producer,** and is illustrated diagrammatically by Fig. 126.

The producer consists essentially of a large air-tight, cylindrical furnace made of sheet iron lined with firebrick, provided with an orifice at the base through which air can be blown, and an outlet for the producer gas at the top. Devices are provided to enable fresh coke to be added at the top and ash to be removed at the bottom, without admission of unwanted air. The producer is filled with coke (which rests on firebars at the bottom) and air is forced through the hot fuel. The air, when it first enters the producer, probably oxidizes some coke to carbon dioxide :

$$C + O_2 = CO_2,$$

which passes further up the furnace, where it is reduced to carbon monoxide by the excess of red-hot coke :

$$CO_2 + C \rightleftharpoons 2CO.$$

There thus passes out of the producer a gas consisting essentially of carbon monoxide and nitrogen from the air used.

There is, in fact, an equilibrium set up in the producer between carbon dioxide and carbon monoxide, as indicated by the last equation.

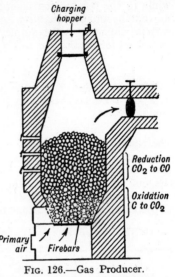

Fig. 126.—Gas Producer.

The relative proportion of carbon dioxide to carbon monoxide, for equilibrium, is determined by the temperature. For instance, any mixture of carbon monoxide and carbon dioxide when heated in the presence of carbon produces at :

Temperature.	Per cent. by volume.	
	CO	CO$_2$
450°	2	98
750°	76	24
1050°	99·6	0·4

This shows that if the temperature of a producer be in the vicinity of 450°, very little combustible gas will be obtained ; and conversely, in the vicinity of 1000°, nearly the maximum possible amount of combustible carbon monoxide will be present. Hence the temperature of the producer should be about 1000° in order to get the maximum yield of carbon monoxide with a minimum loss of heat.

A considerable amount of heat is liberated in the producer, and so the gas comes off at a high temperature. The gas, therefore, should not be allowed to cool before being used, or this heat will be wasted. This is an additional important reason for the production of producer gas *in situ*.

When producer gas is used for heating a retort bench or furnace, the bed of the latter consists of two parts, viz., the producer proper and a combustion chamber. In the former air is admitted in such amount as will form producer gas (this is known as the *primary air*) ; while in the combustion chamber what is called *secondary air* is admitted in suitable quantity so that the carbon monoxide burns to carbon dioxide. An example of this is furnished by the furnace employed for heating the retorts in the gas works (p. 345).

§ 24 Water Gas

When a current of steam is blown through a bed of hot carbon (say in a gas producer), the two interact, forming hydrogen and carbon monoxide :

$$C + H_2O \rightleftharpoons CO + H_2.$$

The resulting mixture has a very high calorific power and it is called water gas. Water gas is almost free from diluting nitrogen. If the reaction occurs below 1000°, carbon dioxide begins to accumulate in the gas, and this the more the lower the temperature of the reaction.

The following table (XXVIII), due to Bunte, shows the proportions of the gases formed at various temperatures.

TABLE XXVIII.—EFFECT OF TEMPERATURE ON FORMATION ON THE COMPOSITION OF WATER GAS.

Temperature.	Per cent. of steam decomposed.	Percentage composition of gas produced.		
		Hydrogen.	Carbon monoxide.	Carbon dioxide.
674°	8·8	65·2	4·9	29·8
1010°	94·0	48·8	49·7	1·5
1125°	99·4	50·9	48·5	0·6

As was the case in the manufacture of producer gas, it is necessary here also that the temperature of the coke should not fall below 1000°.

The reaction which forms water gas proceeds with absorption of heat, that is, it is an endothermic reaction (p. 211) as is shown by the equation :

$$C + H_2O = CO + H_2 - 29 \text{ Cals.}$$

Hence, it follows that when steam is blown over incandescent coke in order to make water gas, the temperature of the fuel will fall. It is, therefore, necessary to provide heat from another source in order to maintain the temperature of the producer sufficiently high to prevent undue amounts of carbon dioxide accumulating in the products of the reaction. In modern water-gas plants, the carbon in the producer is raised to incandescence by a blast of air—the *air blow*—continued for about two minutes. This is followed by a jet of steam until the temperature falls to dull redness—*steam blow*—continued for about four minutes. When the air blow is in progress, the producer is not making water gas, and, in consequence, a damper is used to deflect the stream of gas from the producer elsewhere.

One form of water-gas plant is illustrated in Fig. 127.

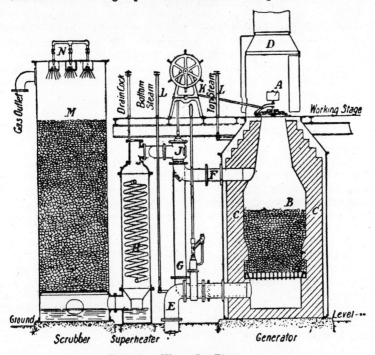

Fig. 127.—Water Gas Plant.
(*From Meade's " Modern Gasworks Practice."*
By permission of Messrs. Eyre & Spottiswoode).

The two operations described above are sometimes combined and just enough air is mixed with the steam to keep the fuel hot. The resulting gas contains nitrogen and a larger proportion of carbon monoxide than water gas, and is known as **semi-water gas.**

Water gas burns with a non-luminous flame, and, though a valuable heating agent, it is useless for lighting purposes unless it be employed in conjunction with, say, a Welsbach's mantle. Hence, if water gas is to be used as an illuminating agent, it is charged with hydrocarbon gases which do not condense on cooling. The mixture is called *carburetted or enriched water gas.* The carburetting is conducted as follows : When the air blast is in progress, the products of combustion from the top of the producer are deflected down a tower containing checkered brickwork, and called the *carburetter* ; then up another tower also containing checkered brickwork, called the *superheater* ; and thence into the air. The result of this is to raise the temperature of both towers—the carburetter and the superheater. The air valve at the top of the superheater is deflected so that the superheater is put in communication with a third tower resembling the *scrubber* of a gas works. A spray of oil is simultaneously directed into the top of the carburetter, and steam is blown into the producer. As the water gas and oil pass down the hot carburetter, the oil is decomposed— " cracked "—and the decomposition is completed in the superheater. In this way, the oil is transformed into gases which do not liquefy when cooled. The gas is purified and washed in the scrubber, and thence passed to the gas holder.

§ 25 Formula and Properties of Carbon Monoxide

Formula

In § 19 (p. 353) it has been shown that carbon dioxide contains its own volume of oxygen. By means of an eudiometer experiment, it can be shown that two volumes of carbon monoxide will unite with one volume of oxygen to form two volumes of carbon dioxide. Hence, by Avogadro's hypothesis, two molecules of carbon monoxide and one molecule of oxygen give two molecules of carbon dioxide. The formula of the latter being CO_2, that of the former is therefore CO. This is confirmed by the vapour density which is 14 ($H_2 = 1$).

In the vast majority of its compounds carbon is found to be quadrivalent ; but it cannot be so in carbon monoxide unless oxygen is also quadrivalent. In consequence it has been generally assumed that in carbon monoxide, the carbon is divalent with two " sleeping " valencies. This is in agreement with the readiness with which carbon monoxide can form addition compounds (see below).

The interpretation of this conclusion in terms of the electronic theory of valency (Ch. IX) has given rise to controversy, since the formula $C = O$, translated into terms of electrons, etc., becomes :

$$: C \, {}^{\circ}_{\circ} \, O \, {}^{\circ}_{\circ}$$

A compound of this structure would, however, have a large dipole moment (p. 149) since it has four electrons at one end and two only at the other, whereas experiment shows that carbon monoxide has zero dipole moment. This has been explained by the formula $C \rightleftharpoons O$, which, in terms of electrons, becomes :

$$: C \, {}_{\circ} \, O$$

This is supported by the fact that in the known addition compounds of carbon monoxide, it behaves as a *donor* but not as an *acceptor*. Thus, it does not combine with water or ammonia, while it forms addition compounds with chlorine, and many metals, such as nickel.

Properties

Carbon monoxide is a colourless, tasteless, and odourless, poisonous gas. One volume of water dissolves about 0·035 volume at 0°, and about 0·023 volume at 20°. The gas condenses to a colourless, transparent liquid at −192°, at atmospheric pressure ; the liquid solidifies at −207°. When a lighted taper is plunged into the gas, the taper is extinguished (non-supporter of combustion), but the gas is inflamed (combustible), and burns with a blue flame. The blue lambent flame which appears on the surface of a clear red coke (or coal) fire, or over the ignited lime in a lime kiln, is carbon monoxide.

On burning in air or oxygen carbon dioxide is formed :

$$2CO + O_2 = 2CO_2.$$

Mixtures of air or oxygen with carbon monoxide are highly explosive in the ordinary way ; but the explosion does not occur easily if the mixture is absolutely dry. This was the first well-investigated case of the effect of intensive drying (see p. 284).

Carbon monoxide is a stable gas and is not decomposed by rise of temperature. It is also a neutral oxide since it does not react or form salts with either acids or bases.

Carbon monoxide readily forms addition products. The formation of carbon dioxide when it burns in air is an example of this. Thus it will combine with chlorine, when a mixture of the two gases is exposed to light, particularly in the presence of charcoal, forming **phosgene** or **carbonyl chloride** :

$$CO + Cl_2 = COCl_2.$$

Similarly, a mixture of carbon monoxide and sulphur vapour combine when passed through a hot tube with the formation of carbonyl sulphide, COS, a reaction analogous to the formation of carbon dioxide when it burns. Again, when heated with caustic soda under pressure, *sodium formate* results :

$$NaOH + CO = H.CO_2Na.$$

This reaction is now used commercially. It also forms an addition product with cuprous chloride, and hence solutions of this salt in hydrochloric acid or ammonia can be used as absorbents for the gas. Carbon monoxide also forms interesting compounds with certain metals (particularly some of those in Group VIII of the Periodic Table). *Nickel carbonyl* is employed in the extraction of nickel from its ores (p. 829).

Carbon monoxide is an important reducing agent, and when passed over the heated oxides of many metals reduces them to the metals themselves. It plays an essential part in the production of iron in the blast furnace (p. 801).

Carbon monoxide is an active poison. When it is respired in the lungs, it unites with the haemoglobin of the blood, forming a bright cherry-red coloured compound carbonyl haemoglobin which prevents the haemoglobin performing its regular work of oxidizing waste tissue. Less than 1 per cent. in the atmosphere is sufficient to cause death when inhaled. J. S. Haldane says that air containing $\frac{1}{20}$ of 1 per cent. of carbon monoxide will produce giddiness on exertion if breathed for from one-half to two hours; and $\frac{1}{10}$ per cent. makes one unable to walk; $\frac{1}{8}$ per cent. leads to loss of consciousness and perhaps death; $\frac{4}{5}$ per cent. means probable death; and 1 per cent. will lead to unconsciousness in a few minutes, followed before long by death. Fatal accidents have arisen from the breathing of carbon monoxide, when its presence has not been suspected. It is formed when a gas flame is exposed to a cold surface as might occur in some " patent water heaters " used in ill-ventilated bathrooms, etc.; in slow combustion stoves, and charcoal pans. It is often present in rooms where gas producers are at work; and in rooms with an escape of coal gas, water gas, etc. The poisonous character of " after-damp " in coal mines is due to the presence of some carbon monoxide along with the carbon dioxide formed during an explosion of fire-damp or coal dust; in air after the use of explosives for blasting; underground fires, etc.

§ 26 Detection and Determination of Carbon Monoxide

The detection of carbon monoxide is not easy. (1) A piece of white filter paper moistened with *platinum* or *palladium chloride*—$PtCl_4$ or $PdCl_2$—is turned pink, green, or black, owing to the reduction of the chloride to the metal. The intensity of the tint is proportional to the amount of carbon monoxide in the given atmosphere (freed from ammonia and hydrogen sulphide).

(2) Iodine pentoxide is reduced by carbon monoxide:

$$5CO + I_2O_5 = I_2 + 5CO_2.$$

This reaction is a sensitive test for the gas. The liberated iodine gives a violet solution with chloroform or carbon disulphide.

(3) *Vogel's blood test* is considered the most reliable. If ordinary blood be diluted with 200 times its volume of water, a yellowish-red solution is obtained, with blood containing carbon monoxide, the solution is distinctly pink.

The spectrum of haemoglobin in normal blood shows two absorption bands, which disappear on the addition of ammonium sulphide, and a single band is seen in between these positions. Blood containing carbonyl haemoglobin gives a very similar spectrum to haemoglobin itself, but ammonium sulphide does not cause any marked change. Hence, if a sample of diluted blood is treated with air suspected of containing carbon monoxide, followed by addition of ammonium sulphide, the presence of *two* absorption bands is evidence of the presence of carbon monoxide.

In ordinary gas analysis, the proportion of carbon monoxide in a mixture may be determined by first removing acid gases such as carbon dioxide by means of a solution of potash, and then absorbing the carbon monoxide in ammoniacal cuprous chloride solution.

§ 27 Uses of Carbon Monoxide

Carbon monoxide, usually either in the form of producer gas or water gas, has many technical applications. One of the most important is in the extraction of metallic nickel from its ores, where its use depends upon the formation and subsequent decomposition of nickel carbonyl (p. 833). It is employed in the manufacture of formates (and hence oxalates), by action on sodium hydroxide under pressure. When mixed with hydrogen (in the form of water gas) it readily forms methane by passage over nickel at a temperature of about 300°. This process has been employed on a large scale for the production, from water gas, of a gas of high calorific power and some illuminating properties also. It has even been suggested that the carbon monoxide present in modern town-gas should be converted into methane in this way, thus making it much less poisonous and increasing its calorific value. By passing a similar mixture at 200 atmospheres pressure over a catalyst consisting of zinc and chromium oxides, at a temperature of 350°-400°, methyl alchohol is made in quantity ; and by modifying the catalyst (e.g., by using an alkalized iron catalyst) higher alcohols and other organic compounds containing up to nine carbon atoms can be obtained. This mixture of products is marketed under the name *synthol*. Carbon monoxide is used also for the manufacture of phosgene which is used in the dye industry, and also finds a use—or abuse—in chemical warfare. Its employment as a reducing agent in metallurgy has already been mentioned ; this use is being extended in some quarters to the reduction of organic compounds. The use of carbon monoxide as a fuel is, of course, of great importance and wide application.

§ 28 Carbon Suboxide, C_3O_2

This is made by the action of phosphorus pentoxide on malonic acid

$$CH_2(CO_2H)_2 - 2H_2O = C_3O_2.$$

Carbon suboxide is a colourless gas, of suffocating odour, which condenses to a liquid at 6°, and decomposes when warmed. It burns with a blue, smoky flame forming carbon dioxide. With water it regenerates malonic acid, so that it may be regarded as malonic anhydride.

§ 29 Carbon Disulphide, CS_2

Carbon disulphide was discovered by W. A. Lampadius in 1796 while studying the action of pyrites on carbon. Clément and Désormes rediscovered it in 1802. It is formed when sulphur vapour is passed over red-hot carbon, in the form of charcoal or coke :

$$C + 2S = CS_2.$$

It is not easy to prepare in the laboratory, but is an important article of commerce.

In the manufacturing process, the charcoal is heated in vertical cast-iron or earthenware retorts set in a suitable furnace. The heat of the furnace also melts the sulphur placed in a vessel near the base of the retort, the sulphur vapour rises through the red-hot charcoal and forms carbon disulphide which escapes at the top. The carbon disulphide is condensed in long condensing coils—30 feet long.

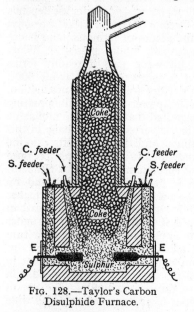

FIG. 128.—Taylor's Carbon Disulphide Furnace.

In Taylor's electric process (1899) a cylindrical furnace 40 feet high and 16 feet in diameter is packed with coke from the top, Fig. 128; the coke is renewed through the side hopper C. An alternating current is sent through the electrodes E set at right angles to one another at the base of the furnace. The heat melts the sulphur on the floor of the furnace; the vapour of sulphur rises through the coke, forming carbon disulphide. Fresh sulphur is introduced through the hopper as shown in the diagram. The carbon disulphide passes off at the top of the furnace, and is condensed in the condensing coils. The electrical process is practically continuous and is free from troublesome leakages and heat losses incidental to the retort process. The crude product by either process can be purified by repeated redistillation.

Carbon disulphide, if pure, is a colourless, mobile, refractive liquid, with an aromatic smell not at all displeasing, although the smell of commercial carbon disulphide is usually disagreeable and rancid. Light slowly decomposes the pure liquid in such a way that a small quantity of some product—possibly a polymer—is formed which raises the boiling point of the liquid and produces an unpleasant smell. Air also seems to affect it, particularly if the temperature is raised a little. So sensitive is purified carbon disulphide to these influences that it has been said : pure carbon disulphide is an ephemeral product. If breathed constantly, in small quantities, carbon disulphide is injurious to health, and in large quantities, fatal. Its specific gravity at 0° is 1·292. It freezes at −111·6° ; and boils at 46·27°. 100 grams of water at 0° dissolve 0·242 gram of carbon disulphide ; and at 20°, 0·210 gram. Most of the alkali salts are insoluble in carbon disulphide ; several salts of the metals are sparingly soluble in this liquid. Carbon disulphide mixes in all proportions with alcohol, ether, benzene, and essential oils. It is also a good solvent for sulphur, phosphorus, iodine, bromine, camphor, gums, resins, waxes, fats, and caoutchouc ; and it is largely employed in the industries on account of its solvent properties. It is also used as an insecticide.

Carbon disulphide reacts under suitable conditions with chlorine to form carbon tetrachloride and sulphur chloride (see below). It also reacts with alkali sulphides, giving substances known as **thiocarbonates** on account of their analogy to the carbonates.

$$CS_2 + Na_2S = Na_2CS_3.$$

§ 30 Carbon Tetrachloride, CCl_4

Carbon tetrachloride is made by the action of chlorine on carbon disulphide containing a little iodine or aluminium chloride in suspension :

$$CS_2 + 3Cl_2 = CCl_4 + S_2Cl_2.$$

The carbon tetrachloride can be separated from the sulphur chloride by distillation. It is purified by washing with dilute sodium hydroxide, and redistillation from bleaching powder.

Carbon tetrachloride is rather important commercially as a solvent for fats—degreasing woollen and linen fabrics, bones, oleaginous seeds, etc. It can replace benzene, which is dangerously inflammable. Carbon tetrachloride is a colourless non-inflammable liquid of specific gravity 1·63, boiling at 76·8°. The liquid attacks metals, particularly if moisture be present, owing to the formation of hydrochloric acid.

Carbon tetrachloride is remarkable in that, being the chloride of a non-metal, it is not decomposed by water. Its behaviour in this respect may be compared with that of silicon tetrachloride (p. 693) and phosphorus trichloride (p. 735), both of which are decomposed even by cold water.

§ 31 Cyanogen and its Compounds

There is a considerable group of compounds, containing the —CN or —NC radical, which are of importance, particularly from the viewpoint of organic chemistry. Certain of them are properly considered in inorganic chemistry. The radical —CN itself shows some resemblance in its reactions to a chlorine atom, and was one of the first radicals, whose behaviour as a group resembles that of a single atom, to be clearly recognized.

Cyanogen, C_2N_2

Cyanogen was first isolated by Gay-Lussac in 1815 by the action of heat on silver cyanide.

Morren (1859) and Berthelot (1879) showed that cyanogen can be obtained directly from its elements by sparking carbon electrodes in nitrogen gas; and cyanides are formed, as indicated on p. 386, by heating the two elements in contact with a metal—preferably of the alkalis or alkaline earths. The endothermic reaction is symbolized :

$$2C + N_2 = C_2N_2 - 82 \text{ Cals.}$$

Cyanogen is a gas made by heating mercuric or silver cyanide in a hard glass tube ; mercuric cyanide is, on the whole, more convenient :

$$Hg(CN)_2 = Hg + C_2N_2.$$

The gas can be collected over water, but it is somewhat soluble and so is best collected over mercury. The yield of cyanogen is much less than the theoretical owing to the formation of a dark brown powder called **paracyanogen**. This substance appears to be a polymer of cyanogen, $(CN)_n$, because, if heated to about 850°, it gives ordinary cyanogen. If the mercuric cyanide be mixed with mercuric chloride, the cyanogen comes off at a lower temperature, and less paracyanogen is formed :

$$Hg(CN)_2 + HgCl_2 = 2HgCl + (C_2N_2).$$

A convenient method for the preparation of cyanogen (though it is liable when prepared thus to contain traces of carbon dioxide and hydrocyanic acid) is to add a solution of potassium cyanide to a warm solution of copper sulphate. Cupric cyanide, $Cu(CN)_2$, is first formed as a yellow precipitate, but it at once decomposes into cuprous cyanide, CuCN, and free cyanogen :

$$CuSO_4 + 2KCN = Cu(CN)_2 + K_2SO_4$$
$$2Cu(CN)_2 = 2CuCN + C_2N_2.$$

This reaction closely resembles that between copper sulphate and potassium iodide (p. 593).

Cyanogen is a colourless poisonous gas with a faint odour which reminds some people of the smell of peaches. Cyanogen burns with a violet-coloured flame, forming carbon dioxide and nitrogen. It condenses to a liquid under a pressure of four atmospheres at ordinary temperatures, and at ordinary pressures it furnishes a liquid boiling at −20·5°. The liquid freezes to a white solid melting at −34·4°. The gas has a vapour density of 26 ($H_2 = 1$), which corresponds with the molecule C_2N_2. The graphic formula is probably $N\equiv C-C\equiv N$. Cyanogen dissolves readily in water. The aqueous solution deposits a peculiar brown flocculent mass—**azulmic acid**—on standing ; ammonium oxalate, hydrogen cyanide, and carbon dioxide are formed at the same time. Cyanogen unites directly with the alkali metals, forming cyanides.

When passed into a solution of potassium hydroxide, potassium cyanide and potassium cyanate are formed :

$$2KOH + C_2N_2 = KCN + KCNO + H_2O$$

a reaction analogous to that of chlorine (p. 508). Owing to these similarities to chlorine and the halogens, and to the fact that all cyanogen compounds contain the group CN, this group is sometimes represented by the symbol Cy.

§ 32 Hydrocyanic Acid, HCN.

K. W. Scheele discovered hydrocyanic acid in 1782 ; and made it by heating sulphuric acid with Prussian blue, hence the old name, *prussic acid* ; and I. von Ittner made the anhydrous compound, HCN, in 1809. J. L. Gay-Lussac established its composition in 1811.

It is found in Nature combined with the sugar glucose and another organic compound as the glucoside *amygdalin* which is found in bitter almonds and other plants.

Hydrogen cyanide is made by distilling a mixture of powdered potassium cyanide with a mixture of equal volumes of sulphuric acid and water ; if concentrated acid be used, a considerable amount of carbon monoxide is evolved.   The vapour is passed through a U-tube containing calcium chloride to remove the water.   The dry hydrogen cyanide is led through a U-tube surrounded by ice ; and the gas condenses to a colourless liquid.   The gas is also made by passing dry hydrogen sulphide over dry mercury cyanide and condensing the vapour to a liquid as before.   Pure hydrogen cyanide is one of the most deadly poisons known, and hence great care must be taken in experiments with hydrogen cyanide, and, indeed, with cyanides generally.   The liquid boils at 26°, and freezes at −14° to a white solid.   It dissolves in water in all proportions, and the solution has the smell familiarly associated with sweet almonds.   The anhydrous acid is a colourless liquid.   It is a very weak acid indeed, and so its salts are strongly hydrolyzed in aqueous solution.   It is used in the fumigation of ships to destroy rats and vermin, and for spraying fruit trees.

Being an acid, it forms salts which are known as **cyanides** ; the most important of these are sodium and potassium cyanides which are much used in industry (see p. 570).   The cyanides of other metals are usually made by double decomposition with potassium cyanide.

Metallic cyanides are noteworthy for their tendency to form complex ions.   Some of these, notably the ferrocyanides (see p. 820), are very stable, while others are less so.   The ferrocyanides of copper and iron are of interest and importance (see pp. 174 and 823) ; while the use of potassium cyanide in the extraction of silver and gold from their ores depends also upon the formation of complex ions of silver and gold cyanides.

Hydrocyanic acid and the cyanides can be formulated either as $H-C{\equiv}N$ where the hydrogen is attached to carbon or as $H-N{\equiv}C$ where the hydrogen is attached to nitrogen, and organic derivatives of both are known.   The exact formulation of the latter form has given rise to controversy in the past ; it is now believed to be as shown, that is, analogous to carbon monoxide.

The acid itself is thought to be an equilibrium mixture :

$$HCN \rightleftharpoons HNC,$$

with the latter predominating.   The corresponding electronic formulae being,

$$H \overset{\bullet}{\underset{\bullet}{\,}} C \overset{\times}{\underset{\times}{\times}} N \overset{\times}{\times} \quad \text{and} \quad H \overset{\circ}{\underset{\circ}{}} N \overset{\times}{\underset{\times}{\times}} C \overset{\bullet}{\underset{\bullet}{\times}}$$

the cyanide *ion* is identical from whichever form it is derived, viz.,

$$\left[\; :N \overset{\bullet}{\underset{\bullet}{\bullet}} C: \; \right]$$

which is in accordance with the chemical behaviour of cyanides in solution.

§ 33 Cyanic Acid and Cyanates

Cyanides, such as those of potassium and sodium, are found to be reducing agents (p. 570) when fused. Thus for example, metallic oxides, such as litharge, are converted into the metals, while the concomitant oxidation of the cyanide produces the corresponding cyanate :

$$KCN + PbO = KCNO + Pb.$$

Cyanates are also formed, as already mentioned above, by the action of cyanogen on solutions of potassium or sodium hydroxides.

Potassium cyanate is usually made by heating the cyanide with an oxidizing agent (e.g., litharge, red lead, or potassium permanganate).

The potassium cyanate is extracted by lixiviating the mass with dilute alcohol, and concentrating the alcoholic solution by evaporation.   Potassium cyanate is a colourless crystalline powder readily soluble in water and in dilute alcohol. The aqueous solution readily decomposes :

$$KOCN + 2H_2O = NH_3 + KHCO_3.$$

The corresponding acid, HOCN, decomposes so rapidly into carbon dioxide and ammonia :

$$HOCN + H_2O = CO_2 + NH_3,$$

that cyanic acid cannot be prepared by the decomposition of its salts with mineral acids.

Pure cyanic acid is a colourless gas which condenses in a freezing mixture to an unstable liquid.   It is obtained by heating **cyanuric acid**, $H_3N_3C_3O_3$, which is formed when urea is distilled.   On keeping, it soon re-polymerizes to cyanuric acid :

$$3HNCO \rightleftharpoons H_3C_3N_3O_3.$$

Ammonium cyanate is of historical interest and importance, since, on heating, it passes into urea ; this being the classical experiment by which in 1829 Wöhler showed that there was no *essential* distinction between inorganic and organic chemistry.

§ 34 Combustion and Flame

The subject of combustion is inextricably interwoven with the history of the elucidation of the nature of the atmosphere, and of the Phlogiston Theory.   These matters have been referred to in Chapter I and Lavoisier's work, and that of others who led the way for him, will receive some attention in Chapter XXI.   Meanwhile, some account of the phenomena of combustion itself and of the nature of flame is appropriate at this point.

Combustion, broadly speaking, may be said to be a reaction taking place at a high temperature, and accompanied by the evolution of sufficient heat to maintain the temperature of the reaction. This can be understood by reference to familiar examples.

Thus, carbon in the form of charcoal burns in air. It has to be heated to a temperature of about 500° in order to start the reaction :

$$C + O_2 = CO_2 + 97 \text{ Cals.}$$

As the equation shows, considerable heat is evolved when this reaction takes place, more than sufficient in fact to keep the charcoal at a sufficiently high temperature for the reaction to continue.

But a substance like mercury will not burn in air. If its temperature is raised suitably it will, as in the classical experiments of Lavoisier, combine with the oxygen of the air forming mercuric oxide (p. 426) ; but the amount of heat evolved in this process is insufficient of itself to keep the temperature of the mercury sufficiently high for the reaction to proceed.

Combustion is, further, a process attended by the development of light and heat, e.g., charcoal as before, or a candle. At one time combustion was thought of as being this kind of process, taking place in air or oxygen only. It is not now usual to restrict the term in this way : it is used to cover all self-maintaining reactions attended with the development of light and heat. So that, for example, we speak of the combustion (or burning) of magnesium in carbon dioxide (p. 359).

It is customary and convenient to distinguish between the combustible substance and the supporter of combustion. Thus, when a jet of coal gas burns in air, the gas is said to be combustible, and the air (or the oxygen it contains) is said to be a supporter of combustion. There is a sense, however, in which this distinction is quite arbitrary, depending upon which gas is being supplied at a jet, and which comprises the atmosphere surrounding it.

This can be illustrated by the following experiment :—

An ordinary lamp cylinder—A, Fig. 129—may be closed at one end with a cork perforated to fit over a bunsen burner, B, and also with a hole in which a glass tube C—about 10 cm. long and 1 cm. diameter —is fitted. The top of the cylinder is covered with a sheet of asbestos D—6 or 7 cm. square—and perforated with a round hole about 2 cm. diameter. The air holes of the bunsen burner are closed ;

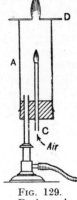

Fig. 129.
Reciprocal
Combustion.

the gas is turned on and the opening in the asbestos is closed by laying a piece of cardboard loosely on the hole. In a few minutes, the apparatus will be filled with coal gas. Light the gas as it issues from C, and simultaneously remove the cardboard which was closing the hole in the asbestos. The flame will pass up the tube drawing the air after it. The upward current of gas causes an upward current of air in the tube C which burns with a feebly luminous flame in the atmosphere of coal gas. The excess of coal gas issuing from the opening in the asbestos may be ignited, and the two flames show air burning in coal gas, and coal gas burning in air.

Flame

The development of flame during combustion is quite an accidental feature. Iron burning in oxygen gives no perceptible flame. The intense light is due to the incandescent solid. Similar remarks apply generally to the combustion of solids which are not volatilized at the temperature developed during combustion. On the other hand, phosphorus, sulphur, bitumen, fat, wax, etc., burn with a flame because these solids are volatilized at the temperature of combustion.

The flame of most of the combustible gases has quite a characteristic appearance—sulphur burns in air with a lavender blue flame ; burning hydrogen is scarcely visible in bright daylight, provided the gas and air are free from dust ; carbon monoxide has a rich blue flame, silicon hydride a pale green flame, the cyanogen flame has a delicate pink tinge, acetylene burns with a highly luminous yellowish flame, while marsh gas burns with a feebly luminous yellowish flame.

It will be obvious that when a stream of gas issues from a tube, the gas can only burn at its surface of contact with the air. The shape of the flame, issuing from, say, a circular jet, is due to the fact that as the gas issues from the jet, a ring of gas, so to speak, next to the tube burns first ; before any more gas can come in contact with the air and burn, it must rise past the first ring of flame, and each successive layer of gas has to pass higher and higher before it can find the supply of air necessary for combustion. The flame thus assumes the form of a cone.

It would be anticipated from the foregoing that in the interior of such a cone of flame, where the gas cannot come into contact with the air, and hence cannot react with it, there will be a region of **unburnt gas.** This is easily shown to be the case by experiments such as the following :—

(1) Cross sections of the flame can be shown by depressing thin sheets of asbestos paper (say, 15 cm. square) for a few moments on the flame of, say, a bunsen burner protected from draughts. The hotter portions of the flame where the gases are burning char the paper, producing a dark ring when the paper is held horizontally, Fig. 130, B, and a more or less elongated cone if the paper be held vertically in the flame A, Fig. 130. The particular " flame figure" produced depends on the part of the flame in which the paper is held : N. Teclu (1891).

Fig. 130.
Flame Sections.

(2) A 5-7 cm. funnel is connected with the gas supply as illustrated in Fig. 131. The broad mouth of the funnel is covered with a piece of fine copper or brass wire gauze. A

small conical heap of gunpowder (1½ cm. base) is placed on the middle of the gauze. The gas is turned on, and a lighted taper slowly depressed from above downwards to the funnel until the gas is ignited. The gunpowder remains on the gauze unconsumed. Ordinary matches can be thrust through the flame and laid on the heap of gunpowder without being ignited.

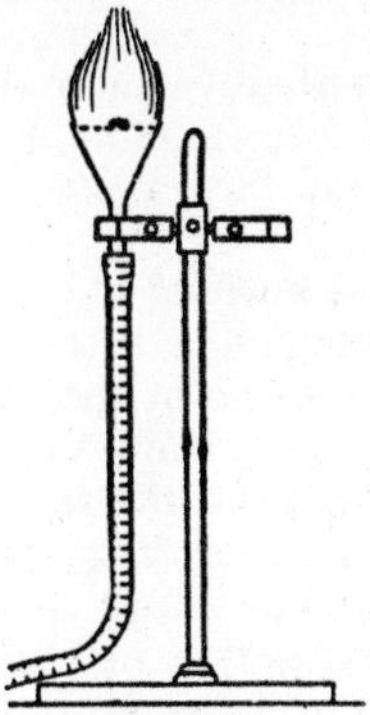

Flames differ considerably in the details of their " construction " according to the nature of the gas or vapour which is burning. For the present, two types of flame will be considered, the single-mantled flame (typified by hydrogen burning in air) and the double-mantled flame (exemplified by a candle or coal-gas flame).

Single-mantled Flames

The flame of hydrogen burning in air or oxygen (Fig. 132) consists of two cones, an inner one, of unburnt gas, and an outer one, in which presumably) the single reaction

Fig. 131.
Hollow ·Flame.

Fig. 132.
Hydrogen Flame.

$$2H_2 + O_2 = 2H_2O$$

is taking place. This is the simplest kind of flame.

Double-mantled Flames

The flames of burning hydrocarbons are much more complex, however, due to the more complicated series of reactions which are taking place in them.

In a candle flame (Fig. 133) or a coal-gas flame (that is, the *luminous*

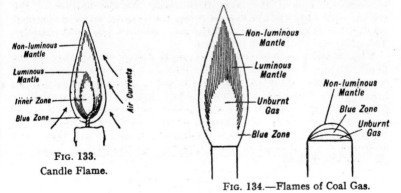

Non-luminous Mantle

Luminous Mantle

Inner Zone

Blue Zone

Air Currents

Fig. 133.
Candle Flame.

Non-luminous Mantle

Luminous Mantle

Unburnt Gas

Blue Zone

Non-luminous Mantle

Blue Zone

Unburnt Gas

Fig. 134.—Flames of Coal Gas.

gas flame, *not* the so-called bunsen flame, concerning which see below, p. 379), four distinct regions may be distinguished. These are :

(i) the dark, inner zone of unburnt gas or vapour ;

(ii) a yellowish-white brightly luminous region or mantle ;

(iii) a small bright blue region at the base of the flame ;

(iv) a faintly visible outer mantle completely enveloping the rest of the flame.

In the case of the gas flame, when the flame is gradually lowered, the inner luminous sheath gradually diminishes in size, and finally disappears. At the same time, the blue region at the base becomes continuous right across the flame, Fig. 134.

The chemical reactions which occur in the flames of burning hydro-carbons have not been satisfactorily elucidated, although a little is known. Tapping the gases from different parts of the flame by means of platinum or porcelain tubes connected with an aspirator, is not very satisfactory because of the changed conditions arising when the reactions take place in contact with solids. Hence, the proof that the flame of burning hydrogen sulphide contains free sulphur ; and that the luminous mantle of burning hydrocarbons contains free carbon, because a cold dish held in the flame receives a deposit of the respective solids, is quite unsatisfactory. It is conceivable that the hydrogen sulphide flame contains free sulphur, and the hydrocarbon flame free carbon when cold porcelain is held in these flames, but not when this disturbing agent is absent ; we therefore prefer demonstrations with methods which do not interfere with the flame itself.

The following is an outline of what is now thought to be the probable nature of the processes which give rise to flames such as have just been described.

In the case of the gas-flame, the burning material is gaseous at the start ; but in the candle, the heat of the flame causes the hydrocarbons of the wax to melt, rise up the wick and vaporize therefrom. In both flames there is, therefore, a region of comparatively cool unburnt gas or vapour. This is the inner dark zone. At the bottom of this region, some of the gas or vapour meets the uprising air, and complete combustion takes place without the separation of any solid particles. This gives rise to the dark blue zone.

Most of the gas or vapour, however, is decomposed higher up the flame, giving rise to the luminous zone owing to the separation of minute particles of carbon which are raised to a high temperature and hence glow, emitting a yellowish-white light. The separation of particles of carbon in this way was formerly explained by the theory of *preferential combustion*, according to which, in a limited supply of air (such as is the case in the inner mantle of a luminous gas flame), the hydrogen of a hydrocarbon burns first, leaving free carbon. Thus, in the case of ethylene,

$$C_2H_4 + O_2 = 2C + 2H_2O.$$

That is to say, the hydrogen was believed to burn first in preference to the carbon. Modern experimental work, notably that of Bone and his collaborators, has shown that, if there be any such preference, it is, in fact, the other way round. They have adduced evidence which suggests that the process takes place by way of hydroxylation, and suggest that the combustion of a hydrocarbon, such as ethane, takes place by way of a series of reactions somewhat as follows :

$$C_2H_6 \overset{O}{\rightarrow} C_2H_5OH \overset{O}{\rightarrow} CH_3.CH(OH)_2 \overset{heat}{\longrightarrow}$$

ethane — alcohol — ethylidene glycol (unstable)

$$H_2O + CH_3CHO \overset{heat}{\longrightarrow} \begin{cases} C + 2H_2O + CO, \text{ etc.} \\ CH_4 + CO, \text{ etc.} \end{cases}$$

aldeyhde

The process is quite likely more complex, but there is a good deal to suggest that this represents its broad outlines.

In the luminous zone, then, a partial combustion takes place which becomes more or less complete in the outermost, non-luminous mantle. Here the carbon and other products of the incomplete combustion come into contact with a plentiful supply of oxygen from the air. The combustion may not be absolutely complete even here ; however, since the air exercises a considerable cooling effect, and occasionally also, even here, the supply of oxygen may not be quite sufficient if the supply of combustible material is very free. In this event the flame smokes.

§ 35 The Luminosity of Flames

It is a well-known fact that many gases give flames which are very bright or luminous. Examples are unsaturated hydrocarbons like ethylene, the vapours of some metals, and phosphorus.

A general explanation of this luminosity is not known. At one period it was believed that all luminous flames contain white hot particles of solid (**Davy's solid particle theory**). It is now known, however, that while some luminous flames do contain such particles, others do not.

The existence of solid particles in the luminous coal-gas flame, for example, has been satisfactorily demonstrated by Soret's optical test (1875) by which it is shown that if the flame of coal gas or of a candle be placed between a strong light and a screen, the luminous portion of the flame throws a dark shadow on the screen, and if the flame be made to smoke, the shadow of the luminous portion extends into the shadow cast by the smoke.

Also the non-luminous portion of the flame gives no shadow. This result was confirmed by Stokes, who focused the image of the sun on to the flame and examined the scattered light. This was found to be polarized—evidence of the existence of minute solid particles. On the other hand, the flames of carbon disulphide and phosphorus, although luminous, are found in this way to contain no solid particles.

In the course of his experiments H. Davy showed that the luminosity of flames is increased by pressure and diminished by rarefaction. The violet blue sheath of the hydrogen flame becomes green, then yellow, orange, and red as the pressure is *reduced* ; and by *increasing* the pressure, the flame becomes luminous.   E. Frankland (1867) found a direct relation between the luminosity of flames and the pressure. Using the flame of hydrogen burning under a pressure of 12 atmospheres, a reduction of the pressure to 3 atmospheres, diminished the luminosity 99 per cent.   Arguing from the fact that luminous flames are known which contain no solids ; that dense gases and vapours give flames more luminous than gases of low density ; and that feebly luminous flames become luminous when the surrounding atmosphere is compressed, Frankland inferred that the luminosity of ordinary flames such as coal gas is due to the glow of dense hydrocarbons rather than to the presence of solid particles.   This is known as **Frankland's dense hydrocarbon theory.**

Lewes considers that the " dense hydrocarbon " in the flame of coal gas and related gases is acetylene, hence, the so-called **acetylene theory of luminosity.**   In the particular case of hydrocarbon flames, as interpreted in the preceding section, it does not appear that this hypothesis is a complete explanation.   When the pressure of the atmosphere is altered, the dense hydrocarbons themselves give opaque flames containing solid matter.   The phenomenon is complicated by changes in the conditions of equilibrium of the products of combustion, and it is probable that the decomposition of the hydrocarbons in the " innermost parts of the flame " is facilitated by increasing the pressure.

However, it is highly probable that dense vapours, as well as incandescent solids, do produce luminosity.   Two distinct effects can be observed in burning hydrogen phosphide : a greenish glow due to the oxidation of the phosphorus which shows best when the phosphide is largely diluted with carbon dioxide ; and a yellowish white light best seen when phosphorus burns in air or oxygen.   This is no doubt due to the glowing of phosphorus pentoxide which, although in the state of *vapour*, can be made to emit a yellowish white glow when the temperature has attained a certain point.   Similar results can be obtained with silicon hydride, but in this case the glow is due to *solid* silica.

Just as a variation of pressure modifies the luminosity of burning gases, so does a variation of temperature.   The temperature attained by the combustion of gases in oxygen is greater than in air, owing to the absence of diluting nitrogen.   In consequence, combustibles burn far more brilliantly in oxygen than in air.   The flame of carbon disulphide in air is nothing like so brilliant as in oxygen ; the flame of hydrogen phosphide in air is brilliant, but in oxygen the flame is of dazzling brilliance.   Phosphorus burns in chlorine with a far more luminous flame when the chlorine is hot than when cold.   Carbon monoxide in oxygen burns with a flame appreciably luminous.   Similarly with flames known to contain solid matter. Magnesium and silicon hydride burn far more brightly in oxygen than in air. The reason for this behaviour is far from certain.

§ 36 The Bunsen Burner

The ordinary luminous flame of a burning hydrocarbon is unsatisfactory for heating purposes ; and, since the invention of the incandescent gas mantle (p. 713) for lighting also. The deposition of soot reduces severely the rate at which heat is transferred to the vessel being heated, as well as involving the loss of much of the potential heat energy of the fuel.

Bunsen in 1855 devised a burner, known by his name, to surmount these objections, and it is now, of course, in universal use. Its construction is quite simple and easily understood.

The burner consists of three parts. (1) The base, A, Fig. 135, supplied with gas by means of a rubber tube connected with the main. The gas escapes from a small opening in the base By lighting the gas issuing from the base, a long thin pencil of flame is obtained. (2) The burner tube, B, has a couple of openings near the base, and these can be closed, partially closed, or opened by turning the air regulator. (3) The air regulator, C, is a short cylindrical tube fitted with holes to correspond with the holes in the burner tube. There are numerous modifications ; that just described may be taken as typical.

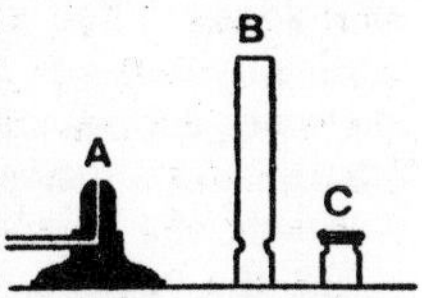

Fig. 135.—Parts of Bunsen Burner.

If the air-holes are closed, an ordinary luminous gas flame is obtained. If the air-holes are opened, the jet of gas from the small orifice produces a partial vacuum in the neighbourhood of the jet, and, in consequence, air is drawn into the air-holes, and mixes with the gas in the burner tube.

A certain ratio must exist between the proportion of air and gas in the burner tube in order to get the gas to burn quietly with a blue flame—the so-called **Bunsen flame.** This is observed by placing the regulator in several different positions and gradually turning off the gas. When the air-holes are fully open, and the gas is gradually turned off, a point is reached when the flame begins to flicker, and finally " strikes back," afterwards burning at the bottom of the tube. As a matter of fact, the mixture of air and gas burning in the bunsen burner is explosive when the gas is burning quietly, the rate at which the flame travels in the explosive mixture of air and gas is less than the rate at which gas is issuing from the burner ; when more air or less gas is introduced, the speed at which the explosive flame can travel is increased ; when the rate of the explosive flame and the speed of the gas issuing from the burner are nearly equal the flame reaches the unstable condition ; any further increase in the amount of air or decrease in the amount of gas gives an explosive mixture in which the

explosive flame can travel faster than the issuing gas ; the flame then
" strikes back."

When burning in its most efficient form, a bunsen flame
can be seen to consist of two cones, Fig. 136.

These cones comprise a very pale blue outer mantle,
surrounding a bright blue inner cone. Inside the inner
cone is a region of unburnt gas. The processes probably
taking place in such a flame are as follows. There is a
vigorous reaction at the surface of the inner cone, partial
oxidation of the gas taking place, and a high temperature
being developed. In the outer cone, complete combustion
of the carbon monoxide, etc., from the inner cone takes
place, but the temperature is not so high.

FIG. 136.
Bunsen
Flame.

The processes taking place in the bunsen flame have
been investigated by means of Smithell's flame separator.

The apparatus consists of two co-axial tubes, A and B, Fig. 137.
The outer wider tube is shorter than the inner tube and fitted with a
rubber union, C, and a brass clip to permit the outer tube to be slid up
and down. The upper ends of the co-axial tubes are fitted one with
a mica cylinder D, and the other with an aluminium, cylinder E. The
narrower tube is clamped over an unlighted Bunsen's
burner and a loose packing of cotton wool, F, placed
between the burner and the glass tube.

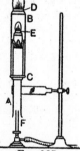

At the beginning of the experiment, the two co-
axial tubes are at the same level, the air-holes of
the burner are closed, and the gas is lighted at
the top of the outer tube, and burns with a luminous
flame. The air-holes of the burner are then opened
until the flame is non-luminous, and the usual two
cones are formed. The outer tube is then slid upwards, and the outer cone ascends with it while the
inner cone remains burning at the top of the inner
tube.

FIG. 137.
Smithell's Flame
Separator.

The gas from the space between the two cones,
on analysis, was found to consist of nitrogen, carbon
monoxide, carbon dioxide, steam and hydrogen. This mixture was
also found to have the same composition if pure methane, unmixed
with free hydrogen, was used. This indicates that the reaction
taking place in the inner cone leads to the formation of carbon monoxide and hydrogen, and if enough oxygen is present, so that some
carbon dioxide is also produced, an equilibrium is set up :

$$CO + H_2O \rightleftharpoons CO_2 + H_2,$$

the same as in the production of water gas (p. 362).

The proportions of gas and air for the normal bunsen flame are
approximately 1 part of gas to 2·5 parts of air, and this proportion
cannot be greatly exceeded without causing the flame to " strike

back." For complete combustion, however, a proportion of about six volumes of air for one of gas is required. Such a mixture clearly cannot be used in a bunsen burner of the ordinary type.

G. Méker, however, has designed a burner in which such a mixture can be burnt—the **Méker burner.** From the sectional diagram, Fig. 138, it will be seen that the air-holes are larger than usual, and a deep nickel grid hinders the flame "striking back." Since the gas issuing from the burner has enough air for complete combustion, the flame is practically a "solid cone" of burning gas, and there is no "inner cone of unburnt gas."

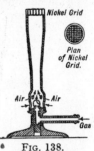

FIG. 138.
Méker Burner.

The maximum temperature attained in this flame is considerably higher than that of the ordinary bunsen flame.

Another way in which the "theoretical" mixture of gas and air has been employed has been developed by Bone and M'Court. In their heater, the mixture of gas and air (sufficient for complete combustion) passes through a porous diaphragm of refractory material. Gas reactions are, as a rule, catalyzed by solid surfaces (p. 230) and very rapid combustion therefore takes place in the outer layer of the diaphragm which is raised to a high temperature. No actual flame is visible when the apparatus is working properly, so that it is sometimes referred to as *flameless* or *surface combustion*. Heaters of this kind have been employed for industrial purposes.

§ 37 The Safety Lamp

Davy was led to investigate the nature of flames by undertaking an investigation into the causes and prevention of explosions in coal mines.

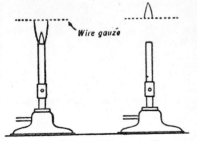

FIG. 139.—Effect of Gauze on Flames.

In the course of his experiments, he found that if a flame is cooled sufficiently, it is extinguished, and that different combustible gases have different **ignition points.**

A familiar experiment is the following. A piece of fine wire gauze is held a little above the top of an unlighted bunsen burner. If the gas be turned on and a lighted match is brought above the gauze, the gas is ignited there, but the flame does not pass through the gauze (Fig. 139).

Conversely, if the gas be ignited below the gauze, the flame will not pass through, although the passage of inflammable gas through the gauze can be demonstrated by bringing a lighted taper above the gauze. If the gauze be heated red hot, the flame will pass through and burn on both sides.

Experiments not unlike these, led Humphry Davy, in 1815, to the idea of "flame sieves," and finally to the "safety lamp for miners." In Davy's safety lamp, Fig. 140, an oil lamp is surrounded by a cylinder—1⅓ inches in diameter, and 6 inches high—made of iron wire gauze, having 28 meshes per linear inch. The cylinder is closed at the top with a double layer of gauze, A, Fig. 140. The lamp is provided with a screw lock to prevent it being opened in the mine, and there is a ring at the top to allow the lamp to be carried or suspended. The lamp is ventilated by air passing through the mesh of the gauze near the flame. The air impinges on the flame, and the products of combustion escape through the gauze in the upper part of the cylinder. When such a lamp is taken into an atmosphere containing a mixture of marsh gas and air, the explosive mixture passes through the gauze and is ignited inside the cylinder. The cylinder may (but should not) be heated red-hot by the combustion of the explosive gases inside. The flame, however, is unable to pass through the gauze and ignite the mixture outside the cylinder. **The gauze acts as a " flame sieve " ; it permits a free passage of gas, air, and light, but it obstructs the passage of the flame.**

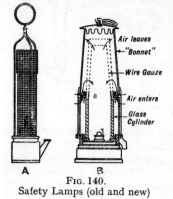

FIG. 140.
Safety Lamps (old and new)

If the gauze should happen to be heated locally above the ignition temperature of the mixture outside ; or if the lamp is exposed in a strong current of air, say, a ventilating shaft, or a "wave" of air sometimes generated in the operations of blasting, the flame may be driven through the meshes of the gauze. Considerable improvements have been made on the original *Davy's lamp*, A, Fig. 140. The modern forms of safety lamp—e.g., *J. B. Marsaut's lamp*, B, Fig. 140—allow the lamp to be used under conditions of great danger with a minimum risk of igniting an explosive mixture of firedamp and air. The old Davy's safety lamp is obsolete. It gives a very poor illumination owing to the obstruction offered by the wire gauze, and the flame may be forced through the gauze when the current of air exceeds 5 feet per second, and in modern mines, the air in some parts of the rapid ventilating roads may attain 20 to 30 feet per second.

CHAPTER XX

NITROGEN

What of nitrogen ? Is not its apparent great simplicity of action all a sham ? —M. FARADAY.

The fixation of nitrogen is vital to the progress of civilized humanity, and unless we can class it among the certainties to come, the great Caucasian race will cease to be the foremost in the world, and will be squeezed out of existence by the races to whom wheaten bread is not the staff of life.—W. CROOKES.

§ 1 Occurrence and Preparation

IT is difficult to state precisely who first isolated nitrogen and recognized it as a definite substance. But D. Rutherford (1772) is generally credited with the discovery of nitrogen. He published a thesis in Latin in 1772 in which he said :

By the respiration of animals, healthy air is not merely rendered mephitic (that is, charged with carbon dioxide), but it also suffers another change, for, after the mephitic portion is absorbed by a solution of caustic alkali, the remaining portion is not rendered salubrious, and, although it occasions no precipitate in lime-water, it nevertheless extinguishes flame, and destroys life.

Rutherford removed oxygen from the air by such combustibles as phosphorus, charcoal, etc., and washed out the products of combustion by alkalis or lime water. The residue was called by him " phlogisticated air."[*] H. Cavendish confirmed this experiment in 1785. Lavoisier first called the residue " mephitic air," and afterwards " azote." J. A. C. Chaptal (1823) suggested the name nitrogéne from the Greek νίτρον (nitron), saltpetre ; and γεννάω (gennao), I produce. —because the gas is a constituent of nitre.

Occurrence

Nitrogen constitutes four-fifths of the total volume of atmospheric air. According to spectroscopic observations it is probable that certain nebulae contain nitrogen. It is also found in certain minerals, where it is probably occluded or adsorbed. It occurs combined in ammonia, nitre, and a great many animal and vegetable products— e.g., white of egg, proteids, etc. It is a constant and essential constituent of all living organisms ; all life seems to depend upon the transformation of proteid compounds.

Preparation

Nitrogen is prepared either :
(i) from the air by removal of oxygen, etc.;
(ii) by suitable decomposition of nitrogen compounds.

From the Air

Nitrogen is easily obtained from air by removing the admixed carbon dioxide and oxygen. This is conveniently done by burning a

---

[*] Hydrogen was also called " phlogisticated air."

piece of phosphorus in a dry crucible floating on the surface of water under a small bell-jar. The phosphorus combines with most of the oxygen, forming phosphorus pentoxide, and this quickly dissolves in water, leaving behind the nitrogen. If the water be alkaline with sodium hydroxide, the carbon dioxide, normally present in air, will also be removed. The nitrogen so prepared is not pure because the phosphorus ceases to burn before all the oxygen has been removed.

It is best to remove the carbon dioxide by first passing the air

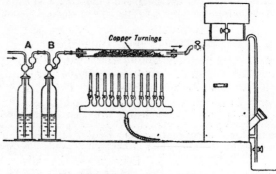

Fig. 141.—Preparation of Nitrogen.

through a solution of sodium hydroxide ; and to absorb the oxygen by means of an element which will form a non-volatile oxide. Copper turnings are generally considered best for the purpose ; the " turnings " offer a large surface of oxidizable metal to the air. The process is as follows :—

Air freed from carbon dioxide in a wash-bottle of sodium hydroxide, A, Fig. 141, and from moisture by passage through sulphuric acid, B, is then passed through a red-hot tube containing copper turnings. The copper removes the oxygen and forms cupric oxide :.

$$2Cu + O_2 = 2CuO.$$

The nitrogen passes on to be collected in a gas jar, or gasholder, etc. In the diagram, the air is supposed to be drawn over the copper, the gasholder being filled with nitrogen. If the gasholder were placed at the end A, and air forced along the tubes, the nitrogen gas could be collected in gas jars.

Cold boiled water should be used in the gasholder so as to lessen the risk of contamination owing to the presence of oxygen dissolved in ordinary water.

Many attempts have been made to modify this process so as to make it practicable for the production of nitrogen commercially. For example, furnace gases contain large quantities of nitrogen, which can be isolated by passing the gases over a heated mixture of copper and copper oxide to remove any residual oxygen and to oxidize any carbon monoxide   The carbon dioxide is removed by sodium hydroxide, or water under pressure, and nitrogen is left.   Nitrogen has also been prepared by burning a mixture of air and hydrogen which is a by-product of many electrolytic processes (e.g., p. 391).

But by far the most important process for the production of nitrogen is the fractionation of liquid air.   This process has been discussed and described in Chapter II (p. 40).

In Chapter XXIV the discovery that nitrogen extracted from the air, as described above, contains small quantities of other gases, known as the inert gases, is described.

From Nitrogen Compounds

Nitrogen called " chemical nitrogen " can be prepared free from argon by heating a concentrated solution of ammonium nitrite in a glass flask or retort :

$$NH_4NO_2 = 2H_2O + N_2.$$

The reaction need only be just started by gently warming the flask, it will then continue, and maybe increase in velocity without a further application of heat because the system itself becomes warmer owing to the degradation of energy.   If heat be continuously applied to the flask, the reaction may become uncontrollably violent.   Instead of using ammonium nitrite, a mixture of ammonium chloride with a concentrated solution of potassium or sodium nitrite is recommended by Corenwinder (1849).   Nitrogen is also made by heating ammonium dichromate :

$$(NH_4)_2Cr_2O_7 = Cr_2O_3 + 4H_2O + N_2 ;$$

or a mixture of ammonium chloride and potassium dichromate ; or a mixture of hypobromites or hypochlorites with urea ; etc.

It can also be obtained by the action of chlorine on ammonia, care being taken that the ammonia is in large excess, otherwise the dangerous explosive nitrogen trichloride may be formed (p. 401) :

$$8NH_3 + 3Cl_2 = 6NH_4Cl + N_2.$$

For the preparation of very pure nitrogen it has been recommended that a mixture of nitric oxide (p. 415) and ammonia be passed over red-hot copper gauze, when the reaction symbolized :

$$4NH_3 + 6NO = 5N_2 + 6H_2O$$

occurs.

§ 2 Properties of Nitrogen

Nitrogen is an odourless colourless gas, not quite so heavy as air.   It is slightly soluble in water ;   100 volumes of water at 0° absorb 2·4 volumes, and at 20°, 1·6 volumes of gas.   At 3500° it is estimated that about 5 per cent. of the nitrogen is dissociated into atoms :

$$N_2 \text{ (95 per cent.) } \rightleftharpoons 2N \text{ (5 per cent.).}$$

Nitrogen has been condensed to a colourless liquid which boils at about $-195\cdot8°$ at ordinary atmospheric pressure ; and solidifies to a white snow-like mass melting at $-209\cdot8°$. Solid nitrogen exists in two forms with a transition temperature $-237\cdot5°$ and the molecular heat of transformation is $53\cdot8$ Cals. Nitrogen cannot be a poisonous gas, for the air we breathe contains a large proportion. The nitrogen dilutes the oxygen as indicated on p. 427. Animals die in nitrogen owing to suffocation, i.e., want of oxygen necessary for respiration. Nitrogen is both incombustible and a non-supporter of ordinary combustion.

The chief characteristic of nitrogen gas is its chemical inertness, due, it is sometimes stated, to " the great affinity of the atoms in the molecule for one another." At any rate, when nitrogen is combined with other elements the converse is true, for the nitrogen compounds generally possess great chemical activity.

The inertness of ordinary nitrogen is a characteristic property at temperatures below 200° C. At and-above a dull red heat, however, many metals combine with nitrogen forming derivatives of trivalent nitrogen known as **nitrides.** Magnesium nitride is a typical example :

$$3Mg + N_2 = Mg_3N_2.$$

and is formed in small quantity along with magnesium oxide, when magnesium burns in air.

These nitrides are decomposed by water with the formation of ammonia, e.g.,

$$Mg_3N_2 + 6H_2O = 2NH_3 + 3Mg(OH)_2.$$

Nitrogen reacts with oxygen to a small extent at very high temperatures forming nitric oxide. This is the basis of the Birkeland-Eyde process for the fixation of nitrogen (p. 406).

With hydrogen, nitrogen will combine under suitable conditions to form ammonia, a reaction which is utilized in the manufacture of synthetic ammonia by the Haber process (p. 390).

Some other non-metallic elements also react to some extent, for example, carbon (which forms cyanogen, p. 369), boron and silicon. Nitrogen will also combine with calcium carbide at a high temperature forming calcium cyanamide :

$$CaC_2 + N_2 = CaCN_2 + C,$$

which is sold for use as a fertilizer under the name *nitrolim.*

§ 3 Active Nitrogen

In 1910 R. J. Strutt observed that when nitrogen at low pressure is subjected to an electric discharge it shows an " after-glow " when the discharge is stopped. At the same time the chemical properties of the gas are changed, for it becomes reactive, combining directly with sulphur, iodine and phosphorus, and with many metals. It also reacts with acetylene forming hydrocyanic acid and with other organic compounds. On account of this behaviour it has been called **active nitrogen.**

It has been found that a trace of oxygen, mercury vapour or certain other substances is necessary for active nitrogen to be formed, although excess destroys it.

The nature of active nitrogen is still uncertain. Strutt suggested that it is atomic nitrogen, but there is some doubt about this since the energy required, in fact, to produce active nitrogen is said to be less than that required to bring about the dissociation $N_2 \rightarrow 2N$. The suggestion that it is N_3 (analogous to ozone) is disproved by the fact that the active form is not condensible in liquid air. Active nitrogen is apparently not ionized nitrogen since the glow persists after ions have been removed from the gas. It is said, at present, that active nitrogen consists of " metastable " molecules associated with a greater quantity of available energy than ordinary nitrogen molecules, together with a few free atoms. This, however, is a vague statement which still leaves the real nature of active nitrogen uncertain.

§ 4 Uses of Nitrogen

Nitrogen is separated on a very large scale for the manufacture of synthetic ammonia (p. 390), and atmospheric air is employed direct in the manufacture of nitrates by the arc process. Smaller quantities of nitrogen are used for gas-filled electric lamps, and high-temperature thermometers.

§ 5 Formula and Atomic Weight of Nitrogen

The molecule of nitrogen is believed to be diatomic for the following reasons. Firstly, the ratio of the specific heats (p. 76) is 1·4 approximately ; and secondly, when ammonia reacts with excess of chlorine or is exploded with oxygen, one volume of nitrogen is formed from two volumes of ammonia (p. 396).

The molecular weight of the volatile compounds of nitrogen indicates a value round about 14 for the atomic weight of nitrogen. The exact value has been determined both by chemical and physical methods.

The chief chemical method has been the determination of the proportion of nitrogen in one or other of the oxides. The principle involved is the decomposition of an exactly known weight of the oxide by an electrically-heated spiral of iron, or nickel, wire. The metal combines with the oxygen and nitrogen remains.

The increase in weight of the metal gives the weight of oxygen in a known weight of oxide. The composition of nitric oxide was determined with a high order of accuracy by this method by Gray in 1905.

Richards's value for the atomic weight of nitrogen is 14·008 (see p. 98).

The limiting density method (p. 103) has been applied with success to the determination of the atomic weight of nitrogen by Gray, who obtained the value 14·008. Similar work by Moles and his collaborators has led to the same value, which is that at present used as the International Value. A further series of experiments by Cawood and Patterson (1936), using an improved microbalance for the determination of the limiting density of nitrous oxide, gave the value 14·007.

§ 6 Detection and Determination

By reason of its inertness at ordinary temperatures, nitrogen is usually identified in a negative way, i.e., by its failure to respond to tests for other gases.   Thus, a sample of gas which does not support combustion, does not burn, is colourless, neutral and does not react with usual reagents (e.g., lime water) is probably nitrogen.   Confirmation is usually sought by passing the suspected gas over heated calcium or magnesium and treating the product with water.   The formation of ammonia indicates the presence of nitrogen in the original gas.

The proportion of nitrogen in a gaseous mixture is similarly determined by removing other gases and measuring the volume of remaining nitrogen and inert gases.   The separation of these latter is tedious and difficult (see Ch. XXIV).   The determination of the proportion of nitrogen in the air is described in Chapter XXI.

The percentage of nitrogen in a compound is often determined by Kjeldahl's process, which depends upon the fact that most compounds yield their nitrogen in the form of ammonium sulphate when heated with concentrated sulphuric acid.   The ammonia formed is then liberated and determined, as described on page 397.   Nitrogen in nitrates (or in organic compounds containing a nitro-group) which do not form ammonia with sulphuric acid can be determined by means of Devarda's alloy (aluminium, 45 per cent. ;   copper, 50 per cent. ; and zinc, 5 per cent.), which reduces them to ammonia in the presence of alkali.

§ 7 Hydrides of Nitrogen.   Ammonia

Nitrogen forms three distinctive compounds with hydrogen, viz.,

$$\text{Ammonia, } NH_3$$
$$\text{Hydrazine, } N_2H_4$$
$$\text{Hydrazoic Acid, } N_3H$$

of which the first is by far the most important.

History and Occurrence of Ammonia

History

Ammonia was known to the early chemists, and Geber describes the preparation of ammonium chloride by heating urine and common salt. Hence the alchemists' term—*spiritus salis urinae.*   Ammonium chloride was first brought to Europe from Egypt, where it was prepared from the " soot " obtained by burning camel's dung.

In 1716 J. Kunckel mentioned the formation of ammonia during fermentation.   S. Hales (1727) noticed that when lime was heated with sal ammoniac in a retort arranged to collect the gas over water, no gas appeared to be given off ;   on the contrary, water was sucked into the retort ;   when J. Priestley (1774) tried the experiment with a mercury gas trough, he obtained ammonia gas which he called " alkaline air."   C. L. Berthollet (1785), H. Davy (1800), and others established the composition of the gas.

Occurrence

Small quantities of ammonia occur in atmospheric air and in natural waters. It is produced by the action of putrefying bacteria (p. 403) on organic matter in the soil, etc. The odour of ammonia can often be detected near stables. Ammonium salts are also deposited on the sides of craters and fissures of the lava streams of active volcanoes; and with boric acid in the fumaroles of Tuscany.

§ 8 Preparation of Ammonia

Ammonia is usually prepared in the laboratory by the action of alkalis on ammonium salts. It is sometimes convenient to use commercial so-called " liquid " ammonia, from which the gas is driven off on heating, as a source of ammonia in the laboratory, but this is hardly to be dignified by the term " preparation." Industrially, very large quantities are obtained from the ammoniacal liquor of the gas works and recovery coke oven plant (pp. 341-350) ; and it is also now manufactured on a large scale directly from its elements by the Haber process (p. 391).

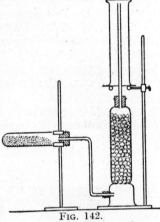

Fig. 142.
Preparation of Ammonia.

Laboratory Preparation of Ammonia

In the laboratory the usual source of ammonia is ammonium chloride (NH_4Cl). This is heated with slaked lime in a tube as shown in Fig. 142.

The reaction is represented by the equation :

$$2NH_4Cl + Ca(OH)_2 = CaCl_2 + 2NH_3 + 2H_2O,$$

so that water is evolved along with the ammonia.

Ammonia combines with the ordinary drying agents—calcium chloride, sulphuric acid, phosphorus pentoxide—and accordingly these agents must not be used with the idea of drying the gas. A tower of quicklime is generally employed.

Ammonia is extremely soluble in water and therefore it is collected by upward delivery, as shown in the diagram. It can be collected over mercury if desired.

A similar apparatus may be employed if it is desired to liberate a sample of the gas from the concentrated commercial solution.

Industrial Preparation

The manufacture of ammonia falls, as shown, under two headings, viz.,

(1) recovery as a by-product of coal distillation;
(2) synthetic production.

Ammonia from Coal

It has been pointed out in the preceding chapter (p. 350) that in the process of the carbonization of coal, whether in coal-gas manufacture or for coke production, there is produced a considerable quantity of ammonia, which is ultimately absorbed in water, partly as free ammonia, partly as salts such as the carbonate, cyanide, sulphide, etc. This is the source of a large amount of the world's ammonia supply. These ammoniacal liquors are, first of all, heated by means of steam which drives off the free ammonia and also that combined as carbonate. After no more ammonia will come off by this heating, milk of lime is added and the heating continued. The remaining ammonium salts are thus decomposed and the ammonia driven off. The mixture of free ammonia and steam obtained in both stages of this process is usually absorbed by means of sulphuric acid, so that a solution of ammonium sulphate results, from which crystals of the salt can be obtained.

Commercial Synthesis of Ammonia

The two gases nitrogen and hydrogen do not react under ordinary conditions, but when subjected to the action of electric sparks a mixture in the proportion of three volumes of hydrogen to one of nitrogen reacts to form ammonia to the extent of about 2 per cent. If ammonia gas be similarly sparked, decomposition takes place until only about 2 per cent. of ammonia remains. The equilibrium represented

$$N_2 + 3H_2 \rightleftharpoons 2NH_3$$

thus lies far over to the left-hand side in these circumstances.

The formation of ammonia from its elements is an exothermic reaction (p. 211). In fact,

$$N_2 + 3H_2 \rightarrow 2NH_3 + 22 \cdot 8 \text{ Cals.}$$

It is evident, therefore, that according to the principle of Le Chatelier (p. 219), since formation of ammonia is attended by reduction in volume and evolution of heat, the equilibrium proportion of ammonia will be greater the higher the pressure and the lower the temperature, which gives broadly the conditions which must be satisfied for a successful synthesis. (See Table XIX, page 220.)

In regard to the use of a low temperature, it is necessary to effect a compromise since the speed of any given reaction is very greatly reduced as the temperature is lowered (p. 222). This points to the use of a catalyst so that the speed of the reaction may be reasonably great at a temperature at which the equilibrium proportion of ammonia is sufficiently high to be worth while.

These considerations form the theoretical basis of the Haber process for the manufacture of synthetic ammonia. A mixture of nitrogen and hydrogen, in the proportion of 1 : 3, is passed over a catalyst at a pressure of about 300 atmospheres and a temperature of 500°.

The hydrogen required is usually obtained from water gas (pp. 255

and 362) and the nitrogen either by fractionation of liquid air (p. 40) or by the combustion of a mixture of air and hydrogen. The exact nature of the catalyst used is not quite certain, but, so far as can be judged from the patent literature, its basis is pure iron, to which is added a promoter (p. 231). The usual promoter appears to be about 1 per cent. of sodium or potassium oxide and about the same amount of silica or alumina.

Under manufacturing conditions the percentage of ammonia formed is only of the order of 10 per cent., so that it is necessary to remove it without releasing the pressure so that the residual nitrogen and hydrogen can be passed over the catalyst again. The heat of the reaction serves to maintain the necessary temperature once the process has got under way ; a heat-interchanger being employed to prevent loss of heat with the issuing gases. The ammonia formed is removed by liquefaction, passage through a spiral tube immersed in cold water being adequate for this purpose at the high pressures employed.

The general arrangement of the details of the catalyst chamber or converter are indicated in Fig. 143 in diagrammatic form.

The action of superheated steam on calcium cyanamide (p. 386), when the following reaction takes place :

$$CaCN_2 + 3H_2O = CaCO_3 + 2NH_3$$

has also been employed for the commercial production of ammonia ; however, it is of less importance than the foregoing, and its use is declining.

The above are the only practical

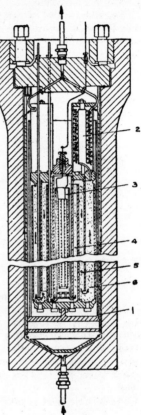

Converter (Diagrammatic).
FIG. 143.–The Haber Process.

methods of any importance for the production of ammonia, but the following reactions, which result in its formation, are of some theoretical or historical interest.

Ammonia is formed during the putrefaction of organic compounds, and when nitrogenous compounds—coal, leather, bones, etc.—are heated in closed vessels. The old term for ammonia—*spiritus cornus cervi* (*spirits of hartshorn*)—refers to an old custom of preparing ammonia by heating hoofs and horns of stags, etc., in closed vessels. The formation of ammonia by heating nitrogenous compounds in closed vessels is particularly noticeable if the organic matter be heated with soda lime—that is, quicklime slaked with a concentrated solution of sodium hydroxide.

The reduction of nitrates, etc., by means of nascent hydrogen (e.g., from Devarda's alloy and acid) resulting in the formation of ammonia has been mentioned above (p. 388) as a means of determination.

§ 9 Properties of Ammonia

Ammonia is a colourless gas with a pungent odour. If inhaled suddenly, it will bring tears to the eyes, if large quantities be inhaled, suffocation may ensue. Ammonia is a little more than half as heavy as air, and consequently, the gas is collected, like hydrogen, by upward delivery.

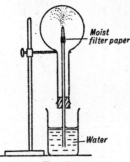

The gas is extremely soluble in water : one volume of water at $0°$ and 760 mm. dissolves 1298 volumes of gas, and at $20°$, 710 volumes. The gas can all be removed from its aqueous solution by boiling. The great solubility of ammonia in water is illustrated by means of the apparatus indicated in Fig. 144.

FIG. 144.
Ammonia Fountain.

The inverted flask is filled with dry ammonia and then attached to the apparatus as shown. A piece of moistened filter paper, A, is attached to the glass tube just below the jet. This moisture dissolves some of the ammonia, thereby creating a partial vacuum and causing water to be driven up the tube. When this emerges from the jet, the first few drops of water are sufficient to dissolve the whole of the ammonia so that water then rushes out of the jet like a fountain, until the flask is full.

Considerable heat is evolved during the solution of the gas :

$$NH_3 + Aq = NH_3Aq + 8.4 \text{ Cals.}$$

If a rapid current of air be driven through a cold solution of ammonia in water, the heat absorbed as the ammonia is expelled from the solution will reduce the temperature so as to freeze a small globule of mercury. The production of cold is best demonstrated by blowing air through a solution of ammonia in a vessel standing on a few drops of water on a block of wood.

The production of cold in this way must not be confused with the use of ammonia in refrigerators and ice-making machines, the operation of which depend upon the properties of liquid ammonia (see below).

Ammonia is readily liquefied, pressure alone being sufficient at ordinary temperatures. The liquid boils at $-33.5°$ and solidifies to

white, transparent crystals at − 78°. Like water, liquid ammonia is
a bad conductor of heat and electricity, but it is an excellent solvent
and many substances which dissolve in it give solutions which conduct
electricity (compare Ch. XII). The behaviour of these solutions has
been considerably investigated and there is now a fair amount of an
ammonia chemistry resembling, in many ways, the water chemistry
with which we are familiar.

Refrigeration

Liquid ammonia is used in refrigerating machinery, for which purpose
it is particularly suitable, since it is very volatile, it is easily obtained
and has a high latent heat of vaporization. The heat of evaporation
of ammonia is 5·7 Cals. at − 33° C., i.e.,

$$NH_3 \rightarrow NH_3 - 5\cdot7 \text{ Cals.}$$
$$\text{liquid} \quad \text{gas}$$

If, therefore, liquid ammonia be evaporated, a relatively large amount
of heat is absorbed
from the surroundings.
Fig. 145 shows in dia-
grammatic form the
arrangement of a re-
frigerating plant using
ammonia.

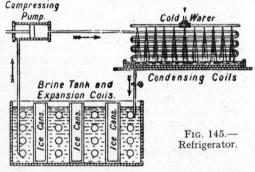

Ammonia gas is
liquefied by compres-
sion in the " condensing
coils " by means of a
pump; the heat genera-
ted as the gas liquefies
is conducted away by

Fig. 145.—
Refrigerator.

the cold water flowing over the condensing pipes, Fig. 145. The
liquid ammonia runs into coils of pipes, " expansion coils " dipping
in brine. The pressure is removed from the liquid ammonia in the
expansion coils, and the heat absorbed by the rapidly evaporating
liquid cools the brine below zero. The gas from the evaporating
liquid is pumped back into the condensing coils ; and so the process
is continuous. Cans of water placed in the brine are frozen into
cakes. In cold storage rooms, the cold brine circulates in coils near
the ceiling of the room to be cooled, and returns to the cooling
tank. Sulphur dioxide and carbon dioxide are also employed for
refrigeration ; but ammonia is more generally used.

Ammonia is a comparatively stable gas at ordinary temperatures ;
but at a red heat, it begins to decompose into nitrogen and hydrogen—
a reaction which is merely the reversal of that by which it is formed
synthetically (see pp. 389-391 above).

Ammonia is a non-supporter of ordinary combustion and does not
readily burn in air, but in oxygen it burns with a yellowish flame,

while mixtures of ammonia and oxygen are explosive. The main reaction is represented by the equation :

$$4NH_3 + 3O_2 = 2N_2 + 6H_2O,$$

but small quantities of ammonium nitrate and nitrogen peroxide are also formed. In presence of red-hot platinum, ammonia may be oxidized by air or oxygen almost completely to oxides of nitrogen, a reaction which is employed in the manufacture of nitric acid from ammonia (p. 407).

Ammonia reacts with chlorine and bromine, nitrogen and ammonium halide being formed if the ammonia is in excess :

$$8NH_3 + 3Cl_2 = N_2 + 4NH_4Cl ;$$

but with excess halogen, explosive nitrogen halides result (p. 401).

Ammonia reacts with some metals. With the alkali metals amides are formed ; for example, sodamide is obtained with sodium and ammonia at a temperature of 300° :

$$2Na + 2NH_3 = 2NaNH_2 + H_2$$

but when magnesium is heated in ammonia gas **magnesium nitride, Mg_3N_2,** is formed.

One of the most striking properties of ammonia, chemically speaking, is the basic character of its aqueous solution. The aqueous solution turns red litmus blue, yellow turmeric paper brown, conducts electricity, and in general reacts like a base.

This behaviour resembles that of aqueous solutions of carbon dioxide (p. 356), and just as that solution is believed to contain a certain amount of carbonic acid, resulting from the combination of a proportion of the carbon dioxide with water, so ammonia solutions are believed to contain some **ammonium hydroxide:**

$$NH_3 + H_2O \rightleftharpoons NH_4OH$$

If the aqueous solution of ammonia be neutralized with an acid— nitric, sulphuric or hydrochloric acid—the corresponding ammonium salt is formed—ammonium nitrate, NH_4NO_3 ; ammonium sulphate, NH_4HSO_4, or $(NH_4)_2SO_4$; ammonium chloride, NH_4Cl. It will be observed that we are here dealing with a univalent radical, NH_4, which is called **ammonium.** This behaves, in reactions such as those mentioned, in a very similar manner to a sodium atom. The more important ammonium salts are described below.

In other ways besides neutralizing acids, a solution of ammonia behaves as a base. Thus, for example, it precipitates many metallic hydroxides from solutions of their salts, and these sometimes dissolve in excess ammonia solution owing to the formation of complex ions. Thus, with ferric salts, ferric hydroxide is precipitated :

$$FeCl_3 + 3NH_4OH = Fe(OH)_3 \downarrow + 3NH_4Cl ;$$

but with copper sulphate solution the cupric hydroxide at first thrown down redissolves in excess of ammonia because of the formation of the complex cuprammonium ion :

$$CuSO_4 + 2NH_4OH = Cu(OH)_2\downarrow + (NH_4)_2SO_4$$
$$Cu(OH)_2 \rightleftharpoons Cu^{\cdot\cdot} + 2OH'$$
$$Cu^{\cdot\cdot} + 4NH_3 \rightleftharpoons Cu(NH_3)_4^{\cdot\cdot}.$$

Reducing agents are without action on ammonia, but it is fairly easily oxidized, particularly at high temperatures. For example, if a stream of the gas be passed over copper oxide heated in a hard glass tube, the oxide is reduced to copper, and the ammonia oxidized to nitrogen :

$$3CuO + 2NH_3 = 3Cu + N_2 + 3H_2O.$$

(Compare the similar action of hydrogen, p. 589.) Oxidizing agents, if sufficiently powerful, will bring about a similar reaction at ordinary temperatures. Thus, for example, with potassium permanganate :

$$2NH_3 + 2KMnO_4 = 2KOH + 2MnO_2 + 2H_2O + N_2.$$

The action of chlorine mentioned on page 394 can be regarded as an oxidation.

The formation from ammonia of complex ions in solution has been mentioned. Many substances containing ammonia combined in this way can be obtained in a crystalline state. This is particularly true of the compounds containing cobalt and platinum which are known as cobalt-ammines and platinum-ammines respectively. These are discussed on pages 841-846. Ammonia also forms double compounds with substances such as calcium chloride, e.g., $CaCl_2.2NH_3$; $CaCl_2.4NH_3$; $CaCl_2.8NH_3$; and similar compounds of zinc, aluminium and mercury are known.

§ 10 Uses of Ammonia

Ammonia finds many important applications. Its use for refrigerating purposes has been discussed. In the form of its salts (e.g., the sulphate) it is a valuable and important fertilizer. It is used also in the manufacture of urea (the other raw material being carbon dioxide) which is an extremely valuable fertilizer, the use of which is increasing. Urea is also used in the manufacture of synthetic resins, particularly of a glass-like kind. Ammonia is employed as a cleansing agent on account of its property of dissolving greases ; in the manufacture of soda by the Solvay process (q.v.) and in chemical operations where a volatile alkali is needed, etc.

It is used also in the manufacture of artificial silk by the cuprammonium process (p. 590).

§ 11 Formula of Ammonia

As indicated above (p. 390), when ammonia gas is sparked, about 98 per cent. of the gas is decomposed into its elements, and if the experiment be performed in an eudiometer it is found that the volume is almost doubled. If oxygen be now added and the mixture sparked, the hydrogen will be removed as water and the volume of the residual nitrogen is found to be very close to half that of the original ammonia. Neglecting the slight amount of ammonia undecomposed by the sparking, and the slight traces of oxides of nitrogen formed in the explosion with oxygen, it is found that :

2 volumes of ammonia form 1 volume of nitrogen plus 3 volumes of hydrogen.

Applying Avogadro's hypothesis it follows that :

2 molecules ammonia → 1 molecule of nitrogen + 3 molecules of hydrogen.

Since the molecules of hydrogen (p. 261) and nitrogen (p. 387) are known to be diatomic,

$$2 \text{ molecules of ammonia} \rightarrow N_2 + 3H_2$$

whence :

$$2NH_3 \rightarrow N_2 + 3H_2,$$

that is to say, the formula of ammonia is NH_3. This experiment, and associated reasoning, serves to establish NH_3 as the *molecular* formula of ammonia and not merely the empirical formula.

The volumetric composition of ammonia may also be demonstrated by the following experiment (sometimes known as Hofmann's experiment). A tube, A (Fig. 146) divided into three equal parts, is filled with chlorine gas, and concentrated ammonia solution is run through the tap funnel, A, drop by drop, until the reaction between the chlorine and the ammonia ceases. The first drop of ammonia gives a yellowish-green flame ; as more ammonia is added, dense clouds of ammonium chloride are formed ; much heat is evolved. Hence it is best to make the experiment with the tube immersed in a cylinder of water. When an excess of ammonia has been added, the excess is neutralized with dilute sulphuric acid. The gas in the tube was originally at atmospheric pressure, it is now under reduced pressure. To restore equilibrium, a long tube is filled with dilute hydrochloric acid, and the long leg allowed to dip in a beaker of dilute hydrochloric acid while the short leg is attached to the funnel as indicated in the diagram, Fig. 146. On opening the stopcock the liquid will run into the tube until it reaches the second mark on the tube. The tube now contains one volume of nitrogen. The interpretation of Hofmann's experiment is as follows : The hydrogen of the ammonia and

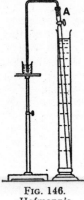

FIG. 146.
Hofmann's
Apparatus.

the chlorine combine in equal volumes to form hydrogen chloride. The hydrogen chloride combines with the ammonia to form ammonium chloride. The tube originally contained three volumes of chlorine. This chlorine has taken three volumes of hydrogen to form hydrogen chloride, etc. The latter dissolves in the liquid in the tube, and hence is without influence on the volume of the residual nitrogen. The three volumes of hydrogen were combined in ammonia with the one volume of nitrogen which remains in the tube.

The empirical formula of ammonia is therefore $(NH_3)_x$, but as the vapour density is 8·5 its molecular weight is 17. From this it follows that the value of x is unity and hence that the formula is NH_3.

The gravimetric analysis of ammonia is effected by passing a measured volume of the gas over heated copper oxide. The resulting water is weighed and the volume of nitrogen passing along is determined, and the corresponding weight computed (p. 77). The numbers so obtained give the combining proportions of hydrogen and nitrogen in ammonia. The result shows that 14·01 parts of nitrogen are combined with 3·024 parts of hydrogen.

The gravimetric result does not discriminate between NH_3 and a multiple of this as the molecular formula of ammonia ; a knowledge of the vapour density is necessary in order to do this.

§ 12 Detection and Determination of Ammonia

Ammonia is easily detected by its pungent and characteristic smell and also by its alkaline reaction with litmus, etc., since no other *gas* (except methylamine and ethylamine) behaves in this way. A very delicate test, used for the detection and determination colorimetrically of minute traces of ammonia in drinking water, is the yellow colour which it gives with **Nessler's solution** (p. 653).

In the ordinary way ammonia is determined by titration, using methyl orange as indicator. The ammonia in an ammonium salt is determined by distilling the salt with excess of sodium hydroxide and passing the distillate into a known volume of standard acid. The excess of acid is determined, after the experiment, by titration with standard alkali in presence of methyl orange.

§ 13 Ammonium Salts

The basic character of ammonia has been referred to above, and the salts which it forms with acids are known as the ammonium salts, being derived from the hypothetical radical ammonium, NH_4. Ammonium salts are white solids, unless they contain a coloured acid radical, and except the perchlorate, cobaltinitrite and chloroplatinate, are readily soluble in water. They decompose or volatilize at temperatures below red heat. When treated with caustic alkalis ammonia is evolved.

The electronic configuration of the ammonium ion will be :

for nitrogen has five electrons in the valency group, and the four hydrogen atoms contribute one each.. There would thus be nine electrons available, one more than is required to make the stable group of eight. One is, therefore, lost to the anion, leaving the group with a single positive charge. The ammonium compounds are thus electrovalent substances. The resemblance to the sodium ion, which is a sodium atom which has lost its outermost (valency) electron leaving a completed group of eight, is also apparent.

Ammonium Chloride, NH_4Cl

Ammonium chloride is manufactured from the ammoniacal liquor of the gas works. The liquor is neutralized with hydrochloric acid, and the resulting solution is evaporated until crystallization occurs. The crude product is purified by heating the solid in a large iron or earthenware pot with a dome-shaped cover, Fig. 147. The ammonium chloride volatilizes and the solid condenses as a white crystalline, fibrous mass inside the cover. Most of the impurities remain in the vessel. The process of vaporizing a solid and condensing the vapour back to the solid condition is called **sublimation.** Ammonium chloride is a white granular, fibrous, crystalline solid, with a sharp saline taste. It dissolves in water and at the same time lowers the temperature. Ammonium chloride is used for charging Leclanché cells ; as a constituent of soldering fluids, to protect metals from oxidation during the soldering. It is also used in galvanizing iron, and in the textile industries.

FIG. 147. — Sublimation of Ammonium Chloride.

It is often known as *sal-ammoniac.*

The action of heat on ammonium chloride vapour is interesting. The salt vaporizes at about 340° C., and the vapour density at 350° is 14·52 ($H_2 = 1$), whereas the theoretical value for NH_4Cl is 26·75. That is, the observed density is very little more than half the value which would be anticipated. This is explained by supposing that the molecule is dissociated into ammonia and hydrogen chloride :

$$NH_4Cl \rightleftharpoons NH_3 + HCl.$$

If complete dissociation has occurred, the vapour density would be 13·375 so that it appears that at 350° the vapour contains about 17 per cent. of ammonium chloride, and 83 per cent. of a mixture of equal volumes of ammonia and hydrogen chloride.

On cooling, the two gases recombine forming ammonium chloride once more, but it is possible to separate the two gases from the hot vapour by diffusion (p. 25), thus proving their presence. This can be done by means of the apparatus shown in Fig. 148.

A little ammonium chloride is placed near the middle of a hard glass tube inclined as shown ; a little lower down is a piece of blue litmus paper. A loose plug of asbestos is put above the salt and then a piece of red litmus paper. On heating the ammonium chloride, ammonia being the lighter gas diffuses more quickly than the hydrogen chloride. Consequently, the blue litmus will be reddened by the excess of slow diffusing hydrogen chloride in the lower part of the tube ; and the red litmus

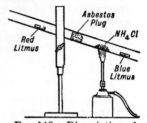

FIG. 148.—Dissociation of Ammonium Chloride.

will be blued by the ammonia which passes to the upper part of the tube before the hydrogen chloride.

Notice that this experiment only proves that *some* dissociation takes place ; it does not prove complete dissociation as the equilibrium :

$$NH_4Cl \rightleftharpoons NH_3 + HCl,$$

is being disturbed (compare p. 237).

Intensively dried ammonia and hydrochloric acid do not combine when mixed, and it has also been claimed by Baker that intensively dried ammonium chloride does not dissociate when heated. There has been much controversy about this point (see p. 285) and it is now thought that even intensively dried ammonium chloride does, in fact, undergo dissociation.

Ammonium Nitrate, NH_4NO_3

Ammonium nitrate is made by neutralizing nitric acid with ammonia, or by double decomposition of ammonium sulphate and sodium nitrate :

$$(NH_4)_2SO_4 + 2NaNO_3 = 2NH_4NO_3 + Na_2SO_4.$$

The sodium sulphate crystallizes out with ten molecules of water of crystallization and the ammonium nitrate is recovered by evaporation.

It exists in colourless crystals which are found in several different forms. It readily dissolves in water, with the absorption of much heat, and so has been employed as a freezing salt, a low temperature being reached when a large amount of the salt is dissolved in a little water. It is also used in the preparation of nitrous oxide (p. 414) and as an explosive. The explosives *amatol* and *ammonal* used in the late war consist largely of ammonium nitrate. (Amatol, 80 per cent. ammonium nitrate and 20 per cent. trinitrotoluene ; ammonal, principally ammonium nitrate, with small quantities of aluminium and sometimes charcoal.)

Ammonium Sulphate, $(NH_4)_2SO_4$

This is the most important commercial salt of ammonia. It is made by neutralizing gas-liquor with sulphuric acid, or by distilling the ammonia from gas-liquor into acid, the salt being obtained by evaporation. It is also made from synthetic ammonia by passing the gas into a suspension of gypsum or anhydrite (calcium sulphate) in water through which a stream of carbon dioxide is also passing. Calcium carbonate is precipitated and ammonium sulphate remains in solution :

$$2NH_3 + CaSO_4 + CO_2 = (NH_4)_2SO_4 + CaCO_3\downarrow.$$

Ammonium sulphate forms large transparent crystals, isomorphous with potassium sulphate. It is very soluble in water. On heating, it loses ammonia even below 100° and forms an **acid sulphate** $NH_4.HSO_4$.

Ammonium sulphate is used extensively as a fertilizer and as a source of ammonium compounds.

Ammonium Carbonate

What is known as ammonium carbonate is made commercially by subliming a mixture of chalk and ammonium chloride or sulphate from iron retorts into lead receivers. There is thus produced a substance which, after re-sublimation with a little water, comes into the market as a white, semi-transparent fibrous mass covered on the outside with a white opaque powder. This powder is **ammonium bicarbonate** $NH_4.HCO_3$, and the main constituent of the rest of the material is now known to be **ammonium carbamate**, $NH_2.CO.ONH_4$

Ammonium carbamate reacts with water giving the carbonate:

$$NH_2.CO.ONH_4 + H_2O = (NH_4)_2CO_3,$$

so that solutions of the solid commercial product contain ammonium carbonate.

Ammonium Sulphides

Bineau in 1839 observed the formation of colourless needles when ammonia and hydrogen sulphide are mixed in equal volumes. These are probably composed of **ammonium hydrosulphide** $(NH_4.HS)$. If hydrogen sulphide be passed through fairly concentrated ammonia solution the resulting liquid contains a mixture of this hydrosulphide with the normal **ammonium sulphide**—$(NH_4)_2S$. *Yellow ammonium sulphide* is a solution of various ammonium polysulphides $(NH_4)_2S_n$, made by digesting flowers of sulphur with the colourless solution obtained by saturating ammonia solution with hydrogen sulphide. The principal constituent is probably the pentasulphide $(NH_4)_2S_5$ (compare p. 443). Solutions of ammonium sulphide (both " colourless " and " yellow ") are used in qualitative analysis.

§ 14 The Action of Halogens on Ammonia and Ammonium Salts

Chlorine, bromine and iodine all react with ammonia, and although the final products are very different it is probable that the initial stages are similar.

The action of chlorine or bromine upon excess of aqueous ammonia solution results in the liberation of nitrogen and the formation of an ammonium salt. It is probable, however, that in the first place substitution takes place, the resulting trihalogen compound combining loosely with another molecule of ammonia, e.g., $NCl_3.NH_3$.

The trichloro and tribromo compounds are very unstable and decompose in presence of excess of ammonia, forming an ammonium salt and free nitrogen :

$$NCl_3.NH_3 + 3NH_3 = N_2 + 3NH_4Cl.$$

The iodine compound is more stable and separates as the insoluble brownish-black so-called nitrogen iodide (see below). When exposed to light in presence of ammonia, however, this decomposes in the same way as the chlorine and bromine derivatives.

If there be not excess of ammonia present, however, iodine is liberated :

$$NI_3.NH_3 = N_2 + 3HI$$
$$NI_3.NH_3 + 3HI \rightleftharpoons 2NH_3 + 3I_2.$$

With ammonium salts, the action is different. Chlorine replaces hydrogen and yellow oily drops of nitrogen chloride (see below) separate.

$$NH_4Cl + 3Cl_2 = NCl_3 + 4HCl.$$

Bromine and iodine are unable to replace hydrogen in the ammonium salt, but combine with it forming perhalides, e.g.,

$$NH_4Br + Br_2 = NH_4Br_3.$$

A number of similarly constituted ammonium perhalides is known, one of the most interesting being the tetrachloroiodide NH_4ICl_4 which is remarkably stable and was one of the earliest compounds of iodine to be discovered (Filhol—1839).

§ 15 Nitrogen Trichloride, NCl_3

Nitrogen chloride was discovered by Dulong in 1811. It separates in yellow drops when chlorine is passed into a solution of ammonium chloride (p. 398), or when such a solution is electrolyzed. It is also formed when a lump of ammonium chloride is suspended in a concentrated solution of hypochlorous acid.

Nitrogen chloride is a yellow liquid and dangerously explosive. Its solution in carbon tetrachloride is safer to handle. When such a solution is shaken with excess of concentrated hydrochloric acid, chlorine is liberated :

$$NCl_3 + 4HCl = NH_4Cl + 3Cl_2.$$

It is slowly hydrolyzed by water into ammonium hypochlorite, this being apparently a reversible reaction (cf. preparation above in which the ammonia is furnished by the ammonium chloride).

$$NCl_3 + 3H_2O \rightleftharpoons NH_3 + 3HOCl.$$

§ 16 Nitrogen Iodide, $NI_3.NH_3$

The brownish-black solid which separates when iodine is added to excess of aqueous ammonia, is known as nitrogen iodide and was formerly thought to vary in composition according to the mode of preparation. Chattaway has, however, definitely established the fact that a single definite compound is always formed viz., $NH_3.NI_3$, and that the various formulae previously suggested were due to the specimens analysed having partially decomposed, e.g., through exposure to light (compare § 14). Chattaway showed that this compound could be obtained crystalline with proper precautions.

Nitrogen iodide explodes very readily indeed when dry, but can be handled safely when moistened with ammonia. It reacts with reducing agents with the formation of hydriodic acid, e.g., with sodium sulphite :

$$NI_3NH_3 + 3Na_2SO_3 + 3H_2O = 3Na_2SO_4 + 2NH_4I + HI,$$

a reaction which can be used for its determination, by titrating the free acid with baryta, the iodide with silver nitrate, and the ammonia set free and titrated with acid. The composition was determined in this way.

§ 17 Fixation of Nitrogen.   The Nitrogen Cycle

All living matter and the waste products of animals contain considerable quantities of combined nitrogen. It is a necessary constituent for the growth of living organisms. During the decay of organic matter through the agency of bacteria, part of the nitrogen finds its way back to the atmosphere, and part passes directly into the soil to be absorbed by plants. Animals cannot assimilate free nitrogen, and they are accordingly dependent upon the plants for their supply. Plants in light transform inorganic compounds into complex organic products surcharged with energy and which are necessary for the life of higher animals. Plants thus form a permanent link between the inorganic and the animal kingdoms. Plants cannot usually obtain their nitrogen direct from the atmosphere. Most plants get their nitrogen from the soil where it is present in the form of nitrates, ammonium salts, or other complex compounds. The organic matter in the soil is attacked by bacteria of various kinds, and part is converted into nitrates and part into free nitrogen. A certain amount is brought back from the atmosphere, during a rain storm, where it has been oxidized into ammonium nitrate by electric discharges—this more particularly in the polar regions. These supplies of available nitrogen, however, do not suffice to maintain the fertility of cultivated soils. It is therefore necessary to make good the constant draining of the available nitrogen by the cultivated plants. This is done by allowing nitrogenous organic matter—manures—to decay away in the soil, or to add a mixture—a fertilizer—containing available nitrogen.

The considerations outlined in the preceding paragraphs indicate the need for supplying nitrogen to the soil to make up for that removed by cultivation. The development of agriculture is largely dependent, therefore, upon the supply of cheap combined nitrogen. The chief sources of supply of combined nitrogen are :

(i) coal, via the gas works, p. 349 ;
(ii) Chile nitrate deposits, p. 565 ;
(iii) nitre plantations (p. 577) and animal excrements :
(iv) fixation of atmospheric nitrogen.

The last of these is of increasing importance since the atmosphere contains a virtually inexhaustible supply of nitrogen. This matter may be discussed under two heads :

(i) fixation by bacteria associated with plants ;
(ii) artificial fixation.

In 1853 G. Ville noticed that while most plants reduce the available nitrogen in soils, some plants, principally the leguminosae—peas, beans, clover, lupins, etc.—enrich the soil so that more available nitrogen is present after a crop has been removed than before. In 1886 H. Hell showed that certain leguminosae appear to live in a kind of partnership —symbiosis (from the Greek συν (syn), with ; βίωσις (biosis), living)—with certain bacteria— e.g., the *bacterium radicula*. The bacteria appear to live as guests in nodules on the rootlets of their host, and probably also in the neighbouring soil. The nodules on the rootlets of a *Phaseolus* (bean) are illustrated in Fig. 149. The symbiotic bacteria convert the nitrogen of the atmosphere into a form available as food for the plant on which they live.

Fig. 149.—Nodules on Root of Bean Plant.

Of artificial methods for the fixation of atmospheric nitrogen, there are at present available three good ones, viz.,

(i) the manufacture of calcium cyanamide (p. 625) ;
(ii) the synthesis of ammonia (p. 390), (Haber process) ;
(iii) the synthesis of nitric oxide (and hence of nitric acid and nitrates)—(p. 406) (Birkeland-Eyde process).

These processes are described in the places named. The first and third are particularly suitable for localities where electric power is

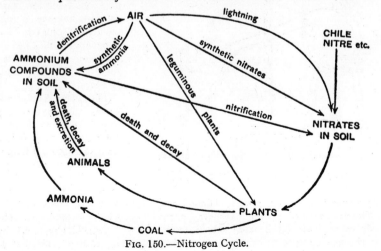

Fig. 150.—Nitrogen Cycle.

very cheap, and hence are to be found in operation at Niagara Falls, and in Norway respectively. The second, the Haber process, requires comparatively little power for its operation and so is worked to an increasing extent in England and Germany.

The artificial fixation of nitrogen, a " problem " at the beginning of the present century, is now a common industrial operation.

It is usual to refer to the succession of changes through which nitrogen passes as described in the preceding pages as the **nitrogen cycle** and the processes involved are summarized in some such diagram as Fig. 150.

§ 18 Nitric Acid, HNO₃. History and Occurrence

History

Nitric acid was probably not known to the ancient Egyptians. Geber says that he made it by distilling copperas with saltpetre and alum ; and J. R. Glauber (1650) made it by distilling a mixture of nitre and sulphuric acid. A. L. Lavoisier (1776) proved that nitric acid is a compound of oxygen, and H. Cavendish (1784-85) demonstrated that it is formed by sparking nitrogen with moist oxygen.

Occurrence

A little nitric acid is formed in the atmosphere by lightning, causing combination of the oxygen and nitrogen of the air (see p. 405 below).

§ 19 Preparation of Nitric Acid

Laboratory Preparation

Nitric acid is prepared in the laboratory by the action of hot concentrated sulphuric acid on a nitrate, potassium nitrate being usually employed. The experiment is carried out in an apparatus such as that indicated in Fig. 151.

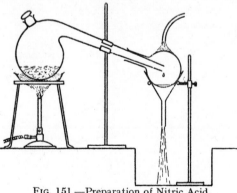

The retort is charged with approximately equal weights of sulphuric acid and potassium nitrate, and heated. Brownish red fumes appear which condense in the cooled

FIG. 151.—Preparation of Nitric Acid.

receiver to a brown liquid. This liquid is nitric acid, coloured by the presence of a little nitrogen peroxide (p. 420), formed by the decomposition of the acid. It is purified by redistillation and by blowing a current of dry air, or carbon dioxide, through the warm nitric acid. The reaction involved in the preparation is represented by the equation :

$$KNO_3 + H_2SO_4 = HNO_3 + KHSO_4.$$

At the temperature at which the operation can be carried out in glass vessels, potassium bisulphate is formed. At the higher temperatures, possible commercially, the normal sulphate results so that less sulphuric acid is required (see below).

The acid so obtained may still contain water. If it be redistilled from concentrated sulphuric acid, and a current of dry air or carbon dioxide passed through the warm acid as before, almost pure anhydrous nitric acid is obtained. The **fuming nitric acid** of commerce is made similarly, but usually without having the nitrogen peroxide removed, so that it is brown in colour.

Industrial Preparation

Nitric acid is now manufactured in three ways, viz.,
(i) from sulphuric acid and sodium nitrate (Chile saltpetre) ;
(ii) by the combination of the nitrogen and oxygen of the air ;
(iii) by the oxidation of ammonia.

Sodium nitrate, also known as Chile saltpetre, is obtained in enormous quantities from the nitre beds of Chile and Peru (p. 565), and is used as a source of nitric acid on a large scale.

The sodium nitrate and sulphuric acid are heated in cast-iron retorts ; the vapour is condensed in earthenware pipes cooled by water, and collected in earthenware jars. The last jar is connected with a tower filled with coke down which a stream of water trickles. The object is to recover the nitrogen peroxide produced by the decomposition of the nitric acid. The retort has an exit pipe from which the sodium sulphate can be run when the action is over. To reduce the amount of nitrogen peroxide formed during the decomposition of the nitric acid by heat, the stills are often worked under a reduced pressure so that the acid may come off at as low a temperature as possible.

If the temperature be high enough, the reaction indicated in the laboratory preparation is succeeded by that represented :

$$NaHSO_4 + NaNO_3 = Na_2SO_4 + HNO_3.$$

In some works this is carried out, but the practice is now becoming commoner of stopping the process at the first stage, and utilizing the sodium hydrogen sulphate (known as *nitre-cake*) for the manufacture of sodium sulphate and hydrochloric acid (p. 500).

Manufacture of Nitric Acid from the Air

J. Priestley (1775) first noticed that an acid is formed when electric sparks are sent through the air, but he seems to have thought that the acidity was due to carbonic acid. H. Cavendish (1785) proved that the product of the action is nitric acid, while M. Berthelot showed that nitric oxide, NO, is an intermediate stage in the process.

When a mixture of nitrogen and oxygen is raised to a very high temperature, the following equilibrium is set up :

$$N_2 + O_2 \rightleftharpoons 2NO - 43 \cdot 2 \text{ Cals.}$$

Examination of this equation in the light of Le Chatelier's principle (p. 219) shows that the amount of nitric oxide present at equilibrium will be greater at high temperatures, since heat is absorbed in the formation of nitric oxide. Similarly, since there is no volume change in the reaction, changes of pressure will be without influence upon the equilibrium. Investigation of this equilibrium by Nernst has shown that it is only at temperatures above 2000° that a useful yield of nitric oxide is obtainable, and even at 3000° the equilibrium proportion is only about 5 per cent. The usual means of obtaining such a temperature is by the use of the electric arc, and this is the basis of the commercial application of this reaction known as the Birkeland-Eyde process, which is worked on a large scale in Norway.

In this process, illustrated by the diagram, Fig. 152, a large alternating current arc is struck between water-cooled copper poles, and

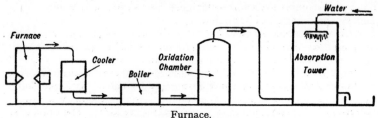

Furnace.
General Arrangement (Diagrammatic).
Fig. 152.—Birkeland-Eyde Process.

spread out by means of an intense magnetic field into a disc of " flame " about six feet in diameter. This is done inside a flat circular furnace made of steel lined with heat-resisting brick and a stream of air is blown through the flame.

As has been said, the proportion of nitric oxide at 3000° is about 5 per cent., but at temperatures even as high as 1500° this proportion is less than half of 1 per cent., so that it is necessary to cool the gases very quickly so as to " freeze " the equilibrium (see p. 222). The rapid passage of the gases and the thinness of the flame makes it possible to arrange that the temperature of the exit gases shall be about 1000° The percentage of nitric oxide actually obtained is round about 1 per cent. The gases are then passed to boilers where they raise steam used for evaporation and other purposes, and finally are cooled to 50° by passage through large aluminium pipes exposed to the air.

When the gases have cooled to 600° formation of nitrogen peroxide begins :

$$2NO + O_2 \rightleftharpoons 2NO_2.$$

This is a rather slow reaction, and in order that it shall be complete, the gases pass through a large empty iron tower before going to the absorption towers. These absorption towers are built of granite and may be up to eighty feet in height; they are packed with broken quartz over which water is circulating.

The principal reaction taking place in the absorption towers is:

$$2NO_2 + H_2O = HNO_2 + HNO_3,$$

that is, a mixture of nitrous and nitric acids is formed. The nitrous acid, however, decomposes into nitric acid and nitric oxide:

$$3HNO_2 = 2NO + HNO_3 + H_2O.$$

The nitric oxide is reoxidized by the air present and is absorbed again as above. The final gases are absorbed in towers fed with sodium carbonate where sodium nitrite (an important salt, p. 566) is formed. From the previous towers, nitric acid of about 30 per cent. strength is obtained and is usually neutralized with limestone, thereby forming calcium nitrate, which is sold as a fertilizer under the name of Norwegian saltpetre. Some of the nitric acid, however, is distilled and concentrated and sold as such.

Manufacture of Nitric Acid from Ammonia

The fact that, in presence of a suitable catalyst, ammonia can be oxidized by the oxygen of the air to nitric oxide, has been mentioned previously (p. 394). This has, of late years, been made the basis for the manufacture of nitric acid (indirectly) from the air in countries where synthetic ammonia is being produced in quantity.

A mixture of ammonia and air in the proportion of about 1 to 7·5 by volume is passed rapidly through a cylinder of

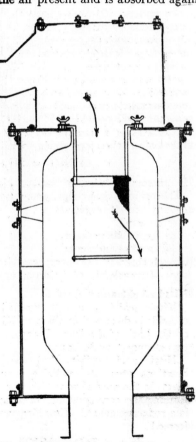

FIG. 153.—Ammonia Oxidation

platinum gauze in an apparatus arranged as shown diagrammatically in Fig. 153.

The platinum gauze is heated electrically in order to start the reaction ; but, once the rate of flow of the gases is properly adjusted, the heat of the reaction itself maintains the necessary temperature (red heat). The nitric oxide formed is converted into nitrogen peroxide and absorbed in much the same way as in the Birkeland-Eyde process.

§ 20 Properties of Nitric Acid

Nitric acid is a colourless mobile liquid which fumes strongly in air. It has a peculiar smell. The pure acid is hygroscopic and rapidly absorbs moisture from the air. It mixes in all proportions with water ; and, as in the case of sulphuric acid, nitric acid contracts when mixed with water, and the mixture rises in temperature. The pure acid boils at 86°, and freezes to a white solid, melting at −42°. An aqueous solution containing 68 per cent. of nitric acid boils at 120·5°, more concentrated solutions, and also more dilute solutions, boil at lower temperatures. A more dilute solution loses water on boiling, and a more concentrated solution loses acid on boiling until 68 per cent. of nitric acid of constant boiling point distils unchanged. This is the concentrated nitric acid of commerce. The specific gravity of the constant boiling acid at 15° is 1·414.

Nitric acid is readily decomposed by heat ; some decomposition takes place, therefore, during distillation :

$$4HNO_3 = 2H_2O + O_2 + 4NO_2.$$

It commences below 68° and at higher temperatures is very marked.

The principal chemical properties of nitric acid fall into three main groups, viz., its reactions as

(i) an acid,
(ii) an oxidizing agent,
(iii) a nitrating agent,

though there are, of course, reactions in which it acts in more than one way—for example its action on copper (p. 585).

Nitric Acid as an Acid

Nitric acid is a very strong acid in the sense in which the strength of acids is discussed in Chapter XII (p. 237), where it is shown that, on the basis of the Ionic Theory, nitric and hydrochloric acids are the two strongest acids known.

Nitric acid exhibits the usual general properties of acids in all reactions where its oxidizing properties are not operative. Thus, it reacts in the normal way with basic oxides, hydroxides and carbonates, forming the corresponding salts, unless the metallic radical concerned is a reducing agent. Thus, for example, with zinc oxide the nitrate is formed :

$$ZnO + 2HNO_3 = Zn(NO_3)_2 + H_2O,$$

while with ferrous oxide, oxidation also takes place so that the *ferric* salt results :

$$3FeO + 10HNO_3 = 3Fe(NO_3)_3 + NO + 5H_2O.$$

The action of nitric acid on metals (see below) is complicated by the oxidizing actions which take place, the acid acting both as an acid and an oxidizing agent.

Owing to its volatility, nitric acid is readily turned out of its salts by weaker, but less volatile acids. The laboratory preparation, using sulphuric acid, is an example of this.

Nitric Acid as an Oxidizing Agent

In consequence of the large proportion of oxygen in nitric acid, and of the ease with which it is decomposed, it would be expected that it would be a powerful oxidizing agent. It is so. Thus, for example, sulphur is oxidized to sulphuric acid, and phosphorus to phosphoric acid :

$$S + 2HNO_3 = H_2SO_4 + 2NO$$
$$3P + 5HNO_3 + 2H_2O = 3H_3PO_4 + 5NO$$

Many metallic sulphides are similarly oxidized to sulphates, e.g.,

$$2FeS_2 + 10HNO_3 = Fe_2(SO_4)_3 + H_2SO_4 + 10NO + 4H_2O.$$

Nitrating Action of Nitric Acid

Nitric acid reacts with a great many organic compounds often merely oxidizing them to carbon dioxide and water. For example, if strong nitric acid be poured on sawdust, the mass often bursts into flame. If a dish of fuming nitric acid be placed in a basin in the bottom of a glass cylinder, and a little turpentine be added from a pipette, the turpentine will burst into flame. Glowing charcoal continues to burn when plunged into the acid.

But it does not always act with such violence, and in many cases causes the replacement of one or more hydrogen atoms of the organic compound by the $-NO_2$ radical, which is known as the **nitro-group.** This process is known as **nitration** and is of great theoretical and practical importance.

§ 21 Action of Nitric Acid on Metals

Nitric acid attacks all metals under appropriate conditions, except gold, platinum, iridium, titanium, tantalum and rhodium. Some metals, however, are rendered *passive* by acid of a certain strength, e.g., iron (p. 812).

As a rule, the reaction is complicated by the simultaneous occurrence of oxidation, and the normal acid reaction. In consequence, hydrogen is not evolved by the action of nitric acid on metals except in the case of cold dilute nitric acid and magnesium, and even then the conditions have to be very carefully adjusted. In all other cases, one or other of the many possible reduction products of the acid is evolved, the nature of which depends upon the metal and the conditions. Thus metals like copper give mainly nitrogen peroxide (p. 420) with the strong acid :

$$Cu + 4HNO_3 = Cu(NO_3)_2 + 2H_2O + 2NO_2$$

and nitric oxide (p. 416) with the dilute :

$$3Cu + 8HNO_3 = 3Cu(NO_3)_2 + 2NO + 4H_2O.$$

Zinc, however, gives mainly nitrous oxide (p. 414) with the dilute acid, but when more concentrated may yield ammonia :

$$4Zn + 10HNO_3 = 4Zn(NO_3)_2 + 5H_2O + N_2O$$
$$4Zn + 9HNO_3 = 4Zn(NO_3)_2 + 3H_2O + NH_3.$$

The ammonia, of course, reacts with excess of nitric acid to form ammonium nitrate. Devarda's alloy, mentioned previously (p. 388) yields ammonia quantitatively. In certain circumstances, hyponitrous acid (p. 413), or nitrogen, may also be formed by the action of nitric acid on a metal.

Two different explanations have been suggested to account for these results. According to one, hydrogen is first formed, but reduces excess of the acid before it can escape ; according to the other oxidation of the metal (with consequent reduction of the nitric acid) first occurs, followed by salt formation by the metallic oxide and excess acid.

It is not possible to decide with certainty between these suggestions. But the metals copper, silver, mercury and bismuth have no perceptible action on cold dilute sulphuric and hydrochloric acids, and accordingly it is not likely that they will reduce nitric acid by the action of nascent hydrogen. In harmony with this, V. H. Veley (1890) proved that these metals have no action on cold dilute nitric acid unless a trace of nitrous acid or a lower nitrogen oxide is present. Nitrous acid may be present in the nitric acid as an impurity ; it may be formed by the incipient decomposition of nitric acid when it is warmed ; or it may be formed in the acid by electrolysis produced by local currents of electricity set up by impurities in the metal (" local action "). Once the action has started, the evolution of nitric oxide, and the formation of nitrate proceed quickly.

§ 22 Uses of Nitric Acid

Nitric acid finds many applications both in the laboratory and in industry. In the former, it is frequently employed as an oxidizing agent as, for example, the preparation of metallic oxides, oxyacids, and in the oxidation of ferrous to ferric salts in qualitative analysis. It is also a constituent of aqua regia (p. 503) and is an important reagent in organic chemistry both for oxidation and nitration.

Industrially nitric acid is used in large quantities for the production of explosives of all kinds ; the manufacture of many nitro-compounds, for use as intermediates, etc., in the dye industry ; in the production of celluloid, collodion, and one variety of artificial silk (nitro-cellulose silk), in the preparation of sulphuric acid by the Chamber process (p. 461) and of silver nitrate for photographic and other purposes. It is also employed for cleaning metals (e.g., before electro-plating) and for etching designs on copper. It is also an essential raw material for the production of many modern plastics and lacquers.

§ 23 Detection and Determination of Nitric Acid

Nitric acid and nitrates are usually detected by the *brown-ring test*. The material to be tested is mixed with excess of concentrated sulphuric acid and cooled. Ferrous sulphate solution is then poured carefully down the side of the test-tube, so as to form a layer on the surface of the sulphuric acid. A brown ring, or layer, at the junction of the two liquids indicates the presence of a nitrate. This is due to the formation of nitric oxide through the reduction of the nitrate by some of the ferrous sulphate. This nitric oxide then forms the dark coloured double compound, $FeSO_4.NO$ (p. 417) with more of the ferrous sulphate.

Another simple qualitative test for a nitrate is to treat with concentrated sulphuric acid and warm, and then to add copper turnings. The formation of brown fumes of nitrogen peroxide indicates the presence of a nitrate.

The quantitative determination of nitric acid and nitrates is rather difficult. The free acid can, in absence of other acids, be titrated with standard alkali. The most usual means of estimation is the use of Devarda's alloy (p. 388), which yields ammonia quantitatively when heated with a nitrate in alkaline solution (p. 410). The ammonia formed is distilled into standard acid (p. 397).

Nitrates can also be determined by shaking a solution containing the nitrate with concentrated sulphuric acid and mercury in a closed tube whereby the nitrate is reduced to nitric oxide. The volume of nitric oxide is accurately measured and the weight of nitrogen present can be calculated. Since nitrites are also reduced to nitric oxide by this process it is necessary to remove or determine them separately.

§ 24 Nitrates

The salts of nitric acid are known as **nitrates**. They are usually readily soluble in water and form well-defined crystals. When heated, nitrates decompose, and there are three types of decomposition according to whether a salt of (i) an alkali metal, (ii) a heavy metal, or (iii) ammonia is concerned.

The nitrates of the alkali metals decompose on heating into the corresponding nitrite and oxygen :

$$2KNO_3 = 2KNO_2 + O_2.$$

The nitrates of the heavy metals give oxygen, nitrogen peroxide (p. 420) and the oxide of the metal, e.g.,

$$2Pb(NO_3)_2 = 2PbO + 4NO_2 + O_2.$$

Ammonium nitrate decomposes on heating into nitrous oxide (p. 414) and water :

$$NH_4NO_3 = N_2O + 2H_2O.$$

§ 25 Nitrous Acid, HNO_2

Nitrous acid is known only in the form of its salts and in dilute solution, on account of the readiness with which the free acid decomposes.

Dilute solutions of nitrous acid are formed when nitrogen trioxide (p. 419) is dissolved in water at 0°, and by the addition to barium nitrite solution, of the exact amount of dilute sulphuric acid theoretically required to precipitate the barium, the whole being cooled to 0° :

$$Ba(NO_2)_2 + H_2SO_4 = BaSO_4 \downarrow + 2HNO_2.$$

The precipitated barium sulphate can be filtered off, when a dilute solution of nitrous acid remains.

Properties

Nitrous acid is very unstable and begins to decompose almost as soon as it is formed even at ordinary temperatures, nitric oxide being evolved and nitric acid formed :

$$3HNO_2 = HNO_3 + 2NO + H_2O.$$

At higher temperatures, it breaks up into a mixture of nitrogen peroxide and nitric oxide :

$$2HNO_2 = NO + NO_2 + H_2O.$$

Nitrous acid is very reactive and behaves either as a reducing agent, or as an oxidizing agent according to the circumstances. Thus, on the one hand, it reduces permanganates, dichromates, chlorine and bromine, e.g. :

$$5KNO_2 + 2KMnO_4 + 3H_2SO_4 =$$
$$5KNO_3 + K_2SO_4 + 2MnSO_4 + 3H_2O$$
$$HNO_2 + Br_2 + H_2O = HNO_3 + 2HBr$$

the former reaction serving for its volumetric determination. On the other hand it oxidizes hydriodic acid to iodine :

$$2HNO_2 + 2HI = 2H_2O + 2NO + I_2,$$

and reducing agents such as sulphur dioxide and stannous chloride are oxidized by it.

Nitrous acid reacts with ammonia and substances (mostly organic) containing the $-NH_2$ radical, eliminating the nitrogen of both substances as the free element, e.g. :

$$NH_3 + HNO_2 = NH_4NO_2 = N_2 + 2H_2O.$$

Formula

Two formulae have been suggested for nitrous acid, viz.,

$$H-N \underset{\searrow O}{\overset{\nearrow O}{\lessgtr}} \quad \text{and} \quad H-O-N=O.$$

The evidence available, some of it drawn from organic chemistry, indicates the existence of derivatives of both forms; the free acid is probably

$$H-O-N=O$$

Nitrites

The salts of nitrous acid are called *nitrites*. They are mostly very soluble salts, the only important exception being silver nitr te which is only sparingly soluble. A number of complex nitrites are known, some of which are noteworthy, e.g., the cobaltinitrites which are used in analysis.

§ 26 Hyponitrous Acid, $H_2N_2O_2$

Hyponitrous acid and hyponitrites are obtained by the reduction of nitrites.
When a solution of potassium or sodium nitrite or nitrate is treated with a solution of metallic sodium in mercury—sodium amalgam—the hydrogen liberated reduces the nitrite or nitrate, forming a new salt—**sodium hyponitrite :**

$$2NaNO_3 + (8H) = 4H_2O + Na_2N_2O_2.$$

The alkaline solution can then be neutralized by acetic acid ; and when silver nitrate is added, a yellow precipitate of **silver hyponitrite,** $Ag_2N_2O_2$, is formed. By treating silver hyponitrite, suspended in dry ether, with a solution of hydrogen chloride in dry ether, and evaporating the clear solution, white deliquescent crystalline plates are obtained. This is **hyponitrous acid.** The solid is very unstable and is liable to explode even below $0°$.
It decomposes slowly when exposed to the air, giving nitrous and nitric acids :

$$2H_2N_2O_2 + 3O_2 = 2HNO_2 + 2HNO_3,$$

but boiling its aqueous solution causes the formation of nitrous oxide.

$$H_2N_2O_2 = H_2O + N_2O.$$

It is a dibasic acid, and the available evidence, derived mainly from organic chemistry, suggests that its formula is : $HO-N=N-OH$.

§ 27 Oxides of Nitrogen

There are five well-established oxides of nitrogen, viz.,

Nitrous oxide, N_2O ;
Nitric oxide, NO ;
Nitrogen trioxide, N_2O_3 ;
Nitrogen peroxide, $NO_2 \rightleftharpoons N_2O_4$;
Nitrogen pentoxide, N_2O_5.

Others, such as NO_3, have been reported but their existence is doubtful.

§ 28 Nitrous Oxide, N_2O.

Nitrous oxide was discovered by J. Priestley (1772), who made it by reducing nitric oxide with moist iron filings :

$$2NO + H_2O + \cdot Fe = N_2O + Fe(OH)_2.$$

It is usually prepared from ammonium nitrate which yields the gas when heated :

$$NH_4NO_3 = N_2O + 2H_2O.$$

The experiment is carried out by means of the apparatus indicated in Fig. 154. A convenient quantity of ammonium nitrate is placed in the round-bottomed flask and heated, care being taken to avoid heating too strongly which causes explosive decomposition. The gas is usually collected over hot water, being fairly soluble in cold. As thus prepared, nitrous oxide may contain traces of nitric oxide and chlorine (from the ammonium chloride sometimes present in ammonium nitrate). These may be removed by washing with ferrous sulphate solution and sodium hydroxide.

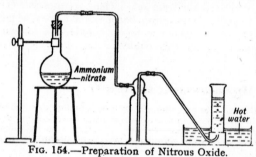

FIG. 154.—Preparation of Nitrous Oxide.

A mixture of sodium nitrate and ammonium sulphate can be used as a source of nitrous oxide ; in this case although evolution of gas takes place more slowly, it is more uniform and the risk of explosion is removed.

Nitrous oxide can also be prepared by heating a mixture of stannous chloride with hydrochloric acid and a little nitric acid, when the reaction occurs as represented by the equation :

$$4SnCl_2 + 2HNO_3 + 8HCl = 4SnCl_4 + N_2O + 5H_2O.$$

Properties

Nitrous oxide is a colourless gas with a faint smell. 100 c.c. of water, at 760 mm. pressure, dissolve 130 volumes of the gas at 0° ; and 63 volumes at 20°. Hence the gas is usually collected over hot water in order to lessen the loss due to its solubility in that liquid. The aqueous solution has a sweetish taste. The gas condenses to a colourless limpid liquid at 0° under a pressure of thirty atmospheres. M. Faraday liquefied the gas in 1823. Liquid nitrous oxide can be purchased in steel cylinders. The liquid boils at −89·5°, and freezes to a snow-like mass when allowed to evaporate. The cubic crystals melt at −102·4°.

Nitrous oxide resembles oxygen in its behaviour towards combustibles. A brightly glowing splinter bursts into flame when plunged into the gas. Ignited phosphorus, sulphur, etc., burn vividly in nitrous oxide gas.

The burning body decomposes the nitrous oxide, unites with the oxygen, and leaves the nitrogen as a residue. If sulphur be but feebly burning, its flame is extinguished when plunged into nitrous oxide, probably because the temperature is not high enough to decompose the gas. It is therefore easy to mistake nitrous oxide for oxygen. One distinguishing test is to add a bubble of the suspected gas to nitric oxide (p. 416) ; if brown fumes are produced the gas is oxygen. Nitrous oxide does not give brown fumes with nitric oxide.

When inhaled nitrous oxide produces unconsciousness, and insensibility to pain. Hence it has long been used as an anaesthetic for small surgical operations, dentistry, etc. But owing to the unpleasant after effects sometimes produced, it is not used so much as formerly. If the inhalation be long continued, it may produce death ; while if but small quantities are inhaled, it may produce a kind of hysteria, or intoxication. Hence the gas is sometimes called " laughing gas."

The formation of nitrous oxide is an endothermic reaction :

$$2N_2 + O_2 = 2N_2O - 36 \text{ Cals.}$$

Nitrous oxide decomposes with an explosion if a fulminating cap be detonated in the gas. Nitrous oxide decomposes into its elements when heated ; two volumes of the gas furnish two volumes of nitrogen and one volume of oxygen—three volumes in all.

In common with the other oxides of nitrogen, nitrous oxide is reduced when passed over red-hot copper :

$$Cu + N_2O = CuO + N_2.$$

Composition and Formula

The gas, when decomposed by means of a heated iron wire in an apparatus such as that employed for the similar experiment with nitric oxide (Fig. 156), yields its own volume of nitrogen. (Copper may be used similarly.) Since the nitrogen molecule is diatomic nitrous oxide must be N_2O_n where n is still to be determined. Its vapour density has been found to be $22(H_2 = 1)$, hence its molecular weight is 44, $n = 1$, and its molecular formula is N_2O. It has recently been shown to have a linear structure, and is now formulated

$$N \equiv N \rightarrow O \text{ or } N \leftharpoons N = O.$$

§ 29 Nitric Oxide, NO

History

J. Priestley (1772) is generally regarded as the discoverer of nitric oxide ; although J. Mayow (1669) made it by treating iron with nitric acid ; and R. Boyle (1671) noted that it formed reddish-brown fumes in contact with air. J. B. van Helmont (c. 1600) knew the gas, although his descriptions seem to confuse it with carbon dioxide, probably because he had one name—gas sylvestre—for a number of different gases.

Preparation

Nitric oxide is formed from its elements at very high temperatures, a reaction already discussed in connection with the manufacture of nitric acid from the air (p. 406).

It is usually prepared in the laboratory by the action of nitric acid, specific gravity 1·2, upon metallic copper or mercury. The copper turnings are placed in a flask (Fig. 155). The flask is about one-fourth filled with water, and about the same volume of concentrated nitric acid is added. A rapid evolution of gas occurs. The gas should be collected as soon as possible because when the reaction has been in progress some time, particularly if the temperature rises during the reaction, nitrous oxide and nitrogen may appear with the nitric oxide.

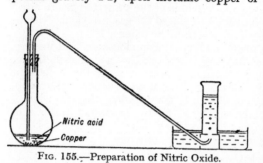

Fig. 155.—Preparation of Nitric Oxide.

At first the flask is seen to be filled with brown fumes due to the formation of nitrogen peroxide by combination of nitric oxide with the oxygen of the air originally in the flask (see below). Nitrogen peroxide is readily soluble in water, whereas nitric oxide is not ; hence the flask soon " clears " and nitric oxide can be collected over water.

A purer gas is obtained by reducing potassium nitrate with ferrous sulphate, acidified with sulphuric acid, or ferrous chloride acidified with hydrochloric acid :

$$KNO_3 + 3FeCl_2 + 4HCl = 3FeCl_3 + KCl + 2H_2O + NO.$$

According to L. W. Winkler (1889), highly pure nitric oxide can be made by dropping a 50 per cent. solution of sulphuric acid upon a mixed solution of potassium iodide and sodium nitrite :

$$2KI + 2NaNO_2 + 2H_2SO_4 = K_2SO_4 + Na_2SO_4 + I_2 + 2H_2O + 2NO.$$

A very pure nitric oxide also results from the action of mercury on cold concentrated sulphuric acid to which nitric acid or a nitrate has been added :

$$2HNO_3 + 3H_2SO_4 + 6Hg = 3Hg_2SO_4 + 4H_2O + 2NO.$$

The gas obtained from copper and nitric acid may be purified by absorption in cold, saturated ferrous sulphate solution (see below) from which it is recovered almost pure on warming. It still contains traces of nitrous oxide on account of the solubility of the latter. The specially pure nitric oxide used by Gray in determining the atomic weight of nitrogen (p. 387) was purified in the following way. The crude gas was first passed through a large volume of water ; then through concentrated aqueous potassium hydroxide solution ; and dried by means of solid potassium hydroxide and phosphorus pentoxide. It was finally liquefied and fractionated twice in special apparatus, to remove nitrous oxide and nitrogen respectively.

Properties

Nitric oxide is a colourless gas, a little heavier than air. When brought in contact with air, it immediately combines with the oxygen, forming brownish-red fumes of nitrogen peroxide. Hence it is not possible to describe the smell and the physiological action of this gas. If the two gases—nitric oxide and oxygen—be thoroughly dried, no combination occurs (compare p. 284).

Nitric oxide is difficult to liquefy. At $-93.5°$, a pressure of 71.2 atmospheres is required to liquefy the gas. The liquid is colourless if air be excluded, otherwise the liquid may be tinted green or blue. The liquid boils at $-151°$, and the white solid melts at $-161°$.

Nitric oxide is very sparingly soluble in water at ordinary temperatures. It dissolves in a solution of ferrous sulphate. A "compound" of nitric oxide and ferrous sulphate appears to be formed. This imparts a dark brown colour to the solution. The "compound" is decomposed when heated to about $60°$, and nitric oxide is evolved. It is not very clear if a true compound is formed between the nitric oxide and the ferrous salt, because its composition seems to vary with the temperature of formation. Thus at $8°$ the composition corresponds with $3FeSO_4.2NO$; from $8°$ to $25°$, about $2FeSO_4.NO$; and above $25°$, $5FeSO_4.NO$. With these facts, and the law of constant composition before us, we cannot very well say that ferrous sulphate forms a true chemical compound with nitric oxide. Ferrous, cobaltous, nickelous, manganous, and chromous chlorides give similar results.

Nitric oxide, however, is one of the most stable of the nitrogen oxides. Decomposition does not begin when it is heated until the temperature reaches $500°$ and is still slight at $900°$. The reaction

$$2NO \rightleftharpoons O_2 + N_2$$

is reversible, as indicated on page 406, so that at still higher temperatures, say, $3000°$, over 4 per cent. of the mixture of nitrogen and oxygen will combine to form nitric oxide.

Nitric oxide is not combustible, and it only supports combustion under special conditions, that is when the temperature is raised sufficiently to decompose the gas. The flame of feebly burning phosphorus is extinguished, but if the phosphorus be burning vigorously, combustion is continued in the gas. Burning sulphur is extinguished, but if the sulphur be boiling when it is plunged in the gas combustion sometimes continues.

Nitric oxide is converted by oxidizing agents into nitrogen peroxide, or nitrates. The gas, as noticed previously, combines directly with oxygen in the cold forming nitrogen peroxide :

$$2NO + O_2 = 2NO_2$$

Other oxidizing agents usually form nitric acid, e.g.,

$$2NO + 3I_2 + 4H_2O = 2HNO_3 + 6HI$$

$$10NO + 6KMnO_4 + 9H_2SO_4 =$$
$$10HNO_3 + 3K_2SO_4 + 6MnSO_4 + 4H_2O.$$

Nitric oxide reacts, however, with many reducing agents and is usually converted into nitrogen, but occasionally ammonia or nitrous oxide is formed. Thus, sparking with hydrogen gives nitrogen :

$$2NO + 2H_2 = N_2 + 2H_2O,$$

but if a mixture of nitric oxide and hydrogen be passed over a catalyst (such as platinum black), ammonia results :

$$2NO + 5H_2 = 2NH_3 + 2H_2O,$$

while with sulphurous acid (or sulphur dioxide in presence of water) nitrous oxide is produced,

$$2NO + H_2SO_3 = N_2O + H_2SO_4.$$

Nitric oxide readily forms addition products, e.g., with oxygen, and metallic salts as above, and also with the halogens :

$$2NO + Cl_2 = 2NOCl$$
$$\text{nitrosyl}$$
$$\text{chloride}$$

Formula

The formula of nitric oxide is determined as in the case of nitrous oxide by means of an apparatus such as that indi-cated in Fig. 156. A spiral of iron or nickel wire is strongly heated electrically in a measured volume of nitric oxide, thereby reducing it to nitrogen. After cooling, the nitrogen is found to occupy half the volume of the nitric oxide from which it is formed. That is, nitric oxide contains *half* its own volume of nitrogen and hence, by Avogadro's hypothesis, its molecular formula is NO_x where x has still to be found. The vapour density of nitric oxide has been found to be $15(H_2 = 1)$, hence its molecular weight is 30, $x = 1$ and the molecular formula is NO.

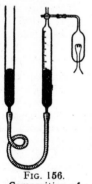

Fig. 156.
Composition of
Nitric Oxide.

This formula cannot be made to fit in with the accepted valencies of nitrogen and oxygen.

If nitrogen be a triad, and oxygen a dyad, there must be one free valency in the graphic formula, $-N = O$. The facts are, if oxygen is bivalent, nitrogen behaves as if it were also bivalent. The ready way in which nitric oxide unites with other elements by direct addition rather lends itself to the idea that nitric oxide has a free valency. Various electronic formulae have been proposed such as

$$\overset{\text{xx}}{\underset{\text{xx}}{N}} \overset{\text{\bf ..}}{\underset{\text{\bf ..}}{O}} \cdot$$

but none is completely satisfactory, and it is difficult to understand why it does not form double molecules (N_2O_2).

§ 30 Nitrogen Trioxide, N_2O_3

When a mixture of nitric oxide and nitrogen peroxide is passed through a tube cooled to about $-30°$, a more or less impure form of nitrogen trioxide—N_2O_3—condenses to a bluish liquid. As soon as the temperature rises, the liquid dissociates, nitric oxide escapes, and leaves a residual yellow liquid of nitrogen peroxide. The melting-point curve of mixtures of nitric oxide and nitrogen peroxide indicates the formation of a compound N_2O_3 melting at about $-102°$.

The trioxide is also produced by the direct union of solid nitrogen peroxide with nitric oxide ; and by the action of oxygen on liquid nitric oxide ; and as a green flocculent powder, resembling chromic hydroxide, when a series of electric discharges are passed through liquid air. The trioxide, not the peroxide, appears to be formed when nitric oxide unites with oxygen at temperatures below $-100°$.

A gas containing a considerable proportion of nitrogen trioxide can be obtained by the action of arsenic trioxide on 60 per cent. nitric acid ; the nitrogen trioxide can be condensed out of the mixture by cooling.

The composition of nitrogen trioxide has been established by passing the products of its decomposition over heated copper, and weighing the copper oxide and the nitrogen.

Nitrogen trioxide derives some interest and importance from the fact that, theoretically, it is the anhydride of nitrous acid. When dissolved in water it gives a mixture of nitric and nitrous acids, but with alkali it combines to give only the nitrite.

According to H. B. Baker (1907), if the liquid be thoroughly dried, it vaporizes without dissociation, forming a gas which has a vapour density never below 38 ($H_2 = 1$), but generally much above that number which corresponds to the formula N_2O_3. If this be confirmed, it is the only direct evidence we have of the existence of the gaseous nitrogen trioxide. The freezing-point method of determining the molecular weight in acetic acid furnished W. Ramsay (1888) with numbers between 80·9 and 92·7—theory for N_2O_3 requires 76·02. Hence the liquid is partly polymerized. B. M. Jones (1914) concluded that the dry liquid consists mainly of N_4O_6 molecules, which on vaporisation give N_2O_3, $NO_2 + NO$ in equal volumes. Many reactions formerly said to yield the trioxide really give a mixture of nitric oxide and nitrogen peroxide.

§ 31 Nitrogen Peroxide, Nitrogen Tetroxide,* $NO_2 \rightleftharpoons N_2O_4$

History

As indicated in discussing nitric oxide, R. Boyle (1671) knew that nitric oxide formed brown fumes in air, and these brown fumes are mentioned in alchemical writings as *the blood of the salamander.* Since nitrogen peroxide is always formed during the preparation of nitric acid, nitrogen peroxide must have been recognized as a gas whenever nitric acid was made. J. L. Gay-Lussac (1816) first made its composition clear.

Preparation

Nitrogen peroxide results when nitric oxide and oxygen are mixed :

$$2NO + O_2 = 2NO_2,$$

but this is an interesting mode of formation rather than a practicable method of preparation. It also results from the action of concentrated nitric acid on copper :

$$Cu + 4HNO_3 = Cu(NO_3)_2 + 2NO_2 + 2H_2O.$$

It can be prepared conveniently in small quantities by heating the nitrate of a heavy metal, lead nitrate being the one most usually employed :

$$2Pb(NO_3)_2 = 2PbO + 4NO_2 + O_2.$$

It is then separated from the oxygen formed at the same time by passing the mixed gases through a U-tube immersed in a freezing mixture (Fig. 157). The nitrogen peroxide condenses to a yellow liquid, while the oxygen escapes.

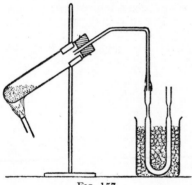

It is also often prepared by the action of arsenic trioxide on ordinary concentrated nitric acid (Sp.Gr. 1·42). When these two substances are warmed together, the nitric acid is reduced. As the reaction proceeds the concentration of the nitric acid diminishes, and consequently the nature of the reduction product changes. As a result a mixture of oxides of nitrogen, containing a considerable proportion of nitrogen peroxide is formed. The gases, as before, are led through a U-tube immersed in a freezing mixture. When evolution of gas has ceased, a current of air or

Fig. 157.
Preparation of Nitrogen Peroxide.

* Nitrogen peroxide is the name commonly applied to the gas obtained at ordinary temperatures, and which is, as explained below, a mixture of two molecular species, NO_2 and N_2O_4, in equilibrium. A more satisfactory nomenclature would be to call NO_2 *nitrogen peroxide*, and N_2O_4 *nitrogen tetroxide*.

oxygen is passed through the liquid until it becomes yellowish-brown to remove or oxidize any nitrogen trioxide present.

Properties

Nitrogen peroxide is a brown gas, the colour of which deepens on heating, due to the larger proportion of NO_2 molecules present at higher temperatures. It has a strong and pungent odour and an acid taste and is very poisonous. When cooled it readily condenses to a yellow liquid (b.p. 26°) and finally freezes to a colourless solid, m.p. −9.3°.

The action of heat on nitrogen peroxide is of interest. On heating the liquid from about the melting point, as the temperature of the liquid rises, it begins to acquire a pale greenish-yellow tint, which becomes deeper and deeper, until at 10°, the liquid is distinctly yellow; at 15°, orange; and at 21.3° the liquid boils and forms a reddish-brown vapour. The colour of the vapour becomes deeper and deeper until, at 40°, it is dark chocolate-brown, and almost opaque; at 140° the vapour is almost black. On cooling the vapour, the same changes occur in the reverse order.

The vapour density of the gas at ordinary temperatures is intermediate between the values corresponding to the formulae NO_2 and N_2O_4 respectively, as seen from the following table.

TABLE XXIX.—VAPOUR DENSITY OF NITROGEN PEROXIDE.

Temperature.	Vapour Density (Hydrogen = 1).	Percentage of NO_2 molecules.
26.7°	38.3	20.0
60.2°	34.5	50.0
100.1°	24.15	79.2
135.0°	23.1	99.0
140°	23.0	100.0

The figures in the last column are obtained as follows :

Let x = fraction of the total volume present as NO_2 molecules. Then $1-x$ = the fraction present as N_2O_4 molecules. Hence the vapour density of the gas

$$= \frac{46x + (1-x)\,92}{2}$$

Whence $x = \dfrac{46 - (\text{Vap. Dens.})}{23}$

Taking, for example, the case where the Vapour Density is 38.3 (i.e., at 26.7°), we have :

$$x = \frac{46 - 38.3}{23}$$

$$= 0.333, \text{ i.e., } 33.3 \text{ per cent. by volume of } NO_2.$$

In these circumstances 1 volume of gas contains 0·333 vols. of NO_2 molecules and 0·667 volumes of N_2O_4 molecules. Each molecule of the latter weighs twice as much as the former, so that the total weight of the gas is 0·333 + 2 × 0·667 units

= 1·667 units when there is 0·333 unit of NO_2 molecules present. Hence there will be

$$\frac{0·333}{1·667} = 0·20 \text{ units}$$

of NO_2 by weight or 20 per cent. of the total weight of the gas will be NO_2 molecules.

At about 500°, an appreciable number of the dark brown molecules of NO_2 begin to dissociate into a colourless mixture of nitric oxide and oxygen :

$$2NO_2 = 2NO + O_2$$

(cf. p. 406). The action of heat on nitrogen peroxide may therefore be represented by the equations :

About 20°	Between 140° and 300°	Above 500°
N_2O_4 $\rightleftharpoons$	$2NO_2$ $\rightleftharpoons$	$2NO+O_2$
Yellow	Dark brown.	Colourless.

Nitrogen peroxide is not combustible, and it extinguishes the flame of a taper. Phosphorus, sulphur, and carbon, if burning vigorously, may continue burning in the gas, but only when the temperature of combustion is sufficiently high to decompose the gas. Nitrogen peroxide is an energetic oxidizing agent. Phosphorus, carbon, potassium, mercury, copper, etc., when heated in the gas, are oxidized, while the gas is decomposed. The gas liberates iodine from potassium iodide ; and it reduces permanganates, forming nitric acid. Nitrous oxide, indeed, is the only gaseous nitrogen oxide which does not decolorize aqueous solutions of potassium permanganate. Nitrogen peroxide resembles ozone and hydrogen peroxide in some of its reactions.

Nitrogen peroxide is decomposed by water. At low temperatures, a mixture of nitric and nitrous acids is formed,

$$2NO_2 + H_2O = HNO_2 + HNO_3,$$

for which reason it is called " a mixed anhydride." The solution of mixed acids is unstable, unless very dilute, the nitrous acid decomposing thus :

$$3HNO_2 = HNO_3 + 2NO + H_2O.$$

This reaction is an important step in the process for the synthesis of nitric acid from the air (p. 406).

When water is treated with an excess of nitrogen peroxide, the solution passes through a series of colour changes—blue, green, orange. This is due to the gradual solution of the nitrogen peroxide in the nitric acid formed as just indicated. If sufficient water be present, the solution finally becomes colourless.

Nitrogen peroxide dissolves in concentrated sulphuric acid forming **nitrosyl hydrogen sulphate,** formerly known as **nitro-sulphuric acid** and nitric acid ;

$$H_2SO_4 + 2NO_2 = NO.HSO_4 + HNO_3.$$

Composition and Formula

When nitrogen peroxide is decomposed with copper, or nickel, as in the similar investigation of nitric oxide (p. 418) the results indicate a percentage composition corresponding to the empirical formula, NO_2. Vapour density measurements, as shown above, point to an equilibrium mixture of NO_2 and N_2O_4. It is thought that NO_2 is best represented by $O=N \rightarrow O$ and that N_2O_4 should be formulated

$$\begin{matrix} O \\ O \end{matrix} \!\!\gtrless\!\! N\!-\!N \!\!\lessgtr\!\! \begin{matrix} O \\ O \end{matrix}.$$

§ 32 Nitrogen Pentoxide

Nitrogen pentoxide is obtained by adding to pure, well-cooled nitric acid contained in a distilling flask twice its weight of phosphorus pentoxide. The temperature is raised to 60-70° and the nitrogen pentoxide distilled in a current of ozonized oxygen, into a series of well-cooled wash-bottles.

$$4HNO_3 + P_4O_{10} = 2N_2O_5 + 4HPO_3.$$

Nitrogen pentoxide also results from the action of ozone on nitrogen peroxide, and from that of chlorine on dry silver nitrate :

$$4AgNO_3 + 2Cl_2 = 4AgCl + 2N_2O_5 + O_2.$$

Properties

Nitrogen peroxide is obtained as above in the form of white crystals. Its melting point is given as 30°, and above its melting point it decomposes ; when rapidly heated it explodes.

$$2N_2O_5 \rightleftharpoons 2N_2O_4 + O_2.$$

It reacts with water, producing nitric acid, and hence it may be regarded as nitric anhydride :

$$N_2O_5 + H_2O = 2HNO_3.$$

Composition

Analysis, by means of copper, indicates the empirical formula N_2O_5. The vapour density has not been determined and the molecular weight, and hence the molecular formula are not known.

§ 33 Other Oxides of Nitrogen

When nitric oxide is passed through liquid air, or liquid oxygen, a green solid is formed which has been assumed to be **nitrogen hexoxide**, NO_3 or N_2O_6. It has also been obtained by the action of a silent discharge on a mixture of nitrogen peroxide and oxygen.

More recently (1925) it has been suggested that this green solid is N_3O_4, but the nature of this substance is still uncertain.

Before dismissing the nitrogen oxides it will be found instructive to draw up a table of their comparable properties.

TABLE XXX.—PROPERTIES OF THE NITROGEN OXIDES.

	Nitrous oxide.	Nitric oxide.	Nitrogen trioxide.	Nitrogen peroxide.	Nitrogen pentoxide.
Formula . .	N_2O	NO	N_2O_3	N_2O_4	N_2O_5
Atomic ratio N : O	2 : 1	2 : 2	2 : 3	2 : 4	2 : 5
State of aggregation	Gas	Gas	Gas	Liquid	Solid
Colour of gas	Colourless	Colourless	Reddish brown	Depends on temperature	White
Melting point .	— 102·4°	— 161°	— 102°	— 9·3°	c. 30°
Boiling point .	— 89·5°	— 151°	—	+ 21·3°	c. 47°
Vapour density (H_2 = 1) . .	22	14·94	Decomposes	Varies with temperature	—
Corresponding acid	HNO	None	HNO_2	None	HNO_3

§ 34 Nitrosyl Chloride, NOCl

Nitrosyl chloride results from the slow union of nitric oxide and chlorine at ordinary temperatures. The reaction is considerably accelerated by the presence of charcoal.

$$2NO + Cl_2 = 2NOCl$$

It can also be obtained by the action of phosphorus pentachloride on potassium nitrite :

$$PCl_5 + KNO_2 = KCl + POCl_3 + NOCl.$$

It is also formed from aqua regia (p. 503).

Nitrosyl chloride is an orange-yellow gas which condenses at — 5·5° to an orange-coloured liquid ; it freezes at —65° to lemon crystals. It is decomposed by water into nitrous and hydrochloric acids.

$$NOCl + H_2O = HNO_2 + HCl.$$

It has no action on gold and platinum, but attacks mercury, forming mercurous chloride and nitric oxide ; it also forms double compounds like $SnCl_4.NOCl$; $FeCl_3.NOCl$, etc.

CHAPTER XXI

THE ATMOSPHERE

I conceive the confused mass of vapour, air, and exhalations which we call the atmosphere, to be nothing else but the particles of all sorts of bodies of which the earth consists, separated from one another and kept at a distance by repulsive forces.—ISAAC NEWTON (1717).

§ 1 General

FROM very early times the air was regarded as an element, though it is open to question whether the conception of an element was then the same as ours in the chemical sense (cf. p. 5). The presence of water vapour was also recognized very early, but it was not thought of as an essential part of the atmosphere.

Mayow (1674) was probably the first to produce reliable evidence for the composite nature of the atmosphere. He showed that a mouse confined in a bell-jar over water causes a diminution in the volume of the air, and also that the same result occurs when combustible substances are burned under similar conditions. He also showed that the residue of gas after these experiments is unfit both for breathing and for combustion. The presence of carbon dioxide in the air was established by Black in 1755, who called it *fixed air*.

The real nature of the atmosphere remained obscure until the time of Lavoisier, chiefly owing to then prevailing phlogiston theory (see Ch. I, p. 9). According to this theory, combustion was attended by the escape of phlogiston, a calx remaining. The original substance could often be regenerated by heating these calces with a substance rich in phlogiston (e.g., copper calx and carbon give the metal again). That the air played some part in this process was indicated by experiments such as those of Mayow, but this was explained by assuming that something had to be present to take up the escaping phlogiston, and that air which would no longer support combustion was " saturated with phlogiston."

As was pointed out in Chapter I, this theory, although erroneous, played an important part in the development of chemistry, but naturally, so long as it held the field, the elemental nature of the air was not seriously questioned.

The true nature of air and the correct theory of combustion were due to the work of Lavoisier, who directed attention to the increase in weight of substances after burning, and interpreted correctly Priestley's discovery of oxygen.

§ 2. Lavoisier's Experiments on the Composition of Air

Antoine Laurent Lavoisier (1774) extended experiments which had been described by Rey in 1630 with more decisive results. Lavoisier heated tin along with air in a *closed* vessel. The vessel containing the air and tin did not increase in weight, although part of the air was

 absorbed. When the flask was opened, air rushed in, and the increase in the weight of the vessel was found to be equal to the increase in weight which the tin alone had suffered. Hence, Lavoisier concluded with Rey, that the increase in the weight of the tin was due solely to an absorption of the air in which the calcination had occurred. There was not sufficient air in the flask to "saturate" all the tin, and yet some air always remained as a residue. Hence, Lavoisier concluded further that **only part of the air can combine with the metal during the calcination;** he also found that *the increase in the weight of the tin during calcination is equal to the decrease in the weight of the air*. Hence, it seems as if air contains at least two con-

FIG. 158.—Lavoisier's Experiment on the Composition of Air.   stituents, only one of which is absorbed by the heated metal.

Lavoisier continued this important work with mercury instead of tin. The mercury was confined in a retort with an S-shaped neck which dipped under a bell-jar in a trough of mercury, as illustrated in Fig. 158. The air in the retort was in communication with the air in the bell-jar. The level of the mercury in the bell-jar was adjusted at a convenient level, and its position " very carefully marked with a strip of gummed paper." By means of a charcoal furnace, the mercury in the retort was heated—not quite to its boiling point. Lavoisier said : " Nothing of note occurred during the first day. The second day I saw little red particles* swimming over the surface of the mercury, and these increased in number and volume during four or five days ; they then stopped increasing and remained in the same condition. At the expiration of twelve days, seeing that the calcination of the mercury made no further progress, I put the fire out." After making allowance for variations of temperature and pressure, Lavoisier noticed that the volume of air in contact with the mercury was about 50 cubic " inches," and after the experiment, between 42 and 43 cubic " inches." About one-sixth of the volume of air in the apparatus was absorbed by the mercury.† The air which remained in the retort was not absorbed by the hot mercury ; it extinguished the flame of a burning candle immersed in the gas ; and a mouse was quickly suffocated when placed in the gas. Hence, Lavoisier called the gas **azote**,

---

* The calx or oxide of mercury is red. It is now called " red oxide of mercury," or " mercuric oxide."

† More recent experiments show that one-fifth is nearer the mark.

" from the ἀ privative of the Greeks, and ζωή, life." In France the gas is still " azote," though in Britain it is called " nitrogen," and in Germany " Stickstoff," that is, " suffocating stuff."

About this time, Lavoisier heard of Priestley's discovery of oxygen (which Priestley called *dephlogisticated air*) and at once perceived its significance in the light of his own experiments.

He collected the red powder formed by heating mercury in the retort, Fig. 158, and by reheating it in a suitable retort, Lavoisier obtained between seven and eight cubic " inches " of a gas which had obviously been previously removed from the air by the hot mercury. When a burning candle was immersed in the gas, the candle burnt with " blinding brilliancy," as Lavoisier expressed it ; a smouldering splinter of wood burst into flame when plunged in the gas ; and the gas did not suffocate a mouse like azote. Lavoisier first called this gas *vital air*, and afterwards *oxygen*. The latter term is its present-day designation. In this manner, Lavoisier proved that **atmospheric air is made up of two gases—oxygen and nitrogen—of different and even opposite natures, the oxygen alone combines with the metal during calcination.**

Assuming that this interpretation of the experiments is correct, Lavoisier inferred that by mixing azote and oxygen in the right proportions, it ought to be possible to reproduce atmospheric air. This Lavoisier did, and the mixture was found to behave with respect to " combustion, respiration, and the calcination of metals similar in every respect to atmospheric air."

In addition to these constituents and the carbon dioxide recognized by Black, in 1777, Carl Wilhelm Scheele inferred that air also contains a little ammonia, because a bottle of hydrochloric acid, when exposed to the air, becomes covered with a deposit of sal-ammoniac (ammonium chloride).

The main constituents of the atmosphere were thus recognized to be, oxygen, nitrogen, carbon dioxide and water vapour, with possible traces of ammonia. In addition to these, it is now known that all manner of other substances occur in traces, e.g., hydrogen, hydro-carbons, hydrogen peroxide, carbon dioxide, sulphur compounds, organic matter, suspended solids, chlorides, ozone, water vapour, argon, helium, krypton, neon, xenon, etc. The five gases last-named are sometimes called the " noble gases " or the " inert gases " of the atmosphere, and they are generally included with the " atmospheric nitrogen " (but see Ch. XXIV). **Dust** is also common in air. Thus the outside air in London contains from 80,000 to 116,000 particles per c.c., whilst inside a room as many as two millions may be present. Over the Pacific Ocean from 280 to 2200 per c.c. have been counted. **Micro-organisms** of various kinds abound in the lower strata of the atmosphere. These cause putrefaction, fermentation, and pathological phenomena. When filtered through asbestos or cotton-wool, air is freed from dust particles, and when a beam of light is passed through dust-free air, it will no longer reveal a multitude of motes constantly in motion. The space is optically empty.

§ 3 The Constituents of the Atmosphere

Oxygen and Nitrogen

Some of the early workers believed that the proportion of oxygen and nitrogen in air varied with respect to time and place, as well as the state of the weather ; but the analyses of Cavendish, Macarty, Sir H. Davy, and C. L. Berthollet rendered it highly probable that only a minute difference is to be found in the proportions of these two elements with air collected in different localities, and this is confirmed by analyses conducted more rigorously with all the refinements known to chemists.

The following analyses are quoted to illustrate the percentage amount of oxygen in air :—

Locality.	Minimum.	Maximum.	Mean.	Number of analyses.	Analyst.
Scotch Hills .	20·80	21·18	20·97	34	R. A. Smith
Paris . .	20·913	20·999	20·96	100	V. Regnault
Dresden . .	20·88	20·97	20·93	46	W. Hempel
Cleveland, Ohio	20·90	20·95	20·93	45	E. W. Morley

Hence, after making due allowance for differences in the methods of analysis by different men, it is clear that **the relative proportions of nitrogen and oxygen in the air collected near sea-level are almost, but not quite, constant.**

Carbon Dioxide

Similar remarks apply to the amount of carbon dioxide. This is rather higher in towns than in the open country ; but diffusion of air by winds, etc., prevents an excessive accumulation in any part— excluding, of course, badly ventilated rooms. Thus, J. Reiset (1882) found 3·027 volumes of carbon dioxide per 10,000 volumes of air in Paris ; and near Dieppe, 2·942 volumes. These numbers may be regarded as normal. The air over the Antarctic ocean contains about 2·05 parts of carbon dioxide per 10,000 parts of air. This is rather less than has been noted elsewhere. The proportion of carbon dioxide in air at high altitudes is less than near sea-level. In towns, during a fog, seven or eight volumes may accumulate ; and in badly ventilated rooms, ten times the normal amount of carbon dioxide may be present. The other constituents—excluding moisture—are usually regarded as impurities. The constituents of normal or average air occur in the following proportions :—

TABLE XXXI.—AVERAGE COMPOSITION OF ATMOSPHERIC AIR.

Per cent. of	By weight.	By volume.
Nitrogen	75·51	78·03
Oxygen . . .	23·15	20·99
Inert gases . .	1·30	0·95
Carbon dioxide . . .	0·04	0·03

Ozone, Hydrogen Peroxide, and Nitrogen Oxides

The ozone and hydrogen peroxide are probably formed by electrical discharges in the atmosphere as indicated previously. The same remark applies to the oxides of nitrogen. Free nitric acid has been reported in the atmosphere of tropical regions, but generally, the nitric acid is combined with ammonia. According to A. Levy (1889), about 3 lbs. of ammoniacal nitrogen, and 1 lb. of nitric acid is returned to the earth per acre per annum with the rain. In rural districts the soil is said to receive between 4 and 6 lbs. of combined nitrogen per acre per annum from the rain.

Ammonia

The ammonia in the atmosphere is largely a product of organic decomposition, and it is returned to the earth by rain in the form of ammonium nitrate, and sometimes as ammonium sulphate or chloride.

Hydrogen and Hydrocarbons

A. Gautier (1901) found that the air of Paris contains per 100 litres —19·4 c.c. of free hydrogen, 12·1 c.c. of methane, 1·7 c.c. of benzene and related hydrocarbons, and 0·2 carbon monoxide with other hydrocarbons. Gautier's estimate is probably rather high. H. Henriet (1904) found 2 to 6 grams of formaldehyde per 100 cubic metres of air. The presence of hydrocarbons explains the oleaginous character of the deposits which form on roofs, leaves of trees, etc., in towns.

Sulphur Compounds

A. Ladureau (1883) reported 1·8 c.c. of sulphur dioxide per cubic metre in the air of Lille. Sulphur compounds are present in small quantities as hydrogen sulphide, sulphur dioxide, and sulphuric acid in the air of towns. According to R. Warrington (1887), about 17¼ lbs. of sulphur trioxide is annually " poured " upon each acre of land at Rothamsted. G. H. Bailey (1892) reported a maximum of 0·0267 gram of sulphur expressed as sulphur trioxide per 100 cu. ft. of air near the surface of the ground in Manchester.

Chlorine Compounds

Rain near the sea brings a certain amo   of chlorine derived from the sea water. The proportion of salt in the air is greatest near the sea, and diminishes rapidly farther away from the coast. E. Kinch (1900) found, as an average of twenty-six years' observations at Cirencester, that 36·1 lbs. of sodium chloride per acre were brought to the earth with the rain. The amount of " wind-borne " sea salt is greatest when the wind blows from the sea. Free hydrochloric acid derived from manufacturing operations is sometimes found in the air of towns.

Moisture

The average amount of moisture, aqueous vapour, in air is rather less than 1 per cent. by volume ; it may reach 4 per cent. in humid climes. The actual amount of aqueous vapour air can carry before it is saturated depends upon the temperature. The higher the temperature, the greater the amount of moisture air can carry. Air seldom contains less than 75 per cent. of the possible amount it is capable of holding ; but much depends on the local conditions—e.g., in the Libyan desert it contains but 9 per cent. of the possible amount.

§4 Is Air a Mixture or a Compound ?

It is not quite clear to what extent the compound nature of air was seriously believed in, but there seems no reason to doubt that for a period after Lavoisier the possibility was at least seriously considered. Consequently, it is of some importance to consider the arguments which are now held to demonstrate conclusively that air is a mixture.

These arguments may be summarized as follows :—

(i) Although the proportions of nitrogen and oxygen show remarkably little variation, variations do in fact occur which lie outside the range of experimental error.

(ii) The characteristic properties of air are those which would be expected for a mixture, in the known proportions, of oxygen and nitrogen, being a mean between those of the constituents. In general, it is known that the physical properties of compounds bear little, if any, resemblance to those of their constituents.

(iii) No heat, no change in volume, or any other sign of chemical change is observed when air is made artificially by mixing oxygen and nitrogen together in the right proportions.

(iv) The constituents of air can be separated by mechanical means : e.g., solution in water (p. 162) ; by diffusion (p. 25) ; by allowing liquid air to vaporize, when the nitrogen distils off before the oxygen (p. 40) ; and J. Dewar has shown that when solidified air is exposed to a magnetic field the oxygen is sucked out of it towards the magnet's poles " so that solid air appears to be a magma of nitrogen and oxygen " separable by a magnet.

(v) The formula of air, if a compound, would be about $N_{15}O_4$, or possibly N_4O. In either case the vapour density of such a gas would be many times that found for air.

Not one of these five reasons is in itself conclusive, but all, taken together, form a long chain of circumstantial evidence which lead to the verdict : Air is a mechanical mixture of nitrogen, oxygen, etc.

§ 5 The Analysis of Air

The gravimetric analysis of air is effected by the method used for preparing nitrogen from the air (p. 384). It was done in this way by J. B. A. Dumas and J. Boussingault (1841) in an apparatus similar in principle to that illustrated in Fig. 159 where a modern furnace is

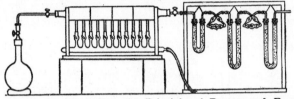

FIG. 159.—Diagram illustrating the Principle of Dumas and Boussingault's Method for the Gravimetric Analysis of Air.

shown in place of the old charcoal furnace, and the number of drying tubes has been reduced. A large globe was evacuated, closed, and weighed in that condition. This globe was connected as indicated in Fig. 159, with a tube containing metallic copper also evacuated, closed, and weighed. The copper tube was connected with a series of bulbs, and tubes containing concentrated sulphuric acid to remove moisture and ammonia from the air ; and with potassium hydroxide to remove carbon dioxide—only a few of the tubes used by Dumas and Boussingault are shown in the diagram. There may be a witness tube to show that the air which passes into the hot tube is free from carbon dioxide and moisture. The tube containing the copper was heated red hot, and air allowed to enter slowly by gradually opening the stopcocks. The air on its way to the glass globe was deprived of all but the nitrogen (atmospheric). When the globe was full, the apparatus was cooled, and the globe and copper tube weighed. The increase in weight gave the amount of nitrogen in the globe. The tube was also weighed. Its increase in weight represented the weight of oxygen which was associated, as air, with the nitrogen in the glass globe ; the tube also contained some nitrogen. The tube was therefore exhausted and weighed again. The difference between the second and third weighings of the tube was taken to represent the nitrogen which must be added to the nitrogen in the globe.

As a mean of six determinations they obtained 23·005 grams of oxygen per 76·995 grams of nitrogen. The gravimetric process is very exact. The error need not exceed 0·00001th part of the whole ; but the experiment requires special apparatus, and occupies much .time. Volumetric processes are not so exact, but they occupy far less time.

Volumetric Processes

In the volumetric processes, the oxygen is usually removed from the nitrogen by absorbents—alkaline sulphides, phosphorus, alkaline pyrogallol, hot copper, nitric oxide, and water, etc.—which do not disengage any gas, and have no action on the residual nitrogen.

One method much used in the early days was Priestley's nitric oxide method. In this, nitric oxide was carefully added to a measured volume of air confined over potassium hydroxide solution. The nitric oxide combines with the oxygen of the air to form nitrogen peroxide which dissolves in the alkali (p. 420). The residual gas is nitrogen and can be measured, while the contraction represents the oxygen originally present.

A satisfactory method is by means of Hempel's apparatus (Fig. 160). The pipette is filled with alkaline pyrogallol (pyrogallic acid dissolved in sodium hydroxide solution) and arranged so that the liquid stands at the level of a mark, A, on the stem. A suitable volume of air is confined over mercury in the burette, B, and, after levelling, its volume pressure and temperature are read and recorded. The tap, T, is opened, the levelling tube, L, is raised, and so the air passes into the bulb of the pipette and is allowed to remain there for some time. The levelling tube is then lowered, and the residual gas drawn back into the burette, leaving the pyrogallol solution at A as before. The volume is then read off and the process repeated until no further change in volume occurs.

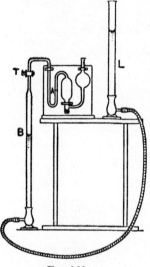

Fig. 160.—
Hempel's Apparatus.

Another method makes use of Jolly's apparatus, which is similar to that used for the determination of the volumetric composition of nitric oxide, illustrated diagrammatically in Fig. 156, p. 418.

A glass globe is provided with an arrangement whereby a piece of copper wire can be heated red hot while inside. The globe is fitted with a three-way stopcock which connects it with the gas-measuring tubes or with the outside air. The gas-measuring tubes are filled with mercury, and the globe is then connected with the air-pump, and exhausted. A jacket containing iced water is placed around the globe. Air dried by passage through wash-bottles containing sulphuric acid is allowed to enter the globe, which is then put in communication with the gas-measuring tube, and the level of the mercury in the levelling tube is read when the mercury in the other tube reaches the mark just below the stopcock. Call this position p_0. The cold jacket is then removed, and the copper wire heated. When the oxygen is all converted into copper oxide, again place the cold jacket in position, and alter the levelling tube until the mercury reaches its former position,

The height of the mercury in the levelling tube is again read. Call this position p. The pressure of the mercury has been reduced to $p_o - p$ owing to the removal of oxygen. Consequently, since the temperature is the same in both cases, the percentage x of oxygen in the air must be $p_o : p_o - p = 100 : x$.

CHAPTER XXII

SULPHUR

§1 History and Occurrence

THE element sulphur has been known from the beginning of history. It is mentioned in the Bible and in Homer. It was placed among the elements by Lavoisier, but for some time previously it was regarded as "the principle of fire." The name is derived from the Sanscrit *sulveri* through the Latin *sulphurium*.

Among the Greeks and Romans sulphur was used for fumigation, and the vapours of burning sulphur were employed for bleaching clothes. It was used medicinally in the Middle Ages, and is a constituent of gunpowder which was introduced into Europe about the beginning of the fourteenth century (p. 579).

Occurrence

Sulphur is widely distributed in nature both as free and as combined sulphur. Deposits of free or native sulphur occur in volcanic districts, Iceland, Italy (Romagna, Marken, Tuscany, Campania, and Calabria), Sicily (chiefly on the southern watershed), Greece (Island of Milo), Russia, Austria, Hungary (Radoboj and Swoscowice), South Frances Spain, Asia Minor, Persia, India, Palestine, Algeria, Morocco, Japan (Sulphur Island), New Zealand (White Island, etc.), United State,

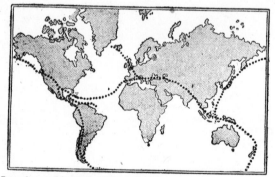

FIG. 161.—Imaginary Lines showing Chief Regions of Volcanic Phenomena and Occurrence of Sulphur Deposits.

(Louisiana, Oregon, Utah, Nevada, Wyoming, Texas), Mexico (Popocatapetl), Chile, Peru, etc. These districts are on or not far from the dotted line, Fig. 161, which indicates the distribution of regions of volcanic activity.

There are two main types of native sulphur : (1) *The solfataric type** found in lava fissures and in extinct volcanic vents (Japan, Mexico). Deposits of this type are forming at the present day in volcanic districts from the mutual action of hydrogen sulphide and sulphur dioxide which occur among volcanic gases.

(2) *The gypsum type.* The sulphur appears to have been liberated from gypsum by the reducing action of bituminous matters found associated with the gypsum. Calcium sulphide is probably formed from the sulphate ; and this, by the action of water and carbon dioxide, forms sulphur, calcium carbonate and hydrogen sulphide. The Sicilian deposits and perhaps the more important sulphur deposits are of this type.

Many important metallic ores are **sulphides,** that is, compounds of sulphur with one or more metals. Thus, *galena* (lead sulphide, PbS) ; *zinc blende* (zinc sulphide, ZnS) ; *cinnabar* (mercury sulphide, HgS) ; *stibnite* (antimony sulphide, Sb_2S_3) ; *copper pyrites* (Cu_2S, Fe_2S_3) ; *iron pyrites* (iron sulphide, FeS_2) etc. Some important **sulphates** also contain sulphur, e.g., *gypsum* (calcium sulphate, $CaSO_4$) ; *heavy spar* (barium sulphate, $BaSO_4$), etc.

Sulphur occurs in many organic compounds, and in animal and vegetable products : onions, garlic, mustard, horseradish, hair, many oils, eggs, proteids, etc. Hydrogen sulphide and its oxidation products are found in the water of many sulphur springs.

§ 2 Manufacture of Sulphur

The " sulphur earth " in Sicily occurs in lodes mixed with limestone and gypsum. The amount of sulphur in " workable " ore varies from 8 up to about 25 per cent. The sulphur is separated by heating the ore, and allowing the molten sulphur to flow away from the mineral impurities. This is effected by stacking the ore on the sloping floor of a circular kiln without a permanent roof. The kilns are called *calcaroni.*

A portion of the sulphur acts as fuel, and melts the remainder which collects at the lowest point of the inclined bottom of the kiln.

About one-third of the sulphur is lost in the calcarone system of extraction. It is, however, cheaper to use the sulphur as a fuel than to import coal. The loss, however, is excessive even then, and in consequence, the calcarone method is being displaced by more economical kilns—Gill's kilns—which are worked in sets.

Fig. 162 shows a plan of a set of such kilns which consist of a series of chambers with domed roofs. The air is admitted into a chamber which contains hot " rock " from which the sulphur has melted out, and thus the air is warmed. It then passes to a chamber containing

---

* Solfatara—a volcanic vent or volcanic area which gives off sulphurous vapours, steam, etc., and which probably represents the last stages of volcanic activity.

hot raw sulphur, some of which burns and so melts out the remaining sulphur in the contents of this chamber. The hot gases then pass

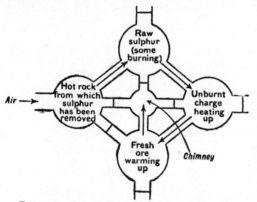

through several other kilns charged with raw sulphur rock which is thus heated up, and so loss of heat is reduced to a minimum.

The American sulphur deposits, which are now the principal source of the world's sulphur, occur at a depth of some 500 feet underneath strata of clay, limestone, etc. Their extraction by ordinary mining is impossible, both on account of the waterlogged nature of the strata concerned, and of the considerable quantities of hydrogen sulphide and sulphur dioxide which occur and make it impossible for men to work in shafts sunk into the sulphur-bearing stratum.

FIG. 162.—Gill Regenerative Sulphur Furnace.

The problem was solved by Frasch who developed the method now in use, consisting of forcing superheated water into the sulphur bed thus melting the sulphur, and forcing it through a tube to the surface in the form of a kind of foam produced by a stream of air bubbles. The method is illustrated in Fig. 163.

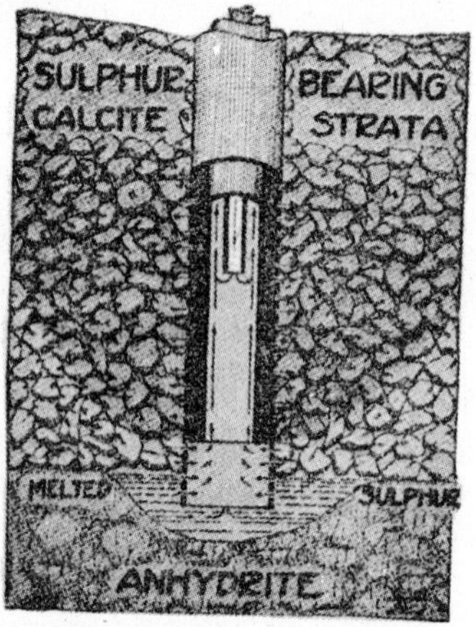

The crude sulphur from the kilns—also called " brimstone " —is graded and put on the market. It may be afterwards purified by distillation from a retort which opens into a large brickwork chamber. The sulphur vapour condenses in the chamber. The

FIG. 163.—Frasch Pump—lower end.
(Courtesy of Texas Gulf Sulphur Co.)

first lot of vapour sublimes as a light powder on the walls. The powder is called *flowers of sulphur*. As the condensing chamber gets hot, the condensed sulphur melts and collects on the floor as a liquid which is drawn off from time to time and cast into large wooden moulds —*rock sulphur*; or in cylindrical wooden moulds—*roll sulphur*.

The sulphur produced by the Frasch process is of a high degree of purity and for most purposes does not need any further purification.

Sulphur is now being produced from the sulphur dioxide contained in the waste gases of metallurgical operations by reducing the dioxide back to sulphur. The reduction is effected by means of carbon in the form of coke, the reaction :

$$SO_2 + C = CO_2 + S$$

taking place rapidly at 1100°, at which temperature it is practically complete. The reaction is exothermic and does not require any external heat for its maintenance, when once the required temperature has been reached.

This process is likely to become increasingly important, since the turning to waste of the sulphur dioxide from metallurgical operations has been largely due to the fact that, on account of the difficulty of transporting it, sulphuric acid must, as a rule, be produced near to where it is to be used. Now that the sulphur of the waste gases can be recovered as such, this obstacle is removed.

Considerable quantities of sulphur can be recovered from the alkali-waste, or tank-waste, of the Leblanc soda process (p. 558), an operation which formerly was of the greatest importance, but the decline in the production of soda by this method has reduced its significance. The alkali waste contains considerable amounts of calcium sulphide and is treated by the **Chance-Claus Process.** The alkali waste is made into a paste with water and then treated with carbon dioxide, evolved from lime-kilns (p. 626), in a series of tall iron cylinders. The carbon dioxide first neutralizes any free lime present and converts the insoluble calcium sulphide into soluble hydrosulphide :

$$2CaS + CO_2 + H_2O = CaCO_3 + Ca(HS)_2.$$

When carbon dioxide has been passing for some time, it becomes in excess when the following action occurs :

$$Ca(HS)_2 + CO_2 + H_2O = CaCO_3 + 2H_2S.$$

The hydrogen sulphide evolved is collected in a gas-holder, and after mixing with the theoretical amount of air, is burnt in a Claus kiln. This consists of a cylindrical furnace filled with layers of iron oxide, where the hydrogen sulphide, in presence of the iron oxide, which acts as a catalyst, burns to sulphur and water. The heat evolved in this reaction keeps the process going once it is started.

$$2H_2S + O_2 = 2H_2O + 2S.$$

§ 3 Allotropy of Sulphur

Sulphur is known in a large number of allotropic forms, and the exact relationship existing between them is complex, and in some cases uncertain.

Three clearly-defined and distinct solid forms are known, viz.,

Octahedral, rhombic or α-sulphur.

Monoclinic, prismatic or β-sulphur.

Amorphous, or δ-sulphur.

In addition to these there have been described :

Plastic sulphur, which is a super-cooled liquid, or possibly a " gel " and so probably a mixture of forms and not a true allotrope ;

Nacreous sulphur, a crystalline form (see below), the exact nature of which seems still doubtful ;

Colloidal sulphur, milk of sulphur, etc., which are composed of amorphous sulphur in various states of division.

Numerous crystalline modifications, e.g., tabular sulphur, Friedel's triclinic sulphur, Engel's rhombohedral sulphur, the precise nature of which in relation to the established forms is dubious.

Liquid sulphur also is now believed to consist of at least two forms, viz.,

λ-sulphur, predominating at lower temperatures ;

and μ-sulphur, predominating at higher temperatures,

while a third liquid form Sπ has also been postulated.

The vapour, too, appears to contain both S_8 and S_2 molecules in equilibrium and possibly S_4 also.

§ 4 Sulphur and the Phase Rule

The diagram (Fig. 164) illustrates the phase rule relationships of the principal forms of sulphur.

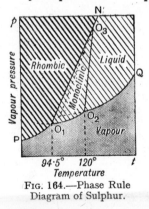

FIG. 164.—Phase Rule Diagram of Sulphur.

By plotting the vapour pressure curve of rhombic sulphur at different temperatures, we get the curve PO_1 ; similarly, by plotting the vapour pressure curve of monoclinic sulphur, we get the curve O_1O_2 ; this variety of sulphur melts at 120° ; however, by continuing the vapour pressure curve of the liquid, we get O_2Q. By plotting the transition points of rhombic sulphur at different pressures, we get the curve O_1O_3 ; and by plotting the melting point of monoclinic sulphur at different pressures, we get the curve O_2O_3. Monoclinic sulphur cannot exist at pressures higher than that represented by the point $_3O$. The continuation of the curve O_3N represents the effect of pressure on the melting point of rhombic sulphur.

The phase rule enables us to form a very clear idea of the conditions of equilibrium. When the condition of the system is represented by a pressure and temperature corresponding with one of the three triple points—O_1, O_2, O_3—the system is invariant, and any change in temperature or pressure will lead to the suppression of one of the three phases ; points on one of the curves PO_1, O_1O_2, O_2Q, etc.—represent univariant systems ; and points in one of the three regions—PQ, QO_2N, NO_1P—represent bivariant systems. It will of course be obvious that we are here dealing with the one component sulphur, and four possible phases—sulphur vapour and liquid, and rhombic and monoclinic sulphur—since an allotropic modification of an element is a true phase.

The metastable states, or states of false equilibrium, are interesting. The QO_2 and the PO_1 curves meet at a point corresponding with the temperature 114·5°. This is the melting point of rhombic sulphur. If the transformation of rhombic to monoclinic were very fast, it would be impossible to state the melting point of rhombic sulphur, because it would pass into the monoclinic form before a determination could be made.

The upward left-to-right slopes of the curves O_1O_3 and O_2O_3 correspond with the fact that the melting point of sulphur is raised by increasing pressures.

§ 5 Rhombic, Octahedral or α-Sulphur

The considerations discussed in the previous section indicate that it is this form which is stable at temperatures below 94·5°, so that this is the form in which sulphur is normally found. To get well-defined crystals, it is necessary to allow sulphur to crystallize from solution in, say, carbon disulphide. A sample of sulphur is ground up and shaken with carbon disulphide, filtered and the solution allowed to evaporate slowly in a crystallizing dish. Octahedral crystals slowly grow, and form transparent, amber-coloured crystals similar to those shown in Fig. 165. When heated to 94·5° they become opaque, owing to the formation of monoclinic sulphur. They have a density of 2·06 and when rapidly heated melt at 114·5°, since the transformation into monoclinic sulphur is so slow.

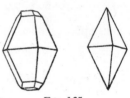

FIG. 165.
Rhombic Sulphur Crystals.

§ 6 Monoclinic, Prismatic or β-Sulphur

This form of sulphur, as can be seen from Fig. 164, is stable between 94·5° and 120° ; and is thus obtained by crystallization within this range of temperature. This is often done by melting sulphur and allowing it to solidify.

If, say, 500 grams of sulphur be melted in a clay or porcelain crucible and the mass allowed to stand until a surface crust is formed, beautiful long prismatic needle-like crystals of waxy yellow sulphur will be found to have grown on the walls of the crucible, and on the underside of the crust when the crust is pierced, and the still fluid sulphur is poured away.

Well-formed crystals of monoclinic sulphur can also be obtained by making a saturated solution of sulphur in boiling toluene (in which it is, however, only sparingly soluble) and allowing it to cool slowly.

The crystalline form of monoclinic sulphur is shown in Fig. 166.

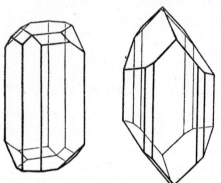

FIG. 166.—Monoclinic Sulphur.

Crystals made by either of the above methods, if allowed to stand for about a day, become light yellow, opaque, brittle, and crumble into powder at the slightest touch. The grains of powder are small rhombic crystals of α-sulphur. If the rhombic crystals be kept a few hours between 108° and 112°, they also become opaque and change to a friable crumbling mass of monoclinic prisms. The two reactions are thus reversible. Experiment shows that the monoclinic prisms are unstable below 94·5°, and slowly pass into the rhombic variety. The change is accelerated by wetting the monoclinic prisms with carbon disulphide, or by bringing the monoclinic sulphur in contact with a crystal of the rhombic variety. Conversely, the rhombic sulphur is unstable above 94·5°, and slowly passes into the monoclinic variety. The change is symbolized :

$$S_{rhombic} \overset{94·5°}{\rightleftharpoons} S_{monoclinic}; \text{ or } \alpha\text{-}S \overset{94·5°}{\rightleftharpoons} \beta\text{-}S.$$

Hence, 94·5° is a transition temperature.

§ 7 Plastic or γ-Sulphur

If sulphur, heated to about 350°, be poured into cold water, a tough elastic material resembling india-rubber—called **plastic sulphur**—is obtained. Plastic sulphur is also obtained by distilling ordinary sulphur from a glass retort, and allowing the liquid sulphur, condensing in the neck of the retort, to flow into cold water. A long continuous thread of plastic sulphur is thus obtained.

The specific gravity of plastic sulphur is about 1·95, nearly the same as monoclinic sulphur ; but unlike the crystalline varieties, this form of sulphur can be moulded between the fingers, and drawn into somewhat elastic threads. Plastic sulphur is probably a super-cooled liquid which has been hurried past its crystallizing temperature and cooled so low that it has formed a viscid mass. If cooled slowly, virtually the whole of the product is crystalline and soluble in carbon disulphide. Plastic sulphur slowly crystallizes on standing. The change is accelerated by rubbing the mass, and is fairly rapid if the mass be heated to about 100°.

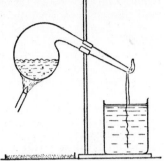

Plastic sulphur is now thought by some to be a gel (cf. p. 249), in support of which it is pointed out that liquid sulphur shows the Tyndall effect (p. 246) which suggests that it may be a sol, which on solidification might well give a gel (compare Ch. XVI).

Fig. 167.
Preparation of Plastic Sulphur.

§ 8 Amorphous or Colloidal Sulphur—δ-Sulphur

Sulphur exists in at least two different colloidal or amorphous conditions in which no signs of crystallization can be detected under the microscope.

If hydrogen sulphide be passed into a saturated aqueous solution of sulphur dioxide at 0° ; or if an alcoholic solution of sulphur be poured into water ; or if a saturated solution of sodium thiosulphate be mixed with twice its volume of concentrated hydrochloric acid, and cooled to 10°, **colloidal, soluble, or δ-sulphur** is formed.

It is a clear, yellow solution containing very minute particles of sulphur in colloidal solution.

On the other hand, by acidifying sodium pentasulphide solution, amorphous sulphur is precipitated in a form soluble in carbon disulphide. This is known as **milk of sulphur,** and is almost white ; on standing at ordinary temperatures, it tends to revert to rhombic sulphur, but some years may be necessary for this to be complete.

§ 9 Liquid Sulphur

Sulphur is pale yellow at ordinary temperatures, and almost colourless at − 50°, and at 100° it is intense yellow. If a piece of ordinary rhombic sulphur be gradually heated in a test-tube, the sulphur crackles and falls to pieces as indicated above. As the temperature rises, the sulphur melts to a clear, limpid, amber-coloured liquid between 113° and 115° ; the colour darkens, and the liquid loses its mobility, until, at about 160°, the mass is almost black, and so viscid that the test-tube can be turned upside down without pouring out the sulphur. The viscosity reaches a maximum at about 180°, for as the temperature rises still higher, the dark colour remains, but the mass becomes more and more mobile until at 444·7° the liquid begins to boil, forming a reddish-orange vapour.   If the liquid be allowed to cool, the sulphur undergoes the same changes, but in the reverse order, and very slowly. If the vapour be heated still higher, it becomes deep red at 500°, and straw-yellow at about 650°.

If α-sulphur be melted at a low temperature, and the pale yellow liquid be suddenly chilled, the crystalline product is almost completely soluble in carbon disulphide ; while, as indicated above, § 7, if the dark brown liquid which is obtained when sulphur is heated to a higher temperature be similarly treated, it forms an amorphous mass almost all insoluble in carbon disulphide.   It is therefore inferred that molten sulphur contains a mixture of two varieties of sulphur—the pale yellow mobile fluid, called λ-**sulphur,** and the dark brown viscid fluid called μ-**sulphur.**   When λ-sulphur solidifies it forms crystalline α- or β-sulphur soluble in carbon disulphide ; and when μ-sulphur solidifies it forms an amorphous plastic mass insoluble in carbon disulphide. The proportion of sulphur soluble and insoluble in carbon disulphide in solidified sulphur depends on the relative amounts of S_λ and S_μ present in the fluid at the time of solidification.   The proportion of the two varieties in any sample of sulphur can be determined by extraction with carbon disulphide, making a small allowance for the very slight solubility of the so-called "insoluble" variety.   Experiment shows that there is a definite relation between the relative amounts of the two varieties present in a system in equilibrium at a definite tempera- ture.   The proportion of μ-sulphur appears to increase with rising temperatures, and for each temperature there appears to be a definite equilibrium constant corresponding with the reversible reaction : $S_\lambda \rightleftharpoons S_\mu$.   The system takes some time to attain equilibrium under any given conditions.   The presence of air, sulphur dioxide, or hydrogen chloride retards, while ammonia, nitrogen, carbon dioxide, iodine, or hydrogen sulphide accelerates the speed of the change.

§ 10   Properties of Sulphur

Sulphur is a yellow solid (sometimes appearing white if in a fine state of sub-division).   It is tasteless and odourless, and is without physiological action on human beings, though its vapour is poisonous to lowly organized forms of life such as fungi, etc.   It is a poor con- ductor of heat, and a non-conductor of electricity.

It is insoluble in water, sparingly soluble in alcohol and ether, and readily soluble in carbon disulphide.

Sulphur burns in air with a blue flame, and sulphur dioxide mixed with small quantities of sulphur trioxide is formed (see pp. 451-458). It burns very brilliantly in oxygen.   When mixed intimately with substances rich in oxygen, an explosive mixture may be formed (e.g., gunpowder, p. 579)..

Sulphur combines directly with carbon, phosphorus, arsenic and with most metals, when the elements are heated together, the corresponding sulphides being formed. The halogens also react with sulphur, forming a variety of sulphur halides (see pp. 480-482).

Sulphur does not react with water, in the cold, but when steam is passed through boiling sulphur, a little hydrogen sulphide and sulphur dioxide are formed :

$$3S + 2H_2O = 2H_2S + SO_2.$$

Nor does it react with acids which are not able to oxidize it. It is readily oxidized by concentrated sulphuric acid or nitric acid, the products being sulphur dioxide and sulphuric acid respectively (pp. 480-482).

It appears to dissolve in caustic alkali solutions, since it reacts with them forming sulphides and thiosulphates, e.g.,

$$4S + 6KOH = K_2S_2O_3 + 2K_2S + 3H_2O$$

$$K_2S + 4S = K_2S_5$$

Similar derivatives of calcium are also readily obtained (p. 632).

§ 11 Uses of Sulphur

Sulphur is used in making sulphur dioxide for bleaching straw, wool, etc. ; for the manufacture of sulphites for bleaching wood fibres, etc. ; and for the manufacture of sulphuric acid. It is also used in making carbon disulphide. Purified sulphur is used in making gunpowder, matches, vermilion, ultramarine, for vulcanizing rubber, in the manufacture of enamels and of metal-glass cements ($S + Fe + NH_4Cl$). Flowers of sulphur is used as an insecticide, and sulphur is also employed in medicine and in industrial organic chemistry (e.g., for the production of dyes).

§ 12 Atomic Weight and Molecular Weight of Sulphur

The vapour densities of very many volatile compounds of sulphur show that these always contain, approximately, at least 32 grams of sulphur per gram-molecule, and hence that the atomic weight of sulphur is round about 32.

Exact values have been determined by several methods, e.g., by heating silver in a tube through which sulphur vapour was passed (Dumas, Stas) ; by reducing silver sulphide in a current of hydrogen ; by converting silver sulphide into silver chloride ; by converting sodium carbonate into sodium sulphate (Richards) ; and by converting silver sulphate into the chloride by passing hydrogen chloride over it in a hot tube (Richards).

The most accurate values are probably those of Richards and his collaborators, who obtained in 1915 the value 32·054. The accepted value at present (1940) is 32·06.

Values for the atomic weight of sulphur have also been obtained from the densities of sulphur dioxide and hydrogen sulphide.

Molecular Weight

At about 500° the vapour density of sulphur is nearly 96 ($H_2 = 1$). This corresponds with the molecule S_6. By raising the temperature or reducing the pressure, the vapour density gradually diminishes until, at 1000°, it reaches 32, corresponding with the molecule S_2. The vapour density then remains constant up to about 1700°; at about 2000° it corresponds to a partial dissociation of 50 per cent. of the S_2 molecules into S atoms.

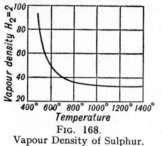

FIG. 168.
Vapour Density of Sulphur.

It may be that at temperatures intermediate between 1000° and 500°, some or all of the molecules S_8, S_6, S_4, and S_2 are present, but the curve is steadily depressed with rising temperatures, and it shows no signs of flattening such as might be expected if any particular type of molecule predominated throughout any particular range of temperature. The freezing and boiling-point methods for the determination of molecular weights show that the molecule of sulphur in a solution of carbon disulphide, bromoform, etc., exists as S_8.

§ 13 Hydrogen Sulphide or Sulphuretted Hydrogen, H_2S
History and Occurrence

Historical

Several references to hydrogen sulphide appear in the writings of the alchemists of the Middle Ages, where it is described under the general term " sulphurous vapour," and their directions for the preparation of this product show that they referred to some fetid solutions of the polysulphides, which probably contained this gas. This liquid excited the attention of the alchemists, for it gave all kinds of colorations with solutions of the different metals ; with vinegar, it gave a precipitate of sulphur and at the same time gave off a gas which blackened silver and some other metals. K. W. Scheele (1777) was the first to investigate the compound systematically.

Occurrence

Hydrogen sulphide occurs in several mineral waters, in the exhalations from volcanic vents, etc. It is also formed during the putrefaction of animal and vegetable matters containing sulphur, and by the action of an aqueous solution of carbonic acid on sulphides which in turn are often formed by the reduction of sulphates by organic matter. Several bacteria during the putrefaction of organic matter produce hydrogen sulphide—the sulphur being derived from protein matters and from the reduction of sulphates—stimulated possibly by sunlight. This is said to occur at the mouths of rivers on the West Coast of

Africa—e.g., the Congo river, which brings organic matter into intimate contact with sulphides. Hence, the atmosphere may be contaminated by hydrogen sulphide derived from these three causes. Hydrogen sulphide is readily oxidized and it cannot therefore persist very long in the atmosphere.

§ 14 Preparation of Hydrogen Sulphide

Hydrogen sulphide is formed in small quantities when a stream of hydrogen is passed through boiling sulphur :

$$H_2 + S \rightleftharpoons H_2S,$$

but the method is not of practical importance. It is also formed when hydrogen is passed over certain heated sulphides, e.g.,

$$Sb_2S_3 + 3H_2 = 2Sb + 3H_2S,$$

and by the action of sulphur upon organic matter when warmed.

The gas is best prepared by the action of dilute hydrochloric or sulphuric acid upon ferrous sulphide, FeS, which, in turn, is made by fusing iron and sulphur together (p. 817). The reactions are symbolized :

$$FeS + H_2SO_4 = FeSO_4 + H_2S \uparrow \; ; \; FeS + 2HCl = FeCl_2 + H_2S \uparrow$$

Hydrochloric acid is generally preferred to sulphuric acid because the resulting ferrous chloride—$FeCl_2$—is not so liable to crystallize as ferrous sulphate—$FeSO_4$. For small quantities, a similar apparatus to that employed for the preparation of hydrogen is used (Fig. 89); and for larger quantities, Kipp's apparatus may be used (Fig. 90). Comparatively large quantities of the gas are required intermittently in a testing laboratory, and scores of different forms of apparatus have been invented for the purpose. The gas is generally washed by passing it through a wash-bottle containing water.

Artificial ferrous sulphide, prepared as indicated above, generally contains a little free iron, and hence some hydrogen will be mixed with the gas. For ordinary purposes, this does not matter. The gas may also contain traces of hydrocarbons, etc., derived from the action of the acids on the impurities in the iron. A more pure gas is made by heating antimony sulphide with concentrated hydrochloric acid, and washing the gas in water :

$$Sb_2S_3 + 6HCl = 2SbCl_3 + 3H_2S \uparrow$$

Aluminium sulphide with water also gives hydrogen sulphide.

Very pure hydrogen sulphide is best obtained by solidifying the crude gas with liquid air. The main impurity is hydrogen, which is not condensed under these conditions and so can be pumped off. The residual solid is allowed to warm up slowly, and after the first portions have been allowed to escape, pure hydrogen sulphide is obtained.

Hydrogen sulphide is rather soluble in cold water and so cannot be collected over it, but like nitrous oxide it can be collected over warm water. It can be dried by means of dehydrated alumina or phosphorus pentoxide, but sulphuric acid must not be used because it is reduced

$$H_2S + H_2SO_4 = SO_2 + S + 2H_2O.$$

Calcium chloride is often used for drying the gas in spite of the fact that slight decomposition occurs :

$$CaCl_2 + H_2S = CaS + 2HCl$$
$$CaCl_2 + 2H_2S = Ca(HS)_2 + 2HCl$$

§ 15 Properties of Hydrogen Sulphide

Hydrogen sulphide is a colourless gas with an unpleasant smell like rotten eggs. It has a sickly taste resembling its smell. It is very poisonous, a proportion of 1 part in 1000 in air proving fatal, if breathed for any length of time. Very dilute chlorine is recommended as an antidote.

Hydrogen sulphide was liquefied by Faraday in 1823. It condenses to a colourless liquid at 10° under a pressure of 15 atmospheres. At ordinary pressures the liquid boils at $-59 \cdot 6°$ and freezes at $-82 \cdot 9°$.

Hydrogen sulphide is slightly heavier than air and is fairly soluble in cold water, which dissolves $4 \cdot 68$ times its volume at 0° and $2 \cdot 7$ volumes at 20°. The solution is called " hydrogen sulphide water " and has a slightly acid reaction. The solution decomposes slowly, depositing sulphur—particularly if exposed to light :

$$2H_2S + O_2 = 2H_2O + 2S.$$

Hydrogen sulphide burns in air with a bluish flame forming sulphur dioxide and water if excess of air be present ; or sulphur and water when there is insufficient air for complete combustion. Sulphur is thus deposited on a cold object placed in the flame :

$$2H_2S + 3O_2 = 2H_2O + 2SO_2$$
$$2H_2S + O_2 = 2H_2O + 2S.$$

A mixture of two volumes of hydrogen sulphide with three volumes of oxygen explodes violently when ignited. A lighted taper dipped into a jar of the gas is extinguished showing that it is a non-supporter of combustion.

Hydrogen sulphide is easily dissociated by passing it through a hot porcelain tube.

$$H_2S \rightleftharpoons H_2 + S.$$

The dissociation begins about 400°, and it is complete at about 1700°. It will be remembered that hydrogen sulphide may be formed by passing hydrogen through boiling sulphur. This means that the reaction belongs to the type of opposing reactions—discussed on p. 212. Hydrogen sulphide is also decomposed by passing electric sparks through the gas confined in a tube over mercury.

Hydrogen sulphide behaves as a reducing agent. Thus it reduces the halogens to halogen acid, e.g.,

$$H_2S + Br_2 = 2HBr + S.$$

(a reaction made use of for the preparation of hydrobromic and hydriodic acids, pp. 521-528) ferric salts to ferrous salts, dichromates to chromic salts, permanganates to manganous salts, sulphuric acid to sulphur dioxide, etc. Its reaction with sulphur dioxide may be noticed, taking place readily when jars of the moist gases are mixed:

$$SO_2 + 2H_2S = 2H_2O + 3S.$$

If the gases be well dried no reaction occurs (compare Ch. XVII).

Hydrogen sulphide behaves in some reactions as a weak acid, e.g., with heated metals, when the sulphide and hydrogen are formed:

$$Sn + H_2S = SnS + H_2,$$

or with alkalis, when hydrosulphides and sulphides are formed:

$$KOH + H_2S = KHS + H_2O$$
$$2KOH + H_2S = K_2S + 2H_2O.$$

§ 16 The Action of Hydrogen Sulphide on Metallic Salt Solutions

Hydrogen sulphide is an important reagent in qualitative analysis since its reactions with the different metallic salts enable the metals to be separated into groups as a preliminary to more detailed examination. Thus:—

I. Sulphides insoluble in dilute acids.
   (a) Soluble in alkaline sulphides—arsenic, antimony, stannic, gold, germanium, molybdenum, tellurium, tungsten, iridium, and platinum sulphides.
   (b) Insoluble in alkaline sulphides—mercury, silver, lead, copper, bismuth, cadmium, and stannous sulphides.

II. Sulphides soluble in dilute mineral acids, but insoluble in the presence of alkalis—iron, cobalt, nickel, manganese, and zinc sulphides.

III. Sulphides not precipitated by hydrogen sulphide—chromium, aluminium, magnesium, barium, strontium, calcium, potassium, and sodium. Chromium and aluminium are precipitated as hydroxides.

The method of classifying certain elements into groups—those which form soluble and those which form insoluble sulphides in hydrochloric acid—frequently conveys wrong ideas of the properties of the sulphides. The solubility of the sulphides depends upon the concentration of the acid. For instance, if hydrogen sulphide be passed into 5 c.c. of a solution of 2 grams of tartar emetic—potassium antimonyl tartrate—in 15 c.c. of hydrochloric acid (sp. gr. 1·175) and 85 c.c. of water, antimony sulphide will be precipitated, but not if 15 c.c. of hydrochloric acid had been employed without the water.

If a metallic sulphide, MS, be treated with hydrochloric acid, hydrogen sulphide and a metallic chloride will be formed :

$$MS + 2HCl = MCl_2 + H_2S.$$

Conversely, when a metallic chloride in aqueous solution is treated with hydrogen sulphide, the metallic sulphide and hydrochloric acid will be produced :

$$MCl_2 + H_2S = MS + 2HCl.$$

Hydrochloric acid thus accumulates in the solution as the action goes on. If any more sulphide be produced, after the hydrochloric acid has attained a certain limiting concentration, the excess of sulphide will be at once decomposed by the acid. There are then two simultaneous opposing reactions : (1) Formation of the metallic sulphide and hydrochloric acid ; and (2) formation of chloride and hydrogen sulphide. In illustration, take the case of lead chloride :

$$PbCl_2 + H_2S \rightleftharpoons PbS + 2HCl.$$

When equilibrium is established, the solution contains lead chloride, hydrogen sulphide, and hydrogen chloride. Using symbols in square brackets to represent the concentrations (gram-molecules per litre) of the respective compounds in the solution, it follows from the equilibrium law, that :

$$\frac{[PbCl_2] \times [H_2S]}{[HCl]^2} = \text{Constant.}$$

This shows that if the concentration of the acid be increased, and the concentration of the hydrogen sulphide be constant, the amount of lead chloride which remains in solutions (that is, escapes precipitation) will increase in order to keep the numerical value of the " constant " always the same. Conversely, if it be desired to keep the amount of lead chloride in the solution as low as possible, it is necessary to keep the concentration of the acid down to a minimum value. A certain amount of acid is usually required to keep other metals in solution ; zinc, for example.

The concentration of the hydrogen sulphide in the solution is practically constant (0·0073 gram-molecules per litre at 20°) when the gas is passing through the solution. If the concentration of the hydrogen sulphide were large and the concentration of the metallic chloride small, a very large excess of acid would be needed to prevent metal being. precipitated by the hydrogen sulphide. It will be observed, however, that the concentration of the hydrogen sulphide under ordinary circumstances is small. In consequence, a comparatively small amount of acid suffices to prevent the separation of sulphides of zinc, iron, nickel, cobalt, manganese.

Under ordinary conditions, the solubilities of the sulphides in hydrochloric acid, starting with the least soluble, are approximately in the order :

As, Hg, Cu, Sb, Bi, Sn(ic), Cd, Pb, Sn(ous), Zn, Fe, Ni, Co, Mn.

Elements wide apart in the list can be easily separated by hydrogen sulphide in acid solutions, but elements close together in the list require a very careful adjustment of the amount of acid in solution before satisfactory separations can be made. For instance, the separation of cadmium or lead from zinc by means of hydrogen sulphide is only satisfactory when the concentration of the acid is very carefully adjusted. If too much acid be present, cadmium or lead will be imperfectly precipitated ; while if too little acid be present, zinc will be precipitated with the cadmium or lead. Hence there is no sharp line of demarcation between metals precipitated and metals not precipitated by hydrogen sulphide from acid solutions. All depends upon the concentration of the acid. This is arbitrarily adjusted (e.g., by making the solution just acid to a suitable indicator such as methyl violet) so that antimony, arsenic, lead, bismuth, cadmium, copper, mercury, and tin are precipitated while the aluminium, iron, zinc, nickel, cobalt, and manganese salts will be found in the filtrate. Barium, strontium, calcium, and magnesium salts will also be found in the filtrate along with the alkalis, because the sulphides of these elements are attacked and decomposed by water and by acids. E.g.,

$$Ca_2S + 2H_2O \rightleftharpoons Ca(OH)_2 + Ca(SH)_2.$$

These facts may be explained by the application of the electrolytic dissociation theory.

No substance is *absolutely* insoluble, although it may be very sparingly soluble indeed. So with the "insoluble" sulphides with which this section is concerned. The very small quantity actually dissolved will ionize, and so there will be the equilibrium :

$$MS \rightleftharpoons MS \rightleftharpoons M^{\cdot\cdot} + S''$$
$$\text{solid} \quad \text{solution}$$

The presence of solid will keep the solution saturated, which means that the concentration of *dissolved* sulphide is kept constant. By the Law of Mass Action :

$$\frac{[M^{\cdot\cdot}][S'']}{[MS]} = \text{constant} = k \text{ (say)}$$

$[MS]$, as above, is also constant, so that

$$[M^{\cdot\cdot}][S''] = [MS] k = \text{constant}$$
$$= P \text{ (say)},$$

where P is the *solubility product* (p. 233) of the sulphide in question.

In order that the sulphide shall be precipitated, the product of the concentrations of the metallic ion and of the sulphide ion must exceed the solubility product. Now, suppose that a series of solutions containing 1 gram-mol. per litre of $M^{\cdot\cdot}$ ion (or any similar predetermined value) are saturated with hydrogen sulphide. Then precipitation will take place when :

$$1 \times [S''] = P.$$

In solution in water, hydrogen sulphide ionizes :

$$H_2S \rightleftharpoons 2H^{\cdot} + S''$$

and, since it is a very weak acid (p. 232), we may apply the Law of Mass Action to its ionization, whence

$$\frac{[H^{\cdot}]^2[S'']}{[H_2S]} = C.$$

When the solution is saturated with hydrogen sulphide $[H_2S]$ is kept constant. Hence :

$$[H^{\cdot}]^2[S''] = C[H_2S] = k' \text{ (say)}$$
$$\therefore [S''] = \frac{k'}{[H^{\cdot}]^2}.$$

That is to say, the concentration of sulphide ion varies inversely as the square of the hydrogen ion concentration.

The addition of acid to a solution of hydrogen sulphide will consequently reduce the concentration of sulphide ion very considerably ; so much so that for many sulphides the product $[M^{\cdot\cdot}][S''.]$ will be less than P, the solubility product. But some sulphides have a solubility product so low that it is exceeded even in this case. Some sulphides, on the contrary, have fairly high solubility products so that a considerable concentration of sulphide ion is necessary for their precipitation. The hydrogen ion concentration must consequently be low for this to occur, and if it be desired to precipitate these sulphides the solution must be made alkaline.

§ 17 Formula of Hydrogen Sulphide

If a known volume of hydrogen sulphide be heated with metallic tin in a tube over mercury, tin sulphide and free hydrogen equal to the original volume of hydrogen sulphide are formed ; similarly, hydrogen sulphide, when decomposed by electric sparks, suffers no change in volume. That is to say, hydrogen sulphide contains its own volume of hydrogen and hence, from Avogadro's hypothesis, it follows at once that one molecule of hydrogen sulphide contains one molecule —two atoms—of hydrogen, and that the formula of hydrogen sulphide is H_2S_n, where n has not been determined.

Its vapour density is 17, hence its molecular weight is 34 and molecular formula H_2S.

§ 18 Detection and Determination of Hydrogen Sulphide

Hydrogen sulphide is very easily detected by its action on solutions of soluble lead salts. Papers soaked in lead acetate solution turn first brown and then black on exposure to the gas, owing to the formation of lead sulphide.

It is determined by treatment with excess of a standard solution of iodine in potassium iodide (p. 526), making use of the reaction :

$$H_2S + I_2 = 2HI + S$$

and then, after a short period, determining the excess iodine by titration with sodium thiosulphate solution.

§ 19 Hydrogen Persulphide or Hydrogen Disulphide

If dilute hydrochloric acid be poured into a solution of sodium polysulphide, e.g., Na_2S_5, milk of sulphur is precipitated (p. 441) :

$$Na_2S_5 + 2HCl = 2NaCl + H_2S + 4S ;$$

but if the polysulphide be poured into the acid, little or no hydrogen sulphide is evolved, and a yellow oily liquid is obtained.

This was once considered to be a mixture of **hydrogen pentasulphide, H_2S_5**, with other hydrogen polysulphides. When the oil is distilled under reduced pressure, the fraction which is obtained at 69° under a pressure of 2 mm. of mercury is a pale yellow oil with a molecular weight, by the freezing-point method, corresponding with H_2S_3—**hydrogen trisulphide**. The fraction which distils at 74°-75°, under atmospheric pressure, has the composition H_2S_2. This is hydrogen disulphide or hydrogen persulphide. The persulphide dissolves in benzene, forming a clear solution. Hydrogen persulphide is a colourless oily liquid with a specific gravity 1·376. It has a pungent irritating smell, and decomposes gradually into hydrogen sulphide and sulphur. The decomposition is faster in presence of water, and particularly alkalis. Mere contact with glass, paper, dust, etc., induces rapid decomposition. Hydrogen persulphide burns with a blue flame. Like its analogue, hydrogen peroxide, it has oxidizing and reducing qualities.

Hydrogen trisulphide, H_2S_3, prepared as just described, resembles the persulphide in many of its properties, but its specific gravity is 1·496, and it solidifies between −52° and −54°. The three hydrogen sulphides—H_2S, H_2S_2, and H_2S_3—are all the hydrogen polysulphides whose individuality has been clearly demonstrated, although a whole ranging from H_2S_5 to H_2S_9 has been reported.

§ 20 Sulphur Dioxide, Sulphurous Anhydride, SO_2

History and Occurrence

The use of sulphur for disinfecting purposes has been known from very early times. It is referred to in Homer where Odysseus, after the slaughter of the suitors, and probably recognizing the need for a general cleansing, calls :

> Quickly, O Nurse, bring fire that I may burn
> Sulphur, the cure of ills.

J. Priestley (1770) prepared the gas by the action of hot concentrated sulphuric acid on mercury. Priestley called it sulphurous acid.

Sulphur dioxide is found among the fumes from volcanic vents ; in the springs of volcanic districts, and in the air of towns where it is derived from the sulphur compounds in coal.

It is also found in the effluent gases from many industrial operations, e.g., the roasting of zinc blende in the smelting of zinc (p. 641). The sulphur dioxide contained in such gases is being increasingly used for the manufacture of sulphuric acid, etc. (p. 461).

Preparation

Sulphur dioxide is formed when sulphur is burned in air :

$$S + O_2 = SO_2.$$

Between 6 and 8 per cent. of the sulphur is simultaneously oxidized to sulphur trioxide, SO_3. If the sulphur be burnt in oxygen gas between 2 and 3 per cent. burns to sulphur trioxide.* The nitrogen in the air seems to favour the production of sulphur trioxide, whereas moisture and carbon dioxide do not affect the result appreciably. The proportion of sulphur trioxide formed increases with the pressure. When sulphur is oxidized by a peroxide—e.g., manganese peroxide— sulphur dioxide is formed :

$$MnO_2 + 2S = MnS + SO_2.$$

Sulphur dioxide is also formed when the sulphides of some metals are roasted in air—e.g., iron or copper pyrites :

$$4FeS_2 + 11O_2 = 2Fe_2O_3 + 8SO_2.$$

This reaction is very commonly used for making the sulphur dioxide employed in the manufacture of sulphuric acid.

Prepared in this way from iron pyrites, the gas frequently contains arsenic, the presence of which, for many purposes, is highly injurious, and so has to be removed.

In the laboratory, the gas is generated, either by the action of moderately concentrated sulphuric acid on sodium sulphite or bi-sulphite, e.g.,

$$NaHSO_3 + H_2SO_4 = NaHSO_4 + H_2O + SO_2,$$

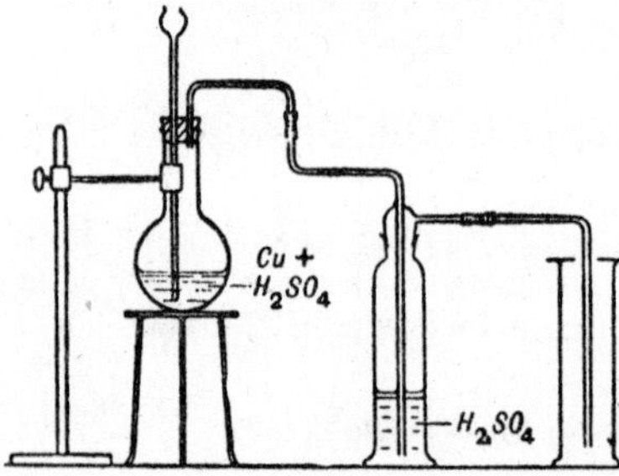

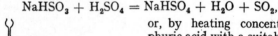

or, by heating concentrated sulphuric acid with a suitable reducing agent such as copper, mercury, sulphur, etc. Copper is usually used for this purpose.

The process is illustrated in Fig. 169. The flask is about one-third filled with copper turnings and sufficient concentrated sulphuric acid is added not quite to cover the copper. On heating, sulphur dioxide is evolved, and may be passed through wash-bottles containing concentrated sulphuric acid

Fig. 169.
Preparation of Sulphur Dioxide.

to dry it. It is collected by downward delivery as shown since it is soluble in water.

The reaction is commonly represented by the equation :

$$Cu + 2H_2SO_4 = CuSO_4 + 2H_2O + SO_2,$$

but it is certainly more complex than this. It is probable that the first action is the oxidation of the copper, with consequent reduction of the sulphuric acid to sulphur dioxide. The copper oxide then reacts with more sulphuric acid, forming the salt—copper sulphate— in the usual way.

* The presence of sulphur trioxide in the sulphur dioxide formed when sulphur burns in air accounts for the " foggy " appearance of the gas. This will be understood when the properties of the trioxide have been studied.

$$Cu + H_2SO_4 = CuO + H_2O + SO_2$$
$$CuO + H_2SO_4 = CuSO_4 + H_2O.$$

An alternative view is that hydrogen is first formed and then reduces excess of sulphuric acid :

$$Cu + H_2SO_4 = CuSO_4 + H_2$$
$$H_2 + H_2SO_4 = SO_2 + 2H_2O.$$

This seems less likely since metals like silver and mercury, which do not yield hydrogen with acids in any circumstances, reduce sulphuric acid to sulphur dioxide almost as readily as metals which do.

In addition to this degree of complexity, some side reaction occurs which results in the formation of cuprous sulphide, which causes the residue in the flask after the experiment to appear black. This may be formed by some such series of reactions as :

$$5Cu + H_2SO_4 = H_2O + Cu_2S + 3CuO$$
$$3CuO + 3H_2SO_4 = 3H_2O + 3CuSO_4$$

which, summarized, leads to the equation :

$$5Cu + 4H_2SO_4 = 4H_2O + Cu_2S + 3CuSO_4.$$

Industrially, sulphur dioxide is prepared by roasting iron pyrites, from waste gases of metallurgical operations and by burning sulphur in air.

§ 21 Properties of Sulphur Dioxide

Sulphur dioxide is a colourless gas with a smell characteristic of burning sulphur. Sulphur dioxide is an acute blood poison. Sulphur dioxide is also injurious to vegetation, and it is one of the " noxious vapours " complained about in manufacturing districts.

The gas is more than twice as heavy as air, and in consequence, it can be collected by downward delivery. It cannot be collected satisfactorily over water because it is easily soluble. One volume of water at $0°$ dissolves $79·8$ volumes of sulphur dioxide ; and at $20°$, $39·4$ volumes. The aqueous solution is strongly acid, and it has the general properties characteristic of acids.

The gas is easily liquefied. A pressure of $1·5$ atmospheres suffices for the condensation of the gas at $0°$; and at $-10°$ the gas liquefies under ordinary pressures. In order to liquefy it, it is therefore sufficient to dry thoroughly the gas obtained by the action of copper on sulphuric acid, and then lead the gas through a condensing tube immersed in a freezing mixture. The gas condenses to a clear, colourless, transparent, limpid liquid which boils at $-10°$ and solidifies at $-72·7°$ to a white snowlike mass. Liquid sulphur dioxide is sold commercially in thick glass " syphons," and where available, the " syphons " are used as a source of sulphur dioxide for laboratory work. By the evaporation of liquid sulphur dioxide a temperature approaching — 50° can be obtained. Hence like ammonia and carbon dioxide, sulphur dioxide is used as a refrigerating agent. Liquid sulphur dioxide is a good solvent for phosphorus, iodine, sulphur, resins, etc. The conductivity of these solutions is sometimes greater than that of aqueous solutions.

Sulphur dioxide is decomposed at high temperatures ; for example, by passage of electric sparks. It is appreciably dissociated at 1200°, sulphur trioxide (or, if moist, sulphuric acid) and sulphur being formed :

$$3SO_2 \rightleftharpoons S + 2SO_3.$$

It is also decomposed by light, for if a beam of light be sent through a long cylinder of the gas, at first, the gas appears to be clear and transparent, but in a few minutes the gas appears to decompose, for misty wavering striae appear, and gradually the whole tube appears to be filled with a fog, due to the decomposition of the sulphur dioxide. If left a short time in the dark, the gas becomes clear owing to the recombination of the sulphur and sulphur trioxide, or to condensation of the solid products on the walls of the apparatus.

Electrical discharge at low pressures appears to convert sulphur dioxide into sulphur monoxide (p. 476).

Sulphur dioxide combines reversibly with oxygen when heated, sulphur trioxide being formed (p. 458).

$$2SO_2 + O_2 \rightleftharpoons 2SO_3.$$

The reaction is only slow in the absence of a catalyst ; the most efficient is platinum (see below, p. 458).

Sulphur dioxide reacts with chlorine, bromine and fluorine, combining directly to form sulphuryl chloride, SO_2Cl_2, sulphuryl bromide, and sulphuryl fluoride, respectively (p. 480), particularly in the presence of camphor, which acts as a catalyst.

The corresponding fluorine and bromine compounds result similarly.

Sulphur dioxide is incombustible and a non-supporter of ordinary combustion. Some substances are able to burn in the gas by abstracting its oxygen. Ignited magnesium ribbon, for instance, continues to burn in the sulphur dioxide. Potassium, calcium, tin, lead, iron, arsenic, and antimony also burn when the finely-divided element is heated in an atmosphere of sulphur dioxide. The products of the reaction are oxides, sulphides, and occasionally free sulphur. Sulphur dioxide is decomposed by carbon at 1100° :

$$SO_2 + C = CO_2 + S.$$

Sulphur is deposited when hydrogen sulphide and sulphur dioxide are brought into contact, say, by placing a jar of sulphur dioxide and of hydrogen sulphide mouth to mouth. The gaseous exhalations from some volcanoes contain these two gases which, on mingling together, mutually decompose with the formation of sulphur (p. 447). This reaction does not occur if the gases are thoroughly dried.

Sulphur dioxide in the presence of moisture is a well-known reducing agent.   (See under sulphurous acid—below.)

§ 22 Uses of Sulphur Dioxide

Sulphur dioxide is used in the manufacture of sulphuric acid, as a refrigerating agent, as a solvent for extracting glue, gelatine, etc., for preserving meats, wines, etc.   It prevents the growth of certain moulds, kills certain disease germs, etc.   It is used in sugar manufacture, as a bleaching agent for straw, silk, wool, and goods too delicate for treatment with chlorine, in refrigerating machines, etc.

On account of its poisonous nature, it was formerly extensively used for fumigation purposes (sulphur candle, etc.), but its use for this purpose has of late years been discontinued in favour of formaldehyde.

Very large quantities are used in the preparation of calcium hydrogen sulphite for the manufacture of paper from wood pulp.

§ 23 Formula of Sulphur Dioxide

When sulphur burns in oxygen no change in volume occurs.   The apparatus shown in Fig. 124 (p. 354) can be used to show this.

A small piece of sulphur in a metal spoon is ignited in *dry* oxygen over *dry* mercury by means of a platinum wire which can be heated electrically.   The result shows that sulphur dioxide contains its own volume of oxygen, and hence, that the formula is S_nO_2, where n is still to be determined.   The vapour density is found to be close to $32(H_2 = 1)$ and hence $n = 1$ and the molecular formula is SO_2.

§ 24 Sulphurous Acid, H_2SO_3

As mentioned above, the aqueous solution of sulphur dioxide is markedly acidic and is believed to contain **sulphurous acid,** H_2SO_3. This acid cannot be isolated, but its presence is inferred from the following facts :—

(i) the solution of sulphur dioxide does not obey Henry's Law (p. 161), even approximately ;

(ii) the solution behaves in many ways like an acid ; witness its effect on indicators, and formation of salts (sulphites) with metals and basic oxides.

The solution smells strongly of sulphur dioxide, and the gas is expelled completely on boiling, hence it is probable that free sulphur dioxide is present in equilibrium with the sulphurous acid :

$$H_2SO_3 \rightleftharpoons SO_2 + H_2O$$

(compare carbonic acid, p. 356).

Moist sulphur dioxide and solutions of the gas are powerful reducing agents owing to the ease with which sulphurous acid is oxidized to sulphuric acid :

$$2H_2SO_3 + O_2 = 2H_2SO_4.$$

It reduces permanganates to manganous salts; chromates to chromic salts; ferric to ferrous salts, etc. The latter reaction is often used in analytical work for the reduction of iron previous to its determination by volumetric processes.

The bleaching effects of sulphurous acid are due to its reducing properties. Moistened red rose-leaves, or fabrics dyed with, say, "magenta" dye, when placed in the gas lose their colour. The sulphur dioxide appears to react with the colouring matter, forming sulphuric acid and hydrogen, and the nascent hydrogen bleaches by reducing the colouring agent. This idea is supported by the fact that the colour of many articles bleached by sulphur dioxide can be restored by exposing the article to oxidizing conditions.

Dry sulphur dioxide, like dry chlorine, does not bleach.

An aqueous solution of sulphur dioxide reduces chlorine, forming hydrochloric and sulphuric acids :

$$SO_2 + 2H_2O + Cl_2 = 2HCl + H_2SO_4.$$

Hence sulphurous acid is used as an " anti-chlor," that is, as an agent to remove the last traces of chlorine from articles bleached with chlorine.

Sulphur dioxide reduces iodine to hydrogen iodide in the presence of water.

On the other hand, concentrated solutions of hydrogen iodide are oxidized by sulphuric acid with liberation of iodine. The reaction is, in fact, a reversible one :

$$SO_2 + 2H_2O + I_2 \rightleftharpoons H_2SO_4 + 2HI$$

$$\text{or} \quad H_2SO_3 + H_2O + I_2 \rightleftharpoons H_2SO_4 + 2HI.$$

This reaction is important because the amount of sulphurous acid or of its salts in a given solution can be determined by adding a solution of iodine of known strength from a burette until the iodine solution is no longer decolorized. The amount of sulphur dioxide must not exceed 0·05 per cent. or the " back reaction " will appreciably affect the results.

Iodates are reduced to iodine by sulphurous acid, a reaction which can be used for the detection of sulphur dioxide :

$$2KIO_3 + 5H_2SO_3 = I_2 + 2KHSO_4 + 3H_2SO_4 + H_2O.$$

The constitution of sulphurous acid is a matter about which there has been much controversy. It is now believed that the sulphite ion is

$$\left[\begin{array}{c} O \\ \uparrow \\ O \leftarrow S \rightarrow O \end{array} \right]'' \quad \text{or written electronically}$$

$$\left[\begin{array}{c} :\ddot{O}: \\ \ddot{O} \times \underset{\times\times}{\overset{\times\times}{S}} \times O \end{array} \right]'' \quad \text{(compare Ch. IX).}$$

a structure which is in agreement with the readiness with which sulphites combine with an oxygen atom to form sulphates (above), or a sulphur atom to form thiosulphates (p. 475).

The structure to be assigned to the non-ionized acid is still in considerable doubt. Many possibilities have been suggested, but the most probable formula seems to be:

$$O \leftarrow S \begin{cases} OH \\ OH \end{cases}$$

which is supported by the formation of the acid from thionyl chloride (p. 479) and water, and explains satisfactorily most of the properties of the acid. At one period, two different sodium potassium sulphites were reported which, if confirmed, would have suggested either:

$$O \leftarrow S \begin{cases} O - OH \\ H \end{cases} \quad \text{or} \quad \begin{matrix} O \\ O \end{matrix} S \begin{cases} OH \\ H \end{cases}$$

as the formula, but this report cannot be confirmed. The existence of two series of organic " esters " seems to require a constitution for sulphurous acid based on one of these latter formulae, but the constitution of esters is sometimes misleading where the constitution of the parent acid is concerned. At present, therefore

$$O \leftarrow S \begin{cases} OH \\ OH \end{cases}$$

seems to be the most satisfactory formula for sulphurous acid.

§ 25 Sulphites

The salts of sulphurous acid are known as sulphites, and two series of these are known, viz., normal sulphites, and acid sulphites or bisulphites, thus indicating that the acid is a dibasic acid. The sulphites of the alkali metals and of the alkaline earths are described later under the heading of the metal concerned.

The normal sulphites are stable, and their solutions do not smell of sulphur dioxide. They decompose with acids forming first, presumably, sulphurous acid, which breaks down into sulphur dioxide (which is evolved as a gas) and water. Sulphites can be distinguished from sulphates since although they give a white precipitate (of barium sulphite) with barium chloride solution, this precipitate is soluble in dilute hydrochloric acid, whereas barium sulphate is not. Sulphites are recognized by the evolution of sulphur dioxide in the cold, on the addition of dilute hydrochloric acid. The sulphur dioxide is identified by its action on a paper soaked in potassium chromate or dichromate solution. A green colour indicates the presence of sulphur dioxide. Sulphites are distinguished from thiosulphates (p. 475) since these give a precipitate of sulphur as well as sulphur dioxide with dilute acids. The sulphites are reducing agents, like sulphurous acid, being readily convertible into sulphates.

§ 26 Sulphur Trioxide, Sulphuric Anhydride, SO$_3$

History

Sulphur trioxide seems to have been made by " B. Valentine " in the seventeenth century, and called " philosophical salt." K. W. Scheele (1777) and G. de Morveau (1786) called it the anhydride of sulphuric acid.

Preparation

Sulphur trioxide can be obtained

(i) by the dry distillation of ferric sulphate :

$$Fe_2(SO_4)_3 = Fe_2O_3 + 3SO_3.$$

Some other sulphates behave similarly;

(ii) by the action of excess of phosphorus pentoxide on concentrated sulphuric acid, when the acid is dehydrated :

$$2H_2SO_4 + P_4O_{10} = 2SO_3 + 4HPO_3 ;$$

(iii) by the direct union of sulphur dioxide and oxygen :

$$2SO_2 + O_2 = 2SO_3.$$

This is now the only important method of making sulphur trioxide.

This last reaction is discussed in some detail on page 466 in connection with the manufacture of sulphuric acid by the contact process (p. 467). A catalyst is necessary ; the most efficient catalyst is platinum in presence of which the reaction proceeds quickly and almost to completion at 400°.

Sulphur trioxide may be prepared in this way in the laboratory using the apparatus sketched in Fig. 170.

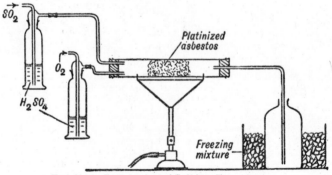

FIG. 170.—Preparation of Sulphur Trioxide.

Sulphur dioxide (prepared as in § 20, or if available a syphon may be used) and oxygen are dried by passing through wash-bottles containing concentrated sulphuric acid and then mixed at the entrance to a hard glass tube containing platinized asbestos (p. 838) which is heated to a temperature of about 400°. Sulphur trioxide is formed in white clouds which condense, in a freezing mixture, in the form of silky needles.

§ 27 Properties of Sulphur Trioxide

Sulphur trioxide exists in more than one form. The relationships between them are not clearly settled, and there seems to be some doubt as to whether two or three distinct forms exist. The following have been described :—

α-Sulphur Trioxide

This is a colourless liquid, boiling at about 44·88°, obtained by repeated distillation of the product of the reactions just mentioned. The liquid fumes strongly in air. It crystallizes in long prismatic needles between 16° and 17°, and melts at 16·8° ; the specific gravity at 20° is 1·9229. The vapour density ($H_2 = 1$) varies from 40·28 to 40·56. The lowering of the freezing point of phosphorus oxychloride also corresponds with a molecular weight of 80 approximately.

β-Sulphur Trioxide

If α-sulphur trioxide be maintained at 16° for some time, it gradually passes into solid crystals which look like asbestos. The mass fumes in air, and gradually passes into the α-form if kept at a temperature between 50° and 100°. The molecular weight by the depression of the freezing point of phosphorus oxychloride is close to 160, the theoretical value for S_2O_6. It melts at 32·5°.

The existence of these two forms has been recognized for a long time, but more recently a third form has been reported and called γ-**sulphur trioxide.** This is said to be obtained by very complete drying of the β-form, and melts at 62·2° under 1743 mm. pressure. At ordinary pressures, it sublimes without melting.

The forms are not very different chemically although the β-sulphur trioxide reacts somewhat less vigorously than the α-variety. Both dissolve in water with a hissing sound as if a piece of red-hot iron were plunged into the water ; much heat is evolved, and sulphuric acid is produced :

$$\alpha\text{-}SO_3 + H_2O = H_2SO_4 + 40 \text{ Cals.}$$

Hence sulphur trioxide is also called **sulphuric anhydride.** The anhydride does not redden blue litmus if extreme precautions be taken to exclude moisture. Sulphur trioxide reacts directly with many metallic oxides, forming the corresponding **sulphates,** e.g., with barium oxide :

$$BaO + SO_3 = BaSO_4.$$

So much heat is evolved that the mass becomes incandescent. Sulphur trioxide also forms curious addition products with some elements, e.g., $I_2(SO_3)_6$, $Te(SO_3)$.

When heated to 1000°, sulphur trioxide decomposes completely into sulphur dioxide and oxygen :

$$2SO_3 = 2SO_2 + O_2.$$

Two volumes of sulphur trioxide produce two volumes of sulphur dioxide and one volume of oxygen. This corresponds with the formula $(SO_3)_n$. The molecular weight of the α-form, indicated above, shows that its formula must be SO_3 ; and the β-form, S_2O_6.

The structure of the sulphur trioxide molecule is still somewhat uncertain. Three formulae have been suggested, viz. :

(i)
$$\begin{matrix} O \\ O \end{matrix} \gtrdot S = O$$

having three double links, which makes sulphur hexavalent, and would involve an outer valency group of twelve electrons (compare SF_6).

(ii)
$$O \leftarrow S \lessgtr \begin{matrix} O \\ O \end{matrix}$$

with two double links and one co-ordinate link which would have ten electrons in the outer electron group.

(iii)
$$\begin{matrix} O \\ O \end{matrix} \gtrdot S = O$$

with two co-ordinate links and one double link corresponding with the presence of eight electrons in the valency group. The last is thought to be the most probable.

§ 28 Sulphuric Acid, H_2SO_4

History and Occurrence

Sulphuric acid does not seem to have been known to the ancient world, and the earliest mention of it is probably in the Latin version of Geber. If the work ascribed in these writings to Geber is really his, sulphuric acid must have been known by the ninth century ; but it is very doubtful if this is so, and hence the discovery of sulphuric acid is more probably to be assigned to the thirteenth century.

It was commonly made in the later middle ages by distilling ferrous sulphate crystals, from which it derives its name *oil of vitriol*.

$$2(FeSO_4.7H_2O) = Fe_2O_3 + H_2SO_4 + SO_2 + 13H_2O.$$

For a long time it was made by burning a mixture of sulphur and nitre over water, this process being the forerunner of the lead chamber process for its manufacture (see below).

Free sulphuric acid is sometimes found in mineral springs whose waters have been in contact with sulphide minerals such as iron pyrites :

$$FeS_2 + 7O_2 + 2H_2O = 2H_2SO_4 + 2FeSO_4.$$

The waters of the Rio Tinto river in Spain contain considerable quantities of sulphuric acid on this account.

§ 29 The Manufacture of Sulphuric Acid

The manufacture of sulphuric acid is a world industry of vast importance, the production in the year 1929 exceeding nine million tons. The bulk of this large production is made either by the **Lead Chamber Process** or by the **Contact Process**.

The Lead Chamber Process

The first beginnings of this process, on a manufacturing scale, were made by Ward who, in 1740, prepared sulphuric acid by burning sulphur with nitre in large glass vessels—40 to 60 gallons capacity—time after time, until the acid which collected on the bottom of the vessels was strong enough to pay for its concentration in glass retorts. The acid was sold as " oil of vitriol made by the bell," to distinguish it from the acid made from ferrous sulphate. Ward's process reduced the price of sulphuric acid from 2s. 6d. per ounce to 2s. per pound. Roebuck and Garbett substituted lead chambers for Ward's glass vessels in a works at Birmingham in 1746. F. Clément and J. B. Désormes, in 1793, showed that the process could be made continuous, and that the nitre plays an intermediary part between the sulphur dioxide and the air.

Fig. 171 is a diagram of the modern plant.

Sulphur dioxide is made in the burners, very often from iron pyrites, but other sources such as native sulphur, spent oxide from gas works (p. 348) and the flue gases produced in smelting ores such as those of zinc and copper may be used instead. The last-named source of sulphur for sulphuric acid manufacture has recently become much more important, since it is now possible to reduce sulphur dioxide to sulphur on a manufacturing scale, and so obviate the transport difficulty (see p. 437).

The type of burner used varies with the material being burnt. If iron pyrites in lumps be the source of sulphur no special arrangements are necessary, but more finely-divided materials require the use of special furnaces, fitted with mechanically-operated stirrers which constantly expose fresh surfaces of the burning material to the air. The air supply is so adjusted that excess of oxygen is present in the gases which leave the burners, ready for the next stage of the process :

$$4FeS_2 + 11O_2 = 2Fe_2O_3 + 8SO_2.$$

The mixed gases are then led over a nitre pot which contains a mixture of sodium nitrate and sulphuric acid, heated by waste heat from the burners. Nitric acid vapour is thus mixed with the gases, passing to the " chambers." (In the most modern practice an apparatus for producing nitrous fumes by the catalytic oxidation of ammonia —p. 407—is now used instead of the nitre pot.)

The gases are then freed from dust and then pass into the base of the Glover's tower. This is a tower, lined with acid-proof material, packed with flints, down which trickles a mixture of a weak acid from the lead chambers and the strong nitrated acid which has been used to absorb nitrous fumes, and recovered in the Gay-Lussac's tower to be described later. The functions of the Glover's tower are : (1) to

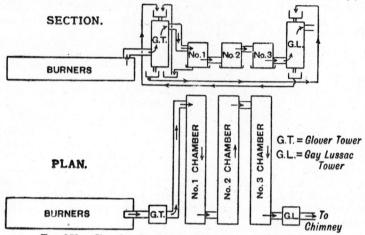

FIG. 171.—Chamber Process for Sulphuric Acid Manufacture.

recover the nitrogen oxides from Gay-Lussac's tower ; (2) to cool the gases from the burners ; (3) to help to concentrate the acid trickling down the tower ; and (4) partly to oxidize the sulphur dioxide from the burners.

The mixture of air, sulphur dioxide, and nitrous fumes passes into a set of three leaden chambers, which may be of a total capacity of 150,000 cubic feet, into which steam, or in more modern plant a spray of water is blown. The gases in the chambers are thus intimately mixed. The oxidation of the sulphur dioxide mainly occurs in the first two chambers. The gases are passed through the chambers slowly so as to allow time for all the sulphur dioxide to be oxidized. The third chamber serves mainly to dry the gases. The chambers are kept cool enough to condense the sulphuric acid which collects on the floor and is drawn off periodically. It is called *chamber acid*. Chamber acid contains between 62 and 70 per cent. H_2SO_4.

The excess air which leaves the lead chambers is highly charged with nitrogen oxides. These are recovered by causing the exit gases from the chambers to pass up a tower called the Gay-Lussac's tower, packed with coke, down which concentrated sulphuric acid is trickling. The concentrated acid absorbs the nitrous fumes. The " nitrated acid " which collects at the foot of the Gay-Lussac's tower is pumped to the top of the Glover's tower along with some of the more dilute chamber acid. The " nitrated acid " trickling down the Glover's tower loses the absorbed nitrous fumes and some water.

On leaving the Gay-Lussac's tower the gases consist almost entirely of the nitrogen of the air used for the burning of the pyrites. These gases pass to a chimney, thus creating a partial vacuum which draws the gases through the plant.

Tower Systems of Sulphuric Acid Manufacture

It has been mentioned above (p. 462), that in the ordinary Chamber process one of the functions of the Glover tower is partly to oxidize the sulphur dioxide from the burner gases—in fact to do a portion of the work for which the lead chambers are provided. In point of fact, the action taking place in the Glover tower is several times more intense than that which occurs in an equal volume of chamber space.

Attempts have accordingly been made to dispense with the use of lead chambers and confine the production of sulphuric acid to towers, like the Glover tower, down which passes sulphuric acid containing dissolved oxides of nitrogen and up which the burner gases (sulphur dioxide, oxygen, etc.) are passing. The sulphuric acid is produced in a similar way to its formation in chambers, but in the liquid instead of the gaseous state, with consequent very considerable saving of space. This system is now a commercial proposition and is being operated with success.

The details of the operations vary with different systems, but the following outline is more or less representative. Six towers are erected, the first five of which act like Glover towers, being fed with sulphuric acid charged with oxides of nitrogen, and being kept hot. The last tower acts as a Gay-Lussac Tower and absorbs any oxides of nitrogen escaping from the previous towers. It is kept cool.

The chief disadvantages of tower systems over the older chamber process are the necessity (i) for pumping large volumes of acid, and (ii) of forcing large quantities of gas against the resistance of the tower packing. However, now that mechanically efficient yet acid-resisting pumping machinery is available, the former difficulty has largely disappeared, and the increased cost of power for both pumping operations is more than offset by the reduced capital cost, the smaller amount of space required and the greater efficiency of the tower system.

The exact nature of the reactions on which the Chamber process depends is still uncertain.

According to an old theory of E. M. Péligot (1844), nitric oxide, NO, unites with the oxygen from the air, forming nitrogen peroxide :

$$2NO + O_2 = 2NO_2.$$

The nitrogen peroxide then oxidizes the sulphur dioxide, and is at the same time reduced to nitric oxide :

$$NO_2 + SO_2 + H_2O = NO + H_2SO_4.$$

The nitric oxide is again oxidized to the peroxide, and so the cycle commences anew.

The nitrogen oxides thus serve to transfer oxygen from the air to the sulphur dioxide.

In some quarters this simple explanation is not accepted, and it is believed by many that an intermediate compound is formed, particularly since experiment shows that if the supply of steam or water be insufficient, crystals of **nitrosyl hydrogen sulphate** (the so-called **chamber crystals**) are formed. This acid decomposes with water, giving sulphuric acid and oxides of nitrogen :

$$NO_2 + NO + 2SO_2 + H_2O + O_2 = 2HO.SO_2.NO_2$$
$$\text{(chamber crystals)}$$

$$2(HO.SO_2.NO_2) + H_2O = H_2SO_4 + NO_2 + NO.$$

Various other intermediate compounds have been suggested, e.g., $H_2N_2SO_6$ (Divers, 1911) ; H_2NSO_5 (Raschig, 1911), etc., but it does not really seem necessary, in the present state of our knowledge, to assume any more complicated series of reactions than the scheme suggested by Péligot. In any case, the mere fact that a definite compound can be isolated by altering the conditions under which a reaction progresses cannot be accepted as a conclusive proof that the compound so isolated is necessarily an intermediate compound when the reaction progresses under other conditions.

A great deal of chamber acid is used as such, but some is concentrated still further for the preparation of the concentrated acid. Prior to the advent of the contact process, all the concentrated acid of commerce was made in this way, and even to-day, although the contact method produces highly concentrated acid directly, a good deal of chamber acid is concentrated and special plant has been devised for this purpose.

FIG. 172.—Cascade Process for Concentrating Sulphuric Acid.

As mentioned above, some chamber acid is concentrated to about 78 per cent. in the Glover tower. If more concentration is required than is produced here, it may be done in flat lead pans utilizing waste heat from the pyrites burners. Acid of this (78 per cent.) strength is known as B.O.V. or brown oil of vitriol (so called on account of its colour, due to the presence of impurities). This is the limit of concentration possible in lead apparatus—the acid attacks lead when more concentrated than 80 per cent.

Further concentration used to be effected in glass or platinum retorts, but it is now done in special forms of apparatus which are more efficient and occasion less loss of acid by decomposition. Among the various types devised may be mentioned the **cascade process,** the **Kessler apparatus** and the **Gaillard Tower.**

The **cascade process,** illustrated in Fig. 172, comprises an arrangement of silica or ferro-silicon beakers and dishes arranged one above the other, on a sort of staircase made of acid-proof bricks. The spout of one dish discharges into the dish next below it. The whole series of dishes is heated by a flue built in the "staircase," and hot air also sweeps over the surface. In this way the vapours from the basins, which consist of steam containing a little acid, pass away at the top of the cascade, and are recovered, while an acid of steadily increasing strength flows down from basin to basin.

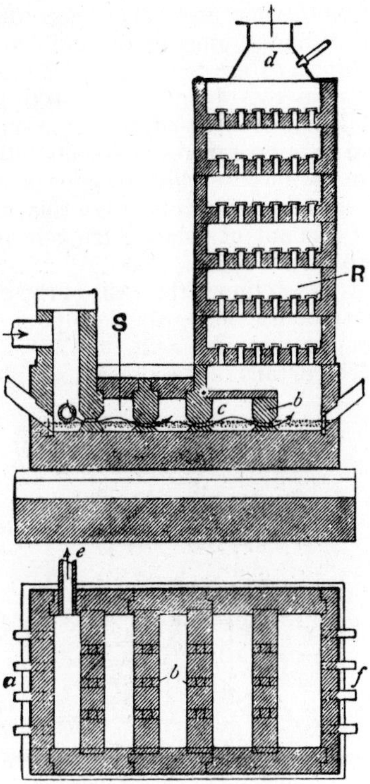

In the **Kessler method** the weak acid is fed down a tower (Fig. 173) which contains a number of perforated plates, having inverted cups over the perforations on to a " dish " of acid-resisting stone. Hot gases from a coke furnace are driven across the dish S and then up the tower R. The concentration of the acid in the dish produces a good deal of acid " fume " which is condensed in the tower, where the temperature is kept at such a point that steam escapes, but sulphuric acid does not. The issuing gases are then passed through a vessel packed

FIG. 173.—Kessler Plant.

with coke drenched with concentrated sulphuric acid which removes any remaining mist of acid droplets.

The **Gaillard Tower** is perhaps the most successful method, particularly when large quantities of acid have to be dealt with. It comprises a tower of acid-resisting stone or brick into the top of which a very fine spray of the acid to be concentrated is introduced. In the tower this spray meets a current of hot gases from a coke furnace. Progressive concentration of the acid takes place as it passes down the furnace, and a strong acid is run off from the bottom.

§ 30 The Contact Process

Sulphur dioxide and oxygen combine to some extent when heated alone, forming sulphur trioxide. The reaction, which may be represented by the equation :

$$2SO_2 + O_2 \rightleftharpoons 2SO_3 + 45 \cdot 2 \text{ Cals.}$$

is exothermic and hence, according to the principle of Le Chatelier (p. 219), the amount of sulphur trioxide present at equilibrium will diminish as the temperature is raised. The reaction is, however, very slow, in the absence of a catalyst, but, as was shown by Peregrine Phillips in 1831, platinum is a very efficient catalyst for this reaction, and at temperatures of 400-500° almost complete conversion of sulphur dioxide into sulphur trioxide can be effected in a reasonable time. At lower temperatures than this, the reaction is too slow, and at higher the amount of sulphur trioxide formed diminishes, falling almost to zero above 1000°.

This reaction is the basis of the **contact process** for the manufacture of sulphuric acid, since sulphur trioxide will combine with water, forming sulphuric acid.

The details of the process are illustrated by Fig. 174.

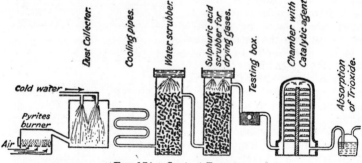

FIG. 174.—Contact Process.

Sulphur dioxide is obtained in a manner similar to the chamber process, but requires very much more thorough purification in order to avoid " poisoning " of the catalyst. It is particularly necessary for the gases to be absolutely free from arsenic.

The gases are cleaned by passage through a chamber—the " dust chamber "—in which steam is injected ; through a series of lead pipes to reduce the temperature down to about 100° ; through a series of towers in each of which the gases meet a descending spray of water. This washes the sulphuric acid, etc., from the gas.

The last traces of suspended matter are removed by electrical precipitation and finally, the gases are dried by passing them up a tower where they meet a descending stream of concentrated sulphuric acid. The gases are periodically tested for dust, arsenic, etc., to make sure the scrubbers, etc., are working efficiently.

The dried gases then pass through a heat interchanger where they are heated up by the outcoming gases (which are themselves thereby cooled). They pass through the catalyst chamber over some form of finely-divided platinum which is often platinized asbestos (*Badische process*), but may consist of platinum deposited on magnesium sulphate (*Grillo process*) or other substances. Sulphur trioxide is formed and heat is evolved. The rate of flow, etc., is so arranged that the temperature in the catalyst chamber is kept at about 400°.

The exit gases consist principally of sulphur trioxide and nitrogen ; on cooling, the former forms a mist of very fine droplets which is absorbed with great difficulty by water or dilute sulphuric acid ; but it is rapidly and completely absorbed by 97 to 98 per cent. sulphuric acid. Hence the gases which leave the contact chamber pass into cast-iron tanks containing 97 to 98 per cent. sulphuric acid. A stream of water or dilute acid is run into the condensing tanks at such a rate that the strength of the acid is maintained at 97 to 98 per cent. By restricting the supply of water in this operation, **oleum** or fuming sulphuric acid is obtained.

The high cost of platinum has led to a search for other contact substances. Ferric oxide which is used in the *Mannheim process* is not so sensitive to poisonous impurities—e.g., arsenic, indeed, it actually absorbs arsenic and so acts as a purifying agent. But it requires a higher temperature (about 700°) to do its work, and the oxidation is incomplete (50 to 60 per cent.).

Sometimes a Mannheim plant and a platinum plant are worked in conjunction, first oxidizing the mixed gases at a high temperature with the ferric oxide catalyst, and absorbing the resulting sulphur trioxide, then passing the remaining gases over platinum at a lower temperature so as to complete the reaction. Recently the use of vanadium pentoxide has been developed. This catalyst is immune to the action of poisons, and with appropriate temperature control, can bring about complete conversion. It seems probable that, in time, vanadium pentoxide will supersede platinum for sulphuric acid manufacture.

§ 31 Properties of Sulphuric Acid

Sulphuric acid is a colourless oily liquid, without odour. It is *extremely corrosive* to the skin and all the body tissues, and so causes very serious burns. Its density is 1·84, and it freezes at 10·5°. The ordinary concentrated acid of the laboratory contains about 2 per cent. of water and, therefore, freezes at a very much lower temperature. It boils with decomposition ; giving off choking fumes of sulphur trioxide and the vapour of the acid.

On mixing sulphuric acid with water the mixture becomes hot and the temperature may rise as high as 120°. This is liable to cause serious accidents if care be not taken when diluting sulphuric acid. The acid should always be added to the water with vigorous stirring.

When sulphuric acid is mixed in water, the volume of the cold mixture is much less than the sum of the volumes of water and acid used. It is remarkable that the greatest contraction occurs with a solution containing about 97·7 per cent. of H_2SO_4, that is, 79·7 per cent. of SO_3. There is another maximum contraction with solutions containing 60 per cent. of free sulphur trioxide, that is a total per cent. of 92·65 SO_3. A curve showing the volume of one gram of different solutions of sulphur trioxide and of sulphuric acid, H_2SO_4, in water is shown in Fig. 175.

Sulphuric acid (H_2SO_4) boils at about 270° with partial decomposition. Some sulphur trioxide passes off as vapour ; the acid in the retort becomes weaker, and the boiling point steadily rises until the acid has attained a strength of about 98 per cent. H_2SO_4 (that is, 80 per cent. SO_3), when it distils over unchanged. Conversely, on boiling dilute solutions of sulphuric acid, the acid becomes stronger and stronger since water or very dilute acid passes over ; at the same time, the boiling point steadily rises as illustrated in Fig. 176, until the acid has attained a strength of 98 per cent. H_2SO_4, when it distils over unchanged, at 317°.

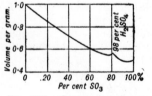

FIG. 175.—Contraction Curve.

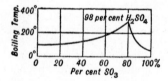

FIG. 176.—Boiling Curve.

Below that temperature, water or dilute sulphuric acid, and above that temperature sulphur trioxide, is evolved. At that temperature (750 mm. pressure) a constant boiling acid is obtained. The specific gravity curve also shows a maximum, or the contraction curve a minimum (Fig. 175), with an acid of nearly that concentration. This acid also absorbs sulphur trioxide more rapidly—" greedily "—than either water or dilute sulphuric acid.

The freezing-point curves of solutions of sulphur trioxide in water are shown in Fig. 173. Maxima occur at points corresponding with $H_2SO_4.4H_2O$, $H_2SO_4.H_2O$, H_2SO_4, and $H_2SO_4.SO_3$ (pyrosulphuric acid). The application of the Phase Rule (p. 158) to freezing-point curves shows that these may be taken to represent the composition of definite compounds of sulphur trioxide and water formed under the conditions stated.

These facts all point to the existence of definite compounds of sulphuric acid and water. In addition, crystals of the composition $H_2SO_4.SO_3$; $H_2SO_4.H_2O$; $H_2SO_4.2H_2O$ and $H_2SO_4.4H_2O$ have been isolated, so that it seems reasonable to assume the formation of such compounds during the dilution of the concentrated acid.

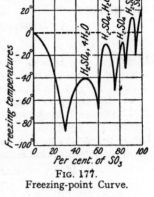

FIG. 177.

Freezing-point Curve.

The great affinity of sulphuric acid for water makes it a useful drying agent. Hence its use in desiccators, and in the balance case for maintaining a dry atmosphere in these vessels, and also for drying gases. Sulphuric acid acts upon solid and liquid substances depriving them of water; or even decomposing the substance—splitting off the elements of water when no ready formed water is present. Wood, paper, sugar, starch, and many organic substances are blackened by concentrated sulphuric acid owing to the separation of carbon which accompanies the removal of the elements of water. This property is utilized for the preparation of carbon monoxide (p. 359); and for the preparation of ethylene (p. 336). The effect is easily demonstrated by stirring 10 grams of powdered cane sugar with 12 grams of concentrated sulphuric acid in a beaker. The sugar first becomes pale brown, rapidly darkens in tint, and finally becomes black; at the same time, much steam is evolved and the mass swells up considerably.

Dilute sulphuric acid shows all the ordinary properties of a strong acid (p. 306) such as turning litmus red, action on metals, etc. According to the Ionic Theory, it is not so strong an acid as nitric and hydrochloric acids, but is stronger than most others (p. 238). The dilute acid reacts with all metals except bismuth, mercury, lead, copper and the noble metals, liberating hydrogen, e.g.,

$$Zn + H_2SO_4 = ZnSO_4 + H_2.$$

(Aluminium, chromium and nickel, which sometimes appear not to react, will do so if the protecting film of oxide is removed.)

Concentrated sulphuric acid does not react with metals in the cold, but when heated oxidizes them, being itself reduced to sulphur dioxide. This is due to the fact that sulphuric acid, when hot, is an oxidizing agent.

A typical example of its action on metals has been discussed in connection with the laboratory preparation of sulphur dioxide (p. 452), using copper. The reaction between concentrated sulphuric acid and other metals is probably similar.

In the case of zinc, for example, hydrogen sulphide, zinc sulphide and free sulphur may be formed, as well as sulphur dioxide.

Many non-metals are also oxidized by sulphuric acid, e.g., carbon, and sulphur :

$$C + 2H_2SO_4 = CO_2 + 2SO_2 + 2H_2O$$
$$S + 2H_2SO_4 = 3SO_2 + 2H_2O.$$

Hydrogen also, even in the cold, is oxidized to a slight extent, forming traces of sulphur dioxide, a fact which has to be borne in mind when drying this gas with concentrated sulphuric acid.

Another familiar example of the oxidizing action of sulphuric acid is its behaviour with bromides and iodides (pp. 522, 528). The hydrobromic and hydriodic acid first formed are oxidized to bromine and iodine respectively, so that these acids cannot be prepared by the action of concentrated sulphuric acid on their salts.

$$H_2SO_4 + 2HBr = Br_2 + SO_2 + 2H_2O$$
$$H_2SO_4 + 6HI = 4H_2O + S + 3I_2$$
$$H_2SO_4 + 8HI = 4H_2O + H_2S + 4I_2.$$

§ 32 Uses of Sulphuric Acid

Sulphuric acid is a very important industrial commodity and its uses are numerous. It was formerly used in very large quantities for making sodium carbonate and nitric acid, but the development of the ammonia-soda process and of the synthetic nitrate industry has reduced the demand for it for these purposes. It is also employed extensively for the manufacture of explosives, fertilizers (e.g., superphosphate and ammonium sulphate) alums, phosphorus, and dyestuffs. Large quantities are used in coal-tar and petroleum refining, in bleaching and dyeing operations, electro-plating, metallurgy, etc. The manufacture of sulphates such as sodium sulphate for the glass industry, and ferrous sulphate for ink manufacture, also absorbs considerable quantities of the acid.

§ 33 Formula of Sulphuric Acid

The formula for sulphuric acid is generally taken to be $SO_2(OH)_2$ or, more fully,

for the following reasons :—

First.—Chlorine can react with concentrated sulphuric acid, forming chlorosulphonic acid $Cl—HSO_3$, where one OH group in sulphuric acid is replaced by chlorine. Phosphorus pentachloride—PCl_5—can displace two OH groups in sulphuric acid, forming sulphuryl chloride Cl—SO$_2$—Cl. Both these chloro-compounds react with water, forming sulphuric acid. The two OH groups can likewise be replaced with other radicals, e.g., NH$_2$. Since two OH groups can be displaced together or separately, we infer from the rule of the constancy of structural arrangement that (1) **sulphuric acid—H$_2$SO$_4$—contains two hydroxyl—OH—groups.**

Second.—It is possible to make but one compound of the type, CH$_3$O—SO$_2$—OK, by replacing the hydrogen of the hydroxyl groups with the radicals like CH$_3$, C$_2$H$_5$, etc. Hence it is inferred (2) **the hydroxyl groups are related to the remainder of the atoms in the molecule H$_2$SO$_4$ in a symmetrical manner.**

Third.—Certain univalent hydrocarbon radicals—C$_2$H$_5$, C$_6$H$_5$, etc. —can replace the chlorine in ClHSO$_3$ and in SO$_2$Cl$_2$ to form, say, ethyl sulphonic acid—C$_2$H$_5$.SO$_2$.OH, and diphenylsulphone—(C$_6$H$_5$)$_2$SO$_2$, respectively. The same compounds can be made by the oxidation of mercaptan—C$_2$H$_5$.SH, and of diphenyl sulphide—(C$_6$H$_5$)$_2$S, in which the radical must be joined directly to the sulphur atom. Assuming that the radicals remain fixed to the sulphur atom during the oxidation, it is inferred that (3) **the hydroxyl groups in sulphuric acid— H$_2$SO$_4$—are directly attached to the sulphur atom.**

Fourth.—The structure $>$S$\nearrow\!\!\searrow^{O}_{O}$ for the $>$SO$_2$ part of the molecule

is preferred to $>$S$<^{O}_{\,|\,}_{O}$ since the latter represents a grouping which,

when it is known to occur, is very unstable.

It is possible that the two oxygen atoms are joined to the sulphur atom by double bonds, thus :

$$\begin{array}{c} HO \\ HO \end{array}\!\!> S \lessless \begin{array}{c} O \\ O \end{array}$$

but the co-ordinate-link formula is considered more probable.

§ 34 Detection and Determination of Sulphuric Acid and Sulphates

The usual method of detection is to add dilute hydrochloric acid and barium chloride solution to a solution of the suspected sulphate. If a white precipitate be formed, it indicates the presence of a sulphate, owing to the formation of insoluble barium sulphate. It is essential to have the solution acid as many barium salts are insoluble in water, but, apart from the fluosilicate, the sulphate is the only one which is insoluble in hydrochloric acid.

The usual confirmatory test is to heat the suspected sulphate on charcoal with sodium carbonate, using the reducing flame, when a sulphide will be formed which when dissolved in water gives a black precipitate with lead acetate solution ; or produces a brown or black stain when a drop is placed upon a silver coin.

§ 35 Sulphates

Sulphuric acid forms salts known as the sulphates when it reacts with certain metals, metallic oxides, hydroxides or carbonates, and many of them are of considerable importance. These will be found described under the heading of the metal concerned.

Sulphates are also prepared by heating the salts of more volatile acids, such as hydrochloric and nitric acids, with sulphuric acid. Sulphuric acid is a dibasic acid and so readily forms two series of salts, viz., acid sulphates, and normal sulphates. With certain poly-acid bases, basic sulphates also occur. There are many important double sulphates also, such as the alums (p. 670).

The sulphates are mostly fairly soluble in water and crystallize well, frequently with several molecules of water of crystallization. The sulphates of lead, calcium, strontium and barium are, however, only very sparingly soluble in water.

The sulphates of the alkali metals and alkaline earths are stable to heat, but those of the heavy metals are decomposed into the oxide of the metal and (usually) sulphur trioxide when very strongly heated, e.g.,

$$CuSO_4 = CuO + SO_3$$

Ferrous sulphate (p. 460) gives sulphur dioxide when heated ; this type of decomposition is unusual.

Most sulphates are reduced to sulphides when heated with carbon, e.g.,

$$Na_2SO_4 + 4C = Na_2S + 4CO.$$

(Compare the production of *black ash* in the manufacture of sodium carbonate by the Leblanc process—p. 558 ; also the manufacture of sodium sulphide—p. 567.)

§ 36 Pyrosulphuric Acid, $H_2S_2O_7$, and the Pyrosulphates

Mention has already been made (p. 467) of the fact that sulphur trioxide will dissolve in concentrated sulphuric acid, forming what is often called **oleum** or **Nordhausen** or **fuming sulphuric acid.** A similar acid is obtained by distilling partially dehydrated ferrous sulphate crystals, $FeSO_4.H_2O$ (preferably with a little sulphuric acid in the receiver). The reaction appears to be represented :

$$6FeSO_4.H_2O = Fe_2(SO_4)_3 + 2Fe_2O_3 + 3SO_2 + 6H_2O$$

followed by :

$$Fe_2(SO_4)_3 = Fe_2O_3 + 3SO_2.$$

The same acid is obtained by heating sodium pyrosulphate with concentrated sulphuric acid :

$$Na_2S_2O_7 + H_2SO_4 = 2NaHSO_4 + H_2S_2O_7.$$

Sodium pyrosulphate is made by heating sodium bisulphate to about 400° :

$$2NaHSO_4 = Na_2S_2O_7 + H_2O.$$

hence the name *pyro* sulphuric acid—from the Greek πῦρ (pyr), fire.

Fuming sulphuric acid is a viscous, oily-looking liquid which is considered to be a solution of variable proportions of sulphur trioxide in concentrated sulphuric acid. The "fuming" of the acid is due to the escape of the sulphur trioxide. If the fuming acid be warmed, sulphur trioxide volatilizes and leaves sulphuric acid, H_2SO_4, behind. This acid has often a brownish colour owing to the presence of a little organic matter. It may also contain other impurities. Fuming sulphuric acid is used in refining petroleums, in the manufacture of dyes, explosives, shoe-blacking, etc. When cooled below 0°, the fuming acid furnishes crystals of pyrosulphuric acid, $H_2S_2O_7$ or $H_2SO_4.SO_3$ or $H_2O.2SO_3$, melting at 35°.

Salts, known as the pyrosulphates, do appear to exist (compare the sodium salt mentioned above) and so it seems probable that the acid is definitely $H_2S_2O_7$.

§ 37 Persulphuric Acids and Persulphates

It will be remembered that when dilute sulphuric acid is electrolyzed, hydrogen and oxygen are obtained in the proportion : two volumes of hydrogen, and one volume of oxygen. As the concentration of the acid is increased, less and less oxygen is evolved ; until, with 50 per cent. sulphuric acid and a cold solution, inappreciable quantities of oxygen will be disengaged at the anode. A new compound is formed—persulphuric acid, $H_2S_2O_8$. The best way of studying this action is to electrolyze a saturated solution of potassium sulphate in sulphuric acid, specific gravity about 1·3.

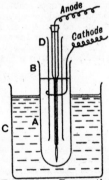

FIG. 178. — Preparation of Persulphuric Acid.

The solution is placed in a test-tube, A, Fig. 178, so that the test-tube is about three-fourths filled. The test-tube is fixed in a large beaker by means of the wire C. A glass cylinder, D, is fixed in the test-tube. A coil of platinum wire—the cathode—is allowed to dip into the solution of potassium sulphate as indicated in the diagram ; and a platinum wire sealed to a piece of glass tube so that about 1½ to 2 cm. of the wire projects from the tube forms the anode. This is fixed within the cylinder. The large beaker is filled with water in which pieces of ice are floating—"iced-water." A current of about one or two amperes is sent through the solution. Hydrogen appears at the cathode ; and a white crystalline mass accumulates at the anode.

The formula $K_2S_2O_8$ is conformable with the change in the molecular conductivity of solutions of the salt with dilution, and with the lowering of the freezing point of solutions of the salt. H. Marshall, who first isolated potassium persulphate in 1891, suggested the formula KSO_4, but later favoured the doubled formula given above.

The Properties of Persulphates

The solid persulphates are fairly stable. Potassium persulphate decomposes on heating into potassium pyrosulphate and oxygen :

$$2K_2S_2O_8 = 2K_2S_2O_7 + O_2.$$

An aqueous solution of a persulphate is a powerful oxidizing agent, and is used for that purpose in analytical work, e.g., it precipitates a brown manganese peroxide from soluble manganese salts. The persulphates *slowly* liberate iodine from solutions of potassium iodide ; oxidize iodine to iodic acid, etc., A solution of a manganese salt gives a precipitate of manganese peroxide with potassium persulphate ; but, in the presence of silver nitrate, is oxidized to pink permanganate—*Marshall's reaction.*

Barium persulphate is readily soluble in water. Hence barium chloride gives no precipitate with the persulphates, although it does give a precipitate with a sulphate, but if the persulphate be decomposed by warming, a precipitate of barium sulphate is obtained. A dilute solution of the acid—**persulphuric acid,** also called **perdisulphuric acid**—can be made by treating the barium persulphate with sulphuric acid. The persulphates are used in photography for " reducing " negatives ; and ammonium persulphate is used in technical organic chemistry.

Caro's acid

If potassium persulphate be digested with 40 per cent. sulphuric acid in a freezing mixture so that there is no rise of temperature ; or if concentrated sulphuric acid and hydrogen peroxide (5 per cent.) be mixed together, a **permonosulphuric acid** is obtained :

$$H_2SO_4 + H_2O_2 \rightleftharpoons H_2O + H_2SO_5.$$

The solution is sometimes called Caro's acid, H_2SO_5—after its discoverer, N. Caro, 1898.

The pure acid forms a white crystalline mass which melts at about 45°, and it is comparatively stable. Like persulphuric acid, Caro's acid has strong oxidizing qualities. Unlike persulphuric acid, it liberates iodine from potassium iodide *at once.* It also oxidizes sulphur dioxide to the trioxide ; ferrous salts to ferric salts ; hydrogen chloride to chlorine, but it is without action on hydrogen fluoride ; and precipitates peroxides from salts of silver, copper, manganese, cobalt, and nickel. It does not bleach permanganates, nor oxidize chromic nor titanium salts, and is therefore distinct from hydrogen peroxide.

The relation believed to exist between persulphuric acid, Caro's acid and pyrosulphuric acid is indicated by the formulae :

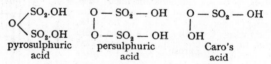

There has been some discussion whether Caro's acid is monobasic, H_2SO_5, or dibasic, $H_2S_2O_6$. The analysis of the potassium salt is not conclusive, since $KHSO_5$ would have the same ultimate composition as the salt $K_2S_2O_9.H_2O$. Benzoyl chloride, $C_6H_5CO.Cl$, reacts with the potassium salt of Caro's acid, forming the benzoyl derivative. This reaction undoubtedly corresponds with the monobasicity of the acid :

$$\begin{matrix} O-SO_2OK \\ | \\ O-H \end{matrix} + C_6H_5.CO.Cl = HCl + \begin{matrix} O-SO_2OK \\ \\ O-CO.C_6H_5. \end{matrix}$$

It is very unlikely that this result would occur if the formula of the salt in question were $K_2S_2O_9.H_2O$. The synthesis of Caro's acid by the action of the calculated quantity of chlorosulphonic acid, $SO_2Cl(OH)$, on pure hydrogen peroxide in the cold :

$$\begin{matrix} SO_2OH \\ | \\ Cl \end{matrix} + H_2O_2 = HCl + \begin{matrix} O-SO_2OH \\ | \\ O-H \end{matrix}$$

is in agreement with the view of the molecular formula just indicated.

§ 38 Thiosulphuric Acid and the Thiosulphates

If an aqueous solution of sodium sulphite, Na_2SO_3, be exposed to the air, one oxygen atom per molecule of sodium sulphite is taken up, and sodium sulphate, Na_2SO_4, is formed. Similarly, if sodium sulphite be digested with finely divided sulphur for some time, one atom of sulphur per molecule of sodium sulphite is taken up, and a new salt, sodium thiosulphate, $Na_2S_2O_3$, is formed:

$$Na_2SO_3 + O = Na_2SO_4$$
$$Na_2SO_3 + S = Na_2S_2O_3.$$

These reactions suggest some analogy in the structure of the thiosulphates and the sulphates; and this is emphasized by the term *thio*-sulphates, meaning *sulpho*-sulphates—from the Greek $\theta\epsilon\hat{\iota}o\nu$ (theīon), sulphur.

The name *sodium hyposulphite* (the photographer's "hypo") was formerly used for this salt, but that name properly belongs to the substance $Na_2S_2O_4$.

Thiosulphates are also formed by the action of caustic alkalis on sulphur (p. 443), and by the oxidation of soluble sulphides (e.g., potassium sulphides) in air:

$$2K_2S_2 + 3O_2 = 2K_2S_2O_3$$

and also, by the action of sulphur dioxide on sodium sulphides:

$$2Na_2S + 3SO_2 = 2Na_2S_2O_3 + S.$$

Thiosulphates were formerly manufactured from alkali waste (p. 558) but are now made from the waste liquors from the production of sodium sulphide (p. 567).

Sodium thiosulphate is also formed when a mixture of sodium sulphide and sulphite is treated with iodine. This is sometimes called *Spring's reaction* (cf. p. 477), and gives a clue to the structure of the thiosulphates:

Thiosulphuric acid has not been isolated. By acting on a thiosulphate with a mineral acid, thiosulphuric acid appears to be formed but it begins to decompose at once into sulphur dioxide and free sulphur. The sulphur only appears after the lapse of a certain time—seconds or minutes, according to the concentration of the solution:

$$Na_2S_2O_3 + 2HCl = 2NaCl + SO_2 + S + H_2O.$$

The evolution of sulphur dioxide with the separation of sulphur on the addition of a dilute mineral acid distinguishes thiosulphates from sulphites in qualitative analysis.

§ 39 Other Oxides of Sulphur

In addition to sulphur dioxide and sulphur trioxide, which have been described above, the following oxides of sulphur have been reported :—

Sulphur monoxide, SO.

Sulphur sesquioxide, S_2O_3.

Sulphur tetroxide, SO_4.

Sulphur heptoxide, S_2O_7.

These are, however, not of any very great importance at this stage of our work.

Sulphur Monoxide, SO

The isolation of this oxide is now claimed by Schenk (1932) by the action of an electric discharge on a mixture of sulphur dioxide and sulphur at low pressures. More recently (1935) he has obtained it (mixed with sulphur dioxide) by the combustion of sulphur under suitable conditions.

It is described as a colourless gas which decomposes very easily, particularly in the presence of water or organic matter. It combines with oxygen when sparked, giving sulphur dioxide, while with metals it forms sulphides.

Sulphur Sesquioxide, S_2O_3

This oxide is supposed to be formed as a malachite-green crystalline mass by the direct union of sulphur and sulphur trioxide, and as a blue solution by the action of flowers of sulphur on Nordhausen sulphuric acid. There is some doubt whether the bluish-green mass is a mixture or a compound. With water, sulphur sesquioxide gives sulphur and a mixture of sulphuric and sulphurous acids, and not hyposulphurous acid. This does not prove that sulphur sesquioxide is not the anhydride of hyposulphurous acid because the latter decomposes in a similar way (see p. 477 below).

Sulphur Tetroxide, SO_4.

This oxide is claimed to have been isolated in 1934 by Schwarz and Achenbach by the action of a glow discharge on a mixture of sulphur dioxide and a large excess of oxygen at 0·5 mm. pressure. It is described as a white solid which begins to decompose at −5° and melts at 3°, forming sulphur heptoxide. It is said to be a good oxidizing agent.

Sulphur Heptoxide, S_2O_7

M. Berthelot (1878) found that when a mixture of oxygen and sulphur dioxide is exposed to the action of a silent discharge (cf. preparation of ozone, p. 313), oily drops of sulphur heptoxide are formed :

$$2SO_2 + O_3 = S_2O_7.$$

The liquid forms white crystals at 0°. It gradually decomposes, on keeping, into sulphur trioxide and oxygen. Sulphur heptoxide combines with water with a hissing noise like sulphur trioxide, but the solution has not the same properties as if sulphur trioxide alone had been dissolved in the water. A similar solution can be obtained by mixing concentrated sulphuric acid with hydrogen peroxide in the cold, and by the electrolysis of concentrated sulphuric acid.

§ 40 Other Acids derived from Sulphur

Besides the important acids already discussed, the following derived from sulphur are known :—

Sulphoxylic acid, H_2SO_2
(in the form of organic derivatives only) ;

Hyposulphurous acid
(hydrosulphurous acid), $H_2S_2O_4$;

The Polythionic Acids, $H_2S_nO_6$
($n = 2, 3, 4, 5$ or 6).

Hyposulphurous Acid, $H_2S_2O_4$

C. L. Berthollet (1789) noticed that iron dissolves in sulphurous acid without giving off a gas ; L. N. Vauquelin and A. F. Fourcroy (1798) found that tin and zinc behaved in a similar way ; and C. F. Schönbein (1852) obtained some reactions with a lower sulphur acid, and which were probably due to what is now called hyposulphurous acid. P. Schützenberger discovered this acid in 1869.

By treating an aqueous solution of sulphur dioxide with finely divided zinc, zinc hyposulphite is obtained :

$$Zn + 2SO_2 = ZnS_2O_4.$$

By using sodium hydrogen sulphite solution similarly, the sodium salt is obtained :

$$2NaHSO_3 + SO_2 + Zn = Na_2S_2O_4 + ZnSO_3 + H_2O.$$

The zinc can be precipitated as hydroxide by treating the solution with lime, and on saturating the filtrate with common salt, sodium hyposulphite crystallizes out.

The free acid can be obtained as a yellow solution by treating calcium hyposulphite with oxalic acid. It readily absorbs oxygen from the air and is a very powerful reducing agent.

The sodium salt is used industrially, and in the chemical laboratory as a reducing agent. For instance, it bleaches sugar, indigo blue, etc. It reduces permanganates ; and also reduces some metallic salts to the metal—e.g., silver nitrate, and gold and platinum chlorides ; and in the case of copper sulphate, a brown **copper hydride,** Cu_2H_2, is formed. It seems to act as an oxidizing agent towards hydrogen sulphide in the presence of moisture, for sulphur is precipitated, and thiosulphate is formed.

The hyposulphites are known commercially as hydrosulphites, since hyposulphurous acid is an old name for thiosulphuric acid (q.v.), and although the use of the term hyposulphite for the salts of the latter acid has been largely given up, it is still retained by photographers, hence giving rise to the possibility of confusion.

§ 41 The Polythionic Acids

There is a remarkable series of five acids—called collectively the polythionic acids—closely related to sulphurous acid and to thiosulphuric acid. The polythionic acids include di-, tri-, tetra-, penta-, and hexa-thionic acids.

These have the general formula $H_2S_nO_6$ and probably have the structure :

$$S_{n\text{-}2}\Big\langle {}^{SO_2OH}_{SO_2OH}$$

Dithionic Acid, $H_2S_2O_6$

The sodium salt is made together with some sulphuric acid, by Spring's reaction with iodine on sodium sulphite :

$$\begin{array}{c} SO_2{<}^{ONa}_{Na} \\ \vdots \\ SO_2{<}^{Na}_{ONa} \end{array} + I_2 = 2NaI + \begin{array}{c} SO_2{-}ONa \\ | \\ SO_2{-}ONa \end{array}$$

The manganese salt, MnS_2O_6, is made by passing sulphur dioxide through water with manganese dioxide in suspension :

$$MnO_2 + 2SO_2 = MnS_2O_6$$

Ferric hydroxide or cobaltic hydroxide forms ferrous or cobaltous sulphate and dithionate when treated with sulphurous acid at a low temperature. Manganese dithionate is converted into barium dithionate, BaS_2O_6, by mixing it with barium hydroxide, $Ba(OH)_2$ and the resulting salt can be purified by crystallization : $BaS_2O_6.2H_2O$ is formed. This gives soluble dithionic acid and insoluble barium sulphate when treated with dilute sulphuric acid. The aqueous solution of the acid can be concentrated by evaporation until its specific gravity is about 1·35, any further concentration decomposes the acid :

$$H_2S_2O_6 = SO_2 + H_2SO_4.$$

Trithionic Acid, $H_2S_3O_6$

The potassium salt of this acid is formed by passing sulphur dioxide through a concentrated solution of potassium thiosulphate :

$$3SO_2 + 2K_2S_2O_3 = S + 2K_2S_3O_6$$

Sodium trithionate is also formed by the action of sulphur chloride, SCl_2, on sodium sulphite, and by warming an aqueous solution of potassium hydrogen sulphite with flowers of sulphur :

$$6KHSO_3 + 2S = 2K_2S_3O_6 + K_2S_2O_2 + 3H_2O.$$

By boiling silver thiosulphate with water, a molecule of Ag_2S splits from two molecules of the thiosulphate and silver trithionate remains :

$$SO_2 < {\overset{OAg \quad AgO}{\underset{S:Ag \quad AgS:}{}}} > SO_2 = Ag_2S + S < {\overset{SO_2.OAg}{\underset{SO_2.OAg.}{}}}$$

The acid itself is formed from the potassium salt by the addition of hydrofluo-silicic acid. Potassium fluosilicate is precipitated, and the trithionic acid remains in solution. The acid and its salts are readily decomposed into sulphur, and sulphuric acid or a sulphate. By the reducing action of sodium amalgam, sodium trithionate is converted back into sodium sulphite and sodium thio-sulphate. According to Chancel and Deacon, when a solution of sodium tri-thionate is boiled with sodium sulphide, sodium thiosulphate is formed. There is thus an intimate relation between thiosulphuric and trithionic acids.

Tetrathionic Acid, $H_2S_4O_6$

The sodium salt is formed by Spring's reaction with iodine and sodium thio-sulphate :

$$\begin{matrix} NaO-SO_2-S \\ \quad \\ NaO-SO_2-S \end{matrix} {\overset{Na}{\underset{Na}{}}} + I_2 = 2NaI + \begin{matrix} NaO-SO_2-S \\ | \\ NaO-SO_2-S. \end{matrix}$$

The barium salt is prepared in a similar manner, and from this the acid itself is obtained by the action of dilute sulphuric acid. The reaction under considera-tion is the last of the set of condensations by the removal of an atom of sodium from each of two molecules of a salt and the condensation of the residues to form a more complex molecule—with sodium thiosulphate, di-, (tri-), and tetrathionate. All these reactions are reversed and the original salts reproduced by treating the complex salts with sodium amalgam. Tetrathionic acid can be made by passing a current of hydrogen sulphide into sulphurous acid until the smell of sulphur dioxide is discharged. The solution can be warmed on a water-bath to get rid of sulphur dioxide and hydrogen sulphide ; the water lost by evaporation being replaced from time to time.

When hydrogen sulphide is passed into a concentrated solution of sulphurous acid at 0°, a solution containing a number of the polythionic acids is formed. It is called **Wackenroder's solution.** It is probable that the first action of the hydrogen sulphide results in the formation of tetrathionic acid :

$$H_2S + 3SO_2 = H_2S_4O_6 ;$$

and that this decomposes into the tri- and pentathionic acids. The passage of the hydrogen sulphide can be continued until the solution contains little more than sulphur and pentathionic acid. The solution containing a mix-ture of sulphur and pentathionic acid can be concentrated by evaporation until its specific gravity is about 1·46, and then saturated with potassium hydroxide ; the solution is filtered to remove the sulphur and allowed to crystal-lize spontaneously. The crystals which separate have the empirical composition : $K_2S_5O_6.3H_2O$. The final products of the action are sulphur and water.

Potassium Hexathionate, K$_2$S$_6$O$_6$, corresponding with the unknown hexathionic acid, H$_2$S$_6$O$_6$, is said to have been prepared in an impure condition from the mother liquid remaining after the separation of potassium pentathionate. The aqueous solution is very unstable.

§ 42 Acid Halides of Sulphur

Acid halides are compounds derived from oxyacids by the replacement of one or more hydroxyl groups by halogen. A whole series of such acid halides are derived from the sulphur acids. Thus, from sulphurous acid, there are :

Thionyl fluoride, SOF$_2$,
Thionyl chloride, SOCl$_2$,
Thionyl bromide, SOBr$_2$;

and, derived from sulphuric acid,

Sulphuryl fluoride, SO$_2$F$_2$,
Sulphuryl chloride, SO$_2$Cl$_2$,
Fluorosulphonic acid, HO.SO$_2$F,
Chlorosulphonic acid, HO.SO$_2$Cl.

Only thionyl chloride, sulphuryl chloride and chlorosulphonic acid are of any great importance.

The remaining possible compounds of bromine and of iodine corresponding to the thionyl and sulphuryl compounds are either unknown, or, if their preparation has been described, their existence is very doubtful.

§ 43 Thionyl Halides

Thionyl Chloride, SOCl$_2$

Thionyl chloride can be prepared by the action of phosphorus pentachloride on sulphur dioxide or sodium sulphite :

$$SO_2 + PCl_5 = SOCl_2 + POCl_3$$
$$Na_2SO_3 + 2PCl_5 = SOCl_2 + 2NaCl + 2POCl_3.$$

It is also formed by the action of sulphur monochloride on sulphur trioxide :

$$SO_3 + S_2Cl_2 = SOCl_2 + SO_2 + S.$$

The first of these methods is often employed in the laboratory ; the last is the usual commercial process, with the modification that chlorine is passed through the mixture in order that the free sulphur formed may be reconverted into sulphur chloride.

Thionyl chloride is a colourless liquid, which fumes in air and boils at 78·8° It is hydrolyzed by water, forming sulphurous acid, and hence is considered to be the acid chloride of sulphurous acid :

$$SOCl_2 + 2H_2O = H_2SO_3 + 2HCl.$$

It finds employment in the laboratory for the replacement of hydroxyl groups by chlorine, since it reacts with hydroxy compounds in a manner similar to phosphorus halides, while having the advantage of giving a gaseous and easily removed by-product, viz., sulphur dioxide. It is used commercially for this purpose in the manufacture of the acid chlorides of organic acids.

Thionyl fluoride is formed by the action of arsenic trifluoride on thionyl chloride, and **thionyl bromide** by treating thionyl chloride with gaseous hydrogen bromide. The reactions of both compounds are similar to those of thionyl chloride.

§ 44 Sulphuryl Compounds

Sulphuryl Chloride, SO_2Cl_2

If a mixture of sulphur dioxide and chlorine be exposed to direct sunlight, especially if a little camphor be present, sulphuryl chloride is obtained :

$$SO_2 + Cl_2 = SO_2Cl_2.$$

It is a colourless liquid, which boils at 69°. It reacts with water in two stages. With a little water, chlorosulphonic acid is formed :

$$SO_2Cl_2 + H_2O = HO.SO_2Cl + HCl ;$$

while, with excess of water, sulphuric acid results :

$$SO_2Cl_2 + 2H_2O = H_2SO_4 + 2HCl.$$

These reactions indicate that sulphuryl chloride is the acid chloride of sulphuric acid.

It is used commercially in the manufacture of organic acid chlorides.

Sulphuryl fluoride, SO_2F_2, has been obtained similarly by the direct union of sulphur dioxide and fluorine. It is a colourless gas and behaves in an analogous manner to the chloride.

Chlorosulphonic Acid, $HO.SO_2Cl$

This acid can be made by direct union of sulphur trioxide and hydrogen chloride :

$$SO_3 + HCl = HO.SO_2Cl ;$$

or by distilling a mixture of concentrated sulphuric acid with phosphorus pentachloride or oxychloride :

$$H_2SO_4 + PCl_5 = HO.SO_2Cl + POCl_3 + HCl$$
$$2H_2SO_4 + POCl_3 = HPO_3 + HCl + 2(HO.SO_2Cl)$$

Chlorosulphonic acid is a colourless liquid which fumes in air and which boils at 151°. It reacts with water with explosive violence, forming a mixture of sulphuric and hydrochloric acids :

$$HO.SO_2Cl + H_2O = H_2SO_4 + HCl.$$

It finds extensive use in organic chemistry both technically (e.g., in the manufacture of saccharine) and in the laboratory.

§ 45 Sulphur Halides

The following halides of sulphur are known with reasonable certainty to exist :—

> Sulphur hexafluoride, SF_6,
> Sulphur decafluoride, S_2F_{10},
> Sulphur monochloride, S_2Cl_2,
> Sulphur dichloride, SCl_2,
> Sulphur tetrachloride, SCl_4,
> Sulphur monobromide, S_2Br_2.

Others have been reported but are more doubtful. No compounds of iodine and sulphur are definitely known, although a solid prepared by the evaporation of a mixed solution of iodine and sulphur in carbon disulphide is prepared and sold under the name of sulphur iodide. This is believed, however, to be either an ordinary mixture or at least a solid solution.

Sulphur Hexafluoride, SF$_6$

Sulphur hexafluoride was obtained by Moissan by the direct action of fluorine on sulphur. It is a colourless, odourless gas, which is comparatively stable and chemically inert. This latter property is particularly exemplified by the fact that it is unaffected by water, whereas the other halides of sulphur are decomposed by water. In this respect sulphur hexafluoride resembles carbon tetrachloride (p. 369), and, with it, differs from most other non-metallic halides.

Sulphur decafluoride, S$_2$F$_{10}$, is reported to have been obtained by the fractionation of the crude hexafluoride (Denbigh and Whytlaw Gray—1934).

Sulphur Monochloride. S$_2$Cl$_2$

When dry chlorine is passed into sulphur heated in a retort, Fig. 179, the two elements combine directly, forming sulphur chloride—S$_2$Cl$_2$—which collects in the receiver cooled by a current of cold water, as a yellow liquid. The oil is purified by redistillation. The pale yellow liquid when pure has a pungent

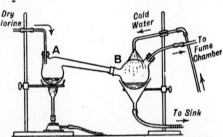

FIG. 179.—Preparation of Sulphur Monochloride.

smell. It boils between 138° and 140°. The liquid fumes in moist air and is decomposed by water, forming sulphur dioxide, hydrochloric acid, and sulphur :

$$2S_2Cl_2 + 3H_2O = 4HCl + H_2SO_3 + 3S .$$

Sulphur chloride is used as a solvent for sulphur in the manufacture of rubber goods ; for decomposing some minerals in analysis ; and in preparing some anhydrous chlorides. Its vapour density is 67·5 (H$_2$ = 1), corresponding with the molecule S$_2$Cl$_2$, not SCl. Hence "sulphur monochloride" does not appear a very appropriate name for this compound.

Sulphur Dichloride, SCl$_2$

If chlorine be passed into sulphur monochloride, cooled in ice, a garnet-red liquid, said to be sulphur dichloride, is obtained :

$$S_2Cl_2 + Cl_2 = 2SCl_2.$$

A mixture of liquid chlorine and sulphur monochloride gradually passes into the same product when kept in a sealed tube at 15°. On heating, it decomposes into sulphur monochloride and chlorine.

Sulphur Tetrachloride, SCl₄

Sulphur tetrachloride is formed by the prolonged action of chlorine on sulphur monochloride at $-22°$:

$$S_2Cl_2 + 3Cl_2 = 2SCl_4.$$

It is a red liquid, which begins to decompose as soon as it is removed from the freezing mixture, forming the dichloride and chlorine. It is now formulated

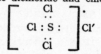

that is as a polar compound.

Sulphur Monobromide, S₂Br₂, is a red liquid which is formed by dissolving sulphur in bromine, or by heating bromine with sulphur. It resembles sulphur monochloride in behaviour.

CHAPTER XXIII

THE HALOGENS

§ 1 The Halogen Group of Elements

THE elements fluorine, chlorine, bromine, and iodine comprise Group VIIB of the Periodic Table (p. 118) and they form one of the best defined families of elements. They are often referred to as **the halogens,** a name given to them by J. J. Berzelius—from the Greek ἅλς (hals), sea salt, and γεννάω (gennao), I produce—since these elements (and in particular chlorine, bromine and iodine) are found in sea water as salts, resembling sea salt, which is sodium chloride. The gradation of properties of these elements, and their compounds, is further discussed at the end of this Chapter (p. 535).

§ 2 Fluorine

Occurrence

Fluorine does not occur free in nature. There is, however, a case recorded by H. Moissan where free fluorine occurs as an inclusion in crystals of fluorspar from Quincié. The compounds of fluorine are widely distributed, though not abundantly, in such minerals as cryolite, fluorspar, etc., and small quantities occur in some of the micas. It is also said to occur in all rocks, thermal waters, and vapours coming from beneath the earth's crust. Traces occur in sea-water, some mineral springs, bones, teeth, blood, milk, plants, etc. The brain of man has about 3 mgrms., and some physiologists believe that the presence of fluorine is necessary in some subtle way, in order that the animal organism can assimilate phosphorus.

History

The fact that glass is attacked when exposed to the fumes produced when fluorspar is warmed with sulphuric acid was known to Schwankhard in 1670, and in 1771 K. W. Scheele stated that fluorspar is the calcium salt of " a peculiar acid "—*fluoric acid.* He prepared this acid by heating fluorspar with sulphuric acid in a tin retort. J. L. Gay-Lussac and J. Thenard (1807) prepared anhydrous hydrogen fluoride, and, following Lavoisier's school, considered fluoric acid to be a compound of water with the oxide of a new element—" fluorium." In 1810 A. Ampère wrote to H. Davy suggesting " many ingenious and original arguments " in favour of the analogy between hydrochloric and hydrofluoric acids. Ampère concluded that hydrofluoric acid contained no oxygen. The close analogies between calcium iodide, bromide, chloride, and fluoride suggested to A. Ampère that fluorspar is a compound of calcium with an unknown element belonging to the same family as chlorine, bromine, and iodine. Ampère's ideas about hydrofluoric acid were established by H. Davy's experimental work, 1813, and the unknown element was named " fluorine " by analogy with chlorine.

Preparation

For many years the isolation of fluorine was one of the major problems of chemistry. No one doubted the existence of fluorine, although it successfully withstood every attempted method of isolation, and for over seventy years had never been seen or handled. Fluorine appeared to be so very powerful that no vessel seemed to be capable of resisting its chemical action ; and it was compared with the *alkahest* or the universal solvent of alchemy.

All kinds of expedients were tried without success, among which may be mentioned the electrolysis of hydrofluoric acid (Davy), which failed on account of the presence of water (see below) ; the electrolysis of *anhydrous* hydrogen fluoride which was attempted by Gore, who found it to be a non-conductor ; and the action of chlorine on mercuric fluoride in fluorspar vessels (G. J. and T. Knox, 1836). The problem was finally solved by Moissan in 1886 by the electrolysis of a solution of potassium fluoride in anhydrous hydrogen fluoride.

When an electric current is passed through a concentrated solution of hydrogen chloride, chlorine is liberated at the anode, and hydrogen at the cathode. When aqueous hydrofluoric acid is treated in the same way, water alone is decomposed, for oxygen is liberated at the anode, and hydrogen at the cathode. The anhydrous acid does not conduct electricity, and it cannot therefore be electrolyzed. Moissan found that if potassium fluoride be dissolved in the liquid hydrogen fluoride, the solution conducts electricity, and when electrolyzed, hydrogen is evolved at the cathode, and fluorine at the anode. The primary products of the electrolysis are fluorine at the anode, potassium at the cathode :

$$2KHF_2 = 2HF + 2K + F_2.$$

The potassium reacts with the hydrogen fluoride, reforming potassium fluoride and liberating hydrogen :

$$2K + 2HF = 2KF + H_2.$$

The electrolysis was first conducted in a U-tube made from an alloy of platinum and iridium which is less attacked by fluorine than platinum alone. Later experiments showed that a tube of copper could be employed. The copper is attacked by the fluorine, forming a surface crust of copper fluoride which protects the tube from further action.

In Moissan's apparatus electrodes of platinum iridium alloy were used and the open ends of the tube were closed with fluorspar stoppers, the joints being made tight with lead washers and shellac. During electrolysis the apparatus was immersed in a bath of evaporating methyl chloride.

More recently the method of preparing fluorine has been improved by Dennis, Veeder and Rochow (1931). In their method (illustrated in Fig. 180) fused, perfectly dry potassium hydrogen fluoride is

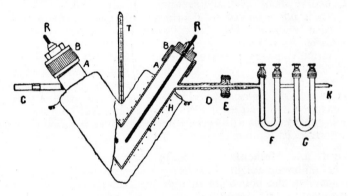

Fig. 180.—Preparation of Fluorine.

electrolyzed between graphite electrodes, in a heavy V-shaped tube A, made of copper, two inches in diameter. The ends are closed with copper caps B, into which the electrodes R are fixed with bakelite cement, which was found to be able to withstand the action of fluorine. The whole cell is lagged with asbestos H, and heated electrically to fuse the potassium hydrogen fluoride. The fluorine evolved is freed from hydrogen fluoride vapour by passing it through U-tubes F, G, filled with sodium fluoride, with which the hydrogen fluoride forms sodium hydrogen fluoride.

Properties

Fluorine is a light canary-yellow gas which condenses to a clear yellow liquid boiling at $-187°$; and freezes to a pale yellow solid melting at $-223°$; at $-252°$ the solid is colourless. Fluorine is probably the most active element known. It combines with hydrogen with explosion, even in the dark, and at low temperatures, say, $-210°$. It decomposes water, forming hydrogen fluoride, and liberates oxygen highly charged with ozone. Sulphur, selenium, and tellurium melt and take fire in the gas, forming a mixture of fluorides. Iodine, bromine, phosphorus, arsenic, and antimony combine with the gas with incandescence; so do crystalline silicon, amorphous boron, powdered charcoal. All metals are acted upon by the gas; some take fire spontaneously—e.g., the metals of the alkalis and alkaline earths:

others—e.g., magnesium, aluminium, nickel, and silver—require warming to start the reaction ; others again require heating to, say, 300°, e.g., gold and platinum. Fluorine also liberates chlorine from sodium chloride and from carbon tetrachloride, CCl_4. Liquid fluorine has no action on silicon, phosphorus, sulphur and glass. It does not react with nitrogen, oxygen, or chlorine, even at the temperature of the electric arc or induction discharge. Palladium and iridium are attacked at about 500°, and rhodium scarcely at all.

Glass is not attacked by fluorine, if the gas is *entirely* free from hydrogen fluoride. This latter substance can only be removed adequately by cooling the fluorine in liquid air.

Fluorine is a very powerful oxidizing agent. It decomposes water with evolution of oxygen charged with ozone, and this oxygen is liberated associated with a very large amount of energy. As an example of this, fluorine passed into an aqueous solution of potassium chlorate, $KClO_3$, oxidizes it to the perchlorate, $KClO_4$

Fluorine combines with each of the other halogens forming a variety of interhalogen compounds (see p. 534).

Atomic and Molecular Weight of Fluorine

The combining weight of fluorine has been established by converting calcium fluoride, potassium fluoride, sodium fluoride, etc., into the corresponding sulphates.

The best determinations by these methods resulted in values between 18·97 and 19·14, and the best representative value is taken to be 19·00. Quite recently Cawood and Patterson (1936) have determined the atomic weight of fluorine by the limiting density method from the densities of carbon tetrafluoride and methyl fluoride. Their value for the atomic weight is 18·996. No known volatile compound of fluorine is known to contain less than 19 parts of fluorine per molecule, and hence this is taken as the atomic weight. The vapour density of fluorine corresponds with the formula F_2.

§ 3 Hydrogen Fluoride, H_2F_2

Hydrofluoric acid—an aqueous solution of hydrogen fluoride—is manufactured by the action of sulphuric acid on calcium fluoride (fluorspar) :

$$CaF_2 + H_2SO_4 = H_2F_2 + CaSO_4.$$

The operation is carried out in a cast-iron pot or retort connected to a series of leaden boxes containing water or dilute hydrofluoric acid to absorb the gas from the retorts. The condensers are submerged in water to keep them cool. A by-product, calcium fluosulphonate, $Ca(FSO_3)_2$, is also formed and remains in the retort. Commercial hydrofluoric acid is marketed in lead, gutta-percha or wax (cerasine) bottles, since it attacks glass.

Pure hydrogen fluoride is prepared in the laboratory by distilling pure, dry potassium hydrogen fluoride in a copper or platinum apparatus ; the pure acid which distils over is collected in a copper bottle cooled in a freezing mixture :

$$2KHF_2 = 2KF + H_2F_2.$$

Copper is not affected by the pure acid ; it is, however, attacked by the aqueous solution. Anhydrous hydrogen fluoride can also be obtained by passing dry hydrogen over dry silver fluoride.

Properties

Anhydrous hydrogen fluoride is a limpid liquid which fumes strongly in air. It is very poisonous and dangerous to manipulate. It forms ulcerated sores if a drop comes in contact with the skin. The metals potassium and sodium dissolve in the pure acid, forming the corresponding fluorides and hydrogen. The liquid acid boils at $19 \cdot 4°$, and freezes at $-102 \cdot 5°$. The crystals melt at $-83°$. Hydrogen fluoride is very soluble in water, forming a corrosive liquid which readily dissolves many metals with evolution of hydrogen, e.g., iron, silver and copper. If the acid be more concentrated than about 36 per cent. HF, it will become weaker on boiling ; and if more dilute, the acid becomes stronger on boiling until an acid containing about 36 per cent. of HF, boiling at $130°$, is formed. This distils unchanged in composition.

Hydrofluoric acid is a weak acid, weaker than phosphoric acid but stronger than nitrous acid. The anhydrous acid resembles water in certain aspects of its behaviour. Thus, it is associated (cf. p. 286 and see below), it has a relatively high boiling point ($19 \cdot 5°$) and it is an ionizing solvent.

The action of hydrofluoric acid on silica and silicates in general (e.g., glass) is interesting and important. When a strong solution of the acid is brought in contact with silica, silicon tetrafluoride is formed, which, in presence of excess of hydrofluoric acid, combines with it to form hydrofluosilicic acid :

$$SiO_2 + 2H_2F_2 = SiF_4 + 2H_2O$$
$$SiF_4 + H_2F_2 = H_2SiF_6.$$

The action on silicates is similar, for instance with ordinary " soda-glass " (p. 691) sodium and calcium fluosilicates are formed :

$$CaSiO_3 + 3H_2F_2 = CaSiF_6 + 3H_2O$$
$$Na_2SiO_3 + 3H_2F_2 = Na_2SiF_6 + 3H_2O.$$

Uses of Hydrofluoric Acid

The action of hydrofluoric acid on silica is used for etching glass. Glass may be etched with the gas or with an aqueous solution of the gas. In the former case, the etching appears opaque and dull ; in the latter case, shining and transparent. For etching, the glass is covered with a film of wax, and the design to be etched on the glass is drawn on the waxed surface with a stylus ; or else the parts of the glass not to be etched are coated with a resistant varnish. The surface is exposed to the action of the acid or gas, and very soon the glass is etched. The wax or varnish is then washed off with turpentine. The process is used for marking the scales on glass instruments.

Hydrofluoric acid is also employed for freeing artificial graphite (p. 326) from silica; and in the dyeing industry, double fluorides of antimony and the alkali metals are now used as mordants in place of tartar emetic. In the spirit and brewing industry, hydrofluoric acid is coming into favour as an antiseptic since its effect on yeast is very small compared with its action on other organisms. It is also employed for freeing iron castings from sand, and has been recommended for cleaning copper. In the laboratory, the solvent action of hydrofluoric acid on silica is made use of in the quantitative analysis of siliceous minerals.

Composition and Formula of Hydrogen Fluoride

G. Gore (1870) measured the volume of hydrogen necessary to form hydrogen fluoride when heated with silver fluoride at 100°, and found that 100 volumes of hydrogen give very nearly 200 volumes of hydrogen fluoride. On the basis of the equation :

$$H_2 + 2AgF = 2HF + 2Ag$$

this indicates the formula HF at this temperature.

The vapour density at 26·4° is 25·59 ($H_2 = 1$), but, as the temperature is raised, it diminishes steadily until at 88° it has fallen to 10·29 This number corresponds with the formula HF. Hence, at lower temperatures, hydrogen fluoride is associated. The effect of hydrogen fluoride on the freezing point of water corresponds also with a molecule H_2F_2, and this is the formula usually adopted, since it is also in agreement with the fact that acid salts (e.g., KHF_2) are readily obtained. The most probable explanation of the facts mentioned seems to be, however, that the pure liquid (and the vapour at the boiling point) contains molecules in various degrees of association, at least up to H_3F_3; the concentrated solution consists mostly of H_2F_2 molecules; dilute solutions and the vapour above 88° are mostly composed of HF molecules.

Fluorides

The salts of hydrofluoric acid are the fluorides and in many ways resemble the chlorides (q.v.). The principal differences are the formation of acid fluorides (e.g., KHF_2) and double salts (e.g., $AlF_3.3NaF$ or Na_3AlF_6), the solubility of silver fluoride and the insolubility of calcium fluoride. (Silver chloride is insoluble and calcium chloride is very soluble.)

Detection and Determination

In testing for fluorides, the substance under examination is warmed with sulphuric acid in a leaden vessel covered with a watch-glass. The watch-glass is coated with wax, and a design ✠ is scratched on the wax with a pin or knife, so as to expose the glass to the action of the acid. The wax is afterwards removed, and if the design is etched on the glass, fluorides were present.

The standard method for the estimation of fluorides, until lately, has been to precipitate the fluorine as calcium fluoride, by addition of calcium chloride solution to a solution made from the substance under examination. Recently, however, new methods have been developed in which the fluorine is precipitated as lead chlorofluoride (PbClF), the process having the advantage of greater accuracy over the old method, as well as being applicable either gravimetrically or volumetrically.

§ 4 Oxygen Compounds of Fluorine

Until comparatively recently, fluorine was believed to be incapable of forming any compound with oxygen, but three oxides, F_2O, F_2O_2 and FO, have now been described and fluorates are also thought to have been made.

(Di)**Fluorine monoxide**, F_2O, was obtained by Lebeau and Damiens (1919) by passing a fine stream of fluorine through a 2 per cent. solution of sodium hydroxide :

$$2NaOH + 2F_2 = 2NaF + F_2O + H_2O.$$

This reaction should be compared with that of chlorine in which sodium hypochlorite and chloride are formed (p. 508). (Di)fluorine monoxide is described as a gas with an irritating odour, which does not attack glass and is a powerful oxidizing agent.

Difluorine dioxide, F_2O_2, is said to be formed by the action of an electric discharge on a mixture of fluorine and oxygen at low pressure and the temperature of liquid air. It is said to be a brown gas which (according to Ruff and Menzel 1933) forms **monofluorine monoxide, FO**, when the temperature rises to $-100°$; this latter gas is colourless and does not revert to F_2O_2 on cooling. According to the most recent work (Frisch and Schumacher—1936) the so-called FO is a mixture of fluorine and oxygen.

Fluorates (XFO_3) are said to have been isolated from the product obtained by electrolyzing a fused mixture of potassium fluoride with potassium hydroxide.

§ 5 Chlorine

History

Chlorine was first isolated by Scheele in 1774 by the action of manganese dioxide on hydrochloric acid, and was named by him *dephlogisticated marine acid air*. After the overthrow of the phlogiston theory by Lavoisier, it was for a time called *oxymuriatic acid* (muriatic acid being the name by which hydrochloric acid was then known). It was believed to contain oxygen, since Lavoisier had thought that all acids contain oxygen. This view of the nature of chlorine and hydrochloric acid was disproved by Davy in 1810 who demonstrated its elementary nature and suggested the name chlorine—from the Greek χλωρόσ (chloros), greenish yellow—on account of its colour.

Occurrence

Chlorine does not occur free in nature, but is found in combination in immense quantities. Among naturally occurring chlorine compounds may be mentioned common salt—sodium chloride—NaCl, which is found in the sea and in the form of rock salt, and potassium chloride (sylvine) and potassium magnesium chloride (carnallite) of the Stassfurt deposits.

The remarkable deposits of potassium, magnesium and sodium salts in the country around Stassfurt, in Prussian Saxony, may be very roughly divided into four strata, illustrated diagrammatically in Fig. 181.

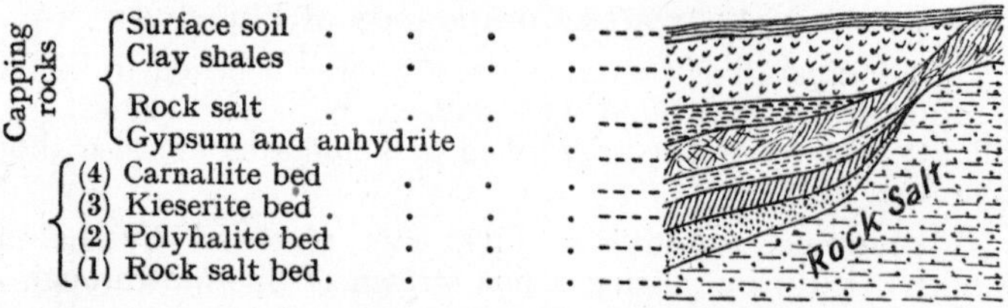

Capping rocks
{ Surface soil . . . .
  Clay shales . . . .
  Rock salt . . . .
  Gypsum and anhydrite . .

{ (4) Carnallite bed . . .
  (3) Kieserite bed . . .
  (2) Polyhalite bed . . .
  (1) Rock salt bed . . .

Fig. 181.—Diagrammatic Geological Section of a Part of the Stassfurt Salt Bed.

(1) *Rock salt bed.*—An immense basal bed of rock salt, broken up at fairly regular intervals with 2 to 5 inch bands of *anhydrite*—$CaSO_4$.

(2) *Polyhalite bed.*—Above the basal salt is a layer of rock salt, sometimes 200 feet thick, mixed with bands of magnesium chloride and *polyhalite*—$2CaSO_4.MgSO_4.K_2SO_4.2H_2O$.

(3) *Kieserite bed.*—Resting on the polyhalite bed is a layer of rock salt, sometimes 100 feet thick, mixed with layers of *kieserite*—$MgSO_4.H_2O$—and other sulphates, about 1 foot thickness.

(4) *Carnallite bed.*—Finally comes a reddish layer of rock salt associated with masses of *kainite*—$K_2SO_4.MgSO_4.MgCl_2.6H_2O$; *carnallite* —$KCl.MgCl_2.6H_2O$; and a few other salts of magnesium and potassium, e.g., *sylvine*—KCl and *leonite*—$MgSO_4.K_2SO_4.4H_2O$.

These deposits are capped by layers of gypsum—$CaSO_4.2H_2O$—and anhydrite—$CaSO_4$; rock salt ; bunter clay shales ; and finally the surface soil. In addition to gypsum ($CaSO_4.2H_2O$), anhydrite ($CaSO_4$), and rock salt (NaCl), the principal salts found in the Stassfurt deposits are :—

Sylvine	.	.	.	.	KCl
Carnallite				.	$KCl.MgCl_2.6H_2O$
Kieserite	.	.	.	.	$MgSO_4.H_2O$
Schönite	.	.	.	.	$MgSO_4.K_2SO_4.6H_2O$
Kainite	.	.	.	.	$MgSO_4.K_2SO_4.MgCl_2.6H_2O$
Polyhalite	.	.	.	.	$MgSO_4.K_2SO_4.2CaSO_4.2H_2O$

along with several other salts of lesser importance. These deposits were the subject of extensive investigation by J. A. Van't Hoff and his pupils in the light of the Phase Rule (p. 158).

It is generally thought that the Stassfurt beds are of marine origin, and have been formed by the natural evaporation of water, during countless years, in an inland prehistoric sea, probably communicating with the ocean by a shallow bar. The sea must have been intermittently replenished by water bringing in more salts, as could occur when driven over the bar by high tides and gales; there must also have been a number of geological elevations and depressions to account for the succession of strata. The order in which salts are deposited from the evaporation of sea-water is very nearly the same as the geological succession observed at Stassfurt. Neglecting the calcium sulphate, the evaporation of sea-water furnishes successively : (1) a deposit of sodium chloride ; (2) sodium chloride mixed with magnesium sulphate ; (3) sodium chloride and leonite ; (4) sodium chloride, leonite, and potassium chloride, or sodium chloride and kainite ; (5) sodium chloride, kieserite, and carnallite ; (6) sodium chloride, kieserite, carnallite, magnesium chloride ; and (7) the solution dries without further change.

§ 6 Preparation and Manufacture of Chlorine

Chlorine is readily obtained either :

(i) by oxidation of hydrochloric acid, or

(ii) by electrolysis of sodium chloride.

The oxidation method was formerly employed almost exclusively, both in the laboratory and industrially, but though still employed in the laboratory it has now given place, to a large extent, to electrolytic processes for the manufacture of chlorine commercially.

Laboratory Preparation of Chlorine

Chlorine is usually prepared in the laboratory by the oxidation of hydrochloric acid, manganese dioxide or potassium permanganate being the oxidizing agents most often used.

With manganese dioxide, the apparatus indicated in Fig. 182 is used.

Manganese dioxide is placed in the flask and concentrated hydrochloric acid, sufficient to cover it, is added through the thistle funnel. The mixture is heated and the chlorine formed is collected by downward delivery, since it is soluble in water. It may previously be passed through a *little* water (to remove hydrogen chloride) and dried by means of concentrated sulphuric

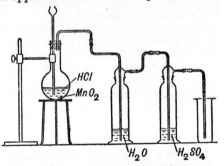

Fig. 182.—Preparation of Chlorine using Manganese Dioxide.

acid. The reaction takes place in two stages, represented by the equations :

$$2MnO_2 + 8HCl = 2MnCl_3 + Cl_2 + 4H_2O$$
$$2MnCl_3 = 2MnCl_2 + Cl_2$$

The first stage takes place even in the cold, the second only on warming.

A mixture of sodium chloride, manganese dioxide and concentrated sulphuric acid is sometimes used instead of hydrochloric acid and manganese dioxide. Hydrogen chloride is first formed (p. 499) and this then reacts as above.

The use of potassium permanganate to oxidize hydrochloric acid is convenient since external heat is not required, and so is often employed. The apparatus, shown in Fig. 183, may be used, the permanganate being placed in the flask and the concentrated hydrochloric acid added through the tap funnel. The reaction is represented :

$$2KMnO_4 + 16HCl = 2KCl + 2MnCl_2 + 5Cl_2 + 8H_2O.$$

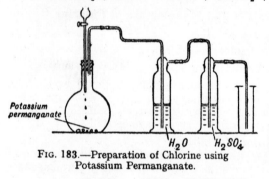

FIG. 183.—Preparation of Chlorine using Potassium Permanganate.

Another very convenient laboratory method for the preparation of chlorine is by the action of an acid (usually hydrochloric acid) upon bleaching powder (q.v. p. 510). The apparatus of Fig. 183 is again suitable.

$$CaOCl_2 + 2HCl = CaCl_2 + Cl_2 + H_2O.$$

Manufacture of Chlorine

Chlorine was formerly manufactured on a large scale by the oxidation of the hydrochloric acid produced in the Leblanc process for the production of sodium carbonate (p. 558). The proportion of the world's total chlorine output made in this way is steadily diminishing through the increasing importance of the electrolytic process for the manufacture of sodium hydroxide, which produces chlorine and hydrogen at the same time.

The principal oxidation processes were those associated with the names of Deacon and Weldon.

Deacon's process utilized air as the oxidizing agent by passing a mixture of air and hydrogen chloride through vertical cylinders containing pieces of porous earthenware impregnated with cuprous chloride, the temperature being kept at about 400°. The final reaction may be represented :

$$4HCl + O_2[+ Cu_2Cl_2] = Cl_2 + 2H_2O[+ Cu_2Cl_2].$$

It is supposed, however, that the reaction takes place in stages, viz.,

(i) $2Cu_2Cl_2 + O_2 = 2Cu_2OCl_2$,

(ii) $Cu_2OCl_2 + 2HCl = 2CuCl_2 + H_2O$,

(iii) $2CuCl_2 = Cu_2Cl_2 + Cl_2$.

The chlorine is necessarily contaminated with undecomposed hydrogen chloride, atmospheric nitrogen, atmospheric oxygen, and steam. The steam and hydrogen chloride can be removed by washing. The chlorine so prepared is used in the manufacture of bleaching powder, where the presence of the impurities does no particular harm. The chlorine produced by Deacon's process is, however, too dilute to be utilized in any other way.

Weldon's process uses crude manganese dioxide, in the form of the mineral *pyrolusite*, to oxidize the hydrochloric acid, thus reproducing, on an industrial scale, the laboratory method described above. The essential feature of the method, as applied technically, is the recovery of the manganese dioxide, the method of recovery used being due to Weldon.

After the chlorine has been driven off, the hot residual liquor, consisting largely of manganous chloride, is treated with excess of milk of lime, and air is blown through the warm mixture for some hours. Heat is evolved in the reaction in sufficient amount to keep it going without the application of external heat. When the suspended solid is fully oxidized (the presence of a base is necessary for the oxidization of the manganese by air), it is allowed to settle out and is used (in this form known as *Weldon mud*) for the oxidation of more hydrochloric acid. The reactions which take place have been said to be :

$$MnCl_2 + Ca(OH)_2 = Mn(OH)_2 + CaCl_2$$
$$2Mn(OH)_2 + 2Ca(OH)_2 + O_2 = 2CaO.MnO_2 + 4H_2O.$$
calcium
manganite

The second reaction is probably more complicated than **this**, for the mud has a composition which varies between that represented by $CaO.MnO_2$ and $CaO.2MnO_2$, and it has been suggested that it consists of a mixture of hydroxides. It is very doubtful if it is actually calcium manganite.

The recovery of the manganese dioxide in this way really makes it a means of utilizing the oxygen of the air indirectly for the oxidation of the hydrochloric acid, but it should be noticed that at least half of the hydrochloric acid is wasted as calcium chloride.

Electrolytic Processes

The electrolysis of aqueous solutions of common salt produces as final products : an aqueous solution of sodium hydroxide, chlorine and hydrogen, and is now carried out on a very large scale. The chlorine might almost be thought of as a by-product (the hydrogen certainly) since of recent years the demand for caustic soda has increased so much more rapidly than that for chlorine that the disposal of the latter has become a problem.

The actions which take place may be represented :

$$NaCl = Na^{.} + Cl'$$
$$2Na + 2H_2O = 2NaOH + H_2 \uparrow$$
$$Cl + Cl = Cl_2 \uparrow$$

In practice, it is necessary to devise some method of separating the caustic soda from the sodium chloride and for preventing the sodium hydroxide and chlorine from mixing. Hence the use of special types of cell.

Two main types of cell have been used, viz.,

(i) cells having a porous diaphragm between the anode and cathode ;

(ii) cells using a mercury " diaphragm " or cathode.

Porous Diaphragm Cells

A great many cells embodying the porous diaphragm principle have been devised, but for the most part they do not differ in principle. A typical example of such a cell is the **Gibbs cell,** used extensively

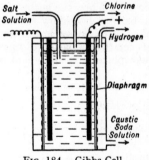

FIG. 184.—Gibbs Cell.

both in this country and in America (Fig. 184). In this cell the anodes (a ring of carbon rods) are separated from the cathode (which is a cylinder of iron gauze) by a diaphragm made of asbestos paper. The brine solution, heated to 85°, is introduced continuously in a slow stream into the anode compartment and caustic soda solution drips out from the bottom of the cathode compartment, and is evaporated (see p. 554). The chlorine escapes from the top of the anode and is led off through earthenware pipes.

Mercury Diaphragm Cells

One of the best-known cells using a mercury diaphragm is the **Kellner-Solvay Cell,** illustrated in Fig. 185. It uses graphite anodes and a mercury cathode. A layer of mercury covers the bottom of the cell through which it flows slowly. A solution of alkali chloride flows through the cell, and is decomposed by the electric current into chlorine at the anode and sodium at the cathode. The latter dissolves in the mercury, at the cathode, and the chlorine at the anodes escapes via the exit pipes. The sodium amalgam then flows out of the cell into a vessel containing water, and there, coming into contact with the water, is immediately decomposed into sodium hydroxide and mercury, and hydrogen is evolved.

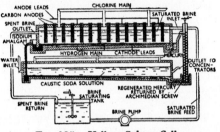

FIG. 185.—Kellner-Solvay Cell.

In earlier forms, the cell was given a slow rocking motion by means of an eccentric so as to make the mercury flow from one compartment to another ; but in later types the cell is stationary and the mercury is moved by means of an archimedean screw. The disadvantage of this type of cell is the heavy capital cost of the mercury required, but the caustic soda is of superior purity.

The chlorine manufactured by any of these processes may be used for the preparation of bleaching powder or other chemicals, or it may be liquefied by compression into steel cylinders and sold in this form.

§ 7 Properties of Chlorine

Chlorine is a yellowish-green gas with an irritating and suffocating smell. It attacks the membrane of the throat, lungs and nose and causes serious injury even at high dilutions. It is thus a very poisonous gas. Chlorine is about two and a half times as heavy as air and so is the heaviest of the common elementary gases. It is readily liquefied and forms a dark greenish-yellow liquid which boils at $-34 \cdot 6°$ at atmospheric pressure. The liquid, contained in steel cylinders (which are not attacked by *dry* chlorine), is an article of commerce. Chlorine is soluble in water, 1 volume of water dissolving 4·61 volumes of the gas at 0°, and 2·26 volumes at 20°. It is also soluble in carbon tetrachloride and this solution is used as a reagent.

The solution of chlorine in water, known as **chlorine water,** has the colour, taste and smell of chlorine. If chlorine water be cooled to 0°, yellow octahedral crystals of **chlorine hydrate** separate. Various formulae have been stated for this substance, but it has usually been taken to be $Cl_2.8H_2O$. When warmed, chlorine hydrate gives off approximately 100 times its volume of chlorine, and in consequence of this property it was used by Faraday in 1823 for the liquefaction of chlorine (p. 37).

The yellow colour of chlorine water gradually disappears on standing and if exposed to sunlight the solution evolves oxygen. This behaviour is due to the formation of hypochlorous acid (p. 508), through the interaction of the chlorine and water :

$$Cl_2 + H_2O = HCl + HOCl.$$

Hypochlorous acid decomposes readily in sunlight, forming hydrochloric acid and oxygen :

$$2HOCl = 2HCl + O_2.$$

Thoroughly dry chlorine is somewhat inert chemically (ct. p. 285), but as ordinarily obtained it is highly reactive. It does not combine directly with oxygen, nitrogen or carbon (although compounds with all three can be obtained indirectly) but with most other non-metals it does so readily. Many, for example, sulphur, phosphorus and arsenic, burn vigorously in chlorine : chlorine forms a number of compounds with the other halogens (p. 534).

The interaction of chlorine and hydrogen is particularly interesting, and has been the subject of a great many researches. In sunlight, or when exposed to the light of burning magnesium, equal volumes of hydrogen and chlorine combine with explosion. Yet hydrogen does not appear to combine with chlorine with appreciable velocity in the dark, but in diffused daylight, the two slowly combine to form hydrogen chloride. The speed of the reaction is proportional to the intensity of the light. Hence, actinometers have been designed to measure the intensity of light in terms of the speed of combination of a mixture of hydrogen and chlorine gases. If light be filtered through a layer of chlorine gas before it impinges on the mixture of hydrogen and chlorine, the light produces no appreciable effect. **Insolated chlorine** rises slightly in temperature, even when the heat rays have been filtered from the incident light. It is therefore inferred that *actinic (light) energy absorbed by chlorine is at once degraded into thermal energy. If hydrogen be associated with the chlorine, when exposed to light, the process of degradation of the actinic energy is accompanied by chemical action* (J. W. Mellor, 1902). The presence of minute traces of impurities in the gases retards the rate of combination in a remarkable way.

Thus a mixture of fairly pure hydrogen and chlorine, when exposed to diffused daylight, exhibits an *induction period* during which no reaction occurs, and after which the gases begin to react and continue to do so steadily until combination is complete. This induction period has been shown to be caused by the presence of traces of an inhibitor (nitrogen chloride, NCl_3, according to D. L. Chapman—1906) which is slowly destroyed by light, so that combination of the hydrogen and chlorine does not take place until the inhibitor has been completely removed.

With the exception of some of the scarcer platinum metals (p. 835) all metals are attacked by free chlorine. Many, such as antimony, copper, tin, zinc, magnesium, alkaline earth and alkali metals burn brightly in the gas ; the compound formed being the highest chloride unless this is definitely unstable.

Hydrides of non-metals react with chlorine giving, as a rule, hydrogen chloride, together with either the non-metallic element itself ; or a chloride of the non-metal :

$$H_2S + Cl_2 = 2HCl + S$$
$$2S + Cl_2 = S_2Cl_2.$$

Ammonia yields nitrogen, or nitrogen trichloride according to the conditions (p. 497). Hydrocarbons react readily with chlorine ; some, e.g., turpentine, inflame spontaneously, carbon being deposited. Others when ignited react similarly, e.g.,

$$CH_4 + 2Cl_2 = 4HCl + C.$$

Chlorine readily displaces bromine and iodine from their compounds with metals, e.g.,

$$Cl_2 + 2KBr = 2KCl + Br_2.$$

Moist chlorine, or chlorine water, is a powerful oxidizing agent. Mention has been made (p. 496) of the action of chlorine on water in sunlight, oxygen being given off and hydrogen chloride formed. In presence of an oxidizable substance, this process occurs even in the absence of light. Thus, for example, chlorine oxidizes sulphites to sulphates :

$$Cl_2 + H_2O + Na_2SO_3 = 2HCl + Na_2SO_4.$$

Chlorine may also act as an oxidizing agent more directly. Thus ferrous chloride is oxidized directly to ferric chloride :

$$2FeCl_2 + Cl_2 = 2FeCl_3,$$

and hydrogen sulphide to sulphur

$$H_2S + Cl_2 = 2HCl + S$$

(but see above).

On account of its oxidizing properties, moist chlorine will bleach many organic colouring matters. If a piece of coloured litmus paper, or a few coloured flower petals or a piece of cloth dyed with turkey red or indigo be placed in a jar of dry chlorine, no appreciable change occurs ; but if moisture be present, the colours are bleached by the chlorine. This bleaching action of chlorine due to *oxidation* should be compared with the bleaching action of sulphur dioxide which is due to *reduction* (p. 456) and which therefore is markedly different in character.

§ 8 Uses of Chlorine

The uses of chlorine are many, although the demand for caustic soda (p. 556) has increased so much of late that the supply of chlorine available is now tending to exceed the demand.

Chlorine is used extensively in the manufacture of bleaching powder (p. 510) and so for bleaching purposes. It is employed in this way for bleaching cellulose fabrics (linen and cotton) which are unaffected by chlorine ; nitrogenous fibres (such as silk and wool) are liable to be damaged by it. Chlorine is also used for bleaching wood-pulp and paper. It finds employment in the extraction of gold, the manufacture of bromine, of carbon tetrachloride, and many other organic solvents and chlorine derivatives, and in the dyestuffs industry. It is used in the manufacture of chloroform, and of chlorates (p. 513). It is also employed for the sterilization of drinking water, and in swimming baths and for the purification of sewage. It is now also used for " de-gassing " molten aluminium before casting. Hydrochloric acid is now manufactured by combining chlorine with hydrogen (p. 501).

§ 9 Formula and Atomic Weight of Chlorine

The combining weight of chlorine has been determined with very great accuracy by Richards, as indicated on page 97. He obtained the value 35·457. Analysis and determinations of the vapour density of volatile chlorine compounds indicate that these never contain less than about $35\frac{1}{2}$ parts by weight of chlorine per molecule. Hence the atomic weight is the same as the combining weight. The accepted value at present (1940) is 35·46.

A very careful determination of the density of hydrogen chloride by the limiting density method (p. 103) by Gray and Burt in 1909 gave results which lead to the value 35·458 for the atomic weight of chlorine ; a value in excellent agreement with that determined chemically.

The vapour density of chlorine below 600° is 35·46 ($H_2 = 1$) corresponding with a molecule Cl_2 ; at higher temperatures the density diminishes, showing that partial dissociation into atoms is taking place :

$$Cl_2 \rightleftharpoons Cl + Cl.$$

Thus, according to Victor Meyer, at 1400° the density ($H_2 = 1$) is 29·29, corresponding to a dissociation of about 21 per cent.

§ 10 Detection and Determination of Chlorine

Traces of free chlorine are readily detected by the fact that chlorine liberates iodine from potassium iodide (cf. p. 497). Free iodine gives a blue colour with starch—a very sensitive reaction. Hence papers dipped in a mixture of starch solution and potassium iodide solution give a blue colour when exposed to chlorine. (It should be noted that a number of other oxidizing agents will also liberate iodine from potassium iodide.) Chlorine in rather larger quantity is detected by its bleaching action on litmus paper.

Free chlorine is determined by passing it into a solution of potassium iodide, and titrating the iodine so liberated with a standard solution of sodium thiosulphate (p. 527).

The detection and determination of chlorine in the form of chlorides is discussed under hydrochloric acid (p. 505).

§ 11 Hydrogen Chloride, Hydrochloric Acid, HCl

History

Judging from the writings attributed to Geber, hydrochloric acid was known to the early Arabian chemists ; but the preparation of the pure acid—*spiritus salis*—seems to have been first described by the author of the writings ascribed to Basil Valentine (1644). The acid appears to have been made by distilling a mixture of common salt and green vitriol (ferrous sulphate). J. R. Glauber (1648) described the preparation of the acid by the action of sulphuric acid on rock salt. Stephen Hales (1727) noticed that a gas very soluble in water was made by heating sulphuric acid with sal ammoniac (ammonium chloride), and J. Priestley, about 1772, collected the gas over mercury, and gave it the name *marine acid air*. It was later re-named *muriatic acid* and, when the elementary nature of chlorine had been established, the name hydrochloric acid was given to it.

Preparation and Manufacture

Laboratory Preparation

Hydrogen chloride is usually made in the laboratory by the action of concentrated sulphuric acid upon common salt. The experiment is performed by means of the apparatus shown in Fig. 182. Salt is placed in the flask, concentrated sulphuric acid is added through the thistle funnel and the mixture is warmed. Hydrogen chloride is evolved as a gas and may be dried by passing through wash-bottles containing concentrated sulphuric acid. It can be collected by downward delivery as shown in the diagram, or over mercury, but **not** over water as it is extremely soluble. At temperatures below a red heat, the reaction is represented :

$$NaCl + H_2SO_4 = NaHSO_4 + HCl.$$

If it is desired to prepare a specimen of the aqueous solution, precautions must be taken when passing the gas into water in order to prevent the liquid from being " sucked back " due to the high solubility of the gas.

Two methods of doing this are indicated in Figs. 186 and 187 and are self explanatory. These methods can be employed in the preparation of solutions of highly soluble gases, in general.

It is often convenient in the laboratory, when the gas is required, to prepare it from the commercial solution. This can easily be done by adding concentrated sulphuric acid by means of a tap-funnel to a quantity of the solution (ordinary concentrated hydrochloric acid) contained in a flask fitted with a delivery tube. The apparatus used for obtaining chlorine (Fig. 183) is convenient.

Manufacture

Hydrochloric acid was for a long time manufactured as a by-product of the Leblanc process for making sodium carbonate (p. 558). With the decline and final aban-donment of this method of alkali manufacture in this country, this has ceased to be the only source of hydrochloric acid ; but there is still a considerable demand for sodium sulphate, the pre-paration of which is the first stage of the Leblanc process, and large quanti-ties of hydrochloric acid are still made in this way.

Two molecular pro-portions of salt and one of sulphuric acid are heated in a shallow cast-iron pan in a furnace similar to that illustrated

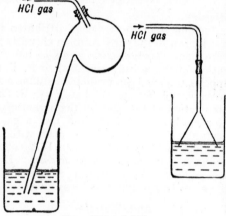

FIGS. 186 and 187.— Anti Suck-back Devices.

in Fig. 188. At the temperature reached in the pan, sodium bisulphate is formed and hydrogen chloride escapes as a gas through a flue as shown. The fused mass is then raked into another part of the furnace,

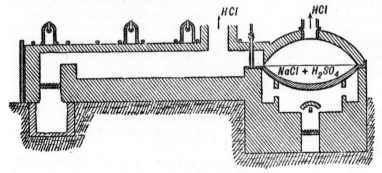

FIG. 188.—Salt-cake Furnace.

where it is heated to redness, when more hydrogen chloride is liberated and sodium sulphate formed :

$$NaHSO_4 + NaCl = Na_2SO_4 + HCl.$$

The hydrogen chloride is led off and is absorbed in water either by passing up a tower filled with coke down which water is trickling, or by means of special counter-current absorption plant such as shown in Fig. 189.

In some works special types of furnace are used which make the operation continuous, but the principle is the same. Also, where nitric acid is being made from sodium nitrate and sulphuric acid, "nitre cake" (crude sodium hydrogen sulphate—p. 405) is used instead of sulphuric acid.

Hydrochloric acid and sodium sulphate are also made from salt and sulphur dioxide by **Hargreave's Process.** In this process salt is heated to 500° in a

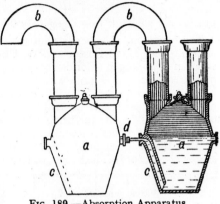

FIG. 189.—Absorption Apparatus.

stream of sulphur dioxide (from pyrites burners, etc.) mixed with excess of air and some steam. Under these conditions, sodium sulphite and hydrogen chloride are formed, the former being then oxidized to sulphate by the oxygen of the air. The final result is represented :

$$4NaCl + 2SO_2 + 2H_2O + O_2 = 2Na_2SO_4 + 4HCl.$$

Hydrochloric acid is now being made in increasing quantities by direct combination of the hydrogen and chlorine obtained as by-products in the manufacture of electrolytic caustic soda (p. 494). The combination is effected by burning chlorine in an atmosphere containing excess of hydrogen by means of burners acting on the same principle as the bunsen burner. The hydrogen chloride produced by this method is very much purer than that made by the older processes, and is absorbed in water by similar methods.

§ 12 Properties of Hydrogen Chloride

Hydrogen chloride is a colourless gas which attacks the mucous membrane when inhaled. It forms dense fumes in moist air on account of the fact that a solution of the gas is less volatile than water. In consequence, a mixture of water vapour and hydrogen chloride condenses to droplets of hydrochloric acid. The gas is heavier than air, having a vapour density of 18·23 ($H_2 = 1$). It is extremely soluble in water : 1 volume of water will dissolve 507 volumes of the gas at 0° and 442 volumes at 20°. In consequence of this high solubility, the "fountain-experiment" described on page 392 can be performed with hydrogen chloride in place of ammonia. Hydrogen chloride is easily condensed to a liquid by pressure, and the liquid so formed boils at −85° at 760 mm. It freezes to a white solid which melts at —111°.　　The gas is stable at temperatures up to 1500° C. after which dissociation occurs :

$$2HCl \rightleftharpoons H_2 + Cl_2,$$

but is only slight at first being only 0·8 per cent. at 2000°.

The behaviour of aqueous solutions of hydrochloric acid on heating is of interest. H. E. Roscoe and W. Dittmar found that if an aqueous solution of hydrogen chloride containing more than 20·24 per cent. HCl be heated, hydrogen chloride with but little water is given off ; the solution becomes less concentrated.　　This continues until the solution contains nearly 20·24 per cent. of HCl, when its boiling point attains the maximum, 110° ; any further boiling does not affect the concentration of the aqueous solution because dilute acid containing 20·24 per cent of HCl distils unchanged.　　Again, if an acid containing less than 20·24 per cent. of HCl be boiled, water accompanied by a little hydrogen chloride passes off ; the boiling point of the solution gradually rises ; and the solution at the same time becomes more concentrated until it contains 20·24 per cent. HCl, when the acid distils over unchanged at 110°.　　Hence 110° is the maximum boiling point of hydrochloric acid at atmospheric pressures.　　Similar phenomena occur with nitric acid and with several other acids.

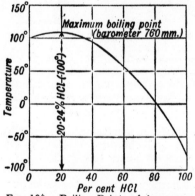

FIG. 190.—Boiling Points of Aqueous Solutions of Hydrogen Chloride.

This behaviour can be understood by reference to the curve, Fig. 190, which shows the relation between the boiling point and composition of aqueous solutions of hydrochloric acid.

It was once thought that the acid which corresponded with the maximum boiling point was an octohydrate—that is, a chemical compound of hydrogen chloride and water—$HCl.8H_2O$; but since the composition of the constant boiling acid varies with the pressure, and since compounds do not vary in composition with changes of pressure, this is clearly not the case.

Hydrogen chloride does not burn and is a non-supporter of combustion.　　It reacts with free oxygen only in presence of catalysts, such as the copper salts used in the Deacon process (p. 492), when chlorine and water are formed.　　It reacts with fluorine, which displaces the chlorine, forming hydrogen fluoride :

$$2HCl + F_2 = H_2F_2 + Cl_2.$$

It does not react with other non-metallic elements.

Its behaviour with metals is such as would be expected of a strong acid. The gas attacks them when heated, and the aqueous solution reacts readily, usually in the cold. Mercury, silver and gold, and the platinum metals are not attacked by hydrochloric acid, and copper only reacts in presence of air or oxygen, but all other metals react forming the chloride and hydrogen, e.g.,

$$Zn + 2HCl = ZnCl_2 + H_2.$$

If more than one chloride exists (e.g., iron) the lower chloride usually results.

The aqueous solution of hydrogen chloride (known as hydrochloric acid) exhibits the properties of a strong acid, reacting with oxides and hydroxides of metals to form salts (chlorides) and displacing weak acids from their salts.

Oxidizing agents, as already mentioned (p. 491) oxidize hydrochloric acid to chlorine ; e.g., peroxides, lead dioxide, dichromates, and permanganates all act upon it in this way.

Nitric acid will also oxidize hydrochloric acid, and this example has an interest of its own since a mixture of nitric and hydrochloric acids, in the proportions of one volume of the former to three or four of the latter, will dissolve gold and platinum and hence is known as **aqua regia**—the kingly water. This name was given to it by the alchemists because it dissolves the very king of metals, gold. The mixture becomes coloured at about 10° and evolves gas at about 30° ; the action is vigorous at 90°, and at 109° a mixture of nitric and hydrochloric acids distils over. The greater oxidizing and solvent properties of aqua regia as compared with nitric acid, etc., are generally attributed to the presence of free chlorine, the reaction being represented by the equation :

$$HNO_3 + 3HCl = NOCl + Cl_2 + 2H_2O,$$

corresponding with the fact that some nitrosyl chloride—NOCl—is also formed. The action is, however, probably more complex than this.

§ 13 Uses of Hydrochloric Acid

Hydrochloric acid is used for the manufacture of chlorine for making bleaching powder, etc. Large quantities are used in the dyestuffs industry and for many minor industrial purposes. Dilute hydrochloric acid is largely used for purifying coke, iron ores and clay, and for regenerating the activity of exhausted animal charcoal ; for " pickling " sheet iron in the galvanizing and tin-plate industries. It is employed in the manufacture of a number of chlorides, and in making pottery. It is an important analytical reagent and, in the form of aqua regia, is used in making gold chloride which is an important photographic chemical.

§ 14 Composition and Formula of Hydrogen Chloride

The composition of hydrogen chloride by volume has been found by decomposing a measured volume of the gas with sodium amalgam in an apparatus such as that indicated in Fig. 191.

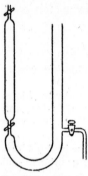

The closed limb of the U-tube is filled with dry hydrogen chloride at atmospheric pressure as far as the lower stopcock, the apparatus having been filled previously with dry mercury which is run out through the tap as the gas enters. The stopcocks are then closed and the remaining mercury replaced by liquid sodium amalgam. The lower stopcock is then opened and the gas brought in contact with the amalgam which decomposes it on standing, forming sodium chloride and hydrogen. The volume of gas remaining, after levelling, is found to be half that of the hydrogen chloride taken. Thus, hydrogen chloride contains half its volume of hydrogen.

FIG. 191.—Volume Composition of Hydrogen Chloride

The composition can be determined also by synthesis, for which purpose the apparatus, Fig. 192, is used.

FIG. 192.—Combination of Hydrogen and Chlorine.

One bulb is filled at atmospheric pressure with hydrogen and the other with chlorine, the bulbs being equal in volume. The apparatus is exposed to diffused daylight and the centre tap opened so as to allow the gases to mix. After some hours the greenish colour of the chlorine will have disappeared, and if one of the end taps be opened under mercury it will be found that no change of volume has occurred. On opening under dilute potassium iodide solution similarly the solution will completely fill the apparatus and no iodine will be liberated. In this way it is shown that hydrogen chloride has been formed, and that no chlorine or hydrogen remains uncombined.

These experiments show that one volume of hydrogen combines with one volume of chlorine to form two volumes of hydrogen chloride. This result is quoted in Chapter IV as evidence that the hydrogen molecule must contain *at least* two atoms. If hydrogen chloride can be shown to be HCl and not H_nCl_n, then the hydrogen molecule is H_2.

Hydrogen chloride is an acid and hence, in common with all acids, contains hydrogen replaceable by metals. Acids differ from each other in the number of stages by which this hydrogen can be displaced (cf. p. 307). Some, such as orthophosphoric acid, can have the hydrogen displaced in *three* stages, so forming three series of salts. Others, like sulphuric acid, form *two* series of salts ; whilst from many others the hydrogen can only be displaced in one step.

If hydrochloric acid had the formula H_nCl_n we should expect to be able to displace the hydrogen in n stages. In fact, it can only be removed in one stage—i.e., all the hydrogen or none is displaced and only one series of chlorides is found. Hence it is inferred that the formula for hydrogen chloride is HCl.

§ 15 Chlorides

The salts of hydrochloric acid, the chlorides, will be found described in the chapters devoted to the metals concerned.

They are mostly well crystallized compounds which are readily soluble in water. Lead chloride and palladous chloride are only very sparingly soluble, and mercurous, cuprous, silver, thallous and aurous chlorides are virtually insoluble. They are not, as a rule, decomposed by heat (gold and platinum chlorides are the only exceptions) and are relatively stable towards water, although some, such as the chlorides of antimony and bismuth, and elements, known as metalloids, which exhibit only feeble metallic properties (p. 114), give oxychlorides with water, e.g.,

$$BiCl_3 + H_2O \rightleftharpoons BiOCl + 2HCl.$$

Detection and Determination

Chlorides are detected in solution by the formation of a white precipitate of silver chloride on addition of silver nitrate solution to a solution acidified with nitric acid. This precipitate is soluble in dilute aqueous ammonia, but is reprecipitated on acidifying with dilute nitric acid, and turns violet in light.

A convenient method for the detection of chlorides in the solid state is to heat a small quantity, mixed with manganese dioxide, with concentrated sulphuric acid. If a chloride is present, chlorine will be evolved. Further confirmation can be obtained by mixing a sample of the substance with potassium dichromate and strong sulphuric acid and warming when red vapours of chromyl chloride (p. 775) are evolved which condense in blood-red drops on the cooler parts of the tube.

The reaction with silver nitrate serves for the determination of chlorides both gravimetrically and volumetrically ; in the former case, the chlorine is weighed as silver chloride ; in the latter, the volume of a standard silver nitrate solution required for the complete precipitation of the chloride present in a known volume of solution is determined

§ 16 Oxides of Chlorine

Chlorine forms three well-known oxides, viz.,

Chlorine monoxide, Cl_2O,
Chlorine dioxide or peroxide, ClO_2,
Chlorine heptoxide, Cl_2O_7.

Two other oxides have also been described :

Chlorine hexoxide, Cl_2O_6
and Chlorine tetroxide $(ClO_4)_x$,

but the latter especially is doubtful.

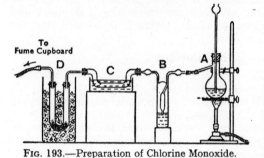

FIG. 193.—Preparation of Chlorine Monoxide.

Chlorine Monoxide, Cl_2O

Chlorine monoxide is made by passing dry chlorine over precipitated mercuric oxide (which has been previously heated to about 400°). The mercuric oxide is placed in a tube C cooled by water as shown in Fig. 193.

Chlorine monoxide is formed and is condensed in a U-tube D immersed in a freezing mixture :

$$2HgO + 2Cl_2 = Hg_2OCl_2 + Cl_2O.$$

Chlorine monoxide is a pale orange-yellow gas at ordinary temperatures ; it readily condenses to a reddish-brown liquid which boils at 3·8 at 766 mm. Both the liquid and the gas are very unstable, and mere contact with sulphur, phosphorus and many carbon compounds (e.g., turpentine) leads to decomposition with explosive violence. The liquid is readily exploded by slight mechanical shock, even by pouring from one vessel to another.

Chlorine monoxide dissolves readily in water, one volume of water dissolving 200 volumes of the gas at 0°, and forms hypochlorous acid (p. 508) :

$$H_2O + Cl_2O = 2HOCl.$$

Chlorine monoxide may thus be regarded as hypochlorous anhydride.

The composition of chlorine monoxide is indicated by the fact that when heated (with suitable precautions to prevent explosion) it is decomposed into chlorine and oxygen ; and it is found two volumes of chlorine and one volume of oxygen are formed. The vapour density is 43·46 ($H_2 = 1$) and hence chlorine monoxide has the formula Cl_2O.

Chlorine Dioxide, Chlorine Peroxide, ClO_2

Chlorine dioxide results when concentrated sulphuric acid acts on chlorates. It was discovered in this way by Davy (1815).

The reactions which take place are usually represented :

$$KClO_3 + H_2SO_4 = KHSO_4 + HClO_3,$$
$$3HClO_3 = 2ClO_2 + HClO_4 + H_2O,$$

the chloric acid first formed decomposing into chlorine peroxide and perchloric acid. It is best prepared by the action of dry chlorine on silver chlorate at 85—95°. (King and Partington, 1926.)

$$2AgClO_3 + Cl_2 = 2ClO_2 + O_2 + 2AgCl.$$

It is separated from the oxygen, formed at the same time, by condensing it in a freezing mixture of solid carbon dioxide and ether, when it is obtained as an orange coloured solid.

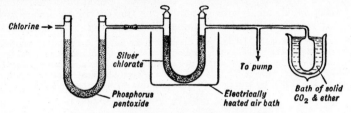

Fig. 194.—Preparation of Chlorine Dioxide.

Chlorine peroxide is a reddish-yellow gas with an unpleasant smell. The gas is much heavier than air, and is collected by downward delivery, since it decomposes in contact with mercury, and it is fairly soluble in water. Water at 4° dissolves about twenty times its volume of the gas. When the solution is cooled to lower temperatures a crystalline hydrate separates—possibly as $ClO_2.8H_2O$. On standing, in the dark, an aqueous solution of chlorine peroxide forms a mixture of chloric and chlorous acids.

$$2ClO_2 + H_2O = HClO_3 + HClO_2.$$

When the gas is cooled, it condenses to a dark red liquid which boils at 11°, and the liquid can be frozen to orange-coloured crystals melting at — 59°. Chlorine peroxide is very unstable. It decomposes with explosive violence if an electric spark be passed through the gas, or if a hot wire be introduced into the gas. Chlorine peroxide also decomposes into its elements if it be exposed to the light. The gas is liable to explode suddenly, especially if in the liquid or solid condition, or if organic matter be present. Chlorine peroxide is a powerful oxidizing agent—a piece of phosphorus, sugar, or other combustible takes fire spontaneously in the gas.

The composition of chlorine dioxide was first determined by Davy, and confirmed in 1875 by Pébal, who obtained by decomposition of the gas one volume of chlorine and two volumes of oxygen. This fact, combined with the knowledge that the vapour density is 33·65, indicates that the formula is ClO_2.

Chlorine heptoxide, Cl_2O_7, is obtained by adding perchloric acid (p. 516) very slowly to phosphorus pentoxide cooled to —10°, and, after standing for a day at this temperature, distilling the mixture at 82°.

$$4HClO_4 + P_4O_{10} = 2Cl_2O_7 + 4HPO_3.$$

It is also obtained by the action of chlorosulphonic acid on potassium perchlorate (F. Meyer, 1921).

The chlorine heptoxide condenses to a colourless volatile oil which decomposes in a few days. It is soluble in benzene which it slowly attacks; it also reacts with iodine, slowly in darkness, rapidly in light, forming what is probably *iodine heptoxide*—I_2O_7; but it does not react with bromine. Chlorine heptoxide explodes in contact with a flame, and by sharp percussion. It may be poured on organic matter —paper, wood, etc.—with impunity for the oil simply volatilizes in air. It reacts with water, forming perchloric acid.

Chlorine Hexoxide, Cl_2O_6, was discovered by Millon in 1843, but overlooked until in 1925 it was rediscovered by Bodenstein. He obtained it as a red liquid, melting at $-1°$ by exposing a mixture of chlorine dioxide and ozone to light.

Chlorine tetroxide (ClO_4)$_n$ is said to have been obtained in ethereal solution by Gomberg (1923) by treating silver perchlorate with iodine:

$$2nAgClO_4 + nI_2 = 2nAgI + 2(ClO_4)n,$$

§ 17 Oxyacids of Chlorine

The known oxyacids of chlorine are:

> Hypochlorous acid, HOCl,
> Chlorous acid, $HClO_2$,
> Chloric acid, $HClO_3$,
> Perchloric acid, $HClO_4$.

Hypochlorous Acid, HOCl

It is probable that a cold, aqueous solution of chlorine contains a certain amount of hypochlorous acid:

$$Cl_2 + H_2O \rightleftharpoons HCl + HOCl,$$

since chlorine water shows an acid reaction to litmus before it bleaches, and some hypochlorous acid can be obtained by distillation of the solution.

A similar reaction occurs between chlorine and *cold* dilute aqueous alkali, e.g.,

$$2NaOH + Cl_2 = NaCl + NaOCl + H_2O.$$

(If the solution is hot, chlorates are formed—p. 513.)

Hypochlorous acid can be prepared by shaking freshly-prepared chlorine water with mercuric oxide and distilling. A dilute solution of the acid collects in the receiver.

$$HgO + H_2O + 2Cl_2 = HgCl_2 + HOCl.$$

Hypochlorous acid is too weak an acid to react with mercuric oxide in these circumstances.

A convenient way of preparing a solution of hypochlorous acid is by the action of dilute nitric acid or boric acid on bleaching powder (q.v., p. 510). The bleaching powder, when dissolved in water, gives a mixture of chloride and hypochlorite:

$$2CaOCl_2 = CaCl_2 + Ca(OCl)_2.$$

The latter is decomposed by the nitric (or boric) acid:

$$Ca(OCl)_2 + 2HNO_3 = Ca(NO_3)_2 + 2HOCl.$$

A dilute solution of the acid may be obtained by distillation as before, and may be concentrated further by evaporation in the cold; but solutions of greater strength than 5 per cent decompose on warming into chloric (p. 512) and hydrochloric acids :

$$3HOCl = HClO_3 + 2HCl.$$

Some chlorine is also evolved by interaction of this hydrochloric acid with unchanged hypochlorous acid :

$$HCl + HOCl = H_2O + Cl_2.$$

In consequence, pure hypochlorous acid free from water, has not been obtained.

When warmed, hypochlorous acid solutions, in addition to the products named above, yield oxygen :

$$2HOCl = 2HCl + O_2.$$

This is particularly the case in sunlight and in presence of oxidizing agents. Thus with silver oxide :

$$Ag_2O + 2HOCl = 2AgCl + H_2O + O_2,$$

or, if a little cobalt nitrate solution be added to a dilute solution of hypochlorous acid, oxygen is readily evolved on warming—the cobalt hydroxide formed acting as a catalyst (p. 229). This is the basis of the method for preparing oxygen from bleaching powder referred to on page 299.

Hypochlorous acid is consequently a powerful oxidizing agent. Thus, if a solution of bleaching powder be boiled for some time with a solution of lead acetate, puce-coloured lead dioxide, PbO_2, will be precipitated ; and if boiled with a solution of a manganous salt, manganese dioxide, MnO_2, will be precipitated. More prolonged boiling may give a green solution of calcium manganate, or a pink-coloured solution of calcium permanganate, $Ca(MnO_4)_2$.

The rapid decomposition of hypochlorous acid in sunlight renders it probable that the action of light on chlorine water results in the formation of the hypochlorous acid by hydrolysis :

$$Cl_2 + H_2O = HCl + HOCl,$$

which is at once decomposed :

$$2HOCl = 2HCl + O_2,$$

so that the hydrolysis goes to completion, and leaves, as final products, hydrochloric acid, water and oxygen.

The salts of hypochlorous acid, the hypochlorites, since they are more readily obtained, and more stable, are of greater importance than the acid itself. The principal ones are sodium hypochlorite and bleaching powder.

Sodium hypochlorite is obtained in solution by passing chlorine into a cold, dilute solution of sodium hydroxide, or sodium carbonate :

$$2NaOH + Cl_2 = NaCl + NaOCl + H_2O,$$
$$Na_2CO_3 + Cl_2 = NaCl + NaOCl + CO_2.$$

A weak solution is now manufactured for disinfecting purposes by electrolyzing a cold solution of sodium chloride under conditions which result in the mixing of the chlorine and caustic soda first formed.

The salt cannot be obtained free from water as it decomposes on warming, forming the chlorate and chloride (cf. the acid) ; but by the evaporation at a low temperature of highly concentrated solutions of sodium hydroxide saturated with chlorine, crystals of the composition $NaOCl.6H_2O$ (slightly contaminated with sodium chloride) have been obtained.

Sodium hypochlorite, like the parent acid, has a strong bleaching and germicidal action, and is a powerful oxidizing agent.

Bleaching Powder, Chloride of Lime

Bleaching powder is made on a large scale by the action of chlorine on slaked lime (quicklime does not react with chlorine at ordinary temperatures). The equation has hitherto been written :

$$Ca(OH)_2 + Cl_2 = CaOCl_2 + H_2O.$$

When the chlorine used has been made by the Weldon process (p. 493), or electrolytically, the following method can be used :—

The lime is spread in 3- or 4-inch layers on perforated shelves in a large chamber, and then raked into furrows. Chlorine is led through the chamber. At first the absorption of chlorine is rapid, but it afterwards slows down. The lime is then turned over from time to time so as to expose a fresh surface. After standing for 12 to 24 hours a shower of fine lime dust is blown into the chamber to absorb the excess of chlorine.

When a very dilute chlorine, such as that produced by Deacon's process (p. 492), is being employed, it is necessary to ensure very close contact between the gas and the slaked lime, and this is effected by the use of special types of plant, such as that indicated in Fig. 195, which illustrates the Hasenclever cylinder apparatus.

It consists of six or eight horizontal cast-iron cylinders arranged one above the other, each provided with an archimedean screw which is kept slowly revolving. Slaked lime is fed into the topmost cylinder, after traversing which, it passes into the next lower cylinder, and so on. Chlorine is fed in at the bottom and passes through the apparatus in a direction opposite to that of the slaked lime.

The amount of chlorine absorbed is never so complete as is represented by the equation quoted above. The commercial value of the bleaching powder depends on the amount of available chlorine it contains. The amount of available chlorine depends upon the method of preparation, temperature, etc. If the temperature be kept between 30° and 40°, a bleaching powder containing about 40 per cent. of available chlorine can be prepared.

The constitution of bleaching powder has been much discussed. Under very favourable conditions, lime can be saturated with no more than 43·5 per cent. of available chlorine, and the facts correspond with the formula, ascribed to W. Odling, viz.,

$$Ca <_{Cl}^{OCl}$$

and for long accepted. It has been suggested that it is a double compound of calcium chloride and hypochlorite, $CaCl_2Ca(OCl)_2$, but it is

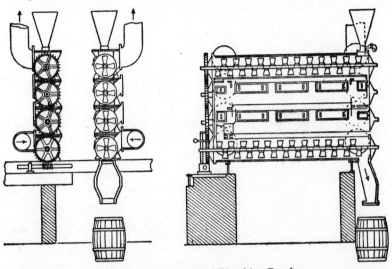

Fɪɢ. 195 —Manufacture of Bleaching Powder.

improbable that bleaching powder contains much calcium chloride because (1) all the chlorine can be expelled from it by the action of carbon dioxide. This would not be the case if calcium chloride were present, unless some reaction like that assumed by Balard takes place, viz.,

$$CO_2 + Ca(OCl)_2 = CaCO_3 + CaCl_2 + Cl_2O,$$

followed by

$$Cl_2O + CO_2 + CaCl_2 = CaCO_3 + Cl_2,$$

which is unlikely ; (2) calcium chloride is very deliquescent, bleaching powder is not ; (3) calcium chloride is readily dissolved by alcohol, whereas an alcoholic solution of bleaching powder contains but traces of calcium chloride ; (4) a deposit of slaked lime is always found as a residue when bleaching powder is treated with water.

It has now been shown (Bunn, Clark and Clifford, 1935) by X-ray examination of slaked lime during the process of chlorination, and comparison of the results with those of the X-ray examination of pure samples of compounds likely to be formed, that ordinary bleaching powder is a mixture of a basic chloride, $CaCl_2.Ca(OH)_2.H_2O$ and a basic hypochlorite $Ca(OCl)_2$, 2 $(Ca(OH)_2)$ in approximately molecular proportions.

The process for the determination of the available chlorine depends upon the fact that sodium arsenite is oxidized to sodium arsenate by an aqueous solution of bleaching powder. Hence a standard solution of sodium arsenite is added to a known amount of an aqueous solution bleaching powder until the solution no longer gives a blue coloration with iodized starch paper. This shows that no available chlorine is present. The amount of sodium arsenite used in the experiment is related with the available chlorine by the following equation :

$$Cl_2 + H_2O + Na_3AsO_3 = Na_3AsO_4 + 2HCl$$

so that the amount of available chlorine can be readily computed. The acid is neutralised by the slaked lime present.

Chlorous Acid, HClO₂ and Chlorites

When an aqueous solution of chlorine dioxide is treated with an alkali such as potassium hydroxide, a mixture of **potassium chlorite**, $KClO_2$, and chlorate is formed :

$$2KOH + 2ClO_2 = KClO_2 + KClO_3 + H_2O,$$

and if sodium peroxide be employed, **sodium chlorite** and oxygen result :

$$Na_2O_2 + 2ClO_2 = 2NaClO_2 + O_2.$$

The colourless, slightly alkaline solution so formed is without action on indigo solution or on starch-iodide paper, and becomes yellow when an acid is added. The acidified solution probably contains **chlorous acid**, $HClO_2$. The chlorites are readily decomposed. **Lead chlorite**, $Pb(ClO_2)_2$, is precipitated when the solution of sodium chlorite is acidified with acetic acid and treated with lead nitrate. Lead chlorite at 100° decomposes with detonation. The soluble chlorites bleach vegetable colouring matters, even after the addition of arsenious acid. This is not the case with the hypochlorites. Pure chlorous acid has not been prepared ; an aqueous solution is obtained by digesting the lead salt with barium carbonate so as to form **barium chlorite**, $Ba(ClO_2)_2$, and finally precipitating the barium as sulphate by $\frac{1}{10}N\text{-}H_2SO_4$. The solution gradually decomposes evolving chlorine dioxide and chlorine :

$$8HClO_2 = 6ClO_2 + Cl_2 + 4H_2O.$$

The anhydride corresponding to chlorous acid, which would be chlorine trioxide, Cl_2O_3, is unknown. H. Davy prepared a gas which he called **euchlorine,** and which was at one time believed to be Cl_2O_3, by the action of concentrated hydrochloric acid on potassium chlorate. Euchlorine is, however, a mixture of chlorine dioxide and chlorine in varying proportions.

§ 18 Chloric Acid, HClO₃, and the Chlorates

As mentioned on page 508, when chlorine is passed into a cold solution of potassium hydroxide, a mixture of potassium chloride and hypochlorite is formed ; and when the solution of the hypochlorite is boiled, it decomposes, forming a mixture of potassium chlorate and chloride ; otherwise expressed, the hypochlorite solution oxidizes itself :

$$3KOCl = 2KCl + KClO_3.$$

Potassium chlorate is likewise obtained when chlorine is passed into a *hot* (70°) aqueous solution of potassium hydroxide

$$6KOH + 3Cl_2 = KClO_3 + 5KCl + 3H_2O.$$

and the two salts—potassium chloride and potassium chlorate—can be separated by fractional crystallization. Potassium chlorate is far less soluble than the corresponding chloride, page 154. C. L. Berthollet (1786-8) first isolated this salt, although it appears to have been known to J. R. Glauber (1658), who mistook it for saltpetre. The above method of preparation is due to J. L. Gay-Lussac (1818).

Potassium chlorate can be prepared in the laboratory in this way, but industrially this method is wasteful, and so a modification due to J. von Liebig (1842) is used.

It will be observed that the amount of chlorate obtained from a given amount of potassium hydroxide is small, because one molecule of potassium chlorate is accompanied by five molecules of potassium chloride as by-product. This loss is serious because the potassium hydroxide is relatively expensive. It is cheaper to substitute a hot solution of slaked lime in water for the potassium hydroxide solution. In that case the reaction may be represented :

$$6Ca(OH)_2 + 6Cl_2 = Ca(ClO_3)_2 + 5CaCl_2 + 6H_2O.$$

The clear solution of calcium chlorate and chloride is concentrated a little by evaporation, and a slight excess of potassium chloride is added. Potassium chlorate has but one-tenth the solubility of the corresponding calcium salt, and is far less soluble than the two chlorides; hence by a further concentration of the solution, the least soluble potassium chlorate separates. The potassium chlorate so obtained is purified by recrystallization.

This old process now has a formidable rival in the electrolytic process, particularly in countries like the United States, Sweden and Switzerland, where abundant water power is available. Hot solutions of potassium chloride are electrolyzed under conditions which result in the products being mixed. This is brought about by the use of special types of cell, one of which is indicated in Fig. 196. In this the potassium chloride solution is passed between a series of electrodes sufficiently close together to cause reaction to take. place between the normal products of

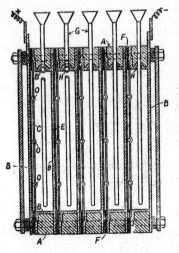

FIG. 196.—Chlorate Cell.

electrolysis (anodes, B, platinum coated lead; cathodes, C, copper wires). The initial and the end stages of these reactions are represented:

$$KCl + 3H_2O = KClO_3 + 3H_2,$$

but no doubt chlorine is first formed ; then potassium hypochlorite ; and finally potassium chlorate. The sparingly soluble potassium chlorate crystallizes from the solution during the electrolysis, and thus gives trouble. Since 100 c.c. of water at 20° dissolve about 99 grams of sodium chlorate ; and 100 c.c. of water, about 7·2 grams of potassium chlorate, it is best to prepare first sodium chlorate by the electrolysis of sodium chloride ; and then treat the solution with potassium chloride as in the case of calcium chlorate described above. Potassium chlorate can be readily isolated by fractional crystallization.

Barium chlorate can be prepared in a similar manner to the above chlorates, either by electrolysis of barium chloride, or by saturating a hot solution of barium hydroxide with chlorine. The separation of barium chlorate and barium chloride is rather difficult because the two salts are almost equally soluble in water.

Barium chlorate is used in the preparation of chloric acid (see below), and in fireworks (green fire).

The chlorates are powerful oxidizing agents. An explosion may occur if a chlorate be mixed with organic matter, charcoal, sulphur, etc., and the mixture struck with a hammer, or heated. Hence mixtures of chlorates with such materials must not be ground together with a pestle and mortar. The materials should be ground separately, and then carefully mixed on paper with a feather. Phosphorus in contact with a chlorate may explode spontaneously. Thus if a drop of a solution of phosphorus in carbon disulphide be allowed to fall on a little potassium chlorate, a loud explosion occurs as soon as the carbon disulphide has evaporated. The oxidizing action of potassium chlorate in neutral or slightly acid solutions is greatly stimulated by traces of osmium tetrachloride, $OsCl_4$, as catalytic agent.

The chlorates are decomposed by heat, with evolution of oxygen, a reaction made use of in the common laboratory preparation of oxygen (p. 297). In the absence of a catalyst the reaction takes place in two stages, the perchlorate (p. 516) being first formed :

$$4KClO_3 = 3KClO_4 + KCl$$
$$3KClO_4 = 3KCl + 6O_2.$$

With concentrated sulphuric acid chlorates evolve chlorine dioxide (p. 506). The heat of the reaction causes the gas to decompose, which it does with loud crackling. Concentrated hydrochloric acid gives with a chlorate a mixture of chlorine and chlorine dioxide, known as euchlorine (p. 512).

The chlorates are all soluble in water. Potassium chlorate is one of the least soluble of the chlorates. The chlorates are recognized by giving no precipitate with silver nitrate ; although, after ignition, the silver nitrate will give a precipitate of silver chloride with an aqueous solution of the residue.   If a few drops of a solution of indigo sulphate be added to an aqueous solution of a chlorate, and the liquid be acidified with sulphuric acid, and sulphurous acid, or a sulphite be added, the chloric acid is reduced to a lower chlorine oxide which bleaches the blue colour of the indigo.   If three or four drops of concentrated sulphuric acid be allowed to run down the side of a test-tube containing a little chlorate solution mixed with aniline sulphate, a blue colour appears where the two liquids meet.   Nitrates and iodates give a brownish red coloration under similar circumstances.

Potassium chlorate is used medicinally in throat lozenges.   It is employed in the manufacture of matches, fireworks and explosives, as an oxidizing agent and for the preparation of oxygen in the laboratory.   Chlorates are also used in calico printing, and in the preparation of dyes.   Sodium chlorate is used as a weed-killer.

Chloric acid, $HClO_3$, was first obtained by J. L. Gay-Lussac (1814).   His method consists in treating an aqueous solution of barium chlorate with an equivalent quantity of dilute sulphuric acid, when barium sulphate is precipitated and chloric acid remains in solution :

$$Ba(ClO_3)_2 + H_2SO_4 = BaSO_4 \downarrow + 2HClO_3.$$

The barium sulphate is filtered off and the filtrate concentrated by evaporation in vacuo over concentrated sulphuric acid.   Solutions of chloric acid of greater concentration than about 40 per cent. cannot be obtained, as stronger solutions decompose into perchloric acid, chlorine, oxygen and water.   This decomposition probably takes place in stages :

$$2HClO_3 = HClO_4 + HClO_2$$
$$HClO_2 + HClO_3 \rightleftharpoons H_2O + 2ClO_2$$
$$2ClO_2 = Cl_2 + 2O_2.$$

(see p. 516).

Properties

The concentrated solution of chloric acid so prepared is a colourless, viscid liquid with a pungent smell.   It readily decomposes on exposure to light.   The solution is stable in darkness provided organic matter be absent.   Wood, paper, etc., decompose the acid at once—very often with spontaneous combustion.   Blue litmus is first reddened and then bleached by the acid.   Even in a dilute solution, chloric acid is a powerful bleaching agent.

The composition of chloric acid was established by J. J. Stas by the analysis of silver chlorate.   A known amount of silver chlorate was reduced to the chloride by means of sulphurous acid.   His results show that the ratio of silver chloride to oxygen in the chlorate is as 1 : 3, i.e., the empirical formula is $AgClO_3$.   The molecular weight of the free acid has not been determined satisfactorily, but it is inferred that the acid is $HClO_3$ from the absence of any acid salts.

§ 19 Perchloric Acid, $HClO_4$, and Perchlorates

Perchloric acid is formed when chloric acid is heated or exposed to light (p. 515) :

$$3HClO_3 = Cl_2 + 2O_2 + HClO_4 + H_2O.$$

It is prepared by the action of sulphuric acid on potassium perchlorate :

$$2KClO_4 + H_2SO_4 = K_2SO_4 + 2HClO_4.$$

Potassium perchlorate is made, as indicated above (p. 514), by the action of heat on potassium chlorate · it is also manufactured electrolytically (see below).

For the preparation of the acid, pure, dry potassium perchlorate is mixed with concentrated sulphuric acid and the mixture distilled under reduced pressure. A white crystalline mass of perchloric acid monohydrate, $HClO_4.H_2O$, collects in the receiver. By redistilling this under reduced pressure, pure perchloric acid can be obtained.

Perchloric acid and the perchlorates are now manufactured by the electrolysis of chloric acid and chlorates respectively. The chlorate is not directly oxidized as was once thought. It is believed that when the chlorate ions are discharged at the anode, they react with the water forming chloric acid which decomposes into perchloric acid, chlorous acid and oxygen as indicated above. The oxygen oxidizes the chlorous acid back to chloric acid, so that the initial and final products may be represented :

$$2KClO_3 + 2H_2O = 2KClO_4 + 2H_2.$$

It has been observed empirically that a trace of potassium dichromate improves the yield.

Perchloric acid is a volatile colourless fuming liquid ; specific gravity 1·764 at 22°, boils at 14° to 18° under a pressure of 15 to 20 mm., and freezes at −112° to a crystalline solid. If a drop of the acid be brought in contact with paper or wood, instantaneous and violent inflammation occurs ; if a drop of the acid be brought in contact with charcoal, a violent explosion occurs. Perchloric acid produces serious wounds in contact with the skin. If the acid be distilled at ordinary pressures, the liquid may gradually become darker and darker in colour, and finally explode violently. The pure acid is also said to be liable to explode after standing some days. .

When dropped into water, the two combine with a hissing sound, and the evolution of much heat :

$$HClO_4 + Aq = HClO_4aq + 20·3 \text{ Cals.}$$

Perchloric acid forms five hydrates containing respectively 1, 2, 2·5, 3, and 3·5 molecules of water. The monohydrate is formed by adding water to the pure acid until crystals begin to appear. This hydrate melts at 50°, and freezes at the same temperature, forming long needle-like crystals. Solutions more concentrated than 71·6 per cent. $HClO_4$ lose $HClO_4$ when distilled, and less concentrated solutions lose water. The " constant boiling acid " contains 71·6 per cent. of $HClO_4$, boils at 203°, and distils unchanged in composition. It fumes slightly in air, and may be preserved indefinitely, even in light. Perchloric acid slowly volatilizes at 138° without decomposition.

Perchlorates

An aqueous solution of perchloric acid reddens litmus, and forms salts—perchlorates—where the radicle " ClO_4 " is univalent. Hence perchloric acid is monobasic. While a dilute aqueous solution of perchloric acid reddens litmus, dilute aqueous solutions of chloric and hypochlorous acids bleach litmus. The potassium salt is one of the least soluble perchlorates. It is practically insoluble in absolute alcohol. When perchloric acid is added to an alcoholic solution of a soluble potassium salt, potassium perchlorate is quantitatively precipitated. The weight of potassium perchlorate so obtained enables the amount of potassium in the given solution to be computed. Unlike the chlorates, the perchlorates are not decomposed by hydrochloric acid ; nor do they yield an explosive gas when warmed with concentrated sulphuric acid. They are not reduced to chlorides by sulphur dioxide ; and they require a higher temperature for their decomposition than the corresponding chlorates. Potassium perchlorate in aqueous solution is quantitatively reduced to the chloride when boiled in the presence of neutral ferrous hydroxide and titanous salts. Sodium perchlorate as well as sodium chlorate occur with sodium nitrate in native Chile saltpetre.

The composition of perchloric acid has been found by preparing pure potassium perchlorate from the acid, decomposing a known weight by heating and weighing the potassium chloride remaining. The composition of potassium chloride being accurately known, it is thus possible to determine the ratio of potassium chloride to oxygen. The results indicate that this is as 1 : 4 and hence the empirical formula of the acid is $HClO_4$. It is inferred that this is also the molecular formula since no acid salt of perchloric acid is known.

§ 20 Bromine

History

Bromine was discovered by A. J. Balard (1826) by the action of chlorine on the residues remaining after crystallization of salt from the water of the salt-marshes of Montpellier. The intensely yellow liquid was extracted with ether, the extract treated with potassium hydroxide, which destroyed the colour, and then evaporated when a white solid was formed. This resembled potassium chloride, but, unlike the chlorides, when heated with manganese dioxide and sulphuric acid, it furnished red fumes which condensed to a dark brown liquid with an unpleasant smell. Balard called this substance " muride," but afterwards changed the name to " bromine "—from the Greek βρῶμος (bromos), stench. Balard demonstrated the elementary nature of bromine, and showed its relation to iodine and chlorine.

J. von Liebig evidently had a sample of bromine in his hands some years previously, but believing it to be iodine chloride (p. 534), paid little attention to it.

Occurrence

Bromine does not occur free in nature. Small quantities occur combined in many silver ores ; and it occurs associated with potassium, sodium, magnesium, or calcium in many mineral waters, salt springs— e.g., the Congress and Excelsior springs of Saratoga, Woodhall Spa, etc.—and sea-water. The water of the Atlantic is said to contain 0·007 per cent. of magnesium bromide ; the water of the Dead Sea, 9 per cent. ; the mineral water of Ohio, from 3·4 to 3·9 per cent. of magnesium bromide.

Bromine is also found in marine animals and plants, in rock salt, etc., human urine, and all commercial products directly or indirectly derived from sea-salt or Stassfurt salts. The saline deposits of Stassfurt contain about 1 per cent. of magnesium bromide.

The main supply of the bromine of commerce was formerly drawn from the Stassfurt deposits, and from the saline springs of Ohio and other parts of America ; large quantities are now being produced from the salts present in the Dead Sea, and from ordinary sea-water.

Manufacture

The mother liquors remaining after the separation of potassium chloride from the carnallite of the Stassfurt deposits contain about 0·25 per cent. of bromine as magnesium bromide. These liquors are allowed to flow down a tower up which a current of chlorine is passing. The chlorine displaces the bromine :

$$MgBr_2 + Cl_2 = MgCl_2 + Br_2,$$

which passes off as a vapour and is condensed in an earthenware coil immersed in water.

An alternative method is by electrolysis of the same mother liquors using carbon electrodes.

The magnesium bromide is decomposed by the electric current before the magnesium chloride, for if any chlorine were formed it would at once decompose the magnesium bromide as just indicated. It is thus possible and practicable to separate the liberated bromine.

Similar methods are employed in the American and Dead Sea plants.

The bromine is purified by redistillation. The chlorine is removed by distillation from calcium or ferrous bromide, or by collecting separately in a receiver the first 1 to 4 per cent. of the distillate in the form of a volatile compound or mixture of chlorine and bromine. If anhydrous bromine be needed, it must be redistilled off concentrated sulphuric acid. If iodine be present, this must be removed by treatment with a copper salt. Cuprous iodide, CuI, is precipitated.

The enormously increased demand for bromine during the past few years in connection with the motor-fuel industry (see below) has led to the initiation of schemes for extracting bromine from sea-water and a successful plant, producing 15,000 lbs. of bromine per day, is now in operation at Cape Fear, N. Carolina. The bromine is displaced by chlorine (as in the above methods) after acidification of the sea-water, and is then removed by a current of air, being finally absorbed in sodium carbonate solution in towers on the counter-current principle :

$$3Br_2 + 3Na_2CO_3 = 5NaBr + NaBrO_3 + 3CO_2.$$

The bromide-bromate mixture is acidified with sulphuric acid and

$$5NaBr + NaBrO_3 + 3H_2SO_4 = 3Na_2SO_4 + 3Br_2 + 3H_2O$$

the bromine removed by steam and condensed as in older methods to the liquid.

Properties

At ordinary temperatures, bromine is a heavy mobile reddish-brown liquid—specific gravity at 0°, 3·1883. It freezes to a yellowish-brown crystalline mass at −7·3°, and boils in air at 58·8°. It is very volatile, and gives off a dark reddish-brown vapour at ordinary temperatures. Bromine separates in the form of carmine-red needle-like crystals, when a solution of bromine in carbon disulphide is cooled to −90°. The solid is almost colourless when cooled to −252°. Bromine has a disagreeable irritating smell, and it attacks the eyes as well as the mucous membrane of the throat and nose. It is poisonous, and attacks the skin, producing troublesome sores. 100 grams of water dissolve 4·3 grams of bromine at 0°, and 3·2 grams at 20°. Bromine is also soluble in chloroform, carbon disulphide, alcohol, ether, and acetic acid. When bromine water is cooled to 0°, it forms **bromine hydrate,** $Br_2.10H_2O$.

Bromine resembles chlorine in general chemical properties, but is not quite so energetic. It only unites slowly with hydrogen in sunlight, or when heated. It reacts with sulphur, phosphorus, arsenic, tin and other metals in a similar manner to chlorine (p. 497), forming the corresponding bromides. Like chlorine, bromine is an oxidizing agent ; it differs from chlorine in that it does not react with water, yet if a substance be present capable of undergoing oxidation, hydrogen bromide is formed and the oxygen of the water is available for oxidation. It reacts with aqueous solutions of the alkalis like chlorine, forming hypobromites and bromates. It has bleaching properties similar to those of chlorine, though it is less vigorous as would be expected from its general behaviour.

Uses

Bromine is used in metallurgy, photography, and the chemical industries. It is also used as a disinfectant, for which purpose it is sold under the name " bromum solidificatum," which is kieselguhr—a siliceous earth—saturated with bromine. Bromine is also used as an oxidizing agent.

It is an important raw material for the manufacture of dyestuffs and of a number of drugs. Of recent years it has been used in large and increasing amount in the preparation of anti-knock motor fuels, of which ethylene dibromide is an important and essential constituent ; the lead present in the actual anti-knock constituent (lead tetraethyl) being eliminated from the cylinder as lead bromide.

Atomic and Molecular Weights

The combining weight of bromine was determined with great accuracy by Richards and Baxter (1906) by the synthesis of silver bromide, and by converting silver chloride into silver bromide. They obtained the value 79·917 Considerations similar to those discussed in connection with chlorine (p. 498) indicate that this is also the atomic weight.

A determination of the density, etc., of hydrobromic acid by Moles by the limiting density method leads to the value 79·92. The value accepted by the International Atomic Weight Committee is 79·916.

At about 100° the vapour density of bromine is 84·65 ($H_2 = 1$), and at 228° it is 79·6, corresponding with the molecule Br_2. At 1570° the vapour density is but two-thirds of its value at 228°, showing that the molecule is probably dissociating into atoms.

Detection and Determination

Free bromine can be detected by the colour of its vapour, formed on warming, provided that it is distinguished from nitrogen peroxide and from chromyl chloride. This may be done by passing the gas into water and shaking the solution with a little carbon disulphide. Bromine, if present, will be extracted by the carbon disulphide which will be coloured orange in consequence. Nitrogen peroxide forms a colourless solution of nitrous and nitric acids ; and chromyl chloride gives a yellow solution, the colour of which is not extracted by carbon disulphide.

Free bromine is determined volumetrically by making it react with excess of potassium iodide solution, and then titrating the liberated iodine with a standard solution of sodium thiosulphate (p. 527).

For the detection and determination of the bromine in hydrobromic acid and bromides, see page 523.

§ 21 Hydrogen Bromide, Hydrobromic Acid, HBr

Hydrogen bromide cannot be prepared by the action of concentrated sulphuric acid on a bromide on account of the ease with which it is oxidized to bromine by sulphuric acid (see below). Phosphoric acid can be used instead of sulphuric acid, but is not commonly employed.

Hydrogen and bromine vapour combine at a red heat, especially in the presence of platinized asbestos, which acts as a catalyst :

$$H_2 + Br_2 = 2HBr.$$

and this method can be employed for its preparation in the laboratory.

The most usual method for making the gas is by the action of bromine and phosphorus on water.

The apparatus indicated in Fig. 197 is used, consisting of a flask containing a mixture of red phosphorus with twice its weight of water

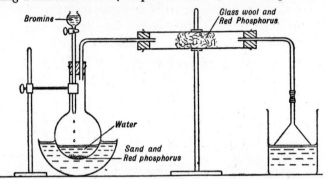

FIG. 197.—Preparation of Hydrobromic Acid (using Phosphorus).

and some clean sand; and fitted with a dropping-funnel containing bromine. The bromine is allowed to drop slowly on to the phosphorus, when hydrogen bromide is given off and heat is evolved, so that in the initial stages of the reaction it may be necessary to cool the flask in a trough of water. The gas is passed through a tube containing glass wool and damp red phosphorus, to remove any unchanged bromine, after which it may be collected over mercury, or by downward delivery since it is heavier than air.

If the solution be required, the gas may be dissolved in water using a funnel, as shown in Fig. 197, to prevent the risk of the water being sucked back. Alternatively, two wash-bottles connected as shown in Fig. 198 may be used.

The reactions which take place are probably as follows :

$$2P + 3Br_2 = 2PBr_3,$$
$$2P + 5Br_2 = 2PBr_5,$$
$$PBr_3 + 3H_2O = H_3PO_3 + 3HBr,$$
$$PBr_5 + 4H_2O = H_3PO_4 + 5HBr.$$

Another convenient method for the preparation of hydrogen bromide is by the action of hydrogen sulphide on bromine, and may be carried out in the apparatus indicated in Fig. 198.

A stream of hydrogen sulphide (p. 445) is passed through bromine mixed with a little water in a wash-bottle. The hydrogen bromide formed is passed through a tube containing damp red phosphorus as before, and then either collected over mercury, or by downward delivery or dissolved in water by means of two wash-bottles as shown. (Alternatively a funnel may be used as in Fig. 197.) The reaction is represented by the equation :

$$H_2S + Br_2 = 2HBr + S.$$

Yet another feasible method is by the action of sulphur dioxide on bromine in presence of a little water. This can be carried out in the

$$Br_2 + SO_2 + 2H_2O = H_2SO_4 + 2HBr$$

apparatus shown in Fig. 198 and gives a very pure product.

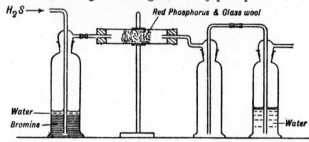

FIG. 198.—Preparation of Hydrobromic Acid (using Hydrogen Sulphide).

Properties

Hydrogen bromide is a colourless gas with a strong penetrating smell. It fumes in air. The gas condenses to a liquid at $-67°$; and solidifies to a colourless solid at $-86°$. The gas is very soluble in water. 100 grams of water at $0°$ dissolve 221 grams of hydrogen bromide, and 199 grams at $20°$. The acid containing 48 per cent. of hydrogen bromide distils unchanged in composition; weaker acids lose much water, while more concentrated acids lose hydrogen bromide until the constant boiling mixture, which boils at $126°$ at 760 mm., is obtained.

Dry hydrogen bromide has no action on litmus. Hydrogen bromide resembles hydrogen chloride very closely in chemical properties, but hydrogen bromide is less energetic. It attacks mercury very slowly, forming hydrogen and mercury bromide. The action is not fast enough to prevent its use in collecting hydrogen bromide. Hydrogen bromide is more easily decomposed than hydrogen chloride; thus at $800°$ the dissociation is appreciable. Slight decomposition also occurs when the gas is exposed to sunlight. Again, it is more readily oxidized than hydrochloric acid; thus sulphuric acid and hydrogen peroxide oxidize it to bromine:

$$2HBr + H_2SO_4 = Br_2 + SO_2 + 2H_2O,$$
$$2HBr + H_2O_2 = Br_2 + 2H_2O,$$

whereas neither of these attacks hydrochloric acid.

Uses

Hydrobromic acid is an important laboratory reagent, especially in organic chemistry. It is also used occasionally in medicine.

The **Composition and Formula** of hydrogen bromide have been determined in a similar manner to those of hydrogen chloride (p. 504).

Bromides

Hydrobromic acid forms bromides in the same way as hydrochloric acid forms chlorides, and the two series of salts are very similar. Thus corresponding salts crystallize in the same forms, and closely resemble each other in chemical behaviour, the principal difference being that the bromides are more readily oxidized. Some bromides, e.g., those of potassium, and silver, are extensively used in photography, and potassium and sodium bromides are used in medicine.

Detection and Determination of Bromides

A common method for the detection of bromides is the formation of free bromine when a bromide is warmed with concentrated sulphuric acid and manganese dioxide. The identity of the bromine is established as indicated on page 520. Another method, available if the salt under investigation is soluble, is to add a few drops of chlorine water to the solution and shake it with a little carbon disulphide. Bromine is liberated and dissolves in the carbon disulphide with an orange colour. Silver nitrate yields an almost white, though slightly cream-coloured, precipitate of silver bromide insoluble in dilute nitric acid and in dilute ammonia, though soluble in strong ammonia. It does not turn violet in light as silver chloride does.

Bromides are determined in the same manner as chlorides, making use of their reaction with silver nitrate.

§ 22 Compounds of Bromine and Oxygen

It is doubtful if any oxides of bromine have been obtained as yet, although such compounds have been described from time to time. The preparation of two such, viz., bromine monoxide, Br_2O, and an oxide of the formula $(Br_3O_8)n$, has been claimed recently (1930). The former is described as a very unstable gas obtained by the action of bromine on specially prepared, very reactive mercuric oxide. The other $(Br_3O_8)n$, is said to be formed by the action of ozone on bromine vapour at temperatures below $0°$, and is also very unstable. Neither of these has received further confirmation. More recently still (1937) the isolation of another oxide of bromine, BrO_2, has been reported by Schwarz and Schmeisser.

Two oxy-acids of bromine are definitely known, viz.,

Hypobromous Acid, HOBr,

Bromic Acid, $HBrO_3$,

while the existence of

Bromous Acid, $HBrO_2$

has been reported, but not confirmed. Neither perbromic acid nor any perbromate has hitherto been obtained.

Hypobromous Acid, HOBr, and Hypobromites

When bromine is added to a cold, aqueous solution of sodium or potassium hydroxide a colourless liquid is obtained which has bleaching properties, and which resembles in many respects a solution of sodium hypochlorite (p. 509). Hence it is inferred that the hypobromite has been formed :

$$2NaOH + Br_2 = NaBr + NaOBr + H_2O.$$

A dilute solution of the corresponding acid can be made by shaking mercuric oxide with a cold, aqueous solution of bromine :

$$HgO + H_2O + 2Br_2 = HgBr_2 + 2HOBr.$$

The aqueous solution of the acid is unstable and decomposes at 60° into bromine and water, although it can be distilled at 40° under reduced pressure.

An alkaline solution of sodium hypobromite is used for the estimation of ammonium salts and urea. Nitrogen is evolved quantitatively and its volume serves as a measure of the ammonium salt, or urea, present in the solution :

$$2NH_4Cl + 3NaOBr + 2NaOH = 3NaBr + 2NaCl + 5H_2O + N_2$$
$$CO(NH_2)_2 + 3NaOBr + 2NaOH = 3NaBr + Na_2CO_3 + 3H_2O + N_2.$$

Bromous Acid, HBrO₂

What is thought to be a solution of bromous acid is formed when an excess of bromine water is shaken with a concentrated solution of silver nitrate. Hypobromous acid is probably first formed, and this is perhaps further oxidized :

$$AgNO_3 + Br_2 + H_2O = HOBr + AgBr + HNO_3,$$
$$2AgNO_3 + Br_2 + H_2O + HOBr = HBrO_2 + 2HNO_3 + 2AgBr.$$

Neither the acid nor its salts have been isolated.

Bromic Acid, HBrO₃, and Bromates

By dropping bromine slowly into a cold aqueous solution of potassium hydroxide a yellow solution is formed which soon deposits crystals of **potassium bromate**, $KBrO_3$:

$$6KOH + 3Br_2 = 5KBr + KBrO_3 + 3H_2O.$$

The crystals can be purified by recrystallization from hot water.

Barium bromate, $Ba(BrO_3)_2.H_2O$, can be prepared similarly from barium hydroxide solution.

By treating barium bromate solution with the calculated quantity of sulphuric acid an aqueous solution of bromic acid is obtained :

$$Ba(BrO_3)_2 + H_2SO_4 = BaSO_4 + 2HBrO_3.$$

The solution can be decanted, or filtered, from the precipitated barium sulphate, and concentrated by evaporation under reduced pressure until it contains about 50 per cent. of the acid. On further concentration, or on heating, decomposition into bromine, oxygen, and water occurs :

$$4HBrO_3 = 2Br_2 + 5O_2 + 2H_2O.$$

The bromates resemble the chlorates, but there is no sign of the formation of perbromates on heating. Some metallic bromates when heated give the oxide, bromine, and oxygen, e.g.,

$$2Mg(BrO_3)_2 = 2MgO + 2Br_2 + 5O_2.$$

§ 23 Iodine

History

In 1811, B. Courtois, a manufacturer of saltpetre, near Paris, used an aqueous extract of varec or kelp* for decomposing the calcium nitrate from the nitre beds (p. 577). Courtois noticed that the copper vats in which the nitrate was decomposed were rapidly corroded by the liquid, and he traced the effect to a reaction between the copper and an unknown substance in the lye obtained by extracting the varec or kelp with water. On evaporating the aqueous extract of the kelp, crystals of potassium sulphate first separate, then follow crystals of sodium sulphate, sodium chloride, and afterwards sodium carbonate. The remaining liquid when heated with sulphuric acid in a retort furnished " a vapour of a superb violet colour " which condensed in the beak of the retort and in the receiver in the form of brilliant crystalline plates. Courtois communicated his discovery to Clément and Désormes, who published some results of their study of this new substance in 1813. A year later Gay-Lussac published an extensive and remarkable memoir on this new substance which was called iodine —from the Greek ἰοειδής (ioeidēs), violet. Gay-Lussac established the elementary nature of iodine, and demonstrated its relationship to chlorine. About the same time, H. Davy confirmed many of Gay-Lussac's results.

Occurrence

Iodine, although widely distributed, is never found free in nature. Varec or kelp contains from 0·1 to 0·3 per cent. of iodine. The kelp derived from deep seas is richer in iodine than that from shallower parts. Iodine also occurs in small quantities in sea water ; sea plants ; sea animals ; in some land plants and animals ; in cod-liver oil ; in the thyroid gland of animals ; and in many mineral springs. It occurs combined with silver in some Mexican ores, and in some South American lead ores. Most of the iodine of commerce is extracted from the mother liquid remaining after the separation of sodium nitrate from caliche in Chile, Peru, etc. Caliche contains about 0·2 per cent. of iodine, and the mother liquid after the extraction of the sodium nitrate, contains 5 to 20 per cent. of sodium iodate (p. 565).

Manufacture

Iodine is manufactured :
(i) from caliche, after removal of the sodium nitrate ;
(ii) from seaweed.

Iodine from Caliche

The mother liquor remaining after the crystallization of the sodium nitrate (p. 565) is treated with sodium bisulphite which first reduces the iodate to iodide, which then reacts with unchanged iodate to form free iodine :

$$NaIO_3 + 3NaHSO_3 = NaI + 3NaHSO_4,$$
$$NaIO_3 + 5NaI + 6NaHSO_4 = 3I_2 + 6Na_2SO_4 + 3H_2O.$$

* During the stormy months of spring, seaweeds are washed on to the western coasts of Ireland, Scotland, and France. The inhabitants collect the weed and burn it in large heaps at as low a temperature as possible. The ash thus obtained is called *kelp* in Scotland and *varec* in Normandy.

The solid iodine which separates is allowed to settle, washed, pressed into blocks, and sublimed from iron retorts into a series of earthenware receivers known as *udells* (Fig. 199).

Iodine from Seaweed

The seaweed is roughly dried and burned, and the fused mass of salts which remains is extracted with water. This aqueous extract is concentrated when potassium sulphate, and chloride, and sodium chloride are deposited.

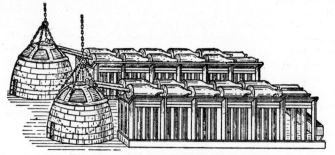

FIG. 199.—Technical Distillation of Iodine.

The mother liquor, which contains iodides and some bromides, is treated with sulphuric acid and manganese dioxide and distilled. Iodine is liberated and condensed in a series of earthenware bottles (udells) arranged as shown in Fig. 199.

Iodine is further purified by mixing it with potassium iodide (to remove chlorine and bromine which are usually present in solid solution) and re-subliming it.

Properties

At ordinary temperatures, iodine is a dark bluish-black crystalline solid. The rhombic crystalline plates have a metallic lustre, and a specific gravity of 4·933 at 4°. Solid iodine has a vapour pressure of 0·030 mm. at 0°, rising to 3·084 mm. at 55°; this agrees with the fact that iodine vaporizes slowly at ordinary temperatures, and it has a slight smell resembling chlorine. It is very sparingly soluble in water: 100 c.c. of a saturated solution at 25° contain about 0·034 gram of iodine, and is coloured a faint brown. The iodine is much more soluble if potassium iodide be also present.

Iodine is readily soluble in carbon disulphide, chloroform, benzene and other hydrocarbons forming violet solutions; it is also soluble in alcohol, ether, acetone, etc., but in these solvents it forms brown solutions.

It is probable that free iodine is present in the violet solutions; and that the brown coloration is due to the formation of a compound of iodine with the solvent. In brown solutions of iodine in potassium iodide, for example, the iodine is present as an unstable **potassium**

tri-iodide, KI_3. This salt has indeed been isolated in the form of dark-coloured, needle-shaped crystals.

A great number of **polyiodides** have been prepared, particularly of the alkali metals : e.g., CsI_5, RbI_3, $RbICl_4$, KI_3, etc.

The tendency of the alkali metals to form polyiodides increases with increasing atomic weight.

Iodine resembles chlorine and bromine in its chemical properties, but it is rather less energetic. Chlorine can displace bromine from bromides, and both chlorine and bromine can displace iodine from iodides. Chlorine can displace bromine from bromates, and iodine appears to displace chlorine from chlorates according to the equation :

$$2KClO_3 + I_2 = 2KIO_3 + Cl_2,$$

but the reaction is probably not one of simple displacement as is explained on page 531.

Iodine does not combine directly with oxygen, and with hydrogen the reaction is very slow, except in the presence of catalysts (see pp. 225, 528).

Of the other non-metals only phosphorus, chlorine and fluorine will combine directly with iodine ; but most metals react energetically with it, although less so than with the other halogens. Thus antimony powder inflames spontaneously when it is shaken with iodine vapour ; iodine and mercury also combine energetically when heated.

When in contact with starch, iodine forms an intense blue coloration. The reaction is delicate enough to reveal the presence of 0·0000001 grm. of iodine per c.c. The blue colour disappears when heated to about 80°, but returns on cooling. The " blued " starch is supposed to be either a solid solution of iodine in the starch, or else an " addition " compound of iodine with starch.

Iodine, like the other halogens, is an oxidizing agent, though much less powerful. It will oxidize, for example, arsenites to arsenates, hydrogen sulphide to sulphur and sulphites to sulphates, reactions which are employed in volumetric analysis in conjunction with a standard solution of sodium thiosulphate :

$$Na_3AsO_3 + I_2 + H_2O = Na_3AsO_4 + 2HI,$$
$$H_2S + I_2 = 2HI + S,$$
$$Na_2SO_3 + I_2 + H_2O = Na_2SO_4 + 2HI.$$

Iodine in solution reacts quantitatively with sodium thiosulphate, sodium tetrathionate being formed :

$$2Na_2S_2O_3 + I_2 = 2NaI + Na_2S_4O_6,$$

and this reaction has many applications in volumetric analysis. It can be employed not only in the determination of iodine itself but for determining the amount of any oxidizing agent which will liberate iodine from an iodide. Examples are chlorine, bromine, copper salts, hypochlorites, and bleaching powder.

Uses

Iodine is largely used in medicine, both in the form of the free element (usually in solution in alcohol called " tincture of iodine ") and in combination. The tincture is an important antiseptic. Iodine is a constituent also of the antiseptics iodoform (CHI_3) and iodole (C_4I_4NH). It is employed in the manufacture of dyes and other organic chemicals, in photography and in analytical chemistry.

Atomic and Molecular Weights

The combining weight of iodine has been determined by the analysis of silver iodide and other iodine compounds such as iodine pentoxide. The atomic weight is seen to be approximately 127 since this is the smallest amount of iodine present in the molecular weight of any known volatile compound. The accepted value for the atomic weight at present (1940) is 126·92.

The vapour density of iodine at 600° is 125·9 ($H_2 = 1$) which corresponds with a molecule I_2. Similarly, the lowering of the freezing points and raising of the boiling points of solutions of iodine in acetic acid, carbon disulphide and chloroform indicate a molecular weight of approximately 254.

When iodine is heated above 700°, the vapour density diminishes steadily up to about 1700°, when it becomes constant at about 63·5 indicating dissociation into atoms.

§ 24 Hydrogen Iodide, Hydriodic Acid, HI

Hydrogen iodide, like hydrogen bromide, cannot be made by the action of concentrated sulphuric acid on iodides on account of the ease with which it is oxidized. It is formed by the direct union of hydrogen and iodine, and although the reaction is reversible and incomplete and also slow in the absence of a catalyst (compare p. 225), it can be utilized for its preparation by passing hydrogen and iodine vapour over heated platinized asbestos.

The gas is usually prepared in the laboratory by the action of phosphorus and iodine on water, using the apparatus (Fig. 197) employed for the similar preparation of hydrogen bromide. Red phosphorus and iodine are mixed in a dry flask, and water is added from a dropping-funnel. (This modified procedure is rendered necessary by the fact that iodine is a solid at ordinary temperatures whereas bromine is a liquid.) Free iodine is removed by passage through a tube containing red phosphorus and glass wool. The gas cannot be collected over mercury as it attacks it ; it is usually collected by downward delivery.

The solution in water (known as hydriodic acid) may be prepared by absorbing the gas obtained as described above, in water (using precautions as in the case of hydrobromic acid, etc., to prevent " sucking-back "), but it is often made in the following way. Powdered iodine is suspended in excess of water and hydrogen sulphide is bubbled slowly through the mixture, until the colour of the iodine has disappeared. A rapid stream of carbon dioxide, or hydrogen, is then passed for a short time to remove hydrogen sulphide. The mixture is then shaken to coagulate the free sulphur which is removed by filtration through glass wool. The solution can be concentrated to about 50 per cent. by distillation. The reaction is represented :

$$H_2S + I_2 = 2HI + S.$$

Properties

Hydrogen iodide is a colourless gas which fumes strongly in air. It condenses to a colourless liquid at $0°$ under 4 atmospheres pressure. This boils at $-35 \cdot 5°$, and freezes to a white solid which melts at $-50 \cdot 8°$. The gas is very soluble in water : one volume of water at $10°$ dissolves about 425 volumes of hydrogen iodide. The solution fumes strongly in air, and it has acid properties.

It forms a constant boiling mixture when distilled, containing 57 per cent. of hydrogen iodide, which boils at $127°$ at 774 mm.

The solution is colourless, when freshly prepared, but turns brown on keeping owing to formation of free iodine on oxidation :

$$4HI + O_2 = 2H_2O + 2I_2.$$

It is a powerful reducing agent on account of the ease with which it is decomposed into hydrogen and iodine and is extensively used for this purpose in organic chemistry. It is also decomposed by exposure to light, and on heating : the following table shows the extent of dissociation at various temperatures.

TABLE XXXII.—DISSOCIATION OF HYDROGEN IODIDE.

Temperature	Per cent. of Dissociation.
$283°$	$17 \cdot 9$
$356°$	$19 \cdot 5$
$444°$	$22 \cdot 0$
$527°$	$24 \cdot 7$

The dissociation of hydrogen iodide was extensively investigated by Bodenstein (1897), whose values are given in Table XXXII

It is interesting to notice that, although hydrogen iodide is an endothermic compound, heat is evolved when it is prepared in solution from iodine and hydrogen sulphide as described on page 528. This is due to the fact that although the formation of hydrogen iodide involves absorption of heat

$$H_2S + I_2 = 2HI + S - 16 \cdot 8 \text{ Cals.}$$

hydrogen iodide evolves $19 \cdot 2$ Cals. per gram molecule when dissolved in water. Consequently the net result of the process is the evolution of heat.

The composition of hydrogen iodide can be determined as indicated for hydrogen chloride and hydrogen bromide. The vapour density is $63 \cdot 94$ ($H_2 = 1$), corresponding with the formula HI.

Iodides

Hydriodic acid resembles hydrobromic and hydrochloric acids, and forms salts—iodides. The chlorides likewise resemble the iodides and bromides, and they all can be prepared by similar processes. It is, however, worth noting that many of the so-called insoluble iodides precipitated by adding a solution of potassium iodide to a solution of a metallic salt, are soluble in an excess of a solution of potassium iodide. Most metallic iodides when heated in air furnish the metal or a metallic oxide and liberate free iodine. The iodides are usually less volatile than the corresponding chlorides and bromides. Many iodides have characteristic colours.

Detection and Determination

Hydriodic acid and iodides are detected by the formation of a pale yellow curdy precipitate with silver nitrate, insoluble in dilute nitric acid and in ammonia. They also give free iodine when warmed with concentrated sulphuric acid, the element being recognized by its violet vapour. Iodides may be determined gravimetrically by precipitation as silver iodide, which is weighed as such. Volumetrically, the iodine liberated by means of a suitable oxidizing agent (cf. p. 527) is titrated with a standard solution of sodium thiosulphate.

§ 25 Oxides of Iodine

Three oxides of iodine have been described :
Iodine Dioxide, IO_2 or I_2O_4,
I_4O_9,
Iodine Pentoxide, I_2O_5,
of which the last-named is the only important one. Also a number of other oxidized compounds of iodine have been reported which are probably mixtures.

Iodine Dioxide, IO_2 or I_2O_4, is said to be formed as a lemon-yellow powder by the action of cold nitric acid on iodine ; also by the action of hot concentrated sulphuric acid on iodic acid. It readily decomposes into iodine and iodine pentoxide on warming.

I_4O_9 is said to result from the action of ozone on dry iodine.

Iodine Pentoxide, I_2O_5

When iodic acid is heated to about 170° it decomposes with loss of water forming iodine pentoxide :

$$2HIO_3 = H_2O + I_2O_5.$$

It is a white, crystalline solid which dissolves in water re-forming iodic acid. It is more stable than any of the oxides of chlorine or bromine, although it decomposes into its elements above 200°

§ 26 Oxyacids of Iodine

Three oxyacids of iodine are known in the form of their salts, viz. :
Hypoiodous Acid, HOI,
Iodic Acid, HIO_3,
Periodic Acid, HIO_4,

but periodic acid itself has probably not been isolated. In addition, a number of salts is known having complicated formulae derived from periodic acid (see below).

Hypoiodous Acid, HOI. Hypoiodites

Iodine will dissolve in cold, aqueous alkaline solutions, like chlorine and bromine, forming a liquid with bleaching properties, believed to contain hypoiodites in solution :

$$2KOH + I_2 = KI + KOI + H_2O.$$

A dilute solution of the corresponding acid can be made by shaking mercuric oxide with a cold aqueous solution of iodine :

$$HgO + 2I_2 + H_2O = HgI_2 + 2HOI.$$

These solutions are very unstable and decompose on standing, forming first iodide and iodate, which (in the case of the free acids) react together with deposition of free iodine :

$$3KOI = 2KI + KIO_3,$$
$$3HOI = 2HI + HIO_3,$$
$$HIO_3 + 5HI = 3I_2 + 3H_2O.$$

Iodic Acid, HIO₃. Iodates

Potassium iodate, KIO_3, can be made by the direct action of potassium chlorate on iodine, as represented by the equation :

$$2KClO_3 + I_2 = 2KIO_3 + Cl_2.$$

This reaction is sometimes considered to be a direct replacement of chlorine, but it is more probably one of oxidation of iodine by the chlorate. This is a convenient method for the preparation of potassium iodate.

Barium Iodate, Ba(IO₃)₂

This salt can be prepared by dissolving iodine in an aqueous solution of barium hydroxide, or by the addition of barium chlorate to an aqueous solution of potassium iodate. White granular barium iodate is precipitated.

The Preparation of Iodic Acid, HIO₃

Iodic acid can be made by the process described for bromic acid (p. 524) of course substituting iodine for bromine, for instance, by the action of dilute sulphuric acid on barium iodate ; or by the action of chlorine on water containing iodine in suspension ; or by the action of an aqueous solution of chloric acid on iodine. Iodic acid, however, is usually made by the direct oxidation of iodine with nitric acid.

The reaction is represented by the equation :

$$10HNO_3 + I_2 = 2HIO_3 + 10NO_2 + 4H_2O,$$

but it is no doubt much more complex.

The powdered iodine is added in small quantities at a time to concentrated colourless nitric acid ; a current of air or carbon dioxide being passed through the apparatus to remove oxides of nitrogen as fast as they are formed. After the iodine has all dissolved and its colour has disappeared, the mixture is allowed to cool and the iodic acid, which separates, is filtered off on an asbestos filter. It is recrystallized from dilute nitric acid.

Properties

Iodic acid is a white crystalline solid, readily soluble in water. The aqueous solution first reddens blue litmus and then bleaches the colour. It does not give a blue colour with starch. It forms salts, the **iodates** which resemble the chlorates and bromates in many ways, but are less easily decomposed by heat. A series of *acid iodates* is known, usually formulated, for example,

$$KIO_3.HIO_3 \; ; \; KIO_3.2HIO_3,$$

from which it might be inferred that iodic acid is a polybasic acid, e.g., $H_2I_2O_6$ or $H_3I_3O_9$; but its constitution is not definitely known.

On heating, iodic acid passes into iodine pentoxide (see above). It is a strong oxidizing agent. It reacts, for example, with hydrogen sulphide, with hydriodic acid and with sulphur dioxide as indicated in the equations :

$$5H_2S + 2HIO_3 = 5S + 6H_2O + I_2,$$
$$5HI + HIO_3 = 3I_2 + 3H_2O,$$
$$5SO_2 + 2HIO_3 + 4H_2O = 5H_2SO_4 + I_2.$$

This latter reaction is used as a test for iodates. The solution is first acidified with hydrochloric acid to liberate the iodic acid, and then mixed with starch paste. Sulphurous acid, or an alkaline sulphite, is then added drop by drop. The liberated iodine forms "blue starch iodide," the characteristic reaction of iodine.

The reaction between sulphurous acid and an iodate is very interesting, because the iodine does not appear immediately the substances are mixed ; there is a well-defined period of time—period of induction —between the moment the reacting substances are mixed, and the moment iodine makes its appearance. The duration of the interval is dependent upon the concentrations of the solutions.

It is supposed that the first action is due to the reduction of the iodic acid to hydriodic acid ; and when all the sulphurous acid has been oxidized this reaction is followed by the oxidation of the hydriodic acid by the excess of iodic acid :

$$3H_2SO_3 + HIO_3 = 3H_2SO_4 + HI,$$
$$5HI + HIO_3 = 3H_2O + 3I_2.$$

(These two equations combined lead to the one quoted previously.)

The first reaction—oxidation of sulphurous acid—must be nearly completed before the second one can start, because, as indicated above, the iodine with sulphurous acid reforms hydriodic acid. Since the maximum amount of iodic and sulphurous acids are present at the start, the first-named reaction must be fastest at the beginning and afterwards gradually slow down. Again, since the velocity of a reaction is proportional to the amount of the reacting substances present in the system, the second reaction will be the slowest at the start, and gradually become faster. The speed of formation of the iodine is therefore the resultant velocity of two consecutive reactions ; and the belated appearance of the iodine—the period of induction—corresponds with the time required for the first reaction to make enough hydriodic acid to enable the second reaction to make sufficient iodine to colour the starch.

Periodic Acid, HIO_4. Periodates

It is not certain if normal periodic acid—HIO_4—has been made, but a large number of related salts, classed as periodates, is known. These are somewhat complicated in composition and are best understood as being salts of acids derived from the hypothetical iodine heptoxide—I_2O_7—by addition of water step by step as shown in the following table.

TABLE XXXIII.—THE PERIODIC ACIDS

I_2O_7 with	Compounds formed.	Empirical formula of acid.	Name of acid.	Salts.
$1H_2O$	$I_2O_6(OH)_2$; or $2IO_3OH$	HIO_4	Meta-periodic acid	KIO_4 ; $AgIO_4$; etc.
$2H_2O$	$I_2O_5(OH)_4$	$H_4I_2O_9$	Dimeso-periodic acid	No salts known
$3H_2O$	$I_2O_4(OH)_6$; or $2IO_2(OH)_3$	H_3IO_5	Meso-periodic acid	Ag_3IO_5 ; $Pb_3(IO_5)_2$; etc.
$4H_2O$	$I_2O_3(OH)_8$	$H_8I_2O_{11}$	Dipara-periodic acid	Salts have been reported ; probably mixtures
$5H_2O$	$I_2O_2(OH)_{10}$; or $2IO(OH)_5$	H_5IO_6	Para-periodic acid	Ag_5IO_6 ; $Ag_2H_3IO_6$; etc.
$6H_2O$	$I_2O(OH)_{12}$	$H_{12}I_2O_{13}$	Diortho-periodic acid	Salts have been reported ; probably mixtures
$7H_2O$	$I_2(OH)_{14}$; or $2I(OH)_7$	H_7IO_7	Ortho-periodic acid	No salts known

Nomenclature of the Periodic Acids and the Periodates

When one anhydride forms a series of acids by union with different amounts of water, the acid containing most water is called the **ortho-acid**—from the Greek ὀρθός (orthos), regular ; the other acids have prefixes, making **para-acid**—from the Greek παρά (para), beside ; **meso-acid**—from the Greek μέρος (meros), middle, intermediate ; and **meta-acid**—from the Greek μετά (meta), beyond, less than the highest. The **di-acids** are supposed to be formed by abstraction of one molecule of water from two molecules of acid. It will be evident that if the acids are polybasic, we can imagine the available hydrogen atoms replaced one by one. If all the available hydrogen atoms are replaced by bases, the **normal salt** is obtained ; if only *one* of the available hydrogen atoms is replaced, the **primary salt** ; if two, the **secondary salt** ; if three, the **tertiary salt.**

Secondary sodium para-periodate has the composition $Na_2H_3IO_6$, thus corresponding with para-periodic acid, or $HIO_4.2H_2O$. It can be prepared as a sparingly soluble salt by passing chlorine into an aqueous solution of sodium iodate and sodium hydroxide :

$$NaIO_3 + 3NaOH + Cl_2 \rightleftharpoons 2NaCl + Na_2H_3IO_6.$$

When sodium periodate is dissolved in nitric acid and silver nitrate is added to the solution, crystals of **silver meta-periodate**—$AgIO_4$—corresponding with meta-periodic acid, separate when the solution is concentrated by evaporation.

Para-periodic Acid

When silver meta-periodate is boiled with water, an insoluble salt, **secondary silver para-periodate**, is formed along with para-periodic acid, H_5IO_6, or $HIO_4.2H_2O$.

Thus

$$2AgIO_4 + 4H_2O = Ag_2H_3IO_6 + H_5IO_6.$$

When the clear solution is concentrated, deliquescent crystals of the para-periodic acid are obtained. This acid melts at 133°, and decomposes into iodine pentoxide, water, and oxygen at 150°. The water cannot be expelled by heat because oxygen is evolved along with the water. Periodic acid and neutral alkali periodates are reduced to iodates by hydrogen peroxide. If concentrated solutions of periodic acid and an excess of hydrogen peroxide be used, much iodine is liberated at the same time as the oxygen. Iodic acid and concentrated solutions of sodium iodate are slowly reduced by 3 per cent. hydrogen peroxide.

A small quantity of potassium periodate is said to occur in native Chile saltpetre, along with some sodium iodate.

§ 27 Interhalogen Compounds

The halogens form a considerable number of compounds among themselves, some of which are described below. These are known as Interhalogen Compounds.

Chlorine monofluoride—ClF—is a colourless gas, obtained by the action of chlorine on hydrogen fluoride at the temperature of liquid air. It is very reactive, acting on some metals more vigorously than fluorine. It is also formed by the action of chlorine on fluorine at 250° ; when excess of fluorine is used in this experiment **chlorine trifluoride**—ClF_3—results as a colourless gas.

Bromine trifluoride—BrF_3—is a colourless liquid, formed by the action of fluorine on bromine or hydrogen bromide ; **bromine pentafluoride**—BrF_5—is obtained similarly with excess of fluorine. It is a colourless solid.

Iodine pentafluoride—IF_5—results from the direct combination of iodine and fluorine, or by the action of fluorine on iodine pentoxide. It is a colourless solid which, when heated to 300° with more fluorine, forms a gas—**iodine heptafluoride**—IF_7.

Iodine monochloride—ICl—is a liquid, superficially indistinguishable from bromine, formed by passing chlorine over iodine. **Iodine trichloride**—ICl_3—is obtained as a yellow solid, by the action of excess of chlorine on iodine. **Iodine monobromide**—IBr—is formed by direct combination of the elements and is a crystalline solid, closely resembling iodine in appearance.

§ 28 Salts of Iodine

Since iodine is the heaviest member of the Halogen Group of elements it might be expected to show indications of the beginning of metallic properties ; it being a general phenomenon that metallic character is more developed in the heavier than in the lighter elements of a group (compare Ch. VIII).

This is found to be the case here since iodine forms a number of compounds of a salt-like nature, in which the iodine is the electro-positive part of the molecule.

Among these might be included the chlorides of iodine mentioned in the preceding section. The following compounds have also been reported, viz. :

Iodine phosphate, IPO_4,

Iodine acetate, $I(C_2H_3O_2)_3$,

Iodine nitrate, $I(NO_3)_3$

§ 29 The Halogen Family of Elements

The halogens (fluorine, chlorine, bromine and iodine) constitute the B sub-group of Group VII of the Periodic System (p. 118). The corresponding A sub-group comprises the elements manganese, masurium and rhenium, and the relationship of these to each other, and to the halogens will be discussed in Chapter XXXIV.

The halogens themselves form a remarkable family of elements.

The gradation in characters which the halogens show with increasing atomic weights from fluorine to iodine yield an almost perfect family series. The family relationship of the halogens is illustrated by—

(1) The *similarity* in the chemical and physical properties of the elements and their corresponding compounds is such that the properties of any one member of the family can be said to summarize or typify the properties of the other members of the series.

(2) The *gradual transition* of chemical and physical properties is such that if the elements be arranged in order : F, Cl, Br, I, the variation in any particular property in passing from fluorine to iodine nearly always proceeds in the same order, and that is the order of their atomic weights.

The relationship in the physical and chemical properties of the halogens can best be emphasized by the tabular scheme.

TABLE XXXIV.—SOME PROPERTIES OF THE HALOGENS.

Property.	Fluorine.	Chlorine.	Bromine.	Iodine.
Atomic weight	19	35·46	79·92	126·92
State of aggregation	Gas	Gas	Liquid	Solid
Melting point	− 223°	− 102°	− 7·3°	+ 113°
Boiling point	− 187°	− 34·6°	58·8°	184·35°
Specific gravity	1·08 (liq.)	1·55 (liq.)	3·19 (liq.)	4·93 (sol.)
Atomic volume*	16·7	22·9	25·1	25·7
Colour of gas	Pale yellow	Greenish yellow	Brownish red	Violet
Solubility (100 grms. water at 20°) dissolves grams	Decomposes water	1·46	4·15	0·0162
Oxidizing action	Strongest	Very strong	Strong	Weak
Oxyacids	—	HClO	HBrO	HIO
	—	$HClO_2$		—
	—	$HClO_3$	$HBrO_3$	HIO_3
	—	$HClO_4$	—	H_5IO_6
Hydrides	H_2F_2	HCl	HBr	HI

* Atomic volume is the atomic weight divided by the specific gravity.

All the halogens form compounds with hydrogen, and the readiness with which union occurs decreases as the atomic weight increases. The properties of the halogen acids and their salts show as striking a relationship as the elements themselves, and are shown in Table XXXV.

TABLE XXXV.—THE PROPERTIES OF THE HALOID ACIDS

Property.	Hydrogen fluoride.	Hydrogen chloride.	Hydrogen bromide.	Hydrogen iodide.
Molecular weight .	20	36·46	80·93	127·93
Boiling point .	19·4°	— 85°	— 67°	— 35·5°
Melting point .	—92·2°	— 115·2°	— 87·9°	— 50·8°
Solubility in water	35·3%	42%	49%	57%
Specific gravity saturated aq. sol.	1·15	1·21	1·49	1·70
Boiling point aq. sol. . . .	130° (36%)	110° (20%)	126° (47%)	127° (57%)
Dissociates at .	—	1500°	800°	180°
Heat of formation (Cals.) .	+ 38·5 gas	+ 22·0 gas	+ 8·4 gas	— 6·4 gas
Heat of formation of K salt (Cals.).	110·6	105·7	95·3	80·1
Heat of neutralization NaOH .	16·3 Cals.	13·9 Cals.	13·84 Cals.	13·78 Cals.
Potassium salt melts . .	885°	790°	750°	705°
Calcium salt melts.	1330°	780°	760°	740°
Solubility Ag salt (20°) per 100 grms. water .	1720	0·00154	0·000084	0·0000028
Solubility Ca salt per 100 c.c. solution . . .	0·0016	42·7	58·8	67·6

Taking almost any property and comparing its magnitude in passing from fluorine to iodine, or from fluorides to iodides, a similar gradual transition will be observed.

The boiling point and composition of the acid of constant composition of hydrofluoric acid is exceptional. Hydrogen fluoride, HF, appears to be polymerized below 88°. Again, while the affinity of the halogens for hydrogen decreases with increasing atomic weight, the reverse is the case with oxygen. But with oxygen the relationship is not so clearly defined. Thus, although fluorine forms two oxides— F_2O, and FO or F_2O_2, numerous compounds of oxygen with chlorine have been obtained ; and, judging by the known compounds with oxygen, the affinity of bromine for oxygen appears to be less, not greater, than is the case with chlorine, although we must remember that bromine has not been investigated so much as chlorine. Bromine occupies an anomalous position with respect to oxygen. Chlorine, bromine, and iodine unite with one another forming an unstable series of compounds analogous, in some ways, with hypochlorites and chlorates, but the bromine analogue of perchlorates has not been prepared.

It is found, when elements are compared that frequently the first element in any group (i.e., the element in the first short period) exhibits properties which cause it to resemble fairly closely an element in a neighbouring group, and which make it, to some extent, separate from the rest of the members of its own group. Some of the properties of fluorine mentioned above illustrate this ; for example, the weakness and association of the hydracid and also in the solubility of the silver and calcium salts.

In many respects fluorine shows considerable resemblance to oxygen. Thus, the heats of formation of many fluorides are nearer to those of the corresponding oxides than of the chlorides ; while the fluorides and oxides resemble each other in solubility, volatility and fusibility more closely, as a rule, than the fluorides and chlorides do. These statements are well illustrated by a comparison of hydrogen fluoride and water. Thus the equivalent heat of formation of water (34·2 Cals.) is closer to that of hydrogen fluoride than to that of any other halogen hydracid ; the boiling point of hydrogen fluoride is nearest to that of water and its range of fluidity most nearly similar. Like water too it is, by comparison with the other hydrogen compounds, a weak acid.

Another point of similarity between fluorine and oxygen is the fact that the fluorides and oxides of the elements are usually compounds in which the element exhibits a higher stable valency than in the chlorides. Thus, for example, SO_3 and SF_6 are stable compounds at ordinary temperatures, whereas SCl_6 cannot exist at ordinary temperatures, and a number of other similar cases could be cited. Again, fluorine will combine directly with carbon (as does oxygen) while the remaining halogens are without effect on it.

To sum up, the halogens, as a group, form one of the most striking examples of family relationship found in the Periodic Table ; but the usually observed tendency of the lightest element to exhibit differences from the remaining members of the group and to show resemblances to its neighbouring element in the next group is found here also.

CHAPTER XXIV

THE INERT GASES

§ 1 History and Preparation

History

IN 1785 Cavendish subjected a sample of air to the action of electric sparks, and absorbed the oxides of nitrogen so formed in caustic alkali solution. When no more contraction would take place, he added more oxygen and continued the sparking. When, at length, even after the addition of yet more oxygen, no further contraction could be brought about, he removed the excess oxygen with liver of sulphur (potassium pentasulphide, p. 579) and found that there remained a small bubble of gas which could not be absorbed by these processes. Cavendish concluded, as a result of these experiments, that " if there is any part of the phlogisticated air (= nitrogen) of our atmosphere which differs from the rest and cannot be reduced to nitrous acid, we may safely conclude that it is not more than $\frac{1}{120}$th part of the whole." This result obtained by Cavendish proved eventually to be remarkably accurate for the date at which it was obtained.

The importance of this observation was not realized for more than a hundred years until, in 1892, Lord Rayleigh, in the course of a series of very accurate determinations of the densities of some of the commoner gases, found that the density of nitrogen derived from the air by removal of oxygen, carbon dioxide, moisture, etc., was about 0·47 per cent. greater than the density of nitrogen prepared from ammonia, etc. The difference is much larger than the experimental error involved in the determinations and so some other cause was sought. Various suggestions were made, such as the presence of a heavy allotrope in atmospheric nitrogen (e.g., N_3) or of hydrogen in the chemical nitrogen ; but these hypotheses were soon shown to be untenable and the cause of the discrepancy to be the presence of a hitherto unrecognized gas. This gas was isolated by Ramsay in 1894 by removing from air freed from carbon dioxide, etc., first, the oxygen by passing it over heated copper, and then, the nitrogen by passage over heated magnesium. Under these conditions :

$$2Cu + O_2 = 2CuO,$$
$$3Mg + N_2 = Mg_3N_2.$$

The new gas, to which the name *argon* was given—from the Greek ἄργος (argos), inert or idle—was found to have a density of about 20 and to be chemically entirely inert and incapable of forming chemical compounds. Owing to its inertness, its atomic weight could not be found by chemical methods ; but since the ratio of its specific heats (p. 74) was found to be 1·67, it was concluded that it is monatomic and hence, that its atomic weight is twice its density, i.e., 40 approximately.

These results encouraged Rayleigh and Ramsay to undertake further investigations, which soon led to the recognition of a whole family of inert gases, viz., helium, neon, argon, krypton and xenon, which were found to fit into the Periodic Table between the strongly electro-negative halogens and the strongly electro-positive alkali metals (see § 7 below).

The last member of this family is the radio-active gas niton, or radon, which is formed as a result of the radio-active disintegration of radium (p. 851). It was first recognized and investigated in 1902 by Rutherford and Soddy. With its discovery the family of Inert Gases became complete.

Preparation

Helium is now extracted in quantity (see below) from natural gas and certain minerals ; radon is obtained as a product of radio-active change ; for the remaining members of the Inert Gas family the atmosphere is the only available source.

Two methods are available for this extraction, both of which were employed by Rayleigh and Ramsay during their investigations. These are :

(i) the removal, by chemical means, of all other constituents ;
(ii) the fractionation of liquid air.

The **chemical method** of extraction by sparking derives, of course, from Cavendish, and was much improved by Rayleigh and Ramsay, whose apparatus is shown diagrammatically in Fig. 200.

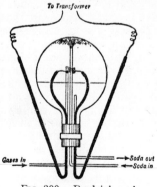

To Transformer

Gases In
Soda out
Soda in

FIG. 200.—Rayleigh and Ramsay's Apparatus.

It consists of a large flask of about 50 litres capacity, closed by a rubber stopper. It was furnished with two substantial platinum electrodes ; with tubes for the circulation of strong caustic alkali solution, and with a tube for the admission of a mixture of air and oxygen, containing approximately 9 parts of air to 11 parts of oxygen. Cooling was effected by passing the alkali solution through a worm condenser. The alkali solution circulated in a closed system so that no argon was lost through solution in it. By this means, the nitrogen is removed from the air by combination with oxygen to form nitric oxide and nitrogen peroxide, as in the fixation of nitrogen by the arc process (p. 406). The reactions which occur are indicated by the equations :

$$N_2 + O_2 = 2NO.$$
$$2NO + O_2 = 2NO_2,$$
$$2NO_2 + 2NaOH = NaNO_2 + NaNO_3 + H_2O.$$

The argon (and other inert gases) accumulate in the flask. The complete separation of the higher members of the series from the argon are only effected by liquefaction and subsequent fractionation.

Ramsay also used hot magnesium for the removal of the nitrogen, but this reaction is very slow. A more efficient modification of this process is the use of calcium carbide, mixed with about 10 per cent. of calcium chloride and heated to 800°. Both oxygen and nitrogen are absorbed according to the equations :

$$CaC_2 + N_2 = CaCN_2 + C,$$
$$C + O_2 = CO_2.$$

Industrially the inert gases are obtained **by the fractionation of liquid air**—a development of the method employed by Rayleigh and Ramsay in the later stages of their investigations. The boiling points of the various gases are, at 760 mm. :

Helium	−268·9° C.
Neon	−245·9° C.
Nitrogen . . .	−195·8° C.
Argon	−185·7° C.
Oxygen . . .	−183° C.
Krypton . . .	−151·8° C.
Xenon	−109° C.

from which it appears that the helium and neon have boiling points very considerably below that of nitrogen. In consequence, in the ordinary nitrogen separation process (p. 41) these two gases escape liquefaction and there accumulates in the liquefying column, above the liquid, a mixture of nitrogen, neon and helium. This mixture is led through a spiral column situated in the stream of evaporating nitrogen, with the result that most of the nitrogen it contains is liquefied. The remaining nitrogen is removed by chemical means (e.g., with calcium carbide). The separation of the neon from the helium (the proportions are usually about 3 parts of neon to 1 part of helium) is then effected, either by cooling in liquid hydrogen when the neon solidifies and the helium passes on, or by selective absorption of the gases in charcoal at a low temperature. Commercial neon usually contains about 2 per cent. of helium.

The boiling point of argon is very close to, and is not far above, that of nitrogen, hence its separation is difficult and is effected in a special type of column. Most of the argon is found in the liquid oxygen obtained in the air-liquefaction process. This mixture is run into the base of a fractionating column round a coil through which compressed air is being circulated. Partial evaporation occurs, the vapour being richer in argon than the liquid. This vapour travels up the column against a descending stream of liquid oxygen. Argon is thus removed from the descending liquid and oxygen from the ascending vapour. The same process is then continued in a second column ; after which the last traces of oxygen (and nitrogen) are removed chemically.

§ 2 Helium, He

Discovery and Preparation

In 1868, P. J. C. Janssen detected a prominent orange line in the spectrum of the sun's photosphere, which did not correspond with the spectral line of any known element. Hence E. Frankland and J. N. Lockyer suggested the existence of a new element to which the name helium (from ήλιος—helios—the sun) was given. The same line was later detected in the spectra of certain stars, and in 1882 Palmieri observed it in the spectrum of the gases flaming from Vesuvius.

In 1882 Hildebrand had reported the presence of a gas which he identified as nitrogen, occluded in certain minerals such as clèveite (a variety of pitchblende), fergussonite, bröggerite, uraninite, etc. After the discovery of argon it was suggested to Ramsay that he should examine this occluded nitrogen to see if it contained any argon. His examination showed that the gas contained no argon, nor did it consist of nitrogen but was, in fact, helium. A little later the presence of helium in the atmosphere was established ; it has also been detected in the gaseous emanations from certain springs, and it occurs to the extent of almost 1 per cent. in the natural gas of the U.S.A.

Helium is now an important article of commerce, particularly in the U.S.A., where it is extracted from natural gas and used for filling airships. Its extraction from certain minerals, in particular from monazite sand (which contains about 1 c.c. per gram of sand, p. 713), is also assuming commercial importance. Its presence in these minerals is due to radio-active changes taking place in certain constituents of the mineral. The helium is obtained from the natural gas by liquefaction and subsequent fractionation ; it is removed from monazite sand by heating to 1000°.

Properties

Helium is a colourless, tasteless and odourless gas, with a density of 2·001 ($H_2 = 1$), so that, next to hydrogen, it is the lightest gas known. It can only be liquefied with the very greatest difficulty. Like hydrogen, it does not cool itself on expansion through a small jet at ordinary temperatures, and in fact must be cooled to —258° before this process will work. It is, therefore, cooled first in boiling liquid hydrogen. It was first liquefied by Kamerlingh Onnes in 1907, and was solidified by Keesom in 1926. By the rapid evaporation of liquid helium, under reduced pressure, a temperature of only 0·82° above the absolute zero was reached.

In common with the other members of the Inert Gas family, helium is usually supposed to form no compounds, and hence its **Atomic Weight** has not been determined by chemical methods, although the existence of compounds with tungsten and mercury has been reported. Thus Boomer in 1925 claimed that electronic bombardment of helium in presence of tungsten leads to the formation of a compound, WHe_2, and Manley in 1927 reported that when subjected to a glow discharge mercury in contact with helium forms HgHe or $HgHe_2$.

The atomic weight of helium has been evaluated from the determination of the density and the ratio of the two specific heats of the gas. This latter ratio, as found from measurements of the velocity of sound in the gas, is 1·67, indicating that helium is monatomic, and hence has an atomic weight equal to twice its density compared to hydrogen. The value at present (1940) recommended by the International Committee is 4·003.

Uses

Helium is used in the United States for filling airships for, although it is not so light as hydrogen its lifting power (p. 264) is still 92 per cent. of that of the latter gas, and it possesses the great advantage of non-inflammability. It also has the advantage over hydrogen of escaping less readily by diffusion through the material of the gas-bags. By reason of its very slight solubility in the blood it is being used as a diluent for oxygen in modern diving apparatus. The very considerable solubility of nitrogen in these circumstances causes the formation of bubbles in the blood when the pressure is released ; a trouble known as caisson disease.

§ 3 Neon, Ne

Discovery and Preparation

Neon was discovered in 1898 by Ramsay and Travers who suspected that a gap existed in the family of Inert Gases previously discovered. It was isolated by the liquefaction of 18 litres of crude argon and fractionation of the resulting liquid.

Neon is now manufactured from the atmosphere by liquefaction, as described above (p. 540).

Properties

Neon is a colourless, tasteless, odourless gas having a density of about 10·1 ($H_2 = 1$). Hence its atomic weight (since it is found to be a monatomic gas) is 20·2 approximately. The value at present accepted by the International Committee is 20·18. It consists of a mixture of three isotopes of mass 20, 21 and 22 respectively, and was the first non-radio-active element for which unmistakable evidence of the existence of isotopes was obtained (compare p. 135).

Uses

Neon is very extensively used in discharge tubes for advertising purposes, since, when subjected to a discharge at 1000 volts at a pressure of 2 mm., it emits a very bright and characteristic orange-red glow. A blue or green colour is similarly obtained by admixture of a little mercury vapour with neon. Argon and mercury vapour are similarly used for producing a blue or green colour, and the so-called ripple tubes contain a trace of an organic compound in addition to the Inert Gas or Gases.

§ 4 Argon, A

Argon is manufactured in considerable quantities from liquid air, as described previously.

It is colourless, tasteless and odourless ; its density is 19·97 and, since it is monatomic, its atomic weight is 39·944. Its atomic weight is thus higher than that of potassium, although it should be lower according to the relative positions of the two elements in the Periodic Table. This anomaly was for long unexplained, but is now known to be due to the preponderance of the heaviest of the three isotopes of which argon is composed (p. 137). Argon is appreciably soluble in water, more so than either oxygen or nitrogen. It is not known with certainty to form any compounds, although the existence of a hydrate A.5 or $6H_2O$ has been reported (Villard, de Forcrand 1902) and Booth and Willson (1935) obtained a freezing-point curve for mixtures of argon and boron trifluoride which is said to indicate the existence of a series of compounds $A.(BF_3)_x$ where $x = 1, 2, 3, 6, 8$ or 16.

Uses

Argon is used to some extent, as mentioned above, in discharge tubes for illumination ; but its principal use at present is in the manufacture of " gas-filled " lamps, in which it is very much more efficient than nitrogen, probably on account of its monatomicity.

§ 5 Krypton and Xenon, Kr and Xe

Krypton and Xenon were discovered by Ramsay and Travers in the final residues from the evaporation of liquid air. They are present only in very minute proportions in the atmosphere and so far have not found any practical applications. Their use in place of argon in electric lamps is said to increase still further the efficiency of the lamps, but their extraction in sufficient quantity for this purpose would involve the handling of enormous quantities of air.

The proportions of the Inert Gases present in the atmosphere are given in Table XXXVI.

TABLE XXXVI.—PROPORTIONS OF INERT GASES IN AIR

Gas	Number of Volumes of Air containing 1 Volume.
Helium	200,000
Neon	65,000
Argon	106
Krypton	1,000,000
Xenon	11,000,000

Very accurate determinations of the densities of krypton and xenon (using an improved form of micro-balance, p. 22) were made in 1931 by Whytlaw-Gray and his collaborators. Their results lead to the values for the atomic weight of 83·7 and 131·3 respectively, and these are now the accepted values.

Like argon, these gases are believed to form hydrates, and the isolation of a crystalline hydrate of xenon has been reported.

§ 6 Niton, or Radon or Emanation, Nt, or Rn, or Em

This gas is a product of radio-active decay, is itself radio-active and exists as three isotopes ; one in each of the three radio-active series (see Ch. XXXVI, p. 854).

It is obtained by dissolving a radium salt in water, when a mixture of oxygen and hydrogen (produced owing to the large amount of energy liberated when radium undergoes radio-active change) and radon is produced. The radon is separated from this mixture by passage through a tube cooled in liquid air, when it is condensed to a liquid.

Radon is only formed in very minute quantities, the largest amount so far obtained pure being 0·0007 mgm. This is in part due to the small amount of radium (or other radio-active source of the gas) available, and in part to the shortness of its period of average life (see p. 853). The density of the gas from radium was determined by Ramsay and Whytlaw-Gray in 1910 by means of the micro-balance and found to be 111·5 corresponding to an atomic weight of 223. Theoretical considerations (α-ray change from radium, p. 133) indicate that its atomic weight should be 222. The present " International ". value is 222. The other two isotopes should have atomic weights similarly of 218 and 220, according as they belong to the actinium or thorium series.

§ 7 The Inert Gas Family of Elements

The Inert Gases comprise Group O of the Periodic Table and fall satisfactorily between the very strongly electro-negative halogens (Group VIIB) and the strongly electro-positive alkali metals (Group IA). Such properties as they possess exhibit a due gradation from member to member as would be expected. Since they form no compounds whose existence has been accepted beyond question (and those which have been reported are extremely few in number) comparison is virtually restricted to the physical properties. The due gradation of these is well illustrated by the figures given in Table XXXVII.

The Inert Gases fall into place very satisfactorily on Lothar Meyer's Atomic Volume Curve, being found just below the alkali metals on the rising portions of the curve (p. 121).

TABLE XXXVII.—PROPERTIES OF THE INERT GASES

Property	Helium.	Neon.	Argon.	Krypton.	Xenon.	Radon.
Atomic Weight	4·003	20·183	39·944	83·7	131·3	222
Melting Point	−272°	−248·67°	−189·2°	−169°	−140°	−71°
Boiling Point	−268·9°	−245·9°	−185·7°	−151·8°	−109°	−61·8°
Critical Temp.	−268°	−228·7°	−122°	−63°	16·6°	104·5°
Critical Press.	2·26	25·9	48	54	58·2	62·5
Compressibility (λ, p. 104)	−0·0005	−0·0004	+0·001	0·0025	0·0069	0·018
Solubility (Vols. in 1 Vol. of water at 0°)	0·01	0·0114	0·0058	0·1105	0·242	0·5

CHAPTER XXV

THE ALKALI METALS

Potash is both wealth and weapon. Our position as sole producer gives us the power of causing grave injury to the agriculture of our enemies by stopping the export of salts so indispensable to them for manurial purposes. If raw materials are refused us, we shall revenge ourselves on the enemy's agriculture with this war cry : " At the enemy with a kilo of potash ! "—*Vossische Zeitung* (November 23rd, 1917.)

§ 1 Group I of the Periodic Table

GROUP I of the Periodic Table comprises eight elements, arranged in two sub-groups, viz., lithium, sodium, potassium, rubidium and caesium in the A sub-group ; whilst copper, silver and gold constitute the B sub-group. As usual, at the extreme ends of the table the relationship between the elements in the two sub-groups is not very marked, but each sub-group forms a family of elements—the A sub-group being very well-defined ; the B sub-group rather less so.

This is well seen in the properties of the elements of Group IA which are known as the alkali metals. The gradation of properties in both sub-groups and the extent of the relationship between them are discussed more fully at the end of Chapter XXVI (p. 611). It may be noted here, however, that they come in the Periodic Table immediately after the Inert Gases which possess, according to modern theory, a very stable electronic configuration ; in each case the outer (or valency) group of electrons of these gases consisting of a completed octet. Consequently, the alkali metals, having a single electron in the outermost group, are characterized by being very strongly electro-positive and persistently monovalent : the tendency to form an electro-positive monovalent ion is thus very marked indeed.

§ 2 Lithium, Li

History and Occurrence

Lithium was discovered by Arfvedson in 1817 during the course of an analysis of the metal petalite. The name lithium (from $\lambda i\theta \epsilon o\varsigma$—litheos—stony) was given to it because it was then believed to be confined to the mineral kingdom. The metal was isolated in 1855 by Bunsen and Matthiessen by electrolysis of the fused chloride.

Lithium is a rare, but widely distributed, element. It occurs in a number of minerals, e.g., in *lepidolite* or lithia mica, which contains up to 6 per cent. of lithia as lithium aluminium fluosilicate ; *spodumene*, a lithium aluminium silicate —$Li_2O.Al_2O_3.4SiO_2$—contains a similar amount, while *amblygonite*, $Li(AlF)PO_4$, and *petalite* contain 7 to 10 per cent. and 3 per cent. respectively. Lithium has been detected in the ash of many plants, notably tobacco ; in milk, blood and in many mineral springs.

Preparation

Various methods have been employed for the extraction of lithium compounds from the minerals containing them. These depend ultimately either upon the sparing solubility of lithium carbonate as compared with the other alkali metals, or upon the solubility of lithium chloride in alcohol (sodium and potassium chlorides being insoluble).

In one of these, the powdered mineral is calcined with a mixture of ammonium chloride and calcium carbonate. The aqueous extract is treated with hydrochloric acid and evaporated to dryness. The lithium chloride is extracted with amyl alcohol or pyridine, in which it is fairly soluble. The solvent is then removed by evaporation. In another process, the powdered mineral is fused with a mixture of barium carbonate, barium sulphate and potassium sulphate. Two layers result—the upper, consisting of lithium and potassium sulphates, is dissolved in water, treated with barium chloride and the lithium chloride extracted as before.

The metal is readily made by electrolysis of the fused chloride, using a carbon anode and an iron cathode, and its production in this way is being undertaken technically now that uses of the element are becoming more numerous (p. 548).

Properties

Lithium is a silvery white metal resembling sodium and potassium in appearance, but harder than they are, and with a higher melting point, viz., 186°. It has a density of only 0·534, which is lower than that of any other solid element at ordinary temperatures. It is fairly volatile, and its vapour imparts a carmine-red colour to a bunsen flame. It has the highest specific heat (0·9408) of any element.

Although chemically an active element, lithium is the least active of the alkali metals. It burns in air, with a brilliant white light resembling that of burning magnesium, forming the monoxide, Li_2O; it does not readily form a higher oxide. It combines readily with hydrogen at a red heat, forming the hydride LiH, and also easily forms a nitride, Li_3N by combination with nitrogen. It also combines directly with the halogens and sulphur.

Lithium reacts with water, forming the hydroxide and hydrogen,

$$2Li + 2H_2O = 2LiOH + H_2,$$

but the hydrogen does not catch fire even if the water be boiling ; neither does the metal melt. As a strongly electro-positive element it reacts vigorously with acids.

The atomic weight of lithium was determined by Richards by conversion of lithium chloride to lithium perchlorate, and to silver chloride, (p. 98). His value 6·94 is that at present accepted.

§ 3 Lithium Hydride, Oxides and Hydroxide

Lithium hydride, LiH, formed by direct combination of the elements, is noteworthy in that electrolysis of the fused compound furnishes hydrogen at the **anode.** When acted upon by water it gives off hydrogen, with evolution of a considerable amount of heat.

Lithium Oxide, Li_2O, can be made by heating the metal in air or, more satisfactorily, by heating the hydroxide to redness in an atmosphere of dry hydrogen. Lithium oxide is a white powder which reacts slowly with water, forming a solution of the hydroxide. The reaction mentioned above is thus reversible :

$$Li_2O + H_2O = 2LiOH.$$

Lithium peroxide, Li_2O_2, is obtained as a double compound with hydrogen peroxide by the action of hydrogen peroxide on lithium hydroxide :

$$2LiOH + 2H_2O_2 + H_2O = Li_2O_2.H_2O_2.3H_2O.$$

This can be dehydrated by keeping over phosphorus pentoxide.

Lithium hydroxide, LiOH, is made by the action of water on the free metal, and is a white crystalline substance rather resembling sodium hydroxide, but less readily soluble in water. It can also be prepared by addition of baryta water to a solution of lithium sulphate.

§ 4 Salts of Lithium

Lithium carbonate, Li_2CO_3, is precipitated as a white solid by the addition of ammonium carbonate solution to a solution of a soluble lithium salt. It is noteworthy in being thus sparingly soluble (100 gms. of water dissolve 1·54 gms. at 0° C. and 1·38 gms. at 15°), for the carbonates of the other alkali metals are all soluble. Further, like the insoluble carbonates of the alkaline earths (Ch. XXVII, pp. 621, 631), it is soluble in presence of excess of carbon dioxide due to the formation of a soluble **lithium bicarbonate,** $LiHCO_3$.

$$2LiCl + (NH_4)_2CO_3 = Li_2CO_3\downarrow + 2NH_4Cl,$$
$$Li_2CO_3 + CO_2 + H_2O = 2LiHCO_3.$$

The solution of the bicarbonate is sold and used medicinally under the name *lithia water*. The normal carbonate, when heated to about 800° in an atmosphere of hydrogen, decomposes into the oxide and carbon dioxide :

$$Li_2CO_3 = Li_2O + CO_2.$$

Lithium chloride, LiCl, is the salt of lithium usually prepared when the element is being extracted from minerals containing it. In general behaviour, etc., it is similar to sodium chloride, but its solubility in water is much greater and it is very deliquescent, being perhaps the most deliquescent substance known.

Of the remaining halides, the **fluoride** is notable for its very sparing solubility in water—in this again lithium resembles the alkaline earths. The **nitrate** is a very deliquescent salt and, like the chloride and sulphate, is soluble in alcohol.

Lithium sulphate crystallizes from water, in which it is readily soluble, with *one* molecule of water of crystallization—$Li_2SO_4.H_2O$.

Lithium (ortho) phosphate, Li_3PO_4, like the carbonate, is virtually insoluble and is precipitated when sodium phosphate solution is added to a solution of a soluble lithium salt such as the chloride. This again shows the similarity of lithium to the elements of the alkaline earth group.

§ 5 Uses of Lithium and Lithium Compounds

Until comparatively recently lithium and its compounds had little use either industrially or in the laboratory, almost the only employment usually mentioned being the use of lithium salts in the treatment of diseases such as gout due to uric acid.

Of late, however, there has been considerable expansion in the manufacture and use of lithium and lithium salts. Thus it is used in the form of an alloy of lead for bearings and for the sheaths of electric cables ; it is used to improve the tensile strength and resistance to corrosion of magnesium alloys (q.v. p. 619), and an alloy of zinc and aluminium, containing in addition about 0·1 per cent. of lithium, possesses elasticity and tensile strength of a similar order to that of mild steel. The calcium-lithium alloy is used for the purification of copper for purposes where a metal of very high conductivity is required.

Lithium hydride has been suggested as a means of transporting hydrogen (cf. p. 256) on account of the large amount of hydrogen it contains in proportion to its weight. Lithium chloride solutions have been used in air-conditioning plant for regulating the humidity of the air, and lithium compounds are now employed in the manufacture of glasses and glazes.

§ 6. Detection and Determination of Lithium Compounds

Lithium is detected by means of the red colouration it imparts to the bunsen flame ; when examined spectroscopically, this flame is seen to give a faint yellow line of slightly longer wave-length than the D lines of sodium, and a brilliant crimson line. Lithium is also recognized by the precipitation of its insoluble phosphate on the addition of sodium phosphate ; a process which is also sometimes employed for its determination. The use of the fluoride has similarly been suggested. It is usual to determine it as sulphate, like sodium (q.v.) and to separate it from the other alkali metals by extraction with amyl alcohol, etc.

§ 7 Sodium, Na. History and Occurrence

Sodium chloride, or common salt, and sodium carbonate have been known since very early times ; for the former is probably a vital necessity and has certainly been employed in food for an indefinitely long period, whilst the latter, which comprises a considerable proportion of the ashes of sea plants, also occurs native and was known to, and employed by, the ancient Egyptians.

Metallic sodium was first obtained by Sir H. Davy in 1807 by electrolysis of fused caustic soda.

Sodium, in the form of compounds, is a widely distributed and abundant element, but on account of its intense chemical activity is never found free.

Sodium chloride occurs in enormous quantities in the sea, and is also found in extensive deposits of rock salt, presumably formed as a result of the evaporation of prehistoric seas. Rock salt is found at Nantwich, Northwich and Middlewich in Cheshire, Droitwich* in Worcestershire, Stassfurt in Saxony, Cardona and Castile in Spain, California, Kansas, Utah, New York, Virginia, Ohio and Michigan in the U.S.A., and numerous other places. The salt mine at Wielicza in Galicia has been worked continuously for 600 years. The salt deposit there is said to be 500 miles long, 20 miles wide and 1,200 feet thick.

Sodium also occurs in large quantities in the form of complex alumino-silicates, such as *soda-felspar* (p. 678) ; and the weathering of rocks and minerals of this type has given rise to sodium carbonate and clay. Much of the sodium carbonate is found in inland seas, etc., but considerable deposits exist, known as *trona*, in Egypt and other places. Large deposits of borax (sodium diborate) are also found, e.g., in Nevada (U.S.A.), and the Chile nitrate beds are largely composed of sodium compounds.

§ 8 Manufacture of Metallic Sodium

Metallic sodium was for many years manufactured by a process due to Castner in which caustic soda was heated with a mixture of carbon and iron at a temperature of 1000° :

$$6NaOH + 2C = 2Na + 3H_2 + 2Na_2CO_3.$$

It is now made using the same principle as that by which Davy first isolated it, viz., the electrolysis of fused caustic soda. The type of plant employed is also due to Castner.

The sodium hydroxide, contained in an iron pot set in brickwork, is melted by means of a ring of gas jets placed underneath ; and kept

---

* The names of these places indicate the antiquity of the salt industry since the Saxon name for a place where salt was dug was " wich."

about 20° above the melting point (318°) of sodium hydroxide. The iron cathode, H, rises through the bottom of the iron pot, A, Fig. 201,

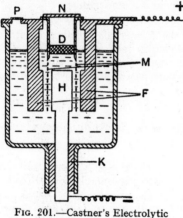

FIG. 201.—Castner's Electrolytic Process for Sodium.

and is maintained in position by a cake, K, of solid sodium hydroxide in the lower part of the pot. The nickel anodes, F, several in number, are suspended around the cathodes from above. A cylindrical vessel, ND, floats in the fused alkali above the cathode, and the sodium and hydrogen liberated at the cathode collect under this cylinder. The hydrogen escapes through the cover, and the atmosphere of hydrogen in the cylinder protects the sodium from oxidation. A nickel wire cage, M, separates the anode, F, from the cathode, H. From time to time the sodium, D, is skimmed off by means of a perforated

ladle which retains the liquid metal, but allows the molten hydroxide to flow back. The oxygen liberated at the anode escapes via the vent P. The fused sodium hydroxide ionizes thus :

$$NaOH \rightleftharpoons Na^{\cdot} + OH'$$

and on electrolysis the sodium is liberated at the cathode, while the hydroxyl ions have their charges neutralized at the anode. They then react together to form oxygen and water :

$$4OH = O_2 + 2H_2O.$$

The oxygen escapes; the water dissolves in the caustic soda, and is itself electrolysed, giving rise to considerable quantities of hydrogen at the cathode.

Attempts have been made to manufacture sodium direct from common salt by electrolysis of the fused salt, but so far these have not proved successful commercially, mainly on account of the high temperature (ca. 800°) required to keep the salt molten.

§ 9 Properties of Sodium

Sodium is a silvery-white, lustrous metal which tarnishes at once when exposed to the air, owing to the formation of a film of oxide. On account of the ease with which it is oxidized (see below), it must be kept immersed in a liquid containing no oxygen. It is lighter than water (sp. gr. 0·93) ; it is soft, so that it can be cut with a knife, and at ordinary temperatures can be moulded between the fingers. Sodium melts at 97·5°, and boils at 880°. The vapour, which is purple when seen in thick layers, has a density of 12·85 ($H_2 = 1$) indicating that it is probably almost entirely monatomic. Sodium is a good conductor of electricity.

Chemically, sodium is a very reactive element. It combines vigorously with oxygen, burning readily in air with a brilliant, yellow flame, and forming a mixture of the oxide and peroxide:

$$4Na + O_2 = 2Na_2O,$$
$$2Na + O_2 = Na_2O_2.$$

It combines directly with the halogens and with phosphorus, taking fire when heated with these elements. It also combines with hydrogen when heated to 360°.

The vigour of its combination with oxygen is such that sodium will react with most oxides, liberating the element previously combined with the oxygen. Thus, it acts energetically with water, forming sodium hydroxide and hydrogen,

$$2Na + 2H_2O = 2NaOH + H_2,$$

and the heat of the reaction is sufficient to melt the sodium, which swims about as a globule on the surface of the water. The heat evolved is, however, not great enough to ignite the hydrogen unless large pieces of sodium are used, or the water warmed. With the oxides of most metals, the metal itself is formed. A similar reaction takes place with metallic chlorides and has been applied to the preparation of metals such as beryllium and uranium, etc.:

$$BeCl_2 + 2Na = Be + 2NaCl.$$

Aluminium also was formerly prepared in this way. Non-metallic oxides are similarly reduced. Thus sodium will burn in carbon dioxide forming carbon and sodium carbonate:

$$3CO_2 + 4Na = 2Na_2CO_3 + C.$$

Sodium will dissolve in liquid ammonia forming a blue solution, but when heated in ammonia gas sodamide results:

$$2Na + 2NH_3 = 2NaNH_2 + H_2.$$

It also dissolves in mercury, forming sodium amalgam (p. 649) and reacts violently with acids.

§ 10 Uses of Sodium

Sodium is used in the manufacture of sodium peroxide, sodium cyanide and sodamide, all of which (particularly the two last-named) are of technical importance. The metal is employed as a reagent in organic chemistry, and an alloy with potassium, which is liquid at ordinary temperatures, is employed in high-temperature thermometers. It was formerly used in the manufacture of aluminium and magnesium, but these are now made by electrolysis (pp. 618, 664). The possibility of using sodium in the production of very light alloys for aircraft is now being investigated, and its alloy with lead is used in the manufacture of lead tetraethyl (the so-called " ethyl-fluid " of commerce) for making anti-knock motor spirit. Like all the alkali metals, sodium exhibits the photo-electric effect (i.e., emission of electrons when exposed to light) in marked degree and hence is used widely for the photo-electric cells on which television, the telegraphic transmission of pictures, the talking-film and many other modern devices depend.

§ 11 Atomic Weight of Sodium

That the atomic weight of sodium lies in the neighbourhood of 23 is indicated by its specific heat (0·283) which, by Dulong and Petit's rule (p. 90), gives 22·6 for the atomic weight. There is much evidence also that it is monovalent (e.g., molecular weight of some of its salts in solution in various solvents) and the equivalent weight is also found to be close to 23.

The best determinations are probably those of Richards and Wells. By conversion of very pure sodium chloride into silver chloride they determined the ratios AgCl/NaCl and Ag/NaCl leading to the values 22·995 and 22·998 respectively for the atomic weight of sodium. The value adopted by the International Committee is 22·997.

§ 12 Hydride and Oxides of Sodium

Sodium hydride, NaH, is prepared by passing dry hydrogen over sodium at about 360°. It is decomposed by water with evolution of hydrogen ; and on heating, the colourless crystals of the hydride dissociate into their elements. As with lithium hydride, when subjected to electrolysis hydrogen is evolved at the **anode** showing that hydrogen can, in these circumstances, form a *negatively*-charged ion :

$$NaH \rightleftharpoons Na^{\cdot} + H'$$

whereas normally it forms a positive ion. Sodium hydride combines with carbon dioxide, forming sodium formate (the sodium salt of the organic acid formic acid) :

$$NaH + CO_2 = H.CO.ONa.$$

Oxides of Sodium

Sodium forms two oxides, viz. :

Sodium monoxide, Na_2O,

Sodium peroxide, Na_2O_2.

Sodium monoxide, Na_2O, is formed, along with the peroxide, when sodium is burned in air or oxygen. It is difficult to obtain pure in this way, even when a limited supply of air is used; and is better made by heating sodium azide with sodium nitrate or nitrite :

$$3NaN_3 + NaNO_2 = 2Na_2O + 5N_2.$$

It is a white solid which combines with water with the evolution of much heat, forming sodium hydroxide.

Sodium peroxide, Na_2O_2, is formed when sodium is burned in oxygen or (along with the monoxide) in air. It is made commercially by passing excess of dry air over sodium contained in aluminium trays in iron tubes heated to about 300°. The product contains about 95 per cent. of sodium peroxide and is usually slightly yellow, although the pure compound is white.

Sodium peroxide is not decomposed by heat and is stable in dry air ; but in moist air, or when acted upon by water, it is decomposed with evolution of oxygen and formation of sodium hydroxide :

$$2Na_2O_2 + 2H_2O = 4NaOH + O_2.$$

If the temperature be kept low, however, water yields hydrogen peroxide, a reaction which is found to be reversible, since a hydrated sodium peroxide, $Na_2O_2.8H_2O$, crystallizes out when hydrogen peroxide is added to a cold concentrated solution of sodium hydroxide :

$$Na_2O_2 + 2H_2O \rightleftharpoons 2NaOH + H_2O_2.$$

Hydrogen peroxide is also formed by the action of acids in the cold.

Sodium peroxide is a powerful oxidizing agent, and is used in the laboratory for oxidizing purposes, and also for decomposing silicate rocks prior to analysis. It combines with carbon monoxide, forming sodium carbonate :

$$Na_2O_2 + CO = Na_2CO_3,$$

and also reacts with carbon dioxide, which it absorbs with liberation of oxygen. It is thus used for the revivification of air which has been vitiated in breathing (e.g., in submarines) :

$$2Na_2O_2 + 2CO_2 = 2Na_2CO_3 + O_2.$$

Sodium peroxide also oxidizes sulphides to sulphates when fused with them, and ammonia to nitrogen, a process often made use of for the estimation of such sulphides.

In addition to the above uses, sodium peroxide is also used for the bleaching of textiles ; for the manufacture of benzoyl peroxide used for bleaching flour ; for the production of calcium peroxide used for the activation of yeast ; in the manufacture of sodium perborate (p. 662), and in the production of dyes and other synthetic organic chemicals.

§ 13 Sodium Hydroxide, Caustic Soda, NaOH

Sodium hydroxide is a very important industrial heavy chemical and is manufactured on a large scale. It can be prepared :

(i) by the action of sodium on water ;
(ii) by the action of milk of lime on sodium carbonate solution ;
(iii) by the electrolysis of solutions of sodium chloride.

The first of these methods is only used for the preparation of small quantities of specially pure sodium hydroxide for use in the laboratory ; both the remaining methods are employed extensively in industry.

Manufacture of Caustic Soda from Sodium Carbonate

This process depends upon the fact that when milk of lime is added to a hot solution of sodium carbonate, calcium carbonate is precipitated and sodium hydroxide remains in solution :

$$Na_2CO_3 + Ca(OH)_2 = 2NaOH + CaCO_3 \downarrow$$

It is known as *causticization* and is carried out industrially in large iron tanks, having a mechanical stirring apparatus and an inlet for a supply of steam. This plant is illustrated diagrammatically in Fig. 202, and is known as a *causticizer*. A solution of commercial sodium

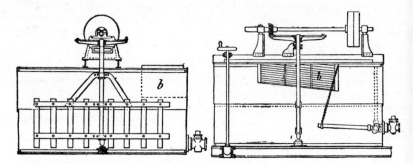

FIG. 202.—Causticizer.

carbonate is run in and quicklime is placed in an iron cage dipping into the solution. The mixture is agitated by means of the stirrer and also by steam, which is blown into the solution to heat it. The sodium carbonate is largely converted into caustic soda, calcium carbonate being precipitated :

$$Na_2CO_3 + Ca(OH)_2 = 2NaOH + CaCO_3 \downarrow .$$

The mixture was formerly run into settling tanks, and after the precipitated calcium carbonate had settled, the clear liquid was run off and concentrated. The sludge remaining contained a considerable proportion of caustic soda which represented so much loss ; but the prevention of this loss by filtering off the calcium carbonate was formerly impracticable owing to the properties of the caustic soda solution. Latterly, however, the use of plant made of monel metal has made this possible and the causticized liquor is filtered off under reduced pressure and evaporated in multiple stage vacuum evaporators heated by steam. Concentration beyond a certain point is not practicable with steam heating and the final stage is effected by heating the concentrated liquor in cast-iron vessels set in brickwork over a free fire until all the water has been driven off and fused caustic soda is left.

On account of the sparing solubility of calcium carbonate the reversible reaction :

$$Na_2CO_3 + Ca(OH)_2 \rightleftharpoons 2NaOH + CaCO_3 \downarrow$$

proceeds almost to completion from left to right, particularly since the presence of excess of lime keeps the solution saturated with respect to this substance.   But the reaction is never quite complete for calcium carbonate is slightly soluble and during the progress of the reaction, as the concentration of sodium hydroxide increases, its solubility steadily increases ; and at the same time the solubility of the calcium hydroxide (never very great) decreases owing to the increasing concentration of the sodium hydroxide.   Consequently, a state of equilibrium is reached when the (molecular) solubilities of these two calcium compounds is equal since no further conversion of one into the other, through solution of one and consequent precipitation of the other, can occur.

These facts are explained on the basis of the Ionic Theory as follows. At the start we have the equilibria

$$Na_2CO_3 \rightleftharpoons 2Na^{\cdot} + CO_3'',$$
$$Ca(OH)_2 \rightleftharpoons Ca^{\cdot\cdot} + 2OH',$$

so that the solution contains sodium, calcium, carbonate and hydroxyl ions. The solubility product (p. 233) of calcium carbonate $[Ca^{\cdot\cdot}][CO_3'']$ is very small, and is consequently largely exceeded so that calcium carbonate is precipitated so long as calcium ions (from the slaked lime) and carbonate ions (from the sodium carbonate) are present in excess of the concentration corresponding to the solubility product of calcium carbonate.   The concentration of calcium ions is, however, also determined by the solubility product of calcium hydroxide, i.e., by the product of the concentration of calcium ions and the square of the concentration of hydroxyl ions present.   As the reaction proceeds the latter is increasing and hence the former (concentration of calcium ions) is decreasing.   Consequently, a point will ultimately be reached when the concentration of calcium will have fallen to a value no longer in excess of that corresponding to the solubility product of calcium carbonate.   At this point equilibrium will be established and the reaction will stop.

The equilibrium is found to be more over to the calcium carbonate side of the equation, the more dilute the solution is as a whole.   This is what would be expected from the ionic theory since the concentration of carbonate ion appears in the equations as the first power, whereas that of the hydroxyl ion is squared.

It is clear that from the manufacturers' point of view a compromise must be effected between the use of dilute solutions which give a purer product but which require a large expenditure for evaporation of the resulting caustic soda solution ; and the use of concentrated solutions which give a product contaminated with carbonate but which are less costly to evaporate. In practice, the sodium carbonate solution used has a concentration of about 10 per cent. and about 92 per cent. causticization is effected.

Manufacture of Caustic Soda by Electrolysis

Large and increasing quantities of caustic soda are now made by the electrolysis of solutions of common salt. Hydrogen and chlorine are formed at the same time. The process has been described in Chapter XXIII (p. 494).

The caustic soda is obtained from these operations in the form of a strong solution from which the solid is obtained by methods similar to those described above.

§ 14 Properties of Sodium Hydroxide

Sodium hydroxide is a white, crystalline solid, which rapidly absorbs moisture and carbon dioxide from the atmosphere. It melts easily (at 318°) and is often sold in sticks formed from the molten material. It is very soluble indeed in water, and much heat is evolved during its solution. The solution has the characteristic soapy feel of an alkali, and is very corrosive. Sodium hydroxide is a very strong alkali; since, according to the Ionic Theory, it is very largely ionized in solution. It is only sparingly soluble in alcohol, in which it differs from potassium hydroxide (q.v.) which is very soluble.

Sodium hydroxide has the properties characteristic of a strong alkali. It changes the colours of indicators (e.g., litmus to blue, methyl orange to yellow; phenolphthalein to pink) and forms salts with all acids. It reacts with solutions of metallic salts (except salts of the alkali metals), precipitating the hydroxide of the metal, e.g., with ferric chloride:

$$FeCl_3 + 3NaOH = Fe(OH)_3 + 3NaCl.$$

In some cases the metal hydroxide re-dissolves in excess of caustic soda solution, e.g., zinc:

$$ZnSO_4 + 2NaOH = Zn(OH)_2 + Na_2SO_4,$$

$$Zn(OH)_2 + 2NaOH = Na_2ZnO_2 + 2H_2O.$$

With ammonium salts ammonia gas is liberated, presumably on account of the very unstable nature of ammonium hydroxide (compare Ch. XX, p. 394).

Sodium hydroxide reacts with many free elements, both metals and non-metals. These reactions are considered in greater detail in the chapters dealing with the elements concerned, but the reactions indicated by the following equations may be mentioned here:

$$2NaOH + Zn = Na_2ZnO_2 + H_2,$$
$$2NaOH + 2Al + 2H_2O = 2NaAlO_2 + 3H_2,$$
$$2NaOH + 2B + 2H_2O = 2NaBO_2 + 3H_2,$$
$$2NaOH + Si + H_2O = Na_2SiO_3 + 2H_2,$$
$$3NaOH + 4P + 3H_2O = PH_3 + 3NaH_2PO_2,$$
$$2NaOH + Cl_2 = NaOCl + NaCl + H_2O,$$
$$6NaOH + 4S = 2Na_2S + Na_2S_2O_3 + 3H_2O.$$

This is probably the primary reaction, but the final product is the polysulphide formed by the action of excess of sulphur :

$$Na_2S + 4S = Na_2S_5.$$

The above reactions take place in aqueous solution ; fused sodium hydroxide will attack most metals (nickel and silver are only slightly attacked), and it also reacts readily with glass and porcelain, in fact, even the aqueous solution has an appreciable action on these materials.

§ 15 Uses of Sodium Hydroxide

Large quantities of sodium hydroxide, usually referred to commercially as caustic soda, are used in bleaching and as dyeing, in the refining of oils and in the manufacture of soap, and of paper. It is also used for the purification of bauxite (p. 664), for the manufacture of aluminium ; in making artificial silks, and in the production of dyes (e.g., alizarin).

§ 16 Sodium Salts, Sodium Carbonate

Sodium hydroxide, being a very strong base, readily forms salts even with very weak acids. Sodium salts are colourless unless derived from a coloured acid, and are almost all soluble in water, the pyroantimonate $(Na_2H_2Sb_2O_7)$ and the complex sodium magnesium uranyl acetate— $NaMg_2(UO_2)_2(C_2H_3O_2)_3$—and the corresponding zinc triple acetate being the only important insoluble ones. Sodium salts often crystallize with considerable quantities of water.

Sodium Carbonate, Na_2CO_3

Sodium carbonate has been known and used from the earliest times. Formerly it was made from the ashes of sea weeds (potassium carbonate was similarly obtained from the ashes of land plants), but at the end of the eighteenth century, largely through the stress of war conditions, alternative sources of supply became essential and a process of manufacture was devised by Leblanc which held its own for over 100 years.

Sodium carbonate is manufactured in four ways, viz.,

(i) by the Leblanc process—now obsolete except as mentioned below ;

(ii) by the ammonia-soda (or Solvay) process ;

(iii) from naturally-occurring sodium carbonate ;

(iv) from electrolytic caustic soda.

The Leblanc Process

This process is now obsolete and has not been worked in this country since 1919 except (as mentioned on pp. 500, 567) for the manufacture of sodium sulphate (salt cake). It has seen a temporary revival in Germany since the war in a modified form for production of sodium carbonate from the large amounts of sodium sulphate accumulated at Stassfurt during the war, as a by-product from the extraction of potassium compounds. Similar use is being made of Russian deposits of natural sodium sulphate.

The Leblanc process proper was conducted in three stages :

(i) The conversion of sodium chloride into sodium sulphate (called *salt-cake*) by heating it with sulphuric acid, as described on page 500 :

$$2NaCl + H_2SO_4 = Na_2SO_4 + 2HCl ;$$

(ii) The conversion of the salt-cake into *black ash* by heating to a high temperature in a revolving furnace with limestone and coke. Black ash is a mixture of calcium sulphide, sodium carbonate, etc. :

$$Na_2SO_4 + CaCO_3 + 2C = Na_2CO_3 + CaS + 2CO_2 ;$$

(iii) The extraction of sodium carbonate from the black ash by leaching it with water, and purifying the product by crystallization. The calcium sulphide which remained (being insoluble in water) was used as a source of sulphur, etc. (see pp. 437, 569).

In working the Stassfurt sodium sulphate into carbonate, use is made of reactions which dispense with the use of calcium carbonate, in which sodium sulphide, made by reduction of the sulphate, page 567, is acted upon by a mixture of carbon dioxide and steam :

$$Na_2SO_4 + 4C = Na_2S + 4CO$$
$$Na_2S + CO_2 + H_2O = Na_2CO_3 + H_2S.$$

The sulphur can be recovered from the hydrogen sulphide as described on page 437.

The Ammonia-Soda, or Solvay, Process

This process depends upon the comparatively low solubility of sodium bicarbonate, particularly in presence of excess of carbon dioxide. When a concentrated solution of sodium chloride is saturated with ammonia and then with carbon dioxide the ammonium carbonate first formed reacts with the sodium chloride forming sodium carbonate, which is then converted by the excess of carbon dioxide into the bicarbonate which is a sparingly soluble salt especially in presence of carbon dioxide :

$$2NH_3 + CO_2 + H_2O = (NH_4)_2CO_3,$$
$$(NH_4)_2CO_3 + 2NaCl = Na_2CO_3 + 2NH_4Cl,$$
$$Na_2CO_3 + CO_2 + H_2O = 2NaHCO_3.$$

The formation of ammonium bicarbonate ($NH_4.HCO_3$) is often stated to be the first stage ; but this is improbable because :

(a) ammonium bicarbonate is just as sparingly soluble in the mother liquors and would itself be precipitated, and

(b) such a reaction would be endothermal whereas the actual reaction is exothermal in agreement with

$$CO_2 + H_2O + Na_2CO_3 = 2NaHCO_3 + 18\cdot4\ Cals.$$

The sodium bicarbonate formed is heated, forming normal carbonate, carbon dioxide (which is used again) and steam.

$$2NaHCO_3 = Na_2CO_3 + CO_2 + H_2O.$$

The ammonia is recovered by heating it with slaked lime.

$$2NH_4Cl + Ca(OH)_2 = 2NH_3 + CaCl_2 + H_2O.$$

The actual manufacture is carried out as follows :—

The raw materials are *brine*, usually obtained by direct pumping *in situ* ; and *carbon dioxide*, obtained by heating limestone in kilns. The quicklime, produced at the same time, is used for the recovery of the ammonia. *Ammonia* is obtained in the first instance, or to make up loss in the process, similarly from external supplies of ammonium chloride.

Ammonia gas is forced up a tower down which the strong brine (about 30 per cent. NaCl) is flowing. This is constructed as shown in Fig. 203. Heat is evolved in this process and so the ammoniated brine is cooled by passing over pipes through which cold water circulates.

The ammoniated brine is then made to run down a *carbonating tower* up which a stream of carbon dioxide is forced. The construction of this

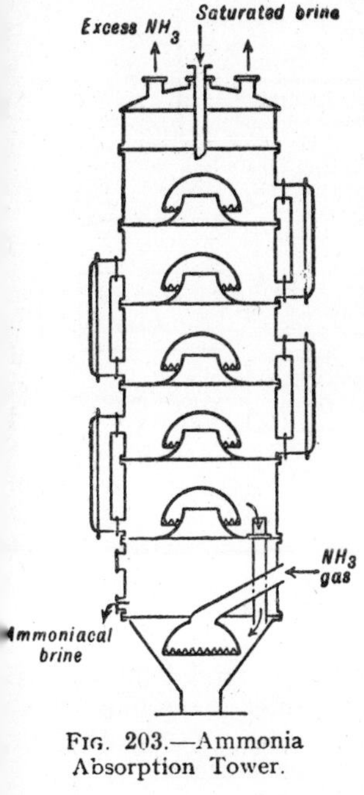

Fig. 203.—Ammonia Absorption Tower.

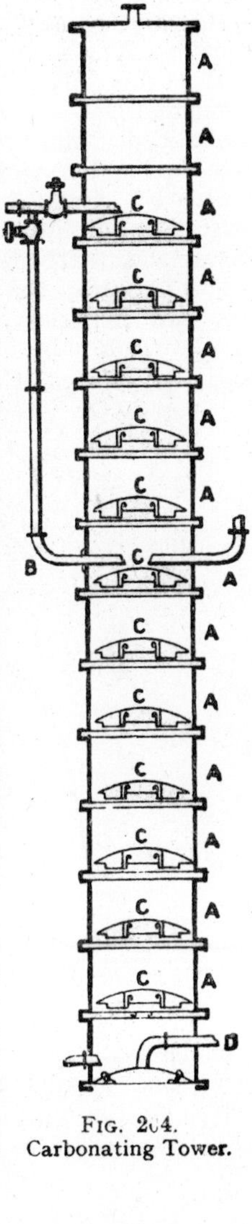

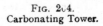

Fig. 204. Carbonating Tower.

tower is indicated by Fig. 204. Ammonium chloride and sodium bicarbonate are formed as indicated above ; the latter, being precipitated, is carried out of the base of the tower as a fine suspension. It is filtered off and washed to free it from ammonia and ammonium salts.

The sodium bicarbonate is then converted into the normal carbonate by heating in special calcining pans which are fitted with scrapers to push the solid along the pan. The carbon dioxide evolved is returned to the plant, along with fresh supplies, and anhydrous sodium carbonate remains. This is known as **soda-ash.**

From this soda-ash, various products are made. By dissolving it in water and crystallizing the solution, **washing-soda,** $Na_2CO_3.10H_2O$ is obtained ; while by evaporation **crystal carbonate,** $Na_2CO_3.H_2O$ is formed and crystallizes from the hot solution. The so-called **concentrated soda crystals,** $Na_2CO_3.NaHCO_3.2H_2O$, result from crystallizing solutions containing equi-molecular quantities of carbonate and bicarbonate.

This outline of the process indicates that limestone and salt are the only raw materials (except fuel) and calcium chloride (from the

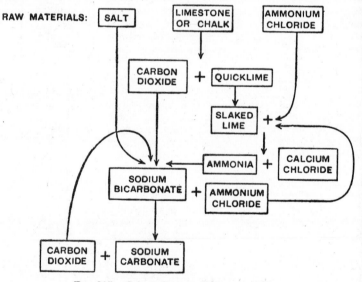

Fig. 205.—Solvay Process (Diagrammatic).

ammonia recovery section) the only waste product. So far no use has been found for the last-named, which constitutes something of a problem in the industry.

Fig. 205 illustrates diagrammatically the whole process.

Sodium Carbonate from Natural Sources

There exist in certain areas (notably at Magadi in British East Africa, and in California) large deposits of sodium carbonate. These are now being utilized, particularly the Magadi deposits. These consist principally of the so-called sesqui-carbonate $Na_2CO_3.NaHCO_3.2H_2O$. The "brine" of the lakes round whose shores these deposits are found is also treated for recovery of sodium carbonate.

Sodium Carbonate from Electrolytic Caustic Soda.

A considerable quantity of sodium carbonate is now being made from electrolytic caustic soda, particularly in America, where electrical energy is relatively cheap. Sodium chloride solution is electrolyzed in a cell of the diaphragm type, thus producing caustic soda, hydrogen and chlorine. Crude carbon dioxide, from furnace gases, gas or oil-engine exhausts and similar sources, is blown through the liquid, thus producing sodium carbonate which is recovered from the solution, as in other methods, by crystallization.

Sodium carbonate can be obtained anhydrous, and also in combination with one, seven or ten molecules of water of crystallization. The anhydrous salt is a white solid which melts at about 850° with slight decomposition. When crystallized from water, at a temperature below 32°, large transparent crystals of $Na_2CO_3.10H_2O$ (washing-soda) are formed. These crystals effloresce (see p. 218) when exposed to the air and gradually crumble to a white powder, probably $Na_2CO_3.H_2O$. If exposed to the air for long periods, a little sodium bicarbonate is said to be formed. Crystallization of solutions between 30° and 50° causes deposition of the hepta-hydrate. Other hydrates have been described, but their individuality is less well established.

Sodium carbonate is alkaline in solution owing to hydrolysis (see p. 239) and is frequently used in volumetric analysis as a standard alkali. It is readily decomposed by acids (compare p. 306) with evolution of carbon dioxide.

Sodium carbonate is used for softening water, and the alkalinity of the resulting solution enhances the detergent properties of the water. Large quantities are used in the manufacture of caustic soda (p. 554), of glass (p. 690), of water glass (sodium silicate, p. 683), and of borax (p. 660). It is also a constituent of many patent soap powders, and is the starting point for the preparation of a number of other sodium salts.

Sodium bicarbonate, $NaHCO_3$, is produced in large quantities as the primary product of the ammonia-soda process ; but is converted into the normal carbonate as described above. Commercial sodium bicarbonate is made from the normal carbonate by saturating a moist mush of crystals with carbon dioxide. The bicarbonate is precipitated, and after washing with cold water is dried in air.

Sodium bicarbonate forms small, white crystals which are somewhat sparingly soluble in water. 100 grams of water will dissolve 9 grms. at

15°. The solution is slightly alkaline owing to partial hydrolysis. We have thus the paradox of an " acid " salt which has an alkaline reaction. This is due to the facts that sodium hydroxide is a very strong base while carbonic acid is a very weak acid. Sodium bicarbonate decomposes at 100° with evolution of carbon dioxide and steam, the normal carbonate being left.

Sodium bicarbonate is used in baking-powders (and hence is sometimes known as *baking-soda*) ; it is also an important constituent of health salts, " Seidlitz powders," etc.

Sodium sesquicarbonate, $Na_2CO_3.NaHCO_3.2H_2O$, known commercially as *concentrated soda crystals*, is obtained by crystallizing a solution of equimolecular quantities of carbonate and bicarbonate. It is extensively used in wool washing.

§ 17 Sodium Halides

Sodium Chloride, NaCl

Sodium chloride, usually known as *common salt* or simply *salt*, is not only the most important source of sodium compounds, but is also important for itself. Its occurrence has been referred to already (p. 549). The production of salt from these natural sources is an important operation.

Manufacture of Common Salt

According to the circumstances, salt is either mined, or extracted from salt beds by solution in water (i.e., in the form of *brine*) or got from the sea by evaporation.

Salt is mined as such at Wielicza in Galicia and the solid salt brought to the surface in lumps. As so obtained, it is usually impure and, though used in this state for some purposes, it is mostly purified by being dissolved in water and crystallized as described below.

In many salt beds (e.g., in Cheshire) the salt is obtained by forcing water into the beds through a boring or well. The brine so formed is afterwards pumped to the surface and the liquid concentrated, sometimes in salterns (making use of the sun and wind—see below), but often by evaporation in shallow pans heated artificially, particularly if fuel is cheap.

A series of these pans is set over a flue, and they are of increasing size the further they are from the fire. The contents of the first pan boil and very small crystals of salt separate. These are removed into wooden moulds while still hot and wet, and on cooling the slight further crystallization of the mother liquor binds the whole into the well-known blocks of salt. The solution in the next pan, which is at a lower temperature and does not actually boil, deposits a coarser-grained salt, used industrially ; the remaining pans, the temperature of which is progressively lower, give salt of still larger grain, used for fish-curing, etc.

Nowadays, the evaporation is frequently carried out in multiple evaporators (Fig. 206.) These consist of a series of closed vessels, so arranged that the steam resulting from the evaporation in one heats the next, in which the pressure is lower. The first of the series is heated with live-steam from a boiler, and the last is connected to an exhaust pump. The salt formed collects at the bottom of long vertical shafts, whose height varies and is adjusted according to the pressure in the pan above them. The salt obtained from multiple

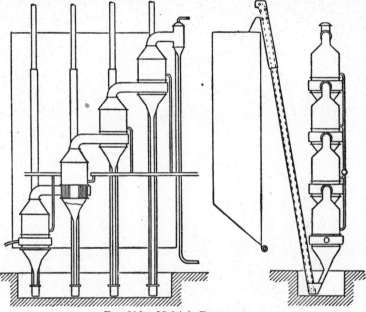

FIG. 206.—Multiple Evaporator.

effect evaporators is fine-grained. If a coarse-grained salt is required open evaporation, as described above, must be employed.

The production of salt from sea-water is only practicable in warm countries or where fuel is very cheap. It is carried on, for instance, in the *salterns* or salt gardens on the shores of the Mediterranean Sea, where the sea-water is concentrated by evaporation in large shallow tanks—" salterns "—exposed to wind and sun. As the solution—" brine "—becomes concentrated, the crystals of salt—*bay salt*—which separate are lifted out by means of perforated shovels, and allowed to drain beside the evaporation tanks. The crystals are allowed to stand in heaps exposed to occasional showers, whereby much of the magnesium chloride is leached out. The product is sometimes called *solar salt*. The mother liquid—" bittern "—was once used for the manufacture of bromine.

The salt obtained by these methods is contaminated with small quantities of other salts as impurities : calcium chloride, magnesium chloride, calcium sulphate, and magnesium sulphate. Cheshire salt for instance, contains about 98·3 per cent. of sodium chloride ; the remaining impurities are mainly insoluble matter, calcium sulphate and magnesium and calcium chlorides. The presence of magnesium chloride makes salt very hygroscopic, so that it becomes lumpy and moist ; some " damp-proof " salts are mixed with, say, 3 per cent. of bone-ash to get over the difficulty to some extent.

The Purification of Sodium Chloride

Sodium chloride can be purified by adding concentrated hydrochloric acid to a cold concentrated aqueous solution of the salts better results are obtained by passing gaseous hydrogen chloride through the salt solution. The impurities remain in solution while the chlorides are precipitated in a very fair state of purity.

This effect is explained by the Ionic Theory as due to the common ion effect (p. 233). The addition of the very soluble hydrogen chloride gas increases largely the concentration of chloride ion, thus causing the solubility product of the salt (the solution being already saturated) to be largely exceeded, salt being precipitated in consequence.

Properties of Sodium Chloride

Sodium chloride crystallizes in cubes and the crystals are anhydrous, though a little water may be mechanically entangled in them. The melting point is about 800° (different temperatures have been recorded by various observers) and it boils at about 1750°. Sodium chloride is moderately soluble in water, 100 grams of water dissolving 36 grams of salt at 20°. The solubility is only very slightly affected by temperature (compare Fig. 49, p. 153). Thus 100 grams of water will dissolve 35·7 grams of salt at 0° and 39·0 grams at 100°. Sodium chloride is almost insoluble in alcohol.

Uses of Sodium Chloride

In addition to its use for seasoning food (for which purpose it should preferably be freed from magnesium and calcium chlorides) common salt is also used for preserving butter, meat and fish, etc., as a starting point for the manufacture of caustic soda (p. 556), sodium carbonate (p. 558) and hence of sodium metal and sodium compounds in general. It is also used in the course of soap manufacture for " salting-out " the soap ; in glazing common pottery (e.g., drainpipes, etc.), and for the manufacture of chlorine and hydrochloric acid (pp. 494, 500) and hence of chlorine compounds in general.

Sodium fluoride, NaF, forms colourless crystals resembling the chloride. It can be made by neutralizing hydrofluoric acid with sodium hydroxide or sodium carbonate. It can also be prepared from cryolite ($AlF_3.3NaF$) by treatment with excess of sodium hydroxide solution. This dissolves the aluminium fluoride, and the undissolved

odium fluoride is extracted with boiling water. It has been used as
a mild disinfectant.

Sodium bromide, NaBr, and **sodium iodide,** NaI, are not much
used, the potassium salts being preferred. They are made in the same
way as the potassium salts (q.v.). Both bromide and iodide crystallize
with two molecules of water of crystallization.

Sodium Nitrate, Chile Saltpetre, NaNO₃

Large quantities of sodium nitrate occur in Argentina, California,
and principally in the rainless districts of the West Coast of South
America—Peru, Bolivia and Chile. Here the salt occurs in large flat
basins, illustrated diagrammatically by Fig. 207.

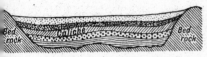

FIG. 207.—Geological Section of
Nitre Bed (Diagrammatic).

There is a thin surface layer
of sand and pebbles, below
which is a 1 to 5-foot layer of
similar material bound together
with clay, salt and sodium
nitrate. This layer is known as
costra and contains 5 to 12 per
cent. of nitrate. Below this is a white stratum of similar thickness,
known as *caliche* which contains an average of 20 to 30 per cent. of
sodium nitrate. Below the caliche is a layer of salt, etc. resembling
costra, a layer of clay, and finally the bed rock of shale and limestone.

The problem of the origin of these nitre beds has not been satisfactorily solved, although it is generally agreed that the nitrogen is of
organic origin. Possibly they are derived from guano, immense
deposits of which exist on the islands off the coast of Peru (though the
absence of phosphate in the nitre beds would then have to be explained);
possibly they are derived from masses of seaweed which have decayed.

The caliche is mined by boring down to the lowest stratum. The
bore is enlarged and charged with blasting powder. The explosion
breaks up the nitre bed within a 50 feet radius of the explosion. The
caliche is sorted out and transported to the leaching works. The
caliche is extracted with water, and the solution is recrystallized so
as to separate the sodium nitrate from the accompanying impurities
—sodium chloride, sodium and calcium sulphates, sodium iodate,
sodium perchlorate, insoluble matter, etc. Commercial Chile saltpetre contains from 95 to 98 per cent. of sodium nitrate. The sodium
iodate which accumulates in the mother liquid is used for the manufacture of iodine (q.v.).

Sodium nitrate forms white, cubic crystals. It is very soluble in
water : 100 grams of water at 20° dissolve 88 grams of the salt. It
melts at 316°, and decomposes at a higher temperature into oxygen
and sodium nitrite. Large quantities are used for fertilizers ; it is
also important for the manufacture of nitric acid, sulphuric acid,
potassium nitrate, sodium arsenate, sodium nitrite, glass, and fireworks, and for curing meat, etc.

The output of natural sodium nitrate from Chile has declined somewhat of late owing to the development of processes for the fixation of nitrogen (see Ch. XX), and a certain amount of sodium nitrate is now made from synthetic nitrogen compounds. In one method, nitrogen oxides (either from the Birkeland-Eyde process, or the ammonia-oxidation method) are absorbed in caustic soda solution, and the resulting liquor mixed with nitric acid and blown in a tower with enriched air (50 per cent. or more oxygen). Attempts are also being made to produce sodium nitrate from nitric acid and sodium chloride; from oxides of nitrogen and sodium chloride; and from sodium sulphate and nitric acid.

Sodium Nitrite, $NaNO_2$

Sodium nitrite is of technical importance in the dyestuffs industry, and is now made on a considerable scale. It is formed by heating sodium nitrate alone above its boiling point, but it used to be made by reducing the nitrate with lead or a mixture of carbon and lime, which enables the conversion to be effected at a lower temperature :

$$2NaNO_3 = 2NaNO_2 + O_2,$$
$$3Pb + 4NaNO_3 = Pb_3O_4 + 4NaNO_2 \text{ or}$$
$$Pb + NaNO_3 = PbO + NaNO_2,$$
$$C + Ca(OH)_2 + 2NaNO_3 = 2NaNO_2 + CaCO_3 + H_2O.$$

Sodium nitrite is now manufactured almost entirely in the course of the processes for the fixation of atmospheric nitrogen (pp. 407-8).

Sodium nitrite is a white, crystalline compound when pure, but is usually slightly yellow as obtained. It has a high solubility in water : 100 grams of water will dissolve 83·3 grams of the salt at 15°, and much heat is absorbed during solution.

Sodium Hydrosulphide, NaHS

Sodium hydrosulphide is formed in solution when aqueous sodium hydroxide is saturated with hydrogen sulphide ; but, on account of hydrolysis, the anhydrous salt cannot be obtained from this solution :

$$2NaOH + H_2S = Na_2S + 2H_2O,$$
$$Na_2S + H_2S = 2NaHS.$$

This can be obtained by heating sodium with hydrogen sulphide gas :

$$2Na + 2H_2S = 2NaHS + H_2,$$

(compare action of sodium on water), or by the action of hydrogen sulphide on sodium ethoxide (the product of the action of sodium on alcohol) :

$$2C_2H_5OH + 2Na = 2C_2H_5ONa + H_2,$$
$$C_2H_5ONa + H_2S = C_2H_5OH + NaHS.$$

Sodium hydrosulphide is a white, deliquescent solid which forms the normal sulphide on heating :

$$2NaHS = Na_2S + H_2S.$$

Sodium sulphide, Na_2S, is formed when hydrogen sulphide is passed into excess of caustic soda solution, or by heating the hydrosulphide, or by adding caustic soda solution in correct amount to the solution of the hydrosulphide. It is now manufactured on a considerable scale, from sodium sulphate. Sodium sulphate is reduced by heating it with coal at 1000°, carbon monoxide being formed at the same time :

$$Na_2SO_4 + 4C = Na_2S + 4CO.$$

The mass is extracted with water and the solution evaporated to give crystals of $Na_2S.9H_2O$. The mother liquor is used for the production of sodium thiosulphate (below).

Sodium sulphide is a buff-coloured solid. It is used extensively in the production of dyes. It is used also for removing the hair from hides before tanning.

Sodium Polysulphides, Na_2S_n—($n = 1$ to 5)

Free sulphur is fairly soluble in solutions of soluble sulphides, such as those of the alkali metals, and the resulting solutions contain various polysulphides. Thus, from sodium sulphide is formed a series ranging from the monosulphide itself to the pentasulphide Na_2S_5. Polysulphides are also formed by direct union of sulphur and sodium. The exact composition and relation between these substances have not been clearly demonstrated, and it is probable that most samples are mixtures of various polysulphides. They are yellow in colour; on exposure to the air they are oxidized to thiosulphates and sulphur :

$$2Na_2S_5 + 3O_2 = 2Na_2S_2O_3 + 6S.$$

With acids, hydrogen persulphide (p. 451) or hydrogen sulphide, and sulphur are formed according to the conditions.

§ 18 Sodium Sulphates and Sulphites, etc.

Sodium Sulphate, Na_2SO_4

Sodium sulphate is an important industrial chemical for which there is an increasing demand. Formerly very considerable quantities were made from nitre-cake (crude sodium bisulphate) which was a by-product of the manufacture of nitric acid (p. 405). Supplies of nitre cake are now diminishing, through the increased production of synthetic nitrates, and the main supply of sodium sulphate is now derived from the action of concentrated sulphuric acid upon common salt, as in the first stage of the now obsolete Leblanc process (compare pp. 500 and 558). Considerable quantities are also obtained as a result of the working of the Stassfurt deposits. The residues from the manufacture of potassium chloride from carnallite (p. 576) contain a large amount of magnesium sulphate. These residues are dissolved in water and treated with common salt. From the solution $Na_2SO_4.10H_2O$ separates, being the least soluble of any of the four salts in the equation :

$$MgSO_4 + 2NaCl = Na_2SO_4 + MgCl_2,$$

provided that the conditions (concentration, etc.) are so adjusted that *astrakanite*—$Na_2SO_4.MgSO_4.4H_2O$—is not formed.

Sodium sulphate occurs native in many parts, particularly in the Western States of America, the western provinces of Canada, and in Russia, and these are now being worked extensively.

Anhydrous sodium sulphate is a white solid, which is fairly readily soluble in water. Solutions which crystallize below 32° deposit the decahydrate $Na_2SO_4.10H_2O$ known as *Glauber's salt*. A heptahydrate is also known (compare p. 155), and is formed by cooling supersaturated solutions of the salt to 5°. Sodium sulphate is one of the easiest salts with which to demonstrate the phenomena of supersaturation.

Sodium sulphate is used in large quantities in the manufacture of glass (p. 690) and of kraft paper. It was formerly made for conversion into sodium carbonate in the Leblanc process; it is still used for making sodium sulphide and sodium thiosulphate (q.v.) and is sometimes employed, instead of the carbonate, for making water-glass (p. 683). It is used in the dyeing and textile industry and Glauber's salt is employed medicinally. Considerable quantities are converted into sodium bisulphate for use in the working of copper-nickel ores.

Sodium Hydrogen Sulphate, Sodium Bisulphate, $NaHSO_4$

This salt is the product of the action of concentrated sulphuric acid on sodium chloride or nitrate at ordinary temperatures (p. 499). The crude product of the nitric acid industry is known as *nitre-cake*. It can be prepared in the laboratory by mixing a solution of two equivalents of sulphuric acid with one equivalent of caustic soda, when $NaHSO_4.H_2O$ crystallizes from the solution in white crystals. This can be dehydrated by heat, and the anhydrous salt can be fused at 300°. At higher temperatures, it decomposes into **sodium pyrosulphate**, $Na_2S_2O_7$ which, on further heating, gives sodium sulphate and sulphur trioxide :

$$2NaHSO_4 = Na_2S_2O_7 + H_2O,$$
$$Na_2S_2O_7 = Na_2SO_4 + SO_3.$$

It is used in the form of nitre-cake in the manufacture of hydrochloric acid and sodium sulphate (pp. 500, 567) and in the laboratory for breaking down some minerals prior to analysis. It is used as a fluxing agent in the extraction of copper-nickel ores.

Sodium Sulphite, Na_2SO_3

This salt is formed when aqueous caustic soda is neutralized with sulphur dioxide, and the solution deposits crystals of the composition $Na_2SO_3.7H_2O$. On the large scale it is made by passing sulphur dioxide through a solution of sodium carbonate, or through a vessel filled with crystals of washing soda ($Na_2CO_3.10H_2O$), until the mixture has an acid reaction. Steam is blown in to prevent deposition of crystals of the bisulphite, after which sodium carbonate is added to the boiling solution until no more carbon dioxide is evolved. The liquid is then evaporated to crystallizing point.

Sodium sulphite forms colourless crystals which are anhydrous if crystallized above 22°, and contain seven molecules of water if separated below that temperature. It is readily soluble in water : 100 grams of water dissolve 25 grams of anhydrous salt at 15°. The solution undergoes oxidation when exposed to the air, sodium sulphate being formed (compare p. 455).

Solutions of sodium sulphite are used as a gentle bleaching agent for wool or silk, as an " anti-chlor " (p. 497) after bleaching with chlorine, as a preservative for foodstuffs, and in the refining of sugar. It is used in photography as a constituent of developers.

Sodium Hydrogen Sulphite, Sodium Bisulphite, NaHSO₃ is produced in solution by saturating a solution of sodium carbonate with sulphur dioxide. It can be isolated from this solution by precipitation with alcohol as a white powder. On heating it decomposes into the sulphate, sulphur dioxide and sulphur. It is used in the manufacture of wood-pulp (sulphite pulp) for the paper-making and artificial silk industries ; as an antichlor, as an antiseptic for preserving food and for sterilizing brewers' casks. It is also a useful reagent in organic chemistry.

Sodium Thiosulphate. $Na_2S_2O_3$

This salt was formerly (wrongly) termed sodium hyposulphite and is still so called by photographers. It has been discussed to some extent already (p. 475) in connection with thiosulphates in general.

Sodium thiosulphate was formerly extensively manufactured from the alkali-waste (p. 558) of the Leblanc process by exposing it to the air for some days, lixiviating with water, adding sodium carbonate, and evaporating and crystallizing the remaining solution. The actions taking place may be represented as in the equations below, but the oxidation is undoubtedly complex and there are probably several intermediate stages :

$$4CaS + 3H_2O + 3O_2 = 3Ca(OH)_2 + CaS_2O_3 + 2S,$$
$$CaS_2O_3 + Na_2CO_3 = CaCO_3 \downarrow + Na_2S_2O_3.$$

It is now made from the waste liquors obtained in the production of sodium sulphide. The crude liquor, obtained by dissolving the melt (p. 567) contains, in addition to the sulphide, sulphate, carbonate and sulphite. On concentration, these salts are deposited and are filtered off, dissolved in water and treated with burner gases containing sulphur dioxide. Sodium thiosulphate is formed according to the equations :

$$2Na_2S + Na_2CO_3 + 4SO_2 = 3Na_2S_2O_3 + CO_2,$$
$$2Na_2S + 3SO_2 + Na_2SO_3 = 3Na_2S_2O_3.$$

Sodium thiosulphate forms large colourless crystals of $Na_2S_2O_3.5H_2O$ when it separates from water. It is freely soluble in water. On heating, it decomposes into sodium sulphate and pentasulphide :

$$4Na_2S_2O_3 = Na_2S_5 + 3Na_2SO_4.$$

The action of acids has been mentioned on page 475 and of iodine solutions on page 527. The former reaction is used qualitatively for the detection of thiosulphates; the latter is of great importance in quantitative volumetric analysis. Some of its applications are referred to on page 527.

§ 19 Sodamide and Sodium Cyanide

Sodamide, $NaNH_2$, is prepared by the action of dry ammonia gas on metallic sodium heated to a temperature of 300-400° in an iron vessel. The reaction may be represented :

$$2Na + 2NH_3 = 2NaNH_2 + H_2.$$

The hydrogen escapes along with the excess of ammonia.
Sodamide is a white wax-like solid, which is decomposed by water :

$$NaNH_2 + H_2O = NaOH + NH_3.$$

When heated in carbon dioxide, cyanamide is formed :

$$2NaNH_2 + 2CO_2 = Na_2CO_3 + CN.NH_2 + H_2O.$$

Sodamide is used as an intermediate product in the manufacture of sodium cyanide (see below) ; and in the dyestuffs industry.
When sodamide is heated in a stream of dry nitrous oxide, **sodium azide,** NaN_3, is formed. It is used as a reagent in organic chemistry and for the preparation of lead azide which is used as a detonator :

$$NaNH_2 + N_2O = NaN_3 + H_2O.$$

Sodium Cyanide, NaCN

Sodium cyanide is now manufactured in large quantities, mostly from metallic sodium. Metallic sodium is converted into sodamide (as above) by the action of ammonia, and this is then run on to red-hot charcoal. Sodium cyanamide is first formed which then reacts with more carbon forming the cyanide :

$$2NaNH_2 + C = Na_2N.CN + 2H_2,$$

$$Na_2N.CN + C = 2NaCN.$$

Crude sodium cyanide (suitable for gold extraction) is also made by fusing calcium cyanamide (nitrolim—p. 386) with salt or sodium carbonate :

$$CaCN_2 + C + 2NaCl = 2NaCN + CaCl_2,$$

$$CaCN_2 + C + Na_2CO_3 = 2NaCN + CaCO_3.$$

Sodium cyanide is also prepared on a considerable scale from the hydrocyanic acid extracted from crude coal gas. One method of doing this is to convert it into potassium (or sodium) ferrocyanide (p. 349) which, when fused with sodium, yields sodium cyanide :

$$Na_4Fe(CN)_6 + 2Na = 6NaCN + Fe.$$

Another (and probably better) process consists in passing the crude gas (containing ammonia as well as hydrocyanic acid) through solutions of copper salts whereby ammonium cuprocyanide—$(NH_4)_2Cu(CN)_3$—is formed. Dilute sulphuric acid is then added and the liberated hydrocyanic acid is absorbed in caustic soda solution, thereby forming sodium cyanide :

$$(NH_4)_2Cu(CN)_3 + H_2SO_4 = (NH_4)_2SO_4 + 2HCN + CuCN,$$
$$2NaOH + 2HCN = 2NaCN + 2H_2O.$$

The cuprous cyanide formed is insoluble and is used again for the absorption of HCN :

$$2NH_3 + 2HCN + CuCN = (NH_4)_2Cu(CN)_3.$$

Sodium cyanide is a white, crystalline substance and, like all cyanides, is extremely poisonous. It is soluble in water, and the solution, owing to hydrolysis (p. 239), is strongly alkaline and smells of hydrocyanic acid.

Sodium cyanide is used in large quantities for the extraction of gold and silver from their ores (pp. 607, 598), and in the laboratory it is employed in the preparation of other cyanides, of some organic compounds and as a reducing agent. It is used industrially for case-hardening iron, in the electro-plating industry, and is the raw material for the production of hydrocyanic acid for spraying fruit trees, fumigation, destruction of vermin, etc.

§ 20 Sodium Phosphates

Sodium (ortho) Phosphates

(Ortho) Phosphoric acid is a tribasic acid and hence should form three sodium salts. These are all known.

Normal sodium phosphate, Na_3PO_4, is usually made by adding the theoretical amount of sodium hydroxide solution to a solution of disodium hydrogen phosphate (the ordinary " sodium phosphate " of commerce and the laboratory) :

$$Na_2HPO_4 + NaOH = Na_3PO_4 + H_2O.$$

On evaporation, white crystals of $Na_3PO_4.12H_2O$ separate. It is readily soluble in water and its solutions are strongly alkaline owing to hydrolysis. It is used commercially under the name *tripsa* for softening boiler feed water : the temporary hardness is removed by precipitation as carbonate owing to presence of free alkali, and permanent hardness is removed also since calcium and magnesium, if present as sulphate or chloride, are both precipitated as phosphates. It is also used as a detergent and degreasing agent ; as an emulsifier in cheese-making and for photographic purposes.

Disodium hydrogen phosphate, Na_2HPO_4, is the ordinary " sodium phosphate " of the laboratory. It is made by neutralizing phosphoric acid with sodium carbonate or caustic soda, using phenolphthalein as indicator. It crystallizes with twelve molecules of water of crystallization, and is used as a reagent in the laboratory. It is efflorescent, forming $Na_2HPO_4.7H_2O$ in ordinary air. It is very soluble in water. On heating, it loses water, forming **sodium pyrophosphate**:

$$2Na_2HPO_4 = Na_4P_2O_7 + H_2O.$$

" Sodium phosphate " is used in the textile industry and for dye-making.

Sodium dihydrogen phosphate, NaH_2PO_4, is made by adding phosphoric acid to a solution of the " ordinary " phosphate until a precipitate is no longer formed when a drop of the solution is added to barium chloride solution. Alternatively, the end point may be fixed by the use of methyl orange as indicator. On evaporation, it crystallizes out as $NaH_2PO_4.H_2O$, in white crystals which are readily soluble. It is used as a constituent of some baking powders. On heating, **sodium metaphosphate** is formed:

$$NaH_2PO_4 = NaPO_3 + H_2O.$$

Sodium ammonium hydrogen phosphate, microcosmic salt, $Na(NH_4).HPO_4.4H_2O$, is formed by dissolving equimolecular amounts of ammonium chloride and ordinary sodium phosphate in a little hot water, filtering off the sodium chloride precipitated and crystallizing. It is used in qualitative analysis for " bead " tests.

§ 21 Detection and Determination of Sodium

Sodium compounds give an intense yellow colour to the bunsen flame ; but as a test this needs to be used with caution, as it is so extremely sensitive that a minute trace of sodium as impurity might be interpreted wrongly.

Sodium may be detected (in a solution from which all metals but the alkali metals have been removed) by addition of a solution of potassium pyroantimonate (p. 753), and allowing the mixture to stand, when a white crystalline precipitate of sodium pyroantimonate $(Na_2H_2Sb_2O_7)$ indicates the presence of sodium. Sodium is also precipitated in similar circumstances from solutions containing magnesium and uranyl acetates as yellow sodium magnesium uranium acetate— $NaMg_2(UO_2)_2(C_2H_3O_2)_3$. The corresponding zinc compound can also be used in this way.

Sodium is usually determined as sulphate. Other metals are removed first (as above) and the remaining solution evaporated with sulphuric acid in a platinum basin or crucible until no further loss of weight occurs. The use of triple uranyl acetates mentioned above for the quantitative determination of sodium is being developed.

§ 22 Potassium, K

History and Occurrence

Potash—the potassium carbonate obtained from the ashes left after wood and land plants have been burned—has long been known ; but it was confused with soda, from which it has been clearly distinguished only since the eighteenth century. Metallic potassium was first obtained by Sir H. Davy in 1808 by the electrolysis of fused potassium hydroxide.

Until comparatively recently the principal source of the world's supplies of potassium compounds was the Stassfurt deposits (p. 490), but during the war of 1914-18 other sources of supply were brought into use. Thus a certain amount of potassium salts was obtained from orthoclase, a felspar consisting of potassium alumino-silicate, and also as a by-product of blast furnace operation. More recently workable deposits of potassium have been discovered, particularly in the Dead Sea, the U.S.A. and in Russia.

All land plants contain considerable quantities of potassium compounds, which are derived from the soil. Under cultivation this is lost from the soil and must be replaced if its fertility is not to be impaired. Hence suitable potassium compounds are important as fertilizers.

It is noteworthy that, notwithstanding the fact that potassium compounds are usually about as soluble as the corresponding sodium salts, the proportion of the former in the sea is very small. This has been attributed to the adsorptive power of the soil for potassium ions being much greater than for sodium ions.

Preparation of Potassium

Potassium has been made by heating potassium carbonate with charcoal :

$$K_2CO_3 + 2C = 2K + 3CO,$$

but explosions are liable to occur when it is made in this way, owing to the formation of **potassium carbonyl,** $K_2(CO)_2$. Potassium can be obtained in the same way as sodium, by electrolysis of the fused hydroxide, but the process is not altogether satisfactory owing to the greater readiness with which the liberated metal dissolves in the fused alkali. It is more satisfactorily obtained using the fused chloride either alone or mixed with calcium chloride. But it is not made on any great scale, as sodium will serve equally well for almost all purposes. It is used to some extent (like sodium) for photo-electric cells (cf. p. 552), and it is occasionally required in the laboratory, particularly in organic chemistry.

Properties

Potassium is a silvery white metal, which rapidly tarnishes when exposed to the air. It is lighter than water (density 0·86). It melts at 62·3° and boils at 760°.

The chemical properties of potassium very closely resemble those of sodium, but its reactions are more vigorous. Thus, when dropped on water the hydrogen evolved, even from a very small piece of potassium, bursts into flame.

Potassium is noteworthy in being very feebly radio-active, emitting β-rays (compare p. 131 and 850). Potassium exists in three isotopes of mass numbers 39, 40 and 41 respectively ; it is believed that the radio-activity is due to the isotope of mass number 41.

Atomic Weight

The atomic weight of potassium has been found in a similar manner to that of sodium ; and also by converting a weighed quantity of pure potassium chlorate into chloride by heat.

The value at present recommended by the International Committee is 39·096.

§ 23 Hydride and Oxides of Potassium

Potassium Hydride, KH

Potassium combines with hydrogen in the same way as sodium, forming slender white needles of the hydride. It is decomposed by water or by heat with formation of hydrogen. Like sodium hydride it combines with carbon dioxide with the formation of the corresponding formate.

Oxides of Potassium

Potassium forms two well-characterized oxides, viz. :

Potassium monoxide, K_2O,
Potassium tetroxide, K_2O_4.

Others have been reported, but their existence is doubtful.

Potassium monoxide, K_2O, is obtained by oxidation of potassium in air or oxygen under reduced pressure, any unoxidized potassium remaining being removed by distillation in vacuo. It closely resembles sodium monoxide in behaviour.

Potassium Tetroxide, K_2O_4

This oxide is formed as a chrome yellow powder by burning potassium in air or oxygen, moisture being rigorously excluded. It acts upon water, forming hydrogen peroxide and oxygen, if the temperature be kept down :

$$K_2O_4 + 2H_2O = 2KOH + H_2O_2 + O_2.$$

If the temperature rise, the hydrogen peroxide is decomposed.

Potassium tetroxide, when heated with carbon monoxide, yields potassium carbonate and oxygen :

$$K_2O_4 + CO = K_2CO_3 + O_2.$$

§ 24 Potassium Hydroxide, KOH

Potassium hydroxide is made in a similar manner to sodium hydroxide (q.v.). Electrolysis of solutions of potassium chloride is the method now most commonly used ; but it has also been made by the action of lime on solutions of the carbonate or sulphate.

It closely resembles sodium hydroxide in properties, but is more soluble both in water and particularly in alcohol. Its solution in this latter solvent is an important reagent in organic chemistry. Potassium hydroxide (or caustic potash) is a very hygroscopic substance and is used as a drying agent for gases ; it is also employed for the absorption of acid gases such as carbon dioxide or sulphur dioxide. It is preferred for this latter purpose over sodium hydroxide owing to the much smaller tendency of the carbonate or sulphite to crystallize out of solution, blocking the flow of gas.

It is used in considerable quantities for the manufacture of soft soap. (Caustic soda yields hard soap.)

§ 25 Potassium Salts

Potassium salts very closely resemble the corresponding sodium salts, the principal differences being that they are, as a rule, less soluble, and do not exhibit the same tendency to separate from solution with water of crystallization. They are often less hygroscopic and hence are preferred for certain purposes, e.g., potassium nitrate in gunpowder, and the potassium salts of acids such as hydriodic, chloric, chromic and permanganic and hydroferrocyanic, being easier to keep on this account, are more commonly used than the sodium salts.

Potassium Carbonate, K_2CO_3

Under the name potash, or pot-ashes, this salt has been known since very early times.

It is now made from potassium chloride by the Leblanc process, exactly as described above for sodium carbonate, except that it will not crystallize out from the liquor obtained after lixiviation of the black ash, and is obtained by evaporating to dryness.

The Solvay process cannot be used for the production of potassium carbonate on account of the too great solubility of the bicarbonate. A good deal is made, however, by adding magnesium carbonate to a solution of potassium chloride and passing in carbon dioxide. A precipitate of magnesium potassium hydrogen carbonate—$MgKH(CO_3)_2.4H_2O$—is formed, which is filtered off:

$$2KCl + 3MgCO_3 + CO_2 + 9H_2O =$$
$$2\{MgKH(CO_3)_2.4H_2O\} \downarrow + MgCl_2.$$

On treating this precipitate with hot water, insoluble magnesium carbonate (which can be used again) and potassium carbonate solution are formed:

$$2\{MgKH(CO_3)_2.4H_2O\} = 2MgCO_3 + K_2CO_3 + CO_2 + 9H_2O.$$

Potassium carbonate can be (and is) extracted from various animal and vegetable products. Thus the *suint* (the oily sweat) extracted from raw wool (which contains up to 30 per cent. of suint), contains a considerable quantity of potassium which is recovered by evaporation of the liquors used for washing the raw wool. A certain amount is also recovered from the residues from beet sugar manufacture, and from the ashes of wood which may contain 15 per cent. of potassium carbonate.

Potassium carbonate is a white, deliquescent substance very soluble in water: 100 grams of water dissolve 112 grams of potassium carbonate at 20°. It is used to some extent in the laboratory as a drying agent. It is also employed for the manufacture of soft soap ; of hard glass (p. 691), in dyeing, and as a starting point for the production of many potassium salts. It is used in the laboratory, mixed with sodium carbonate, as *fusion mixture*.

Hot concentrated aqueous solutions of potassium carbonate at temperatures between 10° and 25° deposit crystals of a **trihydrate**, $K_2CO_3.3H_2O$; these crystals at 100°, lose two molecules of water, forming the **monohydrate**, $K_2CO_3.H_2O$. The latter become anhydrous at 130°.

Potassium bicarbonate, $KHCO_3$, is readily obtained as a white crystalline powder by passing carbon dioxide through a cold, saturated solution of the normal carbonate. It is much less soluble than the latter : 100 grams of water dissolve 27·7 grams of potassium bicarbonate at 10°.

Potassium Chloride, KCl

This salt occurs in large quantities in the Stassfurt deposits either as the mineral *sylvine* (principally KCl) or as *carnallite* (mainly $KCl.MgCl_2.6H_2O$). Most of the potassium chloride of commerce is extracted from carnallite, and from the waters of the Dead Sea.

The crude carnallite is crushed and digested in large tanks with the mother liquor left from preceding operations. This liquid contains chiefly magnesium chloride. The mixture is heated by blowing steam into it, when the potassium and magnesium chlorides dissolve, while most of the sodium chloride and magnesium sulphate, associated with the crude carnallite, remain as an insoluble residue. The liquid is allowed to settle for an hour, and then the supernatant liquid is decanted, while still hot, into large iron vats where, on cooling, crystals of crude potassium chloride (contaminated with sodium chloride and a little magnesium chloride) separate. The crystals of potassium chloride are washed with cold water, to remove the more soluble sodium chloride. Further purification, if required, is effected by recrystallization.

This process depends upon the fact that carnallite is only stable in solution in presence of a large excess of magnesium chloride, being otherwise resolved into its constituent salts.

Potassium chloride crystallizes in white cubes like sodium chloride, which it closely resembles in most respects. It is more soluble than sodium chloride in hot water, but less so in cold. Thus 100 grams of water dissolve 27·6 grams of potassium chloride at 0° and 56·7 grams at 100°. It is used extensively as a fertilizer and in the manufacture of caustic potash and other potassium salts.

Potassium Bromide, KBr

Potassium bromide is made commercially from the crude bromide of iron formed by treating bromine with iron-borings. A solution of this bromide is added to potassium carbonate solution when a mixture of ferrous and ferric hydroxides is precipitated and potassium bromide remains in solution :

$$3Fe + 4Br_2 = Fe_3Br_8,$$
$$Fe_3Br_8 + 4K_2CO_3 + 4H_2O = 8KBr + 2Fe(OH)_3 + Fe(OH)_2 + 4CO_2.$$

The solution is filtered, and the potassium bromide crystallized from the filtrate.

Potassium bromide is thus obtained in white cubic crystals, which are very soluble in water ; 100 grams of water dissolve 65·2 grams of potassium bromide at 20°.

It is used extensively in the manufacture of photographic plates and papers, as a constituent of photographic developers and in medicine.

Potassium iodide, KI, is made commercially in a similar manner to that employed for the bromide, which it resembles in many ways. It crystallizes from water in white cubic crystals, which are very soluble in water: 100 grams of water dissolve 144 grams of potassium iodide at 20°.

Potassium iodide is used in volumetric analysis, partly on account of its solvent action on iodine (due to the formation of the compound KI_3), and as a convenient salt from which iodine may be liberated quantitatively by oxidizing agents, so serving for their determination (see p. 527). Its solution will also dissolve the iodides of several other metals, which are normally insoluble in water. Among these may be mentioned silver iodide and mercuric iodide. The solution of the latter (which contains potassium mercuric iodide, K_2HgI_4) is known as **Nessler's Solution** and is used for the detection of minute traces of ammonia, particularly in water analysis. Nessler's solution gives an intense yellow-brown coloration with ammonia. Potassium iodide is also used in photography, and in medicine.

§ 26 Potassium Nitrate, Nitre, Saltpetre, KNO_3

Potassium nitrate has been known since quite early times and has for a long period found important applications. Although the sodium nitrate of the Chile nitrate beds had become, until the advent of fixation processes, the principal source of the world's supply of nitrates, potassium nitrate was, and is, preferred for many purposes.

Potassium nitrate occurs as an incrustation on the soil in hot countries, particularly in the neighbourhood of villages (e.g., in India), where the ground becomes saturated with crude sewage. The nitrifying bacteria of the soil (p. 402) convert these into nitrates—principally potassium nitrate, since potassium salts are always present in fertile soil. The " nitre " can be extracted by lixiviation.

This process has been imitated (e.g., in France during the Napoleonic Wars) by the construction of *nitre beds*. Soil rich in humus, dung or animal offal is piled into heaps with the debris from buildings, or with lime, or wood ashes, and protected from rain by sheds. Arrangements are made to distribute the liquid excretions of animals over the top of the heap. A white film of nitre grows on the windward side of the pile and is scraped off at intervals. If lime be present, the resulting calcium nitrate is converted into potassium nitrate by means of wood ashes which contain potassium carbonate.

Most of the potassium nitrate of commerce is made by the action of potassium chloride from Stassfurt on sodium nitrate from Chile. The practicability of this process depends upon the fact that of all the four salts which may be present when hot, saturated solutions of these two are mixed :

$$NaNO_3 + KCl \rightleftharpoons KNO_3 + NaCl,$$

the least soluble in the hot mixture will be sodium chloride, which will therefore separate out. If this salt be removed by filtration while still hot, and then cooled to ordinary temperature, the solubility relations are altered and potassium nitrate separates out. The solubility of sodium chloride which might contaminate the nitrate, changes so little with temperature that practically no more separates. These phenomena can be deduced from the solubility curves of Fig. 208.

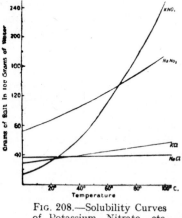

FIG. 208.—Solubility Curves of Potassium Nitrate, etc.

The rise of the synthetic nitrogen industry has stimulated attempts to make potassium nitrate without first preparing sodium nitrate. Direct reaction between nitric acid and potassium chloride has been tried; but the formation of nitrosyl chloride is a difficulty to be overcome. Many other methods have been suggested, e.g., using magnesium nitrate (from kieserite and nitric acid); calcium nitrate or ammonium nitrate and potassium chloride.

Potassium nitrate is obtained in white crystals, which are stable in air, easily soluble in hot water but only sparingly so in cold. 100 grams of water will dissolve 246 grams of potassium nitrate at 100°, and only 32 grams at 20°. On heating, it decomposes like the sodium salt yielding the nitrite. It closely resembles sodium nitrate in chemical properties but, since it is not hygroscopic, it is preferred for such purposes as the production of gunpowder (see below).

The chief use of potassium nitrate is in the manufacture of fireworks and gunpowder. It is also used in pickling meat, and in medicine.

Gunpowder

Roger Bacon (1214-92) is often credited with the discovery of gunpowder, but there is every reason to believe that he derived his information from an Arabian source. It appears to have been introduced into Europe from the Saracens, and is said to have been first used by the English at the battle of Werewater (1327) and also with memorable effect by Edward III at the battle of Crecy (1346).

Gunpowder consists of a mixture of approximately 75 per cent. of potassium nitrate, 12 per cent. of sulphur and 13 per cent. of charcoal, intimately ground under heavy rollers. When ignited, these materials react with explosive violence, producing a very large volume of gas, so much greater than that of the original materials, that if the powder be ignited in a closed space the expanding gases give the mixture the propelling and splitting powers characteristic of explosives. Theoretically, the reaction is represented :

$$4KNO_3 + 2S + 6C = 2K_2S + 2N_2 + 6CO_2,$$

the potassium sulphide remaining as a solid residue, though the reaction is more complicated than this and side reactions cause other products to be formed.

§ 27 Potassium Sulphides and Sulphates

Potassium Sulphides

These compounds closely resemble the corresponding sodium derivatives, and can be prepared in a similar way. A substance known as *liver of sulphur*, which was formerly used in laboratory work (e.g., by Cavendish, p. 538), is prepared by fusing potassium carbonate with an excess of sulphur, and consists largely of potassium pentasulphide, K_2S_5, together with smaller quantities of other sulphides, and potassium sulphate and thiosulphate. A solution of liver of sulphur is used as a garden spray against mildew and insects.

Potassium Sulphate, K_2SO_4

Potassium sulphate occurs in large quantities in various double salts of the Stassfurt deposits, e.g., *schönite*, $K_2SO_4.MgSO_4.6H_2O$, and *kainite*, $K_2SO_4.MgSO_4.MgCl_2.6H_2O$, from which it is prepared. If a hot saturated solution of kainite be allowed to cool, schönite separates. This is treated with sylvine (potassium chloride), when the following reaction occurs :

$$K_2SO_4.MgSO_4.6H_2O + 2KCl = 2K_2SO_4 + MgCl_2 + 6H_2O.$$

The sparingly soluble, anhydrous potassium sulphate separates first— the mother liquor, on concentration, deposits carnallite (p. 576), $KCl.MgCl_2.6H_2O$, from which potassium chloride (p. 576) and magnesium chloride are prepared.

Potassium sulphate crystallizes from aqueous solution in colourless crystals without water of crystallization. It is not very soluble in water : 100 grams of water will dissolve 11·11 grams of potassium sulphate at 20°. It is used for making potash alum, and as a fertilizer, particularly for tobacco, and for wheat in which latter it markedly improves the quality of the straw.

Potassium bisulphate, potassium hydrogen sulphate, $KHSO_4$.

closely resembles the corresponding sodium salt. It is used to attack refractory minerals for analysis.

Potassium cyanide, KCN, was formerly made by heating potassium ferrocyanide either alone or mixed with potassium carbonate :

$$K_4Fe(CN)_6 = 4KCN + FeC_2 + N_2,$$

$$K_4Fe(CN)_6 + K_2CO_3 = 5KCN + KCNO + Fe + CO_2,$$

but prepared in this way always contained some potassium cyanate. It can be made by heating potassium ferrocyanide with metallic potassium :

$$K_4Fe(CN)_6 + 2K = 6KCN + Fe,$$

and the mixture of sodium and potassium cyanides resulting from the similar use of metallic sodium in this process is often sold as potassium cyanide :

$$K_4Fe(CN)_6 + 2Na = 2NaCN + 4KCN + Fe.$$

§ 28 Detection and Determination of Potassium

Potassium salts impart a characteristic lilac colour to the bunsen flame. This is easily obscured by even small traces of sodium, but if the flame be observed through blue glass the lilac potassium flame can be readily detected.

Potassium can be detected in solution (provided other metals than the alkali metals have been removed) by addition of a solution of platinic chloride in concentrated hydrochloric acid, followed by alcohol, when a yellow precipitate of potassium hexachloroplatinate— K_2PtCl_6—indicates the presence of potassium. Perchloric acid (in 20 per cent. solution) and alcohol will similarly give a white precipitate of potassium perchlorate. This is a less expensive reagent than platinic chloride, and equally effective as a test. Another sensitive test is the addition of a solution of sodium cobaltinitrite which gives a yellow precipitate of potassium cobaltinitrite, $K_3Co(NO_2)_6$.

Like sodium, potassium is usually determined as sulphate, but the chloroplatinate has also been used and more recently the reaction with sodium cobaltinitrite has been applied with success to the determination of potassium.

§ 29 Rubidium and Caesium, Rb and Cs

These two elements, which are closely related to sodium and potassium, are both rare elements. Rubidium is widely distributed, but caesium is extremely rare. Rubidium occurs to the extent of about 1 per cent. in the mineral lepidolite (p. 546) ; and carnallite (pp. 490, 618) contains about 0·035 per cent. of rubidium chloride. Both rubidium and caesium occur in very small quantities in certain mineral waters (e.g., Dürkheim in the Palatinate). Caesium is found also in the very rare mineral *pollux*, or *pollucite*, a silicate found on the island of Elba.

Both these elements were discovered in 1861 by Bunsen and Kirchoff by means of the spectroscope. They evaporated down forty tons of the mineral water of Dürkheim, and removed the alkaline earths and lithium by precipitation with ammonium carbonate. Spectroscopic examination of the filtrate gave, besides the lines of lithium, sodium and potassium, two splendid blue lines near the blue strontium line. Since these lines did not correspond with those of any then known element, Bunsen and Kirchoff concluded that they were due to the presence of a new element and gave it the name caesium (from the Latin caesius, the blue of the sky).

Similarly, on extracting the alkalis from lepidolite, and washing the precipitate obtained by treating the solution of the alkalis with hydrochloro-platinic acid with boiling water, they obtained a residue which, when examined spectroscopically, gave, besides those due to strontium and potassium, a number of new lines. Two of these lines lay very far to the red end of the spectrum and hence the new element was named rubidium (from rubidus, dark red).

Both these elements closely resemble potassium. Metallic rubidium has been obtained by heating an intimate mixture of the carbonate and finely divided carbon. Also by heating the chloride with calcium in an exhausted tube of hard glass. It is softer, more fusible (m.p. 38°), more volatile (b.p. 700°) and heavier (d. 1·525) than potassium. Chemically, it is very similar, but its actions are more vigorous. Like potassium, it exhibits feeble radio-activity.

Caesium exhibits similar divergence from potassium to a greater degree. Thus, it melts at 26°, boils at 670°, and its density is 1·9. It is even more vigorous in its chemical activity than rubidium, but is not radio-active. The metal has been obtained by heating the hydroxide with magnesium and by electrolyzing a fused mixture of caesium and barium cyanides and, like rubidium, by means of calcium.

A characteristic property of these two elements, in which they differ from the other alkali metals is in the readiness with which they form stable polyhalides. Among these may be mentioned RbI_3, CsI_3, CsI_4, $CsBr_5$, CsI_2Br, $RbClBrI$, $CsIBr_2$, $RbFICl_3$, $CsFICl_3$.

The atomic weights of rubidium and caesium were determined by conversion of the chlorides and bromides into silver chloride and bromide. The values at present recommended as the most probable are 85·48 for rubidium, and 132·91 for caesium. The atomic weight of caesium has also been found by the action of silica on caesium nitrate, by which means the ratio $Cs_2O:N_2O_5$ can be found.

§ 30 Element No. 87

There is a gap in the Periodic Table between niton and radium, indicated clearly by the atomic numbers of the neighbouring elements. This missing element would be an alkali metal of high atomic weight (approx. 224) and possibly radio-active.

Recently it has been stated that X-ray examination of residues from some minerals relatively rich in caesium reveal a line indicating the presence, in very small amount, of the element of atomic number 87.

The evidence has, however, been reviewed critically by Noddack (who discovered rhenium in 1925) and he concludes that the presence of element No. 87 has not been established.

CHAPTER XXVI

COPPER, SILVER AND GOLD

The properties of an element in two different states of oxidation differ absolutely from one another; and in these two states the element appears in two entirely different rôles.—J. LOCKE.

The extensive use of this metal wherever gorgeous ornament is required, as well as in the simplest designs of art—from the glittering crown of an emperor to the neat little wedding ring of the village maid—has imparted to gold an interest which other metals have failed to excite.—H. SOWERBY.

§ 1 Copper, Cu—History and Occurrence

History

COPPER appears to have been known from prehistoric times—the neolithic age—long before the histories of the ancient peoples were engraved on stone pillars or inscribed on papyri. The "copper age" followed the "stone age." At the time of Ramses II (about 1300 B.C.), copper was so costly that it was stored among the treasures of Egyptian temples. Copper appears to have been used for making utensils and instruments for war before iron. This is probably due to the fact that copper occurs native in a form requiring no metallurgical treatment. The ancients used the terms χαλκός (chalcos) and *aes* for copper, brass, and bronze. In fact, the terms for copper, brass, and bronze are much confused by the old writers, showing that they did not understand the difference—e.g., Pliny. Pliny, by the way, wrote a celebrated *Natural History* at the beginning of this era. In this book he laboriously garnered what he could of facts and fable then known concerning nature ; hence the book is often quoted. Copper was afterwards called *aes cyprium* (i.e., Cyprian brass), since the Romans first obtained it from the Isle of Cyprus ; the term *aes cyprium* was soon abbreviated to *cuprum*. Hence the modern symbol "Cu."

Occurrence

Metallic copper is found in many localities ; e.g., considerable masses have been found in Michigan, on the shores of Lake Superior ; and small quantities in many other places—Cornwall, Siberia, Ural, Australia, Chile, etc. Compounds of copper are distributed in nature as oxide in *cuprite*, or ruby ore, Cu_2O ; as sulphide in *chalcocite*, or copper glance, Cu_2S ; copper pyrites or *chalcopyrite*, $CuFeS_2$ or $Cu_2S.Fe_2S_3$. The real composition of many copper sulphides, as they occur in nature, is exceedingly complex. The same remark is more or less true for the composition of most natural minerals ; at least chemical formulae which follow the analyses closely are very complex. **The formulae for minerals are commonly represented as if pure minerals occurred in nature.** Ideally pure minerals very seldom occur in nature, and accordingly, the formulae represent ideal or imaginary minerals to which real minerals approximate more or less closely. Copper also occurs in many places as basic carbonate, *malachite*, $CuCO_3.Cu(OH)_2$; and *azurite*, $2CuCO_3.Cu(OH)_2$. Copper silicates, arsenates, phosphates, etc., are also known to occur native. Copper has also been found in the feathers of some birds.

§ 2 Manufacture of Copper

The principal source of copper is copper pyrites, which contains varying amounts of copper and iron sulphides, though a good deal is obtained from the deposits of native copper on the shores of Lake Superior, etc.

The precise methods employed in the extraction vary according to the ore and the district but, broadly speaking, are as follows. The stages in the process may be summarized as follows:

1. Concentration of the ore by flotation.

2. Roasting of the ore.

3. Smelting (production of *Matte*).

4. Conversion of Matte to *Blister Copper*.

5. Refining of blister copper.

1. Concentration of the Ore

This is effected by grinding the ore to a fine powder, after which the metal-bearing particles are separated from the gangue, etc., by agitation with water and suitable reagents, so that the froth so formed carries with it a desired constituent of the original ore. The froth is made to overflow and is collected. In this way, quite low-grade ores, which could not formerly be smelted economically, are now concentrated up to 25 per cent. of copper.

2. Roasting the Ore

The ore is next roasted in a furnace consisting of a vertical tier of nine or more circular hearths. Each hearth is provided with a rotating raking device and the whole furnace is so arranged that the ore charged on to the top hearth gradually moves down the furnace from hearth to hearth. No fuel is usually required since the oxidation of the sulphur in the ore furnishes sufficient heat to keep the process going. Copper sulphide oxidizes much less rapidly than iron sulphide and the roasting is so adjusted that, when completed, the amount of sulphur still remaining is just sufficient to combine with all the copper present. The sulphur dioxide may be made into sulphuric acid, or (in the future) will probably be reduced to sulphur (p. 437).

3. Smelting—Production of Matte

This stage in the process was formerly carried out in blast-furnaces but is now done in a reverberatory furnace. The roasted ore (mixed with silica if necessary) is heated in such a furnace and the copper present combines with the sulphur to form cuprous sulphide; the iron oxide formed in the roasting forms a slag with the silica : any excess of sulphur forms iron sulphide. The mixture of copper and iron sulphides melt together to form *matte* and the slag floats on the surface of this. The slag is run off continuously and the molten matte is tipped at intervals into large ladles and conveyed to the converters for the next process.

4. Conversion to Blister Copper

The molten matte is run into a converter (similar to the Bessemer converter used in steel manufacture, p. 807) lined with magnesite, and an appropriate amount of silica is added. A blast of air is blown through the melt, oxidizing the sulphur, iron and many other metals (if present). The volatile oxides are driven off and the iron oxides combine with the silica to form a slag. The blowing is continued until cuprous sulphide and oxide are present in right amount to bring about the reaction :

$$Cu_2S + 2Cu_2O = 6Cu + SO_2.$$

The progress of the operation can be accurately judged by the appearance of the flame issuing from the mouth of the converter. When the matte is completely converted to copper (and the free copper is beginning to oxidize), the blast is stopped and the copper poured off. As the copper cools, the sulphur dioxide dissolved by the metal is expelled, giving the metal a blistered appearance. Hence the product is known as *blister copper*.

5. Refining the Crude Copper

Two methods have been used for copper-refining, viz., roasting in a reverberatory furnace and electrolysis. In the furnace method blister copper is melted in a reverberatory furnace in a stream of air. Any sulphur left is removed as sulphur dioxide, arsenic volatilizes as the trioxide, and other metals, e.g., iron, form a scale of oxide which is skimmed off. The metal thus purified still contains cuprous oxide, which makes it somewhat brittle, and this is removed by stirring it with a log of green wood, when the hydrocarbons formed, in bubbling through the molten metal, reduce it to copper. The product contains about 99·5 per cent. of copper and is known as *Tough Pitch Copper*.

If a metal of very high purity is required (e.g., for electrical purposes) or if gold and silver are present in recoverable quantities the tough pitch copper is further refined by electrolysis. Slabs of crude metal for anodes are suspended between thin cathodes of pure copper in a bath containing about 15 per cent. of copper sulphate and 5 per cent. of sulphuric acid When the current is passed, copper dissolves from the anodes, and pure copper is deposited on the cathodes, the net result being the transference of the copper from anode to cathode. The impurities from the anode either pass into solution or are deposited as a slime near the anode (anode mud). Considerable amounts of silver and gold are obtained from the anode mud. Thus American " copper " furnishes 110 ozs. per ton of silver and $\frac{1}{3}$ oz. per ton of gold, a quantity nearly sufficient to pay for the cost of refining. Electrolytic copper is 99·96 to 99·99 per cent. pure.

§ 3 Properties of Copper

Copper has a characteristic reddish-brown colour when a clean surface is seen by reflected light ; but in transmitted light thin layers are green. It can be obtained in octahedral crystals (cubic system). Copper melts at 1083° if heated in an atmosphere of carbon monoxide ; in air the melting point is some 20° lower owing to the formation of cuprous oxide which dissolves in the molten metal. It is a fairly heavy metal, its specific gravity being 8·92 at 20° and it is an excellent conductor of heat and electricity. The molten metal mixes readily with many other metals forming alloys (see below).

Copper does not burn in air, but is gradually converted into cuprous (Cu_2O) and cupric oxides (CuO) on its surface when heated to redness. The finely-divided metal will burn in chlorine or sulphur vapour. It does not react with steam at any temperature below white heat, and then only to a very slight extent. Copper is below hydrogen in the electro-chemical series (p. 205) and hence does not react with acids unless they are also oxidizing agents, or form complex ions with copper. It is, however, also slowly attacked by some acids in presence of air, due to the slow oxidizing action of the air.

Although unaffected by *dry* air at the ordinary temperature, exposure to moist air causes the formation of a beautiful green coating or patina. This was for long said to be a basic copper carbonate, but Morgan has recently shown that it is, in inland places, a basic sulphate— $CuSO_4.3Cu(OH)_2$, while near the sea this is accompanied by a basic chloride—$CuCl_2.3Cu(OH)_2$.

Copper reacts readily with nitric acid, oxides of nitrogen being formed. With the dilute acid, nitric oxide (along with a little nitrogen peroxide) is formed (compare p. 415), while with the concentrated acid nitrogen peroxide predominates :

$$3Cu + 8HNO_3 = 3Cu(NO_3)_2 + 2NO + 4H_2O,$$
$$Cu + 4HNO_3 = Cu(NO_3)_2 + 2NO_2 + 2H_2O.$$

Suggestions as to the mechanism of these reactions are discussed on page 409. It is curious to note, however, that copper is not attacked by nitric acid which has been completely freed from nitrous acid.

Copper is only attacked by dilute sulphuric acid if air is present, and then only slowly : in that case copper sulphate results :

$$2Cu + 2H_2SO_4 + O_2 = 2CuSO_4 + 2H_2O.$$

Hot strong sulphuric acid readily reacts with copper, sulphur dioxide being evolved (p. 452) :

$$Cu + 2H_2SO_4 = CuSO_4 + SO_2 + 2H_2O.$$

Caustic alkali solutions are without action on copper.

As it is so low in the electro-chemical series, copper is displaced from solutions of its salts by many metals—e.g., zinc or iron.

$$Zn + CuSO_4 = Cu + ZnSO_4,$$
$$Fe + CuSO_4 = Cu + FeSO_4.$$

The familiar experiment of dipping a knife blade into copper sulphate solution, with consequent formation of a layer of copper on the blade, is an example of this. Copper will, in its turn, displace silver, gold or platinum from their solutions since these metals are still lower in the electro-chemical series, e.g.,

$$Cu + 2AgNO_3 = Cu(NO_3)_2 + 2Ag.$$

§ 4 Alloys of Copper

Copper readily forms alloys with other metals and many of these are of considerable importance technically. The following table shows the approximate composition of some of them :—

TABLE XXXVIII. COPPER ALLOYS

Alloy.	Percentage of					
	Copper.	Tin.	Zinc.	Iron.	Nickel.	Other Elements.
Bronze. .	75-90	25-10				
Phosphor-bronze .	86	13				P 0.25
Manganese-bronze.	59	1	up to 40			Mn 0.3
Aluminium-bronze	81·5-90	0-0·5			0-6	Al 7-12
Silicon-bronze .	95-98	2-5				Si 2-5
Brass . . .	60-70		40-30			
Dutch metal. .	80		20			
Bell metal . .	80	20				
Speculum metal .	66-68	34-32				
Gunmetal . .	87	10	3			
German silver .	25-50		35-25		35-10	
Delta metal . .	60		38·2	1·8		
Monel metal . .	27			2-3	68	
Constantan . .	60				40	
British-copper-coinage .	95	1 or more	4 or less			

Bronzes are tough and tenacious materials. Ordinary bronze is used for making statues, coins, ornaments, etc. Phosphor bronze is one of the strongest of non-ferrous metals and is used in bearings, valves, etc., where strength and resistance to wear must be combined with resistance to corrosion. Manganese bronze is used for the propellers of ships and in machinery generally. Aluminium bronze is a hard, light, yellowish-brown alloy, used for making the hulls of yachts, etc. Silicon bronze is used for telegraph wires.

Brass is a fairly soft alloy and can be readily turned on a lathe or otherwise worked. It finds many uses, e.g., as wire for the manufacture of pins, etc., and for many parts of machinery, as well as for ornaments of various kinds, and in making musical instruments. *Bell metal* is used in bell-founding, *gun-metal* was formerly used for making cannon and now finds other uses, particularly for engineering purposes. *Speculum metal* is used for optical instruments, and *german silver* for making resistance coils and for imitating silver. *Delta metal* might be described as a brass to which iron has been added, and is characterized by a very high tensile strength. *Monel metal* is a copper-nickel alloy which also has a high tensile strength and, in addition, is very resistant to chemical action so that it is extensively employed in chemical industry (e.g., caustic soda manufacture, p. 554).

Copper alloys are extensively used in coinage, and gold and silver used in jewellery, etc., are usually alloyed with copper to give them hardness and durability without detracting from their appearance. British copper coins contain 95 per cent. of copper, 4 per cent. of tin, and 1 per cent. of zinc. Some issues since the war have the composition : copper, 95·5 per cent. ; tin, 3·0 per cent. ; and zinc, 1·5 per cent. Gold and silver coins usually contain 8 to 10 per cent. of copper. British silver coins struck before 1920 contained 7·5 per cent. of copper. From 1920-22 they contained 40 per cent. of copper and 10 per cent. of nickel, later issues had 50 per cent. of copper and no nickel. Since 1927 the alloy used has had the composition : silver, 50 ; copper 40 ; zinc 5 ; nickel 5 per cent. Nickel coins (e.g., in Germany and the U.S.A.) contain approximately 75 per cent. of copper.

§ 5 Uses of Copper

Next to iron, copper is the most useful metal we have. Enormous quantities are used in the electrical industries; for household utensils and for brewery vessels. Large quantities are used for the fireboxes of locomotive boilers and for steam pipes in stationary plant. Copper nails, rivets and sheeting are (or were) used for sheathing wooden ships. As mentioned in the preceding section, it is a valuable constituent of many alloys. Copper is notable in having extensive use in the pure condition ; most metals require to have their properties modified by the addition of small quantities of other substances in order to make them most useful. Many compounds of copper have important uses ; these will be mentioned under the heading of the compounds concerned.

§ 6 Atomic Weight of Copper

The atomic weight of copper is shown to be in the neighbourhood of 63·5 by the vapour density of volatile copper compounds, and by the application of Dulong and Petit's rule to the specific heat.

The combining weight has been determined by many methods. The best determinations are those of Richards. Among the methods he employed were the precipitation of silver from an ice-cold solution of silver nitrate by electrolytic copper ; the preparation of pure cuprous bromide by oxidation of electrolytic copper and solution of the oxide in pure hydrobromic acid ; by the preparation of copper sulphate crystals from copper, and by purely electro-chemical methods. His values range from 63·568 to 63·576. The accepted " International " value is 63·57.

§ 7 Copper Hydrides and Oxides

Cuprous Hydride, CuH or Cu_2H_2, is believed to be formed as a red precipitate by the action of hyposulphites (p. 477) or of hypophosphites (p. 730) on solutions of copper sulphate. It is a very unstable, reddish-brown substance and cannot be kept for any length of time, since it decomposes suddenly, leaving a sponge of metallic copper.

Cupric Hydride, CuH_2, has been reported as an intermediate compound in the formation of cuprous hydride, into which it is supposed to decompose with evolution of hydrogen. The existence of a definite compound, CuH_2, is, however, very doubtful.

Copper furnishes three oxides whose existence is established, viz.,

Cuprous oxide, Cu_2O,
Cupric oxide, CuO,
Copper dioxide, CuO_2,

of which only the first two are of any particular importance. In addition, oxides of the formulae Cu_3O and Cu_4O have been reported, but the evidence is indecisive.

Cuprous oxide, Cu_2O

Cuprous oxide is formed when copper or copper oxide is heated to a high temperature, but cannot be prepared pure in this way. It is made either by heating cupric oxide with copper powder,

$$Cu + CuO = Cu_2O,$$

or, better, by the action of glucose on an alkaline solution of a cupric salt. The addition of sodium hydroxide to a solution of copper sulphate causes the precipitation of cupric hydroxide (below, p. 590) ; but if Rochelle salt (sodium potassium tartrate) be first added to the solution, no precipitate results with sodium hydroxide, and a deep blue solution is formed. (This result is probably due to the formation of a complex copper tartrate which is soluble.) If to this solution glucose be added and the mixture warmed, the blue colour disappears and cuprous oxide is precipitated as a red powder.

Cuprous oxide is an insoluble red powder. When heated in air it is partly oxidized to cupric oxide ; and it is easily reduced to metallic copper by heating in a stream of hydrogen or coal gas. With most acids its behaviour is unusual, for instead of forming a cuprous salt, the corresponding cupric salt results and free copper is deposited, e.g.,

$$Cu_2O + H_2SO_4 = CuSO_4 + Cu + H_2O.$$

Yet with hydrochloric acid, cuprous chloride (CuCl) is formed, but dissolves in excess of the acid probably because of the formation of chloro-cuprous acid :

$$Cu_2O + 2HCl = 2CuCl + H_2O,$$
$$2CuCl + 2HCl = H_2Cu_2Cl_4.$$

Cuprous oxide is extensively used in the glass industry, since it imparts a deep red colour to glass. It is also employed in preparing anti-rust paints. Red Chinese flambé glazes are produced by developing glazes containing copper oxide in a reducing atmosphere. The colour is probably colloidal copper suspended in the glaze.

Cupric Oxide, CuO

Cupric oxide or *black copper oxide* can be made by most of the standard methods (compare p. 305). It is prepared in the laboratory by heating the nitrate (obtained from copper and nitric acid), the carbonate or the hydroxide (q.v.).

Commercially it is made by heating *malachite* (the native carbonate) ; and also from the copper scale, etc., which results from the working of copper in boiler shops, etc. This material, which is a mixture of copper, cuprous and cupric oxides, is treated with a little nitric acid and heated to redness, thereby converting the whole into the oxide.

Cupric oxide is a black powder, not affected by water. It is stable to moderate heating, but at high temperatures $(1000°-1200°)$ decomposes into oxygen and cuprous oxide. When heated, it is reduced to the metal by reducing agents, such as hydrogen, carbon monoxide, hydrocarbons, and carbon. It is a typical basic oxide and forms characteristic salts with many acids—the *cupric salts* (pp. 593-595).

It is used in glazes and glasses to which it imparts a green or blue colour ; probably on account of the formation of copper silicate. It is used in the laboratory in the analysis of organic compounds, the carbon and hydrogen of which it oxidizes to carbon dioxide and water respectively.

Copper Peroxide, Copper Dioxide, CuO_2

In 1844 Krüger found that when chlorine is passed through a suspension of cupric hydroxide in potassium hydroxide solution a red-coloured solution results. This he attributed to the presence of an unstable copper peroxide, since the solution rapidly decomposes, liberating oxygen and cupric oxide is precipitated.

Copper dioxide is formed as a yellow-brown powder when a dilute solution of hydrogen peroxide acts upon cupric hydroxide suspended in water at 0°. It is very unstable, and when treated with dilute acids, it gives a cupric salt and hydrogen peroxide. Hence it is probably a true peroxide, or superoxide (p. 304).

§ 8 Hydroxides of Copper

Theoretically two hydroxides would be expected to exist corresponding to cuprous oxide and cupric oxide respectively.

Actually **cuprous hydroxide** seems not to exist. A yellow precipitate is first obtained in the preparation of cuprous oxide (p. 588) which rapidly turns into the red cuprous oxide itself. This yellow precipitate has been thought by some to be cuprous hydroxide ; but is generally supposed to be a colloidal " mixture " of cuprous oxide and water of no fixed composition.

Cupric Hydroxide, Cu(OH)$_2$

When a solution of sodium or potassium hydroxide is added to a cold solution of a cupric salt, a pale blue, gelatinous precipitate of cupric hydroxide is formed :

$$CuSO_4 + 2NaOH = Cu(OH)_2 + Na_2 SO_4.$$

This blue precipitate can be filtered off, but it is very difficult to wash it free from alkali. It can be dried at low temperatures, but on heating to 100° turns black, a substance of the composition 4CuO.H$_2$O being formed. A similar black substance is obtained if the solution used for preparing the hydroxide be boiled either before or after addition of alkali. Stronger heating removes the remaining water forming cupric oxide.

Copper hydroxide reacts readily with acids forming cupric salts, and is also soluble in aqueous ammonia giving the characteristic very deep blue solution.

If aqueous ammonia be added to a solution of a cupric salt, cupric hydroxide is first precipitated as with sodium hydroxide, but this redissolves on addition of excess of ammonia going a deep blue solution. *Schweitzer's reagent*, formed by adding solid copper hydroxide to concentrated ammonia dissolves cellulose (e.g., cotton wool or filter paper). The cellulose is reprecipitated when this " solution " is acidified, and this has been applied in one method for the production of artificial silk. The solution of cellulose in ammoniacal cupric hydroxide solution is squirted through jets into a solution of sulphuric acid (10-50 per cent.) or of sodium hydroxide (5-30 per cent.), and the cellulose is thus obtained in threads with a silk-like lustre.

The solvent effect of ammonia on copper hydroxide is due to the formation of complex compounds known as **copper ammines** or **cuprammonium compounds,** which furnish a complex cuprammonium ion—Cu(NH$_3$)$_4$$\cdots$—which is divalent and forms salts with acidic ions. The effect is explained, in terms of the ionic theory, as follows. The precipitated cupric hydroxide is in equilibrium with its own saturated solution, which contains both undissociated hydroxide and its ions :

$$\underset{\text{(Solid)}}{Cu(OH)_2} \rightleftharpoons \underset{\text{(Solution)}}{Cu(OH)_2} \rightleftharpoons Cu\cdots + 2OH'$$

The ammonia present reacts with the cupric ions, forming cuprammonium ions, thus removing cupric ions from the system and disturbing the equilibrium indicated above. More cupric hydroxide accordingly dissolves and the process continues, provided enough ammonia be present, until all the precipitate has been dissolved.

In the case of the addition of ammonia to a copper sulphate solution, the process may be represented :

$$CuSO_4 \rightleftharpoons Cu^{\cdot\cdot} + SO_4''$$
$$NH_3 + H_2O \rightleftharpoons NH_4OH \rightleftharpoons NH_4^{\cdot} + OH'$$
$$Cu^{\cdot\cdot} + 2OH' \rightleftharpoons Cu(OH)_2 \downarrow$$
$$Cu^{\cdot\cdot} + 4NH_3 \rightleftharpoons Cu(NH_3)_4^{\cdot\cdot}$$
$$Cu(NH_3)_4^{\cdot\cdot} + SO_4'' \rightleftharpoons Cu(NH_3)_4SO_4.$$

Addition of alcohol to the deep blue ammoniacal solution slowly precipitates *copper tetramminosulphate* or *cuprammonium sulphate*, $Cu(NH_3)_4SO_4.4H_2O$, on standing.

§ 9 Salts of Copper. The Equilibrium between Cuprous and Cupric Salts

Copper forms two series of salts, corresponding to the oxides cuprous oxide and cupric oxide, and known consequently as the cuprous and cupric salts.

There is still some doubt concerning the true molecular formula of cuprous salts. The vapour density of cuprous chloride corresponds to a formula Cu_2Cl_2 even at 1600°. On the other hand, the iodide is CuI at 1000° and the freezing points of solutions of cuprous compounds in organic solvents indicate similar differences. The probable conclusion seems to be that univalent copper and the ion $Cu^{\cdot}$ do exist, but that the cuprous compounds have a marked tendency to form double molecules.

The equilibrium between the cuprous and cupric salts is interesting. The soluble cuprous salts decompose in solution in water into cupric salts and copper, e.g., cuprous sulphate, which can be made in absence of water, decomposes at once in water with cupric sulphate and copper. On the other hand, cupric salts of acids whose cuprous salts are insoluble decompose in water into the cuprous salt which is precipitated, e.g., cupric iodide or cyanide, iodine and cyanogen being evolved also. Thus :

$$Cu_2SO_4 = CuSO_4 + Cu.$$

But :

$$2CuI_2 = 2CuI + I_2.$$

In general, it may be said that cuprous salts cannot exist in contact with water unless they are either insoluble or combined in a complex. Cupric salts of acids whose cuprous salts are insoluble are similarly unstable in presence of water, but can be sometimes obtained in the form of co-ordination compounds with organic substances, e.g., cupric iodide forms a stable co-ordination with ethylene diamine :

Similar considerations apply to the soluble cuprous salts.

These facts are interpreted in terms of the Ionic Theory as follows. The interchange between cuprous and cupric salts is represented by the equilibrium :

$$2Cu^{\cdot} \rightleftharpoons Cu^{\cdot\cdot} + Cu.$$

Hence a soluble cuprous salt will furnish a solution containing much $Cu^{\cdot}$ ion and the equilibrium will tend to move to the right. Conversely, when the cupric salt of an acid whose cuprous salt is insoluble is dissolved in water, cuprous ions will be removed by precipitation, and the equilibrium will be moved to the left. The stability conferred by the formation of complexes and co-ordination compounds is similarly due to the removal of, or non-formation of, ions of one or other kind.

§ 10 Cuprous Salts

Cuprous Chloride, CuCl

This salt is made by digesting a solution of cupric chloride in concentrated hydrochloric acid, with metallic copper (usually in the form of turnings) until the green colour has disappeared. The solution is then poured into water, when a white precipitate of cuprous chloride separates. It can be filtered off and washed with water containing a little sulphur dioxide to prevent oxidation and dried by means of alcohol and ether, or in a vacuum desiccator :

$$CuCl_2 + Cu = 2CuCl.$$

The reduction of the cupric to the cuprous salt can also be effected by means of sulphur dioxide. Making use of this fact it is sometimes prepared in the laboratory by passing sulphur dioxide through a solution of equi-molecular amounts of copper sulphate and common salt :

$$2CuSO_4 + 2NaCl + SO_2 + 2H_2O = 2CuCl + 2NaHSO_4 + H_2SO_4.$$

The cuprous chloride is precipitated, and may be filtered off and dried as above.

Cuprous chloride is a white solid, insoluble in water, but soluble in excess of concentrated hydrochloric acid (owing to the formation of the complex $H_2Cu_2Cl_4$). It melts between 415° and 422°. On exposure to air, it gradually turns green on account of the formation of a basic cupric chloride, $CuCl_2.3CuO.3H_2O$. It dissolves also in ammonia forming a dark green solution containing' $CuCl.NH_3$ which, like the solution in hydrochloric acid, readily absorbs carbon monoxide. Both solutions are employed in gas analysis for the absorption of carbon monoxide. The amount of gas absorbed never exceeds the ratio Cu : CO and it is probable that a compound, $CuCl.CO.2H_2O$, is formed.

The ammoniacal solution also absorbs acetylene, which reacts with it, forming a precipitate of **cuprous acetylide,** $Cu_2C_2.H_2O$, a red explosive compound the formation of which is used as a test for acetylene (cf. p. 340).

Cuprous iodide, CuI, is precipitated, mixed with iodine, when aqueous solutions of potassium iodide and of a copper salt (e.g., copper sulphate) are mixed together. It is probable that cupric iodide is first formed, but is unstable and decomposes as soon as it is formed (compare § 9):

$$2CuSO_4 + 4KI = 2CuI_2 + 2K_2SO_4,$$
$$2CuI_2 = 2CuI + I_2.$$

This reaction is employed in the determination of copper (pp. 527, 596), and for separating iodides from chlorides and bromides, since the latter do not give cuprous salts under these conditions.

Cuprous Sulphide, Cu_2S, occurs native as *copper glance*. It is produced when copper is heated with sulphur vapour, when an excess of copper filings is heated with sulphur, and also when copper sulphate solution is warmed with sodium thiosulphate.

Cuprous Sulphate, Cu_2SO_4, probably exists, in small quantity, in aqueous solutions of cupric sulphate in contact with metallic copper, but the action must be very slight at ordinary temperatures. In the case of ammoniacal solutions, a colourless crystalline salt, $Cu_2SO_4 \cdot 4NH_3 \cdot H_2O$, has been isolated. Cuprous sulphate can be prepared as a light grey powder by heating together equivalent amounts of methyl (or ethyl) sulphate and cuprous oxide in the absence of moisture. It is decomposed by water into copper and cupric sulphate:

$$Cu_2SO_4 = CuSO_4 + Cu.$$

Cuprous Cyanide, CuCN, is formed (analogously to cuprous iodide) on mixing solutions of potassium cyanide and copper sulphate, cyanogen gas being evolved (cf. p. 370):

$$CuSO_4 + 2KCN = Cu(CN)_2 + K_2SO_4,$$
$$2Cu(CN)_2 = 2CuCN + C_2N_2.$$

It is a white solid, insoluble in water, but soluble in excess of potassium cyanide forming a stable complex salt potassium cuprocyanide, $KCu(CN)_2$. This property is made use of in the separation of copper from cadmium in qualitative analysis, since the solution does not give the ionic reactions of copper.

§ 11 Cupric Salts

Many cupric salts are soluble in water, yielding blue solutions. Some give green solutions when very concentrated, but go blue when diluted. This behaviour is probably due to differing degrees of hydration of the cupric ion or to the formation of complexes. Many of the salts crystallize with water of crystallization, forming blue or green crystals. The colour of the anhydrous salts varies considerably. Thus, the anhydrous sulphate is white, the carbonate green, the chloride is brown, and sulphide black.

Copper Carbonates

Normal cupric carbonate has not been obtained, but two basic carbonates are known. Both occur naturally, and can be prepared in the laboratory. They are *malachite*, $CuCO_3.Cu(OH)_2$, which is green, and *azurite*, $2CuCO_3.Cu(OH)_2$, which is blue. The copper carbonate of the laboratory resembles malachite in composition, and is obtained as a fine green powder by mixing solutions of copper sulphate and sodium carbonate :

$$2CuSO_4 + 2Na_2CO_3 + H_2O = CuCO_3.Cu(OH)_2 + CO_2 + Na_2SO_4.$$

Cupric chloride, $CuCl_2$, can be obtained by dissolving cupric oxide in hydrochloric acid and concentrating the solution, when green crystals of $CuCl_2.2H_2O$ separate. The anhydrous salt, which is brown, can be obtained by burning copper in chlorine and allowing the product to cool in presence of chlorine. The salt is soluble in excess of concentrated hydrochloric acid, forming a brown solution which, when diluted, becomes first green and then blue. The green colour is restored on concentration. These changes have been ascribed variously to differences in the degree of hydration of the copper ion ; to the formation of complexes, and to the formation of a (supposedly) yellow solution of non-ionized $CuCl_2$ which, mixed with the blue ion, would make the solution appear green.

On heating to redness, dissociation occurs into cuprous chloride and chlorine :

$$2CuCl_2 \rightleftharpoons 2CuCl + Cl_2.$$

This is (or was) made use of in the Deacon process for the manufacture of chlorine.

Cupric Nitrate, Copper Nitrate, $Cu(NO_3)_2$

This salt is most conveniently prepared by dissolving cupric oxide or carbonate in nitric acid and evaporating the solution. Deep blue crystals of the composition $Cu(NO_3)_2.3H_2O$ are deposited. On heating, the crystals lose water and nitric, acid, forming a basic nitrate, $Cu(NO_3)_2.3Cu(OH)_2$; and on further heating give off nitrogen peroxide, oxygen,. and water, leaving copper oxide behind. The anhydrous salt, which is white, is formed when a solution of nitrogen pentoxide in nitric acid is added to the crystalline hydrate.

Cupric Sulphide, CuS

This is usually prepared by passing hydrogen sulphide into a solution of a cupric salt (e.g., copper sulphate). It is then obtained as a black precipitate, which is inclined to pass through a filter paper because it is a hydrosol (colloid) ; it can be coagulated by addition of dilute hydrochloric acid. Cupric sulphide is also obtained as a bluish mass when copper, or cuprous sulphide, is heated with sulphur to a temperature below 114°.

Cupric sulphide is soluble in hot, dilute nitric acid, and in potassium cyanide, forming with the latter a complex—$K_3[Cu(CN)_4]$—from which hydrogen sulphide does not precipitate copper (compare p. 236). Cupric sulphide is insoluble in dilute sulphuric acid (cadmium sulphide is soluble under the same conditions), potassium or sodium sulphides, or ammonium sulphide.

Cupric Sulphate, Copper Sulphate, Blue Vitriol, $CuSO_4.5H_2O$

This is the most important salt of copper and is made commercially on a considerable scale. For this purpose, scrap copper is heated in a reverberatory furnace with sulphur, cuprous sulphide being thus formed. Air is then admitted and the sulphide is oxidized to sulphate. The crude copper sulphate resulting is dissolved in dilute sulphuric acid, insoluble impurities are allowed to settle, and the copper sulphate crystallized out.

It is also made by spraying dilute sulphuric acid on to scrap copper in a lead-lined tower up which air is being blown. The solution so formed is circulated until a sufficient concentration of copper sulphate is reached.

$$2Cu + 2H_2SO_4 + O_2 = 2CuSO_4 + 2H_2O.$$

Copper sulphate is also made by roasting copper sulphide ores so that most of the iron is oxidized. The mass is then digested with "chamber sulphuric acid," in which copper oxide dissolves more readily than iron oxide. The small amount of ferrous sulphate which is present in the product so obtained is not objectionable for many of its applications.

Pure copper sulphate is made in the laboratory by dissolving copper oxide in dilute sulphuric acid and evaporating the solution to crystallizing point ; followed by further recrystallization if necessary.

As so obtained, copper sulphate forms large, transparent, blue crystals of the pentahydrate—$CuSO_4.5H_2O$—which belong to the triclinic system. These are readily soluble in water : 100 grams of water dissolve 38·7 grams of the crystals at 20°.

At 100° the blue crystals lose four molecules of water, and the residual monohydrate is bluish white. At 230° white anhydrous copper sulphate—$CuSO_4$—is formed. It is very hygroscopic, and turns blue by absorption of water ; hence it is used as a test for small amounts of water.

The equilibria among the hydrates of copper sulphate have been considered in Chapter XIV (p. 217).

On further heating, it forms a basic sulphate (see previous page) at 340° and this in turn decomposes into the oxide on very strong heating (650°-750°).

Copper sulphate is used extensively for electroplating, in electric batteries, as a mordant in the dyeing and calico-printing trades, for preserving timber and as an insecticide for fruit trees. For this last purpose it is often applied as a solution mixed with milk of lime (Bordeaux mixture). It is also used for the manufacture of green pigments containing copper carbonates.

Basic copper sulphates are also known. Thus, by digesting copper sulphate with copper oxide for a long time in air, a yellow powder of $CuSO_4.CuO$ is formed. This when thrown into cold water, forms a green insoluble compound, $CuSO_4.3Cu(OH)_2$, and in boiling water, $CuSO_4.2Cu(OH)_2$.

The *green patina* which forms on copper sheeting exposed to the weather (e.g., copper roofing) was for long stated to be a basic carbonate. Recent investigations by Morgan (1929) have shown that it is largely composed of a basic sulphate, $CuSO_4.3Cu(OH)_2$. In locations near the sea the corresponding basic chloride is formed.

Copper Acetates

The *normal acetate*, $Cu(CH_3COO)_2.H_2O$, is used in the manufacture of pigments. It is made by dissolving cupric oxide or verdigris in acetic acid.

Basic copper acetate, verdigris, is made by placing copper plates in the mass of grape' skins and stems left after wine manufacture and which have been allowed to undergo acetous fermentation. When the copper is coated with verdigris, it is exposed to the air for a few days and then immersed again. This is repeated until the whole sheet has been eaten away. The product is *blue verdigris* and is mainly $Cu_2O(CH_3COO)_2$. *Green verdigris*, which is chiefly $CuO.2Cu(CH_3COO)_2$, is made by arranging copper plates and cloths in alternate layers, to which air has access, and which are moistened every few days with acetic acid. It is used in paint manufacture, and sometimes in dyeing and calico printing.

§ 12 Detection and Determination of Copper

Copper salts in solution are easily recognized by their blue colour, which is rendered more intense by the addition of ammonia. In qualitative analysis, , copper is precipitated as sulphide. Copper ferrocyanide (p. 174) is also a characteristic copper salt.

Copper can also be detected by means of certain organic reagents (e.g., *cupron*, α-benzoin oxime, and salicylaldoxime).

When a few drops of a 1 per cent. solution of *cupron* in alcohol are added to a slightly ammoniacal solution of a copper salt a green precipitate of $(C_{14}H_{11}O_2N)Cu$ is formed. This is a sensitive test for copper. Lead, iron, aluminium, cobalt and nickel do not interfere if a soluble tartrate is also present. This condition may be secured by addition of tartaric acid.

When a solution of a copper salt is made slightly alkaline with sodium hydroxide, and then made acid with a considerable excess of acetic acid a yellowish precipitate of the complex $Cu(C_7H_6O_2N)_2$ is formed on addition of 0·5 c.c. of a 1 per cent. solution of salicylaldoxime. This is an extremely sensitive test, and other elements which might interfere do not do so provided that sufficient acetic acid is present.

Copper is very conveniently determined volumetrically by addition of excess of potassium iodide solution to a solution containing a known amount of the material to be analysed. The iodine liberated is then titrated with a standard solution of sodium thiosulphate in the absence of any free acid other than acetic. Usually a slight excess of sodium carbonate is added ; the excess being removed by addition of acetic acid. Each gram-atom of iodine so found indicates the presence of a gram-atom of copper, e.g. :

$$2CuSO_4 + 4KI = 2CuI + 2K_2SO_4 + I_2.$$

(Compare p. 593.)

Copper may be determined gravimetrically by electrolysis on to a previously weighed platinum dish, or by precipitation as sulphide. The former method is slow though accurate ; the latter suffers from the drawback that the ignition of the precipitated sulphide must be carried out in an atmosphere of hydrogen.

The reactions of copper with cupron and salicylaldoxine described above can also be applied to its determination.

§ 13 Silver, Ag. History and Occurrence

History

Silver has been known from ancient times. There are some allusions to silver in the Old Testament, and it was probably used as money as early as gold. The Phoenicians are supposed to have obtained their silver from Armenia and Spain. Silver appears to have been purified by a process of cupellation, but there is little evidence to show that the ancients knew how to separate silver from gold. The old terms for silver refer to its bright white colour—the Hebrew equivalent is derived from the verb " to be white," and the Greek term from ἀργός (argos) to be shining.

Occurrence

Native silver is occasionally found in large masses or crystallized in cubes or octahedra. It is also found associated with metallic copper, gold, etc. The principal ores of silver contain silver glance or *argentite*, Ag_2S, admixed with several other sulphides—antimony, arsenic, and copper. The chief silver ores are found in Mexico, Peru, Chile, Bolivia, Idaho, Arizona, Nevada, Colorado, Norway, Australia, etc. Much silver also occurs associated with lead in galena, and a great deal of the silver in commerce is extracted from argentiferous lead. Silver chloride, AgCl, occurs as *kerargyrite*, or horn silver.

§ 14 Extraction of Silver

Many processes have been employed for the extraction of silver, of which may be mentioned :

    (i) Cyanide process ;
   (ii) Amalgamation process ;
  (iii) Desilverization of lead ;
  (iv) Electrolytic process.

The first of these is now the only important method in use for the treatment of silver ores proper ; while the third and fourth are widely used for the extraction of silver from argentiferous lead and copper respectively. The second method is now only of historical interest.

Cyanide Process (MacArthur-Forrest)

This method depends upon the fact that silver forms soluble complex cyanides with sodium and potassium, so that silver compounds will dissolve in solutions of alkali cyanides. The silver ore, consisting principally of sulphide, is crushed and treated with a solution of sodium cyanide. The following reaction occurs :

$$Ag_2S + 4NaCN \rightleftharpoons 2NaAg(CN)_2 + Na_2S.$$

The accumulation of sodium sulphide in solution tends to stop the reaction, but on exposure of the solution to the air, the sodium sulphide is oxidized to thiosulphate and free sulphur. Thus, free access of air to the solution is an important factor in promoting the dissolution of silver. Frequently a stream of air is blown through the solution. Metallic silver is recovered, after removal of insoluble impurities, by precipitation with zinc or aluminium :

$$2NaAg(CN)_2 + Zn = 2NaCN + Zn(CN)_2 + 2Ag.$$

The precipitated silver is finally purified by fusion with potassium nitrate.

Amalgamation Process

This method was used for over 300 years, but is now obsolete. The ore is mixed with common salt and pyrites which has been roasted, and thus contains a mixture of copper and iron sulphates and oxides, ground to a very fine powder and mixed with water. Mercury is added and the whole thoroughly stirred. It is probable that copper chlorides are first formed which then decompose the silver sulphide :

$$2NaCl + CuSO_4 = CuCl_2 + Na_2SO_4$$
$$CuCl_2 + CuS = 2CuCl + S$$
$$CuCl_2 + Ag_2S = CuS + 2AgCl$$
$$2CuCl + Ag_2S = Cu_2S + 2AgCl.$$

The silver chloride dissolves in the brine and is then reduced by the mercury, liberating silver which dissolves in the excess of mercury :

$$2AgCl + 2Hg = Hg_2Cl_2 + 2Ag.$$

The resulting silver amalgam is separated from the mud by washing and settling, and the excess of mercury squeezed through canvas bags. The solid amalgam remaining is then distilled, when the mercury is recovered, and silver remains behind. The process is wasteful since a considerable amount of mercury is lost as mercurous chloride.

§ 15 Desilverization of Lead

Two processes have been devised for the desilverization of lead, viz., **Pattinson's process** and **Parkes's process.**

The former is now little used. It depended upon the fact that molten argentiferous lead containing less than $2\frac{1}{2}$ per cent. of silver (the eutectic amount) deposits crystals of pure lead, which can be removed by means of a perforated ladle. The enriched lead is finally cupelled for silver (see below).

Parkes's process depends upon the fact that molten lead and zinc do not mix, but form two layers, the zinc being the upper one. Silver is more soluble in the zinc than in the lead, and further, on cooling, the first portion to solidify is the upper layer, which contains most of the silver. Any gold present also passes into the zinc.

The lead is melted in pots of about twenty-five tons capacity and about 1 per cent. of zinc added. The mixture is skimmed frequently as it cools, and the skimmings, consisting of a zinc-silver alloy contaminated with lead, are put into another smaller pot. The contents of this pot are then melted, allowed to cool and skimmed as before. The final skimmings are then distilled with a little charcoal to reduce any oxide present, the zinc being thus recovered, and an alloy of lead and silver remains. The silver is then obtained from this by cupellation (see below). By this process, the silver content of the lead can be reduced to 0·0005 per cent.

Cupellation

This operation has been carried on for over 2,000 years. It consists of heating a lead-silver alloy rich in silver, in a stream of air, in a furnace with a shallow flat hearth made of bone ash or cement. The lead is oxidized to litharge PbO, which is then partly blown from the surface, and partly absorbed by the bone ash. The end of the process is indicated by the " flash " when the clear surface of the pure melted silver appears.

§ 16 Electrolytic Process for Silver

This is principally a process for the refining of crude silver, though the recovery of silver from crude copper in the electrolytic refining of the latter metal (p. 584) is an example of the extraction of silver by electrolysis.

In the electrolytic refining of silver the electrolyte consists of silver nitrate solution with 1 per cent. of free nitric acid. A slab of impure silver is used as anode and a plate of pure silver as cathode. Silver is deposited on the anode, copper dissolves,, and gold, if present, is deposited as a slime. The copper present in solution must not be allowed to exceed 4 to 5 per cent.

§ 17 Properties of Silver

Silver is a white lustrous metal which appears yellow if the light be reflected from its surface many times before it reaches the eye. Very thin layers of silver have a bluish tint. Powdered silver is grey and earthy in appearance. Silver is highly malleable and ductile. Sheets 0·00001 inch thick have been made. Silver melts at 960° in an atmosphere of carbon monoxide, and vaporization commences about 850° and proceeds rapidly between 1200° and 1500°. It can be distilled in the oxy-hydrogen blowpipe, or in the electric furnace. The vapour appears of a greenish colour. Molten silver absorbs oxygen, and rejects most of it on cooling. The evolution of oxygen from cooling silver is often violent enough to spurt some of the metal away from the main mass—hence the term *the spitting of silver*. Silver conducts heat and electricity better than copper. Exposure to the air has no action on silver, but if the air be contaminated with hydrogen sulphide, the silver is blackened owing to the formation of a thin film of silver sulphide on the surface. Nitric acid—hot or cold, dilute or concentrated—readily dissolves the metal, forming silver nitrate. Hot concentrated sulphuric acid gives silver sulphate, but the metal is not perceptibly attacked by the dilute acid. Hydrochloric acid acts very slowly, if at all, at ordinary temperatures, but at a red heat, hydrogen chloride forms silver chloride. The vapour density of silver vapour at 2000° shows that at this temperature the molecules are monatomic.

Colloidal Silver

By the action of certain reducing agents on soluble silver salts, strongly coloured solutions of colloidal silver have been obtained. Very pure materials are required, and the solution must be kept accurately neutral otherwise coagulation is liable to occur. Colloidal silver, stabilized by the addition of albumen, has been used in medicine as a disinfectant.

§ 18 Uses of Silver

Metallic silver is widely used in coinage, and for the manufacture of table ware and ornaments. It is too soft for these purposes in a pure condition and is, therefore, alloyed with other metals such as copper. British silver coinage before 1919 contained 92·5 per cent. of silver. Since 1920 the percentage of silver has been reduced to 50, the remaining constituents being from 1919 to 1922, 40 per cent. copper and 10 per cent. nickel ; since 1922, 50 per cent. copper. The composition of coins struck since 1927 has been : Silver, 50 per cent. ; copper, 40 per cent. ; nickel, 5 per cent. ; and zinc 5 per cent.

Various compounds of silver are used extensively, e.g., in photography (p. 605), in medicine, the making of marking ink, and in the laboratory silver and silver nitrate are very important analytical materials. Large quantities of silver are also employed in electroplating, and in the manufacture of mirrors.

§ 19 Atomic Weight of Silver

The atomic weight of silver is of fundamental importance, since it is by way of silver that the atomic weights of most other elements have been determined (cf. pp. 96-100). The best determinations so far are believed to be those of Richards, whose value 107·88 is the one at present accepted. Richards's methods are described on pages 97, 98 (Ch. VI).

§ 20 Oxides of Silver

Silver forms two oxides, viz. :

Silver oxide, Ag_2O,
Silver peroxide, Ag_2O_2,

which are well characterized, while a third, silver sesquioxide, Ag_2O_3, has also been reported, but its existence is still doubtful.

Silver Oxide, Ag_2O

When sodium or potassium hydroxide solution is added to a solution of silver nitrate, a chocolate-brown precipitate is formed. This might be expected to be silver hydroxide, AgOH, but this is believed not to exist and the precipitate is silver oxide (possibly partially hydrated). It is slightly soluble in water (0·021 grams of oxide will dissolve in 1 litre of water at ordinary temperatures) and the solution has an alkaline reaction and a metallic taste. On heating in air to about 300° it decomposes leaving metallic silver. At lower temperatures (below 120° in air), silver is slowly oxidized, so that the reaction,

$$2Ag_2O \rightleftharpoons 4Ag + O_2,$$

is reversible. Application of the phase rule to the system indicates that it will resemble the decomposition of calcium carbonate by heat (cf. p. 215) since two solid phases and one gaseous phase are involved. The partial pressure of oxygen in air is about 152 mm., and the dissociation pressure of silver oxide has this value at about 121°. Hence, above this temperature, in air, the oxide will decompose ; below it, the metal will slowly oxidize.

Silver oxide is soluble in excess of aqueous ammonia, owing to the formation of the complex ion, $Ag(NH_3)_2$. (Compare pp. 236 and 395.) On standing, the solution deposits black shining crystals of " fulminating silver "—an explosive substance, sometimes said to be **silver nitride**, Ag_3N.

Silver oxide is " reduced " by hydrogen peroxide to metallic silver,

$$Ag_2O + H_2O_2 \rightarrow 2Ag + H_2O + O_2$$

and it rapidly oxidizes sulphur, phosphorus, etc., often with incandescence.

Silver Peroxide, Ag_2O_2

The black powder which collects at the anode when silver nitrate is electrolyzed is considered to be **silver pernitrate**, $AgNO_4$, or a mixture of this with silver peroxide. The product soon decomposes, forming a silver peroxide. When dissolved in acids, silver peroxide gives oxygen or ozone ; and when slowly acted upon by water it gives hydrogen peroxide. When potassium persulphate reacts with silver phosphate, **argentic oxide** with the ultimate composition AgO is formed. This does not give hydrogen peroxide with acids. The same oxide seems to be formed when silver is used as anode in the electrolysis of water in an alkaline solution. If the solution be acid, a **silver sesquioxide,** Ag_2O_3, is said to be formed.

§ 21 Salts of Silver

Most of the salts of silver are insoluble, or at least only sparingly soluble, in water, even those of some strong acids, e.g., sulphate, and chloride. The only common soluble salts are the nitrate, chlorate, perchlorate and fluoride. (The anomalous solubility of silver fluoride has already been referred to—p. 488.)

The formation of characteristic silver salts is made use of in qualitative analysis for the identification of acid radicals. Many silver salts are acted upon by light, a property, first recorded by Gesner (1565), which finds application in photography. (See p. 605.)

Silver carbonate, Ag_2CO_3, is obtained as a faintly yellow precipitate on mixing solution of silver nitrate and a soluble carbonate. It is readily decomposed on heating, yielding first the oxide and then the metal.

Silver fluoride, AgF, obtained by evaporating in vacuo a solution of silver oxide in hydrofluoric acid, is chiefly noticeable in being the only halide of silver which is readily soluble in water : 100 grams of water at 15° dissolving 181 grams of silver fluoride.

Silver chloride, AgCl

Silver chloride occurs in nature as the mineral *horn silver*. It is formed when a solution of a soluble chloride is added to a solution of a silver salt. A white flaky or curdy precipitate is thus formed which melts between 451° and 455° to a yellow liquid, and which solidifies on cooling to a tough horny mass. Silver chloride is virtually insoluble in water : its solubility has been estimated at 1·5 milligrams in a litre of water at 20°. It is, however, easily soluble in solutions of ammonia, potassium cyanide, and sodium thiosulphate. This behaviour is analogous to that of the copper salts described on pages 395, 500, and is explained in terms of the ionic theory as due to the formation of complex ions :

$$AgCl \rightleftharpoons Ag^{\cdot} + Cl',$$
$$(a)\ 2KCN \rightleftharpoons 2K^{\cdot} + 2CN',$$
$$Ag^{\cdot} + 2CN' \rightleftharpoons Ag(CN)_2'.$$
$$(b)\ Ag^{\cdot} + 2NH_3^{\cdot} \rightleftharpoons Ag(NH_3)_2^{\cdot\cdot}.$$
$$(c)\ 3Na_2S_2O_3 \rightleftharpoons 6Na^{\cdot} + 3S_2O_3'',$$
$$2Ag^{\cdot} + 3S_2O_3'' \rightleftharpoons Ag_2(S_2O_3)_3''''.$$

It is supposed that the complex ion in each case is in equilibrium with such very small concentrations of silver ion that the solubility product (p. 233) of silver chloride is not exceeded. In support of this theory, definite complex compounds, $Ag(NH_3)_2Cl$, $KAg(CN)_2$ and $Na_4Ag_2(S_2O_3)_3$, have been isolated.

Silver chloride is otherwise rather unreactive. Like many other silver compounds, it is affected by light (see below), and like them also, absorbs ammonia gas forming such ammines as $AgCl.2NH_3$ and $AgCl.3NH_3$. It can be reduced to silver by heating in a current of hydrogen; by fusion with sodium or potassium carbonate, or by contact with zinc in presence of dilute acid. It is converted into silver bromide or iodide when left in contact with solutions of potassium bromide or iodide. This is due to the fact that the solubility products of the bromide and iodide are much smaller than that of the chloride. Thus, the solubility products of these three salts at ordinary temperature are:

Silver chloride, 1.56×10^{-10}; Silver bromide, 4×10^{-13}; silver iodide, 0.94×10^{-16}.

Silver chloride is used in photography for the manufacture of printing-out papers.

Silver bromide, AgBr, is a pale cream solid which resembles the chloride, and is obtained in a similar way. It does not absorb gaseous ammonia, in which it differs from the chloride and iodide. It is very extensively used in photography for making the sensitive emulsion for plates and films.

Silver iodide, AgI, is a pale yellow crystalline solid which absorbs gaseous ammonia, but which is scarcely soluble in aqueous ammonia. It is interesting in that it contracts on heating and expands on cooling. It is soluble in concentrated solutions of potassium iodide. Silver iodide is used, along with the bromide, in the making of photographic plates and films.

Silver Nitrate, $AgNO_3$

Silver nitrate is usually obtained by the action of nitric acid on the metal. On crystallizing the solution, it is obtained in colourless rhombic plates. It melts at 218° and on cooling solidifies to a fibrous crystalline mass called *lunar caustic*. Silver nitrate is readily soluble in water: 100 grams of water dissolve 122 grams of the salt at 0° and 952 grams at 100°. Both the aqueous solution, and the solid oxidize organic matter, being reduced to silver which is deposited in a black, finely-divided metallic form, especially in light. This property explains its use in medicine, for the treatment of warts, etc., and for marking linen. On heating to 450°, silver nitrate decomposes into **silver nitrite,** $AgNO_2$; and this at higher temperatures is further broken down to metallic silver and oxides of nitrogen. Silver nitrate is used in considerable quantities for the preparation of the silver halides required for making photographic plates, films, etc.

Silver sulphide, Ag_2S, occurs native. It is a black substance which can be made by precipitating it from solutions of soluble silver salts by means of hydrogen sulphide. It is insoluble in ammonia, and dilute acids, but is soluble in potassium cyanide solutions, particularly in the presence of air (cf. p. 598). The tarnishing of silver articles, when exposed to the air of towns, etc., is due to the formation of a very thin layer of silver sulphide.

Silver sulphate, Ag_2SO_4, is obtained by heating the finely-divided metal with concentrated sulphuric acid ; or by mixing strong solutions of silver nitrate and a soluble sulphate, when it is precipitated. It is sparingly soluble in water : 100 grams of water dissolve only 0·77 grams of the salt at 17°.

Silver cyanide, AgCN, is formed as a white insoluble powder when potassium cyanide solution is added to a solution of a soluble silver salt. This precipitate is soluble in excess of potassium cyanide (cf. p. 598), and this solution is employed in electroplating. Its use for this purpose, in preference to salts such as silver nitrate, is due to the fact that it has been found that, in order to obtain a coherent deposit, the solution used must have only a low concentration of silver ion. By using the solution of the complex potassium argento cyanide, this condition can be secured without reducing the conductivity of the solution unduly.

§ 22 Detection and Determination of Silver

Silver is readily detected in solution by the formation of insoluble silver chloride on the addition of hydrochloric acid. Lead and mercurous chlorides are the only others insoluble in these conditions. Lead chloride may be removed, if present, by boiling water, in which it is soluble ; and silver chloride can be separated from mercurous chloride since it is soluble in ammonia solution, from which it can be reprecipitated by acidification with nitric acid.

Silver is determined gravimetrically in a similar way. The silver chloride precipitated is filtered off, washed, dried at 110°-140° and weighed.

Volumetrically, the same process may be used, the end point being determined when another drop of chloride solution causes no further turbidity in the supernatant liquid when the silver chloride precipitate has settled. Alternatively, the end point may be detected (provided the solution is not acid and does not become so in the process of titration) by using a few drops of potassium chromate solution as indicator. When excess of silver is present, red silver chromate is formed, otherwise the solution is pale yellow. Recently, certain dyes, such as eosin, and dichlorofluorescein, have been introduced for use as indicators in this reaction. They become adsorbed on the precipitate and so impart their colour to it when no more chloride ions are present in the solution.

Another volumetric process is known as the **Volhard method.**

This depends upon the fact that a solution of silver in nitric acid when mixed with a solution of potassium thiocyanate gives a precipitate of white silver thiocyanate—AgCNS. If a few drops of a solution of a ferric salt (iron alum is usually employed) be added to the silver solution, the appearance of the blood-red colour of ferric thiocyanate (cf. p. 824) indicates that all the silver has reacted and so marks the end-point of the titration. As a refinement of the method the precipitate of silver thiocyanate is filtered off, or alternatively, the solution is boiled to coagulate it and so make the colour change easier to observe.

§ 23 Photography

The action of light on the halides of silver has been referred to above. Thoroughly dried and purified silver chloride can be exposed to sunlight for several hours without darkening, but if a trace of moisture be present, the chloride darkens, assumes a violet tint and finally turns black. It is now thought that this is due to the decomposition of silver chloride into its elements ; but this is a reversible reaction since, if the darkened chloride be exposed to the action of chlorine in the dark, the chloride is regenerated. Silver bromide and iodide behave similarly.

This sensitiveness of the halides of silver to the action of light is applied in photography. A glass plate or film of celluloid is coated with an emulsion of silver bromide (mixed with a little iodide) in gelatine. (The size of the particles of silver halide has been found to determine the speed of the plate.) The plate is placed in the camera and *exposed* by focussing the image of the object to be photographed on to the plate for a moment. The silver halide granules are affected by the light, and minute nuclei of silver are probably formed, the most intense change occurring where the light was brightest. No visible change is apparent until the plate is *developed*, i.e., treated with a reducing agent such as pyrogallol. This continues the change begun by the light, but is without action on the unexposed parts of the plate. The way in which the nuclei of silver believed to be formed by the light make the grains in which they occur developable is not clearly understood, but as a result of the action of the developer, finely-divided silver is deposited on the parts of the plate illuminated by the light reflected from the object. The deposit is thickest where the light was most intense. Hence, the dark parts of the object appear lightest on the plate, and the light parts dark. The image is thus the reverse of the object, and the plate is accordingly called a *negative*. The silver salt which has not been affected by the light nor by the developer is now removed, and the image thus *fixed* on the plate by immersing the plate in a solution of sodium thiosulphate. The plate is then washed and dried. A *print* is made by laying the negative upon sensitized printing paper—that is, paper prepared in a similar way to the original plate (but silver chloride is usually employed for printing-out paper)— so that the light must pass through the negative before striking the paper. The negative absorbs the light in proportion to the thickness of the deposit of silver, so that the print has the same shading as the object. The paper is then treated with a solution of sodium thiosulphate to fix the image. The print may be *toned* by immersing it in a solution of gold chloride so that some of the silver is replaced by gold ; this gives the print a warm reddish tone ; if a platinum salt be used instead of gold, a steel-grey tone is produced. The image on the print will be the reverse of that on the negative, and will therefore correspond with the object. Hence the print may be called the *positive*.

Gaslight and " bromide " papers are exposed and developed in the same way as the plates of films used in making negatives, and use silver bromide as the principal constituent of the emulsion. Self-toning papers contain gold salts incorporated in the emulsion, and so fixing and toning occur simultaneously when the emulsion is wetted.

§ 24 Gold, Au. History and Occurrence

History

" Gold," said T. Bergman, " occurs in the bowels of the earth native, possessing a complete metallic form, although in general the small particles of it are so interspersed in various matrices that they are entirely invisible." Gold must have been one of the earliest of metals to attract the attention of primitive man, since it occurs free as **virgin gold** in nature, and is found in the rocks and gravels of many rivers. Flint daggers with gilt handles have been reported from excavations in Egypt, and gold is mentioned in the earliest writings of civilized man. Representations of quartz-crushing and gold-refining processes are reported to have been found in Egyptian tombs dated 2500 B.C. ; similar remarks apply to a map showing the gold-mining regions 1350-1330 B.C. The gold mines of Nubia were worked extensively by the early Egyptians. Pliny described the amalgamation process for the extraction of gold. Cupellation processes for the purification of gold were described in the second century, and the same process is probably referred to by Jeremiah in the Old Testament, 600 B.C.

Occurrence

Gold is generally found in a metallic condition in quartz veins as **reef gold** ; and in alluvial gravels as **alluvial gold**—the latter represents the *débris* from the weathering of auriferous rocks which has been washed into river beds, etc. Large nuggets are occasionally found—one from California weighed over 190 lbs. ; and one from Victoria, 183 lbs. Native gold is never found pure, but specimens 99 per cent. purity are sometimes found ; and one from Cripple Creek (Colorado) was reported to be 99·9 per cent. purity.

Metallic gold is very widely distributed in nature in quantities too small to be profitably extracted. Sea-water, for instance, is said to contain about $3\frac{1}{2}$ grains per ton. Granite, on the average, has about 0·37 part per million ; sandstones, 0·03 part per million ; limestones, 0·007 part per million. Gold also occurs in small quantities in clays, iron pyrites, and in almost all silver, copper, bismuth, lead, zinc, tellurium, and antimony ores. Gravels which need not be crushed can sometimes be profitably treated for gold—alluvial gold—if but 2 to 3 grains per ton be present, that is, one part of gold per 5 million parts of worthless material. The mean of the returns for the Rand is something less than half an ounce of gold per ton of material treated.

§ 25 Extraction of Gold

Gold is separated from alluvial gravel by mechanical washing ; but that found in (auriferous—gold-bearing) quartz is extracted by a cyanide process similar to that employed for silver (q.v. p. 598).

Washing Processes

The specific gravity of gold is so much greater than that of the associated materials, that, when the mixture of sand and gravel is agitated with water in large pans or " cradles," and the rocky matters floated off, the fine particles of gold remain on the bottoms of the cradles as " gold dust "—**panning** or **pan washing**. This primitive method of washing has been replaced by **placer mining,** in which the sand containing the gold is agitated in sluices, that is, in long flumes or troughs with transverse cleets along the bottom, and through which powerful streams of water flow. The water sweeps away the sand, and the heavier gold collects on the bottom of the sluices In **hydraulic mining,** water under high pressure is directed against the " earth " containing the gold. The " earth " and gold are washed into the sluices as in placer mining.

Cyanide Process

The gold-bearing quartz is mined by blasting, etc., crushed to a very fine powder in stamper mills, and leached with a dilute aqueous solution of sodium cyanide (0·25 to 1 per cent.), whilst freely exposed to atmospheric air. The gold slowly reacts with the cyanide, forming potassium aurocyanide, and so passes into solution :

$$4Au + 8NaCN + 2H_2O + O_2 = 4NaOH + 4NaAu(CN)_2.$$

The gold is recovered from the solution by passing it through wooden vessels containing zinc turnings, when the gold is precipitated.

$$2NaAu(CN)_2 + Zn = Na_2Zn(CN)_4 + 2 Au.$$

The excess of zinc is removed by dilute acid, when the gold is left as a slime which is collected into a compact mass by fusion. This process enables quartz containing only half an ounce of gold per ton to be worked profitably.

Gold Refining

Crude gold often contains silver and copper. It is then usually purified by **parting with sulphuric acid.** If the alloy contains more than 30 per cent. of gold it is not attacked by acid, and silver is added until the proportion is brought below this amount so as to render it susceptible to attack. The alloy is then boiled with concentrated sulphuric acid, when the silver and copper react with the acid, and the gold remains behind as a porous brown mass. This is washed, dried and fused into a compact mass.

Electrolysis is sometimes used. The alloy to be purified is made the anode, the cathode is pure gold, and the electrolyte a solution of gold chloride in hydrochloric acid. On electrolysis, gold is deposited on the cathode, while the silver forms a deposit of silver chloride near the anode.

Parting by chlorine is sometimes employed. The alloy is melted and chlorine is forced through it. Silver is converted to silver chloride which floats on the surface, other metals are volatilized off as chlorides, but the gold is unaffected.

Cupellation (as described under silver) can be used for removing base metals : the silver and gold remain and must be separated by parting with sulphuric acid or chlorine.

§ 26 Properties of Gold

Gold is a bright yellow metal when seen in the mass by reflected light ; very thin sheets appear green or blue by transmitted light. Gold is one of the most malleable and ductile of metals, and its density, 19·3, is higher than that of all metals except rhenium, platinum, iridium and osmium.

Gold melts at 1063·0° ; and the molten metal appears green. It begins to volatilize at temperatures just below its melting point, say, at 970°. Krafft and Bergfeld say that the metal boils at 2530°. Gold occludes oxygen, hydrogen, and carbon monoxide under suitable conditions. Gold is not acted upon by air or oxygen at any temperature, hence the alchemists called gold a *noble metal* in contrast with *base metals*—like copper, lead, tin, etc.—which are oxidized and lose their metallic character when heated in air. Silver and platinum are noble metals for the same reason as gold.

Gold is scarcely affected by nitric, sulphuric, and hydrochloric acids, but it is dissolved by aqua regia—i.e., a mixture of nitric and hydrochloric acid—or by a mixture of hydrochloric acid with an oxidizing agent which liberates chlorine ; by water containing the halogens chlorine, bromine, or iodine in solution ; and by solutions which can generate the halogens.

Gold is attacked by boiling ferric chloride solutions, hot selenic acid, telluric acid with sulphuric or phosphoric acid, alkaline sulphides and thiosulphates, perchlorates, perbromides, and periodides of the metals, iodic and periodic acids with hot sulphuric acids, and by reacting substances which give large quantities of oxygen—manganese dioxide or potassium permanganate or nitric acid with sulphuric acid—and aqueous solutions of potassium cyanide when exposed to the air. Gold is not appreciably attacked by solutions of the alkalis. The freezing point of a solution of gold in mercury corresponds with a monatomic molecule Au.

Colloidal Gold

Colloidal solutions of gold can be made by several methods and are stable for long periods. They can be obtained, for example, by Bredig's method (p. 246) or by reduction of very pure, very dilute solutions of gold chloride, by means of such reagents as Rochelle salt (potassium sodium tartrate), formaldehyde, etc. Gold is thus formed in very minute particles, and the solution which is blue at first gradually becomes red.

The metallic gold can be removed from its colloidal solution by shaking the solution with precipitated aluminium hydroxide, stannic hydroxide, or barium sulphate. The decolorization here resembles the decolorization of coloured solutions by shaking them with recently ignited charcoal. The gold is absorbed by the precipitating agent. Animal charcoal, if shaken with the solution, adsorbs the gold. The addition of electrolytes—acids, neutral salts, and alkalis—changes the red colour to blue, then violet, and then black. This is due to the coagulation of the particles of gold into clots. The gold then settles to the bottom of the fluid. This behaviour is characteristic of colloidal solutions, as discussed in Chapter XVI.

A form of colloidal gold known as **Purple of Cassius** has long been in use for colouring glass and enamels. It is made by mixing a solution of stannous and stannic chlorides with a very dilute solution of gold chloride. The gold is precipitated along with colloidal stannic acid, the result being a solid solution of the gold in the latter. In this way, the gold particles are " protected " (see p. 246) and so the colour is remarkably stable.

§ 27 Uses of Gold

Gold has for long been the standard for the world's currency, and although it is no longer used for ordinary coinage purposes, it is still the final reserve of wealth and is held as such by all the principal Central Banks of the world in large amounts.

British gold coinage contained $91\frac{2}{3}$ per cent. of gold and $8\frac{1}{3}$ per cent. of copper. The Australian sovereign contained the same quantity of gold, but was alloyed with silver. Its colour was therefore a much less rich yellow than the British sovereign. American gold coinage was 90 per cent. gold and 10 per cent. copper.

Apart from its use as a standard of currency, and a reserve of wealth, the principal use of gold is in jewellery. For this purpose, as with coinage, the pure metal is too soft and it is, therefore, alloyed with other metals—usually copper. The fineness of a gold alloy is usually expressed in " carats." Pure gold is " 24-carat gold " ; the sovereign was 22 carat since it contained 22 parts of gold to 2 parts other metal. Similarly, the other standard gold alloys recognized by law in England are 18-, 15-, 12- and 9-carat gold.

Gold salts are used for toning in photography, and the use of " Purple of Cassius " in colouring glass has been mentioned above.

§ 28 Atomic Weight of Gold

The atomic weight of gold is seen to be in the neighbourhood of 200 from a consideration of its specific heat (0·0316), its position in the Periodic System and the molecular weight of compounds of gold in solution.

The combining weight has been found accurately by conversion of auric chloride into silver chloride, and by determination of the weight of gold remaining when potassium bromoaurate—$KAuBr_4$—is decomposed by heat. Electrolytic methods have also been used.

The best determinations lie between 197·05 and 198·25, and the value 197·2 is that adopted by the International Committee.

§ 29 Oxides and Hydroxides of Gold

Two oxides of gold have been described, viz.,

Aurous oxide, Au_2O,
Auric oxide, Au_2O_3.

The corresponding hydroxides are also known. All these compounds readily decompose on heating, leaving metallic gold.

Aurous oxide, Au_2O, is formed by precipitating a cold solution of gold in aqua regia with potassium bicarbonate. The brown, flocculent precipitate is filtered off, washed, dried at 110° and washed with cold nitric acid to remove the more soluble auric oxide. The residue, after further washing and drying, consists of aurous oxide, possibly contaminated with a little metallic gold.

Auric Oxide, Au_2O_3 is obtained by addition of potassium hydroxide solution to a boiling solution of auric chloride. It is a brown amorphous powder.

Aurous hydroxide, AuOH, is said to be formed as a violet powder, when a dilute solution of potassium hydroxide is added to cold aurous chloride or bromide solution.

Auric hydroxide, $Au(OH)_3$, is obtained as an orange-coloured precipitate when cold solutions of potassium hydroxide and auric chloride are mixed. It loses water at 100° forming AuO.OH ; further heating forms auric oxide, and finally metallic gold. Auric hydroxide is soluble in excess of alkali forming **potassium aurate,** $KAuO_2$, which is precipitated on addition of nitric acid. It is a crystalline salt, soluble in water. Several other aurates are known, and auric hydroxide, though amphoteric, more readily behaves as an acid, and hence is sometimes called **auric acid.**

§ 30 Other Compounds of Gold

Both oxides mentioned above give rise to salts, all of which are unstable and readily decomposed, leaving the metal behind.

Aurous chloride, AuCl, is made by heating auric chloride, freed from traces of hydrochloric acid, to a temperature between 170° and 180°. Any unchanged auric chloride is removed by washing with thoroughly dried ether. In contact with water, it decomposes forming auric chloride and gold : with hydrochloric acid aurous oxide reacts similarly :

$$3AuCl = AuCl_3 + 2Au.$$

When heated above 180°, it reverts to the metal, and when treated with dry chlorine passes into auric chloride.

Auric chloride, $AuCl_3$. If gold be dissolved in a mixture of concentrated hydrochloric and nitric acids (aqua regia) yellow needle-like crystals of **hydro-chloro-auric acid** separate on concentrating the solution. When heated in a current of chlorine at 200°, auric chloride (mixed with a little gold and aurous chloride) is formed in dark red crystals. Auric chloride is readily decomposed on heating, forming first aurous chloride and then metallic gold. The *gold chloride* of commerce is hydrochlorauric acid, which is much more stable, and is used in photography. A series of complex salts called the chloroaurates is known, e.g., $NaAuCl_4.2H_2O$, etc.

§ 31 Detection and Determination of Gold

A very sensitive test for the detection of gold in solution is by the addition of a dilute solution of stannous and stannic chlorides, when the formation (rapidly on warming) of " Purple of Cassius " is evidence of the presence of gold.

It is usually determined by *assaying* which consists in heating a known weight of the gold containing substance (e.g., an ore) with lead oxide, charcoal and soda in a crucible. There is thus formed a bead of metallic lead containing any gold and silver present. This bead is removed and heated on a small cupel (p. 599) until the lead has been oxidized. The silver-gold bead remaining is heated with nitric acid to remove the silver, after which the residue of gold is heated to redness, cooled and weighed.

§ 32 Relationships of the Elements of Group I

The older forms of the Periodic Table, such as that on page 118 placed all the elements considered in this Chapter and Chapter XXV in one group in such a way as to emphasize (or even over-emphasize) the relationship between the two sub-groups. The later form of the table given on page 120, while preserving the connection between the sub-groups, indicates clearly that copper, silver and gold are **transition** elements, and hence that resemblances to neighbouring elements in the same period (i.e., what are sometimes called horizontal relationships) are to be expected.

The alkali metals themselves (viz., lithium, sodium, potassium, rubidium and caesium) form a very satisfactory " family " of elements, showing an appropriate gradation of properties in passing from one to another. The gradation in physical properties is illustrated by Table XXXIX.

TABLE XXXIX.—PHYSICAL PROPERTIES OF THE ALKALI METALS.

	Lithium.	Sodium.	Potassium.	Rubidium.	Caesium.
Atomic weight .	6·94	22·997	39·096	85·48	132·91
Specific gravity .	0·53	0·93	0·859	1·525	1·9
Atomic volume .	11·7	23·5	44·4	55·8	71·0
Melting point .	186°	97·5°	62·3°	38°	26·0°
Boiling point .	1200°	880°	760°	700°	670°
Specific heat at 0°.	0·941	0·2811	0·1728	0·0802	·0·0522
Coefficient expansion	0·000153	0·000274	0·000282	0·000338	0·000345
Heat of fusion (cals.)	32·81	27·21	14·67	6·144	3·766
Increased volume on fusion (per cent.) . .	1·51	2·03	2·44	—	—
Heat of conversion R_2O to R_2O_2 (Cals.) . .	7·91	19·03	22·0	24·1	25·0
Lowest temp. of re-action with water	—	—98°	—105°	—108°	—116°

The metals also are all silvery white, soft enough to be cut with a knife, of very low density and characterized by remarkably intense chemical activity, which increases with increasing atomic weight. They are all strongly electro-positive, becoming more so in passing from lithium to caesium, which is the most electro-positive of all the elements known (though element No. 87—eka caesium—if discovered, should be even more so).

The salts of the alkali metals are nearly all soluble in water, and are the most stable of all metallic salts. Their physical properties show the same order of variation as the atomic weights of the elements. Lithium differs in some respects from the others, an example of the fact that the first member of a family (i.e., the elements of the first short period) often exhibit such differences (compare beryllium, boron, fluorine). Thus, lithium carbonate, phosphate, and fluoride are very much less soluble than the corresponding salts of the other members. And in this respect, lithium resembles the members of the calcium family, and it thus forms a connecting or bridge element between the alkalis and alkaline earths. The alkali sulphates form isomorphous characteristic alums (q.v.), but lithium alum appears to be so soluble that it has not yet been crystallized. Lithium carbonate is sparingly soluble in water, sodium carbonate is not deliquescent, the others are. The salts of sodium and lithium form stable hydrates with water, whereas potassium, rubidium, and caesium salts are nearly all anhydrous. But sodium resembles lithium in the solubility of its chloroplatinate, acid tartrate, and alum so much so that the alkali metals are sometimes divided into two classes : (1) those with sparingly soluble chloroplatinates—viz., potassium, rubidium, and caesium ; and (2) those with soluble chloroplatinates—viz., sodium and lithium.

In the case of the elements of the B sub-group, viz., copper, silver and gold, the relationship is less close than among the alkali metals proper, and, furthermore, marked resemblances are found to the neighbouring transition elements. The relationship between the alkali metals on the one hand, and copper, silver and gold on the other, is very slight.

The principal physical properties of copper, silver and gold are given in Table XL.

TABLE XL.—PHYSICAL PROPERTIES OF COPPER, SILVER, AND GOLD.

—	Copper.	Silver.	Gold.
Atomic weight . . .	63·57	107·88	197·2
Specific gravity . . .	8·93	10·49	19·265
Atomic volume . . .	7·07	10·29	10·11
Melting point . . .	1083·0°	960·0°	1063·0°
Boiling point . . .	2310°	1955°	2530°
Latent heat of fusion (cals.)	43	24·35	16·08
Specific heat . . .	0·09	0·055	0·030

In malleability, ductility, and tenacity, silver is intermediate between copper and gold. While the large atomic volume of the alkali metals was associated with the great chemical activity and affinity for oxygen, the low atomic volume of these elements is related with their weak affinity for oxygen, etc. Copper, for instance, is alone oxidized in air. The oxides of copper, silver, and gold are easily reduced, while the oxides of the alkali metals are reduced with great difficulty. The reduction of copper, silver, and gold by magnesium is the more energetic the greater the atomic weight of the metal—cuprous oxide reduces easily ; silver oxide reduces with explosive violence, and gold oxide breaks down into its constituents below the ignition point of magnesium. Silver appears to be uni-, bi-, and ter-valent, but copper is both uni- and bi-valent, and gold is uni- and ter-valent. Hence these three elements have univalency in common with the alkali metals. Cupric salts are isomorphous with iron, cobalt, and nickel salts. The isomorphism of the silver and sodium sulphates and selenates indicates a relationship of some kind between silver and sodium. The alkali halides, like silver chloride and bromide, crystallize in the cubic system—silver iodide crystallizes in the hexagonal system and the crystals pass into the cubic system at about 146°—on cooling the reverse change takes place—sometimes with explosive violence. Silver seems to be related with copper through argentic oxide, AgO, where silver appears to be bi-valent ; silver pyridine persulphate, $Ag_2S_2O_8.4Py$, is isomorphous with the analogous copper pyridine persulphate, $CuS_2O_8.4Py$; with gold, through silver sesquioxide, Ag_2O_3 ; with the alkalis through argentous oxide, Ag_2O ; and with the magnesium family through mercury. The more salient differences between copper and the alkali metals are : (1) The elements of the alkali metals have a small density, the other metals have a large density ; (2) the alkali metals do not occur free ; (3) the elements of the alkali metals are chemically active, the others not so ; (4) the haloids of the alkalis are all soluble in water, and are not hydrolyzed by water ; copper and silver form sparingly soluble haloids, and the haloids of copper and gold, not silver, are hydrolyzed by water ; (5) the oxides and hydroxides of the alkalis are strongly basic ; the oxides and hydroxides of copper and gold are feebly basic, and they accordingly form basic salts ; (6) the alkali metals do not form complex salts, whereas copper, silver, and gold form many complex salts.

The remarkable difference between the cuprous and cupric salts—whereby the former make copper resemble silver, and the latter relate it to zinc, ferrous iron, and nickel—emphasizes very forcibly the fact that the properties of an element which forms compounds of a particular valency bear no necessary relation with the properties of the same element which forms compounds with a different valency.

Many resemblances are discernible also between silver and mercury. The halides are remarkably similar. The two chlorides are white, the bromides distinctly yellow, and the iodides yellow. The yellow mercurous halides are more intensely coloured than the corresponding silver halides. The same remark applies to the nitrites and hyponitrites. The mode of formation of these salts are similar. Silver and mercurous nitrites (not the nitrates) appear to be the first products of the action of cold nitric acid on the metals. The chemical and physical properties of these salts are also analogous. In some complex mercuroso, or mercuric oxynitrates, silver can isomorphously replace monad mercury. Silver and monad copper can isomorphously replace one another in several salts, e.g., in some complex thiocyanates and thiosulphates. Monad mercury is closely related to monad silver, far more closely than gold to silver.

To a considerable extent these facts are in accord with modern views of the structure of the atom and the nature of valency (cf. Ch. IX). Thus, as in Table XII, the electronic configurations of these elements are :—

Li 2.1.
Na 2.8.1.
K   2.8.8.1.
Rb 2.8.18.8.1.
Cs 2.8.18.18.8.1.

Cu 2.8.18.1.
Ag 2.8.18.18.1.
Au 2.8.18.32.18.1.

The alkali metals thus have a single electron in the outermost orbits, which, when removed, leaves the ion with the very stable inert gas structure. They have, therefore, no tendency to form ions of higher valency, and are very strongly electro-positive. On the other hand, the loss of the outermost electron from the atoms of copper, silver or gold leaves not an inert gas structure, but the less stable group of eighteen electrons. The comparative instability of the eighteen group is indicated by the fact that nickel, palladium, and platinum, which immediately precede copper, silver and gold in their respective periods, are not inert gases but metals (i.e., they readily lose electrons to form metallic ions). The result of this is seen in the variable valency exhibited by copper and gold (and to a much smaller extent by silver) due to the possibility of the removal of one or more of the electrons from the 18-electron orbit.

The metals copper, silver and gold hence differ markedly from the alkali metals in almost every respect except in their univalent compounds, and even here the smaller stability of the 18- as compared with 8-electron shell very considerably modifies the resemblance.

On the other hand, these three metals come close to the end of the series of transition elements in their several periods, i.e., the process of expanding the penultimate shell of electrons from 8 to 18 is just complete. Hence considerable resemblances between them and their "horizontal" neighbours are to be expected, e.g., between nickel, copper and zinc; palladium, silver and cadmium; and between platinum, gold and mercury. Such resemblances are, in fact, very marked, e.g., divalent copper closely resembles nickel and zinc; platinum has many properties similar to gold, and but few to nickel.

Altogether, the classification of copper, silver and gold with the alkali metals in the Periodic System, considered by itself, is far from satisfactory, and even copper, silver and gold are much less closely related to each other than their positions in the Table would seem to imply. But the arrangement is justified to some extent when the elements are considered *as a whole*, and is not likely to be improved upon in any general scheme for the classification of *all* the elements.

CHAPTER XXVII

THE ALKALINE EARTH METALS

§ 1 Group II of the Periodic Table

THE elements of the second group are : beryllium, magnesium, calcium, strontium, barium, and radium in the A sub-group, with zinc, cadmium and mercury in the B sub-group. The relationship between the two sub-groups is much more marked than in Group I, so that opinions differ as to whether magnesium should be particularly associated with calcium, etc., or with zinc, etc. Good reasons can be adduced for either arrangement since magnesium exhibits marked resemblances both to calcium, and to zinc.

The relationships between these elements and the gradations of properties are discussed at the end of Chapter XXVIII.

§ 2 Beryllium

History

While analysing beryl, in 1797, L. N. Vauquelin found that a precipitate which he thought to be aluminium hydroxide, dissolved like aluminium hydroxide in potassium hydroxide ; but unlike aluminium hydroxide, the solution furnished a white precipitate when boiled for some time. Unlike aluminium hydroxide, too, the precipitate was soluble in ammonium carbonate, and behaved in many other ways differently from aluminium hydroxide. Hence L. N. Vauquelin announced the discovery of a new earth—" la terre du Beril," in 1798.

At the time the name glucina—from the Greek γλυκυς (glucus), sweet—was suggested for this " earth " since some of its salts have a sweet taste ; but the term *beryllia* (and hence beryllium for the element itself) is now used almost exclusively. The metal was first isolated by Wöhler in 1828 by the action of potassium on beryllium chloride.

Occurrence and Extraction

The mineral *beryl*, $3BeO.Al_2O_3.6SiO_2$, is the principal source of beryllium. The beryls include the gem-stones : *emerald* and *aquamarine*. Although there are minerals richer in this element, they are scarce and costly. Beryllium is not very abundantly distributed in nature, but small quantities are found in a great many minerals.

Beryllium salts can be obtained from beryl by fusing the mineral with sodium carbonate ; digesting the resulting mass with hydrochloric acid ; evaporating the solution to dryness to separate the silica in an insoluble condition ; extracting the soluble matters with dilute hydrochloric acid ; precipitating a mixture of aluminium and beryllium hydroxides with ammonia ; dissolving the precipitate in potassium hydroxide ; and boiling the solution so as to precipitate the beryllium hydroxide. The precipitate is re-dissolved in acid and re-precipitated from the potash solution a number of times to ensure its freedom from alumina. The hydroxide can then be converted into various salts by dissolving it in the proper acid.

An alternative method now being used consists in fusing beryl at 800° with sodium fluosilicate. The melt is leached with hot water in which the double sodium aluminium fluoride is insoluble, while the corresponding beryllium compound—Na_2BeF_4—dissolves. From this beryllia is precipitated by alkali.

616

The metal is obtained by electrolysis : for example, of a fused mixture of beryllium and potassium chlorides. Its manufacture is now being undertaken by electrolysis of a fused mixture of the double fluorides of beryllium and potassium, using a graphite crucible as anode and a water-cooled iron cathode.

Properties

Beryllium is a hard, silver-white metal of low density (1·8) and high melting point (about 1281°). In chemical properties it is similar in some respects to magnesium ; but it does not react with water, even at a red heat ; while it resembles zinc and aluminium in its reaction with caustic alkali solutions. Its oxide is only feebly basic, its chloride is volatile and fumes in air, like aluminium chloride, and in many respects it closely resembles aluminium. The resemblance of lithium to calcium was mentioned in Chapter XXVI (p. 612) : the similarity between beryllium and aluminium is even more marked.

Uses

Until quite recently beryllium was a chemical curiosity ; but it is now beginning to be made for use in alloys : in particular in the form of beryllium bronzes by alloying with copper. A typical alloy may contain 2·25-2·5 per cent. of beryllium.

These beryllium bronzes are characterized by great hardness and tensile strength ; they can be tempered like spring steel and they are very resistant to fatigue. They are being used for contacts, brush-holder springs, slip-rings for high-speed motors, under-carriage springs for aeroplanes, valve-springs, etc. The alloys of beryllium with aluminium, nickel and cobalt are also being investigated with a view to application in aircraft construction, etc. All these alloys exhibit marked resistance to corrosion. Beryllium itself is now being used for the " windows " of X-ray tubes since it is seventeen times more transparent to X-rays than corresponding amounts of aluminium.

The **atomic weight** of beryllium was for a time uncertain. Its combining weight is in the neighbourhood of 4·5, and for a considerable period, owing to its resemblance to aluminium, it was assumed to be ter-valent and to have an atomic weight approximating to 13·5. Dulong and Petit's rule indicates a value about 15, at ordinary temperatures, but this value rapidly falls at higher temperatures to about 10. The periodic classification, however, has no place for a ter-valent element of atomic weight 13·5, but has a place for a bi-valent one of 9 approximately. Accordingly, it was proposed to put beryllium into this vacant space on the assumption that it is a bi-valent element. This was confirmed by the determination of the vapour density of the chloride which is approximately 40 ($H_2 = 1$). The most recent accurate determinations of the combining weight, made by Hönigschmid by converting pure beryllium chloride into silver chloride, led to the value 9·018 for the atomic weight and 9·02 is the value approved by the International Committee.

Beryllium oxide, BeO, can be obtained by igniting the metal, nitrate, etc., in air, but is usually made from beryl. It is a white, insoluble powder, which forms beryllium salts with acids, and also reacts with caustic alkali solutions forming e.g. K_2BeO_2.

The salts resemble those of magnesium in properties, but they also resemble those of aluminium, e.g., in the volatility and the easy hydrolysis of the chloride. Beryllium also readily forms basic salts.

§ 3 Magnesium, Mg. History and Occurrence

History and Occurrence

In 1695 N. Grew published a pamphlet describing a peculiar salt found in the mineral springs at Epsom. The medicinal properties of this salt attracted some attention ; in England the salt was called " Epsom salt," and on the Continent, " sal anglicum." Magnesia alba (a basic magnesium carbonate) came into commerce from Rome about 1700 ; the term " magnesia alba " was applied to the earth owing to some fanciful contrast with " magnesia nigra," the term then used for black oxide of manganese. In 1755 J. Black clearly distinguished between magnesia and lime by showing that magnesia furnished a soluble sulphate, and lime a sparingly soluble sulphate. When H. Davy isolated the impure metal in 1808, he called it " magnium." At that time, the terms " magnesium " and " manganesium " were applied synonymously to the element (manganese) derived from the mineral pyrolusite (manganese dioxide). To avoid confusion, the term " magnesium " was soon afterwards restricted to the element derived from magnesia alba ; and " manganese " to the element derived from pyrolusite.*

Magnesium occurs in nature combined, not free, as magnesium carbonate in *magnesite*, $MgCO_3$; double carbonate of calcium and magnesium in *dolomite*, $MgCO_3.CaCO_3$; magnesium sulphate in *Epsom salts*, $MgSO_4.7H_2O$; and *kieserite*, $MgSO_4.H_2O$; magnesium chloride in *carnallite* and *kainite* ; magnesium silicate in *olivine*, Mg_2SiO_4 ; *enstatite*, $MgSiO_3$, etc. Magnesium is also common in many other minerals : e.g., asbestos, steatite, spinel, meerschaum, serpentine, talc, etc.

Magnesium compounds also occur in sea-water, which is now being used as a commercial source of magnesium salts in the U.S.A.

§ 4 Preparation of Magnesium

Magnesium is now manufactured on a large scale by the electrolysis of fused carnallite—a double magnesium potassium chloride—or of a

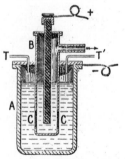

FIG. 209.
Preparation of Magnesium.

mixture of magnesium and sodium chlorides. The operation is carried out in an iron pot A which serves as the cathode (Fig. 209). A carbon rod, surrounded by a porcelain tube BC, to lead off the chlorine which is also formed, is used as anode. The temperature required to fuse carnallite (ca. 700°) is above the melting point of magnesium, which consequently melts and floats on the surface. In order to prevent oxidation or combination with nitrogen, the air in the apparatus is displaced by coal gas' or hydrogen, through T and T'.

Magnesium can also be made by the electrolysis of magnesia in a fused mixture of magnesium, barium and sodium fluorides ; and by the action of metallic sodium on magnesium chloride.

---

* It is not very clear whether the term " magnesia " is a corruption of the word Mangana in the East Indies, or whether " manganese " is a corrupted form of the word Magnesia, a locality in Asia Minor.

§ 5 Properties of Magnesium

Magnesium is a silvery-white metal of low specific gravity (1·74). It melts at 659° and boils at 1110°. It is not affected by dry air at ordinary temperatures; but when heated, burns in air giving a brilliant white light of great actinic power. It reacts readily with most non-metals, e.g., the halogens, sulphur, phosphorus, etc., and nitrogen with which it easily forms a nitride Mg_3N_2. Magnesium reacts very slowly with water at ordinary temperatures, and rather less slowly at 100°; but when heated in a current of steam, it takes fire and continues burning:

$$Mg + 2H_2O = Mg(OH)_2 + H_2.$$

Magnesium reacts readily with dilute acids with liberation of hydrogen, being the only metal which will liberate this gas from dilute nitric acid (the conditions must, however, be very carefully controlled). Solutions of the alkalis do not attack magnesium, which, since it is a strongly electro-positive metal, will displace almost all metals from their salts. (Compare Table XVII, p. 205.) It also reacts with aqueous solutions of ammonium salts forming a double salt with evolution of hydrogen. Thus with ammonium chloride:

$$Mg + 4NH_4Cl = MgCl_2.2NH_4Cl + 2NH_3 + H_2.$$

Magnesium reduces most oxides, and will burn in carbon dioxide, sulphur dioxide, and nitric oxide, for example. It will also reduce sodium and potassium oxides on heating.

§ 6 Uses of Magnesium

Magnesium, in the form of ribbon, is familiar in laboratories; likewise the brilliant white light with which it burns. This property is made use of for flashlight photography, for which purpose it is often mixed in the form of powder with an oxidizing agent such as potassium chlorate. It is also used similarly in fireworks.

On account of its lightness, it is increasingly used as an engineering metal, particularly in the form of " light alloys." With aluminium it forms an alloy known as *magnalium* (95 per cent. aluminium : 1·75 per cent. magnesium). Another alloy which has come to the fore recently is *electron*, an alloy of approximately 95 per cent. magnesium and 5 per cent. zinc. *Duralumin* (p. 666) also contains about 0·5 per cent. of magnesium.

In the laboratory, magnesium is used for the reduction of oxides such as silica, in the preparation of silicon (p. 679), and as a reducing agent generally.

§ 7 Atomic Weight of Magnesium

A value in the neighbourhood of 24 is indicated for the atomic weight of magnesium by the Periodic Table, and the specific heat of metallic magnesium. The best determinations have utilized the conversion of magnesium chloride into silver chloride, or the conversion of the pure oxide into the sulphate. Richards, using the former method, obtained results leading to values very close to 24·32, which is the number at present recommended by the International Committee.

§ 8 Magnesium Oxide and Hydroxide

Magnesium oxide, MgO, can be obtained (mixed with a little nitride) by burning the metal in air, but commercially it is made by heating the carbonate :

$$MgCO_3 = MgO + CO_2,$$

or the hydroxide, made from the waste magnesium chloride of the potash industry (p. 576) by the action of slaked lime :

$$MgCl_2 + Ca(OH)_2 = Mg(OH)_2 + CaCl_2,$$
$$Mg(OH)_2 = MgO + H_2O.$$

Magnesium oxide is a white powder, slightly soluble in water. Thus 100 grams of water dissolve about 0·001 gram of magnesium oxide (or magnesia). The solution has a slightly alkaline reaction. It is curious that the higher the temperature used in calcination, the lower the solubility of the resulting magnesia. This has been ascribed to polymerization, but has not been definitely proved, and it may be that the *rate* of dissolution is lower. In the magnesite brick industry the favourite theory is that the material made at low temperatures is non-crystalline and that made at high-temperatures is crystalline. It is a very refractory material only fusing at about 2500° and so is used as a substitute for lime in the limelight, for making refractory bricks, crucibles, etc. A paste of water and magnesia (calcined at low temperature) " sets " like mortar. It gradually rehydrates and absorbs carbon dioxide from the air and forms a hard mass.

Magnesia is a basic oxide and reacts readily with dilute acids. It is used in medicine for correcting acidity.

Magnesium hydroxide, $Mg(OH)_2$, is precipitated from solutions of magnesium salts by addition of solutions of alkali hydroxides. It is *less* soluble than slaked lime (q.v.), hence it is possible to obtain it as above from magnesium chloride and slaked lime. It is soluble in solutions of ammonium salts and so is incompletely precipitated by ammonia, and if sufficient ammonium salt be present will not be precipitated at all (p. 236).

Magnesium hydroxide is used in the sugar industry for the extraction of sugar from molasses. (Compare similar use of strontium hydroxide, p. 635.)

§ 9 Magnesium Salts

Magnesium hydroxide is a fairly strong base and forms well-defined **salts** with acids. They are colourless (except when formed from a coloured acid) and are not poisonous. Those with strong acids are usually soluble : the carbonate, phosphates and fluoride are sparingly soluble. Many of the salts crystallize with considerable amounts of water, e.g., $MgSO_4.7H_2O$.

Magnesium Carbonate, $MgCO_3$

Magnesium carbonate occurs in enormous quantities associated with calcium carbonate as *dolomite*, $MgCO_3.CaCO_3$; it is also found as *magnesite*, $MgCO_3$. The carbonate can be prepared by adding a solution of sodium bicarbonate saturated with carbon dioxide to a solution of a magnesium salt, when it is slowly deposited as a white powder. If sodium carbonate solution is used instead, various *basic* carbonates result. If the precipitation be carried out in the cold with dilute solutions, the *magnesii carbonas levis* (light magnesium carbonate) of pharmacy results. Hot concentrated solutions similarly yield *magnesii carbonas porderosa* (heavy magnesium carbonate). These have been said to have the compositions $3MgCO_3.Mg(OH)_2.3H_2O$ and $3MgCO_3.Mg(OH)_2.4H_2O$ respectively, but it is very doubtful if either is a pure compound.

The various basic carbonates are extensively used in the salt, rubber and printing ink industries, and also in pharmacy, etc., for the production of tooth pastes, face powders, etc.

All these magnesium carbonates are insoluble in water, and on heating yield magnesium oxide. The normal carbonate is soluble in water saturated with carbon dioxide owing to the formation of **magnesium bicarbonate.**

$$MgCO_3 + H_2O + CO_2 \rightleftharpoons Mg(HCO_3)_2.$$

Like most magnesium salts it is also soluble in solutions of ammonium salts. Magnesium bicarbonate sometimes occurs along with calcium bicarbonate in natural waters, contributing then to their temporary hardness (see p. 275).

Magnesium Chloride, $MgCl_2$

This salt occurs in sea water, and is also found in quantity (e.g., at Stassfurt) as *carnallite*, $KCl.MgCl_2.6H_2O$. It is thus a by-product of the potash industry, and is used as a source of magnesium oxide. Magnesium chloride can be prepared in the laboratory in the usual way, and crystallizes from solutions as $MgCl_2.6H_2O$. This cannot be dehydrated by heat since hydrogen chloride is lost as well as water :

$$2(MgCl_2.6H_2O) = 11H_2O + Mg_2OCl_2 + 2HCl.$$

This oxychloride on heating further, in air, loses chlorine leaving the oxide :

$$2Mg_2OCl_2 + O_2 = 4MgO + 2Cl_2.$$

The anhydrous salt can be obtained by dehydration in a stream of hydrogen chloride. Magnesium chloride is hydrolyzed slightly in water, and hence its presence in boiler feed water is very obnoxious.

The crystallized salt is very deliquescent, and is used in cotton spinning as a lubricant for the thread.

When a concentrated solution of magnesium chloride is made into a thick paste with calcined magnesia, the mixture hardens to a stone-like mass owing to the formation of an oxychloride. This mixture is used under the name of *Sorel's cement* for making artificial stones, floors, etc.

Magnesium bromide, $MgBr_2$, occurs in sea water, and is used as a source of bromine (see p. 518). **Magnesium iodide,** MgI_2, is also found in the sea.

Magnesium sulphate, $MgSO_4$

Magnesium sulphate occurs as *kieserite*, $MgSO_4.H_2O$, in the Stassfurt deposits. When kierserite is digested with water, and the solution purified by recrystallization, colourless rhombic prisms of the hepta-hydrate—$MgSO_4.7H_2O$—separate from the cold solution. When the temperature is about 30°, monoclinic prisms of the hexahydrate—$MgSO_4.6H_2O$—are formed. Several hydrates are revealed when the solubility of magnesium sulphate is studied. At 150° the crystalline salt passes into the monohydrate, *kieserite*, $MgSO_4.H_2O$; and at 200° the anhydrous salt is obtained with partial decomposition. Magnesium sulphate forms a series of double salts—$MgSO_4K_2SO_4.6H_2O$, *schönite*—crystallizing in monoclinic prisms, isomorphous with $MgSO_4.7H_2O$. Like barium sulphate, crystals of the acid salt $MgSO_4.H_2SO_4$ are deposited from a hot solution of magnesium sulphate in sulphuric acid; and from cold solutions, the acid salt $MgSO_4.3H_2SO_4$ is crystallized. Crystalline magnesium sulphate—$MgSO_4.7H_2O$—is also called "Epsom salts," or *epsomite*, because it occurs abundantly in the water of the Epsom springs. This salt is used in medicine; in the tanning and dyeing industries; and in the manufacture of paints and soaps.

Epsom salts are freely soluble in water: 100 grams of water will dissolve 35·5 grams of $MgSO_4$ at 20°.

Magnesium Ammonium Phosphate, $Mg(NH_4)PO_4.6H_2O$

This salt is obtained as a crystalline precipitate when a solution of a soluble phosphate is mixed with ammonia, ammonium chloride and magnesium sulphate or chloride; and conversely, if ammonium phosphate be added to an ammoniacal solution of a magnesium salt the same substance is precipitated. When the precipitated magnesium ammonium phosphate is filtered, washed, dried and heated, it is converted into magnesium pyrophosphate:

$$2[Mg(NH_4)PO_4.6H_2O] = Mg_2P_2O_7 + 2NH_3 + 13H_2O.$$

This reaction is made use of in the determination both of magnesium and of phosphates.

Magnesium Nitride, Mg_3N_2

When magnesium is heated in nitrogen, or in ammonia gas, magnesium nitride is formed. Hence a small quantity is formed, along with the oxide, when magnesium burns in air. This property of magnesium was made use of by Ramsay for the isolation of the Inert Gases (p. 540). Magnesium nitride is a yellowish powder, which is decomposed by water into the hydroxide and ammonia :

$$Mg_3N_2 + 6H_2O = 3Mg(OH)_2 + 2NH_3.$$

§ 10 Detection and Determination of Magnesium

Magnesium is usually detected by the facts that :

(i) in presence of ammonium salts it is not precipitated as sulphide, hydroxide or carbonate ; thus distinguishing it from all except the alkali metals ; (ii) when mixed with ammonia, ammonium chloride and ammonium phosphate the double magnesium ammonium phosphate—$Mg(NH_4)PO_4.6H_2O$—is precipitated.

This same salt is made use of for its determination also since it can be precipitated quantitatively and, on ignition, is quantitatively converted into magnesium pyrophosphate (*vide supra*).

The use of the organic reagent oxine (8-hydroxy quinoline) for the determination of magnesium is growing in favour. In suitable conditions, magnesium is precipitated as $Mg(C_9H_6ON)_2.2H_2O$.

§ 11 Calcium, Ca. History and Occurrence

History

Calcium carbonate has been known since very early times in the form of minerals such as chalk, limestone and marble. Lime-burning was certainly carried on by the Romans, and it is probable that it was an old operation in their day. Chalk, quicklime and slaked lime were first clearly distinguished by J. Black in 1756. Metallic calcium was first prepared by Sir H. Davy in 1808.

Occurrence

Calcium does not occur free, but enormous quantities of its compounds are found. Whole mountain ranges consist of the carbonate, $CaCO_3$, in the forms of *chalk, calcite, limestone* and *marble*. *Dolomite*, $CaCO_3.MgCO_3$, also occurs in this way, while *anhydrite*, $CaSO_4$, and *gypsum*, $CaSO_4.2H_2O$, are common minerals, and the phosphate and silicate are also found.

Natural waters usually contain calcium salts in solution (compare pp. 275-279) and calcium compounds are also an essential constituent of plant and animal tissues, etc. Thus, bones consist largely of calcium phosphate.

§ 12 Preparation of Metallic Calcium

Impure calcium was made by H. Davy in 1808 and the pure metal by H. Moissan in 1898 by reducing calcium iodide with sodium.

The metal is now made by electrolysis of a mixture of fused chloride and fluoride. In G. O. Seward and F. von Kügelgen's process (1908), the cell (Fig. 210) consists of a circular iron box, A, through the bottom of which projects a conical iron cathode, B, insulated from the box at

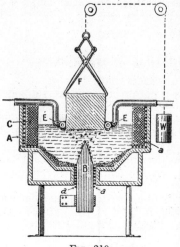

aa. The carbon C, insulated from the box, serves as anode. A water cooled collecting ring E, separates the metal which rises to the surface of the molten chloride. The metal accumulates until the ring is full. The top layer is cooled solid by the air, while the bottom is soft or melted. The solid part is fastened to a hook F, which is gradually raised. The heat due to the current keeps the salt molten. The metal is protected from oxidation by the layer of fused salt.

Crystals of almost pure calcium can be obtained by dissolving calcium in molten sodium, allowing the mixture to cool (when the calcium crystallizes out) and removing the sodium with alcohol.

FIG. 210.
Preparation of Calcium.

§ 13 Properties of Calcium

Calcium is a silver white, lustrous metal. It is softer than most metals, and is very light, its specific gravity being 1·55. It melts at 810°.

Calcium is a very reactive metal. It tarnishes slowly in air, and when heated in an atmosphere of hydrogen, it forms calcium hydride, CaH_2. Similarly in an atmosphere of nitrogen it forms calcium nitride, Ca_3N_2; in air, calcium oxide, CaO; and with chlorine, calcium chloride, $CaCl_2$. With water the action is rapid but not violent, and a crust of calcium hydroxide forms on the surface of the metal and slows down the reaction :

$$Ca + 2H_2O = Ca(OH)_2 + H_2.$$

With acids the action is rather violent : calcium does not react with alkalis.

Uses

No very extensive use has so far been found for metallic calcium, except in the laboratory, where it is sometimes employed as a reducing agent, or as a dehydrating agent. It is used in the preparation of calcium hydride, which has been employed under the name of *hydrolith* as a means of transporting hydrogen (see below). It is also employed in the production of high vacua, and in the preparation of argon (p. 541).

§ 14 Atomic Weight of Calcium

The Periodic Table and the application of Dulong and Petit's rule indicate a value about 40 for the atomic weight of calcium. The exact value has been determined by conversion of pure iceland spar into the oxide, and by conversion of the pure chloride into silver chloride. Hönigschmid, using the latter method (1931), obtained a value for the atomic weight, very close to 40·085. The value at present (1940) recommended by the International Committee is 40·08.

§ 15 Calcium Hydride, Nitride and Carbide

Calcium hydride, CaH_2, is made by passing hydrogen over heated calcium. It is a colourless, crystalline compound which has been used under the name of *hydrolith* for making hydrogen (see p. 256), since with water it readily yields this gas :

$$CaH_2 + 2H_2O = Ca(OH)_2 + 2H_2.$$

Calcium nitride, Ca_3N_2, is prepared by heating calcium in a stream of nitrogen at about 450°. It is a yellowish, crystalline solid, which reacts with water forming ammonia :

$$Ca_3N_2 + 3H_2O = 3Ca(OH)_2 + 2NH_3$$

Calcium carbide, CaC_2, is made in quantity by heating a powdered mixture of quicklime and coke in an electric furnace. The action (which is endothermic) is represented :

$$CaO + 3C = CaC_2 + CO.$$

The carbide formed is molten at the temperature of the furnace and so can be tapped off.

Calcium carbide is a hard, brittle, crystalline solid of specific gravity 2·22. When pure it is white, but commercial calcium carbide is dark grey or bronze coloured owing to the presence of impurities. It reacts with water forming acetylene (p. 339). When heated in an atmosphere of nitrogen to 1000°-1100° it forms **calcium cyanamide**, $CaCN_2$, and so furnishes a means for the fixation of atmospheric nitrogen (see pp. 391, 403).

$$CaC_2 + N_2 = CaCN_2 + C.$$

The mixture of carbon and calcium cyanamide formed is sold under the name of **nitrolim**.

§ 16 Calcium Oxides and Hydroxide

Calcium forms three oxides, viz.,

Calcium oxide, or quicklime, CaO ;
Calcium peroxide, CaO_2 ;
Calcium tetroxide, CaO_4 ;

but only the first named is important.

Calcium Oxide, Quicklime, CaO

Quicklime is made on a large scale by heating calcium carbonate. The reaction which takes place is reversible,

$$CaCO_3 \rightleftharpoons CaO + CO_2,$$

and so does not proceed to completion unless the carbon dioxide formed is allowed to escape. This reaction has been discussed (pp. 215 and 216) from the standpoint of the Law of Mass Action and the Phase Rule. As stated there, there is for each temperature a value for the pressure of carbon dioxide (known as the dissociation pressure) which is in equilibrium with quicklime and calcium carbonate. Some of these values are :—

Temperature	500°	600°	700°	800°	898°	900°	950°
Pressure (mm. of mercury)	0·11	2·35	25·3	168	760	773	1490

It is evident that any temperature above 500° will serve for the

decomposition, provided that the carbon dioxide is removed from the system ; and that at temperatures of 900° or over decomposition will be complete unless the system is confined at a pressure greater than atmospheric. In practice, a temperature of 800°-1000° is used, and the operation is carried out in a lime-kiln (Fig. 211).

Two types of kiln are used : the older type (Fig. 211A) is intermittent in operation, and is

FIG. 211.—Lime Kilns.

rather wasteful in fuel though very cheap to instal. The more modern shaft-kiln (Fig. 211B) is arranged for continuous operation. The limestone gradually works its way down the kiln, which is heated by producer gas, and is converted to lime which is removed at the bottom.

Properties of Calcium Oxide

Calcium oxide, when pure, is a white amorphous powder, but as usually obtained it is in the form of hard white lumps. If heated intensely, e.g., with an oxyhydrogen blowpipe, it becomes incandescent and emits a brilliant white light. This property was formerly made use of in the " lime-light." Its melting point is about 2570°, at which temperature it volatilizes appreciably.

Calcium oxide is a reactive substance, and most non-metals react with it at temperatures of 300° or over. It reacts with water at ordinary temperatures. Thus, if a few drops of water be allowed to fall on a cold lump of freshly " burnt " lime, a hissing noise is produced and clouds of steam are formed :

$$CaO + H_2O = Ca(OH)_2.$$

The lump of lime disintegrates to a fine powder of *slaked lime* or *calcium hydroxide* and the process is known as the slaking of lime. Calcium oxide does not react with gases such as carbon dioxide or sulphur dioxide, in the cold, but combines with them when heated, e.g.,

$$CaO + SO_2 = CaSO_3.$$

Quicklime is used in the preparation of slaked lime for building purposes (see below). It is also a constituent of cement. It is used in the laboratory for drying gases such as ammonia, which react with calcium chloride or sulphuric acid.

Calcium peroxide, $CaO_2.8H_2O$, is formed when hydrogen peroxide is added to lime-water. Its properties are similar to those of barium peroxide (q.v.).

Calcium tetroxide, CaO_4, is obtained as a yellow powder by heating the hydrated peroxide with 30 per cent. hydrogen peroxide solution.

Calcium Hydroxide, Slaked Lime, $Ca(OH)_2$

Slaked lime is obtained, as indicated above, by the action of water on quicklime. It is a white, amorphous powder, which is only sparingly soluble in water : 100 grams of water at 15° C. dissolve 0·17 grams of calcium hydroxide. It is interesting in that its solubility *diminishes* with rise of temperature, whereas the solubility of most solids increases. The solution is known as *lime-water* and has an alkaline reaction. A suspension of a considerable quantity of slaked lime in water is known as *milk of lime*. When exposed to the air lime-water soon becomes " milky " owing to the formation of insoluble calcium carbonate :

$$Ca(OH)_2 + CO_2 = CaCO_3 + H_2O.$$

When heated to 100° calcium hydroxide is not decomposed, but at 400° 30 per cent. of the possible water is expelled, and at 450° nearly all the water can be driven off.

Calcium hydroxide reacts readily with acids and acid gases forming salts. It also absorbs chlorine similarly (see p. 510). It has been shown by J. Kalb (1867) that perfectly dry slaked lime will not absorb carbon dioxide, but that combination takes place readily in presence of a trace of moisture. This furnishes another example of the catalytic action of water (p. 284).

Slaked lime is used in the laboratory for the preparation of lime water (for the detection of carbon dioxide), and as an absorbent for gases such as carbon dioxide, chlorine and acid gases generally.

Industrially it is employed in the manufacture of bleaching powder (p. 510) of caustic soda (p. 544), in the ammonia-soda process (for ammonia recovery), the purification of coal-gas (p. 347) and of sugar, in glass-making and for making mortar and plaster.

Mortar is a thick paste made by mixing slaked lime with sand and water. It sets, on exposure to the air, by loss of water, after which it gradually hardens, by absorbing carbon dioxide with formation of calcium carbonate. This, is, however, a slow process : the mortar of some Roman buildings (2,000 years old) has been found to contain inner cores of slaked lime protected by the outer layers of calcium carbonate.

Portland Cement is made by heating chalk or limestone with clay and sand in a long, slanting cylindrical furnace, slowly rotating, through which a blast of burning coal-dust is blown. The mixture sinters and the resulting " clinker " is ground to a fine powder. When mixed with water and sand, it forms a paste which sets in the course of a few hours, even when under water, to a solid mass which slowly grows harder over a long period. The setting is probably due to the hydrolysis of the calcium aluminates and silicates formed during the burning. The exact nature of the process is not clearly understood, but it is thought possible that the products of hydrolysis form inter-locking crystals, thus giving the material its strength.

Concrete is made by mixing cement with sand and gravel, or broken bricks, etc., and allowing the whole to set. If it is made round a skeleton of steel rods it is known as *reinforced concrete*.

§ 17 Salts of Calcium

Calcium salts are white and give colourless solutions unless derived from a coloured acid. The majority of calcium salts are very sparingly soluble in water, the principal exceptions being the halides (other than the fluoride) and nitrate. They are not poisonous unless derived from poisonous acids. When heated in the flame of a bunsen burner, they impart to it a brick-red colouration.

Calcium Carbonate, $CaCO_3$

Several different minerals occur in nature which have been called different names, although analysis shows that they are all more or less impure forms of one chemical substance—calcium carbonate. These different forms of calcium carbonate may be classed under three heads, although in reality there are but two crystalline forms or mineral species.

1. Calcium Carbonate in Rhombic Crystals

This variety generally occurs in needle-like crystals, and is named *aragonite* after Aragon in Spain. If calcium carbonate be prepared in solutions at temperatures exceeding 30°, crystals corresponding with aragonite are formed, and if at temperatures below 30°, crystals of calcite are formed. Hence, aragonite at temperatures below 30° is in a metastable condition. The fundamental form of crystals of aragonite is illustrated by the outline drawings, Fig. 212, and although there are a great many derived shapes, all are built on the same geometrical plan determined by the inclination of the boundary faces with respect to the axes of the crystal.

2. Calcium Carbonate in Trigonal Crystals

This form of calcium carbonate occurs in more or less well-defined crystals modelled after a rhombohedron, Fig. 213, but exhibiting a great variety of derived shapes which have received special names— " dog's-tooth spar," " nail-headed spar," etc. R. J. Haüy called calcite the *proteus* among minerals because of its presenting what appeared to be a chaotic number of unrelated appearances, yet he also showed that, however diverse the forms of the crystals, they are all related to a primitive geometrical plan which is determined by the inclination of the boundary faces with the crystal axes. All the different forms are subordinate to the primitive type. When transparent and colourless, trigonal calcium carbonate is called *Iceland spar* ; and if opaque and clouded, *calcite* or calcspar. A compact fibrous variety with a satin-like lustre is called " satin spar." *Marble* is made up of minute crystals of calcite. *Onyx* is a variety which is streaked and co oured by associated impurities.

FIG. 212.—Crystals of Aragonite from Cumberland

3. Calcium Carbonate not markedly Crystalline

Chalk and limestone usually occur in large masses sometimes extending over large tracts of country.. This form of calcium carbonate is relatively impure, for it contains more or less magnesium carbonate,

FIG 213.

Crystals of Calcite from Fontainebleau.

clay, and silica. Marl is a mixture of limestone and clay. Egg-shells, sea-shells, pearls, corals, contain a large percentage of calcium carbonate. The microscope shows that *chalk* consists largely of the shells of minute organisms. It is inferred that these organisms once lived in the sea because similar shells are dredged from the bottoms of the oceans to-day.

H. C. Sorby proved that in calcareous organisms a new variety of calcium carbonate is not in question. In every case examined, the shells contained either ealcite or aragonite. Some animal species secrete calcium carbonate as calcite, others as aragonite, and others as both. The pearl, for instance, is mainly aragonite ; the shell of the common whelk is mainly calcite ; and the inner shell of the cuttle-fish is aragonite, the outer portion is calcite.

Calcium carbonate is almost insoluble in water alone, but is soluble in the presence of carbon dioxide owing to the formation of the bicarbonate. When heated it decomposes into calcium oxide and carbon dioxide ; a reaction discussed more fully on pages 215, 626. It is readily attacked by acids with liberation of carbon dioxide : if the acid used form an insoluble calcium salt, the reaction may stop owing to the formation of a protective " skin " unless the carbonate is very finely divided.

Calcium carbonate is used in the manufacture of whiting (which is chalk ground to powder and freed from sandy impurities by levigation in water), in the manufacture of quicklime (and hence of slaked lime and of cement) ; as a flux in the smelting of iron, in the manufacture of sodium carbonate, etc. In the precipitated form it is employed medicinally and in the preparation of tooth pastes.

Chalk and marble are also used in the laboratory as sources of carbon dioxide.

Calcium bicarbonate, $Ca(HCO_3)_2$, is formed in solution by the action of carbon dioxide and water on the normal carbonate. It cannot be isolated, and even in solution decomposes on heating. Its presence in natural waters gives rise to the phenomena of temporary hardness (cf. p. 275).

Calcium Fluoride, CaF₂

Calcium fluoride occurs naturally as *fluorspar* in many places, sometimes (e.g., in Derbyshire) veins of fine crystals are found embedded in limestone. The crystals may be colourless, or tinted by traces of contaminating metallic oxides. " Blue-john " is a familiar example of a tinted variety.

When heated to about 1360°, fluorspar melts to an opaque greyish-white enamel, and its name is derived from this property (Lat. fluere, to flow). It is used as a flux in metallurgy, and in the manufacture of glass, enamels and glazes. It is also the principal source of fluorine compounds (Ch. XXIII). Some of the coloured varieties are used for jewellery, ornamental vases, etc.

Calcium Chloride, CaCl₂

This salt is obtained as a by-product in several manufacturing operations, e.g., the ammonia-soda process, the production of potassium chlorate, etc., but so far it has not been found possible to discover uses for it in any quantity. The anhydrous salt is used in the laboratory as a drying agent for many gases and liquids. (It cannot be used to dry ammonia as this gas combines with it, forming compounds such as $CaCl_2.8NH_3$.)

The anhydrous salt is a white porous mass, extremely deliquescent, and very soluble in water : 100 grams of water will dissolve 63 grams of the anhydrous salt at 10°. Calcium chloride forms several stable hydrates; the hexahydrate being the stable one at ordinary temperatures.

Calcium Sulphide, CaS

This substance has been produced in very large quantities in the form of the " alkali-waste " of the Leblanc process (q.v.). It can also be made by heating slaked lime in an atmosphere of hydrogen sulphide ; or by reducing the sulphate with carbon. When pure it is a white powder, which is stable in air in absence of moisture. It exhibits a very marked phosphorescence (although only if a minute trace of a metallic impurity, e.g., bismuth, be present. The function of the metal in promoting the phosphorescence is not understood).

Calcium sulphide is hydrolyzed by water, forming a mixture of hydroxide and hydrosulphide :

$$2CaS + 2H_2O \rightleftharpoons Ca(OH)_2 + Ca(SH)_2.$$

Calcium hydrosulphide, $Ca(SH)_2$, is made by passing hydrogen sulphide into milk of lime. It is used in tanning for removing the hair from hides.

Calcium Polysulphides, CaS_n

When milk of lime is boiled with sulphur, the sulphur dissolves and calcium polysulphides are formed. It is supposed that the **tetrasulphide** and thiosulphate are first formed :

$$3Ca(OH)_2 + 10S = 2CaS_4 + CaS_2O_3 + 3H_2O,$$

and that the latter decomposes into sulphite and sulphur, while the former forms the **pentasulphide** with excess of sulphur.

Calcium Sulphate, $CaSO_4$

This occurs native, as *anhydrite*, $CaSO_4$; and as *gypsum*, $CaSO_4.2H_2O$. If the gypsum occurs in clean, fine-grained masses it is called *alabaster* ; if in colourless translucent crystals, it is known as *selenite*.

The dihydrate may also be prepared by mixing solutions of sulphates with solutions of calcium salts, or by treating calcium carbonate or hydroxide with dilute sulphuric acid.

Calcium sulphate is sparingly soluble in water : 100 grams of water dissolve 0·18 grams of anhydrous salt at 0°. The presence of calcium sulphate in natural waters causes permanent hardness (p. 275).

Plaster of Paris

When gypsum is heated to about 120° it loses the equivalent of $1\frac{1}{2}$ molecules of water and forms the so-called hemi-hydrate, $(CaSO_4)_2H_2O$. This substance is known as *plaster of Paris* because of the large deposits of gypsum used for the manufacture of plaster at Montmartre (Paris).

When plaster of Paris is wetted with, say, one-third of its weight of water, it forms a plastic mass which " sets " in from 5 to 15 minutes to a white, porous hard mass. A slight expansion occurs during the setting so that it will take a sharp impression of a mould. The setting is due to the formation of an interlacing mass of fine needles of the dihydrate which take up more room. Admixture of alum, borax, etc., with the plaster reduces the rate of setting, while common salt, etc., accelerate it. Alum makes a plaster which when set is much harder ; the mixture of plaster of Paris with alum is known as *Keene's cement*.

If plaster of Paris, or gypsum, be heated above 200° it passes into anhydrous calcium sulphate which does not set when mixed with water, since it takes up water only very slowly. This is known as *dead-burnt* plaster.

Calcium bisulphite, $Ca(HSO_3)_2$, obtained in solution by saturating milk of lime with sulphur dioxide, is extensively employed for the bleaching of wood pulp for paper-making, and as an antiseptic in brewing.

Calcium silicate, $CaSiO_3$, occurs naturally as *wollastonite*. It is an important constituent of glass (p. 690), cement (p. 628), and furnace slag (p. 804).

Calcium Phosphates

The phosphates of calcium are amongst the most important of the salts of phosphoric acid. Pure crystalline **tricalcium phosphate,** $Ca_3(PO_4)_2$, has not been obtained. The nearest approach to it is made by adding sodium phosphate to a solution of calcium chloride in presence of ammonia. Several more or less impure forms of calcium phosphate occur in nature, e.g., *apatite* ; and calcined bones contain 60 to 80 per cent. of the normal phosphate.

Normal calcium phosphate is very sparingly soluble in water : 100 grams of water dissolve 0·003 grams. The presence of alkalis decreases the solubility, while neutral salts and acids increase it. Thus calcium phosphate passes into solution* when treated with dilute acids, but is reprecipitated on addition of alkali. This behaviour is explained by the Ionic Theory as follows. The calcium phosphate furnishes calcium ions and phosphate ions

$$Ca_3(PO_4)_2 \rightleftharpoons \underset{\text{dissolved}}{Ca_3(PO_4)_2} \rightleftharpoons 3Ca^{\cdot\cdot} + 2PO_4^{\prime\prime\prime}.$$
$$\underset{\text{solid}}{}$$

Phosphoric acid is a very weak acid, i.e., it ionizes only to a very slight extent in solution. The addition of a dilute solution of a strong acid increases very largely the hydrogen ion concentration and hence removes phosphate ions from the solution as non-ionized phosphoric acid. This disturbs the equilibrium between the calcium phosphate and its ions, so causing more to dissolve. On adding alkali to this solution, the hydrogen ions are removed, more phosphate ions are formed, thus exceeding the solubility product of calcium phosphate, which is accordingly reprecipitated.

Calcium phosphate is an important fertilizer, but its action is very slow on account of its small solubility. To convert it into a more soluble acid salt it is treated with sulphuric acid—usually chamber acid—in order to turn it into **monocalcium phosphate.**

$$Ca_3(PO_4)_2 + 2H_2SO_4 = Ca(H_2PO_4)_2 + 2CaSO_4.$$

The acid phosphate becomes $Ca(H_2PO_4)_2.H_2O$ and the sulphate $CaSO_4.2H_2O$. This mixture, which is called **superphosphate,** usually contains a little undecomposed normal phosphate.

Another form in which calcium phosphate is obtained is the **basic slag** of the basic Bessemer, and open hearth processes for steel making (pp. 807, 808). It probably consists mainly of calcium silicophosphate, $Ca_3(PO_4)_2.CaSiO_3$. It is an important fertilizer.

Calcium oxalate, $Ca\begin{cases} O.OC \\ | \\ O.OC \end{cases}$, is a very sparingly soluble substance

---

* Objection is sometimes raised to the use of the word *soluble* to describe the behaviour of calcium phosphate with mineral acid and similar reactions in which the solution is the result of chemical action. Many prefer to restrict the terms *dissolve, soluble,* etc., to purely physical processes ; but it is not always easy to draw the line between physical and chemical " solution."

and is used for the estimation of calcium (see below). It is obtained as a white precipitate on addition of ammonium oxalate solution to a soluble calcium salt in presence of ammonia. Mineral acids act upon it in a manner similar to their action on calcium phosphate (p. 633). Calcium oxalate is reformed as a precipitate on addition of alkali.

§ 18 Detection and Determination of Calcium

Calcium salts may be detected by the brick-red colour which, when moistened with hydrochloric acid, they impart to the bunsen flame-- provided that strontium, barium and sodium are absent.

In qualitative analysis calcium, strontium and barium salts are precipitated as carbonates by ammonium carbonate in presence of ammonia. The qualitative separation of these three metals is discussed on page 639.

Calcium is usually determined as oxalate, by adding a boiling solution of ammonium oxalate to a solution of the calcium salt to which ammonia and ammonium chloride have been added. After washing and drying, the precipitate is ignited : if carried out carefully the product is the carbonate, strong ignition yields the oxide :

$$CaC_2O_4 = CaCO_3 + CO,$$
$$CaCO_3 = CaO + CO_2.$$

§ 19 Strontium, Sr

History

A strontium mineral was probably first distinguished in 1791 by Hope, when examining the minerals found in a lead mine at Strontian in Argyllshire. One of these, which was also examined by Kirwan and by Klaproth in 1793, was concluded to be the carbonate of a new earth to which the name *strontia* was given. Strontium was first isolated by Davy in 1808.

Occurrence

Strontium occurs as the carbonate (referred to above) and known as *strontianite* ; and also as the sulphate, *celestine*. Strontium also occurs in small quantities associated with other alkaline earth minerals. Strontium is much scarcer than either calcium or barium.

For the **preparation** of metallic strontium, similar methods can employed to those used for calcium. Usually it is obtained by electrolysis of the fused chloride.

In its **properties** strontium resembles calcium. It is a white metal of low specific gravity (2·6) and is chemically more reactive than calcium.

So far no **uses** have been found for the metal as such, although its employment in photo-electric cells has been suggested. Some of its compounds have commercial uses, however, e.g., the hydroxide in sugar-refining and the nitrate in firework-making, for " red fire," etc.

The **atomic weight** of strontium is in the neighbourhood of 88.

This is in agreement with its place in the Periodic Table and with its specific heat. The exact atomic weight has been determined by methods similar to those used for calcium. Richards, by conversion of the bromide into silver bromide, and of the chloride into silver chloride, obtained values between 87·620 and 87·629. The value recommended by the International Committee is 87·63.

§ 20 Compounds of Strontium

Strontium compounds closely resemble those of calcium ; as a rule the salts of strontium are the less soluble. Strontium salts, moistened with hydrochloric acid, impart a brilliant crimson colour to the flame of a bunsen burner.

Strontium oxide, SrO, is made on a large scale by heating the carbonate in superheated steam : carbon dioxide is evolved and strontium hydroxide is formed :

$$SrCO_3 + H_2O = Sr(OH)_2 + CO_2.$$

The hydroxide on ignition furnishes the oxide. The temperature required for the direct decomposition of the carbonate to the oxide is higher than in the case of calcium.

Strontium oxide is also made commercially from celestine by heating it with carbon and treating the sulphide formed with caustic soda. The sodium sulphide is removed by means of water and the strontium hydroxide converted into the oxide by heating :

$$SrSO_4 + 4C = SrS + 4CO,$$
$$SrS + 2NaOH = Sr(OH)_2 + Na_2S.$$

Strontium oxide resembles quicklime. It "slakes" similarly on addition of water.

Strontium hydroxide, $Sr(OH)_2$, which may be made from celestine as described above, resembles slaked lime, but is more soluble in water : 100 grams of water will dissolve 0·81 grams of strontium hydroxide at 20°. It is a stronger base than slaked lime. It is extensively used in sugar-refining since it combines with cane sugar, forming an insoluble *saccharate*, from which the sugar can be regenerated by carbon dioxide, strontium carbonate being precipitated. Thus by its use a further quantity of sugar can be extracted from the " molasses " left after the first crop of sugar has crystallized out.

Strontium carbonate, $SrCO_3$, occurs native as *strontianite* and is made commercially from celestine by fusion with sodium carbonate. It resembles calcium carbonate, but is less easily decomposed by heat.

Strontium nitrate, $Sr(NO_3)_2$, is made technically by precipitation from concentrated solutions of strontium chloride and sodium nitrate. (Cf. preparation of potassium nitrate from Chile saltpetre, p. 578.) It is extensively used in pyrotechny for " red fires."

Strontium sulphate, $SrSO_4$, occurs naturally as *celestine*. It differs from calcium sulphate, in being less soluble in water, and insoluble in ammonium sulphate. It closely resembles barium sulphate in most of its chemical properties.

Strontium chloride, $SrCl_2$, is made commercially by the action of calcium chloride on strontium carbonate. It resembles calcium chloride in being very soluble in water (100 grams of water dissolve 50 grams of anhydrous salt at 15°) ; it forms a similar hexahydrate, but it is not so hygroscopic.

§ 21 Barium, Ba. History, Occurrence and Extraction

History

V. Casciorolus, in 1602, noticed that when heavy spar was calcined with combustible matters, the product became phosphorescent in the dark. He called the stone *lapis solis*, and later, it was called " Bolognian," or Bononian phosphorus. The heavy spar which furnished *lapis solis* was at first believed to be a peculiar kind of gypsum. K. W. Scheele (1774) found that the mineral contained a new earth which gave a sulphate insoluble in water. G. de Morveau called the earth " barote "—from the Greek βαρύς (barus), heavy—and Lavoisier later altered the word to " baryta," the name now used for this earth.

Occurrence

The principal barium mineral is the sulphate, known as *heavy spar* or *barytes*. The carbonate also occurs and is known as *witherite* ; while an impure barium manganite, $BaO.MnO_2$, is known as *psilomelane*.

Preparation and Properties

Metallic barium, in the form of an amalgam with mercury, was first obtained by Davy in 1808. It is one of the most difficult metals to prepare. It has been obtained by electrolysis of barium chloride using a mercury cathode ; the barium is recovered by distilling off the mercury from the amalgam.

Barium is a silvery white metal, resembling calcium in appearance. It is soft, of specific gravity 3·5, and m.p. 850°. It is very reactive and inflames spontaneously if exposed to the air when finely divided. Its reactions are similar to, but more vigorous than those of calcium.

§ 22 Atomic Weight of Barium

The principal determinations of the atomic weight of barium have been made by conversion of the chloride into the sulphate, or of the chloride or bromide into the corresponding silver salt. Richards using these latter methods obtained values between 137·34 and 137·38. Hönigschmid in 1929, working similarly, obtained a slightly lower value than the mean of Richards' work. The value at present (1940) recommended by the International Committee is 137·36.

§ 23 Barium Oxides and Hydroxides

The principal oxides of barium are :
> Barium oxide, BaO ;
> Barium peroxide, BaO_2 ;

whilst a third,
> Barium suboxide, Ba_2O,

has been reported.

Barium Oxide, Baryta, BaO

Barium oxide is often made by decomposing the hydroxide or nitrate at a red heat ; as the carbonate requires a very high temperature for its decomposition. If the carbonate is to be used, it is mixed with lamp-black or tar before heating. The carbon burns off and the carbonate, at the same time, is decomposed at a much lower temperature :

$$BaCO_3 + C = BaO + 2CO.$$

Barium oxide is a white powder which slakes in contact with water, so much heat being evolved, that if but a little water be used, the mass may become visibly red hot. When heated in air, some barium peroxide is also formed (q.v.).

Barium peroxide, BaO_2, results when barium oxide is heated in air to 400° or over :

$$2BaO + O_2 \rightleftharpoons 2BaO_2 + 24 \cdot 2 \text{ Cal.}$$

The reaction is reversible and since its formation involves the evolution of heat and reduction of volume, a rise in temperature or decrease of pressure, will favour the decomposition of the peroxide. This fact was made use of in the now obsolete Brin's process for the manufacture of oxygen (p. 299). Barium peroxide is also formed by the action of hydrogen peroxide on a solution of barium hydroxide. When made in this way it crystallizes out as $BaO_2.8H_2O$.

Barium peroxide is a white insoluble powder, which reacts with acids forming hydrogen peroxide in the cold (p. 287) ; and oxygen at higher temperatures. It is used for the manufacture of hydrogen peroxide.

Barium Hydroxide, Ba(OH)₂

Barium hydroxide results from the slaking of barium oxide. Commercially, it is made by heating a mixture of barytes with powdered coke or coal, when crude barium sulphide is formed :

$$BaSO_4 + 4C = BaS + 4CO.$$

The latter is then heated in a stream of carbon dioxide, and thus converted into barium carbonate :

$$BaS + CO_2 + H_2O = BaCO_3 + H_2S.$$

The carbonate is converted into the hydroxide by heating in superheated steam as described for strontium hydroxide (p. 635). Sometimes the native carbonate, witherite, is treated similarly.

Barium hydroxide is a white powder which, unlike calcium hydroxide, can be fused without decomposition. It melts at 325° and decomposes if heated to from 600° to 1000°. It is much more soluble in water than either calcium or strontium hydroxide : 100 grams of water dissolve 3·23 grams of barium hydroxide at 15°. The solution, which is strongly alkaline, deposits crystals of $Ba(OH)_2.2H_2O$. Barium hydroxide is used for the titration of weak acids in volumetric analysis, since it is the only reasonably soluble strong base which (owing to the insolubility of its carbonate) is always free from dissolved carbonate.

§ 24 Salts of Barium

Barium salts are white unless derived from a coloured acid, and give colourless solutions. They are poisonous. They are for the most part insoluble or only very sparingly soluble ; the principal soluble ones being the nitrate and chloride. When moistened with hydrochloric acid, and heated in the flame of a bunsen burner, they give it an apple-green coloration.

Barium carbonate, $BaCO_3$, occurs naturally and is also made commercially from barytes, as described under barium hydroxide. It is a white powder resembling chalk in many respects, insoluble in water, dissolving to a small extent in presence of excess of carbon dioxide. It does not decompose on heating at atmospheric pressure under a temperature of about 1842°.

Barium chloride, $BaCl_2$, is made either from the carbonate or from the crude sulphide resulting from reduction of the native sulphate, by dissolving in hydrochloric acid. Technically it is also made by strongly heating a mixture of barytes with coke and calcium chloride, followed by lixiviation with water to extract the barium chloride which is soluble :

$$BaSO_4 + CaCl_2' + 4C = BaCl_2 + 4CO + CaS.$$

The aqueous solution deposits crystals of $BaCl_2.2H_2O$.

The anhydrous salt is a white solid, the hydrated crystals are colourless and transparent. Neither anhydrous nor hydrated salt is deliquescent, in marked contradistinction to calcium chloride. Barium chloride is soluble in water : 100 grams of water dissolve 35·7 grams of anhydrous salt at 20°.

Barium chloride is extensively used in analysis for the detection and determination of sulphates (p. 471).

Barium nitrate, $Ba(NO_3)_2$, is usually made by mixing solutions of sodium nitrate and barium chloride. It forms colourless crystals, which are fairly soluble in water : 100 grams of water dissolve 5·0 grams at 0°. It is used for the preparation of the oxide, and for making " green fire " for fireworks.

Barium sulphide, BaS, is made on a large scale by reduction of barytes for the preparation of other barium compounds. In presence of minute traces of impurities, it exhibits marked phosphorescence like calcium sulphide and like which it was formerly used in making luminous paints.

Barium sulphate, $BaSO_4$, occurs native as *barytes* or *heavy spar.* It is formed as a heavy white precipitate on mixing solutions of a soluble barium salt and a soluble sulphate. It is a white solid, unaffected by heat below 1500°, and is extremely sparingly soluble in water. With concentrated sulphuric acid the acid sulphate is formed, $Ba(HSO_4)_2$, which is moderately soluble in water. It is reduced to the sulphide by heating with carbon as already mentioned ; and is decomposed to some extent when fused with sodium carbonate in excess :

$$BaSO_4 + Na_2CO_3 \rightleftharpoons BaCO_3 + Na_2SO_4.$$

It is used in the manufacture of paint by the name of *permanent white*, also as a " filling " for rubber and for paper making, to increase the opacity and weight of the paper.

§ 25 Detection and Determination of Barium

Barium is frequently detected by the formation of the insoluble sulphate in presence of hydrochloric acid on addition of a solution of a soluble sulphate. It is generally determined by the same method.

In qualitative analysis barium is usually precipitated along with calcium and strontium by addition of ammonium carbonate solution to the solution (containing ammonia and ammonium salts) remaining after removal of metals whose chlorides, sulphides and hydroxides are insoluble.

Several methods are in use for the separation of the mixed carbonates so obtained, of which the following is fairly representative, and depends upon the facts that barium chromate is insoluble in acetic acid, while strontium chromate is soluble in it and calcium chromate is appreciably soluble in water ; and also that calcium sulphate is soluble in presence of acid in concentrated ammonium sulphate solution, whereas strontium sulphate is not.

The carbonates are dissolved in the minimum of dilute acetic acid ; the solution is boiled and potassium chromate added until no more barium chromate is precipitated. The filtrate from this precipitate is mixed with two-thirds of its volume of concentrated hydrochloric acid, then treated with its own volume of ammonium sulphate solution, and left to stand for ten minutes. Any strontium sulphate formed is filtered off, and the filtrate made alkaline with ammonia solution. The addition of boiling ammonium oxalate solution precipitates any calcium present as oxalate.

Radium is, chemically speaking, a member of the alkaline earth family of elements, but as its interest lies very largely in its radio-active properties, it is discussed in Chapter XXXVI along with the other radio-elements.

CHAPTER XXVIII

ZINC, CADMIUM AND MERCURY

§ 1 Zinc, Zn. History and Occurrence

History

BRASS, an alloy of zinc and copper, was known to the ancients, and several references to " brass " occur in the sacred writings. R. Jagnaux says that bracelets made of zinc have been found in the ruins of Cameros which was destroyed about 500 B.C. The word " zinken " appears in the writings ascribed to Basil Valentine, but it is not there referred to as a metal, and it seems to be confused with several other substances. Paracelsus also used the word in the sixteenth century. At that time the term *zinc* appears to have been employed locally by the miners in the Carnia for an earthy ore. Near the beginning of the seventeenth century, zinc was brought from China and the East Indies under the name " tutanego," Indian tin, calamine, or speauter. Libavius (1597) said that the Indian tin and the Goslar metal were the same. About this time, however, there was much confusion as to the meaning of zinc. In 1697, Löhneyes appears to have been the first definitely to apply the term " zink " to the metal now known as zinc. In 1695 W. Homberg, and in 1721 J. F. Henkel, discovered that zinc could be obtained from calamine, and a works for the manufacture of zinc was erected at Bristol about 1740 by J. Champion.

Occurrence

Metallic zinc has been reported in the basaltic rocks of Victoria (Australia) ; but it usually occurs combined : as carbonate, *zinc spar, calamine*, $ZnCO_3$; sulphide, *zinc blende* or *black jack*, ZnS ; oxide, *zincite* or *red zinc ore*, ZnO ; silicate, *willemite*, $2ZnO.SiO_2$; *franklinite*, $(ZnFe)O.Fe_2O_3$; *zinc spinel* or *gahnite*, $ZnO.Al_2O_3$.

§ 2 Extraction of Zinc

The principal ore of zinc used for the manufacture of the metal is the sulphide ; often in the form of a concentrate from which ores of lead, etc., have been removed. The carbonate is also used to some extent.

The process of extraction involves two operations, viz., (i) *roasting* to convert the ore to the oxide ; and (ii) *reduction* to the metal.

The *roasting* of the carbonate presents no difficulty, carbon dioxide being driven off :

$$ZnCO_3 = ZnO + CO_2.$$

In the case of sulphide ores the sulphur is oxidized to sulphur dioxide by calcination in air. This is now effected in furnaces with mechanical stirring or ·other devices to enable the process to take place continuously :

$$2ZnS + 3O_2 = 2ZnO + 2SO_2.$$

The sulphur dioxide was formerly allowed to escape, but the furnace gases are now also used for the manufacture of sulphuric acid after removal of impurities ; the contact process (p. 466) being employed. The manufacture of zinc and sulphuric acid are in this way carried on side by side.

For the *reduction* of the roasted ore, it is mixed with crushed coke or anthracite and heated to 1400°-1450° in fireclay retorts. The heating is usually effected by producer gas using regenerative furnaces for the recovery of the waste heat, similar to those employed in gas works and coke-oven practice (pp. 345, 350). The oxide is reduced with the formation of carbon monoxide :

$$ZnO + C = Zn + CO.$$

Most metallic oxides are reduced by a reaction of the type

$$MO + CO \rightleftharpoons M + CO_2,$$

which is reversible ; but usually the concentration of carbon dioxide necessary for the right-to-left reaction to be appreciable, is very high. In the case of zinc vapour and carbon dioxide, however, the back reaction is marked and hence to complete the reduction of the zinc oxide in the retort, it is necessary to use excess of carbon and so prevent the formation of carbon dioxide. The temperature required for the reduction is considerably above the boiling point of zinc, which therefore distils over and is collected in " condensers " and receivers of fireclay or iron. At first, a bluish-grey powder collects in

the receiver—known as *zinc dust*— but later the metal condenses to a liquid which is drawn off at intervals and cast into blocks—known as *spelter*. The spelter formed in the earlier stages of a distillation is pure enough for commercial use—the later portions require further purification,

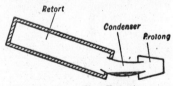

FIG. 214.—Zinc Retort.

by distillation, etc. The retorts used in zinc manufacture, differ to some extent in different works, but have the same main characteristics. A typical retort is illustrated in Fig. 214. It is of elliptical section and measures 8 ins. by 11 ins. inside and is about five feet long. These retorts are arranged in furnaces in three or four tiers ; an average " bank " comprising some 300 retorts.

Of recent years considerable developments have taken place in the electrolytic manufacture of zinc, particularly in America and New Zealand. The stages in this process are :

(i) roasting of the raw ore, as before ; (ii) dissolving out the zinc oxide, using spent electrolyte (sulphuric acid) from stage iv ; (iii) removal of impurities which interfere with electrolysis, or would contaminate the product, e.g., iron, silica, arsenic, antimony, copper, cadmium and cobalt ; (iv) electrolysis of the zinc sulphate solution, using aluminium sheets as cathodes, and lead anodes : this results in the re-formation of sulphuric acid in solution ; (v) melting the cathode zinc and casting into ingots.

By this process zinc of a very high degree of purity can be manufactured.

§ 3 Properties of Zinc

Zinc is a bluish white metal, of sp. gr. about 7·1, being thus a little lighter than iron. It is brittle at ordinary temperatures, loses its brittleness about 120°, but regains it at 200° when it can be readily powdered. As cast, zinc has a crystalline structure and if it be melted and poured on to a non-conducting surface of, say, asbestos, and the liquid portion run off from that which first solidifies, a residue of hexagonal pyramidal crystals will be obtained. Zinc melts at 420° and boils at 907°. It is a good conductor of heat and electricity.

Zinc is slowly oxidized in moist air ; and in water containing air in solution, basic carbonates are formed. When heated to about 1000°, zinc burns in air with a bluish white flame forming a bulky mass of zinc oxide known as *philosopher's wool*. It also reacts readily with chlorine and sulphur. Pure zinc is not attacked by water at the boiling point, but commercial zinc reacts slowly : at a red heat zinc easily decomposes steam :

$$Zn + H_2O = ZnO + H_2.$$

Commercial zinc is readily attacked by dilute acids with evolution of hydrogen in most cases, though not with nitric acid (cf. pp. 253 and 410). Very pure zinc, however, reacts with acids only very slowly if at all. This is thought to be due to the fact that the impurities in commercial zinc form small galvanic " cells " with the zinc which passes into solution in consequence ; whereas with pure zinc no " cells " are formed.

Nitric acid yields zinc nitrate, but the nature of the other product depends upon the concentration of the acid. With concentrated acid, nitrogen peroxide is the principal product ; with a somewhat weaker acid, nitric oxide ; and with dilute acid, ammonia is formed which is not evolved but remains behind as ammonium nitrate. With dilute acid of the right concentration, nitrous oxide may be formed ; possibly through decomposition of ammonium nitrate.

Zinc in presence of an acid such as dilute hydrochloric or sulphuric acid is a very good reducing agent (see p. 260—nascent hydrogen), being more effective than gaseous hydrogen.

Zinc will also react with hot concentrated alkali solutions, evolving hydrogen and forming a solution of sodium zincate, e.g.,

$$Zn + 2NaOH = Na_2ZnO_2 + H_2.$$

Zinc is a very electro-positive metal, being high in the electro-chemical series (p. 205) and, in consequence, will displace many other metals from solutions of their salts. It is used for this purpose in the extraction of gold and silver by the cyanide method (pp. 598 and 607).

§ 4 Uses of Zinc

Zinc is used in large quantities in making electric batteries, and certain utensils. Sheets of zinc have also been employed for roofing purposes, but on account of its softness galvanized iron (see below) is more often employed.

One of the principal uses of zinc is in the manufacture of *galvanized iron*, which is iron covered with a layer of zinc to prevent rusting. It is made by dipping iron, cleaned by " pickling " in dilute hydrochloric acid, into molten zinc. The zinc protects the iron from rusting, and unlike tin, the protection is effective even if the zinc coating becomes broken. This is because zinc is a more electropositive metal than iron and hence is attacked first. Iron articles may also be coated with zinc by heating them and spraying them with zinc-dust. This is known as *sherardizing*.

Another very important use of zinc is in the manufacture of *brass* (p. 586), in which it is alloyed with copper. Other important alloys of zinc are *german silver* and *delta-metal* (p. 586). It is a constituent of recent British silver coins (p. 600).

Many zinc compounds find extensive use, e.g., in the manufacture of paint as a filling for rubber, and in medicine.

§ 5 Atomic Weight of Zinc

The combining weight of zinc has been determined by the analysis of the halogen compounds, the carbonate and the sulphate, and by the synthesis of the oxide. The atomic weight is seen to be in the neighbourhood of 65 from the specific heat of zinc (0·0935) ; the vapour density of volatile zinc compounds and the isomorphism relationships of zinc salts.

The value recommended by the International Committee is 65·38.

§ 6 Zinc Oxides and Hydroxide

Zinc oxide, Philosopher's Wool, ZnO, is formed when the metal is burnt in air. Under the commercial name *zinc white*, it is manufactured by heating zinc in air and passing the fumes into condensing chambers where the powdered oxide collects.

Zinc oxide is a white powder, which appears yellow when hot and white when cold. It is almost insoluble in water, but it reacts with aqueous solutions of acids and alkalis, forming solutions of zinc salts and zincates respectively ; thus behaving as an amphoteric oxide. It is reduced to the metal by carbon at a red-heat, this being the method of manufacture (q.v.).

Zinc oxide is used in place of white lead (p. 707) as a white pigment where white lead might undergo blackening by hydrogen sulphide. It also has the advantage of being non-poisonous. A large quantity of zinc oxide is used as a filler in the manufacture of rubber ; it is also used for making glazes for certain kinds of porcelain and in medicine in *zinc ointment*.

Zinc peroxide, ZnO_2, is a yellowish powder made by the action of hydrogen peroxide on zinc oxide. It is decomposed by dilute acids with the formation of hydrogen peroxide.

Zinc Hydroxide, $Zn(OH)_2$

Zinc hydroxide is precipitated when an alkaline hydroxide is added to a solution of a zinc salt. It decomposes into the oxide and water when heated to 100°. It behaves as an amphoteric hydroxide, reacting with acids to form zinc salts and with alkalis forming zincates. Zinc hydroxide also " dissolves " in aqueous ammonia, and ammonium chloride, not because of the amphoteric nature of zinc hydroxide, but on account of the formation of complex ions : behaviour reminiscent of that of copper (p. 590). The solution contains probably the ion $Zn(NH_3)_4^{..}$.

§ 7 Zinc Salts

Zinc forms only one series of salts, and these are, in general, colourless and very soluble in water. They often crystallize with water of crystallization.

Zinc carbonate, $ZnCO_3$, occurs native as *calamine*. If sodium carbonate solution be added to a solution of a soluble zinc salt, a *basic carbonate*, $ZnCO_3.2Zn(OH)_2.H_2O$, is precipitated ; but the use of sodium bicarbonate results in the formation of zinc carbonate. It is a white powder, which readily decomposes on heating. It is used in medicine for the treatment of skin diseases.

Zinc chloride, $ZnCl_2$, is obtained in solution by dissolving zinc in hydrochloric acid. The concentrated solution deposits crystals of the composition $ZnCl_2.2H_2O$; but the anhydrous salt cannot be obtained from this since hydrochloric acid is also lost and a basic chloride is formed :

$$ZnCl_2.2H_2O = Zn(OH)Cl + HCl + H_2O.$$

The anhydrous salt is obtained by passing chlorine or hydrogen chloride, over heated zinc.

It is a white, very deliquescent solid and is used as a dehydrating agent. It is very soluble in water : 100 grams of water will dissolve 330 grams of anhydrous salt at 10°. It combines with zinc oxide to form a hard and insoluble oxychloride ; this property is applied in dentistry. It is also used (under the name of *killed spirits*) as a flux in soldering.

Zinc sulphide, ZnS, occurs native, and is the principal ore of zinc (p. 640). It is formed as a white, amorphous precipitate when an alkaline sulphide is added to a solution of a zinc salt, or when hydrogen sulphide is passed through an alkaline solution of a zinc salt. It is not acted upon by organic acids, but reacts with mineral acids with evolution of hydrogen sulphide. Although pure zinc sulphide is not phosphorescent, it can readily be obtained in a strongly phosphorescent form. Minute traces of manganese, etc., confer on it this property. (Cf. barium sulphide, p. 638.) Zinc sulphide also finds application as a white pigment.

Zinc Sulphate, White Vitriol, $ZnSO_4.7H_2O$

Zinc sulphate can be obtained by acting upon zinc or zinc oxide with dilute sulphuric acid. The concentrated solution deposits transparent crystals of ·the composition $ZnSO_4.7H_2O$. The crystals are very soluble in water : 100 grams of water dissolve 138 grams of crystals at 10°. It is used in the manufacture of *lithopone*, a white pigment consisting of a mixture of zinc sulphide and barium sulphate made by the interaction of barium sulphide and zinc sulphate. This is a good paint for many purposes, although it has the drawback that its " covering power " is low.

§ 8 Detection and Determination of Zinc

Zinc is often detected by heating the suspected compound on charcoal with sodium carbonate. The formation of an incrustation of zinc oxide, which is yellow when hot and white when cold, is evidence of the presence of zinc. If this incrustation be moistened with a drop of cobalt nitrate solution and heated again, the formation of a green mass indicates the presence of zinc.

Zinc is precipitated in qualitative analysis as its sulphide in *alkaline* solution. It is distinguished from other sulphides precipitated in similar conditions as it is the only white sulphide.

Zinc is conveniently determined gravimetrically by precipitating it as zinc ammonium phosphate, which on ignition is converted into the pyrophosphate. (Compare magnesium, p. 622.)

A 1 per cent. solution of quinaldinic acid gives a white precipitate of $Zn(C_{10}H_6O_2N)_2.H_2O$ when added to a solution of a zinc salt faintly acid with acetic acid. Copper, cadmium, iron and chromium must first be removed, as they also give precipitates ; but cobalt, nickel and manganese do not interfere. This is a very sensitive test for zinc, and can be applied also to its determination.

§ 9 Cadmium, Cd

History and Occurrence

The term καδμεία (cadmeia) was applied by Discorides, and by Pliny, to a zinciferous earth (calamine)—found on the shores of the Black Sea—which when melted with copper furnished brass—aurichalcum. Pliny also applied the term " cadmia " to the tutty (impure zinc oxide) found in the flues of brass-founders' furnaces. In 1817 F. Stromeyer discovered a yellow oxide free from iron in a sample of zinc carbonate used at the smelting works at Salzgitter. This could only be due to the presence of a new metal which he called " cadmium," from *cadmia fornacum*, because the metal was found in the " flowers of zinc," that is, the flue dust of the zinc furnace.

Occurrence

This element does not occur free. It is commonly found accompanying zinc in calamine, and zinc blende. Very few zinc ores contain more than 0·5 per cent. of cadmium. The rare mineral *greenockite*, cadmium sulphide, CdS, is of no commercial importance.

Extraction

The first product of the distillation of zinc ores contains most of the cadmium, partly as metal, partly as oxide. The product, called " crude cadmium," contains some zinc from which it can be separated by repeated distillation, or by electrolysis.

Properties

Cadmium is a white metal, which melts at 321° and boils at 767°. It is ductile at ordinary temperatures. It is very slowly oxidized in moist air, but will burn when heated, forming brown fumes of the oxide. It resembles zinc in many of its chemical properties, though it is usually less active. It differs from zinc principally in that its hydroxide is not amphoteric and its sulphide can be precipitated in presence of dilute acids.

Uses of Cadmium

Cadmium is used as a constituent of fusible metals (e.g., Wood's alloy, which contains bismuth, lead, tin and cadmium in the proportions 4 : 2 : 1 : 1 and melts at 71°). Increasing use has recently been made of cadmium as a plating metal ; electro-plating being effected from a bath of cadmium cyanide dissolved in sodium cyanide solution. Cadmium is also used in conjunction with cadmium sulphate in the Weston cadmium cell which is used as a standard of E.M.F. Cadmium (1 per cent.) is alloyed with copper for overhead tramway wires, and is used in some antifriction alloys and solders. Some compounds of cadmium, e.g., the sulphide and selenide, are used as pigments.

Atomic Weight

The combining weight of cadmium has been determined by the conversion of the metal, and of the oxalate, to the oxide ; the metal into the sulphide or sulphate ; by the reduction of the carbonate to the metal, and by the precipitation of the chloride and bromide with silver nitrate. The most probable value for the atomic weight is considered by the International Committee to be 112·41.

§ 10 Compounds of Cadmium

Cadmous oxide, Cd_2O, is obtained by dissolving cadmium in fused cadmium chloride, treating the product with water, which forms **cadmous hydroxide,** CdOH, and gently heating this. It is a yellow powder.

Cadmium oxide, CdO, is formed when the metal is burnt in air. It has a rich brown colour.

Cadmium hydroxide, $Cd(OH)_2$, is precipitated as a white powder on addition of solutions of alkali hydroxides to a solution of a cadmium salt. Unlike zinc hydroxide, it is not attacked by excess of alkali hydroxide, but, like the zinc compound, it forms a soluble complex compound when treated with ammonia solution.

Cadmium salts are usually colourless and their solubility relations resemble those of zinc. They are notable for the low conductivity of their solutions ; in this respect resembling the compounds of mercury. This behaviour is attributed to the formation of *autocomplexes*. Thus, in solutions of cadmium chloride the following equilibria are believed to exist :—

$$CdCl_2 \rightleftharpoons Cd^{\cdot\cdot} + 2Cl',$$

$$Cd^{\cdot\cdot} + 2Cl' + CdCl_2 \rightleftharpoons Cd[CdCl_4].$$

Cadmium sulphide, CdS, occurs naturally as the rare mineral *greenockite*, and is prepared by the action of hydrogen sulphide on a solution of a cadmium salt. It varies in tint from bright yellow to orange-red, according to the temperature of precipitation, etc. If hydrogen sulphide be passed through a solution of cadmium chloride, the precipitate which forms is an intense orange-red owing to the formation of *cadmium thiochloride* : Cl — Cd — S — Cd — Cl. The thiochloride passes into the sulphide by the continued action of hydrogen sulphide and the precipitate becomes lighter in colour. It is not attacked by dilute, but does react with concentrated, mineral acids, hydrogen sulphide being liberated.

Cadmium sulphide is used as a pigment : but must not be employed in conjunction with white lead, as lead sulphide forms slowly if this is done. It is now used also in the form of *cadmiopone*, the cadmium analogue of lithopone (p. 645).

Cadmium sulphate, $3CdSO_4.8H_2O$, is made by treating cadmium oxide with dilute sulphuric acid. The concentrated solution deposits crystals of the composition shown. (Cf. $ZnSO_4.7H_2O$.) It forms colourless monoclinic crystals, and is soluble in water : 100 grams of water dissolve 76·3 grams of anhydrous salt at 15°.

It is used in the construction of the Weston cadmium cell, which is a standard of E.M.F. This cell has a very low temperature coefficient on account of the small change in the solubility of cadmium sulphate with change of temperature.

§ 11 Detection and Determination of Cadmium

The most characteristic reaction of cadmium salts is the formation of the bright yellow precipitate of the sulphide with hydrogen sulphide. It is distinguished from arsenic sulphide, which is also yellow and precipitated in presence of dilute acid, by being insoluble in yellow ammonium sulphide with which arsenic sulphide forms a soluble compound. Cadmium is separated from other metals whose sulphides are also insoluble in dilute acids and yellow ammonium sulphide, by means of the formation of soluble complex compounds when the hydroxide is treated with ammonia solution. Copper hydroxide also forms a similar soluble complex, but cadmium can be separated from it since hydrogen sulphide precipitates cadmium sulphide from a solution of its cyanide in excess of potassium cyanide solution, whereas copper sulphide is not precipitated under these conditions (see pp. 236, 595).

Cadmium can be determined electrolytically by deposition from cyanide solutions. It can also be precipitated as sulphide from slightly acid solutions ; the sulphide being then converted into the sulphate by the action of sulphuric acid, and weighed as such. It can also be obtained by precipitation as the carbonate ; and the formation of the double ammonium cadmium phosphate has also been employed. The latter salt, on ignition, leaves a residue of cadmium pyrophosphate ($Cd_2P_2O_7$).

§ 12 Mercury, Hg. History, Occurrence and Preparation

History

Mercury was mentioned 300 B.C. by Theophrastus as χυτός ἄργυρος (chutos argyros), quicksilver or liquid silver ; and he states that it can be made by rubbing vinegar with cinnabar in a copper vessel. Discorides called it ὕδωρ ἄργυρος (hydor argyros), liquid silver ; hence the Latin *hydrargyrum*, and the present-day symbol Hg. The metal had a certain fascination for the alchemists, and for a time they believed that it, or something similar, was a constituent of all metals. " Nimble volatile mercury " was named after the mythological Mercury, the messenger of the gods, and accordingly the ancient chemists symbolized the metal by the caduceus or herald's wand ☿, also used for the planet Mercury.

Occurrence

Free mercury in small quantities occurs disseminated in the ores of mercury, which in turn occur in relatively few places in payable quantities. The mercury deposits are usually found along lines of profound volcanic disturbances. *Cinnabar*, HgS, is the chief ore of mercury, and it is mined in Almaden (Spain), Idria (Carniola), Bavarian Palatinate, Peru, California, Japan, China, etc. The great quicksilver mine at Almaden is said to have been worked at least as far back as 415 B.C. Pliny (*c.* A.D. 77) reported that 10,000 lbs. of cinnabar were brought to Rome per annum from this locality. The American deposits range from Alaska along the Pacific slope down to Peru. At one time the output from America rivalled that from Almaden, but, unlike the latter deposits, the American, and indeed most others, decrease in value with increasing depth.

Preparation

Mercury is obtained almost exclusively from cinnabar, HgS. The ore is first crushed dry and then sorted by hand or screen into two grades. The one is a rich ore, the other contains much gangue. The ore is roasted to oxidize the sulphur, and the metal is liberated :

$$HgS + O_2 = Hg + SO_2.$$

The reaction takes place at a temperature higher than the boiling point of mercury which therefore distils, and is condensed. Different condensing arrangements are used at different works. The mercury, for example, may be condensed in large chambers as at Idria ; or in a series of pear-shaped vessels—aludels—connected in rows nearly fifty feet long, as at Almaden.

The crude mercury may be cleaned by filtration through chamois leather ; and purified by distillation from iron retorts. In the laboratory, mercury is often purified by running a fine spray of mercury down a long column of dilute nitric acid, followed by distillation in vacuo. For this purpose a convenient apparatus is that illustrated in Fig. 215.

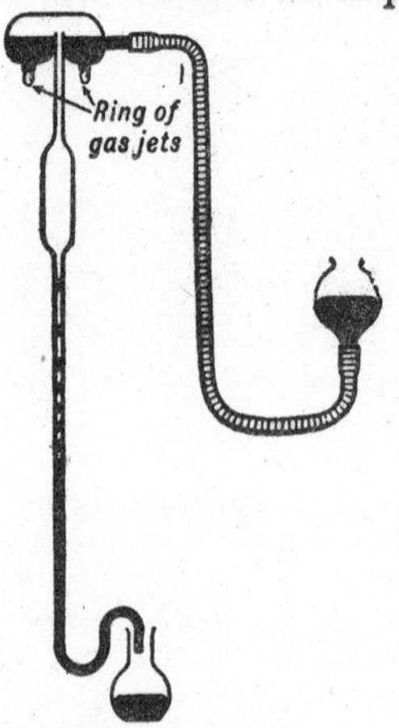

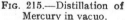

Ring of gas jets

Fig. 215.—Distillation of Mercury in vacuo.

§ 13 Properties of Mercury

Mercury is a silvery-white metal with a bluish tinge : it is the only pure metal which is liquid at the ordinary temperature. Its melting point is $-38.87°$, at which temperature it forms a malleable solid. It boils at $356.9°$. It has a slight vapour pressure, even at ordinary temperatures and the vapour is poisonous.

Mercury does not tarnish in the air in ordinary circumstances, but is slowly oxidized when heated to its boiling point in air or oxygen. It reacts vigorously with chlorine, and combines with iodine and with sulphur if rubbed with them in a mortar. Mercury is not attacked by hydrochloric acid ; concentrated sulphuric acid acts very slowly in the cold ; but when heated mercuric sulphate and sulphur dioxide are formed. Concentrated nitric acid rapidly attacks mercury, forming mercuric nitrate and oxides of nitrogen. Dilute nitric acid acts slowly, giving mercurous nitrate. Alkali hydroxides have no appreciable action on mercury.

Amalgams

Mercury is a good solvent for some of the metals and the solutions are called amalgams. These as a rule appear to be solutions in mercury of the metal or of a compound of the metal and mercury. **Sodium amalgam is** made by pressing pieces of clean sodium under the surface of mercury : a bright flash occurs as each piece of sodium dissolves and a solid compound, NaHg, is formed. Gold, silver, cadmium, tin, bismuth, lead and zinc also readily form amalgams at ordinary temperatures. Finely divided copper readily amalgamates, but in mass the action is slow. Arsenic, antimony and platinum can be amalgamated with difficulty, while cobalt, nickel and iron do not amalgamate directly.

When a little sodium amalgam (containing about 1 per cent. of sodium) is placed in a solution of ammonium chloride the mercury swells up into a buttery mass, thirty times its original volume, which is known as **ammonium amalgam.** Its exact nature is somewhat doubtful, but it is believed that when prepared below 0° it is a true ammonium amalgam, but that at higher temperatures it decomposes into mercury, hydrogen and ammonia.

Uses of Mercury

Mercury is widely used in physical apparatus such as thermometers, barometers, etc. It is used in the manufacture of vermilion (mercuric sulphide) and was employed formerly for the extraction of gold and silver (p. 598). Considerable quantities are used for making mercury fulminate, which is extensively employed as a detonator ; and a certain amount is used in medicine. Tin amalgam, was formerly employed for " silvering " mirrors, and amalgams of gold, copper, and zinc are used in dentistry for stopping teeth. Amalgamated zinc is used in electric batteries, because action takes place only when the circuit is closed. Sodium amalgam is used in the laboratory, in conjunction with water, as a reducing agent.

§ 14 Atomic Weight of Mercury

Several reactions have been used for the determination of the combining weight of mercury, including reduction of the oxide, chloride and bromide to the metal, and the conversion of the chloride and bromide to silver chloride and bromide. Using the last-named method, Hönigschmid obtained results leading to the value 200·61 for the atomic weight of mercury, and this is the value recommended by the International Committee. That the atomic weight lies somewhere near 200 is indicated by the specific heat of mercury (0·333), by the vapour density of volatile compounds and by the position of the element in the Periodic table.

§ 15 Oxides of Mercury

The principal oxide of mercury is **mercuric oxide,** HgO. This appears to exist in two forms, a red and a yellow. Thus, if a solution of mercuric salt be treated with excess of an alkaline hydroxide in the cold, a yellow precipitate is obtained which probably results from the immediate decomposition of the mercuric hydroxide first formed :

$$HgCl_2 + 2NaOH = HgO + H_2O + 2NaCl.$$

If the precipitation be made from hot solutions, an orange precipitate is obtained, while heating mercury in air or ignition of the nitrate gives a red product. The difference appears to be one of particle size only, and the yellow oxide is more active than the red, probably on account of its finer state of subdivision. Hence its use in the preparation of chlorine monoxide (p. 506) and hypochlorous acid (p. 508).

When heated, the yellow oxide becomes red, and the red oxide darkens in colour, finally becoming almost black ; the red colour returning on cooling. If heated to a temperature somewhat above that at which blackening takes place, the oxide decomposes into mercury and oxygen. This is the way in which oxygen was discovered (p. 295). Both forms of the oxide are slightly soluble in water : at 25° one litre of water dissolves 0·0513 gram of the red oxide and 0·0518 gram of the yellow. The solution has an alkaline reaction.

The action of an alkali hydroxide on a solution of a mercurous salt gives a black precipitate—the so-called **mercurous oxide.** It is, however, probably a mixture of mercuric oxide and mercury.

Mercury peroxide, HgO_2, is formed as a red powder by the addition of hydrogen peroxide and alcoholic potash to a solution of mercuric chloride in alcohol.

§ 16 Salts of Mercury

Mercury forms two series of salts, mercurous and mercuric. In the latter the mercury is bivalent, in the former apparently univalent.

There has been some doubt as to the true nature of the mercurous compounds, but the experiments of H. B. Baker on the vapour density of very dry mercurous chloride (p. 651), and of Ogg on the E.M.F. of suitable concentration cells, have shown that the mercurous compounds contain the group — Hg — Hg — so that the metal is actually bivalent.

Mercurous salts are mostly insoluble in water, the nitrate being the only important soluble one. The mercuric salts are more often soluble, the principal insoluble ones being the sulphide and iodide. The mercuric salts are remarkable for the low degree to which they are ionized in solution, as indicated by their very low conductivity. Mercuric cyanide, is the extreme case, for it gives a non-conducting solution which does not give the usual "reactions" of mercuric mercury.

Mercuric salts are reduced to mercurous salts (see, e.g., p. 653) and sometimes to metallic mercury. Mercurous salts are correspondingly oxidized to mercuric by oxidizing agents. Mercury is displaced from solutions of its salts, whether mercurous or mercuric, by all metals except gold and the platinum metals.

§ 17 Mercurous Salts

Mercurous carbonate, Hg_2CO_3, is obtained as a yellow powder by addition of potassium bicarbonate solution to a solution of mercurous nitrate. It decomposes on heating into mercuric oxide, mercury and carbon dioxide.

Mercurous Chloride, Calomel, Hg_2Cl_2

This salt can be obtained by grinding mercuric chloride with mercury and subliming the product, the sublimate being washed with water until free from mercuric chloride :

$$Hg + HgCl_2 = Hg_2Cl_2.$$

It can also be made by the direct union of mercury and chlorine ; and by the addition of a soluble chloride or, better, hydrochloric acid, to a solution of a soluble mercurous salt, when mercurous chloride is precipitated.

Mercurous chloride is a white powder, almost insoluble in water : 1 litre of water dissolves only 0·002 gram at 18°. It sublimes at **373°** and its vapour density is 117·75 ($H_2 = 1$) which seems to indicate a formula HgCl. This value would be equally in accord with the facts if the mercurous chloride vapour were dissociated into mercury and mercuric chloride.

$$Hg_2Cl_2 \rightleftharpoons Hg + HgCl_2.$$

H. B. Baker has claimed that the vapour density of perfectly dried calomel is 235·5, and this supports the view that the formula is Hg_2Cl_2, and that the low value of the vapour density ordinarily obtained is due to dissociation. The lowering of the freezing point of fused mercuric chloride by the addition of calomel also indicates the "double" formula.

Mercurous chloride forms a black compound with ammonia, which appears to be **mercurio amido-chloride,** $Hg(NH_2)Cl$, mixed with metallic mercury. The salt is also blackened by alkalis as well as ammonia, and this may be the origin of the name *calomel*—from the

Greek καλομέλας (kalomelas), black.   The solid also absorbs ammonia gas, forming $Hg_2Cl_2.2NH_3$.

Mercurous chloride is used in medicine as a purgative, etc.   For this purpose it is important that it should be free from the highly poisonous mercuric compound.

Mercurous iodide, Hg_2I_2, is formed when mercuric iodide or iodine is rubbed up with the right proportion of mercury, in presence of alcohol ; or by addition of potassium iodide solution to a solution of a mercurous salt.   It is a greenish, yellow powder slightly soluble in water, which decomposes on standing or heating into mercuric iodide and mercury.

Mercurous nitrate, $Hg_2(NO_3)_2$, is deposited in colourless mono-clinic crystals of $Hg_2(NO_3)_2.2H_2O$ from solutions of mercury in cold, dilute nitric acid, the mercury being kept in excess.   This salt is soluble in water containing a little nitric acid, but excess of water decomposes it, precipitating a **basic nitrate,** $Hg_2(OH)NO_3$.   On boiling this with water, mercuric nitrate and mercury are formed. Dry mercurous nitrate, on heating, decomposes into mercuric oxide and nitrogen peroxide.

Mercurous sulphide, Hg_2S, is said to be formed in brownish-black plates by the prolonged action of cold, concentrated sulphuric acid on mercury, but there is some doubt as to its existence.   The action of hydrogen sulphide on mercurous salts gives a mixture of mercuric sulphide and mercury.

Mercurous sulphate, Hg_2SO_4, is formed by warming sulphuric acid with excess of mercury, or by adding sulphuric acid to a solution of mercurous nitrate.   It is a white solid, very sparingly soluble in water.   It is used in the Weston cadmium cell (p. 646).

§ 18 Mercuric Salts

Mercuric carbonate has not been prepared, and only **basic mercuric carbonates** are known.   The addition of potassium carbonate to a solution of mercuric nitrate gives a brown precipitate of $HgCO_3.2HgO$; whilst that of potassium bicarbonate gives a brown precipitate of $HgCO_3.3HgO$.

Mercuric chloride, corrosive sublimate, $HgCl_2$, is made, on a commercial scale, by heating a mixture of mercuric sulphate with sodium chloride, a little manganese dioxide being usually added to prevent the formation of mercurous chloride :

$$2NaCl + HgSO_4 = Na_2SO_4 + HgCl_2.$$

Mercuric chloride sublimes as a white translucent mass.   It is soluble in water—100 grams of water dissolve 5·6 grams at 10°—and by cooling a hot saturated solution, the salt can be obtained in needle-like rhombic prisms.   It volatilizes at a comparatively low temperature : it melts at 277° and boils at 303°.   It readily forms oxychlorides, e.g.,

$HgCl_2.HgO$, and double salts like $HgCl_2.HCl$. The double salts are more soluble than mercuric chloride itself and they are much used in making antiseptic solutions for taxidermists, etc. Mercuric chloride is a valuable antiseptic, and an aqueous solution (1 : 1000) is used for washing wounds, etc., in surgery. It is a virulent poison.

When solutions of mercuric chloride are treated with reducing agents, a white precipitate of calomel results, and on occasion further reduction occurs resulting in the formation of metallic mercury. Thus, with stannous chloride:

$$SnCl_2 + 2HgCl_2 = SnCl_4 + Hg_2Cl_2,$$
$$SnCl_2 + Hg_2Cl_2 = SnCl_4 + 2Hg.$$

When a solution of mercuric chloride is treated with excess of ammonia solution, a bulky white precipitate of **mercuric amido-chloride** (infusible white precipitate), $NH_2.HgCl$, is formed. If the order of mixing be reversed, or, better, if mercuric chloride be added to a boiling solution of ammonium chloride, **mercuric diammino chloride** (fusible white precipitate), $Hg(NH_3)_2Cl_2$, is formed. It is called fusible white precipitate because, when heated, it fuses and then volatilizes, whereas infusible white precipitate volatilizes without fusing. The relation between the two is indicated:

$$NH_2.HgCl + NH_4Cl \rightleftharpoons Hg(NH_3)_2Cl_2.$$

Mercuric iodide, HgI_2, is obtained by adding potassium iodide solution to mercuric chloride, avoiding excess of potassium iodide. A yellow precipitate is formed which quickly turns a brilliant scarlet.

Mercuric iodide exists in two forms, a red and a yellow. If the red form, which is tetragonal, be heated above 126°, it changes into the yellow (rhombic) form. This reverts to the red form on cooling, and scratching. Mercuric iodide melts at 259° to a red liquid, and a part sublimes forming yellow rhombic needles.

Mercuric iodide reacts with excess of potassium iodide solution, forming a solution containing potassium mercuric iodide, K_2HgI_4. This solution, made alkaline with sodium or potassium hydroxide, is known as *Nessler's Solution*. Nessler's solution is used for the detection and determination of small traces of ammonia, e.g., in water analysis. Ammonia gives a yellow or brown coloration with Nessler's Solution, the intensity of which depends upon the amount of ammonia present.

Mercuric nitrate, $Hg(NO_3)_2$, is prepared by boiling mercury with an excess of nitric acid until the solution gives no precipitate with a little sodium chloride. If evaporated over sulphuric acid, deliquescent crystals of $2Hg(NO_3)_2.H_2O$ are formed. If the mother liquor be boiled, a compound $Hg(NO_3)_2.HgO.2H_2O$, is precipitated, and if this precipitate or mercuric nitrate be treated with excess of cold water, the basic nitrate $Hg(NO_3)_2.2HgO.H_2O$ is precipitated. Thus, like mercurous nitrate, mercuric nitrate has a great tendency to form basic salts.

Mercuric Sulphide, Vermilion, HgS

Mercuric sulphide occurs naturally as the mineral *cinnabar* which is the chief source of mercury.

It is made by rubbing mercury and sulphur together in a mortar, and is also formed as a black precipitate by the action of hydrogen sulphide on a solution of a mercuric salt. When hydrogen sulphide is first passed through the solution (acidified with hydrochloric acid), a white precipitate is formed which is thought to be *mercury thiochloride*, Cl—Hg—S—Hg—S—Hg—Cl. This gradually turns brown and then black as the current of gas is continued.

$$Hg_3S_2Cl_2 + H_2S = 3HgS + 2HCl.$$

The black precipitate is almost unaffected by boiling dilute acids, though hot concentrated nitric acid gradually converts it into a white *mercury thionitrate*, $Hg_3S_2(NO_3)_2$, and finally into mercuric nitrate. It is not attacked by solutions of ammonium sulphide or alkaline hydroxides, but concentrated solutions of alkaline sulphides, more particularly the polysulphides, convert it into solutions of thio-salts, e.g.,

$$HgS + K_2S = Hg(SK)_2.$$

There are three different forms of crystalline mercuric sulphide. Two of these, a black form and a red form, occur in nature. Black *metacinnabar*, which occurs naturally, can be prepared by treating a dilute acid solution of a mercuric salt with sodium thiosulphate. By treating a concentrated solution in the same manner, a scarlet mercuric sulphide is formed with a specific gravity 7·2. This does not occur in nature. *Cinnabar*, the other native sulphide, is red. If the black sulphide be sublimed, a red crystalline sulphide is formed.

Mercuric sulphide is used as a pigment under the name *vermilion*, for which purposes it possesses the advantages of a fine colour and remarkable permanence. Its cost, however, prevents its use on a large scale.

Mercuric sulphate, $HgSO_4$, is prepared by heating mercury with excess of sulphuric acid. On concentrating the solution and allowing it to cool, small silvery-white crystals of mercuric sulphate are formed. It is soluble in cold water, but it reacts with hot water, forming the basic sulphate $HgSO_4.2HgO$, used in pharmacy under the name of *turpeth mineral*.

$$3HgSO_4 + 2H_2O = HgSO_4.2HgO + 2H_2SO_4.$$

Mercuric cyanide, $Hg(CN)_2$, is made by dissolving yellow mercuric oxide in aqueous hydrocyanic acid. It is used in the preparation of cyanogen (p. 370), and is noteworthy in that its solutions are non-conducting (and hence, according to the ionic theory, non-ionized) and do not give the " reactions " of mercury.

Mercuric thiocyanate, $Hg(CNS)_2$, made by adding mercuric chloride to a solution of potassium thiocyanate, is an insoluble white powder which when dried and ignited forms a voluminous ash. Pellets made from the dry powder, when ignited, form long snake-like tubes of ash—the so-called *Pharaoh's serpents*.

§ 19 Detection and Determination of Mercury

Mercury is usually detected by obtaining the separation of the metal. This can be done by warming copper foil with a solution of a mercury salt, when the mercury is deposited on the copper as a grey layer which becomes bright when rubbed, and may be vaporized to condense in globules on the sides of a small test-tube. Similarly, mercury compounds when heated with sodium carbonate yield the metal.

Mercury can also be determined similarly, the experiment being carried out in a crucible covered by a weighed, water-cooled, silver plate, on which the mercury collects. It is, however, usually determined as mercuric sulphide.

§ 20 Relationships of the Elements of Group II

The elements of Group II are somewhat similar to those of Group I in the marked electro-positive character of those in the A sub-group, and in the rather slight relationship between the members of the two sub-groups. Both these characteristics are, however, less noticeable in Group II than in Group I. Also the first two (or "typical") elements are not so clearly related to the A sub-group as in Group I and, as mentioned at the beginning of Chapter XXVII, they have been classified in both ways.

The valency of all the elements of the group is uniformly 2 in the soluble compounds, the mercurous compounds being only an apparent exception (see p. 650). The A sub-group forms a very well-marked triad of elements, which closely resemble each other ; along with them must be included radium, which so far as its chemical properties are known, is very similar to barium. Zinc cadmium and mercury are also a closely-related triad.

The hydroxides of calcium, barium and strontium are soluble, or slightly soluble, in water, those of zinc cadmium and mercury are insoluble. Similarly those of magnesium and the A sub-group are strongly basic, whereas the remainder are only feeble bases and may develop feeble acidic properties. The B sub-group elements also differ from the others in that their compounds are more easily reduced to the metal ; they are all stable in air; their sulphides are stable and insoluble, whereas the others are decomposed by water ; and the hydroxides are more easily decomposed by heat.

Beryllium, the lightest element of the group, shows many resemblances to aluminium, and mercury, which in many respects is a highly individual element, is like copper in some ways, as, for example, in the number of complex compounds it forms with ammonia. Beryllium and magnesium resemble each other quite closely, though the former is sometimes more like zinc in its behaviour than magnesium, which is more like calcium. Magnesium also shows some resemblance to lithium (cf. Chs. XXV and XXVI).

CHAPTER XXIX

THE ELEMENTS OF GROUP III

§ 1 Group III of the Periodic Table

THE third group of the Periodic Table comprises the elements boron and aluminium (the members of the short periods) together with scandium, yttrium, lanthanum, the rare earths and actinium on the one hand ; and gallium, indium and thallium on the other. Boron and aluminium are the only common elements in the group.

As in the case of Group II, there has been considerable discussion as to whether boron and aluminium are to be considered as primarily related to scandium, yttrium, etc., or to gallium, indium and thallium ; but the view is now generally held that the close association of boron and aluminium with gallium, indium and thallium is, on the whole, the best arrangement. This point will be referred to again in § 21.

§ 2 Boron, B

History

Although mentioned in the early Latin writings on chemistry, it is probable that the term " borax " did not always refer to the substance now called " borax," since the Arabians applied the term *buraq* (borax) to many substances used as fluxes. In 1702 W. Homberg made boric acid from borax, and called the acid *sal sedativum* ; H. J. Pott (1741) showed that ordinary Glauber's salt was produced at the same time. Hence, sulphuric acid and borax yields boric acid and Glauber's salt. Baron, 1748, showed that borax is a compound of Homberg's sal sedativum and soda. After Lavoisier's work on acids, the term " boracic acid " was substituted for " sal sedativum," and " boracic acid " was later abbreviated to " boric acid." J. L. Gay-Lussac and J. Thénard isolated the element in a more or less impure condition in 1808.

Occurrence

Boron does not occur free in nature, but it occurs as *boric acid* (also called *Tuscany boric acid*)—and as borates including *borax* and *tincal* ($Na_2B_4O_7.10H_2O$) and *kernite* ($Na_2B_4O_7.4H_2O$). It is also found in the form of complex borates, notably *colemanite* ($Ca_2B_8O_{11}.5H_2O$), in Asia Minor and America ; *boronatrocalcite* ($CaB_4O_7.NaBO_2.8H_2O$) in Chile, and *boracite* ($2Mg_3B_8O_{15}MgCl_2$) at Stassfurt. Boric oxide has been reported in sea-water, and it has been found in small quantities in soils, in most vegetable products, in plant ashes and in some wines. It is not usually present in animal products.

Extraction of Boron

The element boron has usually been obtained by heating the oxide with sodium, potassium, magnesium or aluminium in a covered crucible :

$$B_2O_3 + 6K = 3K_2O + 2B.$$

The fused mass is boiled with dilute hydrochloric acid, and a dark brown powder of **amorphous boron** remains. Of late years boron has been obtained by the electrolysis of a mixture of boric oxide with magnesium oxide and fluoride at 1100°, using a carbon crucible as anode and an iron cathode. The magnesium liberated at the cathode reduces the borate to boron which is deposited on the cathode, and yields amorphous boron on treatment with hydrochloric acid. (Andrieux, 1929.)

Crystalline boron has been made by dissolving boron in molten aluminium at a high temperature. The solution, on cooling, deposits crystals of boron which can be obtained by removing the aluminium by boiling with sodium hydroxide. Some think that this crystalline boron is really an alloy or a compound of boron and aluminium since it always persistently retains aluminium and carbon. A crystalline boron, said to be of 99 per cent. purity, has been made by striking an alternating current arc between water-cooled copper electrodes in a globe containing a mixture of boron trichloride and hydrogen.

Properties

Amorphous boron is a brown powder of specific gravity 2·45. The purest crystalline boron so far obtained is very hard, and has a quasi-metallic lustre, and a sp. gr. 3·3. Boron melts at about 2300° and volatilizes a little at that temperature.

Boron burns to the trioxide (B_2O_3) brilliantly when heated in oxygen, and also burns in air, forming a mixture of oxide and nitride (BN). Oxidizing agents (e.g., nitric acid) oxidize boron to boric acid ; boron also reacts with fused alkali hydroxides, forming borates, with the evolution of hydrogen.

Boron itself has not so far found any applications, but borax and boric acid (q.v.) are important technically.

Atomic Weight of Boron

The vapour densities of volatile compounds of boron, such as the chlorides, and volatile organic compounds, indicate a value for the atomic weight of boron in the neighbourhood of 11. Dulong and Petit's rule gives results which do not agree with this value, but the position of boron in the Periodic system supports the value 11 approx. The exact value has proved difficult to determine with accuracy. It has been attempted by determining the weight of water in a given weight of borax ($Na_2B_4O_7.10H_2O$) and by conversion of the halides into silver halides. The value at present (1940) recommended by the International Committee, is 10·82, based on the determination by Hönigschmid by the last-named method.

§ 3 Compounds of Boron

The compounds of boron exhibit, in general, the properties of the compounds of a non-metal. They indicate that the element is ter-valent. The hydrides (e.g., B_2H_6) seem to indicate the possibility of quadrivalency, but this is probably an incorrect deduction from their formula, though the question is still not definitely settled (see below).

Boron Hydrides

The existence of a hydride of boron was first reported by Sir H. Davy in 1810. F. Jones in 1879 investigated the product of the action of dilute acids on mag-nesium boride (made by strongly heating boron trioxide with magnesium powder), and this reaction was also examined by Ramsay and Hatfield in 1901. The systematic investigation of the subject is due to Stock and his co-workers (1912 onwards).

Stock passed the gases evolved when magnesium boride is dropped into dilute hydrochloric acid through a vessel immersed in liquid air, thus condensing them to a white solid which is a mixture of boron hydrides with silicon hydride, carbon dioxide, and other impurities.

Stock showed that the chief product is a hydride B_4H_{10} which soon breaks up into another, B_2H_6, and hydrogen. Other hydrides isolated by him were shown to have the formulae :

$$B_6H_{10}, \; B_{10}H_{14}, \; B_5H_9 \; and \; B_6H_{12}.$$

The assignment of constitutional formulae to these compounds presents some difficulty at first sight, their molecular formulae seem to suggest that in them boron might be quadrivalent like carbon ; but the position of boron in the Periodic Table and the formulae of its other compounds renders this improbable. A suggestion which gained a good deal of support was that in, for example, B_2H_6 two of the hydrogen atoms were attacked by single-electron links (cf. p. 737) leading to the electronic formula :

$$
\begin{array}{ccc}
\text{H} & & \text{H} \\
\cdot\cdot & & \cdot\cdot \\
\text{H}\cdot\text{B} & : & \text{B}\cdot\text{H} \\
\cdot\cdot & & \cdot\cdot \\
\text{H} & & \text{H}
\end{array}
$$

This view is supported by the great instability of these compounds which very readily lose hydrogen ; but this leaves each boron atom with only seven electrons in the outermost ring.

Stock now considers that these compounds are to be considered as acids and formulated accordingly. Thus, for example, he writes B_2H_6 as $[B_2H_4]H_2$ or written in terms of electrons :

$$
\left[
\begin{array}{ccc}
\text{H}\cdot & & \cdot\text{H} \\
& \text{B} : \text{B} & \\
\text{H} & & \text{H}
\end{array}
\right] \text{H}_2
$$

This is supported by the formation of an ammonium salt and a sodium derivative and by the marked difference in composition and properties between the hydrides and the other compounds of boron. This formula also has the merit of giving each boron atom the normal number of eight electrons in the outer ring, and does not require the doubtful device of single-electron link. Stock has suggested similar formulae for the remaining hydrides.

While Stock's suggestions seem to offer the best explanation at present avail-able for the constitution of these compounds, the matter cannot be said to be definitely settled.

Boron trioxide, boric oxide, B_2O_3, is formed when boron is burned in oxygen, but it is usually prepared by heating boric acid to redness. The fused mass so formed solidifies to a colourless transparent glass, which has no definite melting point. When exposed to the atmosphere, boron trioxide absorbs moisture with which it combines, becoming opaque and finally passing into boric acid :

$$B_2O_3 + H_2O = 2HBO_2$$
metaboric acid

$$HBO_2 + H_2O = H_3BO_3$$
orthoboric acid

Boron trioxide is almost non-volatile, even at a red heat, and consequently it can decompose the compounds of much stronger acids, such as sulphuric acid, when heated with them to very high temperatures :

$$B_2O_3 + 3K_2SO_4 = 2K_3BO_3 + 3SO_3.$$

This behaviour is analogous to that of the preparation of hydrochloric acid from sodium chloride and sulphuric acid (which is a weaker acid than hydrochloric (p. 499). (Compare also the electric furnace method of making phosphorus, p. 719.)

Boron trioxide is mainly an acidic oxide ; but it also exhibits very feeble basic properties. With water it forms boric acid and with basic oxides it forms borates, e.g. :

$$CuO + B_2O_3 = Cu(BO_3)_2.$$

The existence of unstable compounds, like the *acid sulphate*, $B(HSO_4)_3$, and the *phosphate* BPO_4, is evidence of its basic properties. Most of the salts, however, of either kind are largely hydrolyzed by water.

§ 4. The Boric Acids

Several boric acids are known (at least in the form of salts), all derived from boron trioxide with varying amounts of water—thus :

Orthoboric acid	H_3BO_3	or $B_2O_3.3H_2O$,
Metaboric acid	HBO_2	or $B_2O_3.H_2O$,
Pyroboric acid	$H_6B_4O_9$	or $2B_2O_3.3H_2O$,
Tetraboric acid	$H_2B_4O_7$	or $2B_2O_3.H_2O$.

Salts also exist corresponding to more complex, condensed boric acids, e.g., $H_4B_6O_{11}$ and $H_2B_{10}O_{16}$. Of the free acids, orthoboric is the only important one ; of salts *borax*, the most important boron compound, is sodium tetraborate.

Orthoboric Acid, H_3BO_3

Volcanic jets of steam (soffioni) at a temperature between 90° and 120°, issuing from the fumaroles on the so-called Maremme di Toscana —or Tuscany Marshes—carry small quantities of boric acid. The steam condenses in lagoons (lagoni) of water which often surround the jets. The water of the lagoons becomes highly charged with the acid, and the boric acid can be obtained in a crystalline condition by evaporating the water of the lagoons. Artificial lagoons for arresting the jets of steam were established in Tuscany in 1818 ; and artificial soffioni were bored in 1854. The natural heat of the steam is utilized in concentrating the water.

A large proportion of the world's supply of boric acid is now made from the naturally-occurring deposits of calcium borates in California and South America, e.g., colemanite, etc. The mineral is powdered, mixed with boiling water, and sulphur dioxide is passed through the mixture, whereby boric acid and calcium sulphite are formed. On cooling, the boric acid crystallizes out :

$$Ca_2B_6O_{11} + 2SO_2 + 9H_2O = 2CaSO_3 + 6H_3BO_3.$$

Orthoboric acid crystallizes on cooling hot aqueous solutions as white, shining plates belonging to the triclinic system. It is appreciably volatile in steam (hence its presence in the soffioni), and is sparingly soluble in cold water and reasonably soluble in hot : 100 grams of water dissolve 3·6 grams of H_3BO_3 at 10° and 39·65 grams at 100°.

On heating, orthoboric acid loses water : at a temperature of 100°, or a little above, metaboric acid is formed :

$$H_3BO_3 = HBO_2 + H_2O,$$

while at about 160° tetraboric acid, sometimes (wrongly) called pyroboric acid results :

$$4HBO_2 = H_2B_4O_7 + H_2O.$$

When heated to a still higher temperature, it swells to a frothy mass and finally, forms a glass of boron trioxide.

Boric acid is a very weak acid : in aqueous solution it colours litmus claret-red, and moist yellow turmeric paper is coloured brown, but, unlike the brown colour produced by alkalis, the brown stain is not destroyed by acids.

Boric acid is used in medicine as an antiseptic, and large quantities have been employed as a food preservative. Its use, however, for this purpose, is now prohibited in many countries : in this country food preservatives as a whole are forbidden.

Boric acid is also used in the manufacture of glazes, particularly for enamels to be used on metals since borate glazes have a higher coefficient of expansion than silicate glazes.

Metaboric acid, HBO_2, is formed when orthoboric acid is heated to just over 100°. When dissolved in water it reforms the ortho-acid.

§ 5 Sodium Borates. Borax

Sodium Tetraborate, Borax, $Na_2B_4O_7$

Borax occurs naturally as *tincal* in the dried-up inland lakes of some parts of India, Tibet and California. Native tincal contains about 55 per cent. of borax proper, i.e., of $Na_2B_4O_7.10H_2O$. This is extracted by lixiviating the mass with water and evaporating until crystals separate.

Large quantities of borax were at one time made from native calcium borate. The powdered mineral is boiled in drums with a slight excess of aqueous sodium carbonate. Calcium carbonate is precipitated as a mud, and from the clear solution, crystals of borax are obtained.

Sodium metaborate remains in the mother liquor and is converted into borax by blowing carbon dioxide through it.

Since 1926 when kernite (rasorite) was discovered it has been almost the sole source of borax. It is first extracted with hot water, which dissolves the borax ; any silica in solution is precipitated and the hot filtrate, after dilution, treated with an oxidising agent to destroy colouring matter. After further filtration the borax is obtained by crystallisation.

Borax is ordinarily obtained in the form of large colourless crystals of the decahydrate, $Na_2B_4O_7.10H_2O$. It is sparingly soluble in cold water, but is more soluble in hot : 100 grams of water dissolve 3 grams of decahydrate at $10°$ and 99.3 grams at $100°$. If a saturated solution be allowed to crystallize above about $62°$, octahedral crystals of the pentahydrate, $Na_2B_4O_7.5H_2O$ separate ; if the temperature be below $62°$, the decahydrate is formed.

Solutions of borax are alkaline, for, since boric acid is a very weak acid, considerable hydrolysis occurs. Borax solutions can be titrated with standard hydrochloric acid using methyl orange (which is unaffected by boric acid) as indicator.

When heated, borax fuses, loses water, and swells up into a white porous mass, owing to the expulsion of the water. Finally the borax melts to a clear glass—borax glass—which is anhydrous borax. Like boric acid, fused borax dissolves many colouring oxides, giving glasses with a characteristic colour. Borax " beads " fused in a loop of platinum wire are used as tests for oxides which dissolve in the bead, and show characteristic colours as indicated in Table XLI. Thus :

TABLE XLI.—COLOURS OF BORAX BEADS WITH SOME METALLIC OXIDES.

Metallic oxide.	Oxidizing flame.	Reducing flame.
Copper . . .	Green (hot) ; blue (cold)	Colourless or red.
Cobalt . . .	Blue (hot or cold)	Blue.
Chromium . . .	Green or red (hot or cold)	Green.
Iron	Yellow (cold); brown (hot)	Dirty green or olive.
Nickel . . .	Violet (hot) ; brown (cold)	Grey and opaque.
Manganese . . .	Amethyst (hot or cold)	Grey and opaque.

Large quantities of borax are used in the manufacture of enamels, glazes and of optical glass ; in the manufacture of soap and of drying oils ; for stiffening candle wicks ; as a cleansing and stiffening agent in laundry work, and for glazing paper, playing-cards, etc. ; in making varnishes for metals ; with casein, as a substitute for gum arabic ;

and as a flux in soldering and brazing. It is also employed as an antiseptic.

Sodium metaborate, $NaBO_2.4H_2O$, can be obtained by the action of caustic soda solution on boric acid or borax :

$$H_3BO_3 + NaOH = NaBO_2 + 2H_2O,$$
$$Na_2B_4O_7 + 2NaOH = 4NaBO_2 + H_2O.$$

It crystallizes in colourless needles.

Sodium perborate, $NaBO_3.4H_2O$, is obtained when a mixed solution of borax and sodium hydroxide is electrolyzed, or treated with hydrogen peroxide. It has also been made by acting upon boric acid suspended in cold water, with sodium peroxide, and treating the salt which crystallizes out on cooling, with the correct amount of a dilute acid :

$$4H_3BO_3 + Na_2O_2 = Na_2B_4O_8 + 6H_2O,$$
$$Na_2B_4O_8 + HCl + 4H_2O = NaBO_3 + NaCl + 3H_3BO_3.$$

Sodium perborate has strong oxidizing properties and is used as a cleansing and bleaching agent.

§ 6 Other Boron Compounds

Boron nitride, BN, is a white powder formed when boron is burnt in nitrogen, or heated in ammonia. It is decomposed by steam, forming boric acid and ammonia, and the occurrence of both these substances in the vapours of the Soffioni of Tuscany has led to the suggestion that they are there derived from the action of steam on subterranean boron nitride.

Boron sulphide, B_2S_3, is obtained in white needles by direct union of the elements. **Boron pentasulphide,** B_2S_5, is also known.

All four halogens unite with boron to form trihalides. Of these the trifluoride and trichloride are the most important.

Boron trifluoride, BF_3, is a colourless, fuming gas obtained by heating a mixture of concentrated sulphuric acid, calcium fluoride and boron trioxide :

$$B_2O_3 + 3CaF_2 + 3H_2SO_4 = 2BF_3 + 3CaSO_4 + 3H_2O.$$

It reacts vigorously with water forming metaboric and hydrofluoric acids ; the hydrogen fluoride so formed unites with unchanged boron trifluoride to form **hydrofluoboric acid,** HBF_4 :

$$2BF_3 + 4H_2O = 2HBO_2 + 3H_2F_2,$$
$$2BF_3 + H_2F_2 = 2HBF_4.$$

Boron trichloride, BCl_3, is a volatile, colourless, fuming liquid obtained by direct union of the elements ; by heating an intimate mixture of boron trioxide and charcoal in a current of chlorine :

$$B_2O_3 + 3C + 3Cl_2 = 3CO + 2BCl_3.$$

It boils at $12 \cdot 5°$ and is decomposed by water into boric and hydrochloric acids.

§ 7 Detection and Determination of Boron

Boron usually occurs as boric acid or a borate, and if in some other state of combination may be converted into one of these by means of hot concentrated nitric acid. These are then detected by heating with sulphuric acid and a little alcohol. On setting light to the alcohol, a green-edged flame, due to the formation of ethyl borate, indicates the presence of boron. Alternatively, the following procedure may be adopted. The suspected borate is mixed with powdered calcium fluoride and made into a paste with concentrated sulphuric acid. A platinum wire is dipped into the paste and held near to, but not in, a bunsen flame. If boron be present the flame is coloured green owing to the formation of boron trifluoride. Barium and copper, if present, do not colour the flame under these conditions.

Boron in the form of borax can be determined by titration with a mineral acid (such as hydrochloric acid) using methyl-orange as indicator. Boric acid itself can be titrated with caustic soda solution, provided a considerable proportion of glycerol is also present in the solution.

§ 8 Aluminium, Al

History

The word " alumen," or its Greek equivalent, was formerly applied as a grouping term for substances with an astringent taste. Geber and some others classed alum with the " vitriols," but Paracelsus considered it to be radically different, for he pointed out that its " corpus " is not metallic but an intimate mixture of earths. The earthy " corpus " was confused with lime until J. H. Pott, 1746, showed that the base is really an argillaceous earth ; and in 1754, A. S. Marggraf proved clearly that the base is entirely different from lime, and that clay contains the " alum earth " united with silica.

Occurrence

Aluminium (also called in the U.S.A. aluminum) does not occur free in nature, but its compounds are numerous and widely distributed. In abundance, it comes third, after oxygen and silicon.

Corundum, ruby, and *sapphire* are more or less impure forms of the oxide, Al_2O_3 ; *emery* is a mixture of iron oxide and corundum. There are three recognized hydrates occurring in nature—*gibbsite* or *hydrargillite*, $Al_2O_3.3H_2O$, or $Al(OH)_3$; *bauxite*, $Al_2O_3.2H_2O$, or $Al_2O(OH)_4$, and *diaspore*, $Al_2O_3.H_2O$, or $AlO(OH)$. The word **bauxite** is used in rather a general way for native aluminium hydroxides containing the equivalent of, say, 50 to 70 per cent. of Al_2O_3, about 25 to 30 per cent. of water, with varying amounts of ferric oxide, titanic oxide, and silica. Some bauxites approximate to the trihydrate ; others appear to be mixtures of the trihydrate and lower hydrates, and some are considered to be more or less impure monohydrate. The bauxites are often classed as ferruginous, and non-ferruginous. The double fluoride—*cryolite*, $AlF_3.3NaF$, is used in the manufacture of aluminium ; *turquoise* is a hydrated phosphate. The *felspars* and *clays*, as well as a great number of common minerals, are complex silicates of aluminium with other bases. Bauxite and cryolite are the chief compounds used in the preparation of the metal aluminium.

Isolation of the Metal.

Aluminium was first isolated by F. Wöhler in 1827 by warming the anhydrous chloride with potassium, as a light grey metallic powder, but it was not until 1845 that the compact metal was obtained. Deville replaced the potassium by sodium and this, until 1886, was the only method available, so that metallic aluminium until then was little more than a chemical curiosity.

The cheap production of aluminium was made possible by the discovery, by C. M. Hall in 1886, that a solution of alumina in a molten mixture of cryolite and some other fusible fluoride, is an electrolyte, and that when electrolyzed, aluminium collects at the cathode. Aluminium is now made entirely by electrolysis, but the process can be carried on only where electricity is cheap (e.g., where water-power is available).

The raw material is bauxite which is usually too impure to be used without a preliminary purification to remove iron, titanium and silicon oxides, which would seriously contaminate the metallic aluminium. The bauxite is roasted at a low temperature to convert the ferrous oxide into ferric oxide and then digested with a solution of sodium hydroxide under pressure :

$$Al_2O_3 + 2NaOH = 2NaAlO_2 + H_2O.$$

The alumina is reprecipitated from the solution by agitation with a

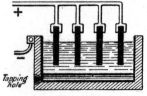

FIG. 216.

Manufacture of Aluminium.

little freshly-precipitated aluminium hydroxide from a previous operation, when the aluminium hydroxide separates from the solution until the ratio Al_2O_3 : Na_2O is about 1 : 6. The hydroxide is then washed, dried and ignited.

The purified oxide is then added to a molten mixture of cryolite and fluorspar, contained in a large electrolytic cell (Fig. 216). This consists of an iron box about eight feet long and six feet wide lined with blocks of carbon and serves as the cathode. The anodes are a set of carbon rods.

The exact nature of the action which takes place is not certain. The following is thought to be probable. The aluminium fluoride (from cryolite) ionizes :

$$AlF_3 \rightleftharpoons Al^{\cdots} + 3F^{\cdot}.$$

The aluminium is discharged at the cathode, while at the anode the fluorine reacts with the bauxite reforming aluminium fluoride, and oxygen which is liberated :

$$2Al_2O_3 + 12F = 4AlF_3 + 3O_2.$$

The resistance of the electrolyte to the current gives enough heat to keep the mass fluid. The liquid metal sinks to the bottom of the cell, whence it is " tapped " from time to time. The oxygen evolved at the anode either escapes as a gas or unites with the carbon to form carbon monoxide, which either burns or escapes. Fresh supplies of bauxite are added when required.

Although clays contain from 20 to 36 per cent. of alumina, no method is known for separating silica from alumina cheaply enough for manufacturing purposes.

§ 9 Properties of Aluminium

Aluminium is a bluish-white metal capable of taking a high polish. The dull surface usually seen on the metal is an effect of a superficial film of oxide. Aluminium is lighter than most metals, its specific gravity is 2·7, and therefore it has nearly the same specific gravity as glass, and one-third the specific gravity of iron. The metal is ductile and malleable at 100° to 150°. With frequent annealing it can be rolled into sheets, wire, and foil. Aluminium is not very tenacious ; at about 530° it undergoes a remarkable change in its physical properties, whereby its toughness and hardness are considerably reduced, and the metal becomes so friable that it can be pulverized. It is a good conductor of heat and electricity. Aluminium melts at about 660° ; and boils at 1800°.

Aluminium remains practically unaltered in dry air, while in moist air and in boiling water, a superficial film of oxide seems to protect the metal from further action. Even at 700° to 800° it oxidizes but slowly ; at higher temperatures it burns brilliantly with the evolution of much heat.

Aluminium, when heated with the halogens and with nitrogen, forms halides and nitride respectively. Aluminium dissolves slowly in cold dilute hydrochloric acid, and rapidly in hot, the concentrated acid giving an aqueous solution of aluminium chloride, and hydrogen gas. Nitric acid, dilute or concentrated, acts so slowly that nitric acid is usually said to have " no action on aluminium." Sulphuric acid has very little action in the cold, but the hot concentrated acid converts it into aluminium sulphate with the evolution of sulphur dioxide. Aluminium is rapidly dissolved by sodium and potassium hydroxides with the evolution of hydrogen and the formation of the alkali aluminate. Organic acids (e.g., acetic acid) are almost without action on the metal at ordinary temperatures, but they are said to have an appreciable solvent action in the presence of sodium chloride. Salt solutions, e.g., sea-water, rapidly corrode the metal.

Aluminium is a very intensely electro-positive element (cf. Table XVII, p. 205) and, in consequence, it is a powerful reducing agent. Thus, carbon monoxide and dioxide are reduced to carbon. Also, aluminium powder, when intimately mixed with many metallic sulphides or oxides—manganese, chromium, tungsten, uranium, iron, etc.—along with some flux, say, fluorspar, and ignited, reduces the oxides or sulphides to the metal. E.g., with pyrites, it forms aluminium sulphide and metallic iron. The mixture becomes very hot during the reaction and a temperature of 3000°-3500° is sometimes attained,

The heat of this reaction can be utilized for softening and welding iron rails, steel castings, etc., when an intense local heat is needed. The rails to be welded are packed in a mixture of iron oxide and aluminium powder together with a special cement to make the mass compact. When the mass is ignited, it burns and heats the rails to a temperature high enough to weld the metals together. The mixture of aluminium powder with various metallic oxides is sold as " thermite," and the process is called H. Goldschmidt's or the alumino-thermic process.

§ 10 Uses of Aluminium

Large quantities of aluminium powder mixed with oil are used as paint for steam-pipes, and other metal objects exposed to heat or the weather. Aluminium is used for cooking utensils ; the metallic parts of military outfits ; certain parts of airships, etc. ; precision instruments ; surgical instruments ; and as an ornamental metal for interior decoration ; and artistic objects, trinkets, etc. The wire is used as a conductor of electricity, because aluminium wire, though thicker than copper for a given conductivity, is not so heavy and does not strain the supports so much. Aluminium is used as a reducing agent in the production of certain metals—chromium, etc.—and in the manufacture of " thermite." The formation of oxides during the melting of many metals is prevented if a little aluminium be present, hence aluminium—0·16 to 0·05 per cent.—is commonly added to molten steel as it comes from the Siemens-Martin's, or Bessemer's furnace. This enables castings to be made more free from " blow holes."

Aluminium forms many useful alloys, which are finding more and more applications. Examples of some of these and their approximate compositions are given in Table XLII.

TABLE XLII.—ALUMINIUM ALLOYS.

Alloy.	Composition (per cent.).						
	Silicon.	Copper.	Mag-nesium.	Mang-anese.	Iron.	Nickel.	Alumin-ium.
Almasilium .	0·8-2		0·8				97·2-98·6
Duralumin .		4	0·5	0·5			95
Y-alloy . .		3·5-4·5				1·8-2·3	93·2-94·7
Hydronalium			7				93
Alpax	10-13						87-90
Magnalium		1·75	1·75		0·4-1		95·5-96·1
Birmabright .			3·5-5	0·5			94·5-96

Aluminium amalgam, made by adding aluminium filings to a 0·5 per cent. solution of mercuric chloride for a couple of minutes, is a valuable neutral reducing agent.

§ 11 Atomic Weight of Aluminium

The vapour density of aluminium chloride and of some organic derivatives of aluminium, and its specific heat indicate a value of approximately 27 for the atomic weight. The exact atomic weight has been determined by measurement of the amount of hydrogen evolved by the action of acids or alkalis, and from the weight of silver chloride or bromide obtained from known weights of aluminium chloride or bromide. The value at present accepted is 26·97, and is based on the determinations made by Krepelka by the silver method.

§ 12 Aluminium Nitride and Carbide

Aluminium nitride, AlN, is formed when alumina is heated with carbon to 1800° in an atmosphere of nitrogen :

$$Al_2O_3 + 3C + N_2 = 2AlN + 3CO.$$

This reaction is the basis of the *Serpek process* for the fixation of nitrogen (p. 402) since, with water, aluminium nitride yields ammonia and aluminium hydroxide, and thus it was hoped to use it for the production of ammonia and, simultaneously, for the purification of bauxite. The method was, however, not a commercial success.

Aluminium carbide, Al_4C_3, is a yellowish powder, made by heating alumina and carbon to a very high temperature. It is decomposed by water forming methane (p. 333).

$$Al_4C_3 + 12H_2O = 3Al(OH)_3 + 3CH_4.$$

§ 13 Aluminium Oxide and Hydroxide

Aluminium Oxide, Al_2O_3

Aluminium oxide, or alumina, occurs in nature as colourless crystalline corundum ; and tinted with various metallic oxides as ruby, sapphire, amethyst, emery, etc. Alumina is prepared as a white powder by the ignition of aluminium hydroxide, aluminium nitrate, or ammonia alum. Alumina fuses at 1900° to 2010°, and it begins to volatilize appreciably at 1750°. Alumina is prepared in a crystalline condition by strongly heating a mixture of aluminium fluoride and boric oxide.

$$2AlF_3 + B_2O_3 = Al_2O_3 + 2BF_3.$$

Artificial rubies have also been prepared : an ingenious method for doing this is due to Verneuil. In this a rod of alumina is heated by an inverted oxy-hydrogen flame, and a little finely-powdered alumina and chromic oxide are sprinkled in the flame. These small particles melt and adhere to the rod, and thus build up a single crystal of alumina coloured by the chromic oxide—an artificial ruby.

Aluminium oxide is a stable and unreactive substance. It is only reduced with great difficulty.

When alumina is heated above about 800° an exothermal change takes place, the alumina changes in some way, for it then becomes almost insoluble in acids ; its specific gravity rises rapidly from 2·8 to 4·0 ; and other physical properties change at the same time. The change is supposed to be due to the formation of a polymorphic modification of alumina.

Apart from its use in the manufacture of aluminium, bauxite is used in making the so-called bauxite bricks, and for lining the bed of basic open hearth furnaces. Fused alumina is also used as a high-grade refractory for muffles, etc.

Alumina is now used in many branches of scientific investigation as an " adsorption filter " ; and by its use some remarkable separations have been effected.

Alumina is a constituent of aluminous cements which are coming into increasing use, being characterized by their quick-setting properties and resistance to sea water.

Aluminium hydroxide, $Al(OH)_3$, is obtained as a colloidal precipitate when ammonia or an alkaline carbonate is added to a solution of an aluminium salt.

Freshly precipitated aluminium hydroxide dissolves easily in acids and in alkaline hydroxides. If the precipitate has stood a long time under water, or if the precipitate be dried, it dissolves very slowly in these reagents.

When aluminium hydroxide is precipitated in a solution containing a colouring matter, the latter is simultaneously precipitated, and the aluminium hydroxide with the absorbed colouring matter is called a lake. Advantage is taken of this property in dyeing cloth. The aluminium hydroxide is first precipitated in the fibres of the cloth, and the fabric is then immersed in the dye, and some of the dye is fixed by the aluminium hydroxide in the fibres. Hence, aluminium hydroxide is a dye-fixing agent or mordant. Dyes which stain the fibres directly need no mordant.

Aluminium hydroxide is an amphoteric oxide for it will easily react with, and form salts with, both acids and alkalis. Both aluminium and the oxide and the hydroxide will react with solutions of the caustic alkalis, forming solutions of sodium or potassium aluminates (e.g., $NaAlO_2$), and aluminates of the alkaline earths are also known. The aluminates are not very stable ; their aqueous solutions are strongly alkaline, on account of hydrolysis, and they are decomposed by carbon dioxide with the precipitation of aluminium hydroxide.

The minerals *spinel*—$MgO.Al_2O_3$, or magnesium meta-aluminate, $Mg(AlO_2)_2$; *chrysoberyl*—$BeO.Al_2O_3$, or beryllium meta-aluminate, $Be(AlO_2)_2$; *gahnite*—$ZnO.Al_2O_3$, or zinc meta-aluminate, $Zn(AlO_2)_2$; *hercynite*, $FeO.Al_2O_3$, or ferrous meta-aluminate—are supposed to be **meta-aluminates** which can be represented by the graphic formulae :

$$KO-Al=O \qquad Mg{<}^{O-Al=O}_{O-Al=O} \qquad Be{<}^{O-Al=O}_{O-Al=O} \qquad Zn{<}^{O-Al=O}_{O-Al=O}$$

Potassium   Spinel.   Chrysoberyl.   Gahnite.
meta-aluminate.

Pleonaste or *ceylonite*, $MgO.Fe_2O_3$; *franklinite*, impure $ZnO.Fe_2O_3$; *magnesioferrite*, $MgO.Fe_2O_3$; *magnetic oxide of iron*, $FeO.Fe_2O_3$; and *chromite*, $FeO.Cr_2O_3$, are sometimes included in this group of minerals with the general name spinels, and general formula $R''O.R'''_2O_3$, where R'' represents the dyad elements Fe, Mn, Mg, Be, Zn ; and R''' the triad elements Fe, Mn, Al, Cr.

§ 14 Salts of Aluminium

Aluminium salts are usually colourless and are not poisonous. Since aluminium hydroxide is a very weak base, the salts with strong acids are very readily hydrolyzed with water, and salts with weak acids can only be obtained, if at all, with great difficulty.

Aluminium Chloride, Al_2Cl_6

Aluminium reacts with hydrochloric acid and the resulting aqueous solution, in presence of excess of acid, deposits crystals of $Al_2Cl_6.12H_2O$. On heating, the hydrate decomposes leaving alumina :

$$Al_2Cl_6.12H_2O = 6HCl + 9H_2O + Al_2O_3.$$

Anhydrous aluminium chloride is made on a large scale by passing chlorine over a mixture of carbon and alumina at a high temperature. The chloride sublimes and is condensed in a receiver carefully protected against access of moisture :

$$Al_2O_3 + 3C + 3Cl_2 = Al_2Cl_6 + 3CO.$$

Anhydrous aluminium chloride can also be made by passing chlorine or hydrogen chloride over heated aluminium turnings.

Anhydrous aluminium chloride fumes strongly in moist air, owing to the formation of hydrogen chloride :

$$Al_2Cl_6 + 6H_2O = 2Al(OH)_3 + 6HCl.$$

It sublimes at 183° and the vapour density, at about 200°, corresponds to the formula Al_2Cl_6.

Aluminium chloride is an important catalyst in organic chemistry. A crude aluminium chloride, made from bauxite, is used in the petroleum industry in the manufacture of " synthetic " lubricating oils.

Aluminium sulphide, Al_2S_3, is a greyish black powder which can be obtained by direct combination of the elements at a high temperature ; by heating very strongly a mixture of alumina, carbon and sulphur ; and by heating aluminium with iron pyrites. It is decomposed by water with evolution of hydrogen sulphide :

$$Al_2S_3 + 6H_2O = 2Al(OH)_3 + 3H_2S,$$

and hence, in qualitative analysis, the action of hydrogen sulphide, or ammonium sulphide, on an aluminium salt in solution precipitates the hydroxide.

§ 15 Aluminium Sulphate. The Alums

Aluminium Sulphate, $Al_2(SO_4)_3$

This salt is prepared by dissolving the hydrated oxide in sulphuric acid. Large quantities too are made by dissolving bauxite, and the purer varieties of clay in the same acid. Clay roasted at a dull red hea is more readily attacked by the acid. · The crude aluminium sulphate so obtained is called " alum-cake," and if much iron is present, " alum ferric cake," used in the purification of sewage on account of its power of precipitating colloids (cf. p. 247).

A purer sulphate is made by heating bauxite with sodium carbonate, or by boiling cryolite with milk of lime. In each case a solution of sodium aluminate—$Al_2O_3.3Na_2O$—almost free from iron is obtained. The sodium aluminate is then decomposed by a current of carbon dioxide, and the precipitated aluminium hydroxide is dissolved in sulphuric acid. When the solution is concentrated, the mass solidifies to a white solid which does not crystallize very readily. The crystalline sulphate has the composition represented by : $Al_2(SO_4)_3.18H_2O$.

The salt is very soluble in water and has an acid reaction on account of hydrolysis. Basic sulphates are formed by boiling the normal sulphate with freshly precipitated aluminium hydroxide.

Aluminium sulphate is used in " foam " fire extinguishers, since when mixed with sodium bicarbonate carbon dioxide is formed along with aluminium hydroxide which renders the bubbles stable, and hence a stable foam results. This foam is particularly valuable for the extinction of oil fires.

It is also employed in sizing paper, tanning leather, waterproofing cloth and as a mordant in dyeing.

Alums

When a hot solution of aluminium sulphate is mixed with potassium sulphate, and the solution is cooled, octahedral crystals of a double sulphate of aluminium and potassium separate. The octahedral form is not always recognizable directly on account of the abnormal development of one or more faces. Thus, shapes like Fig. 217 may be obtained. The salt has the formula, $K_2SO_4.Al_2(SO_4)_3.24H_2O$, or

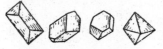

FIG. 217.—Abnormally developed Alum Crystals.

else $KAl(SO_4)_2.12H_2O$. This salt is a typical member of a large number of isomorphous compounds which are called " alums." Their general formula is :

$$R_2^ISO_4.R_2^{III} (SO_4)_3.24H_2O ; \text{ or, } R^IR^{III} (SO_4)_2.12H_2O,$$

where R^I represents an atom of a univalent metal or radicle—potassium, sodium, ammonium, rubidium, caesium, silver, and univalent thallium ; and R^{III} represents an atom of a tervalent metal—aluminium, iron, chromium, manganese, cobalt, rhodium, indium, gallium, and tervalent thallium. An iridium rubidium alum has also been reported. The report of a silver alum has not been confirmed.

Potash-alum or *kalinite* occurs native as the result of the weathering of iron pyrites and alkali rocks. Mixed crystals of different alums are readily obtained by allowing mixed solutions of different alums to crystallize ; and crystals of one alum, say chrome alum, grown on the surface of ordinary alum, or conversely, can be obtained. A series of **selenium alums** has also been made in which the sulphur atom in K_2SO_4 is replaced by an atom of selenium. The selenium alums are isomorphous with the alums proper.

The stability of the alums generally decreases with increasing atomic weight of the tervalent metal, and increases in stability with increasing atomic weight of the univalent metal. For example, sodium forms alums only with the lightest tervalent metals—aluminium, vanadium, and chromium ; potassium forms stable alums only with aluminium and chromium. The ferric and gallic alums readily form basic salts ; and indium does not form a potash-alum, but gives instead the double sulphate $K_2SO_4.In_2(SO_4)_3.6(\text{and } 8)H_2O$; titanium forms an alum only with caesium and rubidium. Lithium alum has been made only recently, and soda alum is not easy to make. The alums are usually much more soluble in hot water than in cold ; and they are deposited from cooling concentrated solutions of the two salts in the form of octahedral or cubical crystals.

When heated, the alums give up their water of crystallization. Potash-alum melts at about 84·5°, and slowly loses all its water of crystallization at 100° ; at higher temperatures, the water is driven off more rapidly, and leaves behind a white porous mass called " burnt alum." Ammonia alum when calcined gives a residue of alumina— Al_2O_3—which may contain traces of sulphates. The soluble sulphates can be removed by washing.

Alum-stone or *alunite* is a kind of basic alum—$K_2SO_4.Al_2(SO_4)_3.$ $4Al(OH)_3$—found near Rome, in Hungary, etc. It is supposed to have been formed by the action of volcanic sulphur dioxide on the felspathic rocks. It is insoluble in water, but, on calcination, it gives a residuum of alumina (mixed with ferric oxide as impurity) and potash-alum passes into solution when the mass is digested with water. Alum prepared in this way is called " Roman alum," and that which occurs in commerce is crystallized in cubes.

Alum is extensively used as a mordant in dyeing and in the leather industry. On account of its power of precipitating colloids, it is used in styptic pencils, etc., for stopping bleeding from small cuts since it causes coagulation of the blood.

Pseudo-alums

A series of double sulphates, sometimes called pseudo-alums, can be made by introducing a bivalent element—manganese, ferrous iron, copper, zinc, magnesium—in place of the univalent element of ordinary alums. Thus,

$$Al_2(SO_4)_3.MnSO_4.24H_2O \qquad Al_2(SO_4)_3.FeSO_4.24H_2O$$

Manganese-aluminium pseudo-alum.   Ferrous-aluminium pseudo-alum.

The latter is related to the mineral *halotrichite*. These alums are not isomorphous with ordinary alums.

Aluminium silicates are important constituents of various minerals, e.g., the felspars, micas, garnets and zeolites. The felspars, such as *orthoclase* or potash felspar ($K_2O.Al_2O_3.6SiO_2$), form part of most igneous rocks ; the micas are double silicates of aluminium and another metal such as magnesium ; and the garnets are double silicates of aluminium (or another trivalent metal) and a divalent metal (e.g., Ca, Mg, or Fe). The zeolites are hydrated double silicates of a metal and aluminium. The sodium compound ($Na_2O.Al_2O_3.2SiO_2.6H_2O$), known as sodium *permutit*, is used for water-softening (p. 278). Alumino-silicates are also important constituents of clays, which are discussed on page 688.

§ 16 Detection and Determination of Aluminium

Aluminium salts are usually recognized in qualitative analysis by the formation of a white, gelatinous precipitate of the hydroxide on addition of ammonia and ammonium chloride. In presence of litmus solution, a blue " lake " is formed. Alumina, when moistened with cobalt nitrate solution and heated on charcoal, gives a bright blue infusible mass.

Aluminium has usually been determined by precipitation as the hydroxide with ammonia and ammonium chloride, followed by ignition to the oxide. Recently precipitation by " oxine " (8-hydroxy quinoline) has been advocated.

§ 17 Gallium, Indium and Thallium

The rare metal **gallium,** Ga, was discovered by Lecoq de Boisbaudran in 1875 while studying a zinc blende from the Pyrenees. Its scarcity has hitherto prevented any extensive investigation of its compounds, but it has recently been found to the extent of some 0·03 per cent. in the ash of certain coals, so that its further investigation is now more practicable.

Indium, In, is another rare metal discovered in 1863 by T. Reich and F. Richter in a zinc ore from Freiberg. Both elements were discovered by the spectroscope. The spark spectrum of gallium contains two violet lines, and indium has a characteristic bright indigo-blue line. The latter element was named from its prominent indigo spectral line. Gallium and indium metals are readily attacked by water, although indium slowly decomposes water at ordinary room temperatures. Gallium and indium are attacked by nitric acid, whereas aluminium under the same conditions appears to be passive. Gallium and indium are related to aluminium much as zinc is related to magnesium. Aluminium, gallium, and indium form oxides R_2O_3. The hydroxides $R(OH)_3$ have weak acidic and basic properties. All three elements form well-defined iso-morphous ammonia alums. Unlike gallium chloride, $GaCl_3$, and aluminium chloride, $AlCl_3$, indium chloride, $InCl_3$, can be obtained by the evaporation of the aqueous solution at 100° with relatively little hydrolysis. All three elements are trivalent, but indium also forms three chlorides : $InCl$, $InCl_2$, and $InCl_3$; and gallium forms $GaCl_2$ and $GaCl_3$.

Thallium, Tl, was discovered by W. Crookes in 1861 while studying the flue dust from a sulphuric acid chamber at Tilkerorde (Hartz mountains). Thallium occurs associated with pyrites in zinc ores, and in the mineral *crookesite*, a copper selenide containing 16 to 18 per cent. of thallium, and 3 to 5 per cent. of silver. Thallium was discovered by the spectroscope. Its spectrum has a characteristic green line—hence its name is derived from the Greek θαλλός (thallos), a green twig.

Thallium shows resemblances to a number of metals outside its own " family." The free metal closely resembles lead ; in its univalent condition, it displays analogies with the alkali metals and with silver and mercurous mercury.

The thallous halides, for instance, like those of silver, are but slightly soluble in water. Mercurous, thallous and silver chlorides are soluble in a solution of sodium thiosulphate. Thallous sulphide, like the silver and lead sulphide, is but sparingly soluble in water ; and thallous hydroxide and carbonate are fairly soluble in water. The thallic salts are not very stable, and they behave somewhat like the auric salts, so that while thallous oxide, Tl_2O, is a strong base, the trioxide, Tl_2O_3, is a feeble base.

The tervalent salts also show resemblances to lead, as well as to aluminium, gallium and indium.

Recently thallium and its compounds have found uses technically. Thus thallous carbonate prevents the growth of mildew in textiles. Some thallium compounds have antiknock properties and an alloy of thallium, aluminium and silver in the proportions of $1 : 1 : 8$ has remarkable resistance to tarnishing. Addition of thallous iodide causes a marked increase in the sensitivity of silver iodide emulsions to light. Certain thallium salts have been used as depilatories, and their administration to sheep in order to induce an artificial moult has been proposed in order to avoid the necessity for shearing.

§ 18 Scandium, Yttrium and Lanthanum

The three rare elements, scandium, yttrium and lanthanum, are related to the aluminium family. They are all triad elements. Their oxides are all of the type R_2O_3, and their halogen compounds : RCl_3, etc. The hydroxides are all basic and insoluble in alkaline hydroxides. The basicity increases in passing from scandium to lanthanum. Scandium, for example, is a very weak base, while lanthanum forms the hydroxide, with the evolution of heat, by the direct action of water on the oxide. All the elements form stable carbonates ; the halides are non-volatile, and are but slightly hydrolysed by water. They form double sulphates—$La_2(SO_4)_3.3K_2SO_4$—with the alkali sulphates, but these compounds are not alums.

The properties of these elements closely resemble those of the rare-earth elements. For reasons explained in the next section, none of them is now classified definitely with rare-earths, though at one time yttrium and lanthanum were so included.

§ 19 Actinium

The ultimate element of Group III is actinium and, like radium, its analogue in Group II, it is radio-active. It is doubtful if it has been obtained in a state of purity and its interest is in its radio-active properties. Consequently it is discussed in Chapter XXXVI along with the remainder of the radio-elements.

§ 20 The Rare-Earth Elements

The group of elements known as the rare-earths comprises a series of elements so closely similar in properties that their separation is extremely difficult, and until comparatively recently it was uncertain how many definite and distinct elements were included.

They occur in a number of minerals, most of which are uncommon. The most important minerals are *cerite*, cerium silicate mixed with the silicates of other rare earths, and *monazite*. Monazite sand is found in considerable quantities in Brazil and in India and contains the phosphates of cerium and other rare earths as well as thorium, lanthanum, yttrium, iron, aluminium, etc. Of late the term *rare* has changed its significance when applied to these elements because some of them are not so scarce as was formerly supposed.

The isolation of the several elements is a difficult matter. They are separated by first digesting the mineral with concentrated sulphuric acid. The clear filtrate is treated with hydrogen sulphide to remove copper, bismuth, etc. The solution of the sulphates is treated with oxalic acid. The precipitate containing the oxalates of the rare earths is then separated into three main groups according to the solubility of their double salts with potassium sulphate. Thus :

Insoluble oxalates.

Insoluble double sulphates		Soluble double sulphates			
		Moderately Soluble		Very Soluble	
Scandium, Sc.	. 45·1	Europium, Eu	. 152·0	Yttrium, Y.	. 88·92
Cerium, Ce .	. 140·13	Gadolinium, Gd.	156·9	Dysprosium, Dy	. 162·46
Lanthanum, La	. 138·92	Terbium .	. 159·2	Holmium, Ho	. 163·5
Praseodymium, Pr	140·92			Erbium, Er	. 167·2
Neodymium, Nd	. 144·27			Thulium, Tm	. 169·4
Samarium, Sa	. 150·43			Ytterbium, Yb	. 173·04
				Lutecium, Lu	. 174·99

It is very difficult to separate further the members of these series and there is some uncertainty whether, as obtained, they are all homogeneous. Repeated fractional precipitation, depending on minute differences in behaviour, has to be used.

In 1794 J. Gadolin discovered a new earth in the mineral gadolinite, which had been named in honour of himself ; and in 1797 A. G. Ekeberg named the new earth yttria, after Ytterby, the place in Sweden where the mineral was found. C. G. Mosander (1843) noticed that what was then called yttria is really a complex earth containing yttria proper, and two other earths, which were oxides of two new elements, **erbium** and **terbium**. In 1880 P. T. Cleve found erbium earth not only contained erbium, but also a new element **thulium**—a name derived from the old Latin *Thule* for the uttermost north—and **holmium**. In 1905 G. Urbain also discovered lutecium in the yttria earths. In 1886 Lecoq de Boisbaudran separated **dysprosium**—from the Greek δύσπρος (dyspros), difficult, in allusion to the trouble involved in its isolation—from the same earth. In the same year, C. Marignac and Lecoq de Boisbaudran showed that terbium earth contained a new element **gadolinium** as well as terbium. In 1878 C. Marignac found the oxide of a new element in gadolinite. This he named **ytterbium**, after Ytterby (Sweden). In 1879 L. F. Nilson, while extracting ytterbia from the mineral euxenite, also separated an unknown earth which he called **scandium**, in honour of his country—Scandinavia—where the mineral was found. In 1839 C. G. Mosander separated the oxide of a new element from an earth which had hitherto been thought to be ceria. This earth he named **lanthanum**, λανθάνειν (lanthanein), to hide. In 1841 C. G. Mosander separated another earth—didymia—from lanthanum. The corresponding element was called **didymium**—from the Greek διδυμος (didymos), a twin, a name suggested by its close relationship and almost invariable occurrence with lanthanum.

By fractional precipitation, Lecoq de Boisbaudran, in 1879, separated **samarium** from **didymium** (discovered by C. G. Mosander in 1841). Samarium was named after the mineral samarskite which, in turn, was named after a Russian, M. Samarsky E. Demarçay, in 1901, separated **europium** from samarium ; the residual didymia was supposed to be the oxide of a distinct metal, didymium, with a definite atomic weight and which furnished salts whose aqueous solutions gave a characteristic absorption spectrum. In 1885, by the fractional crystallization of a nitric acid solution of didymium ammonia-nitrate, A. von Welsbach separated this salt into two other salts, one bright green and the other amethyst blue. The corresponding oxides were respectively pale green, and pale blue. The metal derived from the pale green oxide was called **praseodymium**—from the Greek πράσινος (prasinos), leek green ; and the other was called **neodymium**—from the Greek νέος (neos), new. Aqueous solutions of the two fractions have distinct absorption spectra, but when mixed in the right proportions, the original didymium spectrum is reproduced.

For long the distinctness of these elements, their number and position in the Periodic Table were matters of doubt and dispute. The conception of atomic number, and the discovery by Moseley of means for finding its value for any given element, has enabled the total number of the elements from hydrogen to uranium to be fixed. The investigation of atomic structure, initiated by Rutherford and Bohr, has enabled the relationship of the rare-earths to the rest of the elements, and their place in the Periodic System to be determined.

As explained in Chapters VIII and IX, the first two complete periods of the Table (He—F and Ne—Cl) comprise eight elements each, and are followed by two long periods of eighteen elements each. These long periods are formed by the inclusion of ten *transition elements*, in which an electron shell below the outermost (the penultimate) is increasing while the outermost shell remains almost unaltered. After these two long periods comes a still longer period of 32 elements. In this period, not only is the phenomenon of the transition elements again found, but there is inserted, as it were, into the transition section of the period, a further group of elements (the rare-earths), related to the transition elements of this period in the same way as the transition elements of the third and fourth periods are related to the typical elements. That is to say, the rare earths occur through the increase of an electron shell still deeper in the atom (the ante-penultimate group). This is clearly seen from Table IX on page 120. The rare-earth group is thus defined and is seen to consist of the elements from cerium to ytterbium inclusive, and is foreshadowed by scandium and yttrium which precede lanthanum in the vertical series as starting points of the first and second transition series. The remarkable similarity in properties of all the rare earth elements is thus seen to be due to the fact that their ultimate and penultimate electron groups are all identical.

The rare-earth metals can be extracted from their oxides by the aluminothermic method. An alloy of cerium, lanthanum, praseodymium, neodymium, etc., is made in this way from the residues left after the extraction of the thorium from monazite and is known as *mischmetall*. It is used as a reducing agent for the reduction of refractory oxides such as magnesia. Mischmetall, and cerium-iron alloys, are also used for the so-called " flints " of petrol-lighters, etc. Some of the rare-earth compounds have been used for colouring porcelain and solutions of ceric compounds (e.g., ceric sulphate) are used as oxidizing agents in volumetric analysis.

§ 21 Relationships of the Elements of Group III

The exact sub-classification to be adopted in this group has in the past occasioned some difficulty, but it is now generally agreed that boron and aluminium are best associated with gallium, indium and thallium. This is supported by the conclusions at present accepted for the electronic configurations of these elements which are given in Tables XLIII and XLIV.

TABLE XLIII

Element.	No. of Electrons in Orbit.														
	1	2_1	2_2	3_1	3_2	3_3	4_1	4_2	4_3	4_4	5_1	5_2	5_3	6_1	6_2
Boron	2	2	1												
Aluminium	2	2	6	2	1										
Gallium	2	2	6	2	6	10	2	1							
Indium	2	2	6	2	6	10	2	6	10		2	1			
Thallium	2	2	6	2	6	10	2	6	10	14	2	6	10	2	1

TABLE XLIV.

Element.	No. of Electrons in Orbit.													
	1	2_1	2_2	3_1	3_2	3_3	4_1	4_2	4_3	4_4	5_1	5_2	5_3	6
Scandium	2	2	6	2	6	1	2							
Yttrium	2	2	6	2	6	10	2	6	1		2			
Lanthanum	2	2	6	2	6	10	2	6	10		2	6	1	2
Cerium	2	2	6	2	6	10	2	6	10	1	2	6	1	2
Praseodymium	2	2	6	2	6	10	2	6	10	2	2	6	1	2
Neodymium	2	2	6	2	6	10	2	6	10	3	2	6	1	2
Illinium	2	2	6	2	6	10	2	6	10	4	2	6	1	2
Samarium	2	2	6	2	6	10	2	6	10	5	2	6	1	2
Europium	2	2	6	2	6	10	2	6	10	6	2	6	1	2
Gadolinium	2	2	6	2	6	10	2	6	10	7	2	6	1	2
Terbium	2	2	6	2	6	10	2	6	10	8	2	6	1	2
Dysprosium	2	2	6	2	6	10	2	6	10	9	2	6	1	2
Holmium	2	2	6	2	6	10	2	6	10	10	2	6	1	2
Erbium	2	2	6	2	6	10	2	6	10	11	2	6	1	2
Thulium	2	2	6	2	6	10	2	6	10	12	2	6	1	2
Ytterbium	2	2	6	2	6	10	2	6	10	13	2	6	1	2
Lutecium	2	2	6	2	6	10	2	6	10	14	2	6	1	2

The variation in the physical properties of the five elements boron, aluminium, gallium, indium and thallium with increasing atomic weight is indicated in Table XLV.

TABLE XLV.—PROPERTIES OF THE BORON-ALUMINIUM FAMILY.

—	Boron.	Aluminium.	Gallium.	Indium.	Thallium.
Atomic weight	10·82	26·97	69·72	114·76	204·39
Specific gravity	2·45	2·7	5·9	7·3	11·85
Atomic volume	4·5	10·0	11·8	15·5	17·3
Melting point	2300°	660°	29·75°	155°	303°

With the exception of boron and aluminium, the elements of this series are scarce and rare. The oxides of the metals from aluminium to thallium are obtained by adding ammonia to solutions of salts of the metals. The oxides dissolve in acids forming salts. The haloid salts are volatile. At about 100° thallic chloride breaks down into thallous chloride and chlorine. The chlorides readily form complex salts with other chlorides. The non-metallic characters predominate in boron, and it can almost be said that the properties of boron summarize those of the group, although any particularly striking family trait is wanting. Boric oxide exhibits strongly acidic and very feeble basic properties, for it combines with a few anhydrides—e.g., P_2O_5 and SO_3—of the strong acids to form compounds in which boron acts as a base. Thus *boron phosphate*, BPO_4, is a stable compound, so also is *boron sulphate*, $B(HSO_4)_3$, but is decomposed by heat or water. The other oxides are basic towards most acids, and the basic properties of the elements increase, and the acidic properties decrease with increasing atomic weights in passing from aluminium to thallium. Thus, aluminium is acidic towards strong alkalis, gallium and indium hydroxides are soluble in concentrated potash solutions, and there is evidence of the formation of an unstable potassium thallate in the violet liquid which is produced when thallic hydroxide is suspended in a concentrated solution of potassium hydroxide, and treated with chlorine. The potassium hydroxide solution of indium oxide gives a precipitate of the oxide when boiled and the solution is decomposed by carbon dioxide. The trichloride, $TlCl_3$, for instance, is partially hydrolyzed by water. When thallium is trivalent, its compounds resemble the other members of the group ; the thallic salts are readily reduced to thallous salts. The . . . ic salts are usually soluble in water and, excepting boron, the elements can replace aluminium to form alums—e.g., *gallium alums* $M_2SO_4.Ga_2(SO_4)_3.24H_2O$; *indium alums*, $M_2SO_4.In_2(SO_4)_3.24H_2O$. The grouping of thallium with aluminium is justified by the fact that thallium sesquioxide can replace alumina in the alums. Aluminium, indium, and thallium form complex sulphates with the alkali sulphates crystallizing with eight molecules of water ; but when univalent, thallium behaves like silver and the alkali metals. The kinship of the thallous and alkali salts is illustrated by the fact that (i) thallous salts are stable bodies and usually isomorphous with the corresponding potassium salts ; (ii) thallous sulphate can take the place of the alkali metal to form alums—e.g., $Tl_2SO_4.Al_2(SO_4)_3.24H_2O$; (iii) thallous monoxide, Tl_2O, dissolves in water, forming a corrosive solution which resembles that obtained with caustic alkali—it forms salts when treated with acids ; absorbs carbon dioxide, forming thallous carbonate ; colours red litmus blue ; the carbonate and phosphate are soluble ; the chloroplatinate, like that of potassium, is sparingly soluble ; etc. ; (iv) it forms a tri-iodide, isomorphous with potassium tri-iodide ; and (v) it can replace potassium in potassium chromate, forming $TlKCrO_4$. Thallium itself resembles lead.

The close relationship between scandium, yttrium and lanthanum, and the metals of the rare-earths has been discussed already and seen to lie in the very similar structures of the atoms of these elements. They resemble the other sub-group in being tervalent, and in other ways.

CHAPTER XXX

SILICON, TIN AND LEAD, AND OTHER ELEMENTS OF GROUP IV

§ 1 Group IV of the Periodic Table

GROUP IV comprises the following elements, viz., carbon and silicon, with titanium, zirconium, hafnium, and thorium in the A sub-group; and germanium, tin and lead in the B sub-group.

The two short-period elements are more closely related to the B sub-group, and there is a marked gradation of properties in passing from carbon to lead. This gradation is of such a nature, however, that there are few, if any, obvious resemblances between the extreme members. Thus carbon and lead differ very considerably; far more, for example, than do lithium and caesium, or even beryllium and barium.

§ 2 Silicon, Si

History

Silicon does not occur free in nature, but, as indicated in our study of silica, numerous oxygen compounds are known. The process of manufacturing glass from silicates has been known from ancient times, and J. J. Becher (1669) believed that these silicates contained a peculiar earth which he called *terra vitrescibilis* (vitrifiable earth); this is now called " silica." It was known in the seventeenth century that Becher's vitrifiable earth does not fuse when heated alone, and that a fusible glass is formed when it is heated with other earths. O Tachenius (1660) noticed that the vitrifiable earth had acid rather than alkaline properties; C. W. Scheele (1773) showed it to have the characteristics of a refractory acid; and J. L. M. Smithson (1811) considered it to be an acid rather than an alkaline earth. J. J. Berzelius prepared amorphous silicon in 1823; and H. St. C. Deville prepared crystalline silicon in 1854.

Occurrence

After oxygen, silicon is the most abundant element in the earth's half-mile crust, and silica is one of the most important compounds found in that crust. Silica occurs both free and combined with various bases. Silica occurs free as quartz, flint, sand; examples of natural silicates are *felspar* or *orthoclase*, $K_2O.Al_2O_3.6SiO_2$; *kaolinite*, $Al_2O_3.2SiO_2.2H_2O$, and *anorthite*, $CaO.Al_2O_3.2SiO_2$.

Preparation of Silicon

Two allotropic forms of silicon have been described, known as amorphous and crystalline silicon. There is, however, considerable doubt about their being true allotropes.

Amorphous Silicon

This can be made by heating potassium or sodium in an atmosphere of silicon chloride or silicon fluoride :

$$SiF_4 + 4K = Si + 4KF.$$

The brown mass so formed is washed with water and hydrofluoric acid, heated at a dull red heat, and finally washed and dried. It is also formed by heating a mixture of sodium or potassium fluosilicate with metallic potassium :

$$K_2SiF_6 + 4K = Si + 6KF.$$

The brown mass is cleaned as before. Quartz is reduced to silicon when it is intimately mixed with magnesium powder and heated :

$$SiO_2 + 2Mg = Si + 2MgO.$$

Crystalline Silicon

Crystalline silicon is made by dissolving silicon in molten metals, and on cooling, part of the silicon separates from the solution in a crystalline condition. By passing a stream of silicon tetrachloride vapour over aluminium previously melted in an atmosphere of hydrogen, the volatile aluminium chloride passes on, and the silicon liberated by the reaction :

$$3SiCl_4 + 4Al = 3Si + 4AlCl_3,$$

dissolves in the molten aluminium. As the molten aluminium cools, silicon separates in long lustrous crystals. The aluminium can be separated by treatment with hydrochloric acid. Crystalline silicon is also made by heating a mixture of potassium or sodium silicofluoride, or powdered silica, with an excess of aluminium :

$$4Al + 3K_2SiF_6 = 3Si + 6KF + 4AlF_3.$$

The silicon dissolves in the excess of molten aluminium. The cold solution is treated with hydrochloric acid to remove aluminium, and with hydrofluoric acid to remove silica. Silica is reduced when heated with metallic magnesium :

$$SiO_2 + 2Mg = 2MgO + Si ;$$

if an excess of magnesium be employed, magnesium silicide, Mg_3Si, is formed. Both it and magnesium oxide can be removed by treatment with hydrochloric acid. Crystalline silicon has been made commercially by heating quartz with coke in the electric furnace :

$$SiO_2 + 2C = 2CO + Si.$$

Excess of silica must be used or else carborundum is formed (p. 681).

Properties

As with carbon, the different forms of silica differ in chemical as well as in physical properties.

Amorphous silicon is a dark brown amorphous powder with a specific gravity 2·4. It melts at about 1420°, and volatilizes in the electric arc. When calcined in air, a surface skin of silica is formed which protects the element from complete oxidation. Silicon ignites in chlorine at about 450°, and burns to silicon tetrachloride. If silicon be heated with hydrogen chloride, free hydrogen and silicon tetrachloride are formed :

$$Si + 4HCl = SiCl_4 + 2H_2.$$

Silicon is insoluble in water and most acids ; but it dissolves in hydrofluoric acid forming hydrofluosilicic acid :

$$Si + 6HF = 2H_2 + H_2SiF_6.$$

When boiled with alkaline hydroxides it forms hydrogen and alkaline silicate.

Crystalline silicon forms dark-grey opaque needle-like crystals or octahedral plates (cubic system). It is hard enough to scratch glass. Its specific gravity varies between 2·34 and 3, according to the temperature to which it has been heated. It burns when heated in chlorine and fires spontaneously in fluorine. Silicon is insoluble in acids, but dissolves in a mixture of nitric and hydrofluoric acids. It melts about 1420°, and distils in the electric furnace. Crystalline silicon slightly conducts electricity, amorphous silicon does not. Chemically, crystalline silicon resembles amorphous silicon, but it is not so active. Silicon combines with nitrogen, forming **silicon nitride,** and also with the metals, forming **silicides.**

Uses

Silicon prepared from quartz and coke in an electric furnace is used for making alloys : in particular, a silicon iron which is very resistant to acids and is used, for example, in the distillation of nitric acid ; and silicon bronze (a copper-tin alloy containing a trace of silicon, is used for telegraph and telephone wires). A silicon iron alloy, containing 3-4 per cent. of silicon, known as **stalloy,** has wide applications in the electrical industry on account of its very low hysteresis loss. Certain of the compounds of silicon, notably silica and carborundum, have many applications.

Atomic Weight

The vapour densities of volatile silicon compounds, and the position of silicon in the Periodic Table indicate a value of approximately 28 for the atomic weight of silicon. The best determinations of the combining weight have been made by determining the amount of silver halide produced by dissolving silicon chloride or bromide in water, followed by addition of silver nitrate. In this way the value 28·06 has been obtained and is that recommended by the International Committee.

§ 3 Hydrides and Carbides of Silicon

Hydrides

Silicon forms a number of hydrides, similar in composition to the simpler hydrocarbons. It is evident, however, that the power possessed by carbon of forming long chains of atoms, is only exhibited by silicon to a mild extent. Examples of silicon hydrides are :

Silico-methane, silicane or silane, SiH_4.
Silico-ethane, Si_2H_6.
Silico-propane, Si_3H_8.
Silico-butane, Si_4H_{10}.

Silico-ethylene (Si_2H_4) and silico-acetylene (Si_2H_2)$_n$ have been reported, but their existence is doubtful.

The hydrides of silicon are not very stable, and like many other hydrides, act as reducing agents.

Silico-methane, Silicane, Silane, SiH_4

This gas is most conveniently made by the action of concentrated hydrochloric acid on magnesium silicide :

$$Mg_2Si + 4HCl = 2MgCl_2 + SiH_4.$$

Magnesium silicide is obtained by heating sand with excess of magnesium powder. The silico-methane formed is mixed with hydrogen and other silicon hydrides ; the presence of silico-ethane makes it spontaneously inflammable. These can be separated by liquefying the gases by passing through a vessel cooled in liquid air and fractionating the product.

Silico-methane is a colourless gas, not spontaneously inflammable at ordinary pressure. It burns with a bright flame :

$$SiH_4 + 2O_2 = SiO_2 + 2H_2O.$$

When passed into alkaline solutions, it decomposes :

$$SiH_4 + 2KOH + H_2O = K_2SiO_3 + 4H_2,$$

and when heated to 400° it decomposes into its elements.

Silico-ethane, Si_2H_6, can be obtained as a liquid by fractionation of the residues from the preparation of silico-methane. It is a colourless liquid, b.p. —15°. It decomposes into its elements when heated to 200° in absence of air ; in air it is spontaneously inflammable.

Silicon Carbide, Carbon Silicide, Carborundum, SiC

This compound is made by fusing a mixture of coke and sand in an electric resistance furnace—estimated temperature 3500°. The furnace is a large oblong box with permanent ends, and temporary sides. Large carbon electrodes are fitted into the two ends, and project into the furnace. Granulated coke is packed between the electrodes. A mixture of sand and coke, with some salt to make the mass fusible, and some sawdust to make the mass porous, is packed about the carbon core and held in place by the side walls of loosely packed bricks. A powerful current of electricity is sent through the charge. The change which takes place is represented by the symbols :

$$SiO_2 + 3C = SiC + 2CO.$$

The carbon monoxide burns above the furnace.

The operation is over in about eight hours. The furnace is then allowed to cool ; the side walls are removed, and the silicon carbide removed. The best grades are found nearest the core. The product is crushed and treated with sulphuric acid to remove impurities ; it is then washed, dried, and graded according to size.

Carborundum crystallizes in hexagonal plates when pure ; it may be transparent and colourless, or vary in tint from emerald green to brown or black. The latter varieties are most common. The specific gravity is 3·2. It is not attacked by acids—even hydrofluoric acid. It is decomposed by fusion with alkaline hydroxides. It is nearly as hard as the diamond, and accordingly is largely used as an abrasive powder and made into whetstones, hones, grinding wheels, polishing cloths, etc. It is also very refractory, and when mixed with clay has special uses as a refractory material for protecting furnace walls, etc.

§ 4 Silica, Silicon Dioxide

Silica is a very common constituent of the earth's crust ; some of the ways in which it occurs are mentioned in § 2.

It occurs abundantly in the mineral kingdom, and it is also common in the connective tissue of animals, fibres of vegetables, etc. The so-called *kieselguhr* or " diatomaceous earth " is a friable powder resembling chalk or clay. It is virtually a mass of siliceous skeletons of dead diatoms.

Silica, SiO_2, occurs in nature free and combined with various bases to form numerous mineral silicates. Free silica occurs crystalline and amorphous. There are three main types of crystalline silica : quartz, tridymite, and cristobalite.

Quartz

Quartz occurs in hexagonal prisms (trigonal system) terminating in hexagonal pyramids. A single quartz crystal weighing very nearly one ton has been reported from Calaveras (U.S.A.). The purest varieties of quartz—called *rock crystal*—are colourless ; they have a specific gravity 2·651, and are hard enough to cut glass. The crystals are sometimes coloured with traces of various oxides. Thus, manganese oxide gives *amethyst quartz* ; *smoky quartz* probably owes its colour to the presence of carbonaceous matter ; *milky quartz* owes its opacity to the presence of innumerable air bubbles. Quartz also occurs massive in quartzite and quartzose rocks. Quartzose sands and sandstones are also more or less impure quartz.

Amorphous Silica

Amorphous silica occurs in nature associated with 3 to 12 per cent. of water in the mineral *opal*, which may be colourless or tinted yellowish-brown, etc., with iron oxide, organic matter, etc. Chert, flint, chalcedony, and jasper contain more or less amorphous silica associated with quartz. The silica of diatomaceous earth is opaline and soluble in alkaline carbonate solutions, although the silica in some of the older deposits has begun to crystallize as quartz.

Properties of Silica

Silica melts to a colourless glass—**quartz glass**—in the oxyhydrogen blowpipe. The melting point of quartz is not well defined. Melting commences about 1600°. Silica can be vaporized in the electric furnace. The specific gravity of vitreous silica is about 2·22. The coefficient of thermal expansion of vitreous quartz is remarkably small—nearly 0·0000005—so that quartz glass can be very rapidly cooled without cracking. For instance, quartz glass can be heated red hot in the blowpipe and plunged in cold water without fracture ; under the same conditions, ordinary glass—with a coefficient of thermal expansion of 0·000008—would shatter into small fragments. When heated for some time at about 1250°, the vitreous quartz passes into the crystalline condition (tridymite), and it will not then bear the sudden heating and cooling so well.

Silica is reduced by carbon in the electric furnace and forms carborundum (q.v.) ; it is reduced by magnesium to amorphous silicon. Crystalline and vitreous silica appear to be insoluble in water and in all acids except hydrofluoric acid. Fused silica is readily attacked by phosphoric acid and by the alkalis. Crystalline silica is slowly attacked by aqueous solutions of alkaline hydroxides, and carbonates, but the amorphous variety is rapidly attacked. Silica is also attacked by superheated water, and a small quantity may pass into solution. The necessary conditions seem to prevail in deep-seated cavities in the earth. The water rising to the surface is cooled, and the pressure reduced. Some of the dissolved silica is then deposited at the mouth of the spring as a thick jelly. This afterwards changes into a hard white porous mass called *geyserite*. The Great Geyser of Iceland, for instance, is surrounded by a large mound or hillock of silica with a funnel-like cavity from which the geyser discharges.

Although chemically inactive at ordinary temperatures, silica acts as a powerful acid anhydride at high temperatures, combining with bases and many metallic oxides to form more or less fusible silicates. When silica is fused with sodium carbonate, the carbon dioxide is expelled with effervescence.

The more fusible silicates—e.g., lead silicate—are used in making glasses and pottery glazes. Potassium and sodium silicates are soluble in water, and the aqueous solution is sold as **water glass,** and the solid as **soluble glass.** The powerful acid character of silica at high temperatures turns on the fact that most of the acid anhydrides—SO_3, P_2O_5, etc.—volatilize at much lower temperatures, and consequently, as soon as ever so little, say, sulphur trioxide is displaced, the volatile anhydride passes away and ceases to compete with the silica for the base. At lower temperatures, sulphur trioxide rapidly displaces silica from the bases when competing under equal conditions.

Uses of Silica

In 1839 M. A. Gaudin showed that quartz can be melted and then worked like glass, but the fact attracted no particular attention until comparatively recent years. Quartz glass is used for the manufacture of elastic threads to suspend the delicate parts of electrical instruments. It is made into tubes, flasks, dishes, etc. Sandstone and quartzite are used for building stones, grindstones, whetstones, etc. Sand or sandstone is ground with a little lime or binding clay and made into refractory bricks, etc. Many varieties of quartz are shaped into ornaments and gems. Diatomaceous earth—also called *tripoli, diatomite, kieselguhr*, or (wrongly) *infusorial earth*, etc.—is used as a polishing powder, in the manufacture of cement, soluble glass, and heat-insulating bricks. Its absorbent properties are utilized in pharmacy, etc., for the preparations of solids saturated with liquid, e.g., antiseptics for dry dressings for wounds, and for the absorption of bromine, sulphuric acid, nitroglycerol, etc. The product when nitroglycerol is absorbed in kieselguhr is known as *dynamite*.

Sand is very extensively employed in building, both for cement and mortar, also for the manufacture of artificial stone, of glass and glazes, and of silica bricks used in steel and other furnaces. It is also used in the filter beds of waterworks for the purification of public supplies.

§ 5 The Silicic Acids

The substances called silicic acids are rather indefinite compounds, and it is not certain which, if any, of them have a definite existence. But many silicates are known, derived from various (possibly hypothetical) silicic acids.

When a solution of water glass (sodium or potassium silicate, say, Na_2SiO_3) is acidified with hydrochloric acid, some of the silicic acid separates as a gelatinous mass (hydrogel) and some remains in solution (hydrosol). If the solution be sufficiently dilute, the silicic acid will all remain in solution along with the excess of hydrochloric acid, and the sodium chloride formed in the reaction :

$$Na_2SiO_3 + 2HCl \rightleftharpoons H_2SiO_3 + 2NaCl.$$

The hydrochloric acid and the sodium chloride can be separated from the silicic acid by dialysis (p. 246).

A clear solution containing 5 per cent. of colloidal silica can be obtained as a hydrosol, by dialysis. This solution can be concentrated by boiling in a flask until it contains about 14 per cent. of silicic acid. The solution so prepared gelatinizes, or assumes the hydrogel condition, on standing a few days. The passage of silicic acid from the sol to the gel condition is retarded by the presence of a little hydrochloric acid, or alkali hydroxide, and is accelerated by a little sodium carbonate. If the clear solution of silicic acid be allowed to evaporate *in vacuo* at about 15°, a clear transparent jelly is obtained which, when dried over sulphuric acid, has approximately the composition H_2SiO_3, that is, $SiO_2.H_2O$, and it is called **metasilicic acid.** An acid of the same composition has been made by dehydrating gelatinous silicic acid with 90 to 95 per cent. of alcohol. An acid of approximately the composition $SiO_2.2H_2O$, that is, H_4SiO_4. and called **orthosilicic acid,** has been made by dehydrating gelatinous silicic acid with absolute ether, and drying the amorphous white powder between folds of filter paper ; the same compound is said to be formed by the action of silicon tetrachloride on water. Orthosilicic acid loses water on exposure to the air. A number of other silicic acids is known, e.g., silico-oxalic acid, $HO.OSi—SiO.OH$; silico-mesoxalic acid, $Si_3O_2(OH)_4$; etc.

The formation of metallic silicates is well illustrated by a familiar experiment—*silica garden*. A large beaker is filled with a solution of sodium silicate (sp. gr. 1·1) and crystals of, say, cobalt nitrate, cadmium nitrate, copper sulphate, ferrous sulphate, nickel sulphate, manganese sulphate, zinc sulphate, etc., are allowed to fall into the beaker so as to rest on different parts of the bottom. The whole is allowed to stand overnight in a quiet place, when plant-like shoots appear to grow from the crystals, which have a form and colour characteristic of the metal used as " seed."

Silica Gel

If a solution of sodium silicate be heated to 100° and decomposed by hydrochloric acid, a gelatinous precipitate, known as silica gel, $SiO_2.nH_2O$, is obtained. It is also obtained by the action of sodium hydrogen sulphate on sodium silicate solution. This substance has a remarkable power of absorbing moisture, and it has been used for drying the blast in the smelting of iron (p. 804). It can also adsorb substances from solution and has been applied to the purification of petroleum products from sulphur.

§ 6 The Silicates

The importance of the silicates, comprising, as they do, so large a proportion of the earth's crust, makes the investigation of their constitution a matter of great interest. They are difficult to investigate by chemical methods, since the majority of them appear to exist only in the solid state, and the character of the constituent groups is entirely lost in the course of chemical processes. To avoid hypotheses, the silicate industries usually employ the old system of J. J. Berzelius for the empirical formula ; thus writing potash felspar, for example, $K_2O.Al_2O_3.6SiO_2$, and so on.

Hitherto, for chemical purposes silicates have usually been classified on the basis of a series of hypothetical silicic acids. Thus, starting with ortho-silicic acid, H_4SiO_4 or $\begin{matrix} HO \\ HO \end{matrix}>Si<\begin{matrix} OH \\ OH \end{matrix}$, this is supposed to pass into metasilicic acid, H_2SiO_3 or $\begin{matrix} HO \\ HO \end{matrix}>Si = O$ by the loss of one molecule of water. These acids correspond to ortho- and meta-silicates such as *willemite*, Zn_2SiO_4 ; *olivine* $(Mg, Fe)_2SiO_4$; *zircon*, $ZrSiO_4$ and *tephroite*, Fe_2SiO_4, etc. ; and *wollastonite*, $CaSiO_3$, and *enstatite*, $MgSiO_3$, etc. Two molecules of orthosilicic acid might be condensed into one of orthodisilicic acid, $H_6Si_2O_7$ or

$$\begin{matrix} HO \\ HO—Si—O—Si—OH \\ HO \quad\quad\quad OH \end{matrix}$$

and hence, give rise to a series of ortho-di-silicates such as *serpentine*, $Mg_3Si_2O_7$; *barysilite*, $Pb_3Si_2O_7$, etc. Similarly, two molecules of meta-silicic acid could give rise to meta-di-silicates (derived from $H_2Si_2O_5$) and this process could be continued, forming the basis for ortho- and meta- tri- and poly-silicates. Compound silicates of aluminium and other bases could be formulated similarly.

The difficult problem of the structure of these substances has been considerably elucidated of recent years by means of X-ray analysis, chiefly by W. L. Bragg and by Pauling. This has shown that the difference between the different classes of silicates is a matter of the silicon-oxygen arrangement and only indirectly of the remainder of the structures. Occasionally, the silicon-oxygen structure forms a closed group like an ordinary acid radical, but usually the structure is endless and extends continuously throughout a given crystal.

The silicon atom in the silicates is always associated with four oxygen atoms, tetrahedrally arranged with regard to the silicon. The way in which these tetrahedral groups are related determines the structure of the particular silicate. Some of these possibilities are indicated in the formulae of Figs. 218 to 220.

In the orthosilicate group exemplified by *olivine* (Mg, Fe)$_2$SiO$_4$ and *zircon*, ZrSiO$_4$, the tetrahedral groups are independent like quadrivalent acid radicals. The oxygen atoms each have one negative charge (being attached to the silicon by a single " valency ") and these negative charges attract the metallic ions of the crystal. This represents the simplest silicate type. (Fig. 218A.)

It is possible for these tetrahedral groups to become linked by their corners, that is, through two groups sharing one oxygen atom.

If two tetrahedra are linked in this way by a single corner of each, a grouping (Si$_2$O$_7$) results the effective valency of which is six, since the linking oxygen atom now has no charge (Fig. 218B). Other groups have been observed in which three tetrahedra are united into a ring through the sharing of three oxygen atoms, thus forming a group (Si$_3$O$_9$) whose effective valency is again six (Fig. 218c).

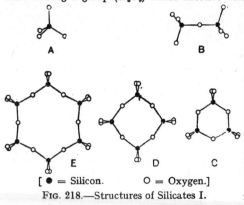

Similarly rings of six such tetrahedra have been found (Fig. 218E). Examples of these are the rare mineral *benitoite* BaTiSi$_3$O$_9$ and *beryl* Be$_3$Al$_2$Si$_6$O$_{18}$ respectively. A ring composed of four tetrahedra (Fig. 218D) has also been detected in certain zeolites.

The process of linking the silicon-oxygen tetrahedra can be continued in long chains and bands such as are found in the pyroxenes and amphiboles respectively. In the chains the tetrahedra are joined corner to corner in a row which extends indefinitely in both directions (Fig. 219F).

[● = Silicon.   O = Oxygen.]

FIG. 218.—Structures of Silicates I.

In the crystal there are thus silicon oxygen structures extending right across the crystal and bound sideways by the positive ions.

In the banded structure of the amphiboles, two of these chains are bound together by the sharing of certain oxygen atoms as indicated in Fig. 219G. It is interesting to note that these two classes of silicate minerals a fibrous structure is exhibited, as for example in asbestos.

A further extension of this process of linking tetrahedra, in which three corners of each are united results in the formation of sheets. The simplest and most usual arrangement in these sheets is a hexagonal network resulting from the

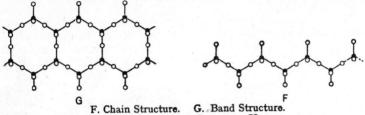

F. Chain Structure.   G. Band Structure.
FIG. 219.—Silicate Structures II.

indefinite extension in a second direction of the process by which chains are bound into bands as above. This is indicated in Fig. 220H. Here each silicon-oxygen tetrahedron has three shared, and only one free oxygen atom. This is the type of structure found in minerals like *mica* and *talc* which are characterized by the ease with which they can be separated into thin leaves. Other ways of forming sheets, as, for example, by the production of rings of four and eight tetrahedra, are also theoretically possible and some of these occur in minerals though they are not common.

If three-dimensional networks be formed, the tetrahedra are linked by all three corners so that there are no oxygen atoms left carrying charges to attract positive ions. The result is then one of the forms of silica itself (e.g., quartz). In most of the structures already considered a certain number of the silicon atoms may be replaced by aluminium. Whenever this occurs each tetrahedral unit of the framework acquires a resultant negative charge, on account of the lower valency (fewer outer-ring electrons) of aluminium, and metallic ions are then incorporated into the interstices of the structure. The felspars are examples of this arrangement.

The silicates thus, for the most part, form crystals

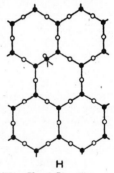

H.   Sheet Structure.

FIG. 220.
Silicate Structures III.

which are not to be thought of as loose aggregations of " simple " molecules but as *giant-molecules* in which the whole mass is bound by chemical linkages, which extend to the limits of the crystal. The infusibility and insolubility of the silicates is presumably the result of these structures.

Weathering of Rocks

Rocks generally show striking differences in behaviour when exposed for long periods of time ; some remain hard and firm, others crumble to powder in a comparatively short time. Many ancient Egyptian and Grecian monuments show but slight symptoms of decay, whereas in other countries buildings made from apparently similar rocks soon deteriorate and are saved from disintegration only by a continued system of renovation. Calcareous building stones—e.g., the Houses of Parliament (London)—decay comparatively quickly when exposed to the acidic vapours which occur in the atmospheres of towns. When potash felspar and many other natural alumino-silicates are exposed to certain natural influences, they are finally converted into insoluble white crystalline or amorphous (colloidal) powder—clay, and other materials.

Formation of Clays

The early stages of the decomposition—weathering—of the felspathic rocks is indicated by the apparent clouding of the crystals of felspar ; the felspar becomes more and more opaque ; and finally disintegrates. The decomposition of silicate rocks exposed to weathering agents apparently furnishes colloidal silica—e.g., opal—and one of the last stages in the decomposition of felspar, and many other aluminosilicates, is clay. Consequently, the **weathering of the aluminosilicates furnishes clay** in a more or less colloidal condition. Granitic rocks, with felspar as a matrix, disintegrate and leave behind the clay mixed with the more or less resistant varieties of mica, quartz, and other minerals which originally formed the granitic rock. The more important agents which facilitate the decomposition and disintegration —weathering—of the aluminium silicates are : (1) Volcanic gases (steam, hydrofluoric acid vapours, etc.). (2) Water draining from peat bogs, and coal beds. This water contains organic acids in solution. (3) Spring or rain water containing carbon dioxide, etc., in solution. The bases derived from the decomposition of the rocks are partly retained by the soil, and partly transformed into carbonates ; the silicic acid is partly carried to the sea where it is utilized for building up the skeletons of various organisms, and partly retained on land where it unites with basic minerals forming steatite, serpentine, etc. The clay may be leached by streams of water from the place where it was formed, transported from the hills, and deposited at lower levels. All kinds of debris from the rocks and soils, etc., over which the clays are carried may be transported along with the clay.

Transported clays are usually, but not always, less pure than the residual primary clays. The residual clays formed by the weathering of the less ferruginous granitic rocks, after an elaborate process of washing and settling, furnish white *china clay*, which has very nearly the empirical composition : $Al_2O_3.2SiO_2.2H_2O$. China clay is often called " kaolin," generally outside the industry. The disintegrated granite from which china clay is washed is called *china clay rock* ; a less disintegrated variety with more unweathered felspar is called *Cornish stone*. The object of the washing china clay rock is to separate the china clay from the unweathered quartz, mica, etc.

The term *clay* is applied industrially to a fine-grained mixture of various minerals which has these qualities : (1) It is plastic enough to be moulded when it is wet ; (2) It retains its shape when dried in spite of a certain amount of contraction ; and (3) When the moulded mass is heated to a high enough temperature it sinters together forming a hard coherent mass without losing its original contour. These properties have given clays a most important place—probably third or fourth

—in the world's industries. Clays are used in the manufacture of building bricks, tiles, firebricks, crucibles, gas retorts, sanitary goods, pottery, etc. ; china clay is also extensively employed for filling paper, cotton, etc. *Fuller's earth* is a kind of non-plastic clay which disintegrates to a fine powder when placed in water. The washed powder was once used for " fulling " cloth—hence the name. It is now largely used for clarifying and deodorizing oils, etc. In this respect, it behaves like charcoal on coloured solutions.

Pottery and Bricks

British pottery is generally made from an intimate mixture of white-burning clay, with flint or quartz, and felspar or Cornish stone. The mixture is made into a slip (slurry) with water ; sieved ; and partly de-watered by filter press or other convenient method, so as to form a plastic mass. The mixture is moulded into the desired shape, dried, and fired between 1000° and 1200° according to the kind of ware being made. This forms the so-called " biscuit " body. A fusible mixture —containing lead boro-silicate, clay, felspar, etc., ground together to form a " slip " with water—is then spread over the surface of the " biscuit body," and the whole is refired to 900° or 1000°. The melted mixture covers the surface of the " body " with a glassy film or "glaze." There are many modifications. The ware may be decorated by painting coloured oxides on the biscuit body before glazing ; or by painting fusible enamels on the glaze and refiring ; or the glaze itself may be coloured with suitable oxides. Glaze and body may be fired in one operation with or without a preliminary baking of the body. There are also considerable variations in the composition of the body and glaze. The chief varieties of pottery are *earthenware*—made from white-burning clays, Cornish stone, and flint ; *vitreous ware*, and *iron-stone*—made from a similar mixture but containing more fluxes and fired at a higher temperature ; *hard porcelain*—made from clays, felspar, and quartz—with or without a little lime ; *bone china*—made from bone ash, clay, and Cornish stone ; *soft porcelain*—made from a calcareous marl and glassy frit ; *parians*—made from a mixture of felspar and clay ; and the commoner varieties of pottery—*terra-cotta ware*, etc.—made from special mixtures—often local clays glazed with a mixture containing galena, etc. There are all grades of porosity varying by insensible gradations from translucent glassy porcelain, to the most porous terra-cotta. No satisfactory basis of classification has been devised. *Drain pipes* are also made from local clays, which burn a buff or red colour, and glazed by throwing salt into the kiln. The salt decrepitates, volatilizes, and the vapours attack the surface of the clayware, covering it with a glass-like skin—*salt glaze*. *Tobacco pipes* (unglazed) are made from siliceous clays, that is, from clays containing more or less finely divided silica. *Firebricks* are made from refractory clays which soften at about 1580°. The refractory clay is moulded by hand or machinery and fired to about 1100°-1200°. Common *building bricks* are usually made from less refractory clays fired at a low temperature.

Ultramarine

Ultramarine or *lapis lazuli*—the sapphire of the Bible—occurs in nature as a blue, green, or violet-coloured mixture of crystalline minerals, the most important of which is *lazurite* (not *lazulite*). It is considered to be a silicate of aluminium and sodium with some combined sulphur ; but its constitution is by no means understood. Artificial ultramarine is a blue pigment made by calcining a mixture of china clay, sodium carbonate, charcoal, and sulphur in the absence of air. The green product is washed with water, dried, mixed with sulphur, and again roasted in air until the mass has acquired the required tint. Ultramarine is decomposed by acids with the evolution of hydrogen sulphide. It is used for neutralizing the yellowish tinge of sugar, cotton and linen goods, and in the laundry. It is also used as a blue pigment. The mineral has been almost superseded by the artificial product which is but one-fifth the price.

Glass

Glass is a congealed or solidified, undercooled solution of several silicates—most commonly potassium, calcium, and lead—and is made by fusing together a mixture of clean sand, limestone, or whiting or lime, sodium or potassium carbonate, and litharge or red lead in the right proportions. Traces of manganese dioxide or selenium are sometimes added to neutralize the yellow or green tinge due to the presence of ferrous or ferric oxide present as impurity in the ingredients used in making the glass. The mixture is melted in fireclay pots, and when the molten mass has cooled to the right temperature, a portion is collected at the end of an iron tube and brought to the desired shape by forcing it into a mould, or blowing into the tube and twisting or swinging the plastic mass of glass as required. Details of the procedure vary with the particular objects being made. Rapidly cooled glass is brittle and liable to fracture, hence the glass is annealed in an annealing kiln where it can be cooled as slowly as desired. If cooled too slowly the glass devitrifies, i e., crystallizes.

It has been said that " few substances in daily use can be compared with glass in point of importance or utility. Glass is so common and so cheap that we are apt to lose sight of its unique qualities. It is durable, transparent, and easily cleaned ; it can be readily coloured with metallic oxides ; it is capable of taking a high polish ; and, while in a fused condition, it can be made to assume almost any desired shape which it retains permanently when cold. It is an indispensable agent in most of the experimental sciences—chemistry, physics, astronomy, etc.—and it is difficult to imagine how many operations could be carried on without its aid. Without glass we should be more than centuries behind in astronomy, bacteriology, and biology." Window glass is a soda-lime silicate. This type of glass is sometimes called " soda-glass " or " soft glass," and it is used for making chemical glass ware. *Window glass, plate glass,* and glass for table ware, and bottles are also made from the same constituents in different proportions and of different degrees of purity. *Bohemian glass* is a potash-lime silicate. It is a hard glass and fuses only at a high temperature, hence it is used for making chemical apparatus designed to withstand high temperatures, gauge-tubes for boilers, etc. It also resists the solvent action of water better than soda-glass. *Jena glass* is a variety of potash-lime glass. *Flint glass* is a lead potash silicate. It is lustrous, and refracts light much better than other types of glass. It is used for making lenses for optical purposes. Some varieties are made into artificial gems and ornamental glass. *Cut glass* is a variety of lead glass which is ground or " cut " on emery or carborundum wheels. Beside these special admixtures, metallic oxides may be added to colour the glass. Translucent or white glass is made by the addition of bone ash, or fluorspar, or cryolite. Boric acid is also used in the manufacture of glass with a high refractive index for optical purposes and for certain kinds of chemical apparatus, known as boro-silicate glass.

Of recent years glass containing a high percentage of silica (e.g., Pyrex, Monax) and which, in consequence, is very resistant to heat (and to sudden changes of temperature) has come into increasing use both for laboratory and oven ware. Pyrex glass, for example, contains approximately 80 per cent. of silica.

§ 7 Silicon Halides

Silicon forms a number of compounds with the halogens of which the most important are :

Silicon tetrafluoride, SiF_4,

and Silicon tetrachloride, $SiCl_4$.

of the others, silicon hexachloride, Si_2Cl_6, silico-chloroform, $SiHCl_3$, and compounds of the formulae Si_2F_6, Si_3Cl_8, $SiBr_4$, Si_2Br_6, $SiHBr_3$, SiI_4, Si_2I_6, $SiHI_3$, have been described, as well as several oxychlorides.

Silicon Tetrafluoride, or Tetrafluosilicomethane, SiF_4

This gaseous compound is important. It was discovered by K. W. Scheele in 1771. It was afterwards made by J. Priestley, and its composition determined by J. L. Gay-Lussac and J. Thénard, 1808 ; J. Davy, 1812 ; and J. J. Berzelius, 1824. Silicon tetrafluoride is made by the direct action of fluorine on amorphous silicon, and also by the action of hydrofluoric acid upon silica or on a silicate—e.g., glass:

$$SiO_2 + 4HF = SiF_4 + 2H_2O.$$

Silicon tetrafluoride is usually made by the action of hydrofluoric acid derived from a mixture of calcium fluoride and sulphuric acid upon silica. The mixture is heated in a flask—illustrated in Fig. 221— fitted with a safety funnel containing mercury. An excess of sulphuric acid is used to absorb the water formed during the reaction.

Silicon tetrafluoride is a colourless gas with a pungent odour resembling hydrogen chloride. The density of the gas corresponds with the formula SiF_4. Silicon tetrafluoride condenses to a colourless liquid which boils at $-65°$ under a pressure of nearly $2\frac{1}{2}$ atmospheres ; and it solidifies when cooled still further, forming a white solid which melts at $-77°$. It can be sublimed without liquefaction at $-90°$ at ordinary pressures. Glass is not attacked by dry silicon tetrafluoride.

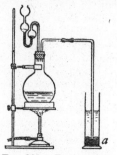

Fig. 221.—Preparation of Hydrofluosilicic Acid.

Hydrofluosilicic acid, H_2SiF_6

If silicon tetrafluoride be passed into water, it decomposes, gelatinous silicic acid is precipitated, and hydrogen fluoride is formed :

$$SiF_4 + 4H_2O = Si(OH)_4 + 4HF.$$

The hydrogen fluoride immediately combines with a molecule of silicon tetrafluoride, producing an aqueous solution of hydrofluosilicic acid. The reactions may be written :

$$SiF_4 + 4H_2O = Si(OH)_4 + 4HF,$$
$$SiF_4 + 2HF = H_2SiF_6,$$

or, combined in one equation,

$$3SiF_4 + 4H_2O = Si(OH)_4 + 2H_2SiF_6.$$

In order to prevent the choking of the delivery tube by the separation of silicic acid when the silicon tetrafluoride is passed into water, it is well to let the delivery tube dip below a little mercury, a, Fig. 221, placed at the bottom of the vessel of water. The aqueous layer is frequently stirred to prevent the formation of channels of silicic acid through which the gas can escape into the atmosphere without coming in contact with the water. This is a good method of making hydrofluosilicic acid. The silicic acid is separated from the aqueous solution by filtration ; the aqueous solution cannot be concentrated very much by evaporation because it decomposes into silicon tetrafluoride and hydrogen fluoride.

Hydrofluosilicic acid reddens blue-litmus, and it is neutralized by the bases forming salts, **fluosilicates.** Most of the fluosilicates are fairly soluble in water, but the potassium and barium fluosilicates are dissolved with difficulty. Hence the use of hydrofluosilicic acid in testing for barium salts, and in the estimation of potassium. Hydrofluosilicic acid is used for giving wood a stone-like surface. The wood is first soaked in lime water and then treated with hydrofluosilicic acid. The acid is also used as an antiseptic in medicine.

Silicon tetrachloride, tetrachlorosilicomethane, $SiCl_4$, can be made by heating silicon, ferrosilicon, silicon carbide, or an intimate mixture of carbon and silica in a stream of chlorine :

$$SiO_2 + 2C + 2Cl_2 = SiCl_4 + 2CO.$$

The liquid which condenses can be freed from the excess of chlorine by shaking it with mercury, and redistilling. The colourless fuming liquid so obtained fumes in moist air. It has a vapour density and composition corresponding with $SiCl_4$. Silicon tetrachloride boils at 57·57° and freezes at −70° ; carbon tetrachloride boils at 76·8° and freezes at −23°. Silicon tetrachloride is decomposed by water into silicic and hydrochloric acids :

$$SiCl_4 + 3H_2O = H_2SiO_3 + 4HCl.$$

§ 8 Germanium, Ge

Germanium was discovered in 1886 by Winkler in a silver mineral *argyrodite* from Saxony, as a result of an apparent discrepancy in the results of his analysis of this mineral. For long germanium was very rare, but recently it has been found to the extent of up to 1 per cent. in the ashes of certain coals, and also the mineral *germanite*, discovered in S.W. Africa in 1916, contains the element as an essential constituent. Germanium is the eka-silicon of Mendeléef (cf. p. 122).

Germanium is a greyish-white, brittle metal which gives rise to two series of compounds in which it is respectively bi- and quadrivalent.

The compounds corresponding with bivalent germanium resemble the compounds of silicon and carbon ; and compounds corresponding with quadrivalent germanium resemble tin and titanium compounds. The analysis and vapour density of germanium tetrachloride correspond with an atomic weight 72·6 (oxygen = 16). This number agrees roughly with the atomic weight calculated from the specific heat 0·08 by Dulong and Petit's rule.

§ 9 Tin, Sn

History

Discoveries of tin in Egyptian tombs show that the metal was fairly common in olden times. It is not certain if the Hebrew word " bedil " in the Pentateuch, translated by the Greek word κασσίτερος (cassiteros), and by the Latin word *stannum*, really means tin. The word " stannum " appears to have been used by the Romans to designate certain alloys containing lead. It is not certain whether the Phoenicians obtained their tin from India, Britain, or Iberia. The resemblance between the Sanscrit word " castira " and the Greek " cassiteros " has been used as an argument in favour of the Indian origin of Phoenician tin. Pliny states that " cassiteron " was obtained from " Cassiterides (British Isles) in the Atlantic Ocean." This no doubt refers to the tin then obtained from the Cornish mines, for " certain islands north of Spain " were often referred to as the *insulae cassiterides*—tin islands. The Romans appear to have distinguished lead from tin by calling lead " plumbum nigrum," and tin " plumbum candidum." The word " stannum " was later restricted to tin proper.

Occurrence

There are several reports of the occurrence of metallic tin in nature—

Bohemia, Bolivia, New South Wales, Nigeria, etc., but *tinstone* or *cassiterite* is the sole source of commercial tin. This mineral occurs in tetragonal crystals coloured brown or black by impurities, chiefly iron. Cassiterite is stannic oxide, SnO_2, contaminated with more or less arsenical pyrites, copper pyrites, tungstates, and various metallic sulphides. *Lode tin* or *vein tin* is cassiterite which is obtained from veins or lodes in primary deposits ; while " stream " tin is cassiterite from alluvial secondary deposits where it occurs in more or less rounded lumps. The miners speak of tinstone as " tin " or *black tin* to distinguish it from the metal which is called *white tin*. The complex sulphide ore, *stannite*, or *tin pyrites*, is a sulphide of copper, tin, iron, and sometimes zinc. It is comparatively rare. About one-third of the world's output of tin is produced in the Malay peninsula—e.g., Banca, which furnishes the so-called *Straits' tin*. Tin is also produced in the Malay archipelago, Bolivia, Nigeria, Australia, Cornwall, South Africa, Bohemia, and Saxony, etc.

It is noteworthy that tin is less abundant than its extensive use would seem to indicate ; it is considerably less abundant, in fact, than titanium, which is often thought of as a scarce element.

Extraction

The method of extracting tin from its ore, the metallurgy of tin, is comparatively simple, owing, no doubt, to the simplicity of the ore— black tin. The ore is first concentrated by washing away the earthy impurities. The high specific gravity of tinstone—6·8 to 7·0—enables this to be done without much trouble, as in the case of washing gold (q.v.). This process usually works well with stream tin ; but vein tin usually requires more complex treatment. The crushed ore is first washed to remove earthy matters. The arsenic and sulphur are removed by an " oxidizing roast." The tungsten and the residue left after the calcination of the pyrites are removed by passing the calcined ore through the intense magnetic field of an " electro-magnetic separator."

The extraction of tin from the concentrates, as they are called, involves the reduction of the ore in a blast furnace or in a reverberatory furnace. To do this, the " concentrated " ore—tinstone—is heated with coal in, say, a reverberatory furnace. The oxide is reduced :

$$SnO_2 + 2C = 2CO + Sn.$$

The molten tin which collects on the bottom of the furnace is drawn off and cast into ingots or blocks—block tin—which contain about 99·5 per cent. of metallic tin. The slag obtained in this operation is also worked up to recover the 20 to 40 per cent. of metal it contains.

Refining Tin

Tin is refined by heating it, at a temperature as little as possible above the melting point of the metal, on the sloping hearth of a reverberatory furnace. The tin flows down the hearth and leaves the oxidized metallic impurities as " refinery dross " behind. This tin may be further purified by stirring the molten metal with a billet of wood. The metal is agitated by the bubbling of the rising gases, and this continually exposes fresh portions of the molten metal to the oxidizing action of the air. The impurities which collect on the surface as a " dross " are skimmed off. The refinery drosses containing a large percentage of tin are re-smelted with the ore.

The recovery of tin from old tin-plate and other scrap materials is an important process and is carried out by treating the scrap material (after washing with alkali to remove grease, etc., and heating to melt off solder) with chlorine in a closed iron cylinder. Volatile stannic chloride is formed which is sometimes converted into the hydrate $SnCl_4.5H_2O$, which finds a use in the silk industry, etc. The iron scrap remaining is smelted in an open-hearth furnace.

§ 10 Properties of Tin

Tin is a white lustrous metal with a pale blue tinge. The metal retains its lustre unimpaired by exposure to air. The metal is soft enough to be cut with a knife, but it is harder than lead, and not so hard as zinc. Tin is very ductile, for it can be beaten into foil—tinfoil —0·01 to 0·1 mm. thick, and drawn into wire. The ductility of tin is greatest at about 100°; at 200° the metal is brittle enough to be pulverized into powder. Tin shows a marked tendency to crystallize on solidification. If a bar of tin be bent, it emits a low crackling noise—" tin cry "—said to be due to the rubbing of the crystal faces upon one another.

Tin melts at 232° and boils at about 2260° ; a perceptible volatiliza-tion occurs at 1200°. Tin exists in three allotropic forms. As ordinarily obtained it forms tetragonal crystals ; but the brittle tin mentioned above is rhombic. Tetragonal tin passes into rhombic at about 170°, which is the transition point of the two forms.

When cooled to a low temperature, tin crumbles to a grey friable powder. Several cases have been reported where tin, during an exceptionally cold winter, has crumbled to powder ; for instance, A. L. Erdmann (1851) noticed some tin organ-pipes in the church at Zeitz crumbled to powder ; and later, the tin buttons of some military uniforms were found to have crumbled to powder while in the depot during a cold winter. The disease is called the " tin pest." The afflicted tin first tarnishes, then shows faint radiating formations, and then wart-like formations, and finally the metal crumbles to a grey pulverulent mass. The afflicted metal contains two kinds of tin—the one, ordinary white bright tin ; and the other grey, dull, pulverulent tin. Grey tin appears to be a third modification of the element.

The transition temperature is 18°. Hence, excepting in warm weather, all ordinary white tin is in a metastable condition ; but, as E. Cohen has pointed out, the speed of the transformation is very slow at ordinary temperatures. The transformation proceeds with a maximum velocity at $-48°$, especially if the tin be in contact with an alcoholic solution of " pink salt," $SnCl_4.2NH_4Cl$. At lower tempera tures, the velocity again slows down. The disease is contagious, for if a piece of tin which has already commenced to change be allowed to remain in contact with a piece of ordinary white tin, the unchanged tin is more quickly affected with the " disease."

Tin is not attacked either by water or air at ordinary temperatures either separately or together ; hence its use as a protective covering. It takes fire when heated in air to between $1500°$ and $1600°$, burning with a white flame to stannic oxide. It combines directly with chlorine forming stannic chloride ; it reacts slowly with dilute hydro-chloric acid and fairly rapidly with the hot concentrated acid forming solutions of stannous chloride :

$$Sn + 2HCl = SnCl_2 + H_2.$$

Tin is but slowly attacked by cold sulphuric acid, but the hot, concentrated acid attacks the metal forming stannic sulphate and sulphur dioxide :

$$Sn + 4H_2SO_4 = Sn(SO_4)_2 + 2SO_2 + 4H_2O.$$

The action of nitric acid depends upon the temperature and concentration of the acid. With cold, very dilute nitric acid, stannous nitrate is formed :

$$4Sn + 10HNO_3 = 4Sn(NO_3)_2 + 3H_2O + NH_4NO_3,$$

with possibly a little stannic nitrate, $Sn(NO_3)_4$. With nitric acid of moderate concentration (e.g., sp. gr. $1·24$), copious fumes are evolved, and a bulky white precipitate of a hydrated oxide, *metastannic acid*, separates. Highly-concentrated, or pure nitric acid, is almost without action on tin. Boiling concentrated alkali hydroxide solutions slowly attack tin forming solutions of stannates, e.g.,

$$Sn + 2KOH + H_2O = K_2SnO_3 + 2H_2.$$

§ 11 Uses of Tin

The most extensive use of tin is in the manufacture of tin-plate. Thin sheets of iron or mild steel are " pickled " by dipping in dilute acid to remove oxide, etc., and are then passed into a bath of molten tin on the surface of which floats a flux such as rosin, zinc chloride, etc.

Tin is also a constituent of many useful alloys, e.g., solder, pewter, type metal, bronze (p. 586), bearing metal, and Britannia metal.

Ordinary *fine solder* consists of **33** per cent. lead and **66** per cent. tin ; *common solder* contains equal parts of lead and tin. *Pewter* contains 75 per cent. of tin and 25 per cent. of lead. *Type metal* has 75 per cent. of lead, 5 per cent. of tin, and 20 per cent. of antimony. A typical *bearing metal*, such as is used in locomotives, contains 82 per cent. of tin, 14 per cent. of antimony and 4 per cent. of copper. *Britannia* *metal*, a somewhat similar alloy, has 93 per cent. of tin, 5 per cent. of antimony, and 2 per cent. of copper.

A white, coarsely crystalline mass known as *phosphor tin* is obtained by adding phosphorus to molten tin. It is used for the manufacture of phosphor-bronze (p. 586).

§ 12 Atomic Weight of Tin

The vapour density of the volatile compounds of tin ; observations on the isomorphism of stannic and titanic oxides, and the specific heat of tin (0·055) indicate a number round about 119 for the atomic weight.

The exact value of the combining weight has been determined from analysis or synthesis of the oxide, chloride, potassium and ammonium stannichlorides ; and by the separation of tin from stannic chloride by electrolysis. The value recommended at present (1940) by the International Committee is 118·7, and is based on the work of Briscoe (1915) who determined the ratio $SnCl_4 : 4Ag$ by breaking bulbs of specially purified stannic chloride in a solution of silver in nitric acid.

§ 13 Oxides and Hydroxides of Tin. Stannic Acids

Tin forms two oxides, viz.,

Stannous oxide, SnO,
Stannic oxide, SnO_2,

and corresponding to them are two series of tin compounds, the stannous and the stannic.

Stannous Oxide, SnO

Stannous oxide can be made by heating stannous oxalate :

$$SnC_2O_4 = SnO + CO + CO_2,$$

or by careful heating of *stannous hydroxide*, $Sn(OH)_2$, in a stream of carbon dioxide. Stannous hydroxide is precipitated on the addition of alkalis to a solution of stannous chloride :

$$SnCl_2 + 2NaOH = Sn(OH)_2 + 2NaCl,$$
$$Sn(OH)_2 = SnO + HO.$$

Stannous oxide is a brown or dark grey powder which burns in air to stannic oxide. It reacts with acids forming stannous salts, and also with alkalis forming *stannites* which are regarded as salts of stannous acid, H_2SnO_2, i.e., of stannous hydroxide reacting as an acid.

Stannic Hydroxide

Stannic hydroxide is precipitated by ammonia, alkali hydroxides, carbonates, etc., from solutions of stannic salts, e.g.,

$$SnCl_4 + 4KOH = Sn(OH)_4 + 4KCl.$$

It is also formed by hydrolysis of stannic chloride in water :

$$SnCl_4 + 4H_2O = Sn(OH)_4 + 4HCl,$$

and when a solution of stannous chloride is exposed to the air. Possibly, in this case, stannic chloride is first formed and then hydrolyzed :

$$2SnCl_2 + O_2 + 6H_2O = 2Sn(OH)_4 + 4HCl.$$

If the precipitate obtained in these ways be dried in air, it has the empirical composition H_4SnO_4 or $Sn(OH)_4$; and if dried over concentrated sulphuric acid, the empirical composition is H_2SnO_3 or $SnO.(OH)_2$. The former is regarded as **orthostannic acid** and the latter as **metastannic acid.**

Stannates, such as $K_2SnO_3\ 3H_2O$, can be made by heating solutions of stannic chloride and alkali carbonates or hydroxides ; from aqueous solutions of these stannates, a metastannic acid, H_2SnO_3, is precipitated by carbon dioxide.

When tin is heated with hot nitric acid (sp. gr. 1·3), stannic hydroxide is formed which, if dried over sulphuric acid, also has the empirical formula H_2SnO_3. But the stannic acids formed by these two processes differ in their behaviour towards many reagents. For convenience, the acid formed by the action of alkalis on solutions of stannic chloride is called the α-acid, and that produced by the action of nitric acid on the metal is known as the β-acid. Some of the differences between the two metastannic acids are indicated in Table XLVI.

TABLE XLVI.—PROPERTIES OF THE METASTANNIC ACIDS.

α-Metastannic acid.	β-Metastannic acid.
Salts dissolve in water easily and are not decomposed. More basic than the β-acid.	Salts dissolve in water with difficulty and form insoluble basic salts and free acid. Less basic than the α-acid.
When moist, dissolves readily in nitric acid.	Insoluble in nitric acid.
Soluble in dilute sulphuric acid and the solution does not gelatinize when boiled.	Insoluble in sulphuric acid even if concentrated.
Easily soluble in hydrochloric and the solution remains clear when boiled.	Unites with hydrochloric acid forming a substance insoluble in acid but soluble in water. The aqueous solution gelatinizes when boiled.

Both varieties dissolve in caustic alkalis and alkali carbonates, and when reprecipitated by acids, they retain the properties they had before being so dissolved. If the β-acid be boiled for a long time with concentrated hydrochloric acid, or concentrated alkali hydroxide solution, it is gradually converted into the α-acid ; and, conversely, the α-acid is gradually changed into the β-acid at ordinary temperatures and more rapidly on boiling with water.

An explanation of the difference between the two acids is not known with certainty ; but it is generally supposed that the β-acid is a polymerized form—$(H_2SnO_3)_5$—of the α-acid—H_2SnO_3 ; and that the two are to be represented :

$$O = Sn{<}{\stackrel{\textstyle OH}{OH}} \qquad {\stackrel{\textstyle HO}{HO}}{>}Sn{<}{\stackrel{\textstyle O{-}Sn(OH)_2{-}O{-}Sn(OH)_2}{O{-}Sn(OH)_2{-}O{-}Sn(OH)_2}}{>}O.$$

The idea is growing in some quarters that the difference is only one of size of grain and that there are not two definite and distinct acids. It is difficult to reconcile this view, however, with the observation that the differences persist after solution in caustic alkali and reprecipitation.

Sodium stannate, $Na_2SnO_3.3H_2O$, is made commercially by fusing tin with a mixture of caustic soda, sodium nitrate and sodium chloride. It is a white crystalline substance, containing 3 molecules of water, and is used as a mordant in calico-printing under the name of *preparing salts*.

Stannic oxide, SnO_2, occurs in nature and is the principal ore of tin. It crystallizes in three different forms and is iso-trimorphous with the corresponding titanium compound (q.v.). It is formed by heating tin in air, or by calcining the stannic acids. It is a white powder which is unattacked by acids except concentrated sulphuric with which it reacts, forming a solution which may contain stannic sulphate, $Sn(SO_4)_2$. On dilution, the oxide is reprecipitated. It also reacts with solutions of alkali hydroxides, forming stannates :

$$SnO_2^{..} + 2KOH = K_2SnO_3 + H_2O.$$

Stannic oxide is used in making white glazes for tiles, and for milk-glass articles such as electric-light shades, etc.

§ 14 Salts of Tin

Tin forms two series of salts, corresponding to the two oxides, known as the stannous salts and the stannic salts respectively. Stannic oxide is a very weak base indeed, and in the quadrivalent state tin forms compounds resembling those of a non-metal ; e.g., stannic chloride is a liquid, readily hydrolyzed by water.

Stannous Chloride, $SnCl_2$

Stannous chloride can be prepared by the action of hydrochloric acid on tin ; the solution on evaporation deposits monoclinic crystals of the dihydrate, $SnCl_2.2H_2O$, known as *tin salt*. When dried in vacuo, the anhydrous salt is formed ; the anhydrous salt also results when tin is heated in a stream of hydrogen chloride, and also by heating a mixture of metallic tin and mercuric chloride, when the mercury volatilizes, and the stannous chloride remains :

$$Sn + HgCl_2 = SnCl_2 + Hg.$$

Stannous chloride dissolves in water, without noticeable change, if only a small quantity is used ; with excess of water, hydrolysis occurs and a basic chloride is precipitated :

$$SnCl_2 + H_2O \rightleftharpoons Sn(OH)Cl + HCl.$$

The precipitate redissolves on addition of hydrochloric acid. Solutions of alkali hydroxides precipitate stannous hydroxide which redissolves in excess, forming stannites.

Stannous chloride is a powerful reducing agent, and readily combines with oxygen or chlorine. Thus it reduces mercuric chloride to mercurous chloride and, if the action be allowed to continue, to metallic mercury :

$$SnCl_2 + 2HgCl_2 = SnCl_4 + Hg_2Cl_2,$$
$$Hg_2Cl_2 + SnCl_2 = SnCl_4 + 2Hg.$$

Ferric salts and cupric salts are reduced by stannous chloride to the ferrous and cuprous states respectively. It acts upon nitric acid with the formation of hydroxylamine (NH_2OH) and it is frequently employed in organic chemistry.

Stannous chloride is used as a mordant in dyeing.

Stannic Chloride, $SnCl_4$

This compound is prepared by the action of chlorine on molten metallic tin, the stannic chloride which is volatile being collected in a cooled receiver. It is a colourless, fuming liquid which boils at 114·1°, and fumes strongly in moist air. The action of a little moisture converts it into a solid pentahydrate, $SnCl_4.5H_2O$, known as *oxymuriate of tin* which is used as a mordant. With excess of water, basic chlorides, and ultimately stannic acid, are formed

$$SnCl_4 + H_2O \rightleftharpoons Sn(OH)Cl_3 + HCl,$$
$$Sn(OH)Cl_3 + 3H_2O \rightleftharpoons Sn(OH)_4 + 3HCl.$$

Stannic chloride forms a series of complex salts, the most important of which is **ammonium chlorostannate**, $(NH_4)_2SnCl_6$, used as a mordant under the name of *pink salt.*

Tin Sulphides

When tin-foil is burned in sulphur vapour, **stannous sulphide,** SnS, is formed. **Stannous hydrosulphide,** $Sn(HS)_2$, is precipitated as a brown powder when hydrogen sulphide is passed through a solution of a stannous salt. The precipitate becomes black on drying. It is soluble in strongly acid solutions, but is reprecipitated on dilution. It is also soluble in alkali and ammonium polysulphides, forming **thiostannates,** e.g.,

$$SnS + K_2S + S = K_2SnS_3,$$

and yellow stannic sulphide is precipitated on acidification. It is insoluble in ammonia, ammonium carbonate and colourless ammonium sulphide.

Stannic sulphide, SnS_2, is precipitated by passing hydrogen sulphide through a (not too strongly acid) solution of a stannic salt. It dissolves in alkali sulphides, forming the same thiostannates as above. It is insoluble in ammonia and ammonium carbonate.

On heating a mixture of tin amalgam, ammonium chloride and

sulphur in a retort, a complex reaction takes place resulting in the formation of a mass of yellow scales of stannic sulphide called *mosaic gold* and used as a pigment.

§ 15 Detection and Determination of Tin

Tin is usually recognized in qualitative analysis by the precipitation of its sulphides, in acid solution, on passing hydrogen sulphide. They are separated from the sulphides of copper, lead, mercury, bismuth and cadmium by the action of yellow ammonium sulphide, with which they react forming soluble thiostannates. Arsenic and antimony sulphides behave similarly with this reagent from which on acidification arsenic and antimony pentasulphides, and stannic sulphide are precipitated. These three may be separated as follows. The arsenic is first removed by adding solid ammonium carbonate and a few drops of water and warming to 40°. After filtering, arsenic pentasulphide is precipitated from the filtrate on addition of dilute hydrochloric acid. The residue (antimony and tin sulphides) after washing with ammonium chloride solution, is warmed to 80° with a little milk of lime. The antimony pentasulphide is converted in a yellow solution of calcium thioantimonate, while the stannic sulphide becomes hydrated stannic oxide. When the precipitate is all colourless, the solution is filtered ; antimony pentasulphide is precipitated on acidification of the filtrate, while the residue, after solution in warm dilute hydrochloric acid, deposits stannic hydroxide as a white gelatinous precipitate on addition of ammonium chloride and ammonia.

Tin is often determined gravimetrically by conversion into stannic oxide by the action of nitric acid followed by ignition. This method is used for alloys, because the other metals present usually form soluble nitrates. The salts are converted to the stannic condition, and then precipitated as stannic hydroxide, which is ignited.

Volumetrically, tin can be determined by means of iodine, provided it is in the stannous condition. The reaction is sometimes expressed :

$$Sn\cdot\cdot + 2I = Sn\cdot\cdot\cdot\cdot + 2I'.$$

Stannic salts can be determined if they are first reduced to stannous by say, iron or nickel in acid solution.

Tin can also be determined by precipitation with "cupferron" $(C_6H_5N(NO)ONH_4)$ by adding a 10 per cent. solution to the cold tin solution. It forms a white precipitate which on ignition leaves stannic oxide, which is weighed.

§ 16 Lead, Pb

History

Lead was known to the ancient Egyptians. It is mentioned several times in the Old Testament. It appears to have been confused with tin (q.v.), and Pliny seems to have distinguished between *plumbum nigrum* (black lead) and *plumbum album* or *plumbum candidum*. The ancient Romans used lead for making water-pipes, and some lead compounds were used as cosmetics, and as paint.

Occurrence

Small quantities of metallic lead are occasionally found in nature. In combination with sulphur, lead occurs as the sulphide, *galena*, PbS. This is the most abundant ore of lead. Commercial lead is obtained almost exclusively from galena. Lead carbonate, *cerussite*, $PbCO_3$, is not uncommon. Lead sulphate, $PbSO_4$, occurs as *anglesite* ; lead chromate, *crocoisite*, $PbCrO_4$; lead molybdate, *wulfenite*, $PbMoO_4$; lead phosphate, *pyromorphite*, $PbCl_2.3Pb_3(PO_4)_2$; lead chloride, *matlockite*, $PbCl_2$. Lead ores come from England, United States, Germany, Mexico, Spain, New South Wales, South America, etc.

Extraction

Three main methods have been employed for the extraction of lead, viz.,

(i) open hearth smelting ;

(ii) reverberatory furnace smelting, and

(iii) the blast furnace method.

Of these, the first two are obsolete or obsolescent ; the last named is coming into increasing use.

The open-hearth method consists essentially in heating the ore on a shallow hearth while a hot blast of air is blown over it. The reaction is sometimes represented :

$$PbS + O_2 = Pb + SO_2,$$

although it is probable that it takes place in two stages (see below).

In the reverberatory furnace, the process is carried out in two stages, known as the *roasting* stage, and the *reaction* stage respectively.

In the roasting stage, the temperature is kept below the melting point of the charge, and air is admitted so that the part of the sulphide is converted into a mixture of oxide and sulphate :

$$2PbS + 3O_2 = 2PbO + 2SO_2,$$
$$PbS + 2O_2 = PbSO_4.$$

In the reaction stage, a higher temperature is employed, the air supply is cut off, and the charge melts, lead being formed according to the reactions :

$$PbS + 2PbO = 3Pb + SO_2,$$
$$PbS + PbSO_4 = 2Pb + 2SO_2.$$

For the blast furnace method, the ore is subjected to a preliminary roasting so as to sinter the finely-divided ore or concentrate into lumps of suitable size ; at the same time most of it is converted into the oxide. This is then mixed with fuel and smelted in a small blast furnace, reduction of the oxide taking place, mainly brought about by carbon and carbon monoxide ; but to a lesser extent by any surviving lead sulphide.

The lead obtained by these processes usually contains small amounts of antimony, tin, copper, etc., which make it hard and brittle ; as well as silver in quantity sufficient to make recovery profitable. Most of the impurities can be removed by heating the metal in a shallow, flat-bottomed, reverberatory furnace, whereby they are oxidized before the lead and rise to the surface as a scum which is skimmed off. Electrolytic methods are now being applied to the refining of lead ; a bath of lead fluosilicate containing some free hydrofluosilicic acid being used. The silver is usually extracted by Parkes's process (p. 599).

§ 17 Properties of Lead

Lead is a bluish-grey metal with a bright metallic lustre when freshly cut, but the lustre soon disappears in ordinary air. Perfectly dry air, and air-free water, have no action on the metal, but if moist air be present, or if the metal be immersed in aerated water, lead is soon covered with a film, probably an oxide, and this is ultimately converted into a basic carbonate. Lead is soft enough to be cut with a knife and scratched with the finger nail. It leaves a grey streak when drawn across paper. Small traces of impurity—antimony, arsenic, copper, zinc—make the lead much harder. Lead is not tough enough to be hammered into foil or drawn into wire ; but it can be pressed into pipes, or rolled into thin sheets or foil. Lead filings under a pressure of about 13 tons per square inch, form a solid block ; and the metal seems to liquefy under a pressure of about 33 tons per square inch. The specific gravity of lead varies from 11·25 to 11·4 according as the metal is cast or rolled. Lead melts at 327°, and boils at about 1620°. When cooled slowly, the molten metal forms a mass of octahedral crystals (cubic system). The crystalline nature of the metal is shown by the electrolysis of a lead salt. Lead is also deposited as an " arborescent " mass of crystals—called a " lead tree "—when a strip of iron or zinc is suspended in a solution of a lead salt.

Lead is fairly rapidly dissolved by nitric acid, but is little affected by dilute hydrochloric or dilute sulphuric acid in the cold, because a crust of insoluble lead chloride or sulphate is formed on the surface, and this protects the metal from further action. Powdered lead is quickly dissolved by boiling concentrated hydrochloric or sulphuric acid. Organic acids—acetic acid (vinegar)—also act as solvents for metallic lead. Hence vessels plated with tin containing lead, if used, for cooking purposes, may contaminate the food with poisonous lead compounds. Water containing sulphates and carbonates in solution forms a coating on the surface of lead which prevents further action. Lead is attacked by water holding air, nitrates, ammonium salts, and carbon dioxide in solution. In the latter case, a soluble acid carbonate may be formed. All soluble lead salts are poisonous, and if the water supply of a town be pure enough to attack lead it may produce lead poisoning. To avoid risk, the water is sometimes filtered through limestone or chalk since carbonates in the water do not corrode the pipes very much. The water then takes up enough carbonates to form a film on the interior of the lead pipes which protects the lead from further action.

§ 18 Uses of Lead

Uses

Lead is largely used in the arts on account of the ease with which it can be worked, cut, bent, soldered, and on account of its power of resisting attack by water and many acids. It is used in the manufacture of pipes for conveying water ; for the manufacture of sheaths for electric wires, sheets for sinks, cisterns, and roofs, lead chambers for sulphuric acid works, evaporation pans in chemical works, etc. It is used in making bullets, shot, accumulator plates, etc. Type metal, solder, pewter, and fusible alloys contain much lead.

§ 19 Atomic Weight of Lead

The atomic weight of lead has been the subject of very many investigations on account of the differing values to be expected for it according to its origin. Thus lead is the end product of radio-active change (see Ch. XXXVI), and its atomic weight, according to modern theory, would be expected to approach 206 or 208 according as it is derived from the uranium or thorium series respectively.

The atomic weight of lead is seen to be in the neighbourhood of 207 from a consideration of its specific heat (0·0309) and the vapour density of its volatile compounds. The exact value to be used has been deduced from the conversion of highly purified lead chloride into silver chloride. For common lead (i.e., from non-radioactive sources) the value 207·22 is that adopted by the International Committee. Values for the atomic weight of radiogenic lead have been obtained as low as 205·93 and as high as 207·92, according to their source, by workers such as Richards, Hönigschmid, Baxter, &c.

§ 20 Oxides of Lead

Lead forms five oxides, viz.,

Lead suboxide, Pb_2O ;
Lead monoxide, litharge, massicot, PbO ;
Triplumbic tetroxide, red lead, minium, Pb_3O_4 ;
Lead sesquioxide, Pb_2O_3 ;
Lead dioxide, PbO_2.

Lead suboxide, Pb_2O, is said to be formed by heating lead oxalate out of contact with air :

$$2PbC_2O_4 = Pb_2O + CO + 3CO_2,$$

and also as a dull grey iridescent coating on the surface of lead melted at a low temperature. Its existence is still in dispute.

Lead Monoxide, Massicot, Litharge, PbO

There seem to be two forms of lead monoxide, known as massicot and litharge respectively. Litharge is the product when it is made at a high temperature so the product fuses, while massicot results when the temperature is kept sufficiently low to prevent melting.

Lead monoxide can be prepared in the laboratory by heating lead nitrate, carbonate, or hydroxide; commercially it is made by heating lead to a temperature considerably above its melting point, and continually skimming off the litharge produced.

Litharge varies in colour from pale yellow to reddish yellow, possibly owing to the existence of two forms, a yellow and a red. It fuses at 877° and is volatile at a red heat. It is slightly soluble in water, probably forming lead hydroxide (q.v.). It reacts with acids forming solutions of lead salts, and also with alkalis forming plumbites, e.g.,

$$2NaOH + PbO = Na_2PbO_2 + H_2O.$$

It is thus an amphoteric oxide.

Litharge is used in preparing oils and varnishes and sometimes in the manufacture of flint glass, although red lead is more often employed (p. 690), as well as for the preparation of some lead salts.

Triplumbic tetroxide, Red Lead, Minium, Pb_3O_4

Red lead is prepared from massicot—unfused lead monoxide—by heating it to a carefully regulated temperature (470°-480°) for several hours. The hot powder acquires a deeper and deeper tint as time goes on and appears to become violet and finally black. On cooling, the colour changes to a brilliant red.

On strong heating, red lead decomposes, forming litharge from which red lead cannot be reformed:

$$2Pb_3O_4 = 6PbO + O_2.$$
$$\text{litharge}$$

Nitric acid converts red lead into lead nitrate and lead dioxide:

$$Pb_3O_4 + 4HNO_3 = 2Pb(NO_3)_2 + PbO_2 + 2H_2O,$$

from which it might appear that red lead is a compound of lead monoxide and dioxide, e.g., plumbous plumbate, $Pb_2.PbO_4$. It is now generally agreed that red lead does not have a definite composition, although it approximates, more or less closely, to that required by the formula Pb_3O_4. With hydrochloric acid, lead chloride is formed and chlorine is liberated; possibly lead dioxide is formed intermediately:

$$Pb_3O_4 + 4HCl = PbCl_2 + PbO_2 + 2H_2O,$$
$$PbO_2 + 4HCl = PbCl_2 + Cl_2 + 2H_2O.$$

Red lead is used for a variety of purposes. It is employed in the glass industry; for making glazes for pottery; and in the manufacture of paint, and of matches.

Lead sesquioxide, Pb_2O_3, is an orange-yellow powder formed when lead hydroxide in alkaline solution is treated in the cold with an oxidizing agent, such as chlorine, bromine, hypochlorites, etc.,

$$2Pb(OH)_2 + NaOCl = Pb_2O_3 + NaCl + H_2O.$$

On heating, lead monoxide and oxygen are formed :

$$2Pb_2O_3 = 4PbO + O_2,$$

whilst with acids a lead salt and lead dioxide result. With hydrochloric acid chlorine is evolved.

Lead dioxide, PbO_2, is prepared by the action of powerful oxidizing agents such as hypochlorites, chlorine, etc., on alkaline suspensions of lead monoxide.

$$PbO + CaOCl_2 = PbO_2 + CaCl_2.$$

It is also deposited on the anode when a solution of a lead salt is electrolyzed, and can be made from red lead by the action of nitric acid.

Lead dioxide is a chocolate coloured powder, which, when heated, decomposes into lead monoxide and oxygen. It is a powerful oxidizing agent. Thus, when lead dioxide is gently rubbed with sulphur on a warm surface, the mass inflames ; when sulphur dioxide is passed over lead dioxide, the two unite to form lead sulphate and the whole mass becomes red hot ; and when hydrogen sulphide is allowed to impinge on a few grams of lead dioxide it bursts into flame.

Lead dioxide is not affected by dilute acids, but it reacts with cold, concentrated hydrochloric acid (probably forming lead tetrachloride, $PbCl_4$, p. 710) ; with hot concentrated hydrochloric acid chlorine is evolved. It also reacts with boiling concentrated aqueous potassium hydroxide, forming *potassium metaplumbate*, K_2PbO_3, analogous to the metastannates. Lead dioxide does not give hydrogen peroxide with acids in any circumstances ; hence the name " lead peroxide " is a misnomer.

Lead dioxide is an important constituent of the *lead accumulator* or storage cell. This consists essentially of an electrolytic cell having an anode of lead dioxide and a cathode of spongy lead immersed in dilute sulphuric acid (about 20 per cent.). In practice, the plates consist of grids, made of lead hardened with a little antimony, into which the active material has been forced. This construction is adopted so as to increase the capacity of the cell and to prevent the active material from becoming detached. If the terminals of such a cell be connected through a suitable resistance a current will flow ; the lead dioxide of the anode and the spongy lead of the cathode are converted into a film of lead sulphate As soon as the dioxide has disappeared the E.M.F. of the cell, originally about two volts, drops rapidly, although it is remarkably constant so long as any dioxide remains. The cell is then said to be discharged ; it can be recharged by passing a current through it in the reverse direction, from some external source. When this is done, hydrogen is formed at the cathode which reduces the lead sulphate to spongy lead again ; the oxygen formed at the anode oxidizes the lead sulphate (probably by way of lead disulphate, $Pb(SO_4)_2$) back to lead dioxide, thus recharging the cell. These effects may be summarized :

$$2PbSO_4 + 2H_2O \rightleftharpoons Pb + PbO_2 + 2H_2SO_4$$

Charge——→   ←———Discharge.

Lead hydroxide, $Pb(OH)_2$, is best made by the addition of a solution of an alkali hydroxide to a lead salt. It is a white solid, which forms lead salts with acids ; it reacts with excess of alkali, forming solutions of **plumbites,** e.g., *potassium plumbite,* K_2PbO_2. It does not react with ammonia, and when heated to 145° changes to the oxide.

§ 21 Lead Salts

Lead forms compounds in which the element is either bivalent or quadrivalent ; but few, if any, of the quadrivalent compounds are true salts. For example, lead tetrachloride, $PbCl_4$ (p. 710), behaves as the acid chloride of plumbic acid.

Lead Carbonates, White Lead

Normal lead carbonate, $PbCO_3$, occurs native as *cerussite* ; it is obtained as a white precipitate when an alkaline bicarbonate is added to a solution of a soluble lead salt, such as the nitrate. Solutions of normal carbonates give a precipitate of a *basic lead carbonate*. Several basic carbonates of lead are known ; the most important is **white**

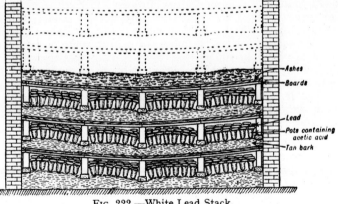

Fig. 222.—White Lead Stack.

lead, $2PbCO_3.Pb(OH)_2$. This has been used as a pigment for centuries and its manufacture is an important technical operation. Several processes have been suggested, but the old, so-called " Dutch " process is said to furnish the best product from the point of view of covering power when used as a pigment or in the manufacture of paints.

The " Dutch " process is illustrated by Fig. 222. There is a brick-work chamber in which is built up a stack. At the bottom is placed a layer of ashes, and then one of spent tan bark which may be up to three feet thick. On this is placed a row of pots, partly filled with dilute acetic acid. (Vinegar is often employed.) On top of these are laid perforated sheets of lead, forming a layer about five inches deep, above which is a row of boards which serve as the foundation for another tier of bark, pots and lead. The temperature of the whole stack is carefully regulated by ventilation and the whole is left to stand for about three months.

The actions taking place in the stack are thought to be as follows. The tan-bark ferments, which causes some carbon dioxide to be evolved, while heat is liberated. The heat volatilizes some of the acetic acid which reacts with the lead, forming basic lead acetate. This is decomposed by the carbon dioxide, forming a mixture of normal lead acetate and basic lead carbonate. The acetate in presence of air and moisture reacts with more lead, forming more basic acetate and so the process goes on. These reactions may be represented :

$$2Pb + 2CH_3COOH + O_2 = Pb(CH_3COO)_2.Pb(OH)_2 ;$$
$$3[Pb(CH_3COO)_2.Pb(OH)_2] + 2CO_2$$
$$= 3Pb(CH_3COO)_2 + 2PbCO_3.Pb(OH)_2 + 2H_2O$$
$$2Pb(CH_3COO)_2 + 2Pb + O_2 + 2H_2O = 2[Pb(CH_3COO)_2.Pb(OH)_2]$$

At the end of three months, the stack is unloaded and the white lead crushed in a mill, any unchanged lumps of lead are removed and the residue of white lead is ground up with water.

Many attempts have been made to speed up this process, but the quality of the products is inferior from the point of view of covering power. White lead paint is the most satisfactory white pigment from this point of view, but suffers from the disadvantages that it is dis-coloured by hydrogen sulphide (always liable to occur in the air of towns) through the formation of black lead sulphide ; and like all lead compounds, it is poisonous. Consequently other materials such as zinc oxide, lithopone (p. 645), etc., are sometimes preferred in spite of their inferior covering power.

Lead Chloride, $PbCl_2$

This salt separates as a white curdy precipitate when hydrochloric acid or a soluble chloride is added to a solution of a lead salt. It is also made by dissolving lead oxide or carbonate in hot hydrochloric acid. On cooling, the solution deposits crystals of lead chloride, $PbCl_2$, which melt at 501°. The salt is generally said to be fairly soluble in hot water, and sparingly soluble in cold water : 100 grams of water at 0° dissolve 0·67 gram of $PbCl_2$; at 50°, 1·70 grams ; and at 100°, 3·34 grams. When lead chloride is heated in air, **lead oxy-chloride**, Pb_2OCl_2, or $PbCl_2.PbO$, is formed. By adding hot limewater to a boiling solution of lead chloride, $PbCl_2PbO.H_2O$, or $Pb(OH)Cl$, separates. This compound is used as a white pigment under the commercial name " Pattinson's white lead," and the pigment " Cassel's yellow " is a mixture containing one or more oxychlorides of lead, approximately $7PbO + PbCl_2$, made by heating lead oxide with ammonium chloride.

Lead iodide, PbI_2, forms glittering golden-yellow crystals which, like the chloride, are almost insoluble in cold water, but which are moderately soluble in hot water. It is interesting to note that the solution is colourless.

Lead Nitrate, $Pb(NO_3)_2$

Lead nitrate is formed by acting upon the metal, oxide, or carbonate with nitric acid. The salt is deposited in regular octahedral crystals which contain no water of crystallization. On heating, lead nitrate decomposes into litharge, nitrogen peroxide and oxygen, a reaction which is sometimes used for the preparation of nitrogen peroxide (p. 420).

$$2Pb(NO_3)_2 = 2PbO + 2NO_2 + O_2.$$

Lead Sulphide, PbS

Lead sulphide occurs in nature as galena in well-formed cubic crystals with a lustre resembling metallic lead. Lead sulphide is formed by reducing the sulphate with carbon, by heating lead in sulphur vapour, and as a black precipitate by passing hydrogen sulphide through neutral, acid, or alkaline solutions of a lead salt. If hydrochloric acid be present, an orange, yellow, or red precipitate of **lead thiochloride,** Pb_2SCl_2, may be formed.

Boiling dilute nitric acid dissolves lead sulphide, forming lead nitrate with the separation of sulphur. Concentrated nitric acid oxidizes it to lead sulphate. Unlike tin sulphide, lead sulphide is insoluble in alkaline hydroxides and sulphides. Synthetic lead sulphide melts at $1114°$, and galena at a lower temperature ; lead sulphide begins to sublime at about $950°$ in vacuo or in a current of an inert gas, forming small cubic crystals. Heated with free access of air, it forms lead sulphate.

Lead sulphate, $PbSO_4$, occurs native as *anglesite*. It is formed as a white precipitate when sulphuric acid or a soluble sulphate is added to a solution of a lead salt. It is noteworthy as one of the few sulphates which are insoluble in water and it is used for the determination of lead.

Lead chromate, $PbCrO_4$, occurs naturally as *crocoisite*. It is precipitated as a bright sulphur yellow solid by adding potassium chromate solution to a solution of a lead salt. It is used as a pigment —known as *chrome yellow, Cologne yellow, lemon chrome*, etc. By boiling with alkali hydroxide solution it is converted into red **basic lead chromate,** $Pb(OH)_2.PbCrO_4$, also used as a pigment—*chrome red*.

Lead acetate, $(CH_3COO)_2Pb$, is important as being one of the two common salts of lead which is easily soluble in water (100 grams of water dissolve 46 grams at 15°). It is made by boiling litharge with acetic acid until a solution results and allowing this solution to crystallize. It is a white crystalline salt with a sweet taste (it is very poisonous) and hence is known as *sugar of lead*. It is used in medicine; as a mordant and in the laboratory for the preparation of lead compounds.

§ 22 Quadrivalent Lead Compounds

In addition to lead dioxide, already discussed, there are a number of compounds of quadrivalent lead. Many of these are more conveniently regarded as organic compounds, (as, for example, lead tetraethyl, $Pb(C_2H_5)_4$, now extensively used as an " anti-knock " in motor fuels), but of the remainder, lead tetrachloride and tetra-acetate may fitly be considered here.

Lead Tetrachloride, $PbCl_4$

The fact that lead dioxide will form a solution with cold concentrated hydrochloric acid has been mentioned (p. 706), and is probably due to the formation of lead tetrachloride, which, in presence of excess of hydrochloric acid, is thought to form the acid H_2PbCl_6. The same deep yellow solution is obtained when chlorine is passed into a suspension of lead dichloride in concentrated hydrochloric acid. If to this solution a concentrated solution of ammonium chloride be added, yellow **ammonium chloroplumbate,** $(NH_4)_2PbCl_6$, separates out. This salt is stable at ordinary temperatures and can be filtered off and dried On adding it to concentrated sulphuric acid in a good freezing mixture, lead tetrachloride is obtained as a heavy yellow liquid :

$$(NH_4)_2PbCl_6 + H_2SO_4 = (NH_4)_2SO_4 + 2HCl + PbCl_4.$$

It is stable under sulphuric acid, but fumes in air, at ordinary temperatures, chlorine being evolved. It is decomposed by water into lead dioxide and hydrochloric acid.

Lead tetra-acetate, $Pb(C_2H_3O_2)_4$, is a white solid, obtained by dissolving red lead in warm glacial acetic acid. On cooling, the solution deposits white needles of the tetra-acetate. It is a reasonably stable compound at ordinary temperatures ; latterly it has been used considerably as an oxidizing agent in organic chemistry. It is decomposed by water forming lead dioxide.

§ 23 Detection and Determination of Lead

Lead salts in solution are detected by the formation of a white precipitate of lead chloride on addition of hydrochloric acid. This precipitate is soluble in hot water and crystallizes out on cooling in fine white needles. Lead salts also give a bright yellow precipitate of lead chromate, with potassium chromate solution.

Lead is usually determined by precipitation as the sulphate.

§ 24 Group IVA of the Periodic Table

The A sub-group of Group IV comprises the elements titanium, zirconium, hafnium and thorium. Cerium is sometimes included in this group, but as mentioned in the previous chapter, the electronic configuration assigned to its atom by Bohr indicated that it is, properly speaking, the first member of the Rare-Earth elements. It shows, in fact, resemblances to both groups.

Titanium, Ti
History and Occurrence

Titanium was discovered in 1791 by W. Gregor while investigating the magnetic sand (*menachanite*) found at Menachan in Cornwall, and was named by him " menachin." Three years later M. H. Klaproth found what he supposed to be a new " earth " in rutile. He called the metal derived from it titanium and showed that it was identical with Gregor's menachin. J. J. Berzelius first isolated the metal—more or less impure—in 1825.

Titanium does not occur free ; but combined it is widely distributed, and in small quantities is quite common since most igneous rocks contain about 0·5 per cent. It is often thought of as a rare element ; in fact, although concentrated deposits are only rarely found, it is about the tenth commonest element and more abundant than any of the common metals except aluminium and iron. The chief minerals are *rutile* (tetragonal), *brookite* (orthochombic) and *anatase* (tetragonal) ; three forms of TiO_2 isotrimorphous with stannic oxide (p. 699) ; titanium also occurs in the minerals *ilmenite* (titaniferous iron ore), $FeTiO_3$; *sphene* or *titanite*, calcium titanium silicate, $CaTiSiO_5$ or $CaO.SiO_2.TiO_2$.

Extraction

In order to obtain the metal, rutile is first purified by dissolving it in strong sulphuric acid, when unstable titanic sulphate is formed, along with sulphates of iron. A little water is added which dissolves the titanium sulphate, leaving most of the iron salts undissolved. The clear solution is diluted when titanic hydroxide is precipitated, and is washed and ignited. The element is then obtained either, by reduction with aluminium (cf. the thermite process—p. 667), or by the action of sodium on the tetrachloride in a steel bomb.

$$3TiO_2 + 4Al = 2Al_2O_3 + 3Ti,$$

$$TiCl_4 + 4Na = 4NaCl + Ti.$$

The free element is not used but the alloy with iron, *ferro-titanium*, is of great importance for the production of titanium steels. It is obtained by adding rutile to a molten mixture of iron and aluminium.

Titanium melts at 1800° ; it is a fairly light metal as its specific gravity is 4·5 approximately. In chemical properties it is closely related with silicon. It burns when heated in oxygen, forming titanium dioxide ; at 800° in nitrogen, it forms the nitride. The metal decomposes boiling water. It is not readily attacked by acids. Hot, dilute sulphuric acid yields a sulphate and hydrogen ; nitric acid converts it into titanic acid, $Ti(OH)_4$, while concentrated sulphuric acid forms the disulphate, $Ti(SO_4)_2$, sulphur dioxide being evolved.

Titanium gives rise to three series of compounds in which the element is bi-, ter- and quadrivalent respectively. The bivalent and tervalent derivatives are coloured, and are powerful reducing agents.

Oxides of Titanium

Three oxides, viz., TiO, Ti_2O_3 and TiO_2, and the corresponding hydroxides, are known. The common oxide is the *dioxide*.

It is obtained from rutile as described above. It is also obtained from iron titanate ores by heating in a mixture of hydrogen chloride and chlorine, by which means the iron is removed as chloride which is volatilized off :

$$FeTiO_3 + 4HCl + Cl_2 = 2FeCl_3 + 2TiO_2 + 2H_2O.$$

Titanium dioxide is a white powder, which reacts only slowly with acids. It forms titanates when fused with alkalis, e.g., **potassium titanate**, K_2TiO_3. It is thus an amphoteric oxide. Titanium dioxide is used as a white pigment, for which it has the advantages, as compared with white lead, that it is not poisonous and does not react with hydrogen sulphide.

Titanium hydroxide, titanic acid, $Ti(OH)_4$, is precipitated from its salts by the action of alkalis and ammonia. It resembles silicic acid in many respects. When dried it appears to form metatitanic acid, H_2TiO_3. There is some doubt about the actual existence of the acid, but well-defined metatitanates are known.

Titanium dichloride, $TiCl_2$, is made by the decomposition of titanium trichloride *in vacuo* :

$$2TiCl_3 = TiCl_2 + TiCl_4.$$

It is a very powerful reducing agent.

Titanium Trichloride, Titanous Chloride, $TiCl_3$

Anhydrous titanous chloride is made by passing a mixture of the tetrachloride and hydrogen through a red-hot tube :

$$2TiCl_4 + H_2 \doteq 2TiCl_3 + 2HCl.$$

In solution, it is readily obtained by reduction of acidified solutions of the dioxide with zinc or tin ; or by electrolytic reduction of the tetrachloride. It is a powerful reducing agent and is used in volumetric analysis for the determination of ferric iron and other oxidizing agents. The solution has a violet colour, and has to be protected from the air, which readily oxidizes it.

Titanium tetrachloride, titanic chloride, $TiCl_4$, is made by passing chlorine over a mixture of titanium dioxide and carbon :

$$TiO_2 + C + 2Cl_2 = TiCl_4 + CO_2.$$

It is a volatile, colourless liquid which boils at $136\cdot4°$. It fumes in air, and reacts with water giving basic chlorides or orthotitanic acid (titanium hydroxide), according to the extent of hydrolysis. In presence of excess of hydrochloric acid, the hydrolysis is almost prevented and from such solutions crystalline hydrates, e.g., $TiCl_4.2H_2O$ and $TiCl_4.5H_2O$, have been obtained.

Zirconium, Zr

Zirconium is widely distributed in the earth's crust in small quantities. It was discovered in 1788 in the mineral zircon by M. H. Klaproth ; the metal was isolated by J. J. Berzelius in 1824.

The principal sources of zirconium are the mineral *zircon*, zirconium silicate, $ZrSiO_4$; and *baddeleyite* zirconium dioxide, ZrO_2. It also occurs as various zirconates.

The metal is made by reducing the dioxide with carbon in an electric furnace, or by heating the dioxide with calcium. It exists in two forms : crystalline and amorphous. It closely resembles silicon in chemical properties. It burns when heated in oxygen at a high temperature forming the dioxide. It forms compounds in which it is bi-, ter- and quadrivalent.

Zirconium dioxide, Zirconia, ZrO_2, is a very hard, infusible white substance which is very stable and scarcely attacked by acids with the exception of hydrofluoric acid.

Zirconium has been used as an oxygen scavenger in the manufacture of special steels ; and the dioxide has been employed as a refractory material for crucibles, etc. The oxide, silicate carbonate and phosphate have been used in paints, and a basic acetate has found application for weighing silk, and as a mordant.

Hafnium, Hf

Indications of the possible existence of a new element resembling the rare-earths were observed by Urbain in 1911 and by Dauvillier in 1922, but its discovery and characterization are due to Coster and Hevesy (1923). They examined a number of zirconium minerals and showed that some of them contained up to 30 per cent. of the oxide of a new element; while all contained traces. The new element was named hafnium, and by examination of its X-ray spectra was shown to have an atomic number 72, and thus to fit into the vacant place in the fifth period of the Periodic Table between *lutecium* and *tantalum* indicated by the work of Bohr and Moseley.

Hafnium was found to be very like zirconium from which it can only be separated by a tedious process of fractional crystallization of the complex ammonium fluorides $(NH_4)_2ZrF_6$ and $(NH_4)_2HfF_6$.

§ 25 Thorium, Th

History

In 1818 J. J. Berzelius believed that he had discovered a new earth in a mineral from Fahlun (Sweden) and gave it the name "thoria" after the Scandinavian god Thor. In 1828 Esmark discovered a mineral from Brevig (Norway) from which Berzelius isolated an earth similar to thoria; and the mineral was subsequently called thorite. In 1898, Madame Curie and Schmidt independently observed that thorium has feeble radio-active properties.

Occurrence

The principal thorium minerals are *thorite* and *orangeite*, which are silicates of very complex composition; and *monazite*, which although essentially a cerium lanthanum phosphate always contains thorium. Monazite sand is the principal commercial source of thorium compounds.

Extraction

The principal form in which thorium is obtained is as the oxide ThO_2. It is prepared from monazite which is dissolved in concentrated sulphuric acid; the solution is then diluted and alkali slowly added. Thorium phosphate is thus precipitated before any of the substances present and is converted into the dioxide by heating it with sodium carbonate. It is interesting to note that helium is evolved to the extent of 1 c.c. per gram (at N.T.P.) when the monazite is heated to 1000°, and this is now being used as a source of helium as large quantities of monazite are dealt with by the gas-mantle industry.

Thorium metal may be prepared by the action of sodium on the chloride (obtained by the action of chlorine on a mixture of the dioxide and carbon):

$$ThO_2 + C + 2Cl_2 = ThCl_4 + CO_2$$
$$ThCl_4 + 4Na = Th + 4NaCl.$$

Thorium dioxide, Thoria, ThO_2, is, so far, the only known oxide of thorium. It is made from monazite as described above, in large quantities for use in the manufacture of gas-mantles. It is a white powder, and is comparatively inert towards reagents.

Incandescent gas-mantles consist essentially of a mixture of 99 per cent. of thorium dioxide (thoria) with 1 per cent. of cerium dioxide (ceria). They are made by weaving a mantle " hose " in ramie fibre or artificial silk and soaking this hose in a solution of thorium and cerium nitrates in the appropriate proportions. The mantle is then dried, the " fibre " burnt away in a high-temperature flame and the skeleton of mixed oxides remaining is dipped in collodion to make it strong enough for packing, etc., until wanted for use. It is a curious fact that thoria only gives a poor light unless. mixed with 1 per cent. of ceria.

§ 26 The Relationships of Group IV Elements

The elements of Group IV occur in the centre of the Periodic Table and so it is to be expected that the marked differences between the A and B sub-groups in other parts of the table would be less pronounced. This is, in fact, the case, the differences here being comparatively slight. It is also to be expected that Group IV elements will be distinctly amphoteric, as is found in practice.

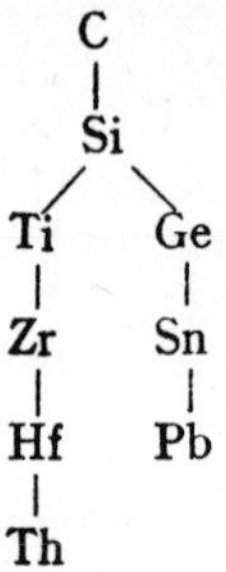

The elements of the Group are divided into sub-groups as indicated in Fig. 223.

With the exception of carbon and silicon which are mainly acidic, the elements of Group IV are metallic in nature, and, except lead and tin, have high melting-points which, with the specific gravities, show the normal gradation of properties with rising atomic number. This is indicated by Tables XLVII and XLVIII.

```
    C
    |
    Si
   / \
 Ti   Ge
  |    |
 Zr   Sn
  |    |
 Hf   Pb
  |
 Th
```

FIG. 223.

TABLE XLVII.

Element.	Melting Point	Specific Gravity.
Titanium .	1800°	4·5
Zirconium .	1700°	6·4
Hafnium .	2227°	13·31
Thorium .	1845°	11·2

TABLE XLVIII.

Element.	Melting Point.	Specific Gravity.
Carbon . .	3500°	2·2-3·5
Silicon . .	1420°	2·4
Germanium .	985·5°	5·36
Tin . .	231·85°	7·31
Lead . .	327·5°	11·34

None of these elements is more than superficially oxidized at ordinary temperatures, while all, when heated strongly, readily oxidize, forming the dioxide (except lead which forms the monoxide or red lead according to the conditions). These dioxides are acidic in the case of the lighter elements, basic character becoming more marked with increasing atomic weight.

All the elements of the Group form quadrivalent compounds, and, except in the case of lead, these are the principal compounds. In all cases divalent compounds are also known, and in some (e.g., lead and titanium) trivalency is also found. One of the most marked common characteristics of the whole group is the formation of characteristic complex halogen salts of the type $M_2^I M^{iv} X_6$.

The marked differences observable in most groups between the first and later members is nowhere more noticeable than in Group IV where carbon, with its seemingly limitless ability to link itself into chains and rings and its essential relation to all forms of life, stands in a class entirely by itself. Silicon resembles carbon in many ways, but its power of forming chains, etc., is feeble by comparison.

The elements of the A sub-group show some resemblance to the rare-earth elements, but are less basic. Titanium shows marked resemblances also to silicon, thus many titanates and silicates are isomorphous, but it is much more basic in character, and this increase in basic character becomes greater with increasing atomic weight. This is shown by the decreasing hydrolysis of the quadrivalent salts on passing from titanium to zirconium, hafnium and thorium.

None of the A sub-group elements forms a definite hydroxide $M(OH)_4$ Attempts to precipitate it yield hydrated oxides which lose water continuously ; and all readily form colloidal solutions.

In the B sub-group, germanium, tin and lead form a well-defined family, and there is a satisfactory gradation of properties from carbon through germanium to lead. But carbon and lead show no resemblance whatever comparable to that between lithium and caesium. In this respect the group more resembles Group III. The principal properties common to carbon silicon and the B sub-group elements are : quadrivalency ; formation of a hydride XH_4 (very unstable in the cases of tin and lead) and oxide XO_2 having acidic properties, and a liquid tetrachloride. The metallic character increases progressively with increasing atomic weight and the tendency to form bivalent compounds increases similarly.

The probable electronic configurations of the atoms of the Group IV elements are shown in Tables XLIX and L. The close resemblance in structure in each sub-group is clear. The A sub-group elements resemble the B sub-group in that the outermost electrons consist of two pairs, but the A sub-group differs in having incomplete cores so that variable valency is more noticeable.

TABLE XLIX.

Element.	Electrons in Orbits.																	
	1	2_1	2_2	3_1	3_2	3_3	4_1	4_2	4_3	4_4	5_1	5_2	5_3	6_1	6_2	6_3	7
Titanium .	2	2	6	2	6	2	2										
Zirconium .	2	2	6	2	6	10	2	6	2		2						
Hafnium .	2	2	6	2	6	10	2	6	10	14	2	6	2	2			
Thorium .	2	2	6	2	6	10	2	6	10	14	2	6	10	2	6	2	2

TABLE L.

Element.	Electrons in Orbits.														
	1	2_1	2_2	3_1	3_2	3_3	4_1	4_2	4_3	4_4	5_1	5_2	5_3	6_1	6_2
Carbon . . .	2	2	2												
Silicon . . .	2	2	6	2	2										
Germanium . .	2	2	6	2	6	10	2	2							
Tin . . .	2	2	6	2	6	10	2	6	10		2	2			
Lead . . .	2	2	6	2	6	10	2	6	10	14	2	6	10	2	2

PHOSPHORUS AND THE REMAINING ELEMENTS OF GROUP V.

§ 1 Group V of the Periodic Table

GROUP V contains the elements nitrogen and phosphorus, with vanadium, niobium, tantalum and protoactinium in the A sub-group ; and arsenic, antimony and bismuth in the B sub-group.

The two light elements, nitrogen and phosphorus, are much more closely related to those of the B than of the A sub-group, and there is a well-graded variation in properties in the series nitrogen, phosphorus, arsenic, antimony and bismuth, although, as in Group IV, there is little, if any, resemblance between the first and last elements.

§ 2 Phosphorus, P. History and Occurrence

History

The following is probably the correct version of the discovery of phosphorus (a matter which has given rise to much confusion and doubt). Phosphorus was discovered in 1674 or 1675 by Brand of Hamburg, by a process involving the distillation of evaporated urine. He obtained the solid, though only in small quantity. At the end of 1675 or early in 1676 his secret was sold to D. Krafft for £37 ; and he also informed J. Kunckel that it was obtained from urine. Kunckel obtained solid phosphorus from urine in 1676 after a few weeks of experimenting. Solid phosphorus was shown to Boyle and others in 1677 by Krafft, who told them that it was obtained from " part of the human body." Boyle succeeded in obtaining solid phosphorus in 1681 and was the first to publish an account of the method of making it.

The name phosphorus is derived from the Greek—$\phi\hat{\omega}s$ (phos), light ; and $\phi\acute{\epsilon}\rho\omega$ (phero), I carry. It was applied to various substances, such as commercial barium and calcium sulphides, which glow in the dark, as well as to phosphorus proper ; but in due course it became restricted to the element.

In 1769 G. Gahn showed that calcium phosphate occurs in bones, and C. W. Scheele obtained phosphorus from bone ash in 1771. The elementary nature of phosphorus was first recognized by A. L. Lavoisier in 1777.

Occurrence

Phosphorus, of course, does not occur free in nature, because it is so very readily oxidized in contact with air. It is, however, rather widely distributed in combination with oxygen—as earthy phosphates —in such minerals as *sombrerite, phosphorite, coprolites,* and " phosphate rock " (of South Carolina, Florida, and Tennessee), all of which are more or less impure calcium phosphates, $Ca_3(PO_4)_2$. It also occurs in *chlor-apatite*—$3Ca_3(PO_4)_2.CaCl_2$; *fluor-apatite*—$3Ca_3(PO_4)_2.CaF_2$; *vivianite*—$Fe_3(PO_4)_2.H_2O$; *wavellite*—$4AlPO_4.2Al(OH)_3.9H_2O$. Some native phosphates are valued for the rare earths associated with the phosphoric acid—e.g., *monazite*, and some phosphates are present in certain gems—*turquoise, lazulite*, etc.

The Phosphorus Cycle in Nature

Small quantities of phosphates are found in granitic rocks. By the weathering and decay of these rocks, the combined phosphorus ultimately finds its way into the soil, spring water, and the sea. All fertile soils contain phosphorus. A ton of average fertile soil contains an average of about a pound of phosphorus—phosphorus is needed to build up certain parts of the essential tissue of growing vegetation. Plants require phosphates from their earliest life, and seeds contain a plentiful supply for the germination of the embryo.

Animals feeding upon plants or upon herbivorous animals concentrate the phosphorus in their bones and tissue. The bones of an adult man furnish about $4\frac{1}{2}$ lbs. of normal calcium phosphate. A normal adult excretes the equivalent of 3-4 grms. of phosphoric acid daily. This is derived from vegetable foods, and partly from the waste of muscular and nervous tissue which involves a decomposition of the phosphorus compounds. The products of decomposition are carried by the blood to the kidneys, and there excreted with the urine—chiefly as sodium ammonium phosphate.

The phosphorus discharged by animals finds its way back to the soil, or rather into the sewage and finally into the sea. The amount returned from the sea as edible fish is insignificant in comparison with that which was formerly drained into the sea as sewage from large towns.

Processes for checking the loss of phosphorus in sewage have attracted much attention, for the growing of repeated crops impoverishes the phosphate content of the soil, and this is made up by the application of phosphatic fertilizers, usually in the form of a phosphatic mineral, e.g., phosphate rock. When supplies of this material begin to run short, a serious situation will arise unless means for the recovery of the phosphorus at present lost in sewage or buried out of reach in cemeteries can be devised.

§ 3 Manufacture of Phosphorus

Phosphorus is made from calcium phosphate. Formerly bones were the principal source of this substance, but this has ceased to be the case, most of the phosphorus and phosphorus compounds of commerce being now derived from mineral phosphate deposits.

The bones were digested with solvents such as benzene, ether, etc., to remove fat, after which the " degreased bones " were digested with water under pressure to remove gelatine. The " degelatinized bones " remaining were heated in air when bone ash, which is mainly calcium phosphate, remains.

Two processes have been used for the manufacture of phosphorus, viz., the retort process, and the electrical process.

The Retort Process

In this process which is now obsolete, the calcium phosphate is treated with sulphuric acid (chamber acid, p. 462, i.e., about 68 per. cent.), thus forming orthophosphoric acid and precipitating calcium sulphate :

$$Ca_3(PO_4)_2 + 3H_2SO_4 = 2H_3PO_4 + 3CaSO_4.$$

The calcium sulphate is removed by decantation and the clear liquid evaporated to a syrup, whereby the orthophosphoric acid is converted to metaphosphoric acid :

$$H_3PO_4 = HPO_3 + H_2O.$$

This is then mixed with about one-fourth of its weight of coke or charcoal, dried by heating in cast-iron pots, after which the mixture is distilled from fireclay retorts whose necks dip under the surface of water. A mixture of hydrogen and carbon monoxide escapes, and crude phosphorus condenses as a dark brown solid :

$$2HPO_3 + 6C = 6CO + H_2 + 2P.$$

The Electrical Process

In this process a mixture of calcium phosphate, sand and coke is fed into an electric furnace illustrated diagrammatically in Fig. 224. At the high temperature of the electric furnace, the silica, on account of its involatility, displaces the phosphoric acid of the phosphate, although the latter is the stronger acid, thus forming phosphoric oxide which is reduced by the carbon to phosphorus. The phosphorus escapes

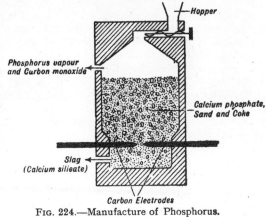

FIG. 224.—Manufacture of Phosphorus.

as a vapour and is condensed as before :

$$Ca_3(PO_4)_2 + 3SiO_2 = 3CaSiO_3 + P_2O_5,$$
$$P_2O_5 + 5C = 2P + 5CO.$$

The electrical method has the advantage of being able to employ hard mineral phosphates (which are only difficultly soluble in sulphuric acid) and also of using cheap sand in place of more expensive sulphuric acid.

Purification

The methods employed for the purification of the crude phosphorus obtained as above are trade secrets. It is said to be purified by distillation from iron retorts, or by warming with a mixture of sulphuric acid and potassium dichromate so as to oxidize some of the impurities; other impurities rise to the surface as a scum, and leave a layer of clear and colourless phosphorus at the bottom of the tank. The molten phosphorus is then allowed to flow into a tube of half-inch bore of such a length that the phosphorus has time to cool before it reaches the end of the tube. The phosphorus is drawn from the tube under water, and cut into sticks.

§ 4 Properties of Phosphorus

Allotropy

Two well-defined allotropic modifications of phosphorus are familiar, viz., yellow (or white) phosphorus and red phosphorus. Many other alleged allotropic forms have been described (e.g., scarlet, violet and black), but it is uncertain how far these are genuine allotropes. It is now usual to consider that there are three distinct forms, yellow, red and black; the others being varieties of these.

When phosphorus vapour condenses, the yellow form results. This is unstable at all temperatures up to the melting point. Phosphorus is thus a monotropic substance. The red form is the stable form, but conversion of the yellow into the red is extremely slow at ordinary temperatures.

When yellow phosphorus is exposed to air and light; or when phosphorus is heated to about 250° in an inert gas or *in vacuo*; or when phosphorus is exposed to an electric discharge—silent or spark—it soon passes into a chocolate-red coloured allotropic modification which sometimes has an iron-grey metallic lustre. This is the variety called red phosphorus.

The change proceeds with almost explosive violence when the phosphorus is heated under pressure to about 350°, that is about 60° above the boiling point of phosphorus; at 300° the change is moderately fast. The speed of the transformation can be accelerated by the addition of a trace of iodine. In the presence of this catalytic agent, the change is fairly fast at 200°.

Red phosphorus is made commercially by heating yellow phosphorus in an iron pot, having a cover through which passes a long narrow, upright iron tube to prevent the development of pressure. The pot is heated to 240°, the temperature being carefully controlled. A little of the phosphorus burns, removing the oxygen from the air initially present ; after which very little if any enters by the long tube. When the conversion to the red form is complete, the product is ground with water and boiled with sodium hydroxide solution to remove any unchanged yellow phosphorus. The red phosphorus is then washed with water and dried ; or, alternatively, preserved under water.

P. W. Bridgman's study of the effect of high pressures on phosphorus furnished him with an hexagonal variety of yellow phosphorus which passes into the ordinary cubic form at the transition point $-76\cdot9°$; and a variety of black phosphorus formed at $200°$ under pressures from 12,000 to 13,000 kilograms per sq. cm.

Properties of Yellow Phosphorus

Yellow phosphorus, which has also been called " octahedral," " common," " colourless," " white," and " non-metallic " phosphorus, is a translucent, almost colourless solid which soon becomes coated with a white opaque crust. If exposed to light, yellow phosphorus rapidly darkens in colour. At $0°$ it is hard and brittle with a crystalline fracture ; at ordinary temperatures it is soft enough to be cut with a knife. It melts at $44\cdot1°$ under atmospheric pressure, and at $52\cdot8°$ under a pressure of 300 atmospheres. When molten phosphorus is cooled, the temperature can be reduced much below the melting point without solidification, owing to the effects of undercooling. Phosphorus boils at $280°$ (760 mm.), and at $165°$ under a pressure of 120 mm., but it vaporizes at a much lower temperature. For instance, when phosphorus is heated to $40°$ in the lower part of a flask in an atmosphere of carbon dioxide, crystals of phosphorus sublime on to the upper part of the flask. Yellow phosphorus also sublimes at ordinary temperatures *in vacuo* when exposed to the light. Yellow phosphorus ignites at about $30°$ in air, saturated with moisture ; the inflammation temperature is higher the dryer the air. When phosphorus burns in air, dense white clouds of phosphorus pentoxide, P_2O_5, are formed. If, however, the phosphorus and oxygen be perfectly dried by exposure to the desiccating action of phosphorus pentoxide, phosphorus may be melted and even distilled in oxygen with very little oxidation.

The inflammation temperature is so low that the heat of the body suffices to raise the temperature of the phosphorus above its kindling temperature, and hence phosphorus should always be " handled " with the forceps, never with the bare fingers unless under water. Burns produced by phosphorus are very painful, and heal very slowly. The fumes of phosphorus are poisonous. Persons constantly exposed to their action are liable to suffer from caries (rotting) of the bones of the jaw and nose—" fossy jaw." Phosphorus itself is poisonous ; it is stated that a $0\cdot1$ gram dose is fatal to man.

On account of its inflammability, phosphorus is usually preserved under water in which it is almost insoluble—one part of phosphorus dissolves in 300,000 parts of water, but it readily dissolves in carbon disulphide, sulphur chloride, phosphorus trichloride, etc. ; and it is also soluble in chloroform, benzene (1·513 per cent. at 0°, and 10·03 per cent. at 81°), turpentine, alcohol, ether (0·43 per cent. at 0°, 2·00 per cent. at 35°), almond oil (1·25 per cent. at 15°), etc. Octahedral crystals of yellow phosphorus are obtained when the solution in carbon disulphide is allowed to evaporate. If a piece of blotting paper be soaked with a solution of phosphorus in carbon disulphide, and the solvent be allowed to evaporate, the finely divided phosphorus which remains behind ignites spontaneously in air owing to its rapid oxidation.

When yellow phosphorus is exposed to ordinary air in the dark, it emits a pale greenish light and gives off white fumes with an unpleasant garlic-like smell.

This glow of phosphorus has been the subject of much investigation, but it is still not completely understood.

Phosphorus does not glow at temperatures much below 0°, and not in inert gases—carbon dioxide, nitrogen, etc. It does not glow in pure oxygen below 15°, but it does phosphoresce if the oxygen be slightly rarefied, or diluted with an inert gas ; and the glow in air is stopped if the air be compressed. Thus a certain critical pressure of the oxygen is needed for phosphorescence to occur. The glow in air is stopped if traces of gases which destroy ozone be present—e.g., hydrogen sulphide, ethylene, turpentine, etc. Hence ozone appears somehow to be connected with the phosphorescence. Ozone is one product of the oxidation of phosphorus in moist air.

The glow is undoubtedly associated with an oxidation of the phosphorus. In moist air the product is mainly P_4O_6 ; in oxygen, at atmospheric pressure, it is P_2O_5 ; but under reduced pressure (18-20 mm.) phosphorus pentoxide and a yellow product (thought by some to be a suboxide, P_4O) are formed.

Phosphorus combines directly with the halogens, forming first the trihalide and with excess of halogen, the pentahalide. It also combines with sulphur and several phosphorus sulphides are known.

Phosphorus unites directly with many metals forming phosphides. In illustration, if very small pieces of sodium and of phosphorus be cautiously heated together, **sodium phosphide,** Na_3P, is formed. The combination occurs with a bright flash.

Phosphorus is a powerful reducing agent ; the yellow variety is more active in this respect than the red. It is oxidized by nitric acid to orthophosphoric acid, and will reduce salts of copper to the metal.

Yellow phosphorus, but not red, also reacts with the alkali hydroxides forming phosphine, etc. (p. 725). Hence the use of sodium hydroxide for the purification of the red form.

Properties of Red Phosphorus

Red phosphorus (sometimes mis-called amorphous phosphorus) is the stable form of phosphorus at ordinary temperatures. It is a violet-red, apparently amorphous, powder which was shown by Pedler and Retgers in 1890 to contain rhombohedral crystals.

Red phosphorus is less chemically active than ordinary yellow phosphorus. This agrees with the fact that the passage of the yellow to the red variety is attended by an evolution of heat :

$$P_{yellow} = P_{red} + 4 \text{ Cals.} ;$$

and hence it is generally stated that red phosphorus contains less available energy than yellow phosphorus. Red phosphorus does not appear to volatilize appreciably below 200°, and only very slightly at 280°. Red phosphorus takes fire when heated in air to about 260° ; and like yellow phosphorus, previously discussed, it burns, forming phosphorus pentoxide. Red phosphorus burns if heated in an atmosphere of chlorine, whereas ordinary phosphorus fires spontaneously in the gas.

The difference in the molecules of red and yellow phosphorus is not known. As is probably the case with monoclinic and rhombic sulphur, it may be due to a difference in the arrangement of identical molecules, or to a difference in the molecular weight, that is, to the number of atoms per molecule. Equal weights of red and yellow phosphorus when burnt separately in an excess of oxygen, give equal weights of phosphorus pentoxide, P_2O_5.

The principal differences between red and yellow phosphorus are summarized in Table LI.

TABLE LI.—COMPARISON OF THE PROPERTIES OF RED AND YELLOW PHOSPHORUS.

Property.	Red phosphorus.	Yellow phosphorus.
Colour	Reddish-violet	Almost colourless
Crystalline form	Rhombohedral system	Cubic system
Smell, etc.	Tasteless, odourless	Garlic-like smell*
Exposed to air.	No phosphorescence no oxidation	Phosphorescence and oxidation
Melting point	589·5 at 43 atm.	44·1°
Physiological action	Non-poisonous	Poisonous
Specific gravity	2·2	1·82
Specific heat	0·170	0·189
Action carbon disulphide	Insoluble	Soluble
Ignition temperature	260°	30°
Electric current	Feeble conductor	Very feeble conductor
Hot sodium hydroxide	Nil	Action
Chlorine gas	Fires if heated	Fires spontaneously
Heat of combustion (Cals.)	363·4	370·8

* When oxidizing.

Although red phosphorus is the stable form, yellow phosphorus does not appear to pass into the red form at ordinary temperatures owing to the extremely slow velocity of the change. By the distillation of red phosphorus at 290°, yellow phosphorus is obtained, and at ordinary pressures the transition point of the stable red into the unstable yellow is masked by the vaporization of the phosphorus. However, when red phosphorus is heated under pressure in capillary tubes so as to prevent distillation, it forms a yellow fluid at 610°, and red particles begin to separate from the cooling solution at 580°. At 570° the mass turns red. Red phosphorus melts at 589·5°, under

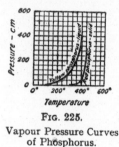

FIG. 225.

Vapour Pressure Curves of Phosphorus.

43 atm. pressure. The vapour pressure of yellow phosphorus is greater than the red; the curves cannot be carried above 400° because the yellow phosphorus passes into the red variety so quickly at about 400°. The two vapour pressure curves are illustrated in Fig. 225. Both curves converge towards the melting point as is the case with allotropic modifications of other elements. It is inferred that both varieties would be in equilibrium with the vapour phase at the melting point—near 600°—were it not for the disturbing phenomenon just indicated.

Other Varieties of Phosphorus

Although red phosphorus is practically insoluble in solvents such as turpentine which dissolve the yellow form, it will dissolve in phosphorus tribromide.

If the solution in phosphorus tribromide be exposed to light, or boiled for some time, what is supposed to be a mixture of red phosphorus and phosphorus tribromide separates as a scarlet red powder— **Schenk's scarlet phosphorus.** This resembles red phosphorus in many of its properties, but is rather more chemically active, as might be expected from its extremely fine state of subdivision. This variety of red phosphorus has not been prepared free from the solvent in which it is formed.

Another variety of red phosphorus has been obtained by heating the ordinary red form with metallic lead in a sealed tube at 500° for eighteen hours.

The lead dissolves the phosphorus at the high temperature, and rejects the dissolved phosphorus on cooling in the form of rhombohedral crystals. The lead can be dissolved away by means of dilute nitric acid followed by boiling with concentrated hydrochloric acid; the residue has a specific gravity varying from 2·34 to 2·39. This dense form of red phosphorus is sometimes called Hittorf's phosphorus, or **metallic phosphorus,** or "rhombohedral" phosphorus. The term "metallic" appears to be a misnomer, for it does not conduct electricity. The specific gravity of red phosphorus varies with its method of preparation from 2·05 to the maximum 2·34 for Hittorf's phosphorus.

§ 5 Uses of Phosphorus

The most important use of elemental phosphorus is for the manufacture of matches. Yellow phosphorus was formerly employed, but on account of its poisonous properties its use has been abandoned.

The modern "strike-anywhere" match head usually contains a phosphorus sulphide, P_4S_3, together with potassium chlorate or manganese dioxide, glue, powdered glass to increase friction, and a colouring matter such as prussian blue or chrome yellow. Safety matches have a head composed of oxidizing agents, such as potassium chlorate and red lead, together with antimony sulphide, and sometimes sulphur and charcoal ; while the box has on it a composition containing glass, phosphorus powdered, etc.

A certain amount of phosphorus is also used in the manufacture of phosphorus tri- and penta-chlorides which are required for some branches of chemical industry, e.g., the manufacture of chloro-sulphonic acid for saccharine manufacture, etc. Phosphorus is also employed in the manufacture of rat-poisons, fireworks, smoke-bombs, etc. ; and is used in the making of phosphor-bronze.

§ 6 Atomic and Molecular Weight of Phosphorus

The atomic weight of phosphorus is seen to lie in the neighbourhood of 31 from a consideration of the molecular weights and composition of its volatile compounds, such as phosphine, phosphorus trichloride, etc. The determination of the accurate value has proved somewhat difficult on account of the nature of the materials involved. Among the methods which have been employed are the deposition of silver from silver nitrate by phosphorus ; the conversion of silver phosphate into silver bromide ; the synthesis of pure phosphorus tribromide from the pure elements and its conversion into silver bromide ; the determination of the density of phosphine ; and the conversion of phos-phorus oxychloride into silver choride. The value at present recommended by the International Committee is 30·98, and is based on the work of Hönigschmidwho in 1937 prepared very pure phosphorous oxychoride, decomposed it with ammonia solution in a closed vessel and thus compared it with silver and silver chloride.

The vapour density of phosphorus at temperatures between 500° and 700° corresponds with a molecule P_4 ; but at higher temperatures dissociation occurs ; probably into molecules of P_2, $P_4 \rightleftharpoons 2P_2$. At very high temperatures, it is probable that still further dissociation into single atoms takes place.

§ 7 Hydrides of Phosphorus

Phosphine, PH_3

Phosphine is probably formed in small quantity by the decay of organic matter ; and the faint luminosity seen over bogs or marshes and described as " will-o'-the-wisp " has been ascribed to it.

It is most conveniently prepared by the action of sodium hydroxide solution on yellow phosphorus, in the apparatus indicated in Fig. 226. A mixture of sodium hydroxide solution and yellow phosphorus is placed in the flask fitted with delivery tube, etc., as illustrated in the diagram. A current of an inert gas—coal gas, hydrogen or carbon dioxide—is first led through the apparatus to drive out the air. The mixture in the flask is then heated. The phosphorus reacts with the alkali, forming sodium hypophosphite, and gaseous phosphine, PH_3, associated with some impurities :

$$3NaOH + 4P + 3H_2O = 3NaH_2PO_2 + PH_3.$$

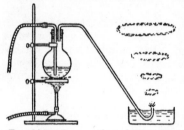

Phosphine, prepared in this way, is spontaneously inflammable on account of the presence of the liquid hydride, P_2H_4. In consequence, as each bubble of gas rises to the surface of the water, and comes into contact with the air, it ignites with a slight explosion and burns with a brilliant flash of light, forming a vortex ring of phosphorus pentoxide. If the gas be passed through a tube immersed in a freezing mixture, it no longer inflames on contact with the air ; pure phosphine is not spontaneously inflammable.

FIG. 226.—Preparation of Phosphine.

Phosphine is a colourless gas, which smells like decaying fish. It liquefies about $-87\cdot4°$, solidifies about $-132\cdot5°$, and ignites when heated to about $100°$. It burns in air forming phosphorus pentoxide :

$$2PH_3 + 4O_2 = P_2O_5 + 3H_2O + 311\cdot2 \text{ Cals.}$$

at constant pressure.

If a mixture of oxygen and phosphine be suddenly rarefied, an explosion occurs. The phenomenon recalls the effect of rarefaction on the luminosity of phosphorus in oxygen gas. Nitric acid or chlorine when brought in contact with the gas cause inflammation. A jet of phosphine inflames and burns, forming phosphorus pentachloride when placed in chlorine gas :

$$PH_3 + 4Cl_2 = 3HCl + PCl_5.$$

Phosphine is slightly soluble in water : 100 volumes of water dissolve about 11 volumes of the gas. The aqueous solution is not alkaline like aqueous ammonia, it decomposes on exposure to light and deposits red phosphorus. The gas possesses reducing properties, e.g., when passed into solutions of copper sulphate, $CuSO_4$, mercuric chloride, $HgCl_2$, phosphine precipitates phosphides of the metals. It combines like ammonia, with some chlorides, for instance, aluminium chloride, stannic chloride, etc.

The Composition of Phosphine

J. B. Dumas determined the composition of phosphine by passing a known volume of the gas over heated copper turnings—zinc, antimony, iron, and potassium have been used in place of copper. The copper forms copper phosphide. The increase in weight of the copper shows the amount of phosphorus in a given volume of the gas. The escaping hydrogen is collected and measured. Experiment shows that 34 parts of phosphine by weight give 31 parts of phosphorus and 3 parts of hydrogen. The empirical formula is therefore PH_3. Similarly, when phosphine is decomposed by the passage of electric sparks through the gas, one volume of phosphine gives $1\frac{1}{2}$ volumes of hydrogen, and red phosphorus, of negligibly small volume in comparison with the volume of the gas, is deposited on the walls of the tube. Hence two volumes of phosphine furnish three volumes of hydrogen; otherwise expressed, by Avogadro's hypothesis, two molecules of phosphine give three molecules of hydrogen:

Hence the formula must be P_nH_3 where n is still to be determined.

The vapour density of phosphine is 17 ($H_2 = 1$), hence $n = 1$, and the formula is PH_3.

Phosphonium Compounds

When dry phosphine is brought into contact with dry hydrogen chloride, bromide or iodide at high pressures, the gases unite forming phosphonium compounds, e.g.,

$$PH_3 + HCl = PH_4Cl.$$

This behaviour is reminiscent of that of ammonia which forms ammonium compounds in a similar manner (p. 394), and the radical, PH_4, phosphonium is analogous to NH_4 ammonium. Phosphine is, however, a very much feebler base than ammonia.

The best known phosphonium salt is **phosphonium iodide**, PH_4I. It is made by dissolving phosphorus and iodine in carbon disulphide in a retort, and then distilling off the carbon disulphide. The residue is then treated drop by drop with the exact quantity of water indicated by the equation (below), and the phosphonium iodide is sublimed through a wide tube into a bottle, in a stream of carbon dioxide. The reaction is represented:

$$5I + 9P + 16H_2O = 5PH_4I + 4H_3PO_4.$$

Phosphonium iodide crystallizes in large quadratic prisms with a brilliant lustre. It is an unstable salt readily dissociating into hydrogen iodide and phosphine, even at as low a temperature as 30°. The crystals can be sublimed without melting. They fume in air, and in contact with water form hydrogen phosphide and hydrogen iodide. With potassium hydroxide, fairly pure phosphine is obtained:

$$PH_4I + KOH = PH_3 + KI + H_2O.$$

Phosphonium iodide is used as a reducing agent, and in the preparation of organic phosphines.

Phosphorus Dihydride, Liquid Hydrogen Phosphide, P_2H_4

When calcium phosphide, Ca_3P_2, is treated with water, and the gas evolved is passed through a spiral tube in order to condense water, and then through a U-tube immersed in a freezing-mixture of ice and salt, a colourless liquid is obtained which is spontaneously inflammable when exposed to air. This is the so-called liquid hydrogen phosphide, and is a colourless liquid which boils at 57° to 58°. It decomposes on standing, yielding the solid hydride (see below). Its empirical formula is PH_2; the vapour density corresponds approximately with the molecular formula P_2H_4, which is analogous with hydrazine N_2H_4.

Solid Phosphorus hydride, $P_{12}H_6$, is also formed in the reaction between calcium phosphide and water, and also when the liquid phosphide is exposed to light, or heated above its boiling point :

$$15P_2H_4 = P_{12}H_6 + 18PH_3.$$

It is a yellow solid, which is decomposed by heat into phosphine and phosphorus. Its empirical formula is P_2H; but the depression of the freezing point of its solution in molten phosphorus corresponds to a molecule, $P_{12}H_6$.

Recently Royen and Hill (1936) have suggested that this hydride consists of phosphorus with an adsorbed layer of phosphine and that it is not a true hydride.

Several other solid hydrides have been reported, but there is some doubt about their real existence.

§ 8 Oxides of Phosphorus

Three oxides of phosphorus are definitely known, viz.,

Phosphorous oxide, phosphorus trioxide, P_2O_3 or P_4O_6 ;
Phosphorus tetroxide, P_2O_4 ;
Phosphorus pentoxide, P_2O_5 or P_4O_{10}.

A suboxide has also been reported, but is probably impure red phosphorus ; a peroxide $(PO_3)_n$, described by Schenk and Platz (1936), awaits confirmation.

Phosphorous oxide, phosphorus trioxide, P_2O_3 or P_4O_6, is formed, along with phosphorus pentoxide, when phosphorus is burned

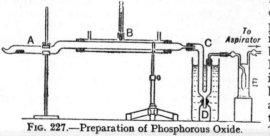

FIG. 227.—Preparation of Phosphorous Oxide.

in a limited supply of air. Some yellow phosphorus is placed in a glass tube A, bent as shown in Fig. 227, and fitted into one end of a long tube cooled by a jacket, B, containing water at 60°. The cooled tube is fitted to a U-tube, C, immersed in a freezing mixture ; a plug of glass-wool is placed in the condenser tube near the U-tube. The phosphorus is ignited, and a slow stream of air is drawn through the apparatus by means of an aspirator connected to the U-tube. The phosphorus pentoxide is arrested by the glass-wool, and phosphorous oxide passes into the U-tube, where it is condensed into a white crystalline mass. The wash-bottle, E, with concentrated sulphuric acid, protects the product from moisture. At the end of the experiment, the solid in the U-tube can be melted and run into the bottle D.

Phosphorous oxide, so obtained, is a mass of monoclinic prisms; which melts at 22·5° and boils at 173°. It smells like garlic and is poisonous. When exposed to the air, it is gradually oxidized to the pentoxide, and when placed in warm oxygen it bursts into flame. It also ignites spontaneously in chlorine. It is slowly attacked by cold water, forming phosphorous acid, H_3PO_3, and with hot water it forms red phosphorus, and phosphine. The vapour density corresponds to the formula P_4O_6, while the lowering of the freezing points of its solutions in benzene and naphthalene indicate the same value.

Phosphorus tetroxide, P_2O_4, is obtained by heating phosphorus trioxide in a sealed tube to 440°, when the trioxide decomposes, and the tetroxide appears as a crystalline sublimate. It is thus obtained in colourless, transparent crystals, which with water form a solution consisting of a mixture of phosphorous and phosphoric acids :

$$P_2O_4 + 3H_2O = H_3PO_3 + H_3PO_4.$$

It is thus analogous to nitrogen tetroxide (p. 422).

Phosphorus Pentoxide, Phosphoric Oxide, P_2O_5 or P_4O_{10}

When phosphorus is burnt in an excess of dried air or oxygen, white clouds of phosphorus pentoxide condense as a voluminous powder. Small quantities of other oxides may be formed at the same time, and it is best purified by heating it to 600°-700° in an iron tube attached to a glass tube through which oxygen is passing at a fairly rapid rate. The pentoxide is vaporized and condenses in the glass tube.

Phosphorus pentoxide is a white solid, which is said to exist in three forms : crystalline, amorphous and vitreous. The exact number and relation of the forms is still in doubt. It sublimes very slowly at 50°, but at 250° the sublimation is rapid. The vapour density at 1400° corresponds with the molecular formula P_4O_{10}; but the simpler formula, P_2O_5, is often adopted for convenience and on account of our ignorance of the molecular formula of the *solid* oxide.

Phosphorus pentoxide is extremely hygroscopic, and it absorbs moisture from the air very quickly ; hence its use for drying gases. When thrown into water, combination occurs with a hissing sound resembling the quenching of red-hot iron, and metaphosphoric acid is formed :

$$P_2O_5 + H_2O = 2HPO_3.$$

When this solution is boiled with water, or when the phosphorus pentoxide is thrown into hot water, orthophosphoric acid is formed :

$$P_2O_5 + 3H_2O = 2H_3PO_4.$$

The affinity of phosphorus pentoxide for water is so great that, as well as being the most powerful drying agent known, it can withdraw the elements of water from many organic and inorganic compounds. Thus, it converts nitric acid into nitrogen pentoxide (p. 423). The acid—$P(OH)_5$, the true ortho-acid—is not known.

§ 9 The Acids of Phosphorus

The best defined acids of phosphorus are :

Hypophosphorous acid, H_3PO_2,
Phosphorous acid, H_3PO_3,
Hypophosphoric acid, $H_4P_2O_6$,
Orthophosphoric acid, H_3PO_4,
Pyrophosphoric acid, $H_4P_2O_7$,
Metaphosphoric acid, HPO_3.

Hypophosphorous Acid, H_3PO_2

When yellow phosphorus is heated with alkalis (as in the preparation of phosphine, p. 725) hypophosphites are formed. If barium hydroxide be used, free hypophosphorous acid can be obtained from the product by addition of the calculated quantity of sulphuric acid :

$$3Ba(OH)_2 + 8P + 6H_2O = 2PH_3 + 3Ba(H_2PO_2)_2,$$
$$3Ba(H_2PO_2)_2 + 3H_2SO_4 = 3BaSO_4 + 6H_3PO_2.$$

After filtering the precipitated barium sulphate, the solution can be concentrated by evaporation and hypophosphorous acid obtained as a colourless crystalline solid, melting at 26·4°.

Hypophosphorous acid is a monobasic acid (i.e., only one of the three hydrogen atoms is replaceable by a metal). The acid and its salts are very powerful reducing agents ; thus, with copper sulphate, a red precipitate, believed to be copper hydride, Cu_2H_2, is obtained :

$$3H_3PO_2 + 6H_2O + 4CuSO_4 = 3H_3PO_4 + 4H_2SO_4 + 2Cu_2H_2.$$

This reaction is used for the detection of hypophosphites.

Hypophosphorous acid is itself reduced by zinc and hydrochloric acid to phosphine. The constitution of the acid is discussed, along with that of other acids of phosphorus, below (p. 733).

Phosphorous Acid, H_3PO_3

This acid is formed by the action of water upon phosphorous oxide :

$$P_4O_6 + 6H_2O = H_3PO_3,$$

or by the action of water on phosphorus trichloride :

$$PCl_3 + 3H_2O = H_3PO_3 + H_3PO_3,$$

or by passing a stream of chlorine through water beneath which phosphorus is melted. The solution is evaporated until the temperature has reached 180°, when, on cooling, it solidifies to a crystalline solid which melts at 73·6°. When heated, phosphorous acid decomposes into phosphine and ortho-phosphoric acid :

$$4H_3PO_3 = 3H_3PO_4 + PH_3.$$

It is a powerful reducing agent and reduces salts of copper, etc., to the metal, e.g.,

$$H_3PO_3 + CuSO_4 + H_2O = H_3PO_4 + H_2SO_4 + Cu.$$

It also absorbs oxygen, forming phosphoric acid ; while it is reduced by zinc and hydrochloric acid to phosphine.

The salts of phosphorous acid—**the phosphites**—are soluble in water, and like the acid are strong reducing agents. Those of the alkali metals have an alkaline reaction in solution. A number of salts is known, derived from various polyphosphorous acids, by removing molecules of water from one or more molecules of an ordinary phosphite. Of these pyrophosphites, from $H_4P_2O_5$, and metaphosphites, from HPO_2 may be mentioned.

Hypophosphoric Acid, $H_4P_2O_6$

A mixture of hypophosphoric, phosphoric and phosphorous acids is formed when phosphorus is exposed to a limited supply of moist air. Hypophosphoric acid can be isolated as follows. Water made slightly acid with sulphuric or formic acid is electrolyzed, using copper phosphide as anode, and copper as cathode. A solution of this salt when treated with lead acetate gives an insoluble precipitate of **lead hypophosphate**, $Pb_2P_2O_6$. This salt is filtered from the solution, and washed with hot water. The precipitate is suspended in water, and a current of hydrogen sulphide passed through the solution. Lead sulphide, PbS, is precipitated, and a solution of free hypophosphoric acid is obtained. On evaporation, the excess of hydrogen sulphide is driven from the solution, but the evaporation cannot be carried very far without decomposing the acid. Hence, the solution must be further evaporated in a desiccator *in vacuo* over sulphuric acid, Fig. 102. In time, tabular, rhombic crystals of the hydrate $H_4P_2O_6.2H_2O$ separate. The crystals melt at 62°. Further desiccation of the crystals over sulphuric acid *in vacuo* gives the anhydrous acid, $H_4P_2O_6$, melting at 70°. The acid is stable at ordinary temperatures, and is hydrolyzed by the mineral acids, forming a mixture of phosphoric and phosphorous acids :

$$H_4P_2O_6 + H_2O = H_3PO_3 + H_3PO_4.$$

The exact molecular formula of this acid was for long in doubt, but it has now been shown that the doubled formula, $H_4P_2O_6$, is the correct one, on the evidence of the diamagnetism of the salts (Bell and Sugden, 1933), and of the rate of hydrolysis of the acid which indicates a unimolecular reaction (Rosenheim and Zilg, 1928).

§ 10 The Phosphoric Acids

Three well-defined phosphoric acids are known, corresponding to various degrees of condensation and dehydration of the ortho-acid.

Theoretically the true ortho-phosphoric acid would be $P(OH)_5$ or H_5PO_5, but this is not known, and the first dehydration product of this hypothetical acid, i.e., H_3PO_4, is called orthophosphoric acid. Two other acids are known derived from this acid, viz., pyrophosphoric acid, $H_4P_2O_7$, by loss of one molecule of water from two molecules of H_3PO_4 ; and metaphosphoric acid, HPO_3, by loss of one molecule of water from one molecule of H_3PO_4.

Orthophosphoric acid, H_3PO_4, is formed when phosphorus pentoxide is added to water and the solution is boiled.

$$P_2O_5 + 3H_2O = 2H_3PO_4.$$

It is also formed when red phosphorus is boiled with 16 parts of nitric acid (of specific gravity between 1·20 and 1·25) and a trace of iodine, in a flask fitted with a reflux condenser. Torrents of nitrous fumes are evolved. When the phosphorus is all oxidized, the solution is evaporated until no more acid fumes are given off, the temperature being kept below 180° in order to prevent decomposition of the ortho-phosphoric acid.

Commercially, orthophosphoric acid is made by the action of sulphuric acid on bone ash as described for the manufacture of phosphorus (p. 719).

Orthophosphoric acid is a colourless, syrupy liquid, which can be obtained by concentration *in vacuo* in six-sided prismatic crystals melting at 42·3°. It is not volatile, but dissolves readily in water with which it is miscible in all proportions. On heating, it decomposes, pyrophosphoric acid being formed at about 250° :

$$2H_3PO_4 = H_4P_2O_7 + H_2O,$$

and metaphosphoric acid on further heating :

$$H_4P_2O_7 = 2HPO_3 + H_2O.$$

Orthophosphoric acid is a tribasic acid, and so forms three series of salts ; e.g., $Na_3PO_4.12H_2O$, $Na_2HPO_4.12H_2O$ and $NaH_2PO_4.H_2O$. The first (the normal salt) is alkaline to litmus, the second is almost neutral, and the third is acidic to litmus. Orthophosphoric acid is comparatively weak and appears to furnish ions thus at moderate dilutions :

$$H_3PO_4 \rightleftharpoons H^{\cdot} + H_2PO_4' \rightleftharpoons 2H^{\cdot} + HPO_4''$$

Even at extreme dilutions, the further dissociation into PO_4''' ions is only partial. The acidic functions of the three hydrogen ions vary greatly ; the first has the strongest, the third the least. So that, when phosphoric acid is titrated with sodium hydroxide solution, using methyl orange as indicator, the colour change takes place when NaH_2PO_4 has been formed. Similarly, if phenolphthalein is used as indicator, the change takes place when Na_2HPO_4 has been formed. The acidity of the last dissociation is so slight that no indicator will indicate the formation of Na_3PO_4.

Pyrophosphoric Acid, $H_4P_2O_7$

This acid is made by heating orthophosphoric acid to between 250° and 260° for some time.

$$2H_3PO_4 = H_4P_2O_7 + H_2O.$$

It is a colourless, low melting solid which is re-converted by boiling water into the ortho-acid. It is a tetrabasic acid, as is shown by the molecular weight of its ethyl ester ; but so far only two series of salts, e.g., $Na_2H_2P_2O_7$ and $Na_4P_2O_7$, have been obtained.

Metaphosphoric Acid, HPO_3

This acid is formed as a viscous solid when phosphorus pentoxide is left exposed to moist air ; it is also obtained by heating ammonium orthophosphate, or pyro- or ortho-phosphoric acid to a red heat :

$$H_3PO_4 = HPO_3 + H_2O.$$

Metaphosphoric acid is a transparent vitreous solid, sometimes called *glacial phosphoric acid*. It fuses at about 38°-41°, and the commercial acid is usually cast in sticks. It is readily soluble in water, and the solution passes, slowly in the cold and rapidly on boiling, into ortho-phosphoric acid.

The Structure of the Acids of Phosphorus

The structures to be assigned to the acids of phosphorus have to take into account the facts about the behaviour of these acids already mentioned ; in particular that

(i) hypophosphorous acid is monobasic ;

(ii) phosphorous acid is probably dibasic—or, at least, exists in a dibasic form ;

(iii) phosphoric acid is tribasic ; is formed from phosphorus oxy-chloride, and hence from phosphorus pentachloride by the action of water.

These facts are now sometimes embodied in the following electronic formulae :

Hypophosphorous acid

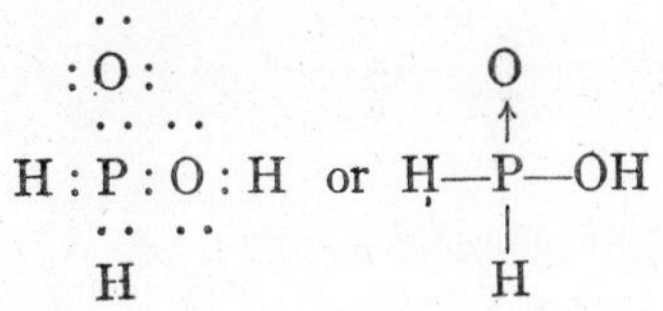

$$
\begin{array}{cc}
:\!\overset{\cdot\cdot}{O}\!: & O \\
\text{H}:\text{P}:\text{O}:\text{H} & \text{H}\!-\!\text{P}\!-\!\text{OH} \\
\text{H} & \text{H}
\end{array}
\quad \text{or}
$$

Phosphorous acid

$$
\begin{array}{ccc}
 & & \text{H} \\
:\!\overset{\cdot\cdot}{O}\!: & & :\!\overset{\cdot\cdot}{O}\!: \\
\text{H}:\text{P}:\text{O}:\text{H} & \rightleftharpoons & :\text{P}:\text{O}:\text{H} \\
:\!O\!: & & :O: \\
\text{H} & & \text{H}
\end{array}
$$

or

$$
\begin{array}{ccc}
O & & \text{OH} \\
\uparrow & & | \\
\text{H}\!-\!\text{P}\!-\!\text{OH} & \rightleftharpoons & \text{P}\!-\!\text{OH} \\
| & & | \\
\text{OH} & & \text{OH}
\end{array}
$$

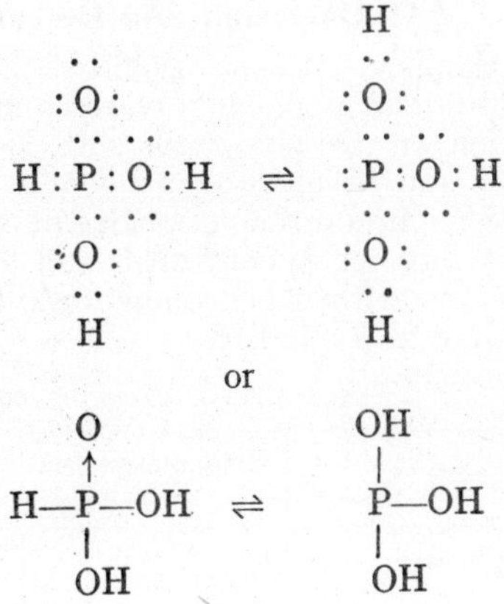

Hypophosphoric acid

$$
\begin{array}{cc}
:\!\overset{\cdot\cdot}{O}\!:\ :\!\overset{\cdot\cdot}{O}\!: & O\ \ O \\
\text{H}:\text{O}:\text{P}\ :\ \text{P}:\text{O}\,\text{H} & \text{HO}\!-\!\text{P}\!-\!\text{P}\!-\!\text{OH} \\
:\!O\!:\ :\!O\!: & \text{OH OH} \\
\text{H}\ \ \ \text{H}
\end{array}
\quad \text{or}
$$

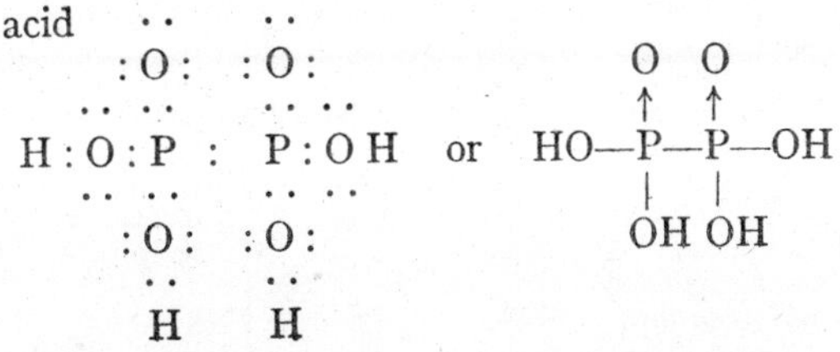

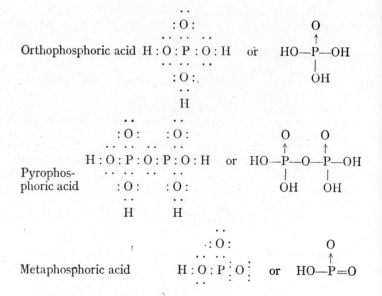

§ 11 Detection and Determination of Phosphates

Orthophosphates are usually detected by the formation of a yellow precipitate of ammonium phospho-molybdate on warming a nitric acid solution of the phosphate with ammonium molybdate. Metaphosphates and pyrophosphates give a similar precipitate since they are converted into orthophosphates by heating with nitric acid.

The three phosphoric acids and their salts are distinguished by the difference in their behaviour towards silver nitrate, albumen, etc., as indicated in Table LII.

TABLE LII.—REACTIONS OF THE PHOSPHORIC ACIDS.

	Orthophosphoric acid.	Pyrophosphoric acid.	Metaphosphoric acid.
Silver nitrate .	Canary-yellow pp.	White cryst. pp.	White gelatinous.
Barium salts . .	No pp. (if alkaline, white pp.).	No pp. (if alkaline, white pp.).	White precipitate.
Albumen . .	Nil.	Nil.	Coagulated.
Zinc acetate .	Nil.	Insoluble pp.	Nil.
Aluminium salts ⎫ Chromium salts ⎭	Soluble in acetic acid.	Insoluble in acetic acid.	Insoluble in acetic acid.
Cobalt salts . .	Blue; soluble in acetic acid.	Red; insoluble in acetic acid.	Red; insoluble in acetic acid.
Copper salts .	Nil.	Precipitate.	Nil.
Bismuth salt alkaline (solution) .	Nil.	Nil.	Precipitate.

Phosphates are determined by precipitation as magnesium ammonium phosphate—$MgNH_4PO_4.6H_2O$—by adding magnesium sulphate or chloride, and ammonium chloride to the solution of the phosphate which has been made alkaline with ammonia. The magnesium ammonium phosphate which is precipitated is filtered off, washed and heated to redness. It is thus converted into magnesium pyrophosphate—$Mg_2P_2O_7$—and is weighed as such.

Phosphates which are soluble in water or acetic acid may be determined volumetrically by titration with uranyl nitrate or acetate solution, in presence of ammonium acetate. Potassium ferrocyanide is used as external indicator :

$$KH_2PO_4 + UO_2(CH_3CO_2)_2 + CH_3CO_2NH_4$$
$$= UO_2.NH_4PO_4 + CH_3CO_2K + 2CH_3CO_2H$$

§ 12 The Halides of Phosphorus

Phosphorus forms two series of compounds with the halogens, represented by the general formulae PX_3 and PX_5. It is doubtful if the penta-iodide has been obtained, but otherwise all the members of both series are known. The oxyhalides POX_3 are also known.

Phosphorus Trifluoride, PF_3

Phosphorus trifluoride is made by the action of copper phosphide on lead fluoride ; or by allowing arsenic fluoride to drop slowly into phosphorus trichloride with the exclusion of moisture :

$$3PbF_2 + Cu_3P_2 = 3Pb + 2Cu + 2PF_3,$$
$$AsF_3 + PCl_3 = AsCl_3 + PF_3.$$

It is a colourless gas, which can be condensed to a liquid boiling at $-95°$, and frozen to a solid, melting at $-160°$. With water, it forms hydrofluoro-phosphoric acid and phosphorous acid :

$$3H_2O + 2PF_3 = H_3PO_3 + HPF_4 + 2HF.$$

When subjected to electric sparks, it decomposes into the pentafluoride :

$$5PF_3 = 3PF_5 + 2P$$

Phosphorus Pentafluoride, PF_5

This compound is made by the action of arsenic trifluoride on phosphorus pentachloride :

$$5AsF_3 + 3PCl_5 = 5AsCl_3 + 3PF_5.$$

It is a colourless gas which is hydrolyzed by water, and which condenses to a liquid boiling at $-75°$, and freezes to a solid, melting at $-83°$.

Phosphoryl fluoride, phosphorus oxyfluoride, POF_3, is a gas resembling the oxychloride (q.v.) in properties, which condenses to a colourless liquid, boiling at $-40°$ and freezes to a white solid m.p. $-68°$.

Phosphorus Trichloride, PCl_3

This compound is made by the action of dry chlorine on yellow phosphorus in the apparatus indicated in Fig. 228.

This consists of a retort containing a layer of sand on which rests a quantity of dry yellow phosphorus. The retort is heated gently on a water bath. Chlorine, dried by sulphuric acid, is passed in by means of a movable tube. The distance of this tube is so arranged that the phosphorus does not distil (which occurs if it is too near), neither is the pentachloride formed (which happens if it is too far off). When the action has begun, a tongue of flame projects from the chlorine tube,

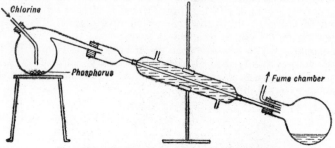

FIG. 228.—Preparation of Phosphorus Trichloride.

and the retort does not need any further heating, until at the end it is warmed gently to drive the last of the trichloride into the receiver. The product is purified by redistilling it over yellow phosphorus to convert any pentachloride present into trichloride.

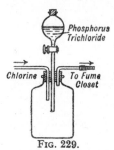

FIG. 229.
Preparation of Phosphorus Pentachloride

Phosphorus trichloride is a mobile liquid with an unpleasant smell. It boils at $73.5°$, fumes in air and is hydrolyzed by water, forming phosphorous acid and hydrochloric acid :

$$PCl_3 + 3H_2O \rightleftharpoons H_3PO_3 + 3HCl.$$

It can be frozen to a solid which melts at about $-112°$.

Phosphorus pentachloride, PCl_5, is best prepared by the action of excess of chlorine on the trichloride. It is convenient to prepare it in the vessel in which it is to be stored, as shown in Fig. 229.

$$PCl_3 + Cl_2 = PCl_5.$$

It can also be made by the direct action of chlorine on yellow phosphorus ; or by the action of sulphur chloride on phosphorus trichloride :

$$3PCl_3 + S_2Cl_2 = PCl_5 + 2PSCl_3.$$

Phosphorus pentachloride when pure is an almost colourless solid ; as obtained it is usually pale greenish-yellow. It sublimes below $100°$, but if heated under pressure melts at $148°$. It reacts violently with water, forming first the oxychloride, and then orthophosphoric acid.

$$PCl_5 + H_2O = POCl_3 + 2HCl,$$
$$POCl_3 + 3H_2O = H_3PO_4 + 3HCl.$$

Like phosphorus trichloride, it is a valuable reagent for transforming hydroxyl compounds into chlorides, and finds extensive use for this purpose in organic chemistry.

The vapour density of phosphorus pentachloride varies with temperature. The following values were obtained by J. B. Dumas :

Temperature	...	182°	200°	250°	300°
Vapour Density	...	73·3	70	57·6	52·4

The theoretical value for PCl_5 is 104·25 (H_2 = 1). It is inferred, therefore, that dissociation is taking place into free chlorine and phosphorus trichloride :

$$PCl_5 \rightleftharpoons PCl_3 + Cl_2.$$

This has been confirmed experimentally by the facts that starch potassium iodide papers give the characteristic blue colouration produced by chlorine when immersed in the vapour of phosphorus pentachloride ; and that addition of chlorine reduces the amount of dissociation as would be expected from the application of the Law of Mass Action to the equilibrium. Thus, with the notation previously employed we have :

$$\frac{[PCl_5]}{[PCl_3][Cl_2]} = K$$

Consequently, if the concentration of chlorine or of phosphorus trichloride be raised, by addition of one or other to the system in equilibrium, some combination will take place, and the concentration of the pentachloride will be thereby increased. That is, its dissociation will be reduced.

This expectation was confirmed experimentally by H. Wurtz in 1873. He found that if the pentachloride be volatilized in an atmosphere of the trichloride, the vapour density is nearly normal, 103·3 between 160° and 175°

It has been argued that because phosphorus pentachloride splits up so readily into the trichloride and chlorine, two of the chlorine atoms in the pentachloride are differently linked to the phosphorus atom. Sugden has used this argument in support of his suggestion that two of the chlorine atoms are united to the phosphorus atom by single-electron links, thus making it possible to construct a model of the molecule without increasing the number of electrons in the outermost (valency) shell of the phosphorus atom beyond eight. The inference is, however, logically invalid, for although a molecule so constructed would indeed be expected to dissociate in the way observed, it does not follow that no other cause of the observed phenomena is possible. Or otherwise expressed, the converse of the statement is not necessarily true. It may be, for instance, that the behaviour of phosphorus pentachloride is due to overcrowding of chlorine atoms round the phosphorus atom.

Phosphoryl Chloride, Phosphorus Oxychloride, $POCl_3$

This compound can be made by very carefully adding water to phosphorus pentachloride until the solid disappears :

$$PCl_5 + H_2O = POCl_3 + 2HCl.$$

It is also made by gradual addition of powdered potassium chlorate to phosphorus trichloride at ordinary temperatures, and distilling the mixture.

Phosphorus oxychloride is a colourless fuming liquid which boils at $107 \cdot 2°$ and can be solidified to a colourless crystalline mass melting at $-1 \cdot 25°$. In aqueous solution it is slowly hydrolyzed to phosphoric and hydrochloric acids.

Phosphorus Tribromide, PBr_3

Phosphorus tribromide is made by gradually adding a solution of bromine in carbon disulphide to dry red phosphorus ; or to a solution of phosphorus in carbon disulphide ; or better, to phosphorus covered with a layer of benzene. After the action is over, the solvent is distilled off; after which the phosphorus tribromide is distilled. It closely resembles the trichloride in properties, but is denser, and it boils at $172 \cdot 9°$.

Phosphorus pentabromide, PBr_5, is made by the action of bromine on phosphorus tribromide. It is a yellow solid, resembling the pentachloride, but less vigorous in its reactions.

Phosphoryl bromide, $POBr_3$, is made similarly to the chloride, and is a colourless liquid boiling at $193°$.

Phosphorus tri-iodide, PI_3, is made by mixing solutions in carbon disulphide of equivalent quantities of iodine and of yellow phosphorus. On distilling off the solvent, the tri-iodide remains as a reddish crystalline solid of m.p. $61°$, which dissociates when heated.

Phosphorus di-iodide, P_2I_4, is obtained in orange-red crystals, which melt at $110°$, when iodine and phosphorus are melted together.

Phosphorus penta-iodide has been reported, but its existence is doubtful.

§ 13 Sulphides of Phosphorus

Several compounds of sulphur and phosphorus have been reported of which P_2S_5, P_4S_7 and P_4S_3 appear to be definite chemical compounds. They are prepared by cautiously heating appropriate proportions of sulphur and red phosphorus in an inert atmosphere (e.g., carbon dioxide).

Phosphorus pentasulphide, P_2S_5, is a pale yellow crystalline mass, which melts at $276°$ and boils at $514°$. It is hydrolyzed by water :

$$P_2S_5 + 8H_2O = 2H_3PO_4 + 5H_2S,$$

and is used in organic chemistry for the replacement of the oxygen of hydroxy groups by sulphur.

Phosphorus sesquisulphide, P_4S_3, is a grey crystalline mass, which dissolves in alkali sulphides, and is slowly attacked by water. It melts at $172 \cdot 5°$ and boils at $407 \cdot 5°$. It is used in the manufacture of matches.

§ 14 Arsenic, As. History, Occurrence and Preparation

History

Arsenic was known to the ancients and considered by them to be a kind of sulphur. Aristotle mentions a substance, σανδαράχη (sandarachē), which appears to have been red arsenic sulphide or realgar, and was called by Theophrastus ἀρσενικόν (arsenikon), meaning " potent " ; the yellow sulphide was called *auripigmentum* and *arsenicum*. The former term was afterwards contracted to *orpiment*, a term which remains with us to-day. The element arsenic was prepared by Albertus Magnus, about 1250, and it was considered by the later alchemists to be a bastard or semi-metal.

Occurrence

The element occurs free, and combined in a great number of minerals —oxide, *arsenolite*, As_4O_6 ; sulphides, *realgar*, As_2S_2 ; *orpiment*, As_2S_3 ; *mispickel* or *arsenical pyrites*, FeAsS ; *cobaltite* or *cobalt glance*, CoAsS ; arsenides—*tin white cobalt*, $CoAs_2$; *arsenical iron*, $FeAs_2$, and Fe_4As_3 ; *nickel glance*, NiAsS ; *kupfernickel*, NiAs. Arsenic also occurs in most samples of pyrites and hence it finds its way into sulphuric acid when sulphur dioxide is made by roasting pyrites. Arsenic is also found in commercial zinc ; and in the smoke from coal when the coal contains pyrites ; hence also arsenic finds its way into the atmosphere of towns, where it can be detected, particularly in foggy weather. Arsenic is also found in some mineral waters—e.g., Levico, Roncegno, etc. A. Gautier says that traces also occur normally in the human body. The mere qualitative detection of arsenic does not therefore give much information unless the operation is more or less quantitative.

Preparation

The element arsenic can be prepared by heating a mixture of the oxide, As_4O_6, with powdered charcoal in a clay crucible :

$$As_4O_6 + 6C = 6CO + 4As.$$

The crucible is provided with a conical iron cap in which the arsenic sublimes. Most of the commercial arsenic is either a natural product, or else it is made by heating mispickel in a clay tube fitted half its length with an inner sheet-iron tube. The arsenic sublimes into the iron tube. By withdrawing and unrolling the tube, the element arsenic is obtained :

$$FeAsS = FeS + As.$$

The arsenic so obtained is not very pure. It is purified by resublimation from a mixture of the crude element and charcoal.

§ 15 Properties, Uses, etc., of Arsenic

Properties

Like phosphorus, arsenic exhibits allotropy, and three forms are ordinarily distinguished.

Ordinary arsenic is a steel-grey, metallic-looking substance, which forms hexagonal rhombohedral crystals with a bright lustre. This is known as **grey arsenic** or **γ-arsenic**. When this form is quickly heated in a current of hydrogen, black glittering hexagonal crystals are deposited nearest the hot portion of the tube, and further on a yellow powder. The former is known as β-**arsenic, black arsenic** or **metallic arsenic,** and is formed by slow condensation of arsenic vapour. Its specific gravity is 4·7. At 360° it passes into the grey variety.

The yellow powder, known as α-**arsenic** or **yellow arsenic,** is formed by rapid condensation of arsenic vapour. It is soluble in carbon disulphide (in which it resembles yellow phosphorus) and it is deposited from this solution in rhombohedral crystals. It is very sensitive to light, which quickly converts it into the grey variety. Its specific gravity is 2·0.

Grey arsenic is brittle, and, like the metals, it is a good conductor of heat. Its specific gravity—5·7—is higher than typical non-metals. In general physical properties grey arsenic resembles the metals, but otherwise it is classed with phosphorus among the non-metals. At atmospheric pressures it sublimes very slowly at about 100°, and very rapidly at a dull red heat, without melting. If heated under pressure, it melts at about 814°, but under ordinary pressures it sublimes without melting. The vapour is lemon-yellow, and it smells like garlic. Arsenic is not altered by exposure to dry air, but in moist air a surface film of oxide is formed. At 180° it burns with a bluish flame, forming arsenious oxide, As_4O_6. It combines directly with chlorine at ordinary temperatures, forming arsenic trichloride, $AsCl_3$. It also combines directly with the other halogens and sulphur. Arsenic is insoluble in solutions of alkali hydroxides and is unattacked by those acids which are not oxidizing agents.

Dilute sulphuric acid has very little action on arsenic, but hot concentrated sulphuric acid dissolves arsenic forming sulphur dioxide and *probably* a very unstable **arsenic sulphate,** $As_2(SO_4)_3$, which immediately decomposes into the oxide. Dilute nitric acid in the cold has very little action, but the hot acid oxidizes the element to arsenic acid—H_3AsO_4, or As_2O_5. The reactions can be represented:

$$6As + 10HNO_3 = 3As_2O_5 + 5H_2O + 10NO.$$

Concentrated nitric acid and *aqua regia* also form arsenic acid.

Uses

Arsenic is used in the manufacture of arsenic compounds, e.g., arsenic trioxide (q.v.) and in certain alloys. It is used in traces for hardening lead for making shot. It is employed for the manufacture of pigments, and, by way of the trioxide, finds many uses in industry. Arsenates, particularly lead arsenate, are extensively employed as insecticides and weed-killers.

Atomic and Molecular Weight of Arsenic

The molecular weights of volatile arsenic compounds, the position of arsenic in the Periodic Table and the application of Dulong and Petit's Law indicate a value in the neighbourhood of 75 for the atomic weight.

Accurate determinations have been made by conversion of silver arsenate into silver bromide and silver chloride. Baxter and his collaborators synthesized very pure arsenic trichloride and tribromide and converted them into the corresponding silver halides. By this method they obtained, as the average of the results of a long series of experiments, the value 74·91. They also hydrolyzed weighed quantities of the trichloride with sodium hydroxide *in vacuo* and determined the amount of iodine pentoxide exactly equivalent to this solution. The mean of these experiments was 74·911. The value at present recommended by the International Committee is 74·91.

The vapour density of arsenic at 860° is 147 ($H_2 = 1$) ; at 1714° it is 79, and at 1736°, 77. The molecular weight at high temperatures thus corresponds to a molecule As_2 and at lower temperatures to As_4.

The effect of yellow arsenic on the boiling point and freezing point of carbon disulphide corresponds with a molecule As_4.

§ 16 Hydrides and Oxides of Arsenic

Arsenic Hydride, Arsine, AsH_3

Arsenic does not unite directly with hydrogen, but the hydride is produced by the action of nascent hydrogen, from zinc or magnesium and dilute hydrochloric or sulphuric acids, upon a solution containing arsenic. Arsine is also formed by the action of the nascent hydrogen from potassium hydroxide and zinc, upon solutions of arsenic compounds.

Prepared in this way, the gas is mixed with much hydrogen. It can be made almost free from hydrogen by the action of dilute sulphuric acid upon sodium arsenide or zinc arsenide :

$$Zn_3As_2 + 3H_2SO_4 = 2AsH_3 + 3ZnSO_4.$$

It can be obtained quite pure by drying, and then liquefying at −100°.

Arsine is a very poisonous gas, one bubble is said to have produced fatal effects. It is colourless, has an unpleasant smell, and is a powerful reducing agent. It liquefies at −55° and solidifies at −113·5°. It is very unstable, and when heated to about 230°, decomposes and deposits arsenic in the form of a metallic film. It is also decomposed by electric sparks, and explodes if detonated with mercury fulminate. Arsine burns in air with a blue flame forming arsenic trioxide ; but if the flame is brought into contact with a cold surface, arsenic is deposited. The formation of arsine is used in Marsh's test for the detection of arsenic (see p. 747).

With concentrated silver nitrate solution, arsine gives a yellow double compound of silver arsenide and silver nitrate :

$$AsH_3 + 6AgNO_3 = Ag_3As.3AgNO_3 + 3HNO_3.$$

This is slowly decomposed by water with the formation of a black precipitate of metallic silver :

$$Ag_3As.3AgNO_3 + 3H_2O = 6Ag + 3HNO_3 + H_3AsO_3.$$

This is the principle of *Gutzeit's test*. If dilute silver nitrate be used, silver is precipitated at once.

The composition of arsine can be determined by passing electric sparks through the gas, when three volumes of hydrogen are formed from two of arsine :

$$2AsH_3 = 2As + 3H_2.$$
$$2 \text{ vols.} \qquad\qquad 3 \text{ vols.}$$

If the gas be passed over hot weighed copper oxide and the resulting water and copper arsenide weighed, the composition can be shown to correspond to AsH_3. The vapour density of arsine ($H_2 = 1$) is 38·95, corresponding to a molecule AsH_3.

Arsenic dihydride—?As_2H_2, is obtained as a velvety brown powder when arsine is partially oxidized ; when a jet of burning arsine impinges on porcelain ; when potassium arsenide, K_3As, obtained by the reaction :

$$3KOH + AsH_3 = K_3As + 3H_2O,$$

furnishes the solid hydride when treated with water :

$$2K_3As + 6H_2O = As_2H_2 + 6KOH + 2H_2 ;$$

when an electric discharge acts on arsine ; and when water is electrolyzed with an arsenic cathode.

Arsenic Trioxide, Arsenious Oxide, As_2O_3 or As_4O_6

This oxide is the most important compound of arsenic, and in commerce is often called *white arsenic*, or simply " arsenic." Small quantities occur free in nature. Arsenic trioxide is formed by oxidizing arsenic with nitric acid, and by the combustion of arsenic, which, unlike phosphorus, only oxidizes to the trioxide when burnt. It is manufactured as a by-product of the roasting of arsenical ores, such as mispickel :

$$FeS_2.FeAs_2 + 5O_2 = Fe_2O_3 + 2SO_2 + As_2O_3.$$

This is done in a revolving, slightly sloping calcining furnace down which the ore moves, whilst furnace gases mixed with arsenic trioxide vapour pass upwards, through a series of brick chambers or flues arranged so as to present an extended surface to the gases. The crude product—*arsenical soot*—is collected and refined by sublimation in a cast-iron pan covered by a bell, or from a reverberatory furnace.

Like phosphorous oxide, arsenious oxide occurs in several different forms. **Amorphous arsenic trioxide,** or vitreous arsenic, is a colourless, non-crystalline, glassy substance produced when the vapour of arsenic trioxide is *slowly* condensed at a temperature slightly below its vaporizing temperature. It melts at about 200°, and volatilizes at 218°. 100 parts of water at 10° dissolve 3·67 parts of vitreous arsenic oxide in six hours, the solubility diminishes on standing. Vitreous arsenic trioxide can be preserved unchanged in a sealed tube, but if it be exposed to the air it gradually becomes opaque and forms crystals of **octahedral arsenic trioxide** belonging to the cubic system. Similar crystals are produced when the vapour of arsenic trioxide is *rapidly* condensed, and when aqueous or hydrochloric acid solutions of the trioxide are allowed to crystallize. Octahedral arsenic trioxide has less than one-third the solubility of the vitreous variety. If a hot saturated solution of arsenic trioxide in water be allowed to cool slowly in a dark room, a flash of light is produced as each crystal is formed. The specific gravity of vitreous arsenic trioxide is 3·74, and

of the octahedral form, 3·63. The passage from the vitreous to the octahedral variety is attended by an evolution of heat, 5·3 Cals. Octahedral arsenic trioxide vaporizes without fusion, but if heated under pressure it melts and forms the vitreous variety.

If a hot saturated solution of arsenic trioxide in potassium hydroxide be cooled, prismatic needle-like crystals of **monoclinic arsenic trioxide** separate. This variety is also formed when either of the preceding forms of arsenic trioxide are heated for a long time at 200°. Its specific gravity is 4·15. If the lower part of a

FIG. 230.

Dimorphism of Arsenic Trioxide.

sealed tube containing arsenic trioxide be heated above 400°, the lower part will contain vitreous, the middle prismatic (monoclinic), and the upper part octahedral (cubic) arsenic trioxide. This experiment is due to H. Debray (1864). A mixture of the prismatic and octahedral crystals will be found in the zone between the octahedral and prismatic crystals. Fig. 230 will give some idea of the crystals in the intermediate zone as they appear magnified under a 1½-inch objective. The vitreous form is the unstable variety, and the octahedral form the stable variety at ordinary temperatures. The vitreous variety can exist at ordinary temperatures because of the slow speed of transformation into the octahedral form. At 100° the speed is quite fast. At higher temperatures still the octahedral form passes into the monoclinic variety. Pressure alone (2500 kgrms. per sq. cm.) at 150° will transform arsenic trioxide into the vitreous variety.

All three varieties of arsenic trioxide vaporize at 218°. The vapour density between 500° and 800° corresponds with the molecule As_4O_6; and at 1732°, with As_2O_3. Arsenic trioxide is quite stable if heated in air or oxygen at 100°. Oxidizing agents—like iodine, hydrogen peroxide, nitric acid, and ozone—transform it into arsenic acid. Arsenic trioxide dissolves in hydrochloric acid, forming arsenic trichloride. Reducing agents—stannous chloride—transform it into arsenic and arsine. Arsenic trioxide is very poisonous—0·06 gram is near the fatal dose for an ordinary man ; but the habitual use of small doses makes the system more or less immune to the effects of much larger quantities.

Arsenic trioxide is used in the manufacture of pigments, e.g.,

Scheele's green, $HCuAsO_3$; *Paris green* or *Schweinfurt green*, $3Cu(AsO_2)_2.Cu(C_2H_3O_2)_2$. It is also used as an insecticide and for rat poison; in preserving the skins of animals and in the manufacture of glass and opaque enamels. It is employed in pyrotechny for the production of " white fire " and its salts are used in medicine (*Fowler's solution*, a weak solution of sodium arsenite, is employed in veterinary surgery) in dyeing and in calico printing. It also finds a use mixed with sodium carbonate for the prevention of boiler incrustations.

Arsenites

Aqueous solutions of arsenic trioxide exhibit a feebly acidic reaction, probably due to the formation of unstable **arsenious acid,** H_3AsO_3. It differs from the corresponding phosphorous acid in being tribasic. The acid has never been isolated; the solution on concentration deposits crystals of the oxide. Salts are known corresponding to ortho-, pyro-, and meta-arsenious acids—H_3AsO_3, $H_4As_2O_5$ and $HAsO_2$.

All the arsenites, except the alkali arsenites, are insoluble in water, and they are decomposed by carbonic and hydrosulphuric acids. The soluble arsenites react alkaline owing to hydrolysis. Arsenious acid and its salts are reducing agents, but not so powerful as phosphorous acid and the phosphites. Arsenious acid precipitates red cuprous oxide from an alkaline cupric solution. When heated, the arsenites are converted into arsenates and free arsenic; and when heated with charcoal, both the arsenates and the arsenites are reduced to elemental arsenic.

Arsenites are oxidized by the halogens, and by bleaching powder, e.g. :

$$H^3AsO_3 + I_2 + H_2O = H_3AsO_4 + 2HI,$$

and these reactions are used for their volumetric determination.

Arsenic Pentoxide, As_2O_5, and Arsenates

Arsenic pentoxide cannot be prepared by burning arsenic in oxygen since the product is the trioxide, but can be obtained by the action of oxidizing agents on arsenic trioxide.

By digesting arsenic trioxide with nitric acid a solution is obtained which, when cold and concentrated, deposits rhombic crystals of $H_3AsO_4.H_2O$. These melt at about 36°, and when heated to 100° lose water, leaving a crystalline powder once called **ortho-arsenic acid,** H_3AsO_4. When this arsenic acid is heated to 210° for about two and a half hours, arsenic pentoxide is obtained as a white deliquescent glassy solid :

$$2H_3AsO_4 = As_2O_5 + 3H_2O.$$

Unlike phosphorus pentoxide, on heating to a higher temperature (ca. 440°) it breaks down into the trioxide and oxygen.

Several **arsenates** are known, among which may be mentioned :

sodium arsenate, $Na_2HAsO_4.12H_2O$, used in calico printing, and **lead arsenate**, $PbHAsO_4$, used for spraying fruit trees.

The soluble arsenates have an alkaline reaction, and give a reddish-brown precipitate of silver arsenate, Ag_3AsO_4, when neutral solutions are treated with silver nitrate. They also react with ammonium molybdate, in presence of nitric acid in a manner similar to the phosphates, giving a yellow precipitate of ammonium arseno-molybdate on heating.

§ 17 Halides and Sulphides of Arsenic

Arsenic trifluoride, AsF_3, is formed as a volatile fuming liquid, boiling at 63°, when arsenious oxide is distilled with calcium fluoride and sulphuric acid. It is decomposed by water.

Arsenic pentafluoride, AsF_5, is obtained as a colourless gas by distilling a mixture of the trifluoride with bromine and antimony pentafluoride at a temperature not exceeding 55° :

$$AsF_3 + 2SbF_5 + Br_2 = AsF_5 + 2SbBrF .$$

Arsenic trichloride, $AsCl_3$, is formed by the direct union of the elements, or by distilling a mixture of arsenic trioxide with hydrochloric acid, or by heating arsenic trioxide with sulphur chloride in a current of chlorine :

$$4As_2O_3 + 3S_2Cl_2 + 9Cl_2 = 8AsCl_3 + 6SO_2.$$

Arsenic trichloride is a heavy, colourless, viscid liquid boiling at 122° ; which freezes to white needle-like crystals at −18°. It is hydrolyzed by water, the reaction being reversible :

$$AsCl_3 + 3H_2O \rightleftharpoons H_3AsO_3 + 3HCl.$$

It is thus intermediate in behaviour between typical non-metallic chlorides such as phosphorus trichloride, and typical metallic chlorides such as calcium or sodium chlorides.

Arsenic pentachloride, $AsCl_5$, is said to be formed when arsenic trichloride is cooled with excess of chlorine ; but there is considerable doubt as to its real existence.

Arsenic tribromide is a liquid which gives colourless prisms when cooled ; and **arsenic tri-iodide** forms orange-red rhombohedral crystals, by direct union of the elements.

Arsenic disulphide, As_2S_2, is found in nature as the mineral *realgar* ; and it can be made by heating together sulphur and arsenic in the right proportions, or by heating arsenic sulphide with arsenic ; or arsenious oxide and sulphur ; or distilling a mixture of iron pyrites and arsenical pyrites. Arsenic disulphide is a red brittle vitreous or crystalline solid, it fuses at 307° and sublimes unchanged. Heated in air it burns with a blue flame forming sulphur dioxide and arsenic trioxide. It is used in pyrotechny ; for instance, in the manufacture of the so-called " Bengal fire," which is a mixture of realgar, sulphur, and nitre.

Arsenic Trisulphide, As_2S_3

This sulphide occurs in nature as the mineral *orpiment*—a term derived from the Latin *auri pigmentum*, golden paint. It is employed as a pigment under the name *King's yellow*. Arsenic trisulphide is formed when powdered arsenic and sulphur are heated together in the proportions indicated by the formula, As_2S_3 ; and it is also precipitated as a canary-yellow solid when hydrogen sulphide is passed into a solution of an arsenious salt acidified with hydrochloric acid.

Arsenic trisulphide is a bright yellow solid, insoluble in water, but " soluble " in alkali hydroxides, ammonium carbonate and alkali sulphides. When dissolved in alkali hydroxides, arsenite and thio-arsenite (see below) are both formed :

$$2As_2S_3 + 4KOH = 3KAsS_2 + KAsO_2 + 2H_2O.$$

But with the alkali sulphides it forms only **thioarsenites,** which may be regarded as salts of the hypothetical thioarsenious acid, H_3AsS_3. Yellow ammonium sulphide, which contains sulphur in solution, oxidizes arsenic trisulphide to a thioarsenate (see below).

The thioarsenites of the alkalis, alkaline earths, and of magnesium are soluble in water, but decompose on boiling. The solutions are also decomposed by acids with the evolution of hydrogen sulphide, and the re-precipitation of arsenic trisulphide. Hydrogen sulphide will not precipitate arsenic sulphide from the normal arsenites, and it is only partially precipitated from the primary and secondary arsenites, because soluble thioarsenites are formed. If sufficient acid be present to prevent the formation of the soluble arsenites, precipitation is complete.

Arsenic pentasulphide, As_2S_5, can be made by fusing together arsenic trisulphide and sulphur in the right proportions. It is precipitated when a rapid stream of hydrogen sulphide is passed through a cold solution of arsenic acid containing a large excess of hydrochloric acid, or through a strongly acidified solution of a soluble arsenate. Both arsenic tri- and pentasulphides are reduced to the disulphide by an hydrochloric acid solution of stannous chloride :

$$As_2S_3 + SnCl_2 + 2HCl = SnCl_4 + H_2S + As_2S_2.$$

This explains the formation of the red precipitate which occurs in the detection of arsenic in the presence of tin.

Like the corresponding trisulphide, the pentasulphide will " dissolve " in alkali hydroxides forming a mixture of arsenate and thio-arsenate ; and in alkali sulphides forming thioarsenates only. Acids decompose the thioarsenates with the re-precipitation of the penta-sulphide.

Solutions of arsenic acid or of arsenates are reduced slowly by hydrogen sulphide, in presence of hydrochloric acid, arsenic trisulphide being ultimately precipitated. It is supposed that the following reactions occur :

(i) the slow formation of an acid, H_3AsSO_3, intermediate in composition between arsenic acid and thioarsenic acid (H_3AsS_4) :

$$H_2S + H_3AsO_4 = H_2O + H_3AsSO_3 ;$$

(ii) reduction of this acid to arsenious acid with separation of sulphur,

$$H_3AsSO_3 = H_3AsO_3 + S ;$$

(iii) decomposition of arsenious acid by hydrogen sulphide :

$$2H_3AsO_3 + 3H_2S = 6H_2O + As_2S_3.$$

Summarized, this leads to the equation :

$$2H_3AsO_4 + 5H_2S = 2S + 8H_2O + As_2S_3.$$

§ 18 Detection of Arsenic

Arsenic is usually detected by means of **Marsh's test,** which depends upon the formation of arsine when nascent hydrogen is produced in a solution containing arsenic.

The standard form of this test is carried out in an apparatus similar to Fig. 231.

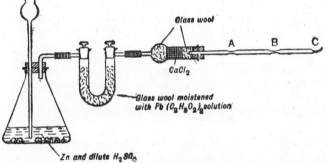

FIG. 231.—Marsh's Test.

Hydrogen is generated in the small flask from arsenic-free zinc and dilute sulphuric acid and then passed along a glass tube heated at one point by a very small flame. Alternatively, the hydrogen may be generated electrolytically. The solution to be tested for the presence of arsenic is run into the flask, and, if arsenic is present, arsine will be formed. When it reaches the hot part of the tube it is decomposed, forming a dark shining " mirror " of arsenic just beyond this point. Antimony forms a similar mirror, but can be distinguished by the fact that with it the mirror is nearer to the flame, and it is insoluble in sodium hypochlorite solution, whereas the arsenic mirror is soluble.

Marsh's test is now often carried out in a different way, as illustrated in Fig. 232.

Hydrogen is produced as before and the suspected solution added. The gases evolved are led up a vertical tube containing a rolled-up lead acetate paper, at the end of which is a sheet of filter paper moistened with mercuric chloride solution, held in position by means of two perforated rubber bungs and a spring clip, as in the diagram. If arsine be present in the gas passing through the paper moistened with mercuric chloride, a yellow stain is produced, which may be compared when produced under standard conditions with standard stains and so used for the estimation of the arsenic present. The exact chemical nature of the yellow compound is uncertain.

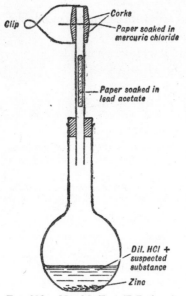

Reinsch's test depends upon the fact that copper will form copper arsenide when boiled with a hydrochloric acid solution of an arsenic compound. The solution suspected of containing arsenic is added to concentrated hydrochloric acid and a piece of bright copper foil. On warming the copper becomes covered with a dark stain of copper arsenide if arsenic be present. This is then dried and heated in a glass tube in a current of hydrogen, when the arsenic sublimes off the copper and condenses in a mirror on the walls of the tube.

FIG. 232.—Marsh's Test (B.P. form).

§ 19 Antimony, Sb. History, Occurrence and Preparation

History

According to Dioscorides and Pliny, *stimmi* and *stibium*—that is, stibnite or antimony sulphide—has long been employed by the women of the East as a medicine, and as an article of toilet for darkening the eyebrows. It is mentioned in this connection in the Old Testament (2 Kings ix. 30 ; Ezekiel xxiii. 40). Pliny terms it *stibium*, and in a Latin translation of Geber, it is called *antimonium*. Both terms were in common use up to the time of Lavoisier for antimony sulphide.

The derivation of the name *antimony* is uncertain ; it has been suggested that it is from *anti* (against) and *moine* (French, a monk), but no weight is attached to this suggestion ; the word had also been referred to the Greek ανθεμώνιον (anthemonion), having reference to the petal-like appearance of the crystals of the naturally occurring mineral (ἀνθος—anthos—a flower).

The preparation of the element, and the known and imagined properties of antimony were described in the writings attributed to

Basil Valentine (supposed to have lived in South Germany in the fifteenth century). The book is entitled *Triumph—Wagen des Antimonii* and is a product of the seventeenth century (cf. p. 7).

Occurrence

Antimony occurs free in small quantities in Borneo and a few other places. It is nearly always accompanied by some arsenic. Antimony occurs combined with oxygen as *antimony bloom*, Sb_2O_3; and as *antimony ochre*, Sb_2O_4; combined with sulphur as *stibnite* or *grey antimony ore*, Sb_2O_3; and as *antimony blende* or *red antimony*, Sb_2S_2O. It also occurs combined with sulphur and the metals.

Preparation

The principal source of antimony is stibnite. Good quality samples are smelted by heating with scrap iron, when the iron combines with the sulphur to form a slag of iron sulphide, which floats on the surface of the molten antimony :

$$Sb_2S_3 + 3Fe = 2Sb + 3FeS.$$

The antimony is purified by re-melting two or three times with a little nitre to oxidize contaminating impurities such as lead and sulphur.

With poorer ores the crude sulphide is melted in such a way that the molten sulphide flows away from the less fusible rocky impurities. This process is called **liquation.**—The liquated sulphide is then mixed with about half its weight of charcoal and carefully roasted so as to convert the sulphide into oxide :

$$2Sb_2S_3 + 9O_2 = 2Sb_2O_3 + 6SO_2.$$

Part of the antimony oxide condenses in the flues, and a residue of Sb_2O_4 and unchanged sulphide remains behind. This is mixed with charcoal and sodium carbonate, and heated in a crucible. The reactions are taken to be :

$$Sb_2O_3 + 3C = 2Sb + 3CO,$$
$$Sb_2O_4 + 4C = 2Sb + 4CO,$$
$$Sb_2S_3 + 3Na_2CO_3 + 6C = 2Sb + 3Na_2S + 9CO.$$

§ 20 Properties, Uses, etc., of Antimony

Like phosphorus and arsenic, antimony exists in allotropic modifications; three such are generally distinguished, viz. :
(i) Crystalline or rhombohedral or β-antimony ;
(ii) Yellow or α-antimony ;
(iii) Explosive antimony.

The first named is the variety ordinarily obtained, and referred to as antimony.

It is a silver-white solid with a high metallic lustre and a crystalline (rhombohedral) structure. It is very brittle and can be easily pulverized. Like the non-metals it is a poor conductor of heat, but it has a high specific gravity—6·684. From its physical properties, antimony, like arsenic, would be classed with the metals, but its metallic characters are more pronounced than those of arsenic. Antimony melts at 630·5° in an atmosphere of carbon monoxide ; and

boils at 1380°. When the molten element is allowed to cool slowly and partially solidify in a crucible, the uncongealed portion may be poured off. The interior of the crucible is then lined with well-formed rhombohedral crystals of antimony isomorphous with arsenic. The reduced photograph, Fig. 233, illustrates the crystalline surface of a sample of 99·5 per cent. antimony. In

FIG. 233.—Crystals of Antimony.

the act of solidification lead contracts, but antimony expands slightly. Hence molten mixtures of antimony with other metals, when poured into moulds, take the fine and sharp impressions of the mould.

Antimony does not tarnish readily on exposure to dry air, but it is oxidized slowly by moist air. Antimony is used to cover other metals like brass and lead alloys. *Antimony black* is finely powdered antimony which is used to coat plaster casts, to make them imitate metals. When heated in air or oxygen, antimony burns with a bright bluish flame forming antimony trioxide, Sb_2O_3. Antimony combines directly with the halogens. The action is vigorous, and the combining element becomes incandescent. With chlorine, antimony trichloride, $SbCl_3$ is formed. Antimony also unites with sulphur, phosphorus, and arsenic, forming sulphides, phosphides, and arsenides respectively. Dilute hydrochloric and sulphuric acids have little or no action upon antimony, but the more concentrated acids respectively form chloride and an unstable antimony sulphate.

$$2Sb + 6HCl = 2SbCl_3 + 3H_2,$$
$$2Sb + 6H_2SO_4 = 6H_2O + 3SO_2 + Sb_2(SO_4)_3.$$

If air be excluded, hydrochloric acid does not attack the element. Antimony thus behaves towards these acids like a typical metal. Dilute nitric acid has scarcely any action, but it probably forms an unstable **antimony nitrate,** $Sb(NO_3)_3$. Concentrated nitric acid does not dissolve the metal but rather oxidizes it to insoluble Sb_2O_3 or Sb_2O_5, or a mixture of Sb_2O_4 and Sb_2O_5.

Yellow, or **α-antimony** is a metastable form which results when antimony hydride, SbH_3, is treated with air at −90° :

$$4SbH_3 + 3O_2 = 4Sb + 6H_2O.$$

This passes into **black antimony** on exposure to light. It is not clear whether black antimony is a definite form or an intermediate form between α- and β-antimony.

Gore (1855) found that if a current of electricity be passed through a solution of antimony trichloride in hydrochloric acid—using an antimony anode, and a platinum cathode—an amorphous powder of specific gravity 5·78 is deposited on the cathode. The cathode has then the appearance of a smooth polished graphite rod. The deposit appears to be solid solution of antimony trichloride in metastable or α-antimony. If this deposit be rubbed or scratched, an explosion occurs. The explosion is attended by the allotropic transformation of the metastable or α-form of antimony into the stable β-form or the rhombohedral variety, at the same time the temperature rises to about 250°, and 19·6 cals. of heat are evolved per gram of antimony. Clouds of antimony trichloride are given off at the same time. Hence the term **explosive antimony** is applied to the solid solution of the trihalide in α-antimony.

Uses

The property possessed by antimony of expanding on solidification leads to its use in a number of alloys. The more important of these are given in Table LIII.

TABLE LIII.—ALLOYS OF ANTIMONY.

	Sn	Pb	Sb	Cu	
Type metal . .	5	75	20		
Stereotype metal .	2·25	84·21	13·54		
Britannia metal .	93·3		4·6	2	
Pewter . . .	83–75	0–20	0–7	0–4	
Anti-friction (Babbit's) metal .	83·3		8·3	8·3	

With copper, a remarkable violet alloy known as *Regulus of Venus* is formed. It is probably a compound, $SbCu_2$.

Antimony is also used in making paints, e.g., antimony white as a substitute for white lead ; antimony black as a bronzing powder for metals and plaster ; and kermes (see below), a brownish-yellow pigment. It is employed in medicine, in the manufacture of enamels, for colouring pottery and tiles, cloth and paper, and for making of mordants (e.g., the oxychloride).

Atomic and Molecular Weights of Antimony

Consideration of the specific heat of antimony (0·046 at 186° and 0·0537 at 300°) together with the molecular weights of volatile compounds such as the trichloride, indicates a value in the neighbourhood of 120 for the atomic weight. The atomic weight has been determined, for example, by conversion of the metal into its chloride and bromide, followed by estimation of the silver chloride and bromide formed from them. The value obtained by different investigators showed considerable variation, but the value 120·2 was accepted until, in 1923, Aston showed that antimony contains two isotopes of weight, 121 and 123, indicating a value for the atomic weight of the ordinary element above 121. Subsequently values were obtained (i) by Hönigschmid and collaborators of 121·76 as the mean of 32 concordant analyses, based on the preparation of pure chloride and bromide ; (ii) by Weatherall, of 121·748, using a similar method ; (iii) by Willard and McAlpine, who found 121·77. The value at present recommended by the International Committee is 121·76.

The vapour density of antimony at 2000° corresponds with a monatomic molecule ; at 1640° it corresponds almost exactly with a molecule Sb_2 and at 1380° (the boiling point) very nearly with Sb_3. By analogy with arsenic and phosphorus this last result is interpreted as indicating an equilibrium :

$$Sb_4 \rightleftharpoons 2Sb_2.$$

§ 21 Hydrides and Oxides of Antimony

Antimony hydride, Stibine, SbH_3, is made in a similar manner to arsenic hydride. It is a colourless, poisonous gas with an unpleasant smell. It begins to decompose into its elements even at ordinary temperatures, and sometimes explodes when heated.

It is a powerful reducing agent and may be distinguished from arsenic hydride by its reaction with silver nitrate, with which it gives a precipitate of silver antimonide, Ag_3Sb, and not metallic silver :

$$SbH_3 + 3AgNO_3 = Ag_3Sb + 3HNO_3.$$

Antimony dihydride, Sb_2H_2, is an amorphous grey solid, formed by the decomposition of stibine by sodium hydroxide solution, or by the reduction of the trichloride with zinc and hydrochloric acid.

Antimony trioxide, antimonious oxide, Sb_2O_3 or Sb_4O_6, is made by burning antimony in air, or by adding hot water to a solution of antimony trichloride or sulphate :

$$4SbCl_3 + 6H_2O \rightleftharpoons Sb_4O_6 + 12HCl.$$

The precipitated oxide is washed with a solution of sodium carbonate to remove the free acid, and finally with water.

Antimonious oxide is a white powder, which volatilizes just over 1500°, when its vapour density corresponds with a molecule Sb_4O_6. The vapour condenses in two distinct forms, isodimorphous with the corresponding crystals of arsenious oxide. Antimonious oxide is very sparingly soluble in water, and the solution has no action on litmus. It is insoluble in dilute nitric and sulphuric acids, but reacts with dilute hydrochloric acid, forming a solution of the trichloride (q.v.) ; and with cold concentrated nitric acid forming **antimony nitrate,** $Sb(NO_3)_3$, and with hot concentrated sulphuric acid forming **antimony**

sulphate, $Sb_2(SO_4)_3$. It also forms a solution with tartaric acid and acid potassium tartrate, giving with the latter *tartar emetic* (q.v.) and with alkalis forming salts, e.g., $NaSbO_2.3H_2O$ derived from the hypothetical **meta-antimonious acid,** $HSbO_2$. **Ortho-antimonious acid,** H_3SbO_3, is obtained as a white solid if sulphuric or nitric acid be added to a solution of tartar emetic, and the resulting precipitate dried at 100°. Its formation is probably due to the hydrolysis of the nitrate or sulphate first formed. A **pyroantimonious acid,** $H_4Sb_2O_5$, has been reported, but there is some doubt if it has been isolated.

Antimony Tetroxide, Sb_2O_4

When antimony trioxide is heated in air, it begins to smoulder, forming antimony tetroxide, which is yellow when hot, and white when cold. It is also formed when the pentoxide is heated to a red heat. It has been thought by some to be a mixed anhydride analogous to N_2O_4 and P_2O_4; and on fusion with alkalis it forms salts known as hypoantimoniates, e.g.,

$$2KOH + Sb_2O_4 = K_2Sb_2O_5 + H_2O$$

Antimony pentoxide, Sb_2O_5, is formed by heating pyroantimonic acid (q.v.) to 300°, or by the repeated evaporation of antimony with concentrated nitric acid.

Antimony pentoxide is a straw yellow powder, almost insoluble in water.

A mixture with water, however, reddens blue litmus. It dissolves in concentrated hydrochloric acid and the mixture has oxidizing properties; for example, it liberates iodine from potassium iodide:

$$Sb_2O_5 + 4KI + 10HCl = 2SbCl_3 + 4KCl + 2I_2 + 5H_2O.$$

Antimonic acids and antimonates

Orthoantimonic acid, H_3SbO_4, is made by oxidizing antimony trichloride with concentrated nitric acid and diluting the solution with water. A white precipitate is obtained, which yields the ortho-acid when dried over concentrated sulphuric acid. On heating to 200°, it passes into

Pyroantimonic acid, $H_4Sb_2O_7$, which is also made by the action of nitric acid on antimony at 100°, and most readily by that of hot water on antimony pentachloride:

$$2SbCl_5 + 7H_2O = 10HCl + H_4Sb_2O_7,$$

the precipitate formed being dried at 100°. At 200° it is said to pass into *meta-antimonic acid*, and at 300° the pentoxide is formed.

Antimoniates are known to be derived from each of these antimonic acids. Among them may be mentioned **Potassium (dihydrogen) pyro-antimonate,** $K_2H_2Sb_2O_7.6H_2O$, which is used as a test for sodium since the corresponding **sodium salt** is one of the very few relatively insoluble salts of sodium. It is made by adding powdered antimony, in small quantities at a time, to four times its weight of **fused** potassium nitrate. When cold the mass (which may contain the ortho-antimonate) is washed with water, and then boiled with more water, when the dihydrogen salt is formed as a granular powder, sparingly soluble in cold water, but easily soluble in hot.

§ 22 Other Compounds of Antimony

Antimony trichloride, $SbCl_3$, is formed by the action of dry chlorine on an excess of antimony, and also by the distillation of an intimate mixture of antimony or antimony sulphide with mercuric chloride. It forms colourless crystals melting at $73·4°$ and boiling at $220·2°$. It is highly deliquescent, and is decomposed by cold water, giving the oxychloride:

$$SbCl_3 + H_2O \rightleftharpoons SbOCl + 2HCl,$$

while with hot water the trioxide is precipitated. The **oxychloride,** which is a white powder, was once used in medicine under the name of " powder of Algaroth."

Antimony pentachloride, $SbCl_5$, is formed when chlorine is passed through fused antimony trichloride. It is a colourless or slightly yellow liquid which crystallizes at $2·8°$, fumes in air, and boils with partial dissociation into antimony trichloride and chlorine at $140°$. In this it resembles phosphorus pentachloride.

Antimony also forms a crystalline trifluoride, tribromide and tri-iodide by direct combination of the elements ; a pentafluoride is also known.

Antimony trisulphide, Sb_2S_3, occurs in two forms ; an orange form and a black form. The latter, known as stibnite, is the principal ore of antimony.

The black form is made by heating antimony with sulphur ; while the orange form is precipitated when hydrogen sulphide is passed through an acidified solution of antimony trichloride:

$$2SbCl_3 + 3H_2S \rightleftharpoons Sb_2S_3 + 6HCl.$$

The orange form passes into the black form on heating.

Antimony trisulphide is used in the manufacture of matches, fireworks, etc. ; whilst a mixture of antimony trisulphide and trioxide, known as *Kermes mineral*, is used in medicine and is made by boiling antimony trisulphide with sodium or potassium carbonate.

Antimony trisulphide reacts with alkalis and alkali sulphides in a similar manner to arsenic trisulphide, forming *thioantimonites* and *thioantimonates*.

Antimony pentasulphide, Sb_2S_5, is made by the action of hydrogen sulphide on a mixture of antimony pentachloride with a little water. It is also obtained by acting upon the trisulphide, along with sulphur, with potassium hydroxide, and decomposing the potassium thioantimonate so formed with dilute hydrochloric acid:

$$3K_2S + Sb_2S_3 = 2K_3SbS_3$$
$$K_3SbS_3 + S = K_3SbS_4$$
$$2K_3SbS_4 + 6HCl = 6KCl + Sb_2S_5 + 3H_2S.$$

Antimony pentasulphide is a reddish yellow solid which combines with alkali sulphides forming thioantimonates. **Schlippe's salt** is sodium thioantimonate, $Na_3SbS_4.9H_2O$. Antimony pentasulphide is used in the vulcanization of rubber.

Tartar Emetic. Potassium Antimonyl Tartrate, $2[K(SbO).C_4H_4O_6].H_2O$

Tartar emetic is made by boiling a solution of " cream of tartar," i.e., potassium hydrogen tartrate, with antimony trioxide. On cooling, the concentrated solution it separates in octahedral crystals :

$$2KHC_4H_4O_6 + Sb_2O_3 = 2K(SbO)C_4H_4O_6 + H_2O.$$

Tartar emetic is the most important salt of antimony in commerce. It is used in medicine in small doses as an emetic ; large doses are poisonous. It is also used for the treatment of some tropical diseases such as kala-azar. Large quantities are used as a mordant.

Detection of Antimony

Antimony is detected by the formation of an orange precipitate of the sulphide when hydrogen sulphide is passed through a not-too-acid solution of an antimony salt. This precipitate can be distinguished from arsenic sulphide by reason of its insolubility in concentrated ammonium carbonate solution. A 2 per cent. solution of " cupferron " gives a yellowish-white precipitate with antimonious compounds, but no precipitate with antimonic compounds.

Marsh's test can also be applied to the detection of antimony as indicated on page 747.

§ 23 Bismuth, Bi. History, Occurrence and Preparation

History

Metallic bismuth was described in the writings ascribed to Basil Valentine under the name marcasite, a name formerly used vaguely for almost any ore with a metallic appearance. Most of the writers of the seventeenth century confused bismuth with antimony or ·zinc. J. H. Pott (1739) first demonstrated the characteristic properties of bismuth, and its reactions were later studied by C. J. Geoffroy (1753) and T. Bergmann (1780). The name bismuth is supposed to be derived from the German " Weissmuth " (white matter).

Occurrence

Bismuth is found in many localities—Bolivia, Saxony, etc.—in a fairly pure condition in a free state. It also occurs combined with sulphur as *bismuth glance*, Bi_2S_3 ; with tellurium as *tetradymite*, Bi_2Te_3 ; and with oxygen as *bismite* or *bismuth ochre*, Bi_2O_3. *Bismuthite* is a hydrated carbonate. Most of the bismuth in commerce comes from Bolivia, and some from Australia and Bohemia.

In the United States much bismuth is now obtained as a by-product in the refining of lead and other metals.

Preparation

The principal ores are the sulphide, and bismuthyl carbonate. The former, after concentration by washing or magnetic separation, is roasted so as to form the oxide :

$$2Bi_2S_3 + 9O_2 = 2Bi_2O_3 + 6SO_2,$$

which is then reduced by heating with charcoal in a reverberatory furnace. The bismuth recovered from lead smelting, etc., occurs in the anode slimes of electrolytic refining processes (e.g., the Bett's process, p. 703). These residues are fused with sodium hydroxide and sodium carbonate, and the resulting material cast into slabs which are refined electrolytically, using a bath of bismuth chloride and hydrochloric acid. A very pure metal can be obtained in this way ; the purification of cruder samples is effected by fusion on an inclined plate in contact with air. Bismuth is only slowly oxidized at the melting point, whereas the impurities are usually readily oxidized or volatilized.

Properties

Bismuth is a greyish-white solid resembling antimony, but it has also a faint reddish tinge. It is hard, brittle, lustrous and crystallizes readily ; and, like antimony, it expands on solidification. It melts at 271°, and if the molten metal be allowed partly to solidify in a crucible, and the uncongealed liquid poured off (as in the preparation of monoclinic sulphur—p. 439) the crucible will be found lined with rhombohedral crystals of the element. Bismuth boils at 1450°, and it distils in an atmosphere of hydrogen if heated over 1100°. It is a very bad conductor of heat, its specific gravity is high (9·8) and it is very strongly diamagnetic (i.e., *repelled* by an ordinary magnet). The metallic properties are more pronounced than with either antimony or arsenic, and whereas in arsenic, non-metallic properties predominate, in bismuth the metallic properties are most pronounced. Bismuth is oxidized only superficially on exposure to the air, but if heated in air it burns, forming the oxide Bi_2O_3. It decomposes steam at a red-heat, but is not affected by cold air-free water. It unites directly with the halogens and with sulphur. It is but slightly attacked by hydrochloric acid and by hot concentrated sulphuric acid, and is readily attacked by dilute and concentrated nitric acid, forming the corresponding salts.

Uses

Bismuth is used in the manufacture of alloys, in particular of fusible metals. Thus *Newton's metal* (tin, 3 ; lead, 5 ; bismuth, 8) melts at 94·5° ; *Rose's fusible metal* (tin, 1 ; lead, 1 ; bismuth, 2) melts at 93·75° ; and *Wood's fusible metal* (tin, 1 ; lead, 2 ; cadmium, 1 ; bismuth, 4) melts at 60·5°—over 150° below the melting point of the most fusible metal. Fusible alloys, which melt at a low temperature, are used for making safety plugs in steam boilers ; fuses in electrical connections ; in fire alarms ; and in automatic sprinklers for buildings so that if a fire breaks out, the heat fuses a plug of the water pipe and thus allows a rush of water from the main. The gas pipe which enters a building can also be fitted with a piece of fusible alloy so that if a fire breaks out, the alloy will melt, choke the gas pipe, and stop the flow of gas. Fireproof doors can also be kept open by fusible plugs which allow the doors to close automatically in the event of fire. The oxide or nitrate is used in making some kinds of optical glass, and in the decoration of pottery with lustres. The basic nitrate was once used as a cosmetic, but is now largely displaced by the cheaper zinc oxide. Some of the bismuth compounds are used medicinally.

It is also used in the construction of thermopiles.

Atomic and Molecular Weights

The atomic weight of bismuth is seen to be in the neighbourhood of 208 from its specific heat (0·0303 at 18°), and the vapour density of volatile compounds such as the chloride. Among the methods employed for its accurate determination are, conversion of the metal into the oxide and vice versa ; conversion of the metal and the oxide into the sulphate, and the formation of silver chloride and bromide from bismuth chloride and bromide. Hönigschmid, by the last method, obtained values between 208·98 and 209·00, and considers the most probable value to be 209·00, which is the value recommended by the International Committee.

The vapour density of bismuth between 1600° and 1700° is about 158 ($H_2 = 1$) corresponding to a mixture of Bi_2 and Bi molecules. At 2000° the molecule is monatomic.

§ 24 Hydride and Oxides of Bismuth

Bismuth Hydride, BiH_3

This substance was first prepared by Paneth and co-workers in 1918. They obtained it in very small quantities by the action of dilute hydrochloric or sulphuric acid on a bismuth-magnesium alloy. Its formation was first detected by the use of the radio-active isotopes of bismuth, radium C and thorium C, which can be detected in very small amounts. It is an exceedingly unstable gas, but can be condensed in liquid air. It decomposes very readily on heating, with separation of bismuth.

Bismuth Oxides

Four oxides of bismuth have been described, viz.,

> Bismuth suboxide, or monoxide, BiO,
> Bismuth trioxide, Bi_2O_3,
> Bismuth dioxide or tetroxide, Bi_2O_4,
> Bismuth pentoxide Bi_2O_5.

The first named is somewhat doubtful.

Bismuth suboxide, BiO, is said to be formed when the trioxide is reduced with carbon monoxide, or when bismuth oxalate is heated. It is a black powder, which has been thought by some to be a mixture of bismuth and bismuth trioxide.

Bismuth Trioxide, Bi_2O_3

This oxide is formed when bismuth is heated in air, or when the hydrated oxide, carbonate or nitrate is calcined. The other oxides also pass into the trioxide when heated in air. It is a cream-coloured powder, which is not acted upon by water. It is readily reduced to the metal when heated with carbon or hydrogen. It exhibits marked basic properties, for it reacts with acids to form salts. It forms a series of hydrates, BiO.OH, $(HO)_2BiOBi(OH)_2$ and $Bi(OH)_3$, which can be obtained by pouring an acid solution of bismuth nitrate into excess of aqueous ammonia, when the trihydrate is formed. This loses water progressively on gentle heating. These hydrates do not exhibit any acidic properties.

Bismuth Dioxide, or Tetroxide, Bi_2O_4

If chlorine be passed into a boiling aqueous solution of potassium hydroxide in which bismuth trioxide is suspended, a dark chocolate-brown precipitate is formed :

$$Bi_2O_3 + KOCl = KCl + Bi_2O_4.$$

The precipitate is washed with water and dilute nitric acid, and dried at 180°. It appears to be a mixture of hydrated bismuth tetroxide, $Bi_2O_4.2H_2O$, with variable amounts of the pentoxide. In some respects this oxide resembles antimony tetroxide, but its mode of formation and many properties are like those of lead dioxide. When heated to 200° it decomposes into the trioxide. With hydrochloric acid it gives chlorine and the trichloride, and with oxyacids it gives oxygen and a bismuth salt.

Bismuth Pentoxide, Bi_2O_5. Bismuthic Acid

If the action of chlorine on an alkaline suspension of bismuth trioxide be continued for a long period the precipitate becomes scarlet red, and has the composition of **potassium metabismuthate,** $KBiO_3$. If this precipitate be washed and boiled for a short time in dilute nitric acid, scarlet-red **metabismuthic acid** is obtained, and when this is dried, bismuth pentoxide is formed as an unstable brown powder. When heated above 120°, it decomposes and bismuth trioxide is formed. With hydrochloric acid and oxyacids it furnishes bismuth salts and chlorine or oxygen ; thus resembling antimony pentoxide in behaving as a basic peroxide. The formation of bismuthates shows that it also exhibits feeble acidic properties.

§ 25 Other Compounds of Bismuth

Bismuth carbonate, bismuthyl carbonate $(BiO)_2CO_3$, is precipitated by addition of carbonate or bicarbonate solutions to bismuth nitrate. It is a basic carbonate, the normal carbonate being unknown ; but it is the only carbonate formed by elements of Group V.

Bismuth chloride, $BiCl_3$, is formed by the direct action of chlorine on bismuth ; by heating bismuth with mercuric chloride ; and by the action of *aqua regia* on bismuth. Bismuth trichloride is a white crystalline mass, deliquescent in air. It melts at 230° and boils at 447°. Its vapour density 164 corresponds with the formula $BiCl_3$.

When bismuth trichloride is dissolved in a little water it forms a syrupy liquid, but with an excess of water, a white precipitate of bismuth oxychloride, BiOCl.

This property is used as a test for bismuth in qualitative analysis.

Bismuth oxychloride, bismuthyl chloride, BiOCl, is obtained as above from the trichloride, or by the interaction of solutions of sodium chloride and bismuth nitrate :

$$Bi(NO_3)_3 + 3NaCl + H_2O = BiOCl + 3NaNO_3 + 2HCl.$$

It differs from the oxychlorides of arsenic and antimony in that it is not decomposed by water ; and from antimony oxychloride in being insoluble in tartaric acid. It has been used as a pigment under the name of " pearl white."

Bismuth nitrate, Bi(NO_3)_3, can be made by the action of nitric acid on bismuth itself, or on the trioxide or carbonate. It is a colourless crystalline deliquescent substance, soluble in water. With a large excess of water, it forms **bismuth subnitrate** which is used in medicine, and was at one time employed as a constituent of face-powder :

$$Bi(NO_3)_3 + H_2O = BiO.NO_3 + 2HNO_3.$$

Bismuth sulphide, Bi_2S_3, occurs native as *bismuth glance* and is formed as a dark brown precipitate when hydrogen sulphide is passed through a solution of a bismuth salt acidified with hydrochloric acid. It differs from the trisulphides of arsenic and antimony is not exhibiting such marked acidic properties ; thus it does not form solutions with alkali hydroxides or hydrosulphide, although it does react to some extent with alkali sulphides.

§ 26 The Elements of Sub-Group VA

Vanadium, V

History

Del Rio, in 1801, expressed the opinion that a Mexican ore which he analysed contained a new metal which he called " erythronium "—from the Greek ἐρυθρός (erythros), red—because it furnished red salts when treated with acids. Del Rio abandoned his opinion when Collet-Descostils, four years later, claimed that the supposed new metal was an impure chromium oxide. In 1830 N. G. Sefström described a new mineral which he found in some Swedish iron ores, and suggested for it the name " vanadium "—from " Vanadis," a Scandinavian goddess. Immediately afterwards, F. Wöhler, 1831, established the identity of Sefström's " vanadium " with Del Rio's " erythronium." F. Wöhler had also found something strange in a Mexican lead ore from Zimapan, before Sefström's announcement, and put it aside for future examination.

J. J. Berzelius, 1831, investigated vanadium, and he appears to have been under the impression that the oxide VO was the metal itself. H. E. Roscoe, in 1867, isolated the metal and established its relationship with the nitrogen family of elements.

Occurrence

Vanadium does not occur free, but is widely distributed in many rocks. The principal ores are *carnotite* (potassium uranyl vanadate), $2U_2O_3.V_2O_5.K_2O.3H_2O$; *patronite*, an impure vanadium sulphide, and *vanadinite*, $Pb_5(VO_4)Cl_3$, which is mined in the Peruvian Andes. The ashes of some Peruvian coals are said to contain up to 48 per cent. of vanadic oxide. Small quantities occur in iron ores, and traces occur in many British fireclays and granitic rocks.

Extraction

For commercial purposes vanadium is not required in the pure metallic state ; most of it is marketed in the form of a ferro-vanadium alloy containing 30 to 40 per cent. of vanadium.

The ores are fused with sodium carbonate and nitrate, and sodium vanadate is formed. This is extracted with water and treated with an ammonium salt, which gives an orange-coloured precipitate of ammonium meta-vanadate, NH_4VO_3. When this salt is heated, more or less impure vanadium pentoxide remains.

The ferro-vanadium is obtained from the pentoxide (or crude vanadates, such as iron vanadate) by reduction of a mixture of the vanadium compound, iron ore or scale, lime or fluorspar and coke in an electric furnace. As an alternative the Goldschmidt thermite process can be used.

Pure vanadium is difficult to obtain even on a small scale on account of the high temperature necessary, and the tendency to re-oxidation. The metal has been obtained by reduction of the pentoxide by the " thermite " method, using *mischmetall* (p. 675) in place of aluminium.

Vanadium forms at least four oxides, viz.,

> Hypovanadous oxide, VO or V_2O_2,
> Vanadous oxide, V_2O_3,
> Hypovanadic oxide, VO_2 or V_2O_4,
> Vanadic oxide (vanadium pentoxide), V_2O_5.

In addition a monoxide V_2O has been reported, though its existence is doubtful.

Hypovanadous oxide, VO or V_2O_5, is made by the reduction of higher oxide, with potassium. It is a black powder which was at one time mistaken for the element. It reacts with acids forming lavender-coloured solutions of hypovanadous salts, from which caustic alkalis precipitate **hypovanadous hydroxide,** $V(OH)_2$, one of the most powerful reducing agents known.

Vanadous oxide, vanadium trioxide, V_2O_3, is made as a black powder by reducing the pentoxide with hydrogen. It burns in air to the pentoxide and only reacts with acids with difficulty. The vanadous salts when obtained are green in solution.

Hypovanadic oxide, V_2O_5, is made by reducing the pentoxide with sulphur dioxide. It is an amphoteric oxide ; thus with alkali hydroxides it forms hypovanadates, e.g., sodium hypovanadate, $Na_2V_4O_9$, while vanadyl salts result with acids, e.g., vanadyl chloride, $VOCl_2$. The vanadyl salts give blue solutions.

Vanadium pentoxide, V_2O_5, results from the oxidation of vanadium compounds in general. It is a yellowish-red powder, sparingly soluble in water, which with alkalis gives rise to a series of vanadates analogous to the phosphates, e.g., Na_3VO_4, $NaVO_3$, $Na_4V_2O_7$.

The basic properties of vanadium oxides become less and less pronounced as the proportion of oxygen increases. The higher oxides exhibit acidic as well as basic properties. The element also forms a series of chlorides : VCl_2, VCl_3, and VCl_1. The existence of VCl_5 is doubtful. There is also a series of vanadyl compounds or oxychlorides—$(VO)_2Cl$, $VOCl$, $VOCl_2$, and $VOCl_3$. Unlike nitrogen and phosphorus, vanadium is undoubtedly a metal. As in the case of phosphorus, the element, if heated to a high temperature, burns to the pentoxide, V_2O_5. The melting point of the metal is about 1710°.

Vanadium is used in making special steels because very small quantities of vanadium modify the properties of steel by increasing the hardness and malleability of the metal. The addition of a half per cent. of vanadium, for instance, raised the tensile strength of a sample of steel from $7\frac{1}{4}$ to 13 tons per square inch.

The high tensile strength and elasticity of vanadium steel has led to its use for motor vehicles, etc.

Vanadium pentoxide is used as a catalyst in the oxidation of naphthalene and in the manufacture of sulphuric acid (modified contact process). Compounds of vanadium are also employed in the manufacture of ink, in dyeing, as accelerators in the drying of paint and varnish, in insecticides, photographic chemicals, therapeutic preparations and in glass manufacture.

History of Niobium and Tantalum

In 1801 C. Hatchett analysed some chromium minerals from Connecticut, and found an earth hitherto unknown. He named the mineral " columbite," after the place of its origin, and the element was designated " columbium " A year later, 1802, A. G. Ekeberg found a new element in some Finnish minerals resembling columbite. To this he gave the name " tantalum," from " Tantalus " of Grecian mythology, in allusion to the " tantalizing " difficulties he encountered in dissolving the mineral in acids. In 1844 H. Rose noticed two new elements in a sample of columbite from Bodenmais : one, tantalum, is similar to Ekeberg's tantalum ; and the other has been called " niobium," from Niobe, the mythological daughter of Tantalus. Hatchett's " columbium " was probably a mixture of both tantalum and niobium. The term " columbium " is often applied to Rose's niobium.

Niobium, Nb, or Columbium, Cb, and Tantalum, Ta

These two elements are found associated in the isomorphous minerals *tantalite*, $Fe(TaO_3)_2$; and columbite or *niobite*, $Fe(NbO_3)_2$. One or both of the elements occur in several rare earths—monazite, and yttrotantalite—and also in tinstone, pitchblende, wolfram, and many other minerals. Niobium forms a mono-, di-, and a penta-oxide ; and tantalum a di- and a penta-oxide. Niobium forms both a tri- and a penta-chloride, while tantalum forms the penta-chloride. Both elements exhibit feeble base-forming qualities, and their chief compounds are the niobates and the tantalates. The elements are produced when the chlorides are reduced in a current of hydrogen. Tantalum forms a series of complex salts with alkaline fluorides. Thus, K_2TaF_7 is formed in rhombic needles when a solution of tantalic acid in hydrofluoric acid is treated with potassium fluoride. The sparing solubility of this salt in hydrofluoric acid enables tantalum to be separated from niobium. Niobium metal melts at about 1950°, tantalum at 2850°.

Tantalum was formerly used for the filaments of electric lamps, but it has now been superseded by tungsten for this purpose. It is used as an electrode in alternating-current rectifiers, and in the manufacture of surgical and dental instruments on account of its resistance to chemical attack, and the hardness of the surface which can be produced by suitable heat treatment.

Protoactinium, Pa

The principal investigations of protoactinium have been connected with its radio-active properties ; and it is discussed from this point of view in Chapter XXXVI. Chemically, it appears to resemble tantalum ; although the pentoxide is slightly basic ; thus it reacts with warm concentrated sulphuric acid ; but is not affected by fused potassium carbonate. In this it resembles its horizontal neighbours in the Periodic Table.

§ 27 The Relationships of the Group V Elements

In this group the relationship between the " typical " elements and the elements of the B sub-group is much more marked than with the A sub-group. This is usual in the later groups of the Periodic Table and is in harmony with present-day views concerning the electronic configurations of the atoms. These configurations are indicated in Tables LIV and LV. From these figures it is evident that the members of the A sub-group are properly regarded as transition elements, since the penultimate electron group is incomplete, and is in process of filling up. On the other hand the elements of the B sub-group have the penultimate group complete. It is also clear that the five elements nitrogen, phosphorus, arsenic, antimony and bismuth are alike in having complete penultimate electron groups, and an identical configuration of the outermost electron group. The close resemblance between vanadium, niobium and tantalum is also indicated, likewise the extent of the resemblances and differences to be anticipated between these three and the other five elements. Thus, as transition elements, they are characterized by very variable valency; the formation of highly coloured ions; they are also paramagnetic, and have marked catalytic power. The variability of valency depends upon the fact that some of the electrons of the incomplete penultimate group can be detached almost as easily as the outermost and, consequently, leads to the expectation that the resemblance to the nitrogen-bismuth series will be mainly confined to the compounds of highest valency (five) in each case.

TABLE LIV.

Element.	Electrons in Orbits.																
	1	2_1	2_2	3_1	3_2	3_3	4_1	4_2	4_3	4_4	5_1	5_2	5_3	6_1	6_2	6_3	7
Vanadium .	2	2	6	2	6	3	2										
Niobium .	2	2	6	2	6	10	2	6	4		1						
Tantalum .	2	2	6	2	6	10	2	6	10	14	2	6	3	2			
Protoactin-ium .	2	2	6	2	6	10	2	6	10	14	2	6	10	2	6	4	1

TABLE LV.

Element.	Electrons in Orbits.														
	1	2_1	2_2	3_1	3_2	3_3	4_1	4_2	4_3	4_4	5_1	5_2	5_3	6_1	6_2
Nitrogen . .	2	2	3												
Phosphorus . .	2	2	6	2	3										
Arsenic . . .	2	2	6	2	6	10	2	3							
Antimony . .	2	2	6	2	6	10	2	6	10		2	3			
Bismuth . . .	2	2	6	2	6	10	2	6	10	14	2	6	10	2	3

Turning now to the general characteristics of the two sections of the group, the properties of nitrogen, phosphorus, arsenic, antimony and bismuth show a gradual transition from the non-metallic nitrogen to the metallic bismuth. The apparent chemical inactivity of nitrogen is in striking contrast with the activity of phosphorus; and the volatility and solubility of the oxides and acids of nitrogen are in similar contrast with the corresponding compounds of phosphorus. The relationship of the physical properties is indicated in Table LVI.

TABLE LVI.—PROPERTIES OF THE NITROGEN-PHOSPHORUS FAMILY.

	Nitrogen.	Phosphorus.	Arsenic.	Antimony.	Bismuth.
Atomic weight	14·008	30·98	74·91	121·76	209
Specific gravity	(solid)1·026	1·82–2·31	4·7–5·7	6·684	9·8
Atomic volume	13·7	about 15	13 to 16	18	21·3
Melting point .	−209·8°	44·1°	[814°]	630·5°	271°
Boiling point .	−195·8°	280°	[615°]	1380°	1450°

The gradual transition of non-metals into metals with increasing atomic weight is brought out very clearly in this family group. The changes in the melting and boiling points are not so regular as the other properties, but this may be related to the fact that phosphorus, arsenic, and antimony have four-atom molecules, whereas bismuth, like nitrogen, has probably a two-atom molecule. The heat of combination of the different elements with hydrogen shows a somewhat similar gradation: NH_3, + 12 Cals.; PH_3, + 4·9 Cals.; AsH_3, − 44·2 Cals.; SbH_3, − 86·8 Cals. Ammonia is a relatively strong base, phosphine a feeble base, while arsine and stibine do not show basic qualities. Hence, as the atomic weight increases, the basicity of the hydride decreases. This is shown by the formation of the ammonium and phosphonium salts, and the non-existence of the arsonium and stibium compounds. The resemblances between nitrogen, phosphorus, arsenic and antimony as foreshadowed by the similarities between their trihydrides is accentuated by a comparison of the compounds $N(C_2H_5)_3$, $P(C_2H_5)_3$, $As(C_2H_5)_3$, $Sb(C_2H_5)_3$, and the analogy becomes still further pronounced in comparing $N(C_2H_5)_4OH$, $P(C_2H_5)_4OH$, $As(C_2H_5)_4OH$, $Sb(C_2H_5)_4OH$, for these bodies are so surprisingly similar that they are almost indistinguishable from one another.

While phosphoric oxide is volatile and stable, the corresponding pentoxides of arsenic, antimony, and bismuth are resolved by heat into the corresponding trioxides and oxygen. Phosphorus pentoxide yields a whole series of polybasic acids, but nitrogen pentoxide gives but one monobasic acid, HNO_3; the corresponding salts are also in strong contrast, for the nitrates are nearly all soluble in water, while the normal, pyro-, and metaphosphates are nearly always sparingly soluble. Similarly with the trioxides, strict analogy is absent. The oxy-acids diminish in strength during the passage from nitric to phosphoric, to arsenic, to antimonic, to bismuthic acid. The acidic properties of the oxides likewise diminish from the strongly acid nitrogen and phosphorus acids to the feebly acidic oxides of arsenic.

antimony and bismuth. The basic property first appears with arsenic and becomes stronger during the passage to antimony and to bismuth. The trichloride of nitrogen is very unstable, while with bismuth the trichloride is quite stable. The boiling points of the trichlorides increase with increasing atomic weights of the elements, thus : NCl_3 boils at 70° ; PCl_3, 73·5° ; $AsCl_3$, 123° ; $SbCl_3$, 220·2° ; and $BiCl_3$, at 447°. The halogen compounds of nitrogen and phosphorus are completely hydrolyzed by water ; arsenic trichloride is also hydrolyzed by water, but it can exist in solution in the presence of hydrochloric acid. Antimony and bismuth halides are incompletely hydrolyzed by water.

In contrast with many of the foregoing properties, the elements of the A sub-group have high melting and boiling points (see Table LVII); are extremely difficult to reduce from their oxides and are all typical metals both in appearance and behaviour. Further, they do not form hydrides. In contrast, the elements of both groups form

TABLE LVII.—PROPERTIES OF THE VANADIUM FAMILY.

	Vanadium.	Columbium, or Niobium.	Tantalum.
Atomic weight .	50·95	92·91	180·88
Colour . . .	Silvery metal	Steel grey metal	Iron grey metal
Specific gravity .	5·96	8·4	16·6
Atomic volume .	9·3	13·3	23
Melting point . .	1710°	1950°	2850°

pentoxides which are acidic. Strongly so in the light elements, becoming less so with increasing atomic number and atomic weight, until bismuth pentoxide is only just acidic.

Thus, in general, the resemblance between the A and B sub-groups, which becomes steadily more marked in passing across the Periodic Table from Group I to Group IV, becomes less so in Group V ; and this reversal of tendency will be seen to continue in proceeding to Groups VI and VII where the resemblance becomes still less noticeable.

CHAPTER XXXII

SELENIUM AND TELLURIUM

§ 1 Group VIB of the Periodic Table

GROUP VI comprises the elements oxygen and sulphur, together with chromium, tungsten, molybdenum and uranium on the one hand ; and selenium and tellurium on the other. (The radio-element polonium also belongs to this subgroup ; but so far it has been obtained in such minute quantities that its chemical and physical properties have hardly been studied. Its radio-active properties are mentioned in Chapter XXXVI.) Here, as is usual in the later part of the Periodic Table, the elements in the short periods are more closely related to the B sub-group than to the A, and so it is found that sulphur, selenium and tellurium form a well-defined family.

Sulphur forms a link between oxygen and selenium and tellurium, but it resembles the former less than the latter elements. Oxygen has been discussed in Chapter XVIII, and sulphur in Chapter XXII. The relationships of Group VI as a whole are described at the end of Chapter XXXIII.

§ 2 Selenium, Se

Selenium is a rather uncommon element, although small quantities are often found associated with sulphur and sulphides, e.g., pyrites. Hence, it is found in the " flue dust " of the pyrites burners in the manufacture of sulphuric acid. It was discovered by J. J. Berzelius, in 1817, and named from the Greek σελήνη (selene), the moon, owing to its resemblance to tellurium, which had been discovered a few years before, and named after the earth (see below).

The principal source of selenium is now the anode mud obtained in the electrolytic refining of copper (p. 584). This mud is roasted in air, which causes the selenium dioxide formed to be volatilized off. It is then dissolved in hydrochloric acid and reduced with sulphur dioxide which causes the precipitation of selenium. A little selenium remains unoxidized after the roasting, and is recovered, along with tellurium (see below), by heating the residue with sodium hydroxide and nitrate, whereby sodium selenite and tellurite are formed. These are extracted with water, and the solution acidified, so causing the precipitation of tellurium dioxide. This is removed and selenium precipitated with sulphur dioxide as before.

Selenium shows considerable resemblance to sulphur, and, like it, exists in several allotropic forms. The most stable form is a grey crystalline variety ; there are also several orange or red crystalline modifications, and at least two amorphous forms.

One of the most interesting properties of selenium is the increase in its electrical conductivity on exposure to light and vice versa—discovered by W. Smith in 1873. The change is proportional to the intensity ·of the light, and red and orange light are the most active. It was formerly supposed that the phenomenon depended upon the change from a feebly conducting to a good conducting allotropic form of selenium ; but it is now thought to be due to the light causing emission of electrons, thus bringing about increase in conductivity. This behaviour has been made use of in various optical and electrical appliances such as telephotography, photometry and detecting devices.

Selenium is mainly used in the glass industry for neutralizing the green tinge of ordinary glass, and for making ruby glass, and in the manufacture of red pigments for enamelled iron. It is also being used in increasing amounts in the rubber industry and in the preparation of pigments and paints. Certain organic derivatives are employed as photographic sensitizers and in froth flotation processes.

Selenium hydride is a gas of obnoxious odour made by the action of dilute hydrochloric acid on ferrous selenide. It resembles hydrogen sulphide, but is more poisonous, and less stable. It is soluble in water, burns in air to selenium dioxide and water, and acts with solutions of metallic salts in a similar manner to hydrogen sulphide.

Selenium dioxide, SeO_2, is formed when selenium burns in dry oxygen, and by evaporating a solution of selenious acid prepared as described below :

$$H_2SeO_3 = SeO_2 + H_2O.$$

It is a white crystalline solid, which sublimes at 300°, and combines with water forming selenious acid. It is used as an oxidizing agent in organic chemistry.

Selenium trioxide, SeO_3, has only recently been prepared (Rheinboldt, Hessel and Schwenzer, 1930). It was obtained by the action of oxygen on selenium under the influence of a high frequency discharge. It is a white, very hygroscopic solid.

Selenious acid, H_2SeO_3, is made by the action of nitric acid on selenium :

$$Se + 4HNO_3 = H_2SeO_3 + H_2O + 4NO_2.$$

It is a colourless, crystalline solid, soluble in water ; the solution resembles sulphurous acid. It decomposes on heating, and is readily reduced to selenium, e.g., by sulphur dioxide. On oxidation, for example, by chlorine or bromine, selenic acid is formed.

Selenic acid, H_2SeO_4, is made by oxidation of aqueous selenious acid by means of chlorine :

$$H_2SeO_3 + Cl_2 + H_2O = H_2SeO_4 + 2HCl.$$

On cautious evaporation of the solution, crystals of the acid can be obtained. It resembles sulphuric acid in many respects, particularly in its vigorous action with water. It is, however, a weaker acid than sulphuric, and is much more readily decomposed by heat, passing at temperatures much below its boiling point into selenium dioxide and oxygen :

$$2H_2SeO_4 = 2H_2O + 2SeO_2 + O_2.$$

The selenates are very similar to the sulphates, with which they are isomorphous.

Selenium forms compounds of the type SeX_4 with fluorine, chlorine and bromine ; it also forms a very stable hexafluoride, but no compounds of selenium and iodine are known.

§ 3 Tellurium, Te

Tellurium, like selenium, is not a plentiful element, although it is widely distributed in small amounts. It occurs as tellurides such as *tetradymite*, Bi_2Te_3, and, with selenium, is found in the anode mud from electrolytic copper refining. This is the principal source of tellurium. It is obtained from the mud as tellurium dioxide, as described under selenium, and is reduced to the element by roasting with coal or charcoal, or by passing sulphur dioxide into its solution in hydrochloric acid. It can also be made from tetradymite by fusion with sodium carbonate, followed by oxidation of the sodium telluride thus formed by passing air through its aqueous solution :

$$Bi_2Te_3 + 3Na_2CO_3 = Bi_2O_3 + 3CO_2 + 3Na_2Te,$$

$$2Na_2Te + O_2 + 2H_2O = 4NaOH + 2Te.$$

Tellurium was discovered in 1782 by Muller von Reichenstein, and named by Klaproth in 1798 from the Latin *tellus*, the earth. It exists in at least two allotropic forms. The stable form is a grey, crystalline solid with a metallic lustre ; the other form is amorphous. Tellurium resembles both sulphur and selenium in chemical properties, but the hydride is even more unstable than hydrogen selenide and the dioxide is amphoteric. It burns in air to the dioxide, and is attacked by chlorine. It is unaffected by acids which are not oxidizing agents ; nitric and sulphuric acids oxidize it.

The addition of tellurium to lead has been suggested, since it increases its resistance to chemical attack, and improves its tensile strength. It has also been used for electroplating silver for the production of a dark finish.

Atomic Weight of Tellurium

From the time when Mendeléef first enunciated the Periodic Law until Moseley's work on atomic numbers, the atomic weights of iodine and tellurium occasioned difficulty. For all determinations of these quantities resulted in values for tellurium higher than those for iodine. These, if followed in drawing up the Periodic Table, would require iodine to come before tellurium, and thus put these two elements in obviously unsuitable places ; iodine with sulphur and selenium, and tellurium with the halogens. Mendeléef himself rightly reversed this order, but predicted that further investigation would show one or both of these atomic weights to be wrong. This prediction has not been fulfilled ; the values at present recommended by the International Committee being 127·61 for tellurium (based on some sixty sets of experiments, particularly those of Hönigschmid) and 126·92 for iodine. The true explanation of these facts was furnished by the work of Moseley, who showed that the position of an element in the Periodic Table is determined by its atomic *number* and not by its atomic weight ; and of Aston who found that tellurium consists of several isotopes of masses 122, 123, 124, 125, 126, 128 and 130, the last two being present in by far the largest proportion, thus giving tellurium an atomic weight substantially greater than that of iodine which is a " pure " element of mass 127. (See also Chapter IX, pp. 133–138.)

Hydrogen telluride, H_2Te, is obtained by the action of dilute hydrochloric acid upon zinc or magnesium telluride :

$$MgTe + 2HCl = MgCl_2 + H_2Te.$$

It is usually contaminated with hydrogen when prepared in this way ; it can be purified by condensation in a freezing mixture, since it boils at $-1·8°$. It is a colourless gas, with an evil smell ; it is even more unstable than hydrogen selenide, decomposing at ordinary temperatures on exposure to light. In the main it resembles hydrogen selenide.

Tellurium dioxide, TeO_2, is obtained, like selenium dioxide, by burning the element in air or oxygen, or by oxidation with nitric acid. It is a colourless solid, very sparingly soluble in water and the solution is neutral to litmus. It reacts with alkali hydroxide solutions forming solutions of *tellurites* ; it also exhibits feeble basic properties forming, for example, a basic nitrate, $2TeO_2.HNO_3$.

Tellurium trioxide, TeO_3, is obtained as an orange-yellow powder by heating telluric acid to dull redness. It is insoluble in water, with which it does not re-combine to form telluric acid.

Telluric acid, H_6TeO_6, is formed by dissolving tellurium in a mixture of nitric and hydrochloric acids, which yields tellurous acid ; and then oxidizing by adding chloric acid in small portions. The resulting solution is evaporated *in vacuo*, when the acid crystallizes out and may be recrystallized from water. It is a colourless crystalline solid of the composition H_6TeO_6 and was formerly considered to be the hydrate $H_2TeO_4.2H_2O$. It is now believed to be not a hydrate, but the true ortho-acid H_6TeO_6, a belief which is confirmed by the preparation of the compound Ca_3TeO_6, and by the molecular weight of the acid in solution. It is a very weak acid, which differs considerably from sulphuric acid. It is reduced to tellurium by sulphur dioxide.

The tellurates somewhat resemble the selenates, but, unlike them, are not isomorphous with the sulphates, and do not form alums.

Tellurium forms halides of the type TeX_4 with all four halogens ; in addition a hexafluoride TeF_6 is known, and the dihalides $TeCl_2$ and $TeBr_2$ have been reported.

CHAPTER XXXIII

CHROMIUM, MOLYBDENUM, TUNGSTEN AND URANIUM

§ 1 Sub-Group VIA of the Periodic Table

THIS sub-group comprises the four elements chromium, molybdenum, tungsten and uranium, which exhibit among themselves a considerable amount of resemblance in their properties, and to a lesser extent justify classification along with the elements of Group VIB. As in Group VA, there are important horizontal relationships.

§ 2 Chromium, Cr. History, Occurrence and Extraction

History

In 1762 J. G. Legmann, in a letter to the naturalist G. L. L. de Buffon, described a new mineral from Siberia. We now know this mineral to be crocoisite, or lead chromate. Both L. N. Vauquelin and Macquart, in 1789, failed to recognize in the mineral a new element, and both reported lead, iron, alumina, and a large amount of oxygen. However, in 1797, L. N. Vauquelin re-examined the mineral and concluded that the lead must be combined with a peculiar acid which he considered to be the oxide of a new metal. This he called chromium —from the Greek $\chi\rho\hat{\omega}\mu\alpha$ (chroma), colour—because its compounds are all coloured. In 1798 L. N. Vauquelin detected the new element in spinel and in smaragdite, and F. Tassaert found chromium in chrome iron ore in 1799.

Occurrence

Metallic chromium does not occur free in nature. It occurs combined with oxygen in *chrome ochre*, which is chromium sesquioxide, Cr_2O_3, associated with more or less earthy matters. *Chromite*, $Fe(CrO_2)_2$, is the chief ore of chromium. It also occurs as lead chromate in *crocoite* or *crocoisite*, $PbCrO_4$. Traces occur in many minerals—emerald, jade, serpentine, etc.

Extraction of Metallic Chromium

The principal source of chromium is chrome iron ore. Chromium comes on to the market principally as sodium or potassium chromate and dichromate, made from the ore, as described on page 774.

Metallic chromium is made in two ways, according to the purpose for which it is required. If the metal is required in bulk, it is made by the " thermite " process (compare p. 665) ; if it is required in the form of chromium plating it is obtained by electrolysis.

For the former process an intimate mixture of chromium sesquioxide and aluminium powder is placed in a refractory clay crucible. A mixture of sodium or barium peroxide and aluminium powder is placed over this ; a piece of magnesium ribbon is stuck into the latter mixture and a layer of powdered fluorspar placed over all.   The crucible is embedded in sand and the magnesium ribbon ignited.   When the flame reaches the peroxide mixture, .the aluminium is oxidized with explosive violence ; the heat of combustion of the aluminium in this ignition mixture starts the reaction between the chromic oxide and aluminium, and it rapidly spreads through the whole mass.   The chromium formed is melted and sinks to the bottom of the crucible, and the alumina forms a slag of artificial corundum :

$$2Al + Cr_2O_3 = 2Cr + Al_2O_3.$$

For chromium plating the conditions require careful control, although the exact details vary somewhat in different works.   The baths used always contain chromium in both the sexivalent and ter-valent conditions, e.g., chromium trioxide (250 gms. per litre) and chromium sulphate (3 gms. per litre), using a lead anode.   Small quantities of other sulphates, such as cobalt, nickel, zinc or cadmium, are sometimes added, as these improve the " throwing-power " of the bath ; and a temperature of 40° is often employed as this results in the formation of a very hard, coherent deposit.   In plating iron it is usual to put on a layer of copper or nickel before the chromium.

§ 3 Properties, Uses and Atomic Weight of Chromium

Chromium is a bluish-white metal, capable of taking a very high polish.   It is extremely hard, being harder than iridium and steel. It has a high melting point, 1830°.   Under ordinary conditions it is stable in air, but it is superficially oxidized when heated in air or oxygen.   It retains a brilliant finish when exposed to all normal atmospheric corroding agents, including rain, snow and sea-water, hydrogen sulphide, sulphur dioxide and sulphur compounds generally. It is slowly attacked by dilute hydrochloric and sulphuric acids, forming chromous salts and hydrogen :

$$Cr + 2HCl = CrCl_2 + H_2.$$

Concentrated sulphuric acid attacks it, yielding sulphur dioxide and chromic sulphate.   When placed in contact with nitric acid, chromium becomes inert or *passive* : it is no longer attacked by acids which dissolve it under normal conditions.   This phenomenon is further considered under iron (p. 812).

Uses

The most important use of chromium is probably the production of special steels.   It is added to the steel in the form of an alloy with iron known as *ferrochrome* (containing 40 to 80 per cent. of chromium) made either by the aluminothermic processs, or by reducing a mixture of iron and chromium oxides with carbon in an electric furnace. *Stainless steel* consists of an alloy of approximately 84 per cent. of iron, 13 per cent. of chromium and 1 per cent. of nickel. A chrome-steel with 1 to $1\frac{1}{2}$ per cent. of carbon and $2\frac{1}{2}$ to 4 per cent. of chromium is so hard that it cannot be worked by ordinary hardened tool-steels so that it is drill-proof. It is used in the manufacture of burglar-proof safes, stamp-mill shoes, railway couplings, etc. Chrome-vanadium steel is very hard and strong, and is now being used for gears, springs, axle-shafts, locomotive wheels, etc. It has the very valuable property that its characteristics can be varied to a surprising extent by heat treatment. Chrome-nickel steels are used for armour plates; and chrome-tungsten and chrome-molybdenum steels are used for high-speed tools.

Nichrome is an important alloy, containing approximately 11 to 25 per cent. of chromium, and 50 to 70 per cent. of nickel (the rest usually being iron) which is remarkably resistant to atmospheric corrosion, even at high temperatures. It is hence used for the windings of electric fires and for similar purposes. *Stellite*, an alloy of chromium, cobalt, and tungsten is used for surgical instruments, and some motor-car parts. It has also been suggested for the manufacture of tools, and possesses remarkable resistance to corrosion.

Chromium is now widely used as a plating metal on account of its remarkable resistance to corrosion, and the high protective power of thin layers.

Of chromium compounds, chromite is used in making the hearths of steel furnaces since it can be used as a neutral refractory material between the basic (magnesian) bricks in the interior of the furnace, and the acidic (siliceous) bricks outside. Chromite bricks are not injured by contact with basic, nor with acid bricks; whereas acidic and basic bricks, when heated in contact with one another, are likely to fuse at the surfaces of contact owing to the formation of fusible silicates. The bricks are very refractory—softening between 2000° and 2100°—and do not crack by sudden heating and cooling.

Potassium and sodium chromates are used in dyeing; in the manufacture of pigments (chrome yellow, chrome red, Guignet's green, etc.); in tanning leather, etc.

Chromium salts are also used as colouring agents in the manufacture of glass and pottery, and are used as mordants in dyeing.

Atomic Weight

The atomic weight of chromium is seen to be in the neighbourhood of 52 from the vapour densities of volatile compounds, such as chromyl chloride and the value of its specific heat (0·12).

The most accurate experimental determinations of the combining weight have been made by preparing pure silver chromate and di-chromate, followed by reduction with sulphur dioxide and in other ways, and the precipitation of the silver, as silver chloride, with all possible precautions. In this way, Baxter obtained the value 52·01 for the atomic weight of chromium and this is that at present recommended by the International Committee.

§ 4 Oxides and Hydroxides of Chromium

Chromium forms three well-defined oxides, viz. :

Chromous oxide, CrO,
Chromium sesquioxide or chromic oxide, Cr_2O_3,
Chromium trioxide, CrO_3.

In addition, several oxides intermediate between the sesquioxide and the trioxide have been reported, and regarded as chromium chromates (e.g., Cr_3O_6 or $Cr_2O_3.CrO_3$), but their individual existence is somewhat doubtful.

Chromous oxide, CrO, is obtained as a black powder by warming chromium amalgam with dilute nitric acid. It is not attacked by nitric acid, but reacts with dilute sulphuric and hydrochloric acids. It is reduced by hydrogen at 1000°, whereas chromic oxide is not affected by hydrogen at 1300°.

Chromous hydroxide, $Cr(OH)_2$, is obtained by the action of alkali hydroxide solutions on solutions of chromous salts. It is a yellowish-brown precipitate which rapidly oxidizes in air, and which decomposes, on heating, into chromic oxide, hydrogen and water :

$$2Cr(OH)_2 = Cr_2O_3 + H_2 + H_2O.$$

Chromium Sesquioxide, Chromic Oxide, Cr_2O_3

This oxide is obtained when chromic hydroxide is heated, and also when ammonium dichromate, or a mixture of potassium dichromate and ammonium chloride, is treated similarly :

$$(NH_4)_2Cr_2O_7 = Cr_2O_3 + N_2 + 4H_2O,$$

$$2NH_4Cl + K_2Cr_2O_7 = Cr_2O_3 + N_2 + 4H_2O + 2KCl.$$

In the latter case, the green residue is washed with water till free from potassium chloride, and dried.

Chromic oxide is a green powder, which is used as a pigment. Thus, *Guignet's green*, for instance, is made by calcining potassium dichromate with boric acid, etc. Chromic sesquioxide, in an extremely fine state of subdivision, appears to be crimson, for if an intimate mixture of stannic oxide, or zinc oxide, or alumina, with a very small proportion of chromic oxide, be heated to a high temperature in an oxidizing atmosphere a red powder is obtained. There is some evidence to show that the red colour is not due to the formation of a chemical compound, and that the " chrome-tin " colour is related to purple of Cassius (q.v.). The " chrome-tin " crimson is used for colouring pottery, glazes, etc.

Chromic oxide is a basic oxide, and forms salts with acids. When, however, it has been calcined at a high temperature it only dissolves in acids very slowly. It also appears to exhibit acidic properties, for, when fused with alkalis, it forms *chromites*, and if air be allowed access or an oxidizing agent such as potassium chlorate be present, yellow chromates result :

$$Cr_2O_3 + 2NaOH = 2NaCrO_2 + H_2O,$$
$$2Cr_2O_3 + 8NaOH + 3O_2 = 4Na_2CrO_4 + 4H_2O.$$

It is thus an amphoteric oxide.

Chromic hydroxide, $Cr(OH)_3$, separates as a bluish-green, gelatinous precipitate when ammonia or alkali hydroxide solution is added to a green chromic salt. When freshly precipitated, it reacts readily with acids forming chromic salts ; but after standing for some time in contact with dilute alkali, its properties change and it then only reacts with difficulty. Another variety, probably a hydrated form, results when alkali is added to solutions of violet chromic salts. Similarly, when freshly precipitated, chromic hydroxide goes into solution in alkali hydroxide solution, possibly with the formation of chromites ; although it has been suggested that these are solutions of colloidal chromium hydroxide. On heating, chromium hydroxide loses water and chromic oxide remains. In presence of alkali solutions, chromic hydroxide is readily oxidized to chromates by chlorine or bromine.

Chromium trioxide, CrO_3, is obtained in long, scarlet, needle-like crystals when a concentrated solution of potassium dichromate is treated with concentrated sulphuric acid and cooled :

$$K_2Cr_2O_7 + H_2SO_4 = K_2SO_4 + H_2O + 2CrO_3.$$

The crystals are filtered on glass wool, washed with concentrated nitric acid to remove sulphates and sulphuric acid, and dried in a current of warm air.

Chromium trioxide forms deep red, very deliquescent, prismatic needles. It can be volatilized at about 110° and melts at 190° with some decomposition. When heated to 250°, it rapidly decomposes into chromic oxide and oxygen :

$$4CrO_3 = 2Cr_2O_3 + 3O_2.$$

It is soluble in water, and the solution probably contains several of the polychromic acids (see below).

Chromium trioxide is a vigorous oxidizing agent owing to the readiness with which it seems to part with oxygen to form chromic oxide, Cr_2O_3. Thus, alcohol dropped on to the oxide takes fire ; when ammonia gas impinges on the crystals, the reduction takes place with incandescence, paper is charred at once ; carbonaceous matter is oxidized to carbon dioxide.

Polychromic Acids

The solution of chromium trioxide in water is strongly acid and deep orange-red in colour, and probably contains several *condensed* chromic acids, e.g., dichromic acid, $H_2Cr_2O_7$; trichromic acid, $H_2Cr_3O_{10}$; and tetrachromic acid, $H_2Cr_4O_{13}$. The chromate ion, CrO_4'', is apparently not stable in presence of acid (or hydrogen ion).

Salts corresponding to these acids are known. Thus potassium dichromate (described below) is the most important compound of chromium; by treating it with chromium trioxide, **potassium trichromate** is formed; and by treating the trichromate with concentrated nitric acid, **potassium tetrachromate** results. These polychromates can be crystallized out. These salts, and the polychromic acids from which they are derived, result from the condensation of two, three or four molecules of chromic acid, with elimination of water, thus:

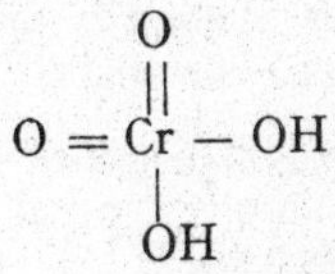

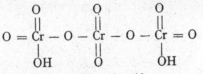

$$O = \overset{\overset{\textstyle O}{\|}}{Cr} - OH \qquad\qquad O = \overset{\overset{\textstyle O}{\|}}{Cr} - O - \overset{\overset{\textstyle O}{\|}}{Cr} = O$$
$$\underset{\textstyle OH}{|} \qquad\qquad\qquad \underset{\textstyle OH}{|} \qquad\quad \underset{\textstyle OH}{|}$$

chromic acid 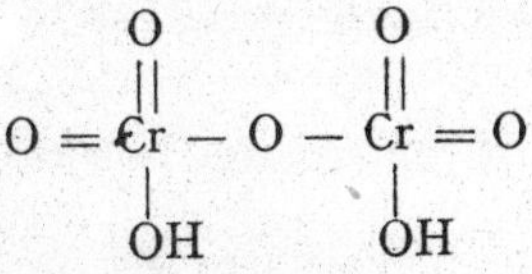　　　　　　　dichromic acid

$$O = \overset{\overset{\textstyle O}{\|}}{Cr} - O - \overset{\overset{\textstyle O}{\|}}{Cr} - O - \overset{\overset{\textstyle O}{\|}}{Cr} = O$$

trichromic acid

$$O = \overset{\overset{\textstyle O}{\|}}{Cr} - O - \overset{\overset{\textstyle O}{\|}}{Cr} - O - \overset{\overset{\textstyle O}{\|}}{Cr} - O - \overset{\overset{\textstyle O}{\|}}{Cr} = O$$

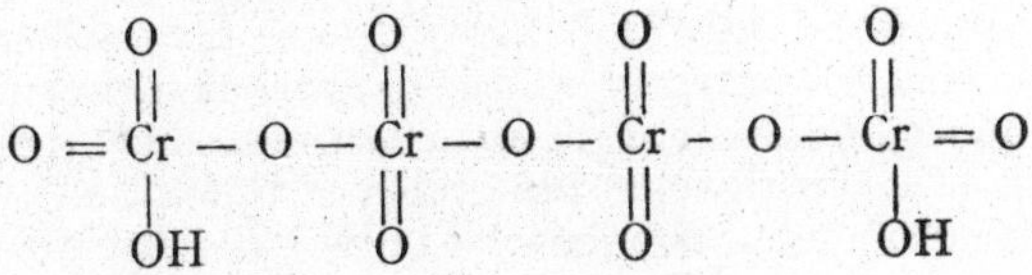

tetrachromic acid

The addition of alkali to any of these polychromates reconverts them into normal chromates; water hydrolyzes them to dichromates. This phenomenon of condensation occurs with a number of oxyacids, e.g., boric iodic and phosphoric acids, and particularly with molybdic and tungstic acids (pp. 780 and 782).

Potassium Chromate and dichromate are the most important compounds of chromium, and are manufactured from chrome iron ore. The ore is finely ground and mixed with calcium carbonate, and then roasted in an oxidizing atmosphere. The roasted mass is then mixed with water, when the ferric oxide remains behind and calcium chromate passes into solution. The reactions which take place are probably:

$$Fe(CrO_2)_2 + CaCO_3 = Ca(CrO_2)_2 + FeO + CO_2,$$
$$2Ca(CrO_2)_2 + 2CaCO_3 + 3O_2 = 4CaCrO_4 + 2CO_2,$$
$$4FeO + O_2 = 2Fe_2O_3.$$

The calcium chromate solution is mixed with potassium carbonate and the solution of potassium chromate which results separated from the chalk which is precipitated. The solution is then allowed to crystallize.

Potassium chromate, K_2CrO_4, is thus obtained in lemon-yellow crystals which are isomorphous with those of potassium sulphate. It is very soluble in water (100 grams of water dissolve 60 grams at 10°) and is stable in the absence of reducing agents, which convert it into chromic hydroxide or oxide. Acids convert chromates into dichromates ; a change which is accompanied by a change in colour of the solution from yellow to orange. This change is reversible in the sense that alkalis convert dichromates into chromates.

Sodium chromate, $Na_2CrO_4.10H_2O$, closely resembles the potassium salt, and is made by using sodium carbonate instead of potassium carbonate in the above process. It is deliquescent.

Sodium dichromate, $Na_2Cr_2O_7.2H_2O$, is made commercially by the addition of sulphuric acid to a solution of sodium chromate :

$$2Na_2CrO_4 + H_2SO_4 = Na_2Cr_2O_7 + Na_2SO_4 + H_2O.$$

Sodium sulphate crystallizes out (with $10H_2O$) and the clear solution is decanted off, and evaporated in iron pans. When it has attained a specific gravity of 1·7, it is filtered from the further crop of sodium sulphate which has separated, and then allowed to cool. Crystals of sodium dichromate separate on standing. This salt is made on a large scale and is preferred to the potassium compound for many purposes, both on account of its cheapness and greater solubility (100 grams of water dissolve 109 grams of the salt at 15°), but it has the drawback of being deliquescent. Its chemical properties closely resemble those of potassium dichromate.

Potassium dichromate, $K_2Cr_2O_7$, is made by mixing concentrated solutions of sodium dichromate and potassium chloride when the less soluble potassium dichromate separates out :

$$Na_2Cr_2O_7 + 2KCl = K_2Cr_2O_7 + 2NaCl.$$

Potassium dichromate forms large red triclinic crystals, which melt at 398°. It is moderately soluble in cold water (100 grams of water dissolve 10 grams of the salt at 15°) and easily soluble in hot water (100 grams of water dissolve about 100 grams at 100°). It is thus readily purified by recrystallization from water.

Potassium dichromate is an important oxidizing agent ; and its solutions are used for this purpose in volumetric analysis. In acid solution, one molecule of potassium dichromate will furnish three atoms (i.e., *six equivalents*) of available oxygen, as indicated in the equation :

$$K_2Cr_2O_7 + 4H_2SO_4 = K_2SO_4 + Cr_2(SO_4)_3 + 4HO + 3O.$$

It will thus oxidize six atoms (or six equivalents) of ferrous iron :

$$K_2Cr_2O_7 + 7H_2SO_4 + 6FeSO_4$$
$$= 3Fe_2(SO_4)_3 + Cr_2(SO_4)_3 + K_2SO_4 + 7H_2O,$$

or three molecules (six equivalents) of sulphur dioxide :

$$K_2Cr_2O_7 + H_2SO_4 + 3SO_2 = Cr_2(SO_4)_3 + K_2SO_4 + H_2O.$$

Potassium dichromate will also oxidize the halogen acids to the free halogens, and is used as an oxidizing agent in organic chemistry.

Ammonium dichromate, $(NH_4)_2Cr_2O_7$, is formed when aqueous solutions of ammonia and chromic acid are mixed. When the solid is heated, nitrogen, water, and a voluminous mass of chromic oxide (resembling green tea) are obtained :

$$(NH_4)_2Cr_2O_7 = Cr_2O_3 + 4H_2O + N_2 \uparrow.$$

Chromyl Chloride, CrO_2Cl_2

When potassium dichromate, a soluble chloride and strong sulphuric acid are heated in a retort, chromyl chloride, an acid chloride, analogous to sulphuryl chloride distils over. The most satisfactory method of preparation is that due to H. D. Law and F. Mollwo Perkin. Chromic acid is dissolved in rather more than the equivalent quantity of concentrated hydrochloric acid, and concentrated sulphuric acid is added in small quantities, the mixture being cooled after each addition. After standing the lower layer of chromyl chloride is run off by means of a tap funnel. Chromyl chloride is a deep-red liquid which boils at $116 \cdot 7°$, and which is hydrolyzed by water into hydrochloric and chromic acids. These reactions are used as a test for chlorides since neither bromides nor iodides form similar compounds. Consequently, if a mixture suspected of containing a chloride be distilled with sulphuric acid and potassium dichromate, and a deep red distillate results which with water gives a solution which responds to the tests for chromic acid, the presence of chlorides may be inferred.

When a solution of potassium dichromate in hydrochloric acid is allowed to crystallize, yellowish red crystals of **potassium chlorochromate** ($KCrO_3Cl$ or $KO.CrO_2Cl$) are formed. This is derived from the unknown *chlorochromic acid*, which is constituted analogously to chlorosulphonic acid. It decomposes on heating into potassium dichromate, chromic oxide, chlorine and oxygen :

$$4KCrO_3Cl = K_2Cr_2O_7 + Cr_2O_3 + 2KCl + Cl_2 + O_2.$$

§ 5 Chromous Salts

Chromium forms two series of salts in which the element behaves as a basic metal, derived respectively from chromous and chromic oxides.

The chromous salts are blue in colour, or give blue solutions, and are powerful reducing agents. They are rapidly oxidized on exposure to the air, forming chromic salts.

Chromous chloride, $CrCl_2$, is made by heating chromic chloride in a current of hydrogen. As thus prepared it is a white, crystalline compound. It dissolves in water forming a blue solution ; in solution, chromous chloride can also be made by reducing chromic chloride by means of zinc and hydrochloric acid.

Chromous sulphate, $CrSO_4.7H_2O$, is obtained in blue crystals, isomorphous with ferrous sulphate, by dissolving chromium, or chromous acetate in dilute sulphuric acid and cooling the solution.

Chromous acetate, $Cr(C_2H_3O_2)_2$, can be obtained by adding a strong solution of chromous chloride (made as above by reduction of chromic chloride with zinc and hydrochloric acid) to a saturated solution of sodium acetate. It is then precipitated in red crystals which can be filtered off and dried *in vacuo*. It is fairly stable, and may be used for the preparation of other chromous salts.

§ 6 Chromic Salts

The chromic salts are derived from chromic oxide (or hydroxide) and while in some respects they exhibit the properties to be expected of the salts of a trivalent radical, and thus resemble the corresponding derivatives of aluminium and iron, they show also some marked peculiarities.

Thus, most of them exist in at least two forms, a violet form and a green form ; and some are found in three varieties. Further, in the green forms they are found to be only partly ionized, and some are known which are not ionized at all.

The explanation of these facts has been suggested by Werner to be similar to that put forward by him to account for the existence and properties of the remarkable complex compounds which chromium, platinum and other transitional metals form with ammonia, cyanides, etc. These, and Werner's theory of their constitution, are discussed in Chapter XXXV (p. 841).

Chromic Chloride, $CrCl_3$

The anhydrous salt is made by passing chlorine over either chromium metal, or a mixture of chromic oxide and carbon heated to redness :

$$Cr_2O_3 + 3C + 3Cl_2 = 2CrCl_3 + 3CO.$$

It is also obtained by the action of sulphur chloride vapour on chromic oxide :

$$6S_2Cl_2 + 2Cr_2O_3 = 4CrCl_3 + 3SO_2 + 9S.$$

It is a pinkish-violet solid, which is virtually insoluble in water, unless a mere trace of a chromous salt be present, when it dissolves easily.

Three crystalline hydrates are known, all having the empirical composition $CrCl_3.6H_2O$. Two of these are green and are known as the α- and γ-salts, and one is violet (the β-salt).

The violet β-salt is made by passing hydrogen chloride into a saturated solution of the oxide in hydrochloric acid at a low temperature (under 10°) ; at a higher temperature the violet solution becomes green, and when saturated with hydrogen chloride deposits green rhombic crystals of the α-salt. The other green salt—the γ-salt—is obtained by treating the mother liquor from the violet crystals with ether, saturated with hydrogen chloride. These three salts are remarkable in that when freshly-prepared solutions are treated with silver nitrate, with the α-salt one-third of the total chlorine present is precipitated as silver chloride ; with the γ-salt two-thirds, and with the violet β-salt the whole is precipitated. Werner symbolizes these results in the formulae :

Green α-salt $[Cr(H_2O)_4Cl_2]Cl.2H_2O$,

Green γ-salt $[Cr(H_2O)_5Cl]Cl_2.H_2O$,

Violet β-salt $[Cr(H_2O)_6]Cl_3$.

In these formulae, the atoms or molecules inside the square brackets are believed to be attached to the chromium atom by covalent or co-ordinate links and are therefore non-ionizable, while those outside the brackets are attached by electrovalent and hence ionizable valencies. (Compare pp. 146 and 841.)

The violet β-salt is practically insoluble in water unless a trace of chromous chloride be present.

Chromic sulphide, Cr_2S_3, is not obtained when hydrogen sulphide is passed into a solution of a chromic salt, as it is completely hydrolyzed and the hydroxide is precipitated. It is made by heating chromic oxide to redness in a stream of hydrogen sulphide. It is a brownish-black amorphous powder.

Chromic sulphate, $Cr_2(SO_4)_3$

The anhydrous salt is obtained in bluish-red crystals by dehydration of a hydrate in air at 400° or in a stream of carbon dioxide at about 300°. It is insoluble in water and acids.

Chromic sulphate forms a variety of hydrates containing varying amounts of water ; both green and violet forms are known ; and the different varieties have varying proportions of their sulphate radicals precipitated by barium chloride.

A violet sulphate, which behaves normally with barium chloride, is obtained by dissolving chromic hydroxide in the calculated quantity of warm sulphuric acid and allowing the green solution which results to stand for a week. It then becomes bluish-violet in colour and deposits violet crystals, said to have the composition $Cr_2(SO_4)_3.18H_2O$.

Alternatively, a green hexahydrate, sometimes known as *Recoura's sulphate*, which is obtained by saturating chromic acid solution at $-4°$ with sulphur dioxide, gives, when freshly prepared, a solution which forms no precipitate with barium chloride. Another green hydrate, containing ten molecules of water, obtained when the green solution formed by reducing chromic acid with sulphur dioxide at 0° and evaporating *in vacuo*, has one-third of its " sulphate " precipitated by barium chloride. A green hydrate is known from which barium chloride precipitates two-thirds of the " sulphate." According to Werner's theory these sulphates are formulated :

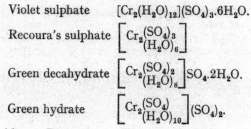

Violet sulphate $\quad[Cr_2(H_2O)_{12}](SO_4)_3.6H_2O.$

Recoura's sulphate $\quad\left[Cr_2\dfrac{(SO_4)_3}{(H_2O)_6}\right]$

Green decahydrate $\quad\left[Cr_2\dfrac{(SO_4)_2}{(H_2O)_8}\right]SO_4.2H_2O.$

Green hydrate $\quad\left[Cr_2\dfrac{(SO_4)}{(H_2O)_{10}}\right](SO_4)_2.$

Chrome Alum, Potassium Chromium Alum,
$K_2SO_4.Cr_2(SO_4)_3.24H_2O$

Chrome alum is readily prepared by reducing potassium dichromate solution, acidified with sulphuric acid, by means of sulphur dioxide and similar reducing agents :

$$K_2Cr_2O_7 + H_2SO_4 + 3SO_2 = \underbrace{K_2SO_4 + Cr_2(SO_4)_3} + H_2O.$$

It is obtained commercially as a by-product in the course of the manufacture of alizarin, for which anthracene is oxidized to anthraquinone by potassium dichromate and sulphuric acid.

Chrome alum crystallizes in deep violet octahedra, isomorphous with the other alums. It is fairly soluble in water (100 grams of water dissolve 24·4 grams of chrome alum at 25°) and forms a violet solution. If this solution be heated above 60° it turns green, and can then only· be made to crystallize with difficulty. Chrome alum is used as a mordant in dyeing, and for tanning leather.

The corresponding sodium and ammonium chromium alums are also known and used.

§ 7 Detection and Determination of Chromium

The presence of chromium is conveniently detected by fusing the compound suspected of containing it with sodium carbonate and a little nitre, when a yellow mass of sodium chromate results if chromium be present. This may be confirmed by dissolving the mass in water, acidifying with acetic acid and adding barium chloride, when a bright yellow precipitate of barium chromate is thrown down.

Chromates are also detected by the formation of a deep blue colour with hydrogen peroxide (compare pp. 292 and 317). The substance causing this blue colour (possibly perchromic acid, H_3CrO_8) dissolves in ether in which it is more stable than in water.

Chromium in the form of chromate or dichromate is determined volumetrically by titrating against a standard ferrous sulphate solution, using potassium ferricyanide as external indicator. Alternatively, a known quantity of acidified chromate or dichromate solution is added to excess of potassium iodide solution ; the liberated iodine is then titrated with standard sodium thiosulphate solution :

$K_2Cr_2O_7 + 6KI + 7H_2SO_4 = Cr_2(SO_4)_3 + 3I_2 + 7H_2O + 4K_2SO.$

If the chromium to be determined be present as a chromic salt it may be treated as above, after oxidation by hydrogen peroxide and sodium hydroxide ; excess peroxide being removed by boiling.

Chromium is determined gravimetrically by precipitation as chromic hydroxide by adding ammonium chloride and ammonia to the solution of a chromic salt. The hydroxide is filtered off and ignited to the oxide which is weighed. Chromates and dichromates must first be reduced to the chromic state, e.g., with sulphur dioxide.

§ 8 Molybdenum, Mo

History and Occurrence

The term $\mu\acute{o}\lambda\upsilon\beta\delta o\varsigma$ (molybdos) was applied by the Greeks to galena and other lead ores. Up to the middle of the eighteenth century, the mineral molybdite or molybdenite was supposed to be identical with graphite, then known as " plumbago " or " black lead." In 1778 K. W. Scheele, in his *Treatise on Molybdena*, showed that, unlike plumbago or graphite, molybdenite forms a " peculiar white earth " when treated with nitric acid. This he proved to have acid properties, and he called it " acidum molybdenae," that is, molybdic acid ; and he correctly considered the mineral molybdenite to be a molybdenum sulphide. In 1790 P. J. Hjelm isolated the element as a metallic powder by heating molybdic acid with charcoal.

The principal ore of molybdenum is *molybdenite*, MoS_2 ; it occurs also as *wulfenite*, $PbMoO_4$, and *molybdite*.

Extraction

The molybdenite is first concentrated mechanically and the concentrate is roasted, whereby it is converted into molybdenum trioxide, MoO_3. From this the metal can be obtained by the alumino thermic process, as in the case of chromium (q.v.).

Properties

Molybdenum is a fairly hard, white metal, which remains unchanged on exposure to air at ordinary temperatures, but is slowly oxidized at a red heat to the trioxide. It has a high melting point, 2620°, and its specific gravity is 10·2. It is only slowly attacked by acids ; but hydrochloric acid, nitric acid and hot concentrated sulphuric acid will react with it.

Uses

Molybdenum is now used industrially to a large extent ; in particular, for the manufacture of alloy steels. For this purpose, a ferro-molybdenum alloy is made by reducing molybdenite with iron and carbon in an electric furnace ; or by reducing a mixture of molybdenum and iron oxides aluminothermically.

Molybdenum steel is used for making rifle barrels, propeller shafts, etc., and particularly **high-speed tool steels**. These steels, unlike ordinary carbon steels, have the peculiar property of retaining their

" temper " when heated to a high degree, so that it is possible to make heavy cuts at high speed, for the steel can be heated to dull redness without impairing its quality. Molybdenum steel contains up to 10 per cent. of molybdenum. Some of the molybdenum and tungsten steels resist the action of acids unusually well, so that these *acid-proof steels* are useful in many chemical industries. Thus, an alloy containing about 60 per cent. of chromium, 35 per cent. of iron, and 2-3 per cent. of molybdenum is scarcely affected by dilute hydrochloric, nitric, or sulphuric acid, or by boiling aqua regia.

Molybdenum is used for the filament supports of electric lamps, and molybdenum compounds can also be used as a blue pigment in porcelain painting ; in silk and woollen dyeing ; and in colouring leather and rubber—it has been, indeed, proposed for dyeing fabrics as a substitute for indigo. Ammonium molybdate is largely used in the determination of phosphorus in iron and steel laboratories.

Molybdenum forms five oxides, viz. :

Molybdenum sesquioxide, Mo_2O_3,
Molybdenum dioxide, MoO_2,
Blue molybdenum oxide, Mo_3O_8,
Molybdenum hemipentoxide, Mo_2O_5,
Molybdenum trioxide, MoO_3.

Of these the **blue oxide** and the trioxide are the most interesting. The former is made by allowing powdered molybdenum to remain for a long time in contact with a suspension of the trioxide in water at the ordinary temperature. It is a dark blue substance which forms a blue colloidal solution. It is used as a pigment for rubber, etc.

Molybdenum trioxide, MoO_3, is made by roasting molybdenite. It can be purified by acting upon it with ammonia, which forms a solution of ammonium molybdate, from which copper, if present, is removed by means of ammonium sulphide. The molybdate is then ignited and molybdenum trioxide remains.

It is a white solid which is sparingly soluble in water, forming an acid solution. With alkalis it forms molybdates, but is much less acidic in nature than the corresponding chromium trioxide, and exhibits an even more marked tendency to form complex or condensed acids.

Molybdic acid, H_2MoO_4, can be prepared from ammonium molybdate, the commonest salt of this acid, by the action of nitric acid. It forms yellow crusts which give colloidal solutions with water.

Molybdates

The molybdates do not, as a rule, have simple formulae, such as X_2MoO_4, because of the readiness with which polymolybdates are formed. **Ammonium molybdate,** for instance, is represented by the formula $(NH_4)_6Mo_7O_{24}.4H_2O$, i.e., as a derivative of a hepta-molybdic acid. It is made by acting upon molybdenum trioxide with aqueous ammonia, and allowing the solution to crystallize.

Ammonium molybdate is important as a reagent for the detection and determination of phosphates (see p. 780). When dissolved in nitric acid and added to a solution of a phosphate, a yellow precipitate of **ammonium phosphomolybdate** is formed. The exact composition of this precipitate varies a little according to the degree of " condensation " or " complexity " of the salt, but is usually $(NH_4)_3PO_4.12MoO_3$ or $(NH_4)_3Mo_{12}PO_{40}$. Silicates, arsenates and vanadates give similar complex molybdate derivatives under appropriate conditions.

Salts of Molybdenum

No salts of molybdenum are known in which the element is definitely present as a basic radical. Chlorides of the following formulae are known, viz., $MoCl_2$, $MoCl_3$, $MoCl_4$, $MoCl_5$ and $MoCl_6$, but they are not true salts; they either form complexes or are volatile, covalent compounds.

§ 9 Tungsten, W

History

Tungsten is now an element óf great commercial and industrial importance, but until relatively recently it was thought of as rare and unimportant.

Up to the middle of the eighteenth century, the mineral scheelite— formerly called " tungsten " (heavy stone)—and wolframite were supposed to be ores of tin, but, in 1781, K. W. Scheele demonstrated that scheelite contains a peculiar acid, which he called tungstic acid, united with lime as a base. The same year, T. Bergmann recognized tungstic acid as an oxide of a new element, tungsten, which was isolated by J. J. y Don Fausto d'Elhuyar in 1783.

Occurrence

The chief tungsten minerals are *wolframite,* which is a mixture of iron and manganese tungstates, $(Fe,Mn)WO_4$; and *scheelite,* calcium tungstate, $CaWO_4$. Other minerals containing tungsten are *stolzite,* $PbWO_4$, *cuproscheelite,* $CuWO_4$, and *tungstenite,* WS_2.

Extraction

Wolframite is the principal source of commercial tungsten. It is a markédly magnetic material, and this property is made use of in a magnetic separator for concentrating the ore. Several methods are in use for obtaining the metal. In one process, the ore is extracted with hydrochloric acid, when a precipitate of tungsten trioxide remains. This is dissolved in ammonia and the tungstate so formed is crystallized and ignited. The trioxide is then reduced by means of hydrogen, or calcium, or by electrolysis in a fused mixture of tungstates. Alternatively, carbon is used as reducing agent when a very pure product is not required. For example, in making ferro-tungsten, for steel manufacture, wolframite is reduced directly in an electric furnace. Another method of obtaining the trioxide from the ore is by heating it with sodium carbonate and extracting the sodium tungstate formed with water ; after which calcium tungstate is precipitated by addition of calcium chloride, and decomposed by acidification. A third method consists in mixing the ore with carbon and heating the mixture in a stream of chlorine. Tungsten oxychloride, mixed with chlorides of iron and manganese is formed ; on addition of water tungsten trioxide results.

Properties

Tungsten is a hard, silvery-white metal. It has the highest melting point (about 3370°) of any metal, and its specific gravity (19·3) is only exceeded by rhenium, iridium, osmium and platinum and equals that of gold.

Tungsten is a very ductile metal, and it is very resistant to chemical action.   It is not oxidized below a bright red heat ; and chlorine only attacks it at this temperature.   Acids are almost without action, but it is readily oxidized by fused potassium chlorate, etc.   In chemical properties. generally, tungsten resembles molybdenum ; but the relationship is less close than between niobium and tantalum.

Uses

The principal uses of tungsten are for making special steels, and the filaments of electric lamps.   Steel containing 16-20 per cent. tungsten and 3-5 per cent. of chromium constitutes a high-speed tool steel since it retains its temper even at high temperatures.

Some compounds of tungsten also have technical applications.   Thus, sodium tungstate is used for " fireproofing " fabrics, and also as a mordant in dyeing.   Lead tungstate has been tried as a substitute for white lead, and the trioxide is used as a yellow pigment.

Tungsten forms three oxides, viz., WO_2, W_2O_5 and WO_3.   **Tungsten dioxide,** WO_2, is obtained by reduction of the trioxide by hydrogen.   **Blue tungsten oxide,** W_2O_5, somewhat resembles the blue oxide of molybdenum.   **Tungsten trioxide,** WO_3, is the most important oxide of tungsten.   Its preparation from wolframite has been described above.   It is a canary-yellow powder, which is insoluble in water, but reacts with alkali hydroxide solutions forming tungstates.

Tungstic acid, H_2WO_4, is obtained when solutions of soluble tungstates, e.g., sodium tungstate, are acidified with hydrochloric acid.   From a cold solution, a-*tungstic acid* is precipitated and has the formula $H_2WO_4.H_2O$.   It is slightly soluble in water ; but hot solutions, when acidified, give β-*tungstic acid*, H_2WO_4.   Tungstic acid resembles molybdic acid, particularly in its ability to form derivatives of condensed and complex acids.   Thus **sodium tungstate** has the formula $Na_{10}W_{12}O_{41}.28H_2O$.   Phosphates, arsenates, silicates and vanadates form complex acids and salts with tungstic, as with molybdic acid.   Phosphotungstic acid, and silicotungstic acid, are used in organic chemistry for the detection and determination of alkaloids.

Tungsten does not appear to form any true salts in which the tungsten is basic.   It forms a number of halides such as WF_6, WCl_4, WCl_5 and WCl_6, but these appear to be covalent compounds.

§ 10 Uranium, U

History

The mineral pitchblende was formerly supposed to be an ore of zinc iron, or tungsten, but M. H. Klaproth (1789) proved that it contained what he styled a " half metallic substance " different from the three elements just named.   This element was named " uranium " in honour of Herschel's discovery of the planet Uranus in 1781.   E. M. Péligot proved that Klaproth's element was really an oxide of uranium, and he isolated the metal itself in 1842.

Occurrence

Uranium occurs as *pitchblende* or *uraninite*, U_3O_8, as *carnotite*, $KUO_2(VO_4).3H_2O$ and in several other minerals.   All uranium minerals are now important as a source of radium.   (See Ch. XXXVI.)

Extraction

The element is best obtained from the oxide aluminothermically (compare chromium).   It can also be obtained by reduction of the oxide with hydrogen, carbon or calcium, or by electrolysis of the fused double chloride Na_2UCl_6.

Properties

Uranium is a white metal in bulk, but as obtained by reduction it is a black powder. Its melting point is about 1850° and its specific gravity is 18·7. It is a somewhat reactive metal, being considerably more readily oxidized and attacked by acids than are molybdenum or tungsten. Many of the most interesting properties of uranium are connected with its radio-activity. These are discussed in Chapter XXXVI.

Uses

Uranium compounds, particularly the yellow trioxide and sodium di-uranate, are used as colours in glass and pottery manufacture. Uranyl nitrate, and acetate, are used for the determination of phosphates, and zinc and magnesium uranyl acetates are reagents for the detection of sodium.

Uranium forms a number of oxides, viz., UO_2, U_2O_5, U_3O_8 and UO_3, and possibly UO_4 also.

Uranous oxide, UO_2, is made by reducing urano-uranic oxide with hydrogen, and was at one time mistaken for the element. (Compare vanadous oxide, p. 760.)

Urano-uranic oxide, U_3O_8, occurs as pitchblende and is made by heating the other oxides in oxygen or by heating uranyl acetate. It is a green powder.

Uranium trioxide, UO_3, is a yellow solid made by heating uranyl nitrate in oxygen :

$$2UO_2(NO_3)_2 = 2UO_3 + 4NO_2 + O_2.$$

It is an amphoteric oxide, forming uranates with alkalis, and uranyl salts with acids.

The **uranates** resemble the chromates ; salts derived from condensed uranic acids are known, analogous to the polychromates. **Sodium di-uranate,** $Na_2U_2O_7.6H_2O$ (also known as *uranium yellow*), is analogous to sodium dichromate. It is made by adding sodium hydroxide to uranium nitrate solution :

$$2UO_2(NO_3)_2 + 6NaOH = Na_2U_2O_7 + 4NaNO_3 + 3H_2O.$$

Salts of Uranium

Uranium forms two series of salts, the uranous salts derived from uranous oxide, and the uranic or uranyl salts in which the group UO_2 acts as a bivalent basic radical. The uranous salts are powerful reducing agents, being readily oxidized to uranyl derivatives. The uranyl salts are characterized by strong fluorescence in solution.

Uranous chloride, UCl_4, is obtained as a dark green solid when chlorine is passed over heated uranium.

Uranyl nitrate, $UO_2(NO_3)_2.6H_2O$, commercially known as uranium nitrate, is made by acting upon any of the oxides of uranium with nitric acid. It is a greenish yellow crystalline solid and is the most important uranium compound. It is readily soluble in water (100 grams of water dissolve 200 grams of the salt at 18°) and its solutions are used for the volumetric estimation of phosphoric acid, since it forms a yellow precipitate of uranyl ammonium phosphate, $UO_2(NH_4)PO_4$, when added to solutions of soluble phosphates. Potassium ferrocyanide is used as external indicator ; it gives a brown colouration when excess of uranyl nitrate is present.

Uranyl acetate, $UO_2(CH_3COO)_2.2H_2O$, is sometimes used instead of the nitrate as a reagent for phosphates. It is also used for the precipitation of sodium as its double salt with zinc or magnesium acetate (p. 572). It is made by dissolving uranium trioxide in acetic acid. It is a yellow crystalline salt, soluble in water (100 grams of water dissolve 7·7 grams of the salt at 15°).

§ 11 The Relationships of the Group VI Elements

The elements of Group VI fall into two well-defined sections ; oxygen, sulphur, selenium, tellurium and polonium comprising one, and the transition elements, chromium, molybdenum, tungsten and uranium the other. As would be expected of a group near to the outside of the table, there are marked differences between the two sub-groups, and the resemblances are not very pronounced. But among themselves the elements of each section show resemblances and relationships such as would be anticipated.

All the members of the group, except oxygen, form trioxides with marked acidic properties, and these trioxides give rise to series of isomorphous salts of the type M_2RO_4 (where M is a monovalent metal and R is an element of Group VI). The trioxides show a great tendency to form condensed and complex derivatives such as the disulphates, polychromates, etc., a tendency particularly noticeable in the A sub-group. Compounds of the type RO_2Cl_2 are also formed by all these elements, and mostly behave as non-metallic chlorides, being readily hydrolyzed by water. With increasing atomic weight, however, the stability increases, and basic character begins to show itself, so that in the case of uranium the basic radical UO_2 gives rise to the most characteristic and stable of the uranium salts.

Most of the elements in Group VI form dioxides, but whereas those of sulphur-tellurium are feebly acidic, the others are basic. All the elements of the group exhibit variable valency. Oxygen is bivalent as a rule, but occasionally quadrivalent; sulphur, selenium and tellurium exhibit valencies of two, four and six. The A sub-group elements show very variable valencies, but all have a valency of six in their most characteristic oxygen compounds.

As mentioned already, in spite of these similarities, the Group falls into two very clearly-defined sections; one predominantly metallic in character, the other mainly non-metallic.

The members of the A sub-group, comprising chromium, molybdenum, tungsten and uranium, are all characteristic metals with high melting points (tungsten has the highest melting point of any metal), and the elements are only extracted from their compounds with difficulty. The gradation in their physical properties with atomic weight is indicated by Table LVIII.

TABLE LVIII.—PHYSICAL PROPERTIES OF THE CHROMIUM FAMILY.

	Chromium.	Molybdenum.	Tungsten.	Uranium.
Atomic weight .	52·01	95·95	183·92	238·07
Specific gravity .	7·1	10·2	19·3	18·7
Atomic volume .	7·7	10·2	9·6	12·7
Melting point .	1830°	2620°	3370°	ca. 1860°

These metals all combine directly with oxygen, sulphur and nitrogen; and their tendency to form complex acids, which reaches a climax in tungsten, is particularly noteworthy.

The probable electronic configurations of these elements are given in

Table LX.   Consideration of this table, along with Table XII (p. 142), shows that the metals of this group are *transition elements*, i.e., they occur in that portion of the table where the penultimate electron shell is expanding.   Consequently, we should expect to find considerable resemblances between these elements and their horizontal neighbours, e.g., between vanadium, chromium and manganese ; and also the development of variable valency and the formation of coloured compounds.   All these expectations are, in fact, realized.

The table shows that in each case the last two electron shells have respectively 13 and 1, or 12 and 2 electrons.   The 13-group is made up of a complete quantum group of 8 electrons and an incomplete one of five or four electrons.   These latter, and the outermost electrons, can be detached for compound formation ; hence the formation of compounds with valencies of 2, 3 and 6.

Turning now to the other section of this group, oxygen, sulphur, selenium, tellurium and polonium are mainly non-metallic in character, although the last three show some signs of metalloid characteristics. All are easily vaporized, have low melting points and can be extracted from their compounds with comparatively little difficulty.   Some of the principal properties are summarized in Table LIX.

TABLE LIX.—PROPERTIES OF THE OXYGEN-SULPHUR FAMILY.

	Oxygen.	Sulphur.	Selenium.	Tellurium.
Atomic weight . .	16	32·016	78·96	127·61
Melting point . .	−252·5°	114°–115°	220°	452°
Boiling point . .	−183°	444·6°	688°	1390°
Specific gravity (solid) .	1·426	1·96–2·07	4·28–4·80	5·93–6·4
Atomic volume (approx.)	11	16	18	21
Colour of solid . .	Pale blue	Yellow	Reddish brown	Black
Heat of union with hydrogen (cals.) . .	69·0	4·8	−25·1	−34·9
State of aggregation of hydride . . .	Liquid	Gas	Gas	Gas

These elements all form hydrogen compounds of the same type (the A sub-group metals do not form hydrides), but whereas the hydrogen compounds of sulphur, selenium and tellurium are foetid-smelling gases at ordinary temperatures, water is a colourless, odourless liquid.   The acidic character of these hydrides increases with increasing atomic weight, and their stability decreases.

All four elements (the properties of polonium have scarcely been examined apart from its radio-activity) exhibit allotropy, give rise to characteristic dioxides and (except oxygen) form salts of the type M_2RO_3, as well as the salts, M_2RO_4, characteristic of the group as a whole.   In this section, the acid H_2RO_4 becomes much less acidic and more unstable, as the atomic weight of R increases.   Thus telluric acid is a very feeble acid, and decomposes on warming (p. 767).

The probable electronic configurations of these elements are given in Table LXI.

TABLE LX.

Element.	Electrons in Orbits.																		
	1	2_1	2_2	3_1	3_2	3_3	4_1	4_2	4_3	4_4	5_1	5_2	5_3	6_1	6_2	6_3	7
Chromium .	2	2	6	2	6	5	1										
Molybdenum	2	2	6	2	6	10	2	6	5		1						
Tungsten .	2	2	6	2	6	10	2	6	10	14	2	6	4	2			
Uranium .	2	2	6	2	6	10	2	6	10	14	2	6	10	2	6	5	1

TABLE LXI.

Element.	Electrons in Orbits.											
	1	2_1	2_2	3_1	3_2	3_3	4_1	4_2	4_3	5_1	5_2
Oxygen . . .	2	2	4								
Sulphur . . .	2	2	6	2	4						
Selenium . . .	2	2	6	2	6	10	2	4			
Tellurium . . .	2	2	6	2	6	10	2	6	10	2	4

CHAPTER XXXIV

MANGANESE, MASURIUM AND RHENIUM

§ 1 Group VII of the Periodic Table

GROUP VII comprises the extremely electronegative halogens, together with, as A sub-group, manganese, and the two recently-discovered elements, masurium and rhenium. The resemblance between these two sub-groups is very slight (see § 8).

§ 2 Manganese, Mn

History

Manganese appears to have been used by the ancient Egyptians and Romans for bleaching glass, for their glass often contains the equivalent of up to 2 per cent. manganese oxide. Pliny mentions its use for this purpose under the name " magnes " ; he considered it to be a variety of loadstone, i.e., a variety of magnetic iron ore. For reasons stated in connection with magnesium, the term " magnesia " in old books may refer to manganese oxide. B. Valentine, and chemists generally towards the end of the eighteenth century, believed wad to be an ore of iron. J. H. Pott (1740) proved that pyrolusite proper does not contain iron, and furnishes a number of salts quite different from those obtained with the iron oxides. C. W. Scheele (1774) made an important investigation on manganese, and T. Bergman (1774) suspected that some metal lay concealed in the mineral earth which he reduced with charcoal, so obtaining a metal regulus. A purer sample was isolated by J. F. John in 1807.

Occurrence

The metal manganese does not occur free in nature. Much of the manganese ore comes from Russia, and the highest grade picked pyrolusite contains 50 per cent. of manganese. Some ore comes from several other countries. The chief minerals are the oxides *pyrolusite*, MnO_2 ; *braunite*, Mn_2O_3 ; *hausmannite*, Mn_3O_4 ; *manganite*, $Mn_2O_3.H_2O$. The carbonate, $MnCO_3$, *dialogite* or *rhodochrosite*, is often associated with siderite ($FeCO_3$) ; manganese also less frequently occurs as sulphide, *manganese blende*, MnS ; and silicate, *rhodonite*, $MnSiO_3$. *Franklinite* usually contains manganese as well as iron, and, after the zinc has been extracted, is used in making spiegeleisen. *Wad* is an impure mixture of manganese oxides often found in damp, low-lying places. Wad is supposed to be a decomposition product of the manganese minerals. Minute quantities of manganese occur in water, plants, and animals ; and traces also appear to be the colouring agent of many amethyst-coloured minerals.

Extraction

Manganese is largely used in the form of spiegeleisen and ferro-manganese (see below), and this is made by reducing a mixture of oxides of manganese and iron with carbon in a blast furnace.

Manganese itself can be obtained by reduction of any of its oxides with carbon, but an inconveniently high temperature is required. It is best obtained by the aluminothermic process, in a similar manner to that described for chromium (p. 768). For this purpose, manganese dioxide is first converted into manganosic oxide, Mn_3O_4, by heating it to redness ; since the reaction between aluminium and the dioxide is too violent for safety and cannot be directly controlled.

The purest metal is made by electrolysis of a solution of manganous chloride, using a mercury cathode. The manganese dissolves in the mercury which is then distilled off *in vacuo*.

Properties

Manganese is a grey metal with a reddish tinge, like bismuth. It is brittle and soft, though harder than pure iron. Its specific gravity is 7·2 and it melts at 1242°. Manganese is superficially oxidized when exposed to the air, but the finely divided metal will burn in air. Pure electrolytic manganese is not attacked by water at ordinary temperatures, but steam attacks it slightly. As ordinarily obtained, however, it is readily attacked by water, manganous hydroxide is formed, and hydrogen is evolved :

$$Mn + 2H_2O = Mn(OH)_2 + H_2.$$

This behaviour is reminiscent of that of zinc with dilute acids (p. 642). When heated in nitrogen, manganese forms the nitride Mn_5N_2 ; heated with ammonia it forms a nitride Mn_3N_2. It readily combines with carbon, sulphur and chlorine ; and dissolves in acids forming manganous salts with the evolution of hydrogen.

Uses

Manganese is used extensively for the manufacture of manganese steel. The addition of small quantities of manganese to steel renders it brittle ; but an alloy containing 12 per cent. of manganese is very hard and tough, and remarkably resistant to shock. It is, therefore, used for rock crushers, railway points and crossings, wagon buffers, and similar purposes. Manganese also enters into the composition of several other useful alloys such as *manganese bronze* (copper alloyed with varying quantities of manganese and zinc), *manganin* (83 per cent. copper, 13 per cent. manganese, 4 per cent. nickel). Manganin is used for resistance coils on account of its very small temperature coefficient of resistance.

Spiegeleisen and *ferro-manganese* are alloys of manganese and iron which are used in the Bessemer process (p. 807) for reducing iron oxide formed in the converter, and to counteract the deleterious effects of phosphorus and sulphur. Alloys containing less than 20 per cent. of iron are called spiegeleisen, the others ferro-manganese.

Cupro-manganese and *Heusler's alloy* (55 per cent. copper, 15 per cent. aluminium and 30 per cent. manganese) are magnetic.

Manganese dioxide is used as an oxidizing agent ; in the manufacture of chlorine and bromine. It is used in decolorizing glass stained a yellowish tinge by the traces of " ferric silicate " present, for the violet colour of manganese silicate masks the complementary yellow tint of the iron. Manganese dioxide is also used as a " drier " for paints and varnishes ; as a depolarizer in battery cells ; colouring pottery bodies and glazes ; etc. Wad is used in the manufacture of paint. A crude mixture of sodium manganate and permanganate is made by fusing sodium hydroxide with pyrolusite, and sold as a disinfectant under the name " Condy's fluid."

Atomic Weight

The atomic weight of manganese is seen to be in the neighbourhood of 55 from the value of its specific heat (0·114). The exact value has been estimated by analyses of silver permanganate, and by conversion of manganous chloride and bromide into the corresponding silver halides. The value recommended at present (1940) by the International Committee is 54·93.

§ 3 Oxides of Manganese

Manganese forms an unusually large number of definite oxides, viz.,

Manganous oxide, MnO,
Manganosic oxide, Mn_3O_4,
Manganese sesquioxide, Mn_2O_3,
Manganese dioxide, MnO_2,
Manganese trioxide, MnO_3,
Manganese heptoxide, Mn_2O_7.

Manganous Oxide, MnO

This oxide can be obtained by reducing any of the other oxides by heating in a stream of hydrogen, and also by heating manganous hydroxide or carbonate in absence of air.

It is a greenish powder which oxidizes rapidly on exposure to air. It reacts with acids forming manganous salts.

Manganous hydroxide, $Mn(OH)_2$, is prepared by adding an alkali hydroxide to a solution of a manganous salt, in absence of air, when it is precipitated as a colourless, flocculent precipitate. In the air, it is quickly oxidized, probably to manganic hydroxide. It is slightly soluble in water, and forms manganous salts with acids.

Manganosic Oxide, Trimanganese Tetroxide, Mn_3O_4

This oxide occurs in nature in red, prismatic crystals of *hausmanite* ; and it is formed as a brownish red powder when any other manganese oxides is ignited in air. It can be obtained, in a crystalline condition, by heating the powdered oxide in a current of hydrogen chloride.

Manganosic oxide reacts with acids with the formation of a soluble manganous salt and insoluble hydrated manganese dioxide, e.g. :

$$Mn_3O_4 + 2H_2SO_4 = 2MnSO_4 + MnO_2 + 2H_2O.$$

It thus appears to be a compound oxide, analogous to red lead (p. 705) and the black oxide of iron (p. 815), and is, therefore, probably manganese ortho-manganite, Mn_2MnO_4 or

$$Mn{<}^O_O{>}Mn{<}^O_O{>}Mn.$$

Manganese Sesquioxide, Mn_2O_3

This oxide, also called red oxide of manganese, occurs in nature as *braunite*, $3Mn_2O_3.MnSiO_3$. It is obtained as a black powder when any other oxide of manganese is heated to about 900° in a current of oxygen. Manganese sesquioxide reacts slowly with cold, dilute acids forming manganic salts ; hot sulphuric acid forms manganous sulphate and manganese dioxide ; when warmed with hydrochloric acid, manganous chloride and chlorine result :

$$Mn_2O_3 + 6HCl = 2MnCl_3 + 3H_2O,$$
$$2MnCl_3 = 2MnCl_2 + Cl_2,$$
$$Mn_2O_3 + H_2SO_4 = MnSO_4 + MnO_2 + H_2O.$$

The corresponding hydroxide, $Mn(OH)_3$, has not been isolated, but the **hydroxide** $MnO.OH$ (or $Mn_2O_3.H_2O$) is obtained by the action of chlorine on a suspension of manganous carbonate in water :

$$3MnCO_3 + Cl_2 + H_2O = 2MnO.OH + MnCl_2 + 3CO_2.$$

This hydroxide also occurs native as the mineral *manganite*.

Manganese Dioxide, MnO_2

This is the most important compound of manganese. It occurs native as *pyrolusite*, *psilomelane*, a hydrated form, and *wad*, a less pure form, contaminated with earthy material. Commercial manganese dioxide is prepared from pyrolusite.

Manganese dioxide, when pure, is a black insoluble powder. On heating to redness it is converted, with loss of oxygen, into manganosic oxide. It is not affected by dilute acids, except hydrochloric acid. Cold concentrated hydrochloric acid dissolves it, giving a dark brown liquid and very little chlorine, if the temperature be kept low. This solution may contain manganese tetrachloride, and probably some trichloride. On warming, chlorine is evolved and manganous chloride remains (see p. 492).

$$MnO_2 + 4HCl = MnCl_4 + 2H_2O,$$
$$2MnCl_4 = 2MnCl_3 + Cl_2,$$
$$MnCl_4 = MnCl_2 + Cl_2$$
$$2MnCl_3 = 2MnCl_2 + Cl_2.$$

When heated with concentrated sulphuric acid, manganous sulphate and oxygen are formed. In the cold, it is possible that a disulphate, $Mn(SO_4)_2$, is formed :

$$2MnO_2 + 2H_2SO_4 = 2MnSO_4 + 2H_2O + O_2.$$

Manganese dioxide appears to be a feeble acidic oxide, for with alkalis it forms compounds which are thought to be manganites (see below). It may also be a very feeble basic oxide ; there is no direct evidence of the existence of the tetrachloride in solution, although complex derivatives, such as K_2MnCl_6, are known. It is not a true peroxide or superoxide, since it does not give hydrogen peroxide with acids. It is, therefore, a polyoxide (p. 304).

Manganese dioxide is used in the preparation of chlorine (p. 491) ; The neutralization of the green colour of glass ; in the manufacture of Leclanché cells (both of the wet and dry type) ; and for the manufacture of permanganates and other manganese compounds in chemical industry.

Hydrated manganese dioxide is obtained when manganese dioxide is precipitated from a reaction in solution. It is probably manganous acid (q.v.).

Manganese Trioxide, MnO_3

If solid potassium permanganate be dissolved in cold concentrated sulphuric acid, and the green solution (probably containing permanganyl-sulphate) dropped upon anhydrous sodium carbonate, violet fumes are evolved which may be condensed to a red, viscid solid, believed to be manganese trioxide :

$$2KMnO_4 + 2H_2SO_4 = (MnO_3)_2SO_4 + K_2SO_4 + 2H_2O,$$
$$2(MnO_3)_2SO_4 + 2Na_2CO_3 = 2Na_2SO_4 + 4MuO_3 + 2CO_2 + O_2.$$

It reacts with water forming manganese dioxide and permanganic acid :

$$3MnO_3 + H_2O = 2HMnO_4 + MnO_2,$$

and with alkali hydroxides, it gives manganates, e.g.,

$$2NaOH + MnO_3 = Na_2MnO_4 + H_2O.$$

It is not finally established that the red solid is manganese trioxide ; it has been thought by some to be a mixture of the heptoxide (q.v.) with a lower oxide.

Manganese Heptoxide, Mn_2O_7

If the green solution obtained by dissolving potassium permanganate in cold concentrated sulphuric acid be treated with a little ice-cold water, oily drops of manganese heptoxide separate. It is a reddish-brown liquid which does not solidify at $-20°$. It is very unstable, and decomposes explosively on warming into manganese dioxide and oxygen. It dissolves in water, forming a violet solution of permanganic acid. It is thus permanganic anhydride. It is a very powerful oxidizing agent, causing wood to inflame when brought into contact with it, and mixed with sulphur or phosphorus, the mixture is violently explosive.

§4 Oxyacids of Manganese

Salts are known derived from three oxyacids of manganese, viz.,

Manganites from manganous acid, H_2MnO_3.
Manganates from manganic acid, H_2MnO_4.
Permanganates from permanganic acid, $HMnO_4$,

of which manganic acid itself has not been isolated.

Manganous Acid, H_2MnO_3

When manganese dioxide is precipitated as the result of reactions in solution, it is usually obtained in a hydrated form, which may be manganous acid—$MnO_2.H_2O$ or H_2MnO_3. It is conveniently made thus by addition of an alkaline hypochlorite solution to an aqueous solution of a manganous salt.

$$2MnCl_2 + 4NaOCl + 2H_2O = 2M_2MnO_3 + 4NaCl + 2Cl_2.$$

Manganese dioxide, particularly in this form, reacts with alkali hydroxide solutions to form manganites. Also, when manganese dioxide is fused with potassium hydroxide in absence of air, **potassium manganite**, K_2MnO_3, is believed to be formed. **Calcium manganite**, $CaMnO_3$, is probably the chief constituent of the *manganese mud* obtained in the Weddon recovery process for chlorine (p. 493).

Manganates

Manganic acid has not so far been isolated, but various manganates are known. When manganese dioxide is fused with potassium or sodium hydroxide, in presence of air or an oxidizing agent such as potassium nitrate or chlorate, the potassium or sodium manganite first formed is converted into the corresponding manganate :

$$MnO_2 + 2KOH = K_2MnO_3 + H_2O,$$
$$2K_2MnO_3 + O_2 = 2K_2MnO_4.$$

The fused mass so obtained has a dark green colour, and when extracted with a small quantity of water it furnishes a dark green solution from which dark green crystals of **potassium manganate**, K_2MnO_4, can be obtained by allowing the solution to evaporate, at ordinary temperatures, *in vacuo*. **Sodium manganate**, $Na_2MnO_4.10H_2O$, can be made similarly, and also by fusing manganese dioxide with sodium peroxide. It is isomorphous with Glauber's salt, $Na_2SO_4.10H_2O$.

The manganates are strong oxidizing agents, but they are so readily converted into the corresponding permanganates (see below), and these are so much more convenient, that manganates are not generally used.

Permanganic Acid, $HMnO_4$

This acid is best made by adding just sufficient sulphuric acid to barium permanganate (see below) to precipitate the barium as sulphate. On evaporating the filtered solution, violet crystals of permanganic acid are obtained. It is a powerful oxidizing agent like perchloric acid, which it resembles also in decomposing in contact with organic matter.

Potassium Permanganate, $KMnO_4$

When the green concentrated solution of potassium manganate, prepared as described above, is gently warmed, or largely diluted with water, the green colour changes to pink owing to the formation of potassium permanganate, and hydrated manganese dioxide is precipitated. It is supposed that the manganate is first hydrolyzed, forming manganic acid, which is so unstable that it is at once converted into permanganic acid :

$$K_2MnO_4 + 2H_2O \rightleftharpoons 2KOH + H_2MnO_4,$$
$$3H_2MnO_4 = 2HMnO_4 + MnO_2.H_2O + H_2O.$$

The manganate is thus self-oxidized and self-reduced ; one part of the compound being oxidized at the expense of the oxygen in another part. Potassium manganate is not hydrolyzed in alkaline solutions, and it is supposed that pure water will not hydrolyze it. If a small trace of acid be present, even carbonic acid derived from the atmosphere, hydrolysis takes place. Hence, if carbon dioxide be passed through potassium manganate solution, it is converted into the permanganate :

$$3K_2MnO_4 + 2CO_2 + H_2O = 2K_2CO_3 + 2KMnO_4 + MnO_2.H_2O.$$

This is the method employed commercially ; the solution is run off from the manganese dioxide deposited, and then evaporated until it begins to crystallize.

Potassium permanganate forms dark purple, almost black, crystals, with a greenish lustre, which are isomorphous with potassium perchlorate. It is only sparingly soluble in water : 100 grams of water dissolve 6·45 grams at 15°. When heated to about 240°, potassium permanganate decomposes, furnishing oxygen and potassium manganate

$$6KMnO_4 = 3K_2MnO_4 + 3MnO_2 + 3O_2.$$

It dissolves in cold concentrated sulphuric acid, forming a green solution of **permanganyl sulphate**, $(MnO_3)_2SO_4$, which is liable to decompose explosively. A similar explosive decomposition occurs if potassium permanganate be warmed with sulphuric acid, and is probably due to the formation of manganese heptoxide :

$$2KMnO_4 + 2H_2SO_4 = (MnO_3)_2SO_4 + K_2SO_4 + 2H_2O,$$
$$(MnO_3)_2SO_4 + H_2O = Mn_2O_7 + H_2SO_4,$$
$$2Mn_2O_7 = 4MnO_2 + 3O_2.$$

Potassium permanganate is a powerful oxidizing agent, and is extensively employed as such in volumetric analysis. When heated with an alkali, potassium permanganate reverts to the manganate :

$$4KMnO_4 + 4KOH = 4K_2MnO_4 + 2H_2O + O_2.$$

If a reducing agent be also present, the alkaline permanganate solution is further reduced to manganese dioxide :

$$4KMnO_4 + 2H_2O = 4MnO_2 + 4KOH + 3O_2.$$

In acid solutions, the reduction proceeds still further, and a manganous salt is formed :

$$4KMnO_4 + 6H_2SO_4 = 2K_2SO_4 + 4MnSO_4 + 6H_2O + 5O_2.$$

There are thus three stages in the reduction of potassium permanganate corresponding with separation of 1, 3 or 5 atoms of available oxygen per two molecules of salt.

For volumetric analysis reduction is always carried out in acid solution, and in this way oxalic acid and oxalates, ferrous sulphate, sulphurous acid and sulphites, hydrogen peroxide, nitrous acid and nitrites, etc., are determined :

$$2KMnO_4 + 5(COOH)_2 + 3H_2SO_4$$
$$= 2MnSO_4 + K_2SO_4 + 10CO_2 + 8H_2O,$$
$$2KMnO_4 + 10FeSO_4 + 8H_2SO_4$$
$$= 2MnSO_4 + K_2SO_4 + 5Fe_2(SO_4)_3 + 8H_2O,$$
$$2KMnO_4 + 5H_2SO_3 = 2MnSO_4 + K_2SO_4 + 2H_2SO_4 + 3H_2O,$$
$$2KMnO_4 + 5H_2O_2 + 3H_2SO_4 = 2MnSO_4 + K_2SO_4 + 8H_2O + 5O_2,$$
$$2KMnO_4 + 5KNO_2 + 3H_2SO_4$$
$$= 2MnSO_4 + K_2SO_4 + 5KNO_3 + 3H_2O.$$

In acid solution potassium permanganate liberates iodine from potassium iodide solution, a process also employed in volumetric analysis :

$$2KMnO_4 + 10KI + 8H_2SO_4 = 2MnSO_4 + 6K_2SO_4 + 5I_2 + 8H_2O,$$

but in alkaline solution it is oxidized to potassium iodate :

$$KI + 2KMnO_4 + H_2O = KIO_3 + 2KOH + 2MnO_2.$$

The use of acid permanganate is very convenient since the solution of the manganous salt formed is colourless, and so, if a solution of potassium permanganate be added to a solution of a reducing agent, a colourless solution results until all the latter has been oxidized when the appearance of a persistent pink colour of permanganate indicates the end of the reaction.

Sodium permanganate, $NaMnO_4$, can be made in a similar way to the potassium salt, but it only crystallizes with difficulty. Consequently it is not much used except in the form of *Condy's fluid*, which is a solution of the crude mixture of sodium manganate and permanganate, made by fusing sodium hydroxide and pyrolusite.

Silver permanganate, $AgMnO_4$, separates as a red precipitate when equivalent quantities of hot concentrated solutions of silver nitrate and potassium permanganate are mixed and allowed to cool.

Barium permanganate, $Ba(MnO_4)_2$, is formed on adding barium chloride solution to a solution of silver permanganate. It is used for the preparation of permanganic acid.

§ 5 Salts of Manganese

Manganese forms two series of salts, which are derived respectively from manganous oxide, and manganese sesquioxide. They are known as the manganous and manganic salts, of which the latter are unstable.

Manganous carbonate, $MnCO_3$, is made by adding sodium carbonate to a solution of a manganous salt, when it is precipitated as a pinkish or buff-coloured powder. It decomposes on heating, the manganous oxide first formed being oxidized to manganese dioxide, if access of air be allowed.

Manganous Chloride, $MnCl_2$

This salt is prepared by dissolving the oxide, or carbonate, in hydrochloric acid and evaporating the solution. It can also be made from manganese dioxide similarly, the heating being continued long enough to drive off all free chlorine. It separates from these solutions in rose-pink crystals of the composition $MnCl_2.4H_2O$. The anhydrous salt is made by heating these crystals in a stream of hydrogen chloride. It is a very deliquescent substance and forms double salts of the type R_2MnCl_4 with the alkali metal chlorides.

Manganous nitrate, $Mn(NO_3)_2$, is made by dissolving manganous carbonate in dilute nitric acid. On heating, manganese dioxide is left :

$$Mn(NO_3)_2 = MnO_2 + 2NO_2.$$

Manganous sulphide, MnS, is formed as a flesh-coloured precipitate when hydrogen sulphide is passed into a neutral or alkaline solution of a manganous salt. It dissolves readily in dilute acids, including acetic acid, which enables it to be distinguished from zinc sulphide which is insoluble in acetic acid.

Manganous sulphate, $MnSO_4.5H_2O$, is made commercially by heating pyrolusite with concentrated sulphuric acid :

$$2MnO_2 + 2H_2SO_4 = 2MnSO_4 + 2H_2O + O_2.$$

It is recrystallized from water, and so obtained in pink triclinic crystals of the composition $MnSO_4.5H_2O$, isomorphous with copper sulphate.

Manganous dithionate, MnS_2O_6, is referred to on page 477.

Manganous ammonium phosphate, $MnNH_4PO_4$, is formed in pink glittering crystals when ammonium chloride, ammonia and sodium phosphate are added to a solution of a manganous salt. It is of importance for the determination of manganese on account of its insolubility and since, on ignition, it is converted into the corresponding pyrophosphate, $Mn_2P_2O_7$.

Manganic salts are unstable and cannot readily be btained pure. The brown solution, which results when manganese dioxide is added to cold concentrated hydrochloric acid (p. 790) probably contains a large proportion of **manganic chloride**, $MnCl_3$. Also, by suspending manganese dioxide in carbon tetrachloride and passing in dry hydrogen chloride, a solid containing manganic chloride results. It is decomposed by water. It forms double salts such as $MnCl_3.2NH_4Cl.H_2O$ or $(NH_4)_2MnCl_5.H_2O$, and $K_2MnCl_5.H_2O$.

Manganic sulphate, $Mn_2(SO_4)_3$, is formed as a dark green powder by the action of sulphuric acid on freshly precipitated manganese dioxide. It dissolves in water to a violet solution which deposits hydrated manganese dioxide on standing. It forms alums such as $K_2SO_4.Mn_2(SO_4)_3.24H_2O$.

§ 6 Detection and Determination of Manganese

Manganese is often detected by the formation of a green manganate when the substance to be tested is fused with caustic alkali and an oxidizing agent (p. 792). On solution in water, a green solution is formed which becomes pink on the addition of dilute sulphuric acid.

Manganese is determined gravimetrically either by precipitation as the double phosphate with ammonia, which on ignition is converted into the pyrophosphate $Mn_2P_2O_7$; or as the sulphide, MnS.

A convenient method for the determination of manganese in iron or steel depends upon the ability of sodium bismuthate to oxidize manganese compounds in solution to permanganates. The solution of the steel in nitric acid is treated with sodium bismuthate. To the resulting permanganate, after filtration, excess of a standard solution of a ferrous salt is added, and the excess of ferrous iron determined by titration with standard permanganate solution.

§ 7 Masurium and Rhenium

When Mendéeleff compiled the first periodic table he left two vacant places in Group VIIA below manganese, which for long has been the only known representative of this sub-group.

Moseley's work (p. 129) confirmed the reality of these gaps corresponding to atomic numbers 43 and 75, but it was not until 1925 that Noddack and Tacke found indications of the existence of these elements on examining the X-ray spectra of concentrates from certain platinum ores and columbite. One of these elements (43) was called **masurium,** Ma, from Masuren, a district in East Prussia, and the other **rhenium,** Re, after the Rhine. Masurium has not been obtained in quantities sufficient to enable its chemical properties to be determined, but the chemistry of rhenium has been investigated to a considerable extent and with the element and its salts are obtainable commercially.

Rhenium is a grey metal of high specific gravity (approx. 20·5) and melting point (3170°). It forms a number of oxides, some of which are analogous to those of manganese, and perrhenates, corresponding to permanganates, are the principal compounds of rhenium. They are much less powerful oxidizing agents than the permanganates, and are colourless.

§ 8 Relationships of the Elements of Group VIIA

Until comparatively recently, manganese was the only known member of this sub-group, and even now so little is known of the chemistry of masurium that comparisons involving it cannot usefully be made.

So far as the chemistry of rhenium has been investigated there seems to be the sort of resemblance to that of manganese which would be expected in view of their positions in the Periodic System. Both elements exhibit very variable valency ; both form a large number of oxides, those with the larger proportions of oxygen being acidic in nature and readily forming salts such as the permanganates and perrhenates.

Since this is one of the extreme groups of the periodic system, it would be anticipated that the resemblance between the two sub-groups would be rather slight, as is found, for example, in the case of Group I, where the relationship between the alkali-metals and the coinage metals is not at all obvious. In point of fact, the resemblance of manganese and rhenium to the halogens is even slighter, and it can hardly be doubted that but for the indication of Mendéeleff's table no such relationship would have been sought for or upheld.

The only property in which manganese shows any real analogy with the halogens is in the formation of a heptoxide, Mn_2O_7, which gives rise to the permanganates, which are in many respects similar to the perchlorates. Thus, the acids are monobasic and are powerful oxidizing agents, and the corresponding salts are often isomorphous. But the force of this fact is somewhat weakened by the isomorphism of the manganates with the sulphates.

In point of fact, the principal analogies in the chemistry of manganese are with its horizontal neighbours in the periodic system, viz., chromium and iron, as might be anticipated from its being a transitional element (in the modern sense). As examples of these resemblances there may be mentioned the isomorphism of the manganites and chromites ; the manganic and ferric alums, and the similarity in the properties of the metals themselves. In all probability, when their chemistry has been more fully investigated, similar relationships will be discerned between molybdenum, masurium and ruthenium ; and between tungsten, rhenium and osmium.

CHAPTER XXXV

IRON, COBALT, NICKEL AND THE PLATINUM METALS

Steel is the mainspring of modern industry. The commercial importance of steel is greater than that of gold, silver, zinc, copper and lead combined, and indeed, the trite saying that this is an age of iron, is well founded.—W. M. Johnson (1914).

The progress which has been made and the considerable exactness actually attained in chemical analysis have been owing in a great measure to the discovery of platina. Without the resources placed at the ready disposal of chemists by this invaluable metal, it is difficult to conceive that the multitude of delicate analytical experiments which have been required to construct the fabric of existing knowledge could have ever been performed.—J. F. W. Herschel.

§ 1 Group VIII of the Periodic Table

Group VIII of the Periodic Table comprises those elements which Mendeléeff termed transition elements (a name which now has a different and more fundamental significance (p. 144). It differs from all the other groups in containing three sets of three elements, each triad being composed of very similar elements whose atomic numbers differ only by one unit each. They are, in fact, situated more or less in the middle of each run of transition elements (in the modern sense, p. 119).

The elements concerned are iron, cobalt and nickel; ruthenium, rhodium and palladium; and osmium, iridium and platinum. The six last named are frequently referred to as a whole as the " platinum metals."

§ 2 Iron, Fe. History and Occurrence

History

Iron is perhaps the most precious of all the metals, for civilized man would probably feel its absence more than would be the case if he were deprived of all the so-called precious metals. Early in the fourteenth century, when iron was scarce, some iron kitchen utensils in the household of Edward III are said to have been classed among the jewels; and iron implements were among the most prized objects of plundering freebooters. The name iron is derived from the Scandinavian *iarn*. Several fabulous stories have been told describing how meteoric iron falling to the earth was sent from heaven as a gift of the gods to man. It requires no such romantic explanation of the discovery when it is remembered how readily iron is reduced from its ores. It has been suggested that " the first iron produced was the result of chance when lumps of iron ore, in place of stones, formed a rude cooking fire associated with some feast, where the fire was maintained long enough to effect the reduction." Then followed the observation that the higher temperatures obtained when the wind was blowing produced better material.   Hence followed various contrivances for producing an artificial blast of wind, and so on by natural stages to the blast furnace.   Iron implements have been used from prehistoric times, one was found during some blasting operations in the pyramid at Gizeh (Egypt), which is probably 5000 years old.   The use of steel in China has been traced as far back as 2550 B.C., and we are told by the philologists that the early Vedic poets mention iron as being in the possession of their prehistoric ancestors, and that the artisans had acquired considerable skill in fashioning iron into tools. Owing to the fact that ancient objects of iron are comparatively rare, while ancient bronze objects are quite abundant, archaeologists affirm that the so-called *bronze age* preceded the *age of iron*.   The argument is much weakened when it is remembered how much more readily iron is corroded by oxidation, and how much more readily bronze would survive atmospheric action.   Still, bronze was more easy to extract and work than iron, and archaeologists consider that bronze ceased to be the dominant tool and weapon of civilized peoples about 500 B.C. The scarcity of copper and the abundance of iron in India makes it probable that with the Hindoos the iron age was not preceded by a bronze age.   The Aryan emigrants who travelled into Europe carried with them a knowledge of producing iron from its ores.   The Etruscans of North Italy were of Aryan stock, and they acquired considerable skill in the working of iron.   Soon after the downfall of the Roman Empire, the manufacture of iron developed in Spain. The famous Toledo steel blades were the product of Spanish artisans. Their fame spread, and Spanish craftsmen were drawn into France and Germany and there they introduced their peculiar Catalan forge which subsequently evolved into the large iron-smelting furnaces. The product of the Catalan forge is either a malleable iron or steel ; the larger furnaces produced a variety of iron which could neither be forged nor tempered, although it was very suitable for all kinds of castings of moderate strength—cast iron.   The discovery of a process by Cort—*vide infra*—whereby cast iron could be converted into wrought iron at a far less cost than was possible in the Catalan forge, gave a great impetus to the manufacture of iron in England.

Iron is frequently mentioned in the sacred writings.   The Chalybes —an ancient nation living near the Black Sea—are supposed by the Greeks to have been the first to smelt iron ores.   Hence the old term *chalybs* for steel, and our modern *chalybeate* for ferruginous.   The process of smelting iron was early practised in the East, and the Hindoos acquired considerable skill in the manufacture of wrought iron and steel.   The old sword blades of Toledo, Bilbao, and Damascus have never been excelled.   The more recent method of smelting by means of the blast furnace is said to have been devised in Germany about 1350; and in Great Britain about 1500. Charcoal was first used as the reducing agent; in 1618 D. Dudley commenced using coal; and in 1713 Darby used coke. Coke and coal gradually displaced the use of charcoal. Some charcoal is still used where wood is cheap, e.g., in a few places on the Continent and in America.

Occurrence

Small quantities of metallic iron occur in some basaltic rocks. An unusual mass, over twenty-five tons, has been found on the Disko Island, Greenland. Since iron rapidly corrodes when exposed to a humid atmosphere, native iron is not at all common. Nearly all *meteorites* or *aerolites* contain iron associated with other metals—chiefly copper, cobalt, and nickel. Traces of iron combined in various ways are found scattered almost universally throughout the mineral kingdom. Ferric oxide, Fe_2O_3, is widely distributed in nature as *red haematite*—from the Greek αἷμα (haima), blood, in reference to the colour of its streak—*red ore*, and *specular iron ore*—from the Latin *speculum*, a mirror, in allusion to the lustrous crystals of this mineral. *Brown haematite* represents a class of hydrated oxides which may be represented by the general formula: $Fe_2O_3.nH_2O$, where n represents the variable amount of water in different varieties—*limonite* is generally taken to be $Fe_2O_3.3H_2O$, that is, $Fe(OH)_3$; *göthite*, $Fe_2O_3.H_2O$; and *bog iron ore* which occurs in Ireland belongs to this class. Limonite and scanthosiderite are considered to be colloidal forms of göthite with various quantities of adsorbed water. *Magnetite*, Fe_3O_4, is called *loadstone*, and *magnetic oxide of iron*. *Siderite*, or *spathic iron ore*, $FeCO_3$, is a ferrous carbonate. *Iron pyrites*, FeS_2, and *chalcopyrites* or cupriferous pyrites, $CuFeS_2$, are not worked directly for iron on account of the difficulty involved in eliminating sulphur from the product so that iron pyrites is often regarded as a sulphur ore. Very few clays, soils and granite rocks are free from small quantities of iron. Iron plays an important part in the nutrition of higher animals and plants since this element seems necessary for their healthy growth.

§ 3 The Extraction of Iron from its Ores

The principal sources of commercial iron are the oxides—magnetite and haematite—and carbonates. These ores frequently contain a certain amount of clay and are then termed *clay ironstones*. The so-called *blackband ironstone* is a ferrous carbonate contaminated with clay and black coaly matters. The ores are usually calcined or roasted to drive off most of the moisture and carbon dioxide; to burn the organic matter and some of the sulphur and arsenic; and to convert ferrous oxide to ferric oxide.

This prevents the early formation of a fusible slag which would attack the lining of the furnace. Ferric oxide does not form a slag at so low a temperature as ferrous oxide. At the same time the ore is made somewhat porous, and this facilitates its reduction to metallic iron at a later stage of the process.

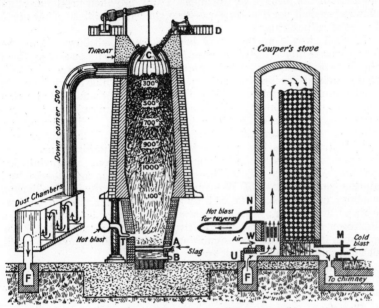

FIG. 234.—Blast Furnace (Diagrammatic).

The reduction of the calcined ore or of ferric oxide is effected in a blast furnace.

The Blast Furnace

The blast furnace is a tall cylindrical furnace—80 to 120 feet high —and shaped approximately as indicated in the section, Fig. 234. The dimensions and constructional details of blast furnaces vary somewhat in different localities. It has an outer shell made of iron plates riveted together. Inside this is a casing of ordinary brickwork, and inside this a lining of firebricks—$1\frac{1}{2}$ feet thick. The parts which are subjected to the greatest heat are built independently so as to facilitate repairs. The greatest internal width is 20 feet. This part is called the *bosh*. The mouth of the furnace is closed by a *cup-and-cone feeder*, C. The materials for charging the furnace are conveyed in trucks to the *charging gallery*, D, at the top of the furnace, and there tipped into the cup of the feeder. When the cup is filled, the cone is depressed, and the charge automatically distributed in the interior of the furnace. The waste gases pass away via the outlet at the throat of the furnace. The furnace narrows below the boshes, and at the hearth the diameter is 8 feet. Molten iron and slag collect on the hearth, and outlets are here provided, one, A, for tapping the slag, and another, B, for tapping the iron. Between six and eight feet from the base of the furnace, six openings, T, are provided for the insertion of water-cooled nozzles—*tuyeres*—through which a blast of hot air is forced into the furnace.

The hot gases from the top of the furnace are led down a flue—the *down-comer*—into a chamber—the *dust-catcher*. The gases pass from the dust-catcher along an underground flue, FF, to a tower—*Cowper's stove*—packed checkerwise with firebricks. The flue gas is burnt in the combustion chamber of the stove, and the products of combustion pass on to the chimney. The secondary air required for the combustion of this gas enters through the ports, W. The burning gas raises the temperature of the checker brickwork. When the temperature of the stove is hot enough, the gases from the blast furnace are deflected, and burnt in an adjoining similar tower ; meanwhile the gas and air valves—U, V, W—in the hot tower are closed ; and another set of valves—M, N—connecting the tuyeres with the blowing machine are opened. The cold air passing through the hot checkerwork of the Cowper's stove on its way to the tuyeres is heated. When the tower has been cooled sufficiently, the adjoining stove is hot. The gas from the blast furnace is again burned in the cooled tower, and the blast is sent through the hot tower.

The chemical changes which take place in the blast furnace during the smelting of iron ore are somewhat complex. Hence the following sketch must be regarded as a simplified description :

1. The Ore

The ore, mixed with coke and limestone, is exposed, in the upper part of the furnace, to the action of reducing gases, principally carbon monoxide, ascending from the lower part of the furnace. The action commences between 200° and 500°, that is, as soon as the charge has commenced its downward descent :

$$Fe_2O_3 + 3CO \rightleftharpoons 2Fe + 3CO_2 ;$$

and reduction continues with increasing velocity as the charge descends into the hotter part of the furnace. There appears to be a complex series of side and intermediate reactions :

$$3Fe_2O_3 + CO = 2Fe_3O_4 + CO_2 ;$$
$$Fe_3O_4 + CO \rightleftharpoons CO_2 + 3FeO ; \text{ and}$$
$$FeO + CO \rightleftharpoons CO_2 + Fe.$$

Below dull redness, the back-reaction

$$Fe + CO \rightleftharpoons FeO + C$$

is known to occur. Most of the oxide is reduced before it has descended ten feet below the level of the charge ; any oxide which has escaped reduction will then be reduced by the carbon :

$$Fe_2O_3 + 3C = 3CO + 2Fe.$$

The hot spongy iron meets the ascending carbon monoxide, and decomposes part :

$$2CO = CO_2 + C.$$

The solid carbon is deposited amidst the spongy iron. The iron undergoes little change until it reaches the zone of fusion. The iron, however, absorbs or dissolves much carbon as it passes down the furnace. The melting point of a mixture of iron and carbon is lower than that of pure iron, so that while the temperature of the blast furnace would not be sufficient to melt pure iron to the necessary fluid condition, the temperature required for iron with carbon in solution is easily maintained. The molten iron trickles down and collects in the well of the furnace below the tuyeres. The iron takes up many other elements in addition to carbon during its descent to the furnace. Thus, silicon, sulphur, phosphorus, and manganese are partly absorbed by the iron, and partly by the slag.

2. The Ascending Gases

The oxygen of the hot air blast burns the carbon of the hot coke

$$C + O_2 = CO_2 ;$$

and the carbon dioxide is at once reduced by the hot carbon :

$$CO_2 + C = 2CO.$$

The ascending gases warm up the descending charge. When the temperature reaches about 600°, the limestone begins to decompose :

$$CaCO_3 = CO_2 + CaO.$$

Most of the carbon dioxide thus formed is at once reduced by the excess of carbon to carbon monoxide. At this stage, the reduction of the iron oxide to spongy metallic iron is practically complete. An excess of carbon monoxide is needed for the reduction because the reaction, Fe_2O_3

$$Fe_2O_3 + 3CO \rightleftharpoons 3CO_2 + 2Fe,$$

is reversible, and a condition of equilibrium would be attained when only a certain proportion of the ferric oxide is reduced. An excess of carbon monoxide favours a more complete reduction of the ferric oxide. There are quite a number of concurrent reactions taking place at the same time. If any water is present in the blast, it will be reduced :

$$H_2O + C = CO + H_2 ;$$

and the nitrogen of the air, brought in with the gas, forms a little cyanogen. The net result is a combustible gas, containing approximately :

CO	CO$_2$	N	H	Hydrocarbons.
25·3	10·5	58·1	4·3	1·6 per cent.

The combustible gas is utilized for heating the blast ; and if there be any surplus, it is used for heating the boilers which run the blowing engine ; for calcining the ore, and for general heating purposes. If coal be used in place of coke, tar, etc., separate from the gas at the base of the down-comer and that mixture is treated by the process described under coal gas.

3. The Slag

When the charge in the furnace has descended about twenty or thirty feet, and the temperature is about 600°, it has formed a mixture of spongy iron, earthy gangue, coke, and limestone or quicklime. Little further change occurs until the temperature is hot enough to melt the mixture. At this temperature, a fusible slag is formed containing approximately 55 per cent. SiO_2, 30 per cent. CaO, and 15 per cent. Al_2O_3. The fused slag trickles down into the well, and floats on the surface of the molten iron. The slag is drawn from the furnace at intervals, and, when cool enough, tipped on the slag heap.

The fact that any water present in the blast is reduced during the operation of the blast furnace has been mentioned. This is a strongly endothermic reaction as shown by the equation :

$$H_2O + C = CO + H_2 - 29 \text{ Cals.}$$

The heat absorbed in this reaction is taken from that being liberated in the furnace in general and lowers the working temperature, besides using up valuable fuel. Hence, processes for drying the blast are now being tried. One of the most promising methods seems to be the use of silica gel (p. 685) which can absorb up to 20 per cent. of its weight of moisture, and can be re-vivified simply by heating to a suitable temperature. The gel is made by mixing solutions of sodium hydrogen sulphate and sodium silicate, and is placed on suitable perforated trays in a chamber through which the air for the blast passes. It is interesting to note that if the amount of moisture be reduced below 1·25 grains per cu. ft., the furnace will not operate : a discovery in harmony with the results obtained by Dixon and by Baker on the effects of intensive drying (p. 284).

The molten metal which collects on the hearth of the blast furnace is tapped at intervals and run into sand moulds, or into chilled moulds and allowed to solidify. In this form it is known as pig-iron or cast iron. If it is to be used for steel making, the charge is sometimes conveyed in the molten state direct to the converter or furnace in which this is to be done so as to save the cost of fuel required for remelting the solid pig-iron.

Pig-iron is a relatively impure form of iron, containing between 1·5 and 4 per cent of carbon (partly free and partly combined as Fe_3C) together with phosphorus, sulphur, silicon and traces of other elements. It is a brittle material, and cannot be worked under the hammer, for when heated it passes immediately from the solid brittle condition to the liquid state, when it can be *cast* or poured into moulds ; hence it is known as cast iron. Cast iron is used for the production of a large number of articles of all kinds which do not have to withstand undue strain or shock, among which may be mentioned iron bedsteads, gutter pipes, stoves, railings and similar objects.

§ 4 Wrought Iron

Wrought iron is practically pure iron and was formerly extensively used, but it has now been very largely superseded by mild steel.

Wrought iron is now made by melting pig-iron with " scrap " iron on the bed of a reverberatory furnace, Fig. 235, lined with iron ore (Fe_2O_3). The reverberatory furnace —here called a *puddling furnace*— was first used for iron by T. and G. Granage in 1776, and more successfully by H. Cort in 1784, although similar furnaces had been used by copper smelters for some time. Rogers, in 1816, improved the furnace by introducing a bed of iron oxide in place of siliceous matters previously used.

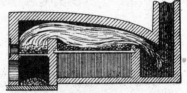

Fig. 235.

Puddling Furnace (Diagrammatic).

When the pigs of cast iron are melted in the puddling furnace, part of the carbon, silicon, sulphur, and phosphorus of the cast iron are oxidized by the furnace lining, and the metal melts to a fluid mass on the bed of the furnace (*melting stage*). The puddler then thoroughly mixes the charge so as to bring the molten metal into intimate contact with the iron oxide of the furnace bed. The puddler works the iron through an opening in the side of the furnace. The sulphur, phosphorus, and silicon are partly oxidized. Jets of flame soon appear on the surface of the molten metal—" puddler's candles " (*fluid stage*). The carbon is oxidized to carbon monoxide which burns to carbon dioxide. The other impurities are also oxidized, and form a slag with the lining of the furnace (*boiling stage*). The iron then becomes " pasty " because purified iron melts at a higher temperature than the less pure iron. The molten mass is stirred, puddled, and finally gathered into large " balls " or " blooms," each ball about 80 lbs. in weight (*balling stage*). The balls are removed from the furnace, and squeezed nearly free from slag by working under a steam hammer. The iron is then rolled into sheets so as to give the finished product a fibrous structure.

While cast iron melts at about 1200°, wrought iron melts at about 1527°. Wrought iron softens at about 1000°, and it can then be forged and welded. Wrought iron is tough and malleable, and fibrous in structure ; cast iron is brittle, and it has a crystalline structure. Under the microscope, wrought iron appears to be composed of a bundle of fibres surrounded by some slag of magnetic oxide, etc. ; each bundle seems to consist of a series of fibres of metallic iron, interlaced with a little ferrous silicide. These fibres give wrought iron its characteristic structure and enable it to withstand severe longitudinal stresses. Wrought iron was formerly used for shipbuilding, bridge construction and similar purposes, but on account of the very arduous nature of the work involved in its manufacture, and its high cost, it has now been largely replaced by mild steel. Thus the production of wrought iron in this country has declined from nearly three million tons in 1882 to little over 100,000 tons in 1930, although the total production of iron in all forms has increased in the same period. It is still probably unequalled for smith's work in general and has advantages over steel for the manufacture of chains and hooks.

§ 5 The Manufacture of Steel

By far the largest proportion of the iron produced in modern industry is converted into some form of steel, which is iron containing from 0·5 to 1·5 per cent. of carbon, and only the merest traces of sulphur and phosphorus. Other metals (e.g., tungsten, chromium, molybdenum, vanadium, manganese, nickel, cobalt) may be added in considerable quantities for the production of alloy steels for special purposes.

The amount of carbon in steel is thus intermediate between that in cast iron and in wrought iron, so that steel can be made by decarbonizing cast iron or by carbonizing wrought iron. At one time steel was almost entirely made in the latter way ; but now only comparatively small quantities are made thus.

The principal methods of making steel are :
(i) the cementation process ;
(ii) the crucible process ;
(iii) acid and basic Bessemer processes ;
(iv) acid and basic open-hearth (Siemens-Martin) processes ;
(v) electrical processes.

The Cementation Process

This is the oldest method of steel making. Bars of specially pure varieties of wrought iron—e.g., Swedish iron—are packed with charcoal in boxes made of firebrick, and sealed with a lute of refuse from the troughs below the grindstones of the steel grinders. The boxes are heated in a furnace for eight to eleven days at about 1000°. The time and temperature depend upon the amount of carbon to be incorporated with the wrought iron. The bars, when removed from the cold furnace, have a blistered appearance, hence the term *blister steel*. The bars are broken and sorted by experts who estimate the quality from the appearance of fractured surfaces. The blistered steel is then heated, and hammered into bars. The product is a high-class tool steel called *shear steel*.

Blister steel is also melted in crucibles, and cast into ingots for high-grade cast steels.

During cementation, carbon slowly diffuses into the iron. Possibly carbon monoxide is formed, occluded in the iron and there decomposed depositing carbon ; the carbon dioxide resulting would then escape into the box of charcoal and re-form the monoxide.

The Crucible Process

Bars of wrought iron are melted with a definite amount of charcoal in fireclay crucibles. The result is a high-grade crucible steel used for razors, shears and various tools. A less pure product is obtained by heating a mixture of wrought iron with the right amount of cast iron.

The Bessemer Process

In 1852 Kelly patented a process for purifying pig-iron, based on the fact that if air be forced through a mass of molten pig-iron, in a suitable vessel, the impurities—carbon, silicon, phosphorus, etc.—which prevent the pig-iron being ductile and malleable are oxidized first, and a bath of molten metal, virtually wrought iron, is obtained. In 1856 H. Bessemer patented a converter suitable for the process. Bessemer afterwards bought Kelly's patents. The metal in the converter can be mixed with a known amount of spiegeleisen—i.e., a ferro-manganese containing a known amount of carbon.

The manganese is oxidized by the remaining oxygen of the iron, while the carbon brings the composition of the metal to that of mild steel.

In the Bessemer process about ten tons of molten pig-iron are run into a large egg-shaped vessel, called the *converter* (Fig. 236). The converter is made of iron plates lined with siliceous bricks (often *ganister* is used: a silica mineral), and provided with holes at the bottom through which a powerful blast of air can be blown. When the converter has been charged and the blast is turned on, the temperature rises owing to the heat evolved by the oxidation and combustion of the impurities—silicon, manganese and carbon. The carbon forms

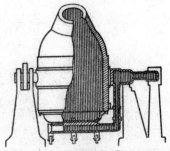

FIG. 236.—Bessemer Converter.

carbon monoxide, which burns at the mouth of the converter: the other oxides form a slag with the lining. By observing the flame, the right moment to stop the blast can be determined. The right amount of spiegeleisen is then added, the blast is turned on again for a few moments, and the metal is then cast into moulds.

This process revolutionized steel-making when first introduced, and brought down the price of steel from £70 per ton to the neighbourhood of £15, besides making possible the production of very large quantities. Unfortunately, in its original form it can only be employed for pig-iron free from phosphorus, since this, if present, is not removed, and renders the resulting steel brittle and useless.

In 1878, S. G. Thomas and P. C. Gilchrist showed that, if the converter be lined with, say, dolomite (basic lining), and some lime be added to the charge of pig-iron, and the blast continued a little longer, the oxides of phosphorus, sulphur and silicon formed are absorbed by the furnace lining. The operation is otherwise conducted as before. The process gives rise to *basic slag*, which is used as a fertilizer on account of the phosphorus it contains. If the lining is siliceous, the operation is called the *acid Bessemer process* ; and if the lining be dolomite, the *basic Bessemer process*.

The Siemens-Martin Open-Hearth Process

This is now the method in widest use for the manufacture of steel.

In this process, the furnace is charged with a mixture of pig-iron, scrap iron and good haematite ore free from carbon. The mixture is

Producer Gas
from hot chambers

Flue Gas to
cold chambers

FIG. 237.—Hearth of Siemens-
Martin Process (Diagrammatic)

melted in a shallow rectangular trough or hearth. The furnace is heated by producer gas. Both the gas and the secondary air for the combustion of the gas are pre-heated so that a very high temperature can be obtained. A general idea of the process can be gathered from Fig. 237, which shows a section through the hearth. The air port is not shown in the diagram. The gas and air burn on the left, the flue gases travel down the flue on the right, and in doing so heat up two chambers packed with checker brickwork. The direction of the burning gas is then reversed. Gas and air pass separately through the heated chambers, and the flue gases heat up another pair of similar chambers below the hearth. The direction travelled by the burning gas is reversed about every half-hour, and the heat of the flue gases is utilized in warming up chambers through which the unburnt gas and air will pass later on. The furnace is called *Siemens' regenerative furnace*. When a test shows that the metal contains the right amount of carbon, ferro-manganese is added as in the case of Bessemer's steel. If the bed of the furnace is made of siliceous materials—*acid process*— the proportion of carbon, silicon, and manganese are reduced during the treatment, but the amounts of sulphur and phosphorus remain fairly constant. In the *basic process*, the furnace is bedded with, say, dolomite, and there is a steady fall in the amount of phosphorus and sulphur during the treatment, just as was the case with the basic Bessemer process.

The open-hearth process owes its commanding position in the steel industry to the readiness with which the composition of the steel can be controlled, the uniformity of the product, the ability to use up steel scrap, the relatively smaller loss of iron in the process (4 per cent. as against 15 per cent. in Bessemer), and the large quantities which can be dealt with at one operation. Its principal disadvantage, in comparison with the Bessemer process, is the necessity for heating the furnace externally.

Electrical Processes

Electric furnaces, usually of the arc-type, are used in the production of special high-quality steels. The absence of contact with furnace-gases reduces the chance of contamination by impurities and lessens the risk of the finished product containing " blow-holes." The purity of the product renders these methods important, especially where electric power is cheap as in Sweden, for the manufacture of high-grade products and special alloy steels.

§ 6 The Constitution and Properties of Iron and Steel

Pure iron is a laboratory curiosity ; all commercial forms of iron contain impurities, notably carbon ; and their properties depend upon the nature and amount of these impurities.

Iron appears to exist in several allotropic modifications.

If the temperature of a cooling bar of almost pure iron be recorded every half minute by a recording pyrometer the cooling process does not appear to be uniform and continuous, because the metal cools down to about 860°, and then becomes hotter ; the cooling is then resumed until, at about 750°, the temperature again begins to oscillate. These temperature fluctuations are supposed to be due to the transition of iron from one allotropic modification to another. Each transition temperature corresponds with a change in the mechanical and physical properties of the iron. The sequence of changes is reversed when the cold iron is heated. Iron below 680° is called α-**ferrite** ; between 750° and 860°, β-**ferrite** ; and above 860°, γ-**ferrite**. Some consider that the alleged β-iron is a solid solution of γ-iron in α-iron. If the iron contains some carbon in solution, both the transition points approach 720°. The proximity of these points to 720° depends on the amount of carbon in solution. A new disturbance then appears in the cooling curve at about 660°. There is a marked evolution of heat at this temperature, for the red-hot cooling steel glows more brightly than before. This phenomenon was called by its discoverer—Barrett (1874) —the **recalescence** of steel.

Iron at about 1240° dissolves 5 percen t. of carbon, the amount dissolved increases with the temperature, so that at about 2380°, nearly 10 per cent. is dissolved. A sample of iron of 99·98 per cent. purity melted at about 1520° ; and the freezing point of iron is lowered by the presence of carbon in the same way that the freezing point of water is lowered by salt. The freezing point curve for solutions of carbon in iron is shown in Fig. 238. If a molten saturated solution of carbon

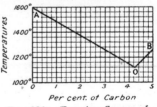

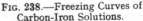

FIG. 238.—Freezing Curves of Carbon-Iron Solutions.

in iron be slowly cooled, the excess of carbon separates as graphite, and the still molten mother liquid becomes poorer in carbon ;

DD*

as the temperature falls, graphite continues separating as illustrated by the curve *BO*, Fig. 238. When the mother liquid has 4·3 per cent. of carbon in solution, it solidifies, *en masse* at 1130°, corresponding with the point *O*. The mixture containing 4·3 per cent of carbon is the most fusible mixture of carbon and iron—the eutectic mixture, and 1130° is the eutectic temperature. If the cooling fluid contains less than 4·3 per cent. of carbon, a solid solution of about 2 per cent. of carbon commences to separate, and continues separating as the solution cools until the remaining fluid has the eutectic composition, which solidifies *en masse* at 1130°. The carbon which is rejected as the solution cools is called **graphitic carbon.** It is not attacked when the metal is digested in boiling hydrochloric acid, nor by nitric acid of specific gravity 1·2. When steel free from graphitic carbon is digested in dilute hydrochloric or sulphuric acid, part of the carbon—called **hardening carbon**—appears to be combined with the metal, for it is evolved as a hydrocarbon gas along with the escaping hydrogen. A portion of the carbon—called **cementite carbon**—remains undissolved. The cementite carbon, however, does dissolve in dilute nitric acid, forming a brown solution. The intensity of the colour is proportional to the amount of carbon dissolved, and by comparing the colour of the solution with the colour of the solutions made up with steels containing known amounts of carbon, the amount of carbon in solution can be estimated. This is the so-called *Eggertz's colour test for combined carbon in steel.*

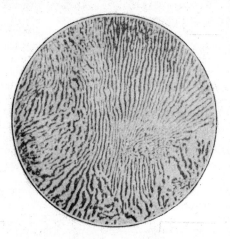

FIG. 239.—Pearlite.

Iron above 860° is in the γ-condition ; and between 860° and 750° in the β-condition. The solid solution of carbon in γ ferrite above 860° is called **austenite**—after W. C. Roberts-Austen ; and the solid solution of carbon in β-ferrite, **martensite**—after A. Martens. α-ferrite does not appear to form a solid solution of carbon in the same way as do β- and γ-ferrite. J. O. Arnold calls a solid solution of iron with 0·89 per cent. of carbon, **hardenite.** Hardenite has a constant composition containing 0·89 per cent. carbon.

If hardenite be cooled slowly, it decomposes just below 700° into a mixture of ferrite (iron) and cementite. There is a marked evolution of heat during the decomposition of the hardenite. This corresponds with the recalescence of cooling steel just below 700°. **Cementite** is an iron carbide, Fe_3C, or a solid solution containing Fe_3C with traces of several other carbides. The mixture of cementite and ferrite forms alternate layers of different degrees of hardness. When the surface of the metal is polished the harder parts stand out in relief. This gives the surface an iridescent appearance resembling mother-of-pearl when viewed at certain angles. Hence the mixture has been called " the pearly constituent of steel," or simply **pearlite.** The alternate layers, under the microscope, have an appearance resembling that shown in Fig. 239. If the solid solution—hardenite—be cooled so quickly that the decomposition products of the hardenite have not time to segregate into alternate layers, but produce a more or less ill-defined mixture of cementite and ferrite, the mixture is called **sorbite**—after H. C. Sorby. With slowly cooled steels the pearlitic structure is well developed ; and with more quickly cooled steels, the sorbitic structure prevails. If the iron has less than 0·89 per cent. of carbon, ferrite separates from the cooling solid solution until a mixture of ferrite embedded in a matrix of hardenite with 0·89 per cent. of carbon remains ; the hardenite then dissociates as indicated above. Similarly, if the solution has more than 0·89 per cent. of carbon, cementite separates until a matrix of cementite imbedded in hardenite, with 0·89 per cent. of carbon, is formed ; the hardenite then dissociates as before. It will be noticed that pearlite and sorbite are not definite constituents ; the terms refer to the mode in which certain constituents of a mixture are aggregated together. Metallographists are not all agreed in their interpretations of the observed phenomena, and details are still in dispute.

The sudden quenching of the steel while these changes are in progress may arrest or inhibit further change. Similarly, re-heating followed by sudden quenching may completely alter the structure, and accordingly also the properties of the metal. The hardness of steel thus depends upon its composition and its history—the way the metal has been cooled, and on its subsequent heat treatment. A typical steel containing nearly 1 per cent. of carbon when heated to a high temperature and suddenly chilled, becomes so hard that it will scratch glass, and so brittle that it will not bend very far without breaking. The operation is called **hardening steel.** The hardenite of hardened steel is preserved more or less undecomposed when the steel is suddenly chilled—hence the term " hardenite." If the hardened steel be re-heated to its original high temperature, and slowly cooled—" letting down," or **annealing steel**—it becomes soft and ductile. By re-heating hardened steel to certain definite temperatures—200° and upwards—and then cooling under definite conditions, steels can be obtained of varying, yet definite, degrees of hardness and ductility. This has been traced to changes in the constitution of the metal. The process of re-heating a hardened steel to a temperature far short of that employed when the steel was hardened is called **tempering steel.**

Properties of Pure Iron

Pure iron is a grey, lustrous metal which crystallizes in the cubic system. It melts at 1527°, and boils at 3000° ; its density is 7·87 and its specific heat 0·11. One of the most noteworthy of the physical properties of iron is its magnetism. Almost every element exhibits some slight magnetic phenomena ; but its extent in iron is remarkable and unique. Pronounced magnetic properties appear to be possessed only by α-ferrite ; the other forms are apparently non-magnetic.

Iron is readily oxidized ; it burns brilliantly in oxygen, and, when finely divided, will also burn in air, the magnetic oxide (Fe_3O_4) being formed. Iron also burns in chlorine and in sulphur vapour ; ferric chloride and ferrous sulphide being the respective products. When heated to redness, iron also reacts readily with steam, hydrogen and the magnetic oxide resulting.

Iron dissolves in dilute acids ; sulphuric acid furnishes ferrous sulphate and hydrogen ; and hydrochloric acid furnishes ferrous chloride and hydrogen. With cold dilute nitric acid (specific gravity below 1·034) hydrogen is not evolved, but the acid is reduced to ammonia, and this reacts with the excess of nitric acid to form ammonium nitrate ; with an acid of specific gravity 1·034 to 1·115, *ferrous nitrate* is the main product ; and with an acid of greater specific gravity than 1·115, say 1·3, *ferric nitrate* is the main product. With concentrated nitric acid (specific gravity 1·45), the iron does not dissolve. The iron in contact with the concentrated acid appears to have changed, for it behaves differently from a piece of the same sample of iron which has not been in contact with concentrated nitric acid. The sample which has not been in contact with the strong acid will precipitate copper from copper sulphate solutions, lead from lead nitrate, and silver from silver nitrate ; the other sample will not. The inert iron is said to be in the passive condition. **Passive iron** does not dissolve when dipped in dilute nitric acid. Other oxidizing agents, chromic acid, hydrogen peroxide, will make iron passive. It is now thought that the cause of passivity is that a thin film of oxide is formed on the metal by contact with the oxidizing agent. The passivity can be removed by scratching the surface of the iron, by heating it in a reducing gas, by strongly rubbing the surface, and by bringing the passive iron in contact with zinc while immersed in the dilute nitric acid. Other metals also exhibit passivity, e.g., cobalt, nickel, chromium, and bismuth.

Iron is not appreciably attacked by alkalis, except at high temperatures.

The Rusting of Iron

It has been estimated that the world's annual loss by corrosion of iron, steel and the ferrous metals generally, is in the neighbourhood of 700 millions sterling (Hadfield). It is, therefore, evident that the problem of the protection of iron and steel articles, so as to render them resistant to corrosion, is of paramount importance.

When commercial iron is exposed to a humid atmosphere for a short time, it soon becomes covered with a reddish-brown film which is called *rust*. Iron rust seems to be an indefinite mixture which on analysis furnishes numbers which vary according to the age of the rust, etc. Rust usually contains ferrous oxide, ferric oxide, carbon dioxide, and water. Analyses show that rust is probably a mixture of ferric oxide, hydrated ferrous and ferric oxides, and basic ferrous and ferric carbonates. If the rust has been long exposed to the air, the amount of ferric oxide is relatively large, and the amounts of ferrous oxide and carbon dioxide small. Rusting is a complex process, and workers are by no means agreed on the simple facts. Dry iron in dry air does not rust, moisture must be present before rusting can occur.

It also appears to be true that water alone (in the absence of air) will not cause rusting to take place. There is still some dispute as to whether pure iron will rust in the presence of pure water and pure oxygen only, and although it is quite possible that rusting does not occur under these conditions, nevertheless, this particular question is of academic interest only.

Some deny, others affirm, that the presence of an acid and water are necessary. It is exceedingly difficult to free water and the surface of glass from carbon dioxide ; and silicic acid can be dissolved from the glass vessels used and from particles of slag in the iron. However, where careful attention has been taken to eliminate the disturbing factors, the evidence seems in favour of the conclusion that the presence of an acid is necessary for rusting ; that an acid is always present when the iron dissolves ; and it is highly probable that pure iron does not undergo appreciable oxidation when exposed to pure water and to pure oxygen. Films of moisture frequently condense on the surface of iron exposed to the air, and the moisture holds carbonic acid and oxygen in solution. The mechanism of the " atmospheric rusting " of iron may then proceed according to the following scheme : An acid ferrous carbonate, $Fe(HCO_3)_2$; or a basic carbonate, $Fe(OH)(HCO_3)$, is first formed. The ferrous carbonate in contact with oxygen is oxidized to basic ferric carbonate, $Fe(OH)_2(HCO_3)$; or to $Fe(OH)(HCO_3)_2$; or both. The basic ferric carbonate is then hydrolyzed by the water, forming ferric hydroxide, $Fe(OH)_3$; and the ferric hydroxide is subsequently more or less dehydrated, forming ferric oxide. Ferric oxide is more or less hygroscopic, so that once rusting has started, at any point, subsequent corrosion is quicker because the ferric oxide helps to keep the surface of the iron adjacent to the rust spot moist. Several other hypotheses have been suggested, and the subject is still *sub judice*.

It has recently been shown by U. R. Evans that an important cause of the rusting of iron is differential aëration, and in so doing he has provided an explanation of the peculiar phenomenon of pitting. It is fairly clear that the corrosion of iron is an electro-chemical phenomenon connected with the different electrical condition of different portions of the metal ; for, if one piece of a metal becomes electro-positive to another, that piece will dissolve more rapidly in contact with an electrolyte, just as pure zinc dissolves more readily in acids when in contact with copper. If a cell be made in which the electrodes are two portions of iron, one of which is immersed in air-free water, and the other in water through which air is bubbled, a current is found to flow and the iron which is screened from air dissolves. Thus corrosion occurs at a point which is most screened from the air and so rusting, having once started, will tend to be worst at the deepest point in a rust patch, thus producing pits.

Alloys of Iron

Iron forms many valuable alloys with other elements, particularly in the form of special steels. Among the alloying elements may be mentioned vanadium, titanium, chromium, molybdenum, tungsten, manganese, nickel and cobalt. These, and their properties, are referred to briefly under the heading of the element concerned. In addition, the presence of more than the normal proportion of silicon produces a material of remarkable resistance to acids and other reagents, but it is very brittle and is not to be regarded as a steel. In certain circumstances silicon-steels can be made (see p. 680).

Atomic Weight

The values found for the vapour densities of volatile compounds of iron, such as iron carbonyls and ferric chloride, and the specific heat (0·116), indicate a value in the neighbourhood of 56 for the atomic weight of iron.

Accurate values have been determined by conversion of pure ferrous chloride and bromide into silver chloride and bromide, and by reduction of pure ferric oxide in a stream of hydrogen. By the bromide method Hönigschmid obtained values between 55·847 and 55·854. The mean of 18 experiments was 55·85 and this is the value recommended by the International Committee at the present time (1940).

§ 7 Oxides and Hydroxides of Iron

Iron forms three oxides, viz. :

Ferrous oxide, FeO ;
Ferrosic oxide (magnetic oxide), Fe_3O_4 ;
Ferric oxide, Fe_2O_3.

Ferrous oxide, FeO, is formed as a black, crystalline, magnetic substance when carbon dioxide is reduced by hot metallic iron. It is also formed when ferrous oxalate is heated out of contact with the air :

$$FeC_2O_4 = FeO + CO + CO_2.$$

When exposed to the air, it oxidizes readily, sometimes burning spontaneously, to ferric oxide. It is a basic oxide, and dissolves readily in acids forming ferrous salts.

Ferrous hydroxide, $Fe(OH)_2$, is obtained as a white precipitate when solutions of alkali hydroxides or ammonia are added to a solution of ferrous salt, with complete exclusion of air. If the solutions contain dissolved air, the precipitate has a greenish colour. It rapidly absorbs oxygen and passes into brown ferric hydroxide. It dissolves readily in acids, giving ferrous salts.

Ferrosic Oxide, Magnetic Oxide of Iron, Fe_3O_4

This compound occurs in nature as the mineral *magnetite* in black, octahedral crystals which are magnetic.

It is the most stable oxide, and is formed when iron or iron oxides are heated in air or oxygen. According to Moissan, there are two modifications of ferrosic oxide : the one is formed by heating ferric oxide from 350° to 400° in a current of hydrogen or carbon monoxide ; and the other by reactions at a high temperature, e.g., the combustion of iron in oxygen. The former is attacked by nitric acid, and has a specific gravity of 4·86 ; the latter is not attacked by the same acid, and has a specific gravity 5·0 to 5·1. The phenomenon is thus analogous with the general effect of high temperatures on oxides like alumina, chromic oxide, ferric oxide, etc. Ferrosic oxide is not a basic oxide since it forms a mixture of ferric and ferrous salts when treated with acids. It is probably a " compound " oxide, analogous with manganosic oxide, Mn_3O_4, and red lead, Pb_3O_4.

On this assumption, ferrosic oxide is a *ferrous ferrite*, $Fe(FeO_2)_2$. Several other ferrites are known (see below).

Ferric oxide, Fe_2O_3, occurs naturally in large quantities as *haematite* and *specular iron ore*—a crystalline form. It is obtained as one of the products of the roasting of iron pyrites for the manufacture of sulphuric acid (p. 461). It is formed as a reddish-brown powder when ferrous sulphate, or carbonate, or hydroxide, or many organic salts of iron are calcined in air. It is stable at a red heat, but at temperatures above about 1300° it decomposes into Fe_3O_4.

The finely-divided oxide, obtained by calcining ferrous sulphate, is known as *jeweller's rouge* and is used as a pigment. *Red ochre* and *venetian red* are also forms of ferric oxide. The particular tint of the pigment depends upon the temperature of calcination, which appears to determine the size of the particles.

When prepared at a low temperature, ferric oxide dissolves fairly easily in acids, forming ferric salts ; but if it be heated to a temperature above 600°, acids only attack it with difficulty.

Ferric Hydroxides

A voluminous red precipitate is formed when ammonium hydroxide is added to a solution of a ferric salt, and this appears to be the fully hydrated oxide, $Fe(OH)_3$. On drying and heating, this passes into ferric oxide. It readily reacts with acids, forming solutions of ferric salts, although it is a very weak base and its salts are largely hydrolyzed in solution.

Ferric hydroxide can readily be obtained in the form of a colloidal solution as described on page 246.

A hydrate of the composition $FeO(OH)$ or $Fe_2O_3.H_2O$ occurs naturally as the mineral göthite, and is also obtained by the action of water on sodium ferrite. It may be **ferrous acid**, $HFeO_2$.

On heating an intimate mixture of ferric oxide with sodium carbonate, **sodium ferrite**, $NaFeO_2$, is formed. Similarly, other ferrites result when ferric oxide is heated with basic oxides, e.g. :

$$ZnO + Fe_2O_3 = Zn(FeO_2)_2.$$

In these reactions ferric oxide exhibits an acidic character : it is thus an amphoteric oxide like aluminium oxide and chromic oxide.

Ferrates

When chlorine is passed through a concentrated solution of potassium hydroxide in which ferric hydroxide is suspended, the solution assumes a purple colour, and a black powder of **potassium ferrate**, K_2FeO_4, separates. The reaction is usually represented :

$$2Fe(OH)_3 + 10KOH + 3Cl_2 = 2K_2FeO_4 + 6KCl + 8H_2O.$$

The black powder appears to be analogous with potassium manganate, K_2MnO_4, with potassium chromate, K_2CrO_4, and with potassium sulphate, K_2SO_4. The salt dissolves in water, forming a rose-red solution which, on crystallization, furnishes dark-red crystals isomorphous with potassium sulphate and chromate. Potassium ferrate is unstable and its solution readily decomposes :

$$4K_2FeO_4 + 10H_2O = 8KOH + 4Fe(OH)_3 + 3O_2.$$

The barium salt, $BaFeO_4$, is a dark carmine-red and fairly stable. By analogy with the chromates and sulphates, it is inferred that the ferrates are derived from an unknown ferric acid, H_2FeO_4 ; which in turn is derived from an unknown ferric anhydride, FeO_3, analogous with sulphur and chromic trioxides.

§ 8 Salts of Iron. Ferrous Salts

Iron forms two series of salts derived respectively from ferrous oxide and ferric oxide.

Ferrous Salts

The ferrous salts are usually colourless when anhydrous, and form green crystalline hydrates and faintly green solutions. They are readily oxidized in acid solution by most oxidizing agents and, hence, are useful reducing agents. They are stable in air in presence of acid, but otherwise are readily oxidized in contact with the atmosphere. This probably occurs through the formation of the hydroxide which is precipitated in alkaline solutions, and is present in neutral solutions on account of hydrolysis.

Ferrous salts are distinguished from ferric salts in that they give a green precipitate with ammonia or alkali solutions, and a blue precipitate of Turnbull's blue with potassium ferricyanide solution (see p. 823).

Ferrous carbonate, $FeCO_3$, occurs naturally as *spathic iron ore*, and can be obtained as a white precipitate by mixing air-free solutions of sodium carbonate and ferrous sulphate. It rapidly oxidizes in contact with the air, becoming green, and finally red, through formation of ferric hydroxide.

Ferrous chloride, $FeCl_2$, is obtained in solution by dissolving pure iron wire in dilute hydrochloric acid. On concentration, the solution deposits bluish-green crystals having the composition $FeCl_2.4H_2O$. On heating, it decomposes so that the anhydrous salt cannot be obtained in this way. It is made by passing dry hydrogen chloride over heated iron, when white feathery crystals are produced.

Ferrous chloride is very soluble in water (100 grams of water dissolve 67 grams of anhydrous salt at 15° C.), and the solution has an acid reaction, probably on account of hydrolysis. Like the sulphate, the solution absorbs nitric oxide forming a black or very dark brown solution. On heating in air, ferrous chloride decomposes into ferric oxide and chloride :

$$12FeCl_2 + 3O_2 = 2Fe_2O_3 + 8FeCl_3.$$

With ammonia gas, at room temperatures, ferrous chloride forms $FeCl_2.6NH_3$, which passes into $FeCl_2.2NH_3$ at about 300°. It readily forms double salts, of which $FeCl_2.2NH_4Cl$—or $(NH_4)_2FeCl_4$—ferrous ammonium chloride is the most important.

Ferrous nitrate, $Fe(NO_3)_2.6H_2O$, forms unstable green crystals. It is obtained by grinding together equivalent quantities of ferrous sulphate and lead nitrate with a little alcohol :

$$Pb(NO_3)_2 + FeSO_4.7H_2O = Fe(NO_3)_2.6H_2O + PbSO_4 + H_2O.$$

Ferrous sulphide, FeS, is made by heating iron filings and sulphur, considerable heat being evolved in the process ; or by dipping iron rods into molten sulphur. A certain amount is precipitated when hydrogen sulphide is passed into alkaline solutions of ferrous salts. It is a black, insoluble substance with a metallic lustre in mass. It readily reacts with dilute acids, yielding hydrogen sulphide, and is used for the preparation of this gas (p. 445).

Ferrous Sulphate, Green Vitriol, $FeSO_4.7H_2O$

Ferrous sulphate occurs native as *copperas* or *melanterite*. It was known to the Ancient World and used for making ink, and in medicine. It is still used for the former purpose ; also for the preparation of blue pigments, and as a mordant. It is made commercially from iron pyrites. This is stacked in heaps exposed to air and moisture. Oxidation occurs, and the liquid which drains away contains ferrous and ferric sulphates and sulphuric acid; the " drainage solution " is converted into ferrous sulphate by scrap iron ; on crystallization, the solution furnishes pale green, rhombic prisms of the composition $FeSO_4.7H_2O$.

$$2FeS_2 + 7O_2 + 2H_2O = 2FeSO_4 + 2H_2SO_4,$$
$$4FeSO_4 + 2H_2SO_4 + O_2 = 2Fe_2(SO_4)_3 + 2H_2O,$$
$$Fe + H_2SO_4 = 2FeSO_4 + 2H,$$
$$2Fe_2(SO_4)_3 + 2H = 2FeSO_4 + H_2SO_4.$$

Pure ferrous sulphate is made in the laboratory by dissolving pure iron in sulphuric acid, precautions being taken to exclude air.

Ferrous sulphate, prepared as above, is a green crystalline solid, soluble in water (100 grams of water dissolve 43·5 grams of $FeSO_4.7H_2O$ at 15°). On heating, it decomposes, losing water, sulphur dioxide and trioxide :

$$2FeSO_4 = Fe_2O_3 + SO_2 + SO_3.$$

This reaction was at one period used for making sulphuric acid. On exposure to the air, the crystals turn brown, presumably owing to the formation of a basic ferric sulphate. Solutions of ferrous sulphate absorb nitric oxide, forming a black or dark-brown solution, a property made use of in the brown-ring test for nitrates (p. 411), and in the preparation of nitric oxide (p. 416).

Ferrous sulphate crystals are isomorphous with the corresponding salts of beryllium, magnesium, zinc, cadmium, manganese, chromium, cobalt and nickel, all of which crystallize with seven molecules of water. These are known as vitriols, e.g., green vitriol is ferrous sulphate ; white vitriol, zinc sulphate. It is interesting to note that copper sulphate normally crystallizes with $5H_2O$, but a salt isomorphous with the above series and of the composition $CuSO_4.7H_2O$, is formed when copper sulphate in admixture with the sulphate of iron, zinc or magnesium, is allowed to crystallize.

Ferrous ammonium sulphate, Mohr's salt, $FeSO_4.(NH_4)_2SO_4.$ $6H_2O$, is made by adding a saturated solution of ammonium sulphate at 40° to a solution of ferrous sulphate in as little air-free water at 40° as possible, in presence of a trace of sulphuric acid. Pale green crystals of the double salt separate on cooling. It is soluble in water (100 grams of water dissolve 20 grams of the salt at 15°), and both the solid and solution are less readily oxidized by contact with the atmosphere than ferrous sulphate. It is used in volumetric analysis.

Ferrosic chloride, $Fe_3Cl_8.18H_2O$, is analogous in composition to the magnetic oxide. It is made by dissolving that oxide in concentrated hydrochloric acid and evaporating the solution in a desiccator containing concentrated sulphuric acid. It forms yellow deliquescent crystals.

§ 9 Ferric Salts

The ferric salts are usually yellow, although in solution they often appear darker on account of the formation of ferric hydroxide by hydrolysis. They are found to be more easily hydrolyzed than the ferrous salts, i.e., ferric hydroxide is a weaker base than ferrous hydroxide.

Ferric salts are readily reduced to the corresponding ferrous salts by many reducing agents, e.g., nascent hydrogen, sulphur dioxide, etc. They are thus weak oxidizing agents. Some ferric salts (e.g., the oxalate) are reduced by the action of light ; a fact which is made use of in the blue-print process for reproducing diagrams, etc.

Ferric Chloride, $FeCl_3$ or Fe_2Cl_6

Anhydrous ferric chloride is made by passing dry chlorine over iron heated in a combustion tube. The ferric chloride formed is volatile and can be condensed in a bottle attached to the outlet of the tube. (See Fig. 240.) It forms glistening scales which appear greenish by reflected light, and dark red by transmitted light.

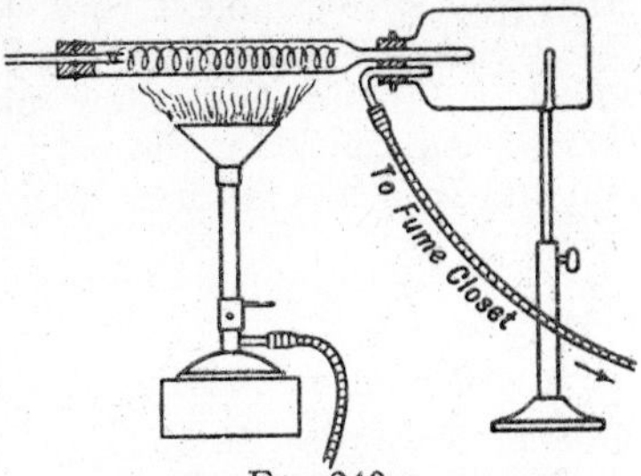

FIG. 240.
Preparation of Ferric Chloride.

Ferric chloride is ordinarily met with in the hydrated form, which is prepared by the action of iron, ferrous carbonate or ferric oxide on hydrochloric acid, to which a little nitric acid has been added. Several hydrates are known ; the one formed by allowing the solution made as above to crystallize has the composition $FeCl_3.6H_2O$.

Ferric chloride is very soluble in water (100 grams of water dissolve 92 grams of the anhydrous salt at 20°), but undergoes considerable hydrolysis, unless excess of hydrochloric acid be present. Colloidal ferric hydroxide is formed in this way, and may be separated by dialysis (p. 246).

The anhydrous salt boils at 315°, and at temperatures below 400° the vapour density corresponds with the formula Fe_2Cl_6 ; from 400° to 750° the vapour density steadily diminishes to the value corresponding to $FeCl_3$. At still higher temperatures, a further slight fall in vapour density occurs ; probably on account of dissociation into ferrous chloride and chlorine :

$$2FeCl_3 \rightleftharpoons 2FeCl_2 + Cl_2.$$

The elevation of the boiling point of ether or alcohol when ferric chloride is dissolved in them indicates a formula $FeCl_3$.

Ferric chloride solutions are yellow when dissociation does not occur (e.g., in ether or benzene) or has been prevented by addition of hydrochloric acid. Otherwise they are reddish on account of the formation of the hydroxide.

Ferric chloride forms a number of double salts which are garnet, red crystalline substances, e.g., $K_2FeCl_5.H_2O$; $(NH_4)_2FeCl_5.H_2O$.

Ferric nitrate, $Fe(NO_3)_3$, can be made by treating iron with moderately dilute nitric acid (sp. gr. ca. 1·3). On addition of more concentrated nitric acid, almost colourless crystals of the composition $Fe(NO_3)_3.9H_2O$ separate.

Ferric sulphide, Fe_2S_3, can be obtained by fusing equal weights of iron and sulphur at about 550° ; and by passing a current of hydrogen sulphide over warm ferric oxide, as in the purification of coal gas (p. 348).

Iron Disulphide, Iron Pyrites, FeS$_2$

Although ferrous sulphide is rare in nature, iron pyrites is very common indeed. It occurs in two forms : one, *pyrite*, crystallizes in the cubic system and is very slowly oxidized in air ; the other, *marcasite*, crystallizes in the rhombic system and oxidizes comparatively quickly. It is a hard yellow substance with an appearance resembling brass, and can be made artificially by heating iron with excess of sulphur at a low red heat, 500°.

When heated to 700°, it loses sulphur, and when heated in air it burns to ferric oxide and sulphur dioxide, and is extensively used as a source of sulphur dioxide for sulphuric acid manufacture (see p. 461). It is also used for making ferrous sulphate (p. 817).

Ferric Sulphate, Fe$_2$(SO$_4$)$_3$

This salt is prepared by adding sulphuric acid and an oxidizing agent, such as nitric acid or hydrogen peroxide to ferrous sulphate solution and boiling the mixture until it ceases to give a blue precipitate with potassium ferricyanide :

$$2FeSO_4 + H_2SO_4 + H_2O_2 = Fe_2(SO_4)_3 + 2H_2O.$$

After concentration, the solution deposits, when cooled, a whitish mass which has the composition Fe$_2$(SO$_4$)$_3$.9H$_2$O. The anhydrous salt can be obtained by heating the hydrate.

Ferric sulphate forms alums with the sulphates of the alkali metals, etc., the most important of which is **iron alum,** K$_2$SO$_4$.Fe$_2$(SO$_4$)$_3$. 24H$_2$O. It is used in analytical work as a standard of ferric iron as it is almost the only ferric salt which can be purified readily by crystallization.

§ 10 Ferrocyanides and Ferricyanides

Diesbach, a colour manufacturer of Berlin, accidentally discovered the colour now known as Prussian or Berlin blue, about 1704, and he mentioned the fact to the alchemist, Dippel, who investigated the subject, and according to Woodward (1724) prepared it by melting dried blood with potash salts and treating the aqueous extract of the mass with ferrous sulphate. J. Brown (1725) showed that animal flesh, and St. Geoffroy (1725) that other animal substances, could be used instead of blood. In 1752 Macquer noticed that when Prussian blue was boiled with an alkali, iron oxide separated from the solution and the mother-liquid contained a substance which separated in yellow crystals. It was then called *phlogisticated potash* and afterwards *prussiate of potash*, it is now known as *potassium ferrocyanide*. K. W. Scheele (1782-5) showed that when distilled with dilute acids, Prussian blue furnishes an acid which he named *prussic acid*. C. L. Berthollet (1787) showed that iron, as well as potash and prussic acid, is an essential constituent of the so-called prussiate of potash.

Potassium Ferrocyanide, K$_4$Fe(CN)$_6$

When nitrogenous refuse (blood, horns, leather scraps, etc.) is charred, and the black mass is ignited with potash and iron filings, something is formed which passes into solution when the mass is lixiviated with water. The aqueous solution on evaporation gives yellow crystals of potassium ferrocyanide with the empirical composition, $K_4FeC_6N_6.3H_2O$. The same salt is obtained from the " spent oxide " of the " purifiers " of gas works which are used (q.v.) to remove the sulphur and cyanogen,compounds from the gases formed during the distillation of coal. The " spent oxide " is boiled with lime. The soluble calcium ferrocyanide is leached from the mass, and converted into potassium salt by the treatment with potassium carbonate. The resulting potassium ferrocyanide is purified by crystallization. Sometimes the cyanogen compounds are removed from the coal gas before it reaches the purifiers by washing the gas in an alkaline solution with ferrous carbonate in suspension. **Sodium ferrocyanide**, $Na_4Fe(CN)_6.10H_2O$, is produced in an analogous way.

Properties of Potassium Ferrocyanide

Potassium ferrocyanide crystallizes in laminated, sulphur-yellow crystals with three molecules of " water of crystallization," $K_4Fe(CN)_6$. $3H_2O$. The salt is soluble in water, but not in alcohol or ether. The aqueous solution has a bitter taste, but is not particularly poisonous. The salt loses its " water of crystallization " on warming, and the anhydrous salt remains behind as a white powder. The salt is decomposed when heated, forming potassium cyanide, KCN, and an impure iron carbide, generally symbolized FeC_2, thus,

$$K_4Fe(CN)_6 \rightarrow 4KCN + FeC_2 + N_2,$$

although it is probably much more complicated than this. When warmed with *dilute* sulphuric acid, hydrogen cyanide (q.v.) is formed ; with *concentrated* sulphuric acid, carbon monoxide is evolved :

$K_4Fe(CN)_6 + 6H_2O + 6H_2SO_4$
$$= 2K_2SO_4 + FeSO_4 + 3(NH_4)_2SO_4 + 6CO.$$

Potassium ferrocyanide decomposes when ignited out of contact with the air and forms a complex mixture of potassium cyanide, iron carbide, etc.

Ferrocyanic Acid, $H_4Fe(CN)_6$

When a saturated solution of potassium ferrocyanide, freed from dissolved air by boiling, is treated with concentrated hydrochloric acid in the cold, a white crystalline powder called ferrocyanic acid is formed, it has the empirical formula, $H_4Fe(CN)_6$. Ferrocyanic acid turns blue on exposure to the air owing to the partial decomposition of the salt and the formation of Prussian blue (q.v.), and when heated *in vacuo* at about 300° it furnishes a pale yellow powder with the empirical formula $Fe(CN)_2$; this powder is probably not a simple cyanide, but rather a ferrous ferrocyanide (*vide infra*).

Sodium nitroprusside, $Na_2Fe(NO)(CN)_5.2H_2O$

When, say, four grams of powdered potassium ferrocyanide are boiled for half an hour with 4 c.c. of concentrated nitric acid diluted with its own volume of water, and the cold solution made alkaline with sodium hydroxide, ruby-red crystals of sodium nitroprusside are obtained. The sodium ferrocyanide is first oxidised to the ferricyanide, which reacts with NO:

$$Na_3Fe(CN)_6 + NO = NaCN + Na_2Fe(NO)(CN)_5.$$

When sodium nitroprusside is treated with alkalis, it furnishes sodium ferrocyanide, ferrous hydroxide, etc. :

$$6Na_2Fe(NO)(CN)_5 + 14NaOH = Fe(OH)_2 + 5Na_4Fe(CN)_6 + 6NaNO_2 + 6H_2O,$$

showing that tne iron is probably present in the ferrous condition. The salt is sometimes called *sodium nitroferrocyanide*. A solution of sodium nitroprusside is sometimes used as a test for sulphides since it gives a deep violet coloration with soluble sulphides.

Nitroprussic acid, $H_2Fe(NO)(CN)_5$, has been obtained in dark-red monoclinic crystals by treating the silver salt with hydrochloric acid, or the barium salt with dilute sulphuric acid.

Potassium Ferricyanide, $K_3Fe(CN)_6$

If an aqueous solution of potassium ferrocyanide be treated with oxidizing agents like chlorine, bromine, nitric acid, hydrogen peroxide, etc., it acquires a dark reddish colour, and crystals of potassium ferricyanide separate when the solution is concentrated by evaporation :

$$2K_4Fe(CN)_6 + Cl_2 = 2KCl + 2K_3Fe(CN)_6.$$

The potassium ferricyanide is separated from potassium chloride by re-crystallization. If an excess of chlorine be passed into a solution of potassium ferricyanide, the solution deposits a greenish precipitate—called *Prussian green*. The oxidation of the ferrocyanide to ferricyanide is now conducted by the electrolysis of slightly alkaline solutions—hydrogen and potassium hydroxide are formed at the cathode :

$$2K_4Fe(CN)_6 + 2H_2O \rightarrow 2K_3Fe(CN)_6 + 2KOH + H_2.$$

The ferricyanide is separated by crystallization. Potassium ferricyanide, also called *red prussiate of potash*, is a mild oxidizing agent in alkaline solutions, for it oxidizes " reducing agents " like sodium thiosulphate, hydrogen sulphide, etc., re-forming potassium ferrocyanide :

$$4K_3Fe(CN)_6 + 4KOH = 2H_2O + 4K_4Fe(CN)_6 + O_2.$$

Thus, an aqueous solution of the ferricyanide is converted into ferrocyanide by potassium or sodium amalgam. Potassium ferricyanide, is rather more soluble in water than the ferrocyanide : thus, 100 grams of water at 0° dissolve 31 grams of potassium ferricyanide, and 13 grams of ferrocyanide ; at 10° these numbers are respectively 36 and 20. Potassium ferricyanide is not soluble in alcohol. When a saturated solution of potassium ferricyanide is treated with concentrated hydrochloric acid, in the cold, reddish-brown, acidular crystals of tribasic **ferricyanic acid,** $H_3Fe(CN)_2$, separate from the solution concentrated by evaporation *in vacuo*.

Various salts of ferrocyanic and ferricyanic acids have characteristic colours, as indicated in Table LXII, and consequently, potassium ferrocyanide and ferricyanide—particularly the former—are used in qualitative analysis.

TABLE LXII.—PROPERTIES OF FERRO- AND FERRI-CYANIDES.

	Ferrocyanides added to	Ferricyanides added to
Ferric chloride .	Deep blue precipitate of Prussian blue, insoluble in hydrochloric acid, soluble in oxalic acid.	No precipitate in neutral solutions, but the solution is coloured green or blue.
Ferrous chloride	Bluish-white precipitate which rapidly darkens on exposure to air, or by adding a drop of bromine.	Deep blue precipitate of Turnbull's blue.
Copper sulphate	Reddish-brown precipitate.	Yellowish-green precipitate.
Zinc sulphate .	White precipitate.	Orange precipitate.
Silver nitrate .	White precipitate.	Reddish-brown precipitate.

Prussian blue, or *Berlin blue*, is formed, as indicated in the preceding table, when a solution of potassium ferrocyanide is added to a solution of a ferric salt. It is insoluble in hydrochloric acid, but soluble in oxalic acid, forming a deep blue solution. When heated with concentrated sulphuric acid Prussian blue yields hydrocyanic acid ; and when boiled with alkaline hydroxides, ferric hydroxide is precipitated, and alkaline ferrocyanide remains in solution. Besides the " insoluble " Prussian blue, a *soluble or colloidal Prussian blue* is formed when a ferric salt is added to a solution of potassium ferrocyanide, or a ferrous salt to a solution of potassium ferricyanide. By the addition of salt to the solution, the " soluble " Prussian blue is coagulated or " salted out," and the precipitate is then " insoluble " Prussian blue.

It is probable that these two " forms " of Prussian blue differ only in the size of the particles composing them.

When potassium ferricyanide solution is added to neutral or acid solutions of a ferrous salt, a dark blue precipitate called " Turnbull's blue " is formed.

Prussian blue and Turnbull's blue should thus be ferric ferrocyanide, $Fe_4[Fe(CN)_6]_3$, and ferrous ferricyanide, $Fe_3[Fe(CN)_6]_2$, but it is not at all certain that they are, in fact, distinct chemically. The two " blues " are said to give identical results on analysis and consequently it has been suggested that ferrous ions, ferric ions, ferrocyanide ions and ferricyanide ions are all present. It is thought that in making Prussian blue, some of the ferrocyanide will be oxidized to ferricyanide by the ferric ion which is consequently reduced to ferrous ; in preparing Turnbull's blue, some ferricyanide ion oxidizes ferrous ion to ferric and is itself reduced to ferrocyanide.

§ 11 Iron Carbonyls

Iron forms three compounds with carbon monoxide, known as carbonyls. If carbon monoxide be passed over finely-divided iron at 120°, **iron pentacarbonyl,** $Fe(CO)_5$, is formed as a pale yellow viscous liquid. On exposure to light, it decomposes, forming **iron enneacarbonyl,** $Fe_2(CO)_9$. This latter compound decomposes when heated, forming carbon monoxide and the pentacarbonyl. If the enneacarbonyl be heated in an inert atmosphere, and in presence of an organic solvent, green crystals of a polymer of **iron tetracarbonyl** $[Fe(CO)_4]_3$, are formed.

$$2Fe(CO)_5 \rightleftharpoons Fe_2(CO)_9 + CO.$$

§ 12 Detection and Determination of Iron

Iron can be detected in compounds by fusion on charcoal with sodium carbonate, using a reducing flame, when the metal results and can be recognized by its magnetic properties.

In solution, iron is detected by means of the reactions of ferrous and ferric salts with ferrocyanides, ferricyanides and thiocyanates (the latter give a blood-red coloration with ferric salts).

Iron is determined volumetrically, when in the ferrous state by titration with potassium permanganate or dichromate. Ferric salts may be titrated with titanous chloride, or they must be reduced to the ferrous state and dealt with as before.

Gravimetrically, iron is determined by conversion first to the ferric state, by means of nitric acid ; after which it is precipitated as hydroxide by ammonium hydroxide or sodium hydroxide solution. The ferric hydroxide is filtered off, washed, dried, ignited and weighed as ferric oxide.

§ 13 Cobalt, Co

History

The word " kobalt " occurs in the writings of B. Valentine and Paracelsus to denote a goblin supposed by the old Teutons and Scandinavians to haunt the mines, destroying the work of the miners, and giving them a lot of unnecessary trouble. The word is derived from the German *kobald*, an evil spirit. The church service in some mining districts once included a prayer that God would preserve the miners and their work from kobalds and other evil spirits. The term was applied to what were called " false ores," that is, ores which did not give metals when treated by the processes then in vogue for the extraction of the metals ; and also to ores which had an objectionable smell. The term was gradually confined to the minerals used for colouring glass blue, and which are still used for making smalt. In 1735 Brandt stated that the blue colouring principle is due to the presence of a peculiar metal or semi-metal which he called " cobalt rex," hence our " cobalt." Brandt isolated the metal in 1742.

Occurrence

Cobalt is nearly always found in association with nickel, chiefly as arsenides, e.g., in *smaltite* or *cobalt speiss*, $CoAs_2$; *cobaltite* or *cobalt glance*, CoAsS.   The principal deposits occur near Ontario in Canada, along with nickel and silver ores, and in the Belgian Congo.

Extraction

Cobalt ores are principally worked in order to get cobalt salts and not the metal.   The ore is first roasted in a small blast furnace to remove arsenic as trioxide, which is condensed and used as a source of that element (p. 742).   The remainder of the ore forms a " speiss " of crude cobalt, nickel, etc., which is heated with common salt and then extracted with water.   The insoluble residue is worked up for silver and the aqueous solution contains cobalt, nickel and copper chlorides.   The copper is precipitated by adding metallic iron, and then cobalt and nickel as hydroxides by caustic soda.   The mixed hydroxides are then heated so as to give the oxides.

Several methods are in use for separating cobalt and nickel ; one of the most important being the Mond process for obtaining nickel by way of the carbonyl (p. 829).   Of other methods there may be mentioned the use of bleaching powder.   The mixed oxides are dissolved in hydrochloric acid and the resulting solution neutralized with chalk. The clear solution is treated with bleaching powder which precipitates cobaltic hydroxide practically uncontaminated by nickel :

$$2CoCl_2 + 2Ca(OH)_2 + CaOCl_2 + H_2O = 2Co(OH)_3 + 3CaCl_2.$$

If the metal itself be required, it can be obtained by reducing the oxide in a current of hydrogen ; by the aluminothermic method, or by electrolysis of cobalt ammonium sulphate solution.

Properties

Cobalt is a white malleable and ductile metal rather harder than iron.   It is feebly magnetic, and melts at 1480°.   It is not attacked by air at ordinary temperatures, and only reacts slowly with oxygen at a red heat.   Dilute hydrochloric and sulphuric acids attack cobalt slowly and nitric acid dissolves it fairly readily.

Uses

Cobalt has been used in electro-plating and has been suggested for use as a coinage metal.   As a constituent of alloys it is beginning to be used more extensively.   Some of these, e.g., stellite (p. 770), and high-speed tool steels (p. 782) have been mentioned already ; in addition, reference may be made to *cochrome* (Co 60, Cr 14-16, Fe 24-26 per cent.) which is similar to nichrome (p. 770) and is used for similar purposes.

Cobalt oxides and silicates are used for colouring glass, and pottery glazes.   *Smalt*, much used for these purposes, is a potassium cobalt alumino-silicate.   *Cobalt yellow* is a pigment which is a potassium cobalt nitrite.   Cobalt salts of organic acids are used as driers in the manufacture of paints and varnishes.

Atomic Weight

The specific heat of cobalt (0·103), and the position of the element in the Periodic System indicate a value for the atomic weight in the neighbourhood of 59. The most satisfactory method of determining an accurate value is by conversion of the chloride and bromide into the corresponding silver salts. As a result of the work of Baxter and his collaborators, the International Committee has recommended the value 58·94.

§ 14 Oxides and Hydroxides of Cobalt

Cobalt forms four oxides, viz.,

Cobaltous oxide, CoO ;
Cobaltosic oxide, Co_3O_4 ;
Cobaltic oxide, Co_2O_3 ;
Cobalt peroxide, CoO_2.

Cobaltous oxide, CoO, is obtained by heating cobaltous hydroxide, carbonate or nitrate to 1000° in absence of air. It is a dark-brown or olive-green powder, which is stable in air, but when heated to between 600° and 700°, it absorbs oxygen and forms Co_3O_4. At still higher temperatures, CoO is reformed. When heated in hydrogen or carbon monoxide, it is reduced to the metal. It reacts with acids forming cobaltous salts.

Cobaltous hydroxide, $Co(OH)_2$, is obtained when alkali hydroxides are added to solutions of cobaltous salts. It exists in two forms : a blue form, which is converted into a rose-pink form on boiling the suspension of the blue form in the solution from which it was precipitated. Both forms turn brown on exposure to the air because of the absorption of oxygen.

Cobaltosic oxide, Co_3O_4, is obtained as a black powder by strongly heating cobalt nitrate :

$$3Co(NO_3)_2 = Co_3O_4 + 6NO_2 + O_2.$$

It reacts with hydrochloric acid, chlorine being liberated, and a solution of cobalt chloride is formed.

Cobaltic Oxide, Co_2O_3

Cobaltic oxide is obtained by heating cobaltous nitrate or carbonate in air. It is a dark grey or brownish-black powder which forms an oxide corresponding with cobaltosic, Co_3O_4, when heated between the dissociation temperature 373° (760 mm.) and about 700°. **Cobaltic hydroxide,** $Co(OH)_3$, is formed as a black precipitate when a cobaltous salt is treated with alkaline hypochlorite. Both the oxide and the hydroxide dissolve in acids, forming brown solutions which contain unstable cobaltic salts ; these salts decompose when warmed, forming cobaltous salts and oxygen or its equivalent. Hence cobaltic oxide behaves as a feebly basic oxide and as a peroxide like nickelic oxide and manganese dioxide.

Cobalt Peroxide, Cobalt Dioxide, CoO_2

When a solution of cobalt sulphate is treated with iodine and sodium hydroxide, a black precipitate results, believed to be cobalt dioxide.

If cobalt hydroxide be suspended in water and then treated with hydrogen peroxide, the resulting liquid, after filtration, is strongly acid and is believed to contain **cobaltous acid,** H_2CoO_3 ; a green unstable solution of **potassium cobaltite,** K_2CoO_3, is formed by the addition of potassium hydrogen carbonate to the solution of cobaltous acid.

§ 15 Salts of Cobalt

In one sense cobalt gives rise to two series of salts derived respectively from cobaltous oxide and cobaltic oxide ; but the latter are only stable in the form of complex compounds. The cobaltous salts are thus the ordinary salts of this element.

Cobalt carbonate, $CoCO_3$, is obtained as a bright red powder by addition of sodium bicarbonate solution, saturated with carbon dioxide, to a solution of a cobalt salt. If the reaction be carried out at a low temperature, $CoCO_3.6H_2O$, is formed ; at a temperature of 140° the anhydrous salt results.

Cobalt Chloride, $CoCl_2$

The hydrated salt—$CoCl_2.6H_2O$—crystallizes from solutions of the oxide or carbonate in hydrochloric acid in ruby-red monoclinic crystals, easily soluble in water (100 grams of water dissolve 32 grams of anhydrous salt at 15°). The crystals at 100° form the monohydrate $CoCl_2.H_2O$; and at about 120° the anhydrous chloride $CoCl_2$. The latter is deep blue but gives pink solutions when dissolved in cold water. The solution also changes colour when heated, becoming blue at about 50°. It is now thought that the pink solutions contain various hydrated ions such as $Co(H_2O)_6^{..}$; but that the blue solutions contain complex ions like $CoCl_4''$ or $[Co(H_2O)Cl_3]'$ (Bassett, 1930-34).

$$CoCl_2 \rightleftharpoons Co^{..} + 2Cl',$$
$$Co^{..} + 6H_2O \rightleftharpoons Co(H_2O)_6^{..}$$
$$Co(H_2O)_6^{..} + 3Cl' \rightleftharpoons [Co(H_2O)Cl_3]' + 5H_2O,$$
$$Co(H_2O)_6^{..} + 4Cl' \rightleftharpoons CoCl_4'' + 6H_2O.$$

Solutions of cobalt chloride have been used for sympathetic ink. The pink solution is not visible when used for writing ; but becomes blue when the paper bearing it is warmed. On cooling in moist air, the blue colour fades again.

Cobalt Nitrate, $Co(NO_3)_2$

The anhydrous salt is made by the action of nitrogen pentoxide, or a solution of nitrogen pentoxide in nitric acid, on the hydrated salt. It is a slightly pink powder which decomposes on heating with evolution of nitrous fumes.

Cobalt nitrate can be obtained in aqueous solution by dissolving the carbonate in dilute nitric acid. On evaporation, reddish crystals of the composition $Co(NO_3)_2.6H_2O$ are obtained.

Cobalt sulphide, CoS, is formed as a black precipitate on addition of ammonium sulphide to a solution of a cobalt salt or on passing hydrogen sulphide through a similar ammoniacal solution. It is amorphous in appearance when first precipitated, and soluble in acids ; on heating, it becomes insoluble and crystalline in character.

Cobalt sulphate, $CoSO_4.7H_2O$, is made by dissolving the monoxide or carbonate in dilute sulphuric acid. It crystallizes below 40° with 7 molecules of water forming rose-coloured crystals isomorphous with $FeSO_4.7H_2O$ and $NiSO_4.7H_2O$.

It readily forms a double salt with ammonium sulphate $(NH_4)_2SO_4.$ $CoSO_4.6H_2O$, analogous to ferrous ammonium sulphate.

Simple **cobaltic salts** are unstable, but give rise to a number of stable complex compounds such as cobalt alums, cobalticyanides, cobaltinitrites, and cobaltammines. The cobalt alums are isomorphous with other alums ; an important one is **ammonium cobalt alum,** $(NH_4)_2SO_4.Co_2(SO_4)_3.24H_2O$, which is bright blue. Both cobalto- and cobalti-cyanides are known, analogous to the ferro- and ferricyanides.

The cobaltinitrites are of some importance in analysis. If potassium nitrite be added to a solution of a cobaltous salt, acidified with acetic acid, a bright yellow crystalline precipitate of **potassium cobalti-nitrite,** $K_3Co(NO_2)_6.nH_2O$, is formed. This substance is practically insoluble in water, whereas the corresponding sodium salt is soluble. Hence its formation serves as a test for the presence of potassium. Also nickel salts give a similar but *soluble* nickel nitrite and so the formation of the cobaltinitrite serves for the detection of cobalt in presence of nickel.

$$CoCl_2 + 2KNO_2 = Co(NO_2)_2 + 2KCl,$$
$$2Co(NO_2)_2 + 4HNO_2 = 2Co(NO_2)_3 + 2H_2O + 2NO$$
$$3KNO_2 + Co(NO_2)_3 = K_3Co(NO_2)_6.$$

The probable formula for potassium cobaltinitrite is,

$$K_3[Co(NO_2)_6]$$

since it does not give the reactions of nitrites.

Cobaltammines are formed on addition of excess of ammonia to a solution of a cobalt salt ; the mixture being then allowed to stand in contact with the air. They are discussed at the end of this chapter (p. 841) along with other similar complex compounds.

Cobalt Carbonyls

Two cobalt carbonyls are known. By the action of carbon monoxide on cobalt at 30 atmospheres pressure and 150°, orange-red crystals of $Co_2(CO)_8$ are formed. These melt at 51° and at 60° decompose into black $Co(CO)_3$.

§ 16 Detection and Determination of Cobalt

Cobalt is easily recognized by the blue colour of the borax bead which its compounds give when fused with borax on a platinum wire. In solution, the formation of potassium cobaltinitrite (described above) is a useful method of detection and of separation from nickel.

Cobalt is commonly determined by addition of potassium hypo-bromite solution to the solution of the cobalt salt whereby an indefinite mixture of hydroxides results. This is washed, dried and ignited, giving a mixture of oxides, which are reduced to the metal in a current of hydrogen. If nickel be present, it is separated first by the cyanide process (p. 833). Cobalt can be both detected and determined in presence of nickel by means of a solution of α-nitroso-β-naphthol in dilute acetic acid, which forms a dark red precipitate.

§ 17 Nickel, Ni

History

Nickel seems to have been known to the Chinese in early times. In Europe, towards the end of the seventeenth century, the German term *kupfer-nickel* (false-copper) was applied to an ore which, while possessing the general appearance of a copper ore, yet gave no copper when treated by the general process then used for the extraction of copper. Nevertheless, the mineral was supposed to be an ore of copper, or a species of cobalt or arsenic united with copper. A. F. Cronstedt, 1751-1754, stated that kupfer-nickel contains a metal which gives a brown, not a blue colour, with glass. Cronstedt's views were not accepted generally until T. Bergman had shown clearly that Cronstedt's metal was a new element in an impure condition. Bergman's arguments were mainly directed to controvert the view that nickel is a compound of cobalt, iron, arsenic, and copper, advocated by le Sage. He showed that nickel retains its individuality when arsenic is absent, and when no signs of cobalt or copper can be detected in solutions of the metal. Bergman also tried unsuccessfully to make nickel synthetically from mixtures of the elements in question.

Occurrence

Cobalt and nickel are nearly always found associated with one another; both occur free in some meteorites. Nickel occurs as *kupfernickel* or *nicollite*, NiAs; *millerite*, or nickel blende, NiS; *nickel glance*, NiAsS; and *garnierite*, a silicate of magnesium and nickel $(NiMg)H_2SiO_4$, found in New Caledonia. The most important ores come from Sudbury in Ontario.

Extraction

The Sudbury ores contain chalcopyrite and other copper and iron minerals, as well as nickel; often these are embedded in other rocky materials. Preliminary concentration of the nickel ore is effected by flotation, and it is then roasted to remove some of the sulphur. The roasted ore is then smelted with quartz, coke, and limestone in a small blast furnace, when an impure mixture of nickel and copper sulphides, and some iron remains. The product is then " blown " in a Bessemer type converter with a basic lining, to oxidize away the iron and most of the sulphur. There thus results a *matte* of nickel and copper, which can be used as it is for the manufacture of some alloys (e.g., monel metal). To get pure nickel, the matte is roasted to convert it into oxides, which are then extracted with hot, dilute sulphuric acid with which the copper oxide reacts, thus passing into solution and the nickel oxide remains. This is reduced by means of water gas at 300°, after which carbon monoxide is passed over the mixture of metals at 50-80°.

The nickel forms nickel carbonyl, $Ni(CO)_4$, which is volatile and is conveyed, along with excess carbon monoxide, to towers containing pellets of pure nickel at 180°. The carbonyl is decomposed into almost pure nickel, and carbon monoxide which is used again. This is the *Mond Nickel Process*.

Properties

Nickel is a moderately hard, white metal, which melts at 1450°, and is very slightly magnetic. It is stable in air at ordinary temperatures, and burns in oxygen forming nickelous oxide NiO. It is not affected by water, but decomposes steam at a red heat ; it is only slowly acted upon by dilute hydrochloric and sulphuric acids; but nitric acid attacks nickel readily, forming nickel nitrate.

Alloys and Uses

Nickel is much used for " nickel plating " other metals on account of its silvery appearance, and the fact that it does not readily tarnish in air. The nickel is deposited from a double sulphate of ammonium and nickel by a process similar to that used for " silver and gold plating." Nickel is used in making several important alloys : e.g., *German silver* is the trade-name for a series of white alloys consisting of a mixture of copper, nickel, and other metals. The standard might be regarded as : copper 50 ; nickel 25 ; zinc 25 per cent. Additions of lead, tin, cadmium and iron are used in different proportions to suit various uses to which the alloy may be put and to accentuate maybe hardness, ductility, surface polish, electrical conductivity, etc. Naturally several other trade-names are used—*nickel silver, silveroid, argentoid, nickeline*, etc. *Manganin* is an alloy used in making electrical resistances. It is a kind of German silver with manganese in place of zinc—e.g., manganese 12, copper 85, nickel 3. *Nickel steel* is hard and tough, and is used for parts of machinery designed to withstand continuous wear and shocks, and in the manufacture of armour plates, burglar-proof safes, etc. A nickel steel containing about 35 per cent. of nickel has a very small coefficient of thermal expansion, and is consequently useful for making measuring instruments, pendulums, etc. It is called *invar* ; an alloy with about 40 per cent. of nickel expands at about the same rate as glass, and hence it can be sealed into glass in the manufacture of incandescent electric lamps, etc. This alloy is called *platinite*. Nickel coins contain about 25 per cent. of nickel, and 75 per cent. of copper. An alloy of nickel 68, copper 27-30, is called *monel metal*. It is said to be less liable to corrode than brass or bronze and nearly as strong as steel. An alloy containing 80 to 95 per cent. of copper and 5 to 20 per cent. of a cobalt-tin (2 : 3) alloy is one of the so-called *non-corrosive alloys* because it resists fairly well the attack by many acids which rapidly corrode copper. Finely divided nickel is used as a catalytic agent since, in the presence of hydrogen, it is able to reduce or hydrogenize many organic and inorganic compounds.   Traces of sulphur or chlorine in the gas rapidly makes the nickel lose its activity.

Atomic Weight

The atomic weight of nickel has been determined in a manner similar to that of cobalt.   The International Committee recommends, at present, the value 58·69, based on the work of Richards and of Baxter and their collaborators.

§ 18 Oxides and Hydroxides of Nickel

A number of oxides of nickel has been reported, but only two seem to be unquestioned, viz.,

$$Nickelous\ oxide,\ NiO\ ;$$
$$Nickel\ dioxide,\ NiO_2.$$

In addition to these, a sesquioxide, Ni_2O_3, nickelosic oxide, Ni_3O_4, and a peroxide, NiO_4, have been reported.

Nickelous oxide, NiO, is obtained as a greenish powder when the hydroxide or carbonate are heated out of contact with the air.   On heating, it is said to form the sesquioxide, and it reacts with acids forming nickelous salts.

Nickelous hydroxide, $Ni(OH)_2$

When potassium hydroxide is added to a solution of a nickel salt, a pale green precipitate of nickelous hydroxide separates.   Unlike ferrous and cobaltous hydroxides, this precipitate does not oxidize on exposure to the air.   It dissolves in ammonia and ammonium salts, forming ammines, and unlike the corresponding cobalt solution does not absorb oxygen from the air.   It reacts with acids forming nickelous salts.

Nickel Dioxide, NiO_2

Two probably isomeric **nickel dioxides** have been reported—a black dioxide is made by the action of bromine, or hypochlorites or hypobromites on nickelous hydroxide ; and a green one by the action of hydrogen peroxide on nickelous chloride in the cold, followed by treatment with alcoholic potash.   The green oxide is remarkably like hydrogen dioxide in its chemical properties, and is different from the black oxide.   Hence it has been suggested that the green oxide is a peroxide or super oxide with nickel bivalent ; and the black oxide is a dioxide or polyoxide, nickel quadrivalent.

If nickel oxide be heated with barium carbonate in an electric furnace, a dark coloured crystalline mass of **barium nickelite,** $BaO.2NiO_2$, is formed.   Barium nickelite is decomposed by water.

Nickelic oxide, Ni_2O_3, is said to be formed as a black powder when nickelous oxide is heated in air, and when the nitrate or carbonate is ignited in air at a low temperature, but it is thought to be actually a mixture of NiO_2 and NiO.

Nickelic hydroxide, $Ni(OH)_3$, is precipitated when chlorine is passed through water or alkali hydroxide solution in which nickelous oxide is suspended, or when a nickel salt is treated with a solution of bleaching powder.   The oxide (if it exists) and hydroxide do not appear to be basic, for when treated with acids nickelous salts and oxygen result.

Nickelosic oxide, Ni_3O_4, is reported to be formed when moist oxygen is passed over nickel chloride at 400°. There are doubts about its existence ; it is thought by some to be a mixture of NiO and NiO_2.

§ 19 Salts of Nickel

Nickel forms only one stable series of salts, although, as with cobalt, some complex nickelic derivatives are known.

Nickel carbonate, $NiCO_3$, is obtained in green crystals by adding nickel sulphate to a solution of sodium bicarbonate saturated with carbon dioxide. The addition of sodium carbonate to solutions of nickel salts precipitates basic nickel carbonates.

Nickel chloride, $NiCl_2$, is obtained in solution by the action of dilute hydrochloric acid on the oxide or carbonate. It crystallizes from this solution in green crystals of the composition, $NiCl_2.6H_2O$, which effloresce slightly in air. On heating, the anhydrous salt can be obtained ; it is also formed by the action of chlorine on finely-divided nickel. It is a golden yellow solid, which combines with ammonia.

Nickel Nitrate $Ni(NO_3)_2$

Nickel dissolves readily in dilute nitric acid, and on evaporation, the solution deposits green monoclinic crystals of the composition $Ni(NO_3)_2.6H_2O$. These are very soluble in water. On heating, some of the water of crystallization is driven off, but the nitrate decomposes before it has become anhydrous, yielding nickelous oxide, nitrogen peroxide and oxygen :

$$Ni(NO_3)_2 = NiO + 2NO_2 + O_2.$$

Nickel sulphide, NiS, is formed as a black precipitate when ammonium sulphide is added to a solution of a nickel salt, or by passing hydrogen sulphide through an alkaline nickel solution. As thus precipitated, it is soluble in acids, but on standing, or on boiling, it is quickly converted into a form which is insoluble in acids. It thus resembles cobalt sulphide in that neither sulphide is precipitated by hydrogen sulphide in acid solution ; yet, as obtained by precipitation in alkaline solution, it is insoluble in acids, after quite a short time. It is supposed to exist in three forms (Thiel and Gessner, 1914).

Nickel Sulphate, $NiSO_4.7H_2O$

By adding nickelous oxide or carbonate to dilute sulphuric acid and evaporating the resulting solution, green crystals of nickel sulphate heptahydrate separate, which are isomorphous with the corresponding hydrates of ferrous sulphate, magnesium sulphate, etc. It is the best known of the nickel salts, and is readily soluble in water. It combines with ammonia gas forming an unstable, dark blue compound analogous to the corresponding compound of copper sulphate. It also forms a stable double compound with ammonium sulphate, **nickel ammonium**

sulphate, $(NH_4)_2SO_4.NiSO_4.6H_2O$, analogous to ferrous ammonium sulphate, which is used extensively in nickel-plating.

Nickel carbonyl, $Ni(CO)_4$, is a colourless liquid, obtained by passing carbon monoxide over reduced nickel at $50°-80°$. It boils at $43°$, and on heating decomposes into nickel and carbon monoxide. It is used industrially for the purification of nickel by the Mond process (p. 829).

§ 20 Detection and Determination of Nickel

Nickel salts give green solutions, black sulphide precipitates with hydrogen sulphide in alkaline solution, and with ammonium hydroxide a pale green precipitate, soluble in excess to give a blue solution. When cobalt is also present, the nickel may be detected by adding excess of potassium cyanide to the solution until the precipitates first formed re-dissolve, owing to the formation of cobalto- and nickelo-cyanides. On boiling the solution, the cobalto-cyanide is oxidized to the cobalti-cyanide, and if sodium hypochlorite or hypobromite solution be now added, hydrated nickel dioxide is obtained as a black precipitate, while the cobalt remains in solution.

Alternatively, dimethyl glyoxime (which is also used for the quantitative determination of nickel) may be employed. In neutral or alkaline solution this reagent precipitates nickel quantitatively as a scarlet solid, but does not precipitate cobalt. This affords a very delicate test for nickel and for the estimation, the precipitate can be dried at $110°$ and weighed as such—$Ni(C_4H_7O_2N_2)_2$—or ignited and weighed as the oxide, NiO.

§ 21 The Platinum Metals

The " platinum metals " are the two heaviest triads of the eighth group, and thus include ruthenium, Ru ; rhodium, Rh ; and palladium, Pd ; and osmium, Os ; iridium, Ir ; and platinum, Pt, itself. They occur together and have many properties in common (see below).

History

There is supposed to be a reference to platinum in Pliny's *Natural History* under the name " aluta." The term " platina del Pinto " for a white metal resembling silver, has been for a long time in general use by the Spaniards in South America. " Platina " is the diminutive form of the Spanish *plata*, silver, and " Pinto " has reference to the river where it was discovered. At one time its export from South America was forbidden by the Spanish Government, who ordered it to be thrown into the sea to prevent its being used for adulterating gold. In 1788, the Spanish Government bought it for about 8s. per lb., presumably for adulterating gold. It is now worth from £13 to £20 per troy oz. It was brought to Europe in 1735 by C. Wood, and W. Brownrigg and R. Watson described its properties in 1750. The platina del Pinto of Choca (Colombia) attracted the attention of

Antonio de Ulloa in 1748 ; J. J. Scaliger of Leydon, 1558, also referred to an infusible metal which has been taken to have been platinum. The metal attracted much attention at the time. Before 1823, most of the platinum in commerce came from South America. Platinum was discovered in Ural in 1819, and in 1824 Russia began exporting platinum ; since that time, most of the platinum of commerce has come from that source.

Osmium and iridium were discovered by S. Tennant, 1802 to 1803 ; rhodium and palladium by W. H. Wollaston, 1803 to 1804 ; and ruthenium by K. Claus in 1845. All these metals were found during the study of native platinum.. " Osmium " is named from the Greek ὀσμή (osme), a smell ; " iridium " is named from the Greek ἴρις (iris), a rainbow, from the varying tint of its salts ; " rhodium " is named from the Greek ῥόδον (rhodon), a rose, from the **rose-red** colour of its salts ; " palladium " is named after the planet Pallas, discovered the same year as palladium, 1802 ; " ruthenium " is named after *ruthen*, for Russia.

Occurrence

The platinum metals occur in a metallic condition in gravels and sands associated together as mixtures or compounds along with magnetite, gold, chromite, etc., principally in that part of the Perm district in the neighbourhood of Nizhni Tagilsk drained by the Tura river and particularly its tributaries, the Iss and the Veeya, and Mount Blgodat in the Ural mountains (Russia), and in smaller quantities in California, Sumatra, Abyssinia, New Granada, Brazil, Australia, etc. The world's production amounts to about 6·5 tons per annum ; and of this, about six tons comes from the Urals, and a little less than half a ton from the Choco district in Colombia (S. America), and other localities.

The platinum metals associated with the nickel ores at Sudbury, Ontario, are now being recovered on an important scale from the residues after the removal of the nickel.

The world's production of iridium amounts to about 5000 ozs. The platiniferous sands and gravels are washed as in the case of alluvial gold. " Platinum concentrates " consist of more or less rounded grains which sometimes show signs of cubic crystallization, flattened scales, and small nuggets containing approximately the following percentage composition :

Platinum.	Iridium.	Rhodium.	Palladium.	Gold.	Copper.	Iron.	Osmiridium.	Sand.
76·4	4·3	0·3	1·4	0·4	4·1	11·7	0·5	1·4

The platinum content may vary from 50-86 per cent., nuggets weighing up to 20 lbs. have been found on rare occasions. When the native metal contains a preponderating proportion of iridium (say up to 75 per cent.), it is called *platiniridium*. This variety is rare ; it is white and harder and denser than platinum. *Iridosmium*, or *osmiridium* is a native metallic alloy containing approximately :

Platinum.	Iridium.	Rhodium.	Osmium.	Ruthenium.
10·1	52·5	1·5	27·2	5·9

with traces of palladium, copper, and iron.

Extraction of the Metals

The gold can be removed from the platinum concentrates by the amalgamation process. About 1860, the platinum, contaminated more or less with other metals, was extracted by a smelting process ; to-day, a wet process is used. Details of the process are a " trade secret." In a general way it may be said that the concentrates are digested with dilute aqua regia under pressure. The insoluble residue contains sand (gangue) and osmiridium. Osmium and ruthenium form volatile oxygen compounds which can be easily removed from the solution by distillation. The solution of crude platinum in aqua regia is evaporated to dryness and heated to 125° ; the residue is then dissolved in water ; acidified with hydrochloric acid ; and treated with ammonium chloride, when a precipitate containing platinum and iridium compounds is obtained from which the metals are obtained by ignition. Aqua regia dissolves the residual platinum, not iridium. The platinum can be obtained by precipitation as before. The mother liquid is worked over for palladium and rhodium. The further separation of the platinum metals from one another is a difficult and laborious operation because the properties of the metals are so much alike ; and because the behaviour of the salts of one element is modified by the presence of others. Thus, iridium does not dissolve in aqua regia, but if iridium be alloyed with platinum, some iridium passes into solution when the alloy is digested in aqua regia.

§ 22 Properties and Uses of the Platinum Metals

The metals are greyish-white and lustrous. They all melt at a high temperature. They are not acted upon by air or oxygen at ordinary temperatures. Osmium alone burns when strongly heated in air forming the tetroxide OsO_4 ; the others are scarcely affected, chemically, at any temperature. Palladium readily dissolves in hot nitric acid and very sparingly in hydrochloric acid, but the other metals are scarcely affected by hot acids. Aqua regia attacks osmium, forming osmium tetroxide, OsO_4 ; and it dissolves platinum forming the tetrachloride, $PtCl_4$; ruthenium is slowly dissolved, while iridium and rhodium are not appreciably attacked, unless in a very finely-divided condition. The native platinum alloy stubbornly resists attack by chemical reagents—even aqua regia. The metals are readily reduced from their compounds, which fact probably accounts for their occurrence free in nature. The metals fall naturally into two groups with nearly equal atomic weights. The *light platinum metals* include ruthenium, rhodium, and palladium ; the *heavy platinum metals* include osmium, iridium, and platinum. Palladium is related to silver, and platinum to gold, as indicated in Table LXII. Unlike the other platinum metals, osmium vaporizes without melting.

TABLE LXIII.—PROPERTIES OF THE PLATINUM METALS.

	Light.				Heavy.			
	Ru	Rh	Pd	Ag	Os	Ir	Pt	Au
Atomic weight	101·7	102·91	106·7	107·88	190·2	193·1	195·23	197·23
Specific gravity	12·25	12·12	12	10·5	22·48	22·4	21·45	19·3
Atomic volume	8·3	8·5	8·9	10·1	8·5	8·6	9·1	11
Melting point	2450°	1955°	1555°	960·5°	2700°	2350°	1755°	1063°
Boiling point	2700°	2200°	2540°	1950°	5300°	4800°	4300°	2600°
Valency	2, 3, 4, 6, 7, 8	2, 3, 4,	2, 4	1, 2, 3	2, 3, 4, 8	1, 2, 3, 4, 6	2, 3, 4	1, 3

Platinum is a greyish-white metal with a brilliant lustre. It is harder than copper, silver or gold. It is ductile and malleable, and usually comes on the market in the form of foil or wire. Platinum has also the valuable quality that it softens like iron before melting, so that like iron it can be welded. Platinum melts between 1750° and 1755° ; and boils at about 4300°. Platinum and rhodium do not volatilize appreciably at 900°, but at 1300° volatilization can be detected. Appreciable quantities of the metals palladium, iridium, and ruthenium volatilize at 900°, and at 1300° the effect is very marked. Iridium is readily oxidized to a volatile sesquioxide when heated just below 1000° ; but it is doubtful if platinum is oxidized below 1300°. Molten platinum, like molten silver, absorbs oxygen which is given off as the molten metal cools, hence it is liable to " spitting." Platinum is not attacked by pure hydrofluoric, hydrochloric, nitric and sulphuric acids. It is readily dissolved by aqua regia and by solutions containing chlorine : cf. Gold. When platinum is alloyed with silver, copper, lead, zinc, etc., it is attacked and partly dissolved by nitric acid, probably forming a **platinum nitrate.**

The high fusing temperature, and the fact that platinum is not attacked by air and strong acids enables it to be used in the manufacture of apparatus—dishes, crucibles, stills, etc.—for many chemical operations which could not be readily performed with apparatus made from other available metals. The unfortunate steady advance in the price will lead to the use of gold crucibles for many purposes. The analysis of many minerals could not be so readily conducted as at present if it were not for the valuable qualities of platinum.

Platinum is attacked by alkalis, nitrates, cyanides, and phosphates under reducing conditions. With phosphorus it forms **platinum phosphide** ; with sulphur, **platinum sulphide,** PtS ; with sulphur and dry alkali, **platinum disulphide,** PtS_2 ; with arsenic, **platinum arsenide,** Pt_2As_3. An arsenide called *sperrylite,* $PtAs_2$, associated with nickel sulphide occurs at Sudbury (Ontario). Platinum also alloys directly with metals like lead, silver, zinc, etc., but not mercury. Hence platinum crucibles must not be heated with these metals. Carbon alloys with platinum forming a brittle **platinum carbide,** and hence platinum crucibles must not be heated in a smoky flame.

Platinum has nearly the same coefficient of expansion as glass, and platinum wires can be fused in glass so as to make gas-tight joints. Platinum is also a good conductor of electricity, and large quantities are used in the electric light industry. Short pieces of platinum wire are fused into the glass at the base of the bulb, and connected with the filament inside. The bulb is then exhausted and sealed. The platinum wires outside are then put in communication with the wire carrying the current. The filament is thus heated under reduced pressure to form the " incandescent electric light." Platinum is used in dentistry, photography, in jewellery, and in making scientific and surgical instruments, etc. One-third of the world's supply of platinum is said to be used in dentistry, and another third in electro-technical work. The stock of platinum is gradually dissipated by wear in the laboratory, etc. ; and, owing to the very limited occurrence of this metal, the reserves must also be approaching exhaustion. The demand for platinum outstrips the supply, and this naturally explains the enormous increase in price. One of the most serious problems in certain branches of technical chemistry and in electro-technical work is based on the limited occurrence of this metal.

Platinum-iridium alloys are hard and elastic ; malleable and ductile ; and less fusible than platinum. If more than 20 per cent. of iridium be present, the alloys are exceedingly difficult to work. An alloy of 10 per cent. iridium and 90 per cent. platinum was chosen by the International Committee on Weights and Measures for preserving the standards of length and weight. Platinum-iridium wire with platinum wire are used as thermo-couples for temperatures up to 1000° ; and platinum-rhodium wires are used with platinum in a similar way for temperatures up to 1400°. Commercial platinum has 2 per cent. of iridium, and it appears to gradually lose this constituent when heated to a high temperature. The result is that platinum crucibles made from commercial platinum lose in weight every time they are heated for some time in the gas blowpipe. This is a source of annoyance. The high fusing temperature of osmium led to its use for the manufacture of filaments for incandescent electric lamps—" osmium lamps." These lamps gave twice the illuminating power of the carbon filament lamp with an equal consumption of energy for an equal time. The glass bulb also remains unblackened even to the end of the life of the lamp ; but other metal filament lamps have displaced the osmium lamp. An alloy of iridium and osmium is used for tipping gold nibs on account of its hardness. The alloy is called *iridosmium* or *osmiridium*. Palladium is used for absorbing hydrogen, for the detection of carbon monoxide, and for the separation of iodine as indicated above. Osmium tetroxide is used for staining and hardening organic tissues in histology.

When platinum is precipitated from solutions of the tetrachloride by reducing agents, a velvet black powder called **platinum black** is obtained ; when ammonium chloroplatinate is calcined, the metal remains behind as a spongy mass called **spongy platinum** ; and if asbestos be soaked in a solution of platinum chloride and ignited, the asbestos permeated with platinum is called **platinized asbestos.** Platinum sponge, platinum black, and platinized asbestos absorb large quantities of oxygen gas, and they can then be used as oxidizing agents. Platinum black can absorb 100 times its volume of oxygen and 110 times its volume of hydrogen. Palladium black absorbs about 900 times its volume of hydrogen. This property of occluding gases is shown in a less marked degree by iron, nickel and cobalt, as well as by copper, gold and silver. Spongy platinum will cause a mixture of hydrogen and oxygen to unite with explosion ; spongy palladium without explosion. A jet of hydrogen directed on to finely-divided platinum will cause the platinum to glow and finally ignite the jet of gas. Alcohol dropped on to iridium black takes fire. Similarly coal gas can be ignited by spongy platinum, and this property was utilized in making the so-called " self-lighting Bunsen burners." The catalytic properties of the finely divided platinum metals are used in some industries for promoting chemical changes, e.g., the contact process for sulphuric acid.

§ 23 Oxides and Hydroxides of the Platinum Metals

When a solution of potassium chloroplatinite or of platinous chloride is treated with an alkaline hydroxide, **platinous hydroxide,** $Pt(OH)_2$, is precipitated as a black powder. It is soluble in the haloid acids—hydrochloric and hydrobromic acids—and in sulphurous acid, but not in the other oxy-acids, and thus forms the corresponding platinous salts. The hydroxide is decomposed into the metal and **platinum dioxide,** PtO_2, by boiling alkaline hydroxides :

$$2Pt(OH)_2 = PtO_2 + Pt + 2H_2O.$$

When gently ignited, platinous hydroxide forms the corresponding **platinous oxide,** PtO, as a dark powder insoluble in water and in most acids. It is doubtful if IrO has been made. Palladium black warmed in air furnishes a dark bluish-green **palladous oxide,** PdO, which decomposes into the metal and oxide at a higher temperature.

When a boiling solution of potassium hydroxide is added to a solution of platinum tetrachloride, and the precipitated **platinic hydroxide,** $Pt(OH)_4$, is washed with acetic acid to remove the potash, a yellowish powder is obtained which dissolves in acids, forming **platinic salts,** and in bases forming a series of salts called the **platinates.** For instance, with sodium hydroxide, yellow crystals of **sodium platinate,** $Na_2O.3PtO_2.6H_2O$, are obtained. Hence platinic hydroxide is an acidic and a basic compound. Platinic hydroxide, $Pt(OH)_4$, is a type of similar compounds formed by the whole six of the platinum metals. The hydroxides when heated form dark grey powders of the dioxide—e.g., PtO_2, IrO_2, etc.

Ruthenium, osmium, iridium, and rhodium form **sesquioxides** : Ru_2O_3 ; Os_2O_3 ; Ir_2O_3 ; Rh_2O_3. Ruthenium and osmium form compounds corresponding with the **trioxides,** RuO_3 and OsO_3.   A more or less impure IrO_3 has been made. Thus, **potassium ruthenate,** K_2RuO_4; and **potassium perruthenate,** $KRuO_4$, call to mind potassium manganate and permanganate.   Ruthenium and osmium also form **tetroxides** of the type RuO_4 and OsO_4 respectively. These compounds represent the highest known state of oxidation of any single metal.   The nearest approach to this state of oxidation occurs with perchloric and permanganic acids.   The tetroxides dissolve in water but the solutions are not acid : (1) they are neutral to litmus ; (2) do not decompose carbonates ; and (3) form crystalline salts.   The acids show no signs of hydrolysis.   The term " osmic acid " for osmium tetroxide is thus a misnomer.   Both tetroxides, RuO_4 and OsO_4, melt at a low temperature, about $+40°$, and boil at about $100°$ giving irritating vapours.   Osmium tetroxide vapours are very poisonous, and seriously injure the eyes.   They decompose on further heating into the dioxide and oxygen.   The solutions are reduced by organic matters and the finely divided metal is precipitated.   The doubt whether, say, osmium is really octovalent in the tetroxide was lessened when osmium octofluoride, OsF_8, was obtained with a vapour density of 355—theory for OsF_8 being 343—by the action of fluorine on osmium.   *En passant,* it may be added that osmium tetrafluoride, OsF_4, and osmium hexafluoride, OsF_6, are formed at the same time.   The tetrafluoride predominates when the action occurs at about $100°$, and the other two fluorides, when the action occurs at about $250°$.   The octofluoride is separated in lemon-yellow crystals, melting at $34·5°$, by cooling the product *in vacuo* in liquid air.

§ 24 Other Compounds of the Platinum Metals

Platinum Tetrachloride, $PtCl_4$

Platinum dissolves in aqua regia.   If the solution of hydrochloro-platinic acid, H_2PtCl_6, be evaporated to dryness, and the residue gently heated, a solution of the residue in hot water deposits reddish-brown crystals of $PtCl_4.5H_2O$ on cooling.   The anhydrous chloride, $PtCl_4$, can be made by drying the crystals over sulphuric acid and warming them in a current of chlorine ; or by heating hydrochloroplatinic acid in a current of hydrogen chloride between $165°$ and $200°$.

If a stream of chlorine be passed over hydrochloroplatinic acid between $364°$ and $374°$, the tetrachloride is formed ; between $430°$ and $440°$ what appears to be the trichloride, $PtCl_3$; about $582°$, platinum dichloride appears, and it has been reported that at the same temperature some monochloride is formed, but this lacks confirmation. Iridium chlorides $IrCl_4$, $IrCl_3$, $IrCl_2$, and $IrCl$ have been reported to be formed under similar circumstances respectively at $100°$, $763°$, $773°$, and $798°$.   Chlorides of all six platinum metals of the type $PtCl_4$ are known.   **Palladium tetrachloride** is not known in a free state, but double chlorides with potassium, etc., are known.

Chloroplatinates

If platinum chloride be crystallized from a solution acidified with hydrochloric acid, or if an aqua regia solution of the metal be evaporated a number of times with an excess of hydrochloric acid to drive off the nitric acid, reddish-brown deliquescent crystals of the complex acid $H_2PtCl_6.6H_2O$ are formed.   This substance—the " platinum chloride " of commerce—is really **hydrochloroplatinic acid.**   The acid is dibasic, and it forms a characteristic series of complex salts—the chloroplatinates.   **Potassium chloroplatinate,** K_2PtCl_6, for example, is a yellow crystalline precipitate made by adding the acid to a solution of potassium chloride. While the solubilities of the normal alkali chlorides in water *increase* in passing from lithium to caesium, the chloroplatinates *decrease* in solubility in passing from lithium to caesium. For instance, 100 c.c. of water at 10° dissolves, in grams :

Li_2PtCl_6	Na_2PtCl_6	K_2PtCl_6	Rb_2PtCl_6	Cs_2PtCl_6
Very Soluble	1·15	0·90	0·15	0·05

The solubility of **ammonium chloroplatinate**, $(NH_4)_2PtCl_6$, is 0·6 at 10°, and it thus comes between potassium and rubidium chloroplatinates. The fact that the sodium salt is fairly soluble in 80 per cent. alcohol, while the potassium salt is almost insoluble, enables a mixture of the chloroplatinates of sodium and potassium to be separated. The ammonium salt behaves like the potassium salt. During the electrolysis of ordinary salts—silver nitrate, potassium chloride, etc.—the metal is deposited on the cathode ; with the chloroplatinates, some of the platinum migrates as a $PtCl_6''$-ion to the anode compartment. Again, silver nitrate precipitates Ag_2PtCl_6, not AgCl, thus confirming the deduction that " $PtCl_6$ " is a bivalent complex acid radicle or that the solution of the acid furnishes the ions $2H^{\cdot}$ and $PtCl_6''$ on electrolysis. The constitution of the chloroplatinates will be discussed later.

Platinum Dichloride, $PtCl_2$

If hydrochloroplatinic acid be heated between 250° and 300°, it furnishes a grey granular powder of platinum dichloride, $PtCl_2$, insoluble in water ; at higher temperatures, it decomposes into platinum and chlorine. Platinum dichloride is also formed when platinum is heated to about 582° in chlorine gas. All six metals of the platinum series form salts of the type $PtCl_2$. Dihydrated **palladium dichloride**, $PdCl_2.2H_2O$ is obtained by the simultaneous action of hydrochloric acid and chlorine, or a little nitric acid, upon palladium. The solution deposits brownish-red crystals of the dihydrate on evaporation under reduced pressure. The anhydrous salt is formed if the crystals are warmed ; and also by the action of chlorine on the warm sulphide. The garnet-red crystals of the anhydrous salt decompose at a red-heat, forming what has been reported as monochloride, PdCl, but this is not certain. **Palladous iodide**, PdI_2, is precipitated as a black insoluble powder when potassium iodide is added to solutions of palladous chloride. This reaction is used sometimes for the separation of iodine from the other halogens, since the other halogen salts of palladium are soluble. It is difficult to precipitate the palladium quantitatively, because the iodide is very soluble in the presence of an excess of potassium iodide. Carbon monoxide unites with platinous chloride forming **carbonyl platinous chlorides**, $CO.PtCl_2$; $2CO.PtCl_2$; $3CO.2PtCl_2$. ; carbon monoxide also reduces a solution of the chloride even in the cold.

Chloroplatinites

When platinum dichloride is digested with hydrochloric acid, it furnishes a reddish-brown solution which is supposed to contain **hydrochloroplatinous acid**, H_2PtCl_4. The acid has not been isolated, but the salts—chloroplatinites— are formed by treating the solution with, say, potassium chloride. **Potassium chloroplatinite**, K_2PtCl_4, forms rose-red crystals. The same salt is formed by reducing potassium chloroplatinate with moist cuprous chloride, CuCl. Potassium chloroplatinite is used in platinum printing in photography. This chloride is reduced to metallic platinum by the action of light on ferrous oxalate. Palladium forms a similar series of **chloropalladites.**

Platinum-ammonia Compounds

The platinum metals behave in a peculiar manner with ammonia. Thus, when ammonia is added to a solution of platinum tetrachloride, $PtCl_4$, in hydrochloric acid, a green precipitate is formed. If the mixture be boiled, a green insoluble compound, $PtCl_2.4NH_3 + H_2O$, called **Magnus's green salt,** is formed and $PtCl_2.2NH_3$ remains in solution. If the precipitate be heated to $250°$, a yellow crystalline substance sparingly soluble in water is formed, $PtCl_2.2NH_3$. Both compounds can be oxidized with chlorine to $PtCl_4.2NH_3$. These two compounds may be taken to represent two well-defined series of platinum ammonia compounds. One series is derived from $PtCl_2$ and the other from $PtCl_4$. These will be discussed very shortly along with other complex ammines, etc.

A solution of platinum salts give a brown precipitate of the sulphide when treated with hydrogen sulphide, and the precipitate is soluble in alkali sulphide solution. Platinum salts also give a yellow crystalline precipitate with ammonium or potassium chloride. Most platinum salts decompose when ignited, and the metal is obtained on washing away the soluble products of decomposition   The metal itself is not affected by treatment with the mineral acids, although it is dissolved by aqua regia.   Most platinum salts in solution are reduced by reducing agents.

§ 25 Complex Compounds of the Elements of Group VIII and Similar Substances

Many compounds are known, such as the ferrocyanides and ferricyanides potassium cobaltinitrite and the ammines of chromium, cobalt, platinum, etc. which presented great difficulties in formulation according to the usual valencies of the elements concerned. Thus, the formula for potassium ferrocyanide will only fit in with the usual valencies of potassium (one), iron, (two or three) and the cyanogen radical (one) if it be written $4KCN.Fe(CN)_2$, that is, as an ordinary double salt. But there are several facts about the behaviour of this substance which render this formula unsatisfactory ; in particular, it does not give the reactions of cyanides, but appears to furnish a tetravalent anion $[Fe(CN)_6]''''$.

Similar problems occur in even more acute form when the complex metallic ammines are considered, for additional peculiarities are noticeable. For example, in some of these, only a proportion of the acid radical present is detectable as such ; thus with some complex chloride derivatives only a portion of the chlorine is precipitated by addition of silver nitrate solution. Compounds in which this behaviour is observable have already been noticed, e.g., the chromic chlorides (p. 777). Again some complex derivatives are known whose solutions do not conduct electricity, and hence furnish no ions, although made from ordinary salts, etc.

Werner was the first to systematize the compounds of this type in a satisfactory way. In its original form, his theory distinguished two kinds of valency which he termed main, or principal ; and auxiliary valencies. According to this, primary valencies represent those manifestations of chemical affinity which enable the combining capacities (valencies) of the elements to be expressed in terms of hydrogen atoms or their equivalents, e.g.,Cl—, Na—, NO_2—, CH_3—, . . .

Auxiliary valencies similarly represent those manifestations of (residual) chemical affinity which are able to bring about the stable union of molecules as if the molecules were themselves radicals able to exist as independent molecules, e.g., H_2O—, NH_3—, HCl—, $CrCl_3$—, . . .

In illustration, antimony pentachloride, $SbCl_5$; sulphur tetrachloride, SCl_4 ; phosphorus oxychloride, $POCl_3$; phosphorus pentachloride, PCl_5 ; and hydrogen cyanide, HCN, may all be regarded as compounds in which the primary valencies of the elements are exhausted, yet, in virtue of their residual affinity, compounds like $SbCl_5.4H_2O$, $SbCl_5.3HCN$, $SbCl_5.SCl_4$, $SbCl_5.PCl_5$, $SbCl_5.POCl_3$, etc., are readily formed.

At a later stage, Werner came to the conclusion that the difference between principal and auxiliary valencies is not so marked as he had at first supposed, and is one of degree rather than of kind. This is supported by modern electronic views of valency (see below).

Werner considered that when the binding capacity of an elementary atom appears exhausted, it can still link up with or co-ordinate other molecules, and build up more complex structures, but that there is an upper limit to this process. The maximum number of atoms, radicals or molecular groups—independently of their valencies—which can be directly linked with a central atom he called the co-ordination number of that atom.

The co-ordination number of most atoms, curiously enough is six; in a few cases it is four; and with molybdenum and the addition products of the chlorides of the alkaline earths, the co-ordination number appears to be eight. The fact that the co-ordination number for so many elements is six, and is generally independent of the nature of the co-ordinated groups, has made Werner suggest that the number is decided by available *space* rather than affinity and that six is usually the maximum number which can be fitted about the central atom to form a stable system. Consequently the co-ordination number represents a property of the atom which enables the constitution of " molecular compounds " to be referred back to actual linkings between definite atoms.

When the co-ordination number is six, Werner suggested, consequently, that the atoms or groups arrange themselves symmetrically about the central atom in the form of an octahedron. Evidence for the correctness of this assumption is given below. Similarly, when the co-ordination number is four, either a plane or a tetrahedral arrangement is theoretically possible. Examples of both arrangements are known.

The central atom with its surrounding co-ordinated atoms or groups constitutes, according to Werner, a unit which is not a salt (hence it does not itself ionize), but it may be a radical which can combine with other radicals to form a salt-like compound. The effective valency of the co-ordinated group depends both in magnitude and sign upon the nature of the atoms or groups attached to the central atom, as can be seen from the examples quoted below.

In illustration of the way in which Werner's theory systematized the formulation, and hence advanced the comprehension, of these complex compounds, some platinum-ammines may be mentioned, and also some of the cobalt derivatives.

Thus, two well-defined series of platinum-ammines is known, derivable respectively from platinous and platinic chlorides, in which the co-ordination numbers are respectively four and six. Thus :

TABLE LXIV.—PLATINUM-AMMINES DERIVED FROM PLATINOUS CHLORIDE.

Empirical Formula.	Werner's Formula.	Effective Valency of Complex.	Proportion of Ionizable Chlorine, etc.
$Pt(NH_3)_4Cl_2$	$[Pt(NH_3)_4]Cl_2$	$+2$	the whole
$Pt(NH_3)_3Cl_2$	$[Pt(NH_3)_3Cl]Cl$	$+1$	half
$Pt(NH_3)_2Cl_2$	$[Pt(NH_3)_2Cl_2]$	0	none : non-electrolyte
$Pt(NH_3)Cl_3K$	$[Pt(NH_3)Cl_3]K$	-1	none : one $K^\cdot$ ion
$PtCl_4K_2$	$[PtCl_4]K_2$	-2	none : two $K^\cdot$ ions

TABLE LXV.—PLATINUM-AMMINES DERIVED FROM PLATINIC CHLORIDE.

Empirical Formula.	Werner's Formula.	Effective Valency of Complex.	Proportion of Ionizable Chlorine, etc.
$Pt(NH_3)_6Cl_4$	$[Pt(NH_3)_6]Cl_4$	$+ 4$	the whole
$Pt(NH_3)_5Cl_4$	$[Pt(NH_3)_5Cl]Cl_3$	$+ 3$	three-quarters
$Pt(NH_3)_4Cl_4$	$[Pt(NH_3)_4Cl_2]Cl_2$	$+ 2$	one-half
$Pt(NH_3)_3Cl_4$	$[Pt(NH_3)_3Cl_3]Cl$	$+ 1$	one-quarter
$Pt(NH_3)_2Cl_4$	$[Pt(NH_3)_2Cl_4]$	0	none : non-electrolyte
$Pt(NH_3)Cl_5K$	$[Pt(NH_3)Cl_5]K$	$- 1$	none : one K·ion
$PtCl_6K_2$	$[PtCl_6]K_2$	$- 2$	none : two K··ions

The simple or compound radicals which form the complex represented within the square brackets, are directly united with the central atom of platinum.   The complex takes part in chemical reactions as if it were one individual radical. The basic ammonia in the complex can be successively replaced by acidic radicals —Cl, Br, NO$_3$, CO$_3$, SO$_4$, etc.—until the complex becomes acidic instead of basic and the platinic ammine complexes finally pass from electro-negative (basic) radicals to electro-positive (acidic) radicals.   Potassium chloroplatinate is the limit of the platinic ammines and potassium chloroplatinite is the limit of the platinous ammines.   It will be obvious that an enormous number of derivatives is conceivable and, in fact, a very large number indeed is known, derived not only from platinum, but also from chromium, iron, cobalt, nickel, ruthenium, rhodium, palladium, osmium, iridium and platinum.

Nomenclature of the Metal Ammines

Werner's system of naming the metal-ammonia compounds has been almost universally adopted.   The constituents of the complex are taken first ; and of these, the acid radicals with the suffix " o " come first ; then follow any groups which behave like ammonia, e.g., H$_2$O is called *aquo* ; NO$_2$, *nitrito* or *nitro* ; NO$_3$, *nitrato* ; CO$_3$, *carbonato* ; SO$_3$, *sulphito* ; SO$_4$, *sulphato* ; SCN, *thiocyanato* ; etc.   And lastly, preceding the metal itself, the ammonia molecules are designated " ammines," and spelt with a double " m " to distinguish the word from the " amines " or substituted ammonias.   The prefixes di, tri, . . . indicate the number of each.   The whole is written as one word.   Examples appear in the above list.

As examples of this nomenclature, the second and third compounds in each of the above tables may be taken.   These will be, according to Werner's system :

> Chlorotriamminoplatinous chloride,
> Dichlorodiaminino platinum,
> Chloropentammino platinic chloride,
> Dichlorotetrammino platinic chloride.

The valency of the complex is numerically equal to the difference between the ordinary valency of the central atom and the number of negative (acidic) groups or elements attached to the metal. Thus, the normal valency of platinum in the compounds of Table LXV is 4, hence the valency of $[Pt(NH_3)_5Cl]$, with one negative (acidic) group " Cl," will be 3 ; this means that the complex in question acts as a tervalent electropositive (basic) radical ; and it can unite with three univalent electro-negative (acidic) radicals.   The valency of $[Pt(NH_3)Cl_5]$ with five negative (acidic) groups, " Cl," will be -1.   This means that the complex under consideration will act as a univalent electro-negative (acidic) radical, and it can accordingly unite with one electropositive (basic) radical like potassium, sodium, etc.   If the valency of the acidic radicals in the complex are numerically equal to the normal valency of the central atom, the complex will be nullvalent.   This is the case, for instance, with the complex $[Pt(NH_3)_2Cl_4]$.

One of the features of Werner's theory was that it provided an explanation of the isomerism which exists among some of these complex compounds, and also predicted the existence of isomers of types which had not previously been observed.

Thus, dinitritotetramminocobaltic chloride exists in two forms, the flaveo (golden yellow) and croceo (saffron) forms. These are accounted for satisfactorily by Werner's assumption of an octahedral configuration for the complex ; thus :

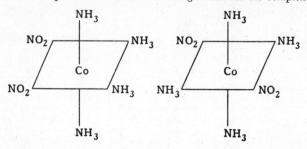

Again, there are two isomers of dichlorodiammineplatinum and two isomers of tetrachlorodiammineplatinum. In the former, $[Cl_2Pt(NH_3)_2]$, the four radicals are attached to the central atom of platinum in pairs. If the four groups were attached in space, say at the angular points of a regular tetrahedron, isomerism could hardly be expected because the four groups could be interchanged without altering their relations one with another. Hence it is inferred that the groups are arranged about the central atom of platinum in one plane. The resulting isomerism can be graphically illustrated by the schemes :

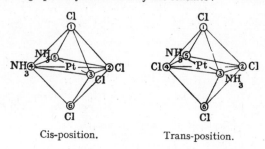

Cis-position.   Trans-position.

Similarly, on the assumption of an octahedral arrangement, the two isomers of $[Pt(NH_3)_2Cl_4]$ can be represented by :

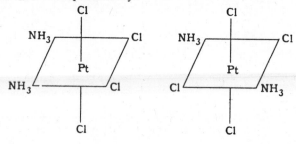

Werner has also applied this theory to salt hydrates, alums, etc., but its principal importance has laid in its elucidation of the structure of compounds of the types discussed above, and those represented by such substances as potassium mercuriodide, cuprammonium sulphate, potassium cobalticyanide, etc.

§ 26 The Electronic Theory of Valency and Werner's Theory

The enunciation of Werner's theory was a great step forward, and gave a considerable stimulus to the investigation of complex compounds, but it was not until the Bohr theory of the atom (p. 131) came to be applied to the problem of valency that any satisfactory explanation for the peculiar behaviour of what became known as the Werner compounds could be given.

The application of the conception of the co-ordinate valency (p. 148), along with the general ideas of valency as explained on the basis of the Bohr atom, to the complex ammines and related compounds affords results in complete harmony with the experimental observations already indicated.

Considering, for example, the case of the platinum ammines.

In the platinous ammines, starting with the central platinous ion, :Pt:, with a group of four valency electrons, the tetrammine is formed by the introduction of four ammonia molecules, in which each molecule shares a pair of electrons with the platinum atom by means of a duplet linkage.   This raises the number of electrons in the ring to twelve so that there is a stable group of twelve outer electrons.   If one of the ammonia molecules be replaced by, say, a neutral chlorine atom, the ammonia molecule taking away with it two shared electrons, and the chlorine atom bringing in only one electron, means that there is an electron short.   This is made good by the complex bringing in an electron from outside, thus reducing the positive charge of the complex by one unit.   In that way, $[Pt(NH_3)_4]^{++}$ passes into $[Pt(NH_3)_3Cl]^+$, and so on with successive replacements of NH_3-groups by Cl-atoms, until, at the limit, a chloroplatinite, $[PtCl_4]^{--}$ say potassium chloroplatinite, $K_2[PtCl_4]$, is formed :

$$\begin{bmatrix} NH_3 \overset{\times\bullet}{\underset{\times\bullet}{\times}} NH_3 \\ NH_3 \overset{\times\bullet}{\underset{\times\bullet}{\times}} NH_3 \end{bmatrix}^{+2} \quad \begin{bmatrix} NH_3 \overset{\times\bullet}{\underset{\times\bullet}{\times}} NH_3 \\ NH_3 \overset{\times}{\underset{\bullet\bullet}{\times}} Cl \end{bmatrix}^+ \quad \begin{bmatrix} NH_3 \overset{\times\bullet}{\underset{\times\bullet}{\times}} Cl \\ NH_3 \overset{\times}{\underset{\bullet\circ}{\times}} Cl \end{bmatrix}^0 \quad \begin{bmatrix} NH_3 \overset{\times\bullet\circ}{\underset{\bullet\circ}{}} Cl \\ Cl \overset{\circ\bullet\circ}{\underset{\bullet\circ}{}} Cl \end{bmatrix}^- \quad \begin{bmatrix} Cl \overset{\circ\bullet\circ}{\underset{\circ\bullet\circ}{}} Cl \\ Cl \overset{\circ\bullet\circ}{\underset{\circ\bullet}{}} Cl \end{bmatrix}^{--}$$

$[Pt(NH_3)_4]^{..}$-ion $[Pt(NH_3)_3Cl]^{.}$-ion $[Pt(NH_3)_2Cl_2]$ $[Pt(NH_3)Cl_3]^{'}$-ion $[PtCl_4]^{''}$-ion

where ● denotes the electrons of platinum ; ○, those of chlorine ; and ×, those of ammonia.   Since the symbol → is used to indicate a valency bond in which two shared electrons are supplied by one atom, or atomic group, as donor, and the symbol — for an ordinary valency bond formed by two atoms sharing a pair of electrons, the alternative symbols for these compounds are of the type

$$\begin{bmatrix} NH_3 \\ NH_3 \end{bmatrix} \!\!\!\! \underset{\diagdown}{\overset{\diagup}{Pt}} \!\!\!\! \begin{bmatrix} NH_3 \\ H_3 \end{bmatrix}^{++} \quad \begin{bmatrix} NH_3 \\ NH_3 \end{bmatrix} \!\!\!\! \underset{\diagdown}{\overset{\diagup}{Pt}} \!\!\!\! \begin{bmatrix} NH_3 \\ Cl \end{bmatrix}^+ \quad \begin{bmatrix} NH_3 \\ NH_3 \end{bmatrix} \!\!\!\! \rightarrow Pt \!\!\!\! \begin{bmatrix} Cl \\ Cl \end{bmatrix}^0 \quad \begin{bmatrix} Cl \\ Cl \end{bmatrix} \!\!\!\! > Pt \!\!\!\! < \begin{bmatrix} Cl \\ Cl \end{bmatrix}^{--}$$

Similar results apply to the platinic ammines where the central platinum ion, :Pt:, has a group of six valency electrons, and, in forming the hexammine, it takes up six ammonia molecules, so as to make a stable group of eighteen outer electrons.

Similar considerations apply also to the ferrocyanides, ferricyanides, cobalti-nitrites and, in fact, to the complex compounds in general. Thus, the substances named can be represented :

$$
\begin{bmatrix} CN & \cdot \ ^{\circ} \ ^{\cdot} \ ^{\circ} & CN \\ CN \ ^{\circ} & Fe & ^{\circ} \ CN \\ CN \ ^{\circ} \ ^{\cdot} \ ^{\circ} \ ^{\cdot} & CN \end{bmatrix}^{\prime\prime\prime\prime} \quad
\begin{bmatrix} CN & \cdot \ ^{\circ} \ ^{\cdot} \ ^{\circ} & CN \\ CN \ ^{\circ} & Fe & ^{\cdot} \ CN \\ CN \ ^{\cdot} \ ^{\circ} \ ^{\circ} \ ^{\cdot} & CN \end{bmatrix}^{\prime\prime\prime} \quad
\begin{bmatrix} NO_2 & ^{\circ} \ ^{\cdot} \ ^{\circ} \ ^{\cdot} & NO_2 \\ NO_2 \ ^{\cdot} & CO & ^{\circ} \ NO_2 \\ NO_2 \ ^{\cdot} \ ^{\cdot} \ ^{\circ} & NO_2 \end{bmatrix}^{\prime\prime\prime}
$$

Ferrocyanide ion   **Ferricyanide ion**   **Cobaltinitrite ion**

The electronic theory of valency thus has the merit of being able to explain the formation and behaviour of the complex (or Werner) compounds, along with the rest of chemical compounds, without resorting to any special assumptions. Its application to these substances also shows that Werner's original distinction between principal and auxiliary valencies can no longer be maintained, since when established, a link is the same whether both of the electrons of the pair are derived from a single atom (co-ordinate link) or one from each of the two linking atoms (covalent link).

§ 27 Relationships of the Group VIII Elements

As mentioned in § 1 this group of Mendeléeff's Table differed from the others in consisting not of single elements, but of three triads of elements, and further, the members of each triad show much more closely related properties, and have atomic weights closer together than is usual in successive elements. The modern form of the Periodic Table indicates that these triads are the central ones of the transition elements of the long periods so that the gradation of properties now recognized in these (horizontal) series would be expected to include the Group VIII elements. This is, in fact, the case, for the series, chromium, manganese, iron, cobalt, nickel, copper and zinc shows a steady gradation of properties ; likewise molybdenum (masurium), ruthenium, rhodium, palladium, silver and cadmium ; and also tungsten, rhenium, osmium, iridium, platinum, gold and mercury.

All the elements of the group are metals of high melting point, which exhibit marked catalytic activity. They are all characterized by very variable valency, and the property of forming complex compounds is developed to a high degree with all of them.

Some of the physical properties of these elements are given in Table LXIII, page 836. Corresponding properties of iron, cobalt and

TABLE LXVI.—PHYSICAL PROPERTIES OF THE IRON FAMILY.

	Iron.	Cobalt.	Nickel.
Atomic weight . . .	55·85	58·94	58·69
Specific gravity . . .	7·86	8·9	8·9
Atomic volume . . .	7·16	6·94	6·68
Melting point	1527°	1480°	1450°
Boiling point	3000°	2900°	2900° ?

nickel are given in Table LXVI. Close resemblances within the triads are thus observable, and similar resemblances are to be found in the chemical properties.

In addition to these similarities, among the triads themselves there is also a certain amount of resemblance between each element and its vertical analogues, particularly the last two members in each case. Thus iron, ruthenium and osmium have certain common properties, as also have cobalt, rhodium, and iridium ; and nickel, palladium and platinum.

Iron, ruthenium and osmium all form dichlorides and trichlorides, and these also form complex chlorides or double chlorides such as $FeCl_3.2KCl.H_2O$ (or $K_2FeCl_5.H_2O$), K_2RuCl_5, K_3OsCl_6, etc. All three elements form monoxides and sesquioxides, and at any rate derivatives of dioxides. Ruthenium and osmium form complex cyanides analogous to the ferrocyanides ; but do not give rise to analogues of the ferricyanides.

Interesting comparisons are possible between cobalt, rhodium and iridium. The stable chloride of cobalt is a dichloride, while the stable chlorides of the other two elements are trichlorides ; all three form double halides such as $LiCoCl_4$, K_3RhCl_6, K_3IrCl_6. Only cobalt forms a monoxide, but there are sesquioxides and dioxides of all three, the last named being slightly acidic in nature, and suggests thus a relationship to iron, ruthenium and osmium, but to chromium and manganese also. All three elements form similar sulphates, alums, and double cyanides, as well as complex ammine-derivatives like those of palladium and platinum.

Nickel, palladium and platinum are similar in their power of occluding hydrogen (notably palladium) ; they all yield a dichloride, and palladium and platinum at least form double chlorides ; these two also give rise to trichlorides and double salts derived therefrom. All three form monoxides and dioxides ; the latter displaying feeble acidic properties ; they all form double cyanides like $K_2Pt(CN)_4$.

As regards horizontal relationships, iron, cobalt and nickel are all fairly hard and high-melting, decidedly para-magnetic, and exhibit similar variability of valency. They give rise to isomorphous and closely similar complex compounds, such as the complex cyanides, etc. According to the electronic theory, this similarity is due to their all having two electrons in the outermost valency group, differing only in the composition of the preceding electron group (see Table XII).

While there are thus many resemblances observable among the members of the group, there are also considerable differences noticeable. Thus, relationship between iron and platinum is somewhat remote, and as regards close resemblance, is almost confined to the ease with which all the metals of the group give rise to complex compounds. This difficulty, however, is no greater than is found in many other groups, and is much smaller than, say, those occasioned by the inclusion of the halogens and manganese in the same group.

CHAPTER XXXVI

RADIO-ACTIVITY AND THE RADIO ELEMENTS

The discovery that there are metals which, so to speak, are bleeding to death by the irrestrainable welling forth of strange aerial substances from their intimate parts was a novelty which held chemists spellbound with astonishment.—ANON.

Radio-activity is the least manageable of natural processes. It will not be hurried or controlled. Nature keeps the management of this particular department in her own hands. Man views the phenomenon with hungry eyes, but his interference is barred out. He can only look on in wonder while it deploys its irresistible unknown forces.—ANON (1907).

§ 1 Discovery of Radio-activity and of Radium

ABOUT the same time as Röntgen discovered X-rays (1895), H. Becquerel (1896) placed fragments of several phosphorescent substances on photographic plates wrapped in two sheets of black paper. In about twenty-four hours, when the plates were developed, a silhouette of the phosphorescent substance appeared on the plate. Hence, it was inferred that " *the phosphorescent salts of uranium must emit radiations which are capable of passing through black paper opaque to ordinary light, and of reducing the silver salts of the photographic plate,* even when the uranium compound has been completely sheltered from the light." The radiations emitted by the phosphorescent substance are called **Becquerel rays,** though Niepce, thirty years previously, noticed that uranium salts could effect photographic plates in the dark, and G. le Bon (1896) called the radiations *lumière noire*—" black light." A substance which possesses the property of emitting these penetrative rays is said to be " radio-active," and the property itself is called **radio-activity.**

Becquerel also found that when uranium is brought near to a charged gold-leaf electroscope, the gold leaf gradually collapses. The rate at which an electroscope is discharged is a measure of the efficiency of the specimen in emitting rays. The charged electroscope, indeed, is more sensitive than the photographic plate for detecting Becquerel rays. Air which has been in contact with uranium and its compounds, like air which has been exposed to Röntgen rays, will discharge an electroscope, for exposure to these radiations makes air a conductor.

G. C. Schmidt (1898) found that thorium is radio-active in the same sense that uranium is radio-active, and curiously enough, these two elements have the highest atomic weight—Th, 232 ; U, 238. The radio-activity of thorium is readily shown by flattening an ordinary new gas mantle on the sensitive side of a photographic plate, and leaving all in darkness for about a week. When the plate is developed in the usual way, a photograph of the flattened mantle will be produced.

The mantle contains sufficient thorium, as oxide, to demonstrate the effect.

Investigation soon showed that all substances containing uranium are radio-active, and it was also soon found that this property does not depend upon light or heat ; the emission of the rays appears to be a permanent and abiding property of uranium and its compounds ; and it is independent of temperature and of all known physical conditions. No sign of a diminution or increase of the property has been detected whether the substance be heated towards 2000° or cooled towards −200°. The same weight of uranium, no matter how combined, emits the same amount of radiation. *The chemical properties of the elements—excepting perhaps the helium family—can be modified and controlled by changes in the chemical and physical conditions ; but radio-activity is independent of these conditions.*

Not long after Becquerel's discovery, Mme. Curie in examining the radio-activity of a number of uranium minerals found that some uraniferous minerals are much more active than the uranium which they contain. This was particularly marked in pitchblende from Joachimstahl in Bohemia, and the effect was traced to the presence in the pitchblende of a substance different from uranium or any other known body and very highly radio-active. This substance, isolated by Mme. Curie, turned out to be a new element, more than a million times more radio-active than uranium, to which the name radium was given.

§ 2 The Nature of the Radiations

The radiations from radium, upon investigation, were found to be capable of bringing about many effects in addition to their effects on a photographic plate or of discharging electroscopes. The chemical and physiological changes which they cause, although interesting in themselves, are of lesser importance for an understanding of the phenomena of radio-activity than the physical effects.

A few sheets of paper or a couple of sheets of aluminium foil will cut off a large part of the radiations, and a sheet of lead, about half a centimetre thick, will cut off nearly all the radiations. A residuum still remains unsuppressed even after passing through 15 cm. of lead or through a far thicker block of iron. Hence, **the radiations from radium are not homogeneous.** Again, the radiations from radium are not affected in the same way by a magnet. Some of the rays are not influenced, for they do not bend when placed in a magnetic field ; these are called the γ-rays. Others are bent *towards* or in a direction parallel to the magnet, and they are called the β-rays ; while others are bent *away* from the magnet, and are called the α-rays.

The characteristics of these three types of radiation are as follows :

Alpha Rays

The α-rays are slightly bent by intense magnetic forces ; the effect of an electric field on them shows that they are positively charged and their behaviour is similar to that of canal rays or positive rays (p. 134). Later experimental evidence showed that they consist of particles of mass 4 (relative to the mass of an oxygen atom as 16) positively charged ; and in 1908, Rutherford and Royds showed that these particles are, in fact, charged atoms of helium. This was accomplished by sealing radium emanation (see below) in a thin glass tube, when the α-particles passed through the walls into an outer evacuated tube. On passing an electric discharge through the latter after some time, the helium spectrum slowly developed. α-rays are easily absorbed by thin metal foil and have a limited range in air ; the fastest have a range of about 7 cm.

Beta Rays

The β-rays have more penetrating power than α-rays, but they differ in being deflected in the opposite direction by magnetic and electric fields. Investigation has shown that they closely resemble cathode rays (p. 127) and, in fact, that they consist of electrons projected with enormous velocity (sometimes approaching that of light).

Gamma Rays

The γ-rays are not affected by the most intense magnetic forces. Their penetrative power is very intense, and they can manifest their presence after passing through several inches of metallic lead or several feet of metallic iron. The relative penetrative powers of the three types of rays for aluminium are roughly as $\alpha : \beta : \gamma = 10 : 10^3 : 10^5$. The γ-rays do not appear to be material particles at all, but the experimental evidence shows that **the γ-rays are similar to, if not identical with, Röntgen rays.** A diagrammatic illustration of the three types of radiation from radium can now be given, Fig. 241. A piece of radium is supposed to be placed in a lead vessel, A, sufficiently thick to prevent rays travelling through the walls. Under the influence of an intense magnetic field, the rays no longer travel in straight lines, but they are deflected as shown in the diagram.

It is now known that a single radio-active element never emits all three types of radiation ; either an α-particle is emitted, or β-particles together with γ-rays. Radium appears to produce all three on account of its disintegration into other substances which are themselves radio-active (see below).

§ 3 Radium Emanation

The investigation of the properties of radium soon showed that there is a continuous evolution of a substance from radium which behaves as though it were a radio-active gas. This gas emits only α-rays, and was termed by Rutherford, who first observed it, *emanation*.

The **radium emanation** is quite distinct from the three types of rays emitted by radium and its salts. The amount is very small, but

the supply is continuous.   If the temperature be raised the absorbed
emanation is given off, for a short time, much more copiously than in
the cold.   There is now little doubt that it is a gas, for it has a characteristic spectrum, somewhat resembling the
spectrum of xenon ; it can be condensed
by liquid air to a minute drop of liquid
(microscopic) of specific gravity 5·7 ; and
at still lower temperatures, the liquid solidifies.   The solid melts at about −71°,
and the liquid boils at about −62°.   The
radio-active gas is chemically inert, for it
resists attack by every chemical reagent
hitherto tried, it has a characteristic
spectrum, and distinctive chemical and
physical properties, and in consequence,
the radium emanation has been placed with
the argon-helium group of the periodic table.

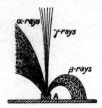

FIG.   241. — Diagrammatic
Analysis of the Radium Radiations by a Magnet.

The atomic weight of the emanation has
been determined by measurements of its density, rate of diffusion,
etc., and found to be 222.   It is now known as **niton** or **radon**
(Ch. XXIV).

The emanation, if kept by itself, slowly disappears.   After about
four days, only about half the original quantity remains.   In fact, the
**radium emanation decomposes, continuously and spontane-
ously, into a radio-active solid and helium gas.**

This radio-active solid is known as the " active deposit," and it has
been found to decay into a series of radio-active products ending with
lead.   The period of average life of these products varies, and the
" active deposit " thus contains, when radio-active equilibrium has
been established, a proportion of each substance greater or less according to the rate at which it is being formed and decomposed.   Each
change is associated with either the expulsion of an α-particle or the
production of β- and γ-rays.

§ 4 Theory of Atomic Disintegration

Many hypotheses have been suggested to account for the observed
facts of radio-activity.   That which is generally accepted is due to
Rutherford and Soddy, and is known as the theory of atomic disintegration.   According to this theory, ordinary atoms are supposed to be
small intricate systems (Ch. IX) linked together by forces of tremendous
power.   The properties of the different elementary atoms are determined by the number and configuration of the intra-atomic electrons.
Radio-activity is an atomic property, and it is an effect of the instability
of certain atomic systems.   The disintegration of the unstable atoms
is marked by the emission of rays.   The radio-active elements are
therefore unstable, and are continually and spontaneously changing by

numerous intermediate stages into more stable elements. This hypothesis is called **Rutherford and Soddy's theory of the disintegration of the atoms,** because they established its claim to serious consideration, and have done valuable work with its aid. Their hypothesis is orthodox and fashionable. If this hypothesis should survive that struggle for existence which all neoteric hypotheses must undergo, then radio-activity will be cited as proof of the **devolution of the elements.** Astro-spectral observations leave little room for doubt that in the " cooling stars " a process of **evolution of the elements** is in progress.

It is further assumed that the radio-active elements are not unique among the elements in containing abnormal stores of internal energy, but—excluding potassium and possibly rubidium—the other elements are either immutable or else they are changing so slowly that no signs of mutation have yet been detected. According to the atom disintegration hypothesis of radio-activity, Nature is continually changing the elements with the largest atomic weights such as uranium (238·07) and thorium (232·12) into simpler elements. The latter, in turn, are said to be stable simply because no signs of radio-activity have yet been detected. It is possible that if ever elements existed on earth with larger atomic weights, and by inference, with more complex atoms, they have all degraded into simpler forms, and are now probably **extinct elements.**

The elements with the smallest atomic weights, and those which are found in greatest abundance on the earth—hydrogen, helium, calcium, oxygen, sodium, silicon, etc.—are usually considered to be the most stable, and to contain least infra-atomic energy. Hydrogen and helium, occurring in the hottest stars, are supposed to have a tendency to form aggregates, and pass into common terrestrial elements during the cooling of the hot stars. It seems as if uranium and thorium must have been exposed to peculiar conditions—possibly of pressure and temperature—whereby they were elaborated beyond the limits of stability, and absorbed stores of energy which are now being slowly released because the conditions necessary for their stability no longer obtain.

It might be asked why the comparatively conspicuous self-destructive activities of radium have not led to its extinction long ago? Rutherford estimates that the radium now on earth will be disintegrated and the whole virtually extinct in about 25,000 years. There can thus be little doubt that if there had not been a continuous source of supply, radium would have been an extinct element long ago. The decay of the heaviest known element, uranium, is so extraordinarily slow that it can just be detected, and a rough estimate made of its life—8,000,000,000 years.

The Distribution of the Elements

The reasons for thinking that the supplies of radium are continually renewed turn on the facts :

1. Radium and uranium always occur together, and the two elements are not sufficiently common for this to be due to mere chance ; and

2. The proportion of radium to uranium in the uraniferous minerals is almost invariable—1 : 35,000,000. This approximate constancy is clearly the result of an equilibrium between production and decay. The supply of radium is regulated by its relative rates of formation and degradation ; and when the birth and death rates are balanced, the ratio radium : uranium must be constant. It is interesting to observe in this connection that a very small amount of helium is always found occluded in uraniferous minerals. Assuming that no helium escapes, the small amount found in a given rock will be a measure of the time which has elapsed since the birth of that particular sample, but this gas must be constantly leaking into the atmosphere, and, consequently, the " age " so computed will be a minimum age of the mineral, for the mineral may be older, but not younger than the age so computed. Hence, by determining the relative amounts of uranium and helium in a mineral, its minimum age can be estimated. In this way, Strutt estimated that it requires eleven million years to produce one c.c. of helium per gram of uranium. Lead also has been detected in over forty uraniferous minerals ; and in many of these cases lead does not occur near the uranium deposit. Hence it is considered unlikely that the lead has been deposited about the uranium by subterranean streams, and hence may be taken as confirmation of the view that lead is the end product of radio-active change.

According to this theory, therefore, an atom is at any moment liable to explode, and its expectation of life is expressed by a simple law discovered by Rutherford. He showed that the fraction of the total number of atoms undergoing disintegration in unit time is constant ; or otherwise expressed, the activity diminishes exponentially with the time. The reciprocal of the fraction which disintegrates in unit time is called the **period of average life** of the element. The period after which half the atoms have disintegrated is called the **half-life period,** and is 1/1·443 of the period of average life. Each radio-element is characterized by its average life, and in radio-active equilibrium the amounts of each element present are proportional to the half-life period.

Investigation has shown that there are three series of radio-active changes, known respectively, as the uranium, thorium and actinium series. Actinium is a new element separated from the residues of pitchblende by Debierne in 1899. It is not the first member of the series, being preceded by another new element, protoactinium. It is believed that protoactinium itself is derived from the uranium series, as shown by the dotted line in Table LXVIII, but the exact position at which branching occurs is still a matter of controversy.

These series of changes are shown below, and also the nature of the rays emitted at each step. The half-life period, and atomic weight of each element, are given in Table LXVII.

Uranium Series

$$UI \xrightarrow{a} UX_1 \xrightarrow{\beta\gamma} UX_2 \xrightarrow{\beta\gamma} UII \xrightarrow{a} Io \xrightarrow{a} Ra \xrightarrow{a} RaEm \xrightarrow{a} RaA \xrightarrow{a} RaB \xrightarrow{\beta\gamma}$$

$$\xrightarrow{} RaC \underset{a}{\overset{\beta\gamma}{\underset{\diagdown RaC''}{\diagup RaC'}}} \overset{a}{\underset{\beta\gamma}{}} RaD \xrightarrow{\beta} RaE \xrightarrow{\beta} Po \xrightarrow{a} Lead.$$

Thorium Series

$$Th \xrightarrow{a} MsThI \xrightarrow{\beta\gamma} MsThII \xrightarrow{\beta\gamma} RaTh \xrightarrow{a} ThX \xrightarrow{a} ThEm \xrightarrow{a} ThA \xrightarrow{a} ThB \xrightarrow{\beta\gamma}$$

$$\xrightarrow{} ThC \underset{a}{\overset{\beta\gamma}{\underset{\diagdown ThC''}{\diagup ThC'}}} \overset{a}{\underset{\beta\gamma}{}} Lead.$$

Actinium Series

$$Pa \xrightarrow{a} Ac \xrightarrow{\beta\gamma} RaAc \xrightarrow{a} AcX \xrightarrow{a} AcEm \xrightarrow{a} AcA \xrightarrow{a} AcB \xrightarrow{\beta\gamma}$$

$$AcC \underset{a}{\overset{\beta\gamma}{\underset{\diagdown AcC''}{\diagup AcC'}}} \overset{a}{\underset{\beta\gamma}{}} Lead$$

TABLE LXVII.—CHARACTERISTICS OF RADIO-ELEMENTS.

Element.	Symbol.	Half-life period.		Atomic Weight.
Uranium I	UI	$4 \cdot 5 \times 10^9$	years	238·07
Uranium X$_1$	UX$_1$	23·8	days	234
Uranium X$_2$	UX$_2$	1·15	mins.	234
Uranium II	UII	ca. 2×10^6	years	234
Ionium	Io	ca. 9×10^4	years	230
Radium	Ra	1580	years	226·05
Radium Emanation	RaEm	3·82	days	222
Radium A	RaA	3·05	mins.	218
Radium B	RaB	26·8	mins.	214
Radium C	RaC	19·7	mins.	214
Radium C′	RaC′	10·7	secs.	214
Radium C″	RaC″	1·32	mins.	210
Radium D	RaD	16	years	210
Radium E	RaE	5	days	210
Polonium	Po	136·5	days	210

TABLE LXVII.—CHARACTERISTICS OF RADIO-ELEMENTS (*contd.*)

Thorium	Th	2.2×10^{10}	years	232·12
Mesothorium I	MsTh I	6·7	years	228
Mesothorium II	MsThII	6·2	hours	228
Radiothorium	RdTh	1·90	years	228
Thorium X	ThX	3·64	days	224
Thorium Emanation	ThEm	54	secs.	220
Thorium A	ThA	0·14	secs.	216
Thorium B	ThB	10·6	hours	212
Thorium C	ThC	60	mins.	212
Thorium C'	ThC'	10^{-11}	secs.	212
Thorium C''	ThC''	3·2	mins.	208
Protoactinium	Pa	ca. 10^4	years	231
Actinium	Ac	20	years	227
Radioactinium	RdAc	19	days	227
Actinium X	AcX	11·2	days	223
Actinium Emanation	AcEm	3·9	secs.	219
Actinium A	AcA	·002	secs.	215
Actinium B	AcB	36	mins.	211
Actinium C	AcC	2·16	mins.	211
Actinium C'	AcC'	10^{-3}	secs.	211
Actinium C''	AcC''	4·76	mins.	207

§ 5 Radio-elements and the Periodic Table

The position of the radio-elements in the Periodic Table and the discovery of isotopes have been discussed in Chapter IX (pp. 133-138). The relation between the nature of the change (whether α-ray or β-ray) by which a particular element is formed and its position in the table is also explained together with the enunciation of the displacement law. These facts are summarized in the portion of the Periodic Table reproduced in Table LXVIII on page 856.

Artificial Radio-elements

It has been shown recently by Mme. Curie and F. Joliot and other workers that certain of the ordinary non-radio-active elements, after bombardment by α-rays exhibit feeble radio-activity. It is thought that the α-particles " combine " with the nucleus and thus form unstable isotopes of the element next but one higher in the Periodic Table. One of the most interesting of these observations is that of Fermi who obtained, in this way, a new artificial radio-element from uranium. This will have an atomic number of 93 or 94, and an atomic weight approximately 242, and so is the heaviest element so far known. This part of the subject is being energetically investigated at the present time, and a number of artificially produced radio-active elements (some of them isotopes of common elements) have been reported.

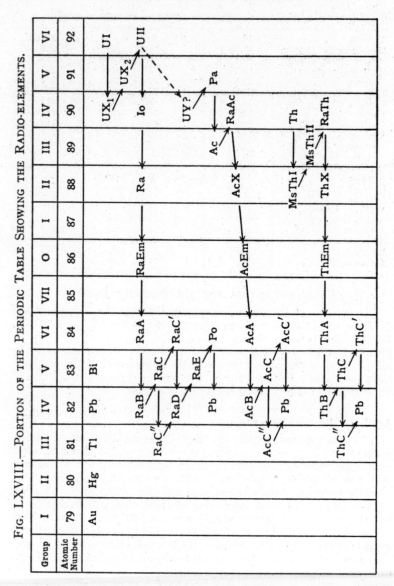

Fig. LXVIII.—Portion of the Periodic Table Showing the Radio-elements.

QUESTIONS

1. Give an account of the Phlogistic Theory of combusion, explaining clearly how it accounted for both oxidation and reduction. What was the chief fallacy in this theory? (Cambridge, H.S.C.)

CHAPTER II

1. Under what conditions do gases exhibit deviations from Boyle's Law? To what factors do you attribute these deviations, and on what lines has the attempt been made to give a quantitive account of them? (London, B.Sc.)

2. Give an account of the work of (a) Andrews, (b) Faraday, (c) Dewar, on the liquefaction of gases. Describe some modern technical applications of liquid gases. (London, B.Sc.)

3. Explain why temperature is defined in terms of the properties of a perfect gas. (Oxford Univ.)

4. Describe how real gases are found to deviate from the ideal gas laws. Discuss how far these deviations are accounted for by the theory of Van der Waals. (Oxford Univ.)

5. Explain and justify the assumptions underlying the kinetic theory of gases, and show that from them it is possible to deduce Boyle's Law. (Inst. of Chem.)

6. What is meant by gaseous diffusion? How would you attempt to compare quantitatively the rates of diffusion of two gases?
127 c.c. of a certain gas is diffused in the same time as 100 c.c. of chlorine under the same conditions. Calculate the molecular weight of the gas. (O. & C.J.B.H.C.)

7. On the basis of the Kinetic Theory deduce the relationship between the pressure of a gas and the velocity and the density of its molecules. Calculate the molecular weight of an unknown gas which under precisely similar conditions takes 1·117 times as long as oxygen to diffuse through an aperture. (Sheffield Univ.)

8. How do you understand that the principle of the Conservation of Energy applies to a case in which a coiled spring (as of brass) is compressed within a vessel of glass or porcelain, and then completely dissolved in acid? (Massachusetts Inst. of Technology.)

9. What do you understand by the kinetic theory of gases? How can you utilize your knowledge to formulate a proof of Avogadro's Hypothesis? (Punjab Univ.)

10. What is meant by a chemical change? In what respects does chemical action differ from gravitation? What properties of matter do we define as chemical properties, and what are physical properties? (Punjab Univ.)

CHAPTER III

1. Trace the development and application in chemistry of the law of conservation of mass, dealing especially with the scope and degree of precision of the experimental evidence on which it is based. (London B.Sc.)

2. How may a chemical compound be distinguished from a mixture? Illustrate your answer by examples. (O. & C.J.B.H.C.)

3. State the law of multiple proportions. Describe experiments which you would perform to demonstrate its accuracy. What do you know about the history of the discovery of this law? (Cambridge H.S.C.)

4. Show that the laws of multiple and reciprocal proportions are a necessary consequence of the atomic theory. (Cambridge H.S.C.)

5. Matter is said to be indestructible ; what does this mean ? What evidence is there that this is so ? (Science and Art Dept.)

6. Distinguish as clearly as you can between changes in matter which are classed as chemical and those classed as physical. Which of the following do you think are chemical, and which are physical : freezing ice cream ; souring milk ; burning a candle ; distilling water ; magnetizing iron ; electrolysis of a solution of copper sulphate ?

7. Give a brief account of the Atomic Theory, together with its history. (Princeton Univ.)

8. Define the laws of definite and multiple proportions. Show how the following analysis of three oxides of nitrogen illustrate the law of multiple proportions.

	A.	B.	C.
Nitrogen	63·65	46·68	25·94
Oxygen	36·35	53·32	74·06

(Manchester Univ.)

9. Describe in detail how you would separate the constituents of ordinary black gunpowder, and ascertain the percentage of each constituent in the mixture. (St. Andrew's Univ.)

Chapter IV

1. Explain the relation between Gay-Lussac's law of gaseous volumes, and Avogadro's hypothesis. (O. & C.J.B.H.C.)

2. Describe one method you would use to measure the vapour density of a given liquid. Explain why this value enables you to deduce the molecular weight of the substance in the form of vapour. (London Inter B.Sc.)

3. 0·6 grm. of a liquid when vapourized at 150°c. and at a pressure of 750 m.m. occupied 176 c.c. What is the value of (a) its vapour density referred to hydrogen, (b) its molecular weight ? (London Inter B.Sc.)

4. State Avogadro's Hypothesis. Explain how experiments on the composition by volume of hydrogen chloride have led to the conclusion that the molecules of hydrogen and chlorine contain at least two atoms. (London Inter B.Sc.)

5. Describe a method for the determination of molecular weights by the relative lowering in the vapour pressure of a pure solvent, produced by a non-volatile solute.

At 0°c. the vapour pressure of water = 4·62 m.m., and that of a solution of 2·28 grms. of $CaCl_2$ in 100 grms. of water = 4·584 m.m. Calculate the degree of dissociation of the salt. (London B.Sc.)

6. Describe a method by which the vapour density of a volatile liquid may be measured. Explain why the molecular weight of the substance in the form of vapour may be easily calculated from the vapour density.

One grm. of liquid vapourized at 150°c. and 750 m.m. pressure occupied 238 c.c. Calculate its molecular weight. (O. & C.J.B.H.C.)

7. Trace the steps in the proof of the relationship which exists between the vapour density and the molecular weight of a gas.

Three compounds of a certain element contained 94·1, 50·0, and 21·9 per cent. of the element, and had vapour densities of 17, 32 and 73 respectively. What is the probable atomic weight of the element ? (O. & C.J.B.H.C.)

8. Describe fully how you would determine the vapour density of a substance, whose boiling point is well below 100°c. How does the fact that a vapour does not behave as a perfect gas, affect the relation between vapour density and molecular weight ? (Oxford H.S.C.)

9. Which of the following gases are lighter, and which are heavier than air :— O_2, CO, CH_4, NH_3, SO_2, H_2S ? Calculate the weight of 10 litres of CO_2 at N.T.P. (Board of Educ.)

10. Explain the reasons for believing that " the molecular weight of any gas is twice its density compared with hydrogen." (Madras Univ.)

CHAPTER V

1. Explain the term " equivalent weight " as applied to a metal. Calculate the numerical value in each of the following cases :

(a) aluminium ; given that it burns with an increase of 88·8 per cent. of its weight.

(b) magnesium ; which when treated with acids yields 922 c.c. of hydrogen (measured at S.T.P.) per grm. (Durham Inter B.Sc.)

2. What is meant by a normal solution of, a base, and an oxidizing agent ?

When the salt $KNaC_4H_4O_6.4H_2O$ (molecular weight 282) is ignited, there is a residue of sodium carbonate and of potassium carbonate. A grm. of this salt gave a residue which required 63·8 c.c. of N/10 hydrochloric acid for neutralization, methyl orange being used as indicator. Calculate the percentage purity of the salt. (O. & C.J.B.H.C.)

3. Show that the symbol H_2O best represents the formula for water, quite independent of the atomic theory.

CHAPTER VI

1. Discuss with full details two different methods which have been used in the determination of atomic weights. (Durham B.Sc.)

2. Give an account of the methods employed in the accurate determination of atomic weights. (Durham B.Sc.)

3. Write an historical and critical essay on the principles underlying the determination of the atomic weights of the elements. (London B.Sc.)

4. From the following data, calculate the atomic weight of the metal M, and write the formula of its chloride :—

(a) 0·45 grm. of the metal displaces 560 c.c. of hydrogen from an acid (measured at S.T.P.).

(b) 0·50 grm. of the anhydrous chloride when volatilized in a Victor Meyer apparatus displaces 42·3 c.c. of air (at S.T.P.).

(c) The specific heat of the metal is 0·214. (Oxford H.S.C.)

5. Explain how Avogadro's hypothesis can be used to find the atomic weight of an element which forms a number of volatile compounds. Calculate the probable atomic weight of carbon (to the nearest whole number) from the following data :—

Substance	CO	CS_2	C_2H_4	C_3H_8	C_6H_6
Vap. Dens.	14	38	14	22	39
% of carbon	42·86	15·79	85·73	81·81	92·31

(Cambridge H.S.C.)

6. Give a simple and elementary definition of valency. Classify the following elements according to their valencies, quoting the formulae of suitable compounds and indicating any cases where more than one valency is shown :—S, Cl, N, C Ca, Pb, Fe, P, Al, Zn, Cu, K. (J.M.B.H.S.C.)

7. Discuss the question whether H, = 1 or O = 16 should be used as the standard for atomic weights. (Board of Educ.)

8. What is meant by the " equivalent " of an element, and what relation does it bear to the atomic weight ? (London Univ.)

9. An element may exhibit several combining or equivalent weights, but only one atomic weight. Explain this phenomenon clearly and briefly.

10. State the law of Dulong and Petit, and explain its application. Discuss its limitations to the determination of atomic weights.

11. An oxide of a metal contains 48·0 per cent. of oxygen. What is the exact equivalent of the metal ? If the specific heat of the metal was found to be 0·123, what is the probable atomic weight and valency of the metal, and what would be the probable nature of the oxide ? (Manchester Univ.)

12. State the law of isomorphism, and give examples of its utility in fixing the atomic weights of the elements.

Chapter VII

1. Explain in words the precise meaning of the expression,
" $Mg + H_2SO_4 = MgSO_4 + H_2$ "
(Punjab Univ.)

2. According to C. R. A. Wright (1874), " neither the molecular theory nor the atomic theory, generally so called, is taken for granted in the formation of chemical equations." Discuss this quotation.

3. Explain the connection between the terms Equivalent, and Atomic weight. 0·100 grm. of a metal gave on treatment with dilute acid 34·2 c.c. of hydrogen measured at S.T.P. Calculate the equivalent of the metal. What further information is required in order to deduce the atomic weight? (Aberystwyth Univ.)

4. State the law of diffusion of gases, and state carefully the ratio of the rate of diffusion of oxygen (molecular weight 32) to that of air (density 14·4).

5. Ten grms. of water are (a) decomposed by sodium, (b) passed as steam over red hot iron, (c) decomposed by an electric current. What volume of gas under standard conditions is produced in each case?

6. Calculate the weight of anhydrous zinc sulphate and the volume of hydrogen at 29°C. and 735 mm. pressure produced by the action of dilute sulphuric acid on 12 grms. of zinc. Hydrated zinc sulphate on heating to 100°C. loses 37·64 per cent. of water, and on heating to a higher temperature 6·27 per cent. more. Calculate the simplest molecular formula for hydrated zinc sulphate and find how many molecules of water are lost in the first heating. (Cape Univ.)

7. Oxygen is to be obtained from mercuric oxide, or manganese dioxide, or from potassium chlorate. What is the cheapest method of making oxygen per litre, so far as raw materials are concerned, if 100 grms. of mercuric oxide cost 9d. ; 1 kilo of manganese dioxide 10d. ; and 1 kilo of potassium chlorate 1s. 3d. ?

8. The atomic weight of an element M is 56. An oxide of this element is found to consist of 53·8 per cent. metal, and 46·2 per cent. oxygen. Calculate the formula of the oxide. (London Univ.)

9. Calculate the percentage composition of potassium nitrate, sulphuric acid, common salt, phosphine, manganese dioxide.

10. C. Rammelsberg (1841) analysed a crystalline salt obtained by treating antimony pentasulphide with concentrated potassium hydroxide, and found : K, 23·40 ; Sb, 37·80 ; S, 18·19 ; O, 7·30 ; water, 13·30 ; and he considered these numbers agreed satisfactorily with the formula $K_3SbS_4.KSbO_3.5H_2O$. Is this formula in accord with the observed data?

Chapter VIII

1. Discuss the missing elements in the periodic classification. (Durham B.Sc.)

2. Give an historical account of the methods which have been adopted for the classification of the chemical elements. Indicate the advantages and disadvantages of each method. (London B.Sc.)

3. Explain the statement that " the properties of elements are a periodic function of their atomic weight," and illustrate it by reference to *one* physical and *two* chemical properties. Discuss the chemical resemblances between sulphur and (a) oxygen, (b) chromium. (Oxford H.S.C.)

4. Compare the commonest hydrides of fluorine, chlorine, oxygen, sulphur, nitrogen, and phosphorus with the object of illustrating the way in which their properties vary with the position of these elements in the Periodic Table. (Oxford H.S.C.)

5. A new elementary body, a metal, is placed in your hands. What means would you take to (a) ascertain its atomic weight, (b) find its position in Mendeléeff's Table? (Science and Art Dept.)

6. State the general characteristics of the magnesium-zinc-cadmium family of metals, and indicate their relationships with the alkaline earths on the one hand, and to aluminium on the other. (Science and Art Dept.)

7. What grounds had Mendeléeff for predicting the existence of the elements gallium, scandium, and germanium ? (Science and Art Dept.)

8. Why is manganese included with chlorine in the same group of the periodic table ? With what elements besides the halogens, is manganese related, and how is this relationship displayed ? (London Univ.)

9. What substances stand on the border line between metals and non-metals ? Illustrate the fact that such classification is always approximate, and that nearly all the laws of chemical combination or chemical relations, like Prout's Law are approximately true. (New Zealand Univ.)

10. Explain how the valency of an element is connected with the position of the element in the periodic table. What are the reasons for the positions assigned to (a) hydrogen, (b) manganese or copper, in the table ? (Board of Educ.)

CHAPTER IX

1. Discuss, from the historical standpoint and with regard to present conceptions, the use of the term " element." (London B.Sc.)

2. What is the experimental evidence for the electron as a constituent of the atom ? (Durham B.Sc.)

3. Write concise but full notes on *two* of the following :—
  (a) the determination of atomic number,
  (b) the separation of isotopes
  (c) the mass spectrograph. (Durham B.Sc.)

4. Survey the experimental evidence for the existence and relative abundance of isotopes. (Durham B.Sc.)

5. Survey the experimental evidence for the electron as an atomic constituent, and indicate how the electrons in a given atom can be counted. (Durham B.Sc.)

6. Give an account of the recent determinations of the atomic weight of lead, and explain the probable reason for the different values obtained with lead obtained from different sources. (London B.Sc.)

7. Give a concise account of the modern views of the structure of matter, *or* indicate some of the important applications in inorganic chemistry of the electronic theory of valency. (Inst. of Chem.)

8. What types of valency are recognized in modern chemical theory ? Give *two* examples of compounds illustrating each type and write down their detailed electronic formulae. (Inst. of Chem.)

9. Write a short essay on isotopes. (Inst. of Chem.)

10. Describe briefly the significance of the atomic number of an element. (Inst. of Chem.)

11. Give an account of the electron theory of valency, and discuss the polar and covalent links in simple compounds. Illustrate your answer by suitable examples. (O. & C.J.B.H.C.)

12. Dalton regarded the atom as a homogeneous and indivisible unit. Give an account of any evidence within your knowledge which leads to the conclusion that the atom is neither homogeneous nor indivisible. (J.M.B.H.S.C.)

CHAPTER X

1. State the phase rule, and explain the terms used. Discuss the aqueous vapour pressures of hydrated salts from the standpoint of this rule and indicate the conditions governing efflorescence and deliquescence. (Inst. of Chem.)

2. Give an account of the methods employed in the determination of the solubility of gases in liquids. In what way does the solubility of a gas in a liquid depend on (a) pressure, (b) temperature ? (Inst. of Chem.)

3. Discuss what happens when (a) a dilute solution, (b) a saturated solution, of sodium chloride is slowly cooled. (O. & C.J.B.H.C.)

4. How do changes of temperature and pressure influence the solubility of

gases in liquids ? Describe how you would determine the solubility of nitrogen in water at 20°C. (O. & C.J.B.H.C.)

5. How is the adsorption coefficient of a gas defined ? How would you measure the solubility in water of (a) oxygen, (b) hydrogen chloride? (Cambridge H.S.C.)

6. On what factor does the solubility of a gas or a mixture of gases in water depend ? At S.T.P. 1·0 c.c. of water dissolves 0·0489 c.c. of oxygen and 0·0235 c.c. of nitrogren. Supposing that air consists of 79 per cent. of nitrogen and 21 per cent. of oxygen by volume, calculate the percentage composition by volume at S.T.P. of the gas dissolved from air by water. (J.M.B.H.S.C.)

7. Describe and explain the phenomena of efflorescence and deliquescence. (J.M.B.H.S.C.)

8. Write a short account of the phase rule, and indicate clearly some useful applications of this generalization. (Board of Educ.)

9. 100 grms. of water dissolve the following quantities of zinc sulphate at the temperatures named :

Temp.° C.	0	25	39	50	70	80	90	100
ZnSO₄	41·9	57·9	70·1	76·8	88·7	86·6	83·7	80·8 grms.

Plot the results on squared paper so as to show a solubility curve.

10. Define the terms : degree of freedom, phase, component, and variant, in Gibbs's rule. In the case of a system containing salt and water, and the phases, salt, saturated solution, and vapour, how many variants must be fixed in order to establish equilibrium ? Discuss the reasons for your statement. (Sydney Univ.)

11. Plot curves to represent the following tabulated numbers representing the number of grms. of salt in 100 grms. of water at the temperatures named :

Temp.° C.	0	10	20	30	40	50	60	70	80	90	100
Na₂SO₄	5·0	9·0	19·4	40	48·8	46·7	45·3	44·4	43·7	43·1	42·5
K-alum	3·9	7·5	15·1	22·0	30·3	44·1	66·6	90·7	134·5	209·3	257·5

Answer by reference to the resulting diagram ; (a) two saturated solution. contain 26·5 grms. sodium sulphate and potash. alum respectively in 100 grms of water. At what temps. were the two solutions made up ? (b) a saturated solution of potash alum in 100 grms. of water was made up at 64° C. and another of sodium sulphate at 72° C. If both solutions were cooled to 15° C. how many more grms. of potash alum would separate out than of sodium sulphate ? (Staffs County Major Scholarship.)

12. " Sodium sulphite Na₂SO₃.7H₂O, forms colourless *monoclinic crystals*, with a *saline taste* and *alkaline reaction*. The crystals *effloresce* in dry air ; they are *soluble* in water ; and become *anhydrous* when heated to 150° C. At a higher temperature the crystals *decompose*, forming a yellow liquid." Explain the words in italics in this quotation.

13. Explain the meaning of the terms, saturated solution, solution, and crystallization. Show how it can be proved experimentally that hot water is generally a better solvent than cold water. (Cape Univ.)

14. If the solubility of sodium chloride in water at 20° C. is 35·6, how much water will be needed at this temperature for the solution of a kilogram of the salt ?

15. The adsorption coefficient of nitrogen dissolved in water is 0·0152 at 12·6° C. What volume of the gas measured at standard temp. and pressure is adsorbed by one litre of water at 12·6° C. at each of the following pressures : 1000 mm. 748·2 mm. 391 mm. and 14·3 mm. ? (New Zealand Univ.)

16. Water at 15° can absorb 756 times its volume of ammonia. What mass of ammonia can be dissolved in one litre at 15° under a pressure of 10 atmospheres, the volume of one grm. of ammonia at 0° C. and a pressure of 760 mm. being 1317 c.c. ? (Sydney Univ.)

Chapter XI

1. Give a precise account of the freezing of pure substances and of solutions of pure substances ; showing in detail how the facts afford a quantitative knowledge of the condition of dissolved substances. (Durham Inter. B.Sc.)

2. Give an account of the procedure involved in the determination of the osmotic pressure of a concentrated solution of cane sugar. (London B.Sc.)

3. The aqueous solution of a certain non-electrolyte containing 0·3 grm. of the substance per 100 c.c. has an osmotic pressure of 81 mm. of mercury at 30° C. What is the molecular weight of the substance ? (London B.Sc.)

4. When 0·3 grm. of a substance with molecular weight 150 is dissolved in 42 grms. of a certain solvent, the freezing point of the latter is lowered by 0·233° C. When 0·27 grm of another substance is dissolved in 56 grm. of the same solvent the observed depression of the freezing point is 0·218° C. Calculate the molecular weight of the second solute. (London B.Sc.)

5. What is the evidence for the view that the solute molecules in a dilute solution behave like gas molecules ? Assuming that the osmotic pressure P of a dilute solution is given by P = RTc (c = concentration of solute in grm. molecules per litre) deduce Raoult's Law. (Inst. of Chem.)

6. Describe how the osmotic pressure of a dilute sugar solution may be quantitatively demonstrated. State how the osmotic pressure of such a solution (a) varies with temperature, (b) is related to the molecular weight of the solute. (J.M.B.H.S.C.)

7. Describe in detail how the molecular weight of a non-volatile substance may be determined by observations of the freezing points of its solutions, and point out all the precautions necessary.

A solution of 8·55 grm. of cane sugar $C_{12}H_{22}O_{11}$ in 100 grm. of water froze at −0·472° C. and a solution of 7·24 grm. of an unknown substance in 100 grm. of water at −0·930° C. Calculate the molecular weight of the unknown substance. (O. & C.J.B.H.C.)

8. What do you understand by the statement that the osmotic pressure of a certain solution is H cm. of mercury ? Describe two experiments which illustrate osmosis, and state the laws of osmotic pressure.

An aqueous solution which contains 1 grm. mol. of the solute AB in 10 litres, has an osmotic pressure of 300 mm. at 0° C. What conclusion can be drawn as to the state of the substance in solution ? Calculate the approximate freezing point of the solution. (Molecular depression for water = 18·6° for 100 grm.) (Oxford H.S.C.)

9. Describe the effects produced by soluble and insoluble substances on the boiling and melting points of water. What explanation can be given of the differences observed when common salt and sugar are respectively dissolved in sufficient pure water to form dilute solutions of the same molecular concentration ? To what other properties of solutions does this explanation apply ? (Punjab Univ.)

10. What do you understand by the term " osmotic pressure " ? Describe in outline any two processes, one direct, the other indirect, for measuring osmotic pressure. Explain carefully how the molecular weight of a substance in solution can be determined, when the osmotic pressure which it sets up is known. (Board of Educ.)

11. What is osmotic pressure ? Has this any connection with the pressure of a gas ? Alcohol is said to be normal in regard to its vapour pressure and its osmotic pressure ; ammonium chloride has an abnormal vapour pressure and osmotic pressure. Explain the meaning of the terms " normal " and " abnormal " used here. (Sydney Univ.)

Chapter XII

1. Describe with practical details the determination of the electrical conductivity of an aqueous salt solution.

A potential difference of 20 volts applied to the end of a column of N/10 silver nitrate, 4 cm. in diameter, and 12 cm. in length, gives a current of 0·198 amp. Calculate the specific and equivalent conductivity of the solution. (London B.Sc.)

2. Outline the evidence for the existence of ions in aqueous solutions of electrolytes. (Durham Inter B.Sc.)

3. Discuss in outline the modern ionic theory and its applications in chemistry. (Inst. of Chem.)

4. State the laws of electrolysis. Describe and explain what occurs when a current of electricity is passed through cells containing solutions of (a) sodium chloride, (b) copper sulphate (with copper electrodes), (c) sodium acetate. (Oxford H.S.C.)

5. State as clearly as you can the Arrhenius theory of electrolytic dissociation, pointing out the evidence in favour of the theory, and also any facts which it fails to explain. (J.M.B.H.S.C.)

6. What is meant by electrolysis? Illustrate your answer by reference to the electrolysis of aqueous solutions of metallic salts. (St. Andrews Univ.)

7. Give an account of the ionic theory of solution, stating clearly the facts on which it is based. (Aberystwyth Univ.)

8. A current passes simultaneously, through acidulated water, a solution of copper sulphate, and molten silver chloride. What substances are produced in each cell, and how many grms. of each in the time that 10 c.c. of hydrogen are liberated from water? (New Zealand Univ.)

9. H. J. Gladstone and W. Hibbert (1889) passed the same current of electricity through solutions of zinc and silver salts, and obtained quantities of these metals in the ratio $Zn : Ag = 1 : 3 \cdot 298$. If the equivalent of silver is $107 \cdot 88$, what is that of zinc?

10. One. and the same electric current is simultaneously passed through solutions (a) hydrochloric acid, (b) copper sulphate, (c) silver sulphate. Draw a diagram of the apparatus required, and indicate what products would be obtained in each case. Calculate also the weights of these products which would be formed during the time that 1000 c.c. of dry hydrogen (at N.T.P.) were collected from the hydrochloric acid solution. (London Univ.)

Chapter XIII

1. The heats of formation of ferric oxide and aluminium oxide being 195,600 cal. and 392,600 cal. respectively, calculate the heat of reduction of ferric oxide by aluminium. (London B.Sc.)

2. What do you understand by the term " thermal dissociation "? Describe and explain how changes in pressure affect the equilibrium between the following substances, and their dissociation products : hydriodic acid, nitrogen peroxide, calcium carbonate. Show how the degree of dissociation of nitrogen peroxide may be calculated from a knowledge of its vapour density. (Oxford H.S.C.)

3. Explain the meaning of the terms " heat of combustion," and " heat of formation." What information about the combustion of carbon and carbon monoxide can be gained from the following equations?

$$C + O_2 = CO_2 + 96K,$$
$$2CO + O_2 = 2CO_2 + 136K.$$

Deduce the amount of heat involved in the production of 1 litre of carbon monoxide from its elements (volume at S.T.P.). Calculate also the thermal value of the reaction

$$CO_2 + C = 2CO. \qquad \text{(Oxford H.S.C.)}$$

4. What is meant by the terms " endothermic " and " exothermic " compounds? To what class do substances known as explosives belong? Account for the great activity of ozone compared with that of oxygen on thermochemical grounds, and for its resolution into oxygen by compression. (Science and Art. Dept.)

5. What is the heat of formation of zinc chloride in solution when the reaction is given by :—

$$Zn + 2HCl_{aq} = ZnCl_{2aq} + H_2 + 34 \cdot 4 \text{ cals.}$$

and the heat of formation of an aqueous solution of hydrogen chloride, is given by the equation :

$$H_2 + Cl_2 = 2HCl + 78 \cdot 6 \text{ cals. ?} \qquad \text{(French Coll.)}$$

6. How may a chemical reaction be modified so as to represent not only a redistribution of matter, but also a redistribution of energy ? Explain what is meant by the heat of formation of a compound. From the following data, find the heat of formation of acetylene : When 24 grms. of carbon, 2 grms. of hydrogen, and 26 grms. of acetylene are burnt separately in an excess of oxygen, 194,000 ; 68,000 ; and 310,000 cals. are respectively evolved. (Cape Univ.)

7. Find the amount of heat K liberated in the reaction,

$$AlCl_3 + 3Na = 3NaCl + Al + xK.$$

The heat of formation of aluminium chloride is 1610 K, and of sodium chloride 976 K.

8. What amount of heat is evolved when 46 grms of metallic sodium react with an excess of water, given the heats of formation of water as 69 Cals., and of sodium hydroxide 112·5 Cals.?

9. Find the heat of formation of acetaldehyde (C_2H_4O) from its elements when it is (a) liquid and (b) gaseous.

> Data :—$C_2H_4O + 5O = 2CO_2 + 2H_2O$;
> (C_2H_4O, 5O) liquid 275·5 Cals.$_2$; (CO_2) 96·6 Cals. ;
> (H_2, O) liquid 68·4 Cals ; (H_2, O) gaseous 58·7 Cals. ;
> (C_2H_4O, 5O) gaseous, 266·0 Cals.

CHAPTER XIV

1. Outline the chief phenomena of catalysis, with reference to typical examples, and indicate the explanations of catalytic action which have been advanced. (Durham B.Sc.)

2. Write an historical essay on the Law of Mass Action. (London B.Sc.)

3. Give a statement of the principle known as Le Chatelier's Theorem. Illustrate its widespread application by four examples. (Inst. of Chem.)

4. Outline the more important views upon the phenomenon of catalysis illustrating your answer by examples of industrial importance. (Inst. of Chem.)

5. What is meant by a reversible reaction ? Describe experiments which could be carried out to illustrate the effect on chemical equilibrium of changes in (a) temperature, (b) the concentration of the reacting substances. (O. & C.J.B.H.C.)

6. What do you understand by the term " thermal dissociation " ? Describe and explain how changes in pressure affect the equlibrium between the following substances and their dissociation products :· hydriodic acid, nitrogen peroxide, calcium carbonate. (Oxford H.S.C.)

7. Explain giving the illustrative examples what is meant by a balanced reaction. State Le Chatelier's Principle and show its application to the examples you have chosen. (J.M.B.H.S.C.)

8. Describe how you would prove that the reaction between iron and steam is reversible. Describe short experiments which you would carry out to illustrate the reversibility of two other chemical reactions. (Cambridge H.S.C.)

9. What do you understand by a " catalyst " ? Give an account of an experiment you would carry out yourself in which a catalyst is used, and describe with necessary detail how you would show that the behaviour of the catalyst is in accordance with your statements. (Cambridge H.S.C.)

10. What do you understand by a reversible chemical reaction ? Cite examples and point out the conditions affecting the course of the action. (St. Andrews Univ.)

11. Define and give examples of thermal dissociation, kinetic equilibrium, reversible reaction, electrolysis, and reduction. (Princeton Univ.)

12. The rate of chemical change may be altered by (a) temperature, (b) catalysis, and (c) solution. Describe accurately one experiment illustrating the change in rate of a reaction which may be brought about by each of these factors. (London Univ.)

Chapter XV

1. What is meant by the strength of an acid ? Describe the different methods which have been employed in ascertaining the relative strength of two acids. (London B.Sc.)

2. What do you understand by the term " solubility product " ? Explain the importance of this quantity in qualitative analysis. (Inst. of Chem.)

3. Discuss briefly the meaning of the terms " strong " and " weak " as applied to acids. If you were supplied with a normal solution of an acid, describe with necessary detail *two* experiments you would carry out to decide whether the acid was a strong or weak one. (Cambridge H.S.C.)

4. What is Ostwald's Dilution Formula for weak electrolytes ? Deduce it theoretically, and explain clearly how the constant is experimentally obtained. (St. Andrews Univ.)

5. In terms of the ionic theory, what is a strong acid ?—a strong base ?—a weak acid ?—a weak base ?—In these terms classify the following :—HCl, NH_4OH, KOH, H_2S, H_2CO_3, $Al(OH)_3$. (Amhurst Coll., U.S.A.)

6. How is the following phenomenon explained ? When dilute solutions of any strong acid and base are mixed together in equivalent proportions, approximately the same amount of heat is given out (13,700 cals.), although the heats of formation of the various salts formed have very different values. (Madras Univ.)

7. What is an indicator ? Give some account of the theory of indicators as employed in acidimetry, and alkalimetry.

Chapter XVI

1. What are crystalloids and colloids ? Give examples. Discuss some of the most important properties of colloids. (Durham B.Sc.)

2. Give an account of the chief methods available for the preparation of a collodial solution. What are the characteristics of such solutions. (London B.Sc.)

3. Write a concise account of the collodial state with particular reference to the distinction between colloids and other forms of matter. (Inst. of Chem.)

Chapter XVII

1. Write an essay on the effects of intensive drying on physical and chemical properties. (London B.Sc.)

2. What is meant by the terms temporary hardness and permanent hardness of natural water ? How would you compare these ? How would you treat a water for boiler purposes which contains substances producing both temporary and permanent hardness ? (London B.Sc.)

3. Describe *three* modern methods for the production of hydrogen on an industrial scale, and discuss its use in processes of technical importance. (Inst. of Chem.)

4. How is atomic hydrogen prepared ? Give some account of the isotopes of hydrogen. (Inst. of Chem.)

5. What processes are in common use for the removal of hardness from water for industrial purposes ? (Inst. of Chem.)

6. Describe how you would prepare in the laboratory as pure a specimen of hydrogen as possible. Give reasons for what you would do. Give an account of the industrial uses of hydrogen. (O. & C.J.B.H.C.)

7. Describe the preparation of a concentrated aqueous solution of hydrogen peroxide starting from a metallic peroxide. Mention *two* other reactions in which hydrogen peroxide is produced. How does hydrogen peroxide react with *three* of the following :—(a) sodium carbonate, (b) titanic sulphate, (c) chromic sulphate, (d) chlorine ? (Cambridge H.S.C.)

8. Indicate by means of equations four methods of preparing hydrogen. What weight of zinc is required to produce 100 litres of hydrogen gas measured at 27° C. and 680 mm. pressure ? (St. Andrews Univ.)

9. How would you proceed in order to find the volumes in which hydrogen and oxygen combine to form water ? What modification of your apparatus would you make, if you were asked in addition to measure the volume of steam formed ? What volume of gas is formed when 72 grms. of water are decomposed, (a) electrolytically, (b) by means of sodium, (c) by heated iron ? (Victoria Univ.)

10. How would you prove that the composition of water may be expressed by the formula H_2O ? Mention everything that this formula implies. What volume would 9 grm. of vapour occupy at 273° C. and 380 mm. pressure ? (Aberdeen Univ.)

11. What facts would you adduce to prove that the molecule of water contains *two* atoms of hydrogen and not more nor less than two. (Science and Art Dept.)

12. How would you prove that the body formed by the combustion of hydrogen and oxygen is water ? (Science and Art Dept.)

13. What are the chief properties of hydrogen peroxide ? 20 c.c. of a solution of this substance after acidification with dilute hydrochloric acid, reduced 24 c.c. of 1/10 N potassium permanganate. Calculate the percentage of hydrogen peroxide in the solution. (St. Andrews Univ.)

14. How is hydrogen peroxide prepared ? Mention any instances known to you of its action; (i) as an oxidising agent, and (ii) as a reducing agent. What is the evidence that its molecule contains twice as much oxygen as a molecule of water ? (London Univ.)

Chapter XVIII

1. Describe the preparation and properties of ozone. How was the composition of ozone ascertained ? How does ozone react with (a) mercury, (b) finely divided silver, (c) a solution of potassium iodide ? What occurs when ozonized oxygen is strongly heated and cooled. (London Inter B.Sc.)

2. How would you prepare oxygen in a very pure state ? Describe the action of oxygen on (a) hydrogen, (b) phosphorus, (c) sodium. (Oxford Univ.)

3. Discuss the conditions under which (a) oxygen may be converted into ozone, (b) ozone converted into oxygen. Describe how you would make use of the action of ozone on potassium iodide solution to determine the composition of ozonized oxygen. How would you discover whether the action of a specimen of air on starch iodide paper were due to traces of ozone or traces of chlorine ? (Oxford H.S.C.)

4. Explain the meaning of the terms " oxidation " and " reduction." State the conditions under which the following substances react together, and point out in each case how the reaction involves oxidation and reduction : (a) chlorine and ammonia, (b) hydrogen sulphide and sulphur dioxide, (c) lead dioxide and sulphur dioxide, (d) copper and sulphuric acid. (Cambridge H.S.C.)

5. There are reasons to believe that the equations :—

$$2KClO_3 \rightarrow KCl + KClO_4 + O_2 \text{ and}$$
$$KClO_4 \rightarrow KCl + 2O_2$$

do not actually represent the decomposition of potassium chlorate when heated. Describe the experiments you would make in order to test the validity of these equations. (New Zealand Univ.)

6. Write an account of the chemistry of ozone. In what way is the composition of ozone deduced ? (St. Andrews Univ.)

7. What substances besides ozone have the power of turning starch iodized paper blue ? How are they distinguished from ozone ? (Science and Art Dept.)

Chapter XIX

1. Describe and comment on the experiments which serve to elucidate the nature of flame. (Durham Inter B.Sc.)

2. What is the action of (a) carbon dioxide, (b) steam, upon red-hot carbon, and what is the importance of these reactions for technical purposes ? (O. & C.J.B.H.C.)

3. Give *two* methods for preparing carbon dioxide. What are the properties of this substance? How would you determine (a) its composition, (b) its molecular weight? (Oxford H.S.C.)

4. Give an account of the natural phenomena that follow from the fact that carbon dioxide is soluble in water. (Oxford H.S.C.)

5. How would you prepare carbon monoxide in the laboratory? How is it obtained on a commercial scale? What is its action on (a) ferric oxide, (b) nickel, (c) chlorine?

Mention the conditions necessary for chemical reaction in each case. (London Inter B.Sc.)

6. What do you know of the reactions which occur when coal gas is burnt in a bunsen flame? Describe experiments which could be performed in support of your statements. (O. & C.J.B.H.C.)

7. How is sodium (or potassium) cyanide prepared on a large scale, and for what purposes is it employed? (Oxford H.S.C.)

8. How is water gas produced? For what purposes is it used? Assuming that it consists of equal volumes of the two main constituents, calculate (a) the volume in litres produced per grm. of carbon consumed, (b) the volume in cubic feet of air necessary to burn one cubic foot of the gas, (c) the volume of gases produced by combustion of one cubic foot, at S.T.P. (Oxford H.S.C.)

9. Write an account of the part played by carbon in *three* natural processes. (J.M.B.H.S.C.)

10. Give the chief chemical and physical properties of CO_2 and CS_2. (Owen's College.)

11. Explain how the quantitative and qualitative composition of carbon dioxide and carbon monoxide have been ascertained. (St. Andrews Univ.)

12. The acid formed by dissolution of carbon dioxide in water might have its structure represented by the formula, $CO(OH)_2$ or $C(OH)_4$. State fully the evidence on which the existence of carbonic acid in such a solution may be assumed, and give the evidence in favour of both these formulae. (Board of Educ.)

13. How do you account for the fact that in spite of the large amount of oxygen consumed in respiration and combustion, the percentage of oxygen in the atmosphere remains practically unaltered? (Vict. Univ.)

14. How is coal gas manufactured and purified? What are the by-products? Name the diluents, impurities, and illuminants present in ordinary coal gas. (Princeton Univ.)

15. 10 c.c. of a gaseous hydrocarbon are exploded with an excess of oxygen. A contraction of 15 c.c. is observed. After the explosion, a contraction of 20 c.c. is observed on treating the resulting gases with potassium hydroxide solution. What is the molecular formula of the hydrocarbon? (Customs and Excise).

16. Describe properties of carbon which tend to show that diamonds could not have been formed at a temperature at which pure iron melts. How would you show that carbon dioxide is a compound of carbon and oxygen, and that it contains very nearly its own volume of oxygen? (London Univ.)

17. What is charcoal, and how can it be made on a large scale? Describe the differences between peat, lignite, bituminous coal, anthracite, and graphite. (Bombay Univ.)

18. Give three reasons for the non-luminosity of the flame of a bunsen burner. When will such a flame strike back? What causes the luminosity of an ordinary gas flame? Why does the amount of carbon dioxide in the atmosphere remain practically the same? (Cornell Univ.)

19. Describe the construction of a Davy Lamp, and indicate the principles on which its action as a safety lamp depends. (London Univ.)

CHAPTER XX

1. Describe *three* reactions by which nitrogen can be made to combine with another element. Explain the importance of *one* of these reactions. (O. & C.J.B.H.C.)

2. Describe a process for converting the nitrogen of the atmosphere into nitrates. State briefly how sodium nitrite may be obtained from the nitrate. By what test could you distinguish between these two compounds ? (O. & C.J.B.H.C.)

3. Under what conditions and with what results does nitrogen combine with (a) hydrogen, (b) oxygen, (c) magnesium, (d) calcium carbide ? (London B.Sc.)

4. Give an account of the processes used in the fixation of atmospheric nitrogen. (Oxford Univ.)

5. What happens when a series of sparks is passed through a mixture of nitrogen with (a) hydrogen, (b) oxygen ?
Describe briefly how one of these reactions is used on the large scale for fixing atmospheric nitrogen. What reactions would you use in order to prepare fairly pure specimens of nitric oxide and nitrogen peroxide from nitric acid ? (Oxford H.S.C.)

6. How would you prove that nitric acid acts both as an oxidizing and as a reducing agent ? (London Univ.)

7. Give illustrations of the behaviour of different metals towards nitric acid. (Aberdeen Univ.)

8. What is the action of concentrated nitric acid on tin ; iodine ; and sulphurous acid solution. (St. Andrews Univ.)

9. What is observed, and what products are obtained when each of the following nitrates is heated until any decomposition which occurs is complete : copper nitrate, mercuric nitrate, ammonium nitrate, sodium nitrate ? How would nitrogen be isolated from one of these nitrates ? (Sheffield Univ.)

10. Calculate the vapour density of ammonium chloride. By experiment it is found to be 13·345. How do you explain the difference between the calculated and the observed results ? Can you give any experimental evidence in support of your explanation ? Do you know of any other similar cases ? (Science and Art Dept.)

11. Why are the compounds formed by the union of acids with ammonia termed ammonium compounds ? Quote facts which may be regarded as evidence that a solution of ammonia in water contains ammonium hydroxide. (London Univ.)

12. What change takes place when chlorine is passed into a solution of ammonia ? How can the experiment be conducted so as to afford evidence of the constitution of ammonia ? (Board of Educ.)

Chapter XXI

1. How may the composition of the air be determined ? Would the composition of the air be represented by either of the formulae N_4O or $N_4 + O$? Give reasons, for your answer. (Cambridge Senior Locals).

2. A given volume of air is left in contact with lime, (calcium oxide) ; a second volume of air is shaken up with acidified solution of ferrous sulphate. Carefully describe the changes which occur in the air and in the reagent in each case. (Univ. North Wales.)

3. Name the gases which form the atmosphere and describe the part which each plays in connection with animal and vegetable life. (Tasmania Univ.)

Chapter XXII

1. Discuss with the help of graphical methods of representation the equilibria between the different forms of sulphur. (London B.Sc.)

2. Describe the occurrence of sulphur in nature. Given crude sulphur containing calcium sulphate and sand, how could you prepare a pure specimen of the element, and what tests would you apply to demonstrate its purity ?
Indicate precisely the reactions involved in preparing a specimen of sodium thiosulphate from sulphur and caustic soda. (Durham B.Sc.)

3. Describe as fully as possible from your own laboratory experiments the chemistry of the compounds of sulphur. (Durham B.Sc.)

4. How is sulphur dioxide prepared on a large scale ? Under what conditions

does it react with oxygen ? What reactions occur when sulphur dioxide is passed into (a) chlorine water, (b) hydrogen sulphide solution, (c) an acidified solution of potassium dichromate. (O. & C.J.B.H.C.)

5. Hydrogen sulphide in aqueous solution is (a) a dibasic acid, (b) a reducing agent, (c) a useful reagent in qualitative analysis. Justify the description and quote experiments in illustration. (O. & C.J.B.H.C.)

6. Give an account of the lead chamber process for the manufacture of sulphuric acid. (O. & C.J.B.H.C.)

7. Describe and explain *three* different chemical reactions of sulphuric acid. (O. & C.J.B.H.C.)

8. Describe experiments to demonstrate that sulphuric acid is (a) a dibasic acid, (b) a dehydrating agent, (c) an oxidizing agent. Why is sulphuric acid sometimes used in preparing other acids from their salts, and what are the limitations of this method of preparation ? (Cambridge H.S.C.)

9. Give an account of the occurrence of the element sulphur, and its compounds in nature. Describe the preparation and properties of the various modifications of sulphur. (St. Andrews Univ.)

10. What do you know regarding the general behaviour of metallic sulphides towards (a) water, (b) hydrochloric acid, (c) caustic soda ? Give equations. (St. Andrews Univ.)

11. You are required to convert a given weight of sulphur into hydrogen sulphide as completely as possible. How would you proceed ? What are the reactions of gaseous hydrogen sulphide respectively with (a) gaseous ammonia, (b) aqueous sodium hydroxide, (c) aqueous copper sulphate, and (d) gaseous sulphur dioxide ? (Univ. North Wales.)

12. How does sulphur occur in nature, and how is it obtained as stick sulphur and flowers of sulphur ? Describe the changes which sulphur undergoes when heated and give some account of its allotropic forms. (New Zealand Univ.)

13. Describe the means you would adopt in order to prepare from sodium sulphite (a) sodium hyposulphite and (b) sodium thiosulphate. Discuss the existing evidence concerning the constitution of each of these three compounds. (Science and Art Dept.)

14. Explain the reaction involved in the production of sulphuric acid in the " Chamber Process " and the means adopted to prevent the escape of nitrous gases into the atmosphere. Give two illustrations of the use of sulphuric acid as (a) a dehydrating agent, (b) an oxidizing agent. (Sheffield Univ.)

15. What happens on heating with sulphuric acid, (a) manganese dioxide, (b) cuprous oxide ; with nitric acid, (a) black oxide of iron, (b) red lead ; with hydrochloric acid, (a) red oxide of iron, (b) black oxide of manganese ? (London Univ.)

16. Give graphic formulae for sulphurous and sulphuric acids, with a clear account of the facts which have led to their adoption. What happens when a solution of sulphur dioxide is treated with zinc ? (Board of Educ.)

17. How is sodium thiosulphate made ? What is the meaning of the name " thiosulphate " ? Why is the name " hyposulphite " often applied to this salt inappropriately ? Describe the true hyposulphites. (Board of Educ.)

Chapter XXIII

1. Show how fluorine differs in chemical behaviour from the other halogens and give any explanation you can of its abnormality. (Durham B.Sc.)

2. Write explanatory notes upon the following reactions and show how they illustrate the general chemistry of iodine :—

     (a) Iodine and sulphurous acid,
     (b) Sodium iodide and nitrous acid,
     (c) Iodine and aqueous sodium hydroxide,
     (d) Iodine and aqueous sodium iodide,
     (e) Iodine and concentrated nitric acid.

                      (Durham Inter B.Sc.)

3. Give an account of the oxides and oxyacids of the halogens. (Durham Inter B.Sc.)

4. Outline the methods by which the halogens can be isolated from their compounds and with the aid of a tabular statement of the formulae and properties of their compounds indicate, (a) why the halogens are regarded as a family of related elements, and (b) what important differences exist among them. (Durham, B.Sc.)

5. Compare the chemistry of iodine with that of the other halogens. Explain how pure iodine may be prepared from crude iodine. (O. & C.J.B.H.C.)

6. Discuss and comment on the following statement : " the economic disposal of by-product chlorine is one of the problems of industrial chemistry." (Cambridge H.S.C.)

7. Describe and explain the behaviour of an aqueous solution of chlorine, (a) when exposed to sunlight, (b) when distilled, (c) when added to a cold solution of sodium hydroxide, (d) when added to a suspension of chalk, (e) when added to a suspension of yellow mercuric oxide. (London Inter B.Sc.)

8. Why was fluorine regarded as an element and classed with the halogens before it had been isolated ? Give a brief account of its chemical and physical properties. (London Inter. B.Sc.)

9. Explain the method for extracting iodine from the mother liquors of Chile saltpetre manufacture. What action has each of the following substances upon the element : nitric acid, chlorine, potassium chlorate, sulphurous acid ? Specify the conditions needed for each of the reactions given. (London, Inter. B.Sc.)

10. How does fluorine occur naturally and how may it be isolated ? Summarize the main points of the chemistry of which justify placing it in the halogen group. (Inst. of Chem.)

11. Tabulate the oxygen compounds of the halogens and write notes on those which are remarkable either for theoretical interest or practical importance. (Inst. of Chem.)

12. Write a short account of the chemistry of the compounds of fluorine with (a) oxygen, and (b) the other halogens. (Inst. of Chem.)

13. Give an outline of the methods by which (a) iodic acid, (b) potassium iodide, (c) hydrogen iodide, may be prepared directly from iodine. Describe and explain how potassium iodide solution reacts with (a) chlorine, (b) copper sulphate solution, (c) mercuric chloride solution. (Oxford H.S.C.)

CHAPTER XXIV

1. Give an account of the discovery of the inert gases, and the part they have played in the discovery of the classification of the elements. (London Inter. B.Sc.)

2. Give a succinct account of the early experiments of Cavendish on the composition of the air, and the further experiments of Lord Rayleigh and Prof. Ramsay which led to the discovery of a new constituent of the atmosphere. (Science and Art Dept.)

3. Discuss the position of the helium family in the Periodic Classification. (St. Andrews Univ.)

CHAPTER XXV

1. What is the chief natural source of potassium ? Describe how pure potassium chloride is obtained therefrom and how this material is subsequently converted into potassium carbonate.

Contrast the chemical properties of potassium with those of sodium. (Durham B.Sc.)

2. Describe the Solvay ammonia-soda process for making sodium carbonate from sodium chloride. Why should there be such a great demand for sodium carbonate ? (London Inter. B.Sc.)

3. Describe concisely with diagrams, how (a) sodium carbonate, (b) sodium hydroxide, are obtained from common salt. (O. & C.J.B.H.C.)

4. From what minerals are the salts of potassium prepared and where do they occur? How is potassium nitrate prepared from potassium chloride? How would you show the presence of potassium in the presence of a mixture of calcium, sodium, and potassium chlorides? (Aberdeen Univ.)

5. Name two compounds containing lithium and describe the preparation of lithium chloride from one of them. In what respects do lithium compounds resemble or differ from corresponding derivatives of other alkali metals? (Board of Educ.)

6. How is potassium chloride converted into (a) caustic potash, (b) potassium chlorate? Starting from carnallite, the double chloride of magnesium and potassium, show briefly how the metals magnesium and calcium can be prepared. (Owen's College.)

CHAPTER XXVI

1. Give an account of the chemistry of silver and its compounds. Contrast the behaviour of silver with that of other metals forming monovalent cations. (Oxford Univ.)

2. To what properties is the usefulness of copper due? Starting with copper sulphate solution, how may (a) cuprous chloride, (b) cuprous iodide. and (c) metallic copper, be prepared? (O. & C.J.B.H.C.)

3. Describe the successive phenomena observed when ammonium hydroxide solution is added drop by drop to a solution of cupric sulphate and indicate by formulae or equations the nature of the changes that occur. (Massachusetts Polytech.)

4. (a) In the laboratory you passed dry hydrogen over copper oxide which was heated in a tube. How does this experiment illustrate: a synthetic reaction; an analytical reaction; oxidation and reduction? (b) If you started with an unknown mixture of copper oxide and copper, say 10 grms., and after heating and passing hydrogen over it, the resulting weight of pure copper was 9·2 grms. how much of the original weight of the mixture was copper oxide and how much was metallic copper? (Worcester Polytech., U.S.A.)

5. (a) Show the analogy between the reactions of copper on nitric acid and copper on sulphuric acid. (b) What products are formed when the concentrated sulphuric acid is warmed with potassium iodide? (c) What reasons have you for thinking that no nascent hydrogen is formed in the reactions mentioned under (a)? (Amherst Coll., U.S.A.)

CHAPTER XXVII

1. What are the chief compounds of calcium occurring in nature and for what purposes are they used?

How and under what conditions does calcium hydroxide react with (a) sodium carbonate, (b) chlorine, (c) carbon dioxide. (O. & C.J.B.H.C.)

2. Briefly describe the chief properties of the metal calcium. In what way and under what conditions does slaked lime react with (a) sodium carbonate, (b) chlorine, (c) ferric chloride, (d) sulphur. (London Inter. B.Sc.)

3. What are (a) plaster of Paris, (b) Portland cement? How are they made and how do you explain their setting? (Inst. of Chem.)

4. Compare the properties of beryllium, magnesium, and the elements of the alkaline earths. (Inst. of Chem.)

5. How is metallic calcium obtained from calcium chloride? Mention two naturally occurring compounds of calcium other than calcium carbonate and state the use of one of them. Outline the preparation of (a) anhydrous calcium chloride, (b) calcium carbide, (c) calcium sulphide. (d) calcium cyanamide. (J.M.B.H.S.C.)

6. What is lime? How is it obtained? What takes place (a) when lime is

mixed with water? (b) when it is heated strongly with sand? (c) when it is exposed to carbon dioxide gas? Give equations. (Aberdeen Univ.)

7. Give the names of formulae of the four principal minerals containing calcium. How is metallic calcium prepared? By what reactions would it be possible to prepare from the metal specimens of (a) calcium hydroxide, (b) calcium carbonate, (c) bleaching powder? (London Univ.)

8. How does calcium occur in nature? What are its principal compounds in everyday use, and how are they made from naturally occurring compounds? How is metallic calcium made? Give the formulae of the typical salts of calcium and the ions formed on solution of these salts in water. (Sydney Univ.)

Chapter XXVIII

1. What are the chief ores of zinc? Describe in detail the extraction of the metal from one of these ores, and indicate the industrial applications of zinc and its compounds. (London B.Sc.)

2. How does mercury occur in nature and how is it obtained from its ores? How would you prepare chemically pure mercury from a commercial specimen? (London Inter. B.Sc.)

3. Describe the occurrence, isolation, and properties of the metal cadmium. Show that in chemical behaviour cadmium resembles zinc and mercury. (London B.Sc.)

4. Compare the chemical properties of the elements zinc, cadmium, and mercury and their chief compounds. (Oxford Univ.)

5. How can mercuric and mercurous chloride be obtained from mercuric sulphate? What is the action of mercuric chloride solution with solutions of (a) potassium iodide, (b) stannous chloride, (c) ammonia, (d) sodium hydroxide? (London Univ.)

6. Mercury forms two classes of salts—mercurous and mercuric salts. Illustrate by examples how these salts differ in composition from each other. How would you discover whether a given mercury salt was mercurous or mercuric salt? (London Univ.)

7. Give an account of the metal mercury and of its behaviour towards the common acids. Give the formula and names (systematic and trivial) of its chief compounds. (London Univ.)

8. What are the chief ores found in Europe from which zinc is extracted? Describe the process used for the extraction of zinc and for its purification. What other less common elements are found associated with zinc, and how are they separated? What are the common impurities in commercial zinc? (Science and Art. Dept.)

Chapter XXIX

1. Describe in detail the production of aluminium and indicate the various uses to which the metal is now put. (London, Inter. B.Sc.)

2. How is metallic aluminium obtained? How would you prepare from it the anhydrous chloride? Why cannot this substance be obtained when an aqueous solution of aluminium oxide in hydrochloric acid is evaporated to dryness and the residue ignited? (London Inter. B.Sc.)

3. How does aluminium react with three of the following: (a) hydrochloric acid, (b) nitric acid, (c) sodium hydroxide, (d) ferric oxide, (e) the atmosphere? Specify the conditions needed for the reactions you mention. (London Inter. B.Sc.)

4. Describe briefly the chemical characteristics of boron and its compounds. Discuss the relationship of this element to (a) aluminium, (b) silicon. (London B.Sc.)

5. Give an account of the compounds of hydrogen and boron. (Inst. of Chem.)

6. Describe the action of aluminium from bauxite. What do you know of the chemical properties of the metal? (Oxford, H.S.C.)

FF*

7. Discuss the chemical and physical properties of aluminium which render it commercially important. (J.M.B.H.S.C.)

8. Write the formulae of the chief " alums " known. Point out their characters as a class. State and explain the principle they illustrate. (London Univ.)

9. What is the composition of borax and to what class of salts does it belong ? Mention some examples of other salts of similar composition. What is the action of a solution of borax on litmus ? (London Univ.)

10. Explain how a high temperature is obtained in the " aluminothermic " processes, and why so much heat can be made effective as compared with many other processes of combustion. (Worcester Polyt. Inst., U.S.A.)

11. Aluminium is often regarded as a triad metal. State the facts on which that conclusion is based, and cite any evidence which seems to conflict with that view of the valency of the element. (Science and Art Dept.)

Chapter XXX

1. Write concise but full notes on the silicic acids and the silicates. (Durham B.Sc.)

2. How would you proceed to prepare from litharge specimens of red lead and lead dioxide ? Give details of the experimental procedure and describe precisely how you would estimate the percentage of metal in either of the above materials. (Durham B.Sc.)

3. Describe with special reference to the reactions involved the preparation of pure lead from galena and of the several oxides from the metal. Give a brief account of the properties and uses of these oxides. (Durham B.Sc.)

4. How may silica be obtained in a pure state from sand ? How may silicon be obtained from silica ? How would you prepare (a) silicon tetrachloride, (b) silicon tetrafluoride from silica. (London Inter. B.Sc.)

5. The elements carbon silicon and tin fall in the same group of the periodic table. How far are their properties in harmony with this common grouping ? (London B.Sc.)

6. Describe the process of extracting tin from its ores. What are the properties to which the usefulness of tin is due ? How may (a) stannic oxide, (b) stannic chloride, (c) sodium stannate, be obtained from the metal ? (London Inter. B.Sc.)

7. Describe the process of extracting lead from its ores. To what properties is the usefulness of lead due ? Starting with the metal, how may lead chloride and lead sulphide be obtained ? (O. & C.J.B.H.C.)

8. Describe the preparation, starting with metallic lead, of (a) lead dioxide, (b) lead acetate, (c) lead iodide. Give an account of the properties and uses of lead dioxide. (O. & C.J.B.H.C.)

9. Describe the preparation, properties and reactions of the compounds of silicon with hydrogen, with chlorine, and with fluorine. (Aberdeen Univ.)

10. How can (a) silicon, and (b) silicon carbide be obtained from sand, and for what purposes are these substances used ? How can silicon chloride be obtained from silica, and converted into silica ? (Sheffield Univ.)

11. Compare and contrast the elements carbon and silicon by a discussion of their analogous inorganic compounds. (Sheffield Univ.)

12. Make a comparison of the compounds of carbon and silicon, so as to reveal the relationship existing between them. What suggestion can be made to account for the fact that carbon dioxide is a gas whereas silica is a solid of high melting point ? What abnormalities are found in connection with the specific heats of the two elements ? (Board of Educ.)

13. Give an account of the element silicon. Discuss the classification of the silicates. (Cape Univ.)

14. Give the names and formulae of the oxides of lead, and describe all that can be observed when each of these oxides is heated in an open crucible. From 1 grm. of one of the oxides of lead, 1·269 grms. of lead sulphate can be obtained ; which of the oxides is it ? (Sheffield Univ.)

15. What would be produced if tin foil were introduced into solutions of the

following salts : silver nitrate, lead acetate, copper sulphate, copper chloride, stannous chloride, alum, ferric chloride ? Give equations. (London Univ.)

16. Starting from lead sulphide, describe how you would prepare (a) lead, (b) litharge, (c) red lead, (d) white lead. How would you detect the presence of lead peroxide and of lead chloride in a mixture of these two substances ? (Board of Educ.)

17. Explain the modern processes adopted for the smelting of lead from galena, and in the desilverization and softening of the crude metal. (Board of Educ.)

CHAPTER XXXI

1. Give an account of the allotropes of phosphorus, and explain how each form can be converted into the other. How may (a) orthophosphoric acid, and (b) phosphine be prepared from the element ? (O. & C.J.B.H.C.)

2. Compare the properties and methods of preparation of the hydrides of nitrogen, phosphorus, arsenic, antimony and bismuth. (London B.Sc.)

3. Give an account of the preparation and properties of metallic arsenic, arsine, arsenious oxide and arsenates. (Oxford Univ.)

4. Give an account of the oxyacids of phosphorus and their salts, indicating those which have industrial applications. (Oxford Univ.)

5. What changes take place when metallic antimony is (a) heated in air, (b) treated with nitric acid ? How may antimony compounds be distinguished from arsenic compounds ? (Inst. of Chem.)

6. Describe in outline how you would prepare the following compounds of phosphorus, starting from the element : (a) phosphorus pentoxide, (b) phosphine, (c) orthophosphoric acid. How would you test qualitatively for phosphates ? (Cambridge H.S.C.)

7. Give the names and approximate chemical composition of *two* compounds of arsenic which occur in nature, and state how you would prepare a specimen of the element from one of them. Compare and contrast (a) arsenic and antimony, (b) arsenates and phosphates. (J.M.B.H.S.C.)

8. Describe the chlorides of phosphorus and give all the details essential for the preparation of a pure specimen of phosphorus pentachloride. (Board of Educ.)

9. Describe how the law of mass action can be applied to the dissociation of phosphorus pentachloride, both by itself, and in the presence of chlorine gas, and state and explain what influence change of pressure and temperature have on this dissociation. (Madras Univ.)

10. How are phosphorus trioxide and phosphorus pentoxide respectively prepared ? What happens when phosphorus pentoxide is dissolved in cold water and then the solution is boiled ? What is the action of heat on orthophosphoric acid ? (Aberdeen Univ.)

11. How may the different modifications of phosphoric acid be obtained, and by what tests may they be distinguished ? (Aberdeen Univ.)

12. How is yellow phosphorus converted into the red variety, and how can the reverse change be accomplished ? What substances can be formed when phosphorus is (a) heated in air, (b) heated with nitric acid, and what is the relationship between them ? (Board of Educ.)

13. Compare the hydrides of nitrogen, phosphorus, arsenic and antimony. (Univ. Pennsylvania.)

14. Describe carefully the preparation of the gaseous hydride of phosphorus and compare its properties with those of the corresponding hydrides of nitrogen and arsenic. (Sheffield Univ.)

15. How is arsenic obtained ; and how would you prepare arsenic chloride, arsenic trioxide, and arsenic acid from arsenic ? What are the more characteristic properties of these substances ? (Board of Educ.)

16. What is the evidence for the existence of antimonyl and bismuthyl compounds ? Describe the preparation of an antimonyl compound from antimony,

and of a bismuthyl compound from bismuth ; give briefly the properties of each; and explain the reactions that occur when each is boiled with sodium carbonate solution. (Punjab Univ.)

CHAPTER XXXIII

1. Give a careful account of the chemistry of the less common elements of the Sixth Group of the Periodic Table and compare and contrast them with other elements in that part of the Table. (Durham B.Sc.)

2. Starting in each case with potassium dichromate describe the preparation of (a) chromic anhydride, (b) chromium sesquioxide, (c) chrome alum, (d) chromyl chloride, (e) potassium chromate. (London Inter. B.Sc.)

3. How are tungsten and molybdenum produced on the large scale from their ores, and what are the chief uses of these elements ? (Inst. of Chem.)

4. Given an ore of chromium, explain how you might obtain from it specimens of (a) $K_2Cr_2O_7$, (b) CrO_3, (c) Cr_2O_3, (d) the metal itself. (O. & C.J.B.H.C.)

5. The oxide of chromium, Cr_2O_3, and the hydroxide, $Cr(OH)_3$, are weak basic and still more weakly acidic. How does this statement accord with the fact that the salt $Cr_2(SO_4)_3$, is stable in water while the corresponding carbonate and sulphide are not stable ? What compound is formed when sodium carbonate is added to a solution of a chromic salt ? (Massachusetts, Inst. Technology.)

6. What happens when sodium hydroxide is mixed with a solution of a chromic salt ? Of a potassium chromate solution ? Of a potassium dichromate solution ? Give four reactions which distinguish chromium from all other elements. (Amherst Coll., U.S.A.)

7. Nillson and Petterson found that 0·0859 gram of chromium chloride when volatilized at 1200° displaced 12·049 c.c. of gas (reduced to 0° C. and 760 mm. pressure). Calculate density of the vapour compared with hydrogen and the formula to which it corresponds. How would you prepare potassium chromate, potassium dichromate, and chromic acid ? (Owens Coll.)

8. Calculate the number of cubic centimetres of decinormal potassium dichromate solution required to oxidize 0·5 gram of iron dissolved in dilute hydrochloric acid. In an actual experiment 88·5 cubic centimetres were used. How do you account for the difference ? (Trinity Coll.)

CHAPTER XXXIV

1. How does manganese occur in nature and how is the metal usually prepared for commercial use ? What other elements are associated with manganese in the periodic classification ? (Inst. of Chem.)

2. Show how the chemistry of manganese can be correlated with its position in the periodic table, and point out any features by which it is distinguished from neighbouring elements. (Oxford Univ.)

3. Describe the preparation of potassium permanganate from pyrolusite. When reduced in solution it yields, according to the agent employed, either a colourless solution or a dark brown precipitate, or a green solution. Explain these results and compare the weights of permanganate needed to provide equal amounts of oxygen in the three cases. How would you prepare the dark brown compound from the colourless solution ? (Oxford, H.S.C.)

CHAPTER XXXV

1. Give an account of the compounds of nickel and cobalt, with special regard to the points of similarity and difference between the chemical properties of the two elements. (London B.Sc.)

2. Give an account of the ammine compounds of cobalt and platinum, clearly explaining how the constitution of typical compounds is usually represented. (Inst. of Chem.)

3. Compare and contrast the chemical properties, etc., of the elements usually associated with platinum in nature. (Inst. of Chem.)

4. Describe and explain the types of isomerism exhibited by the ammine compounds of cobalt. (Oxford Univ.)

5. Starting in each case with the metal, describe how you would prepare specimens of (a) crystalline ferrous sulphate, (b) anhydrous ferric chloride, (c) ferric oxide. Describe the appearance of each of these compounds. (O. & C.J.B.H.C.)

6. State the essential chemical difference between the Bessemer and the open-hearth processes for the production of steel. What changes are common to both processes? What is the " basic Bessemer process," and why is it of importance? (Worcester Polytechnic Inst., U.S.A.)

7. How would you make (1) ferrous chloride from iron, (2) ferrous sulphide from ferrous chloride, (3) ferrous sulphate from ferrous sulphide, (4) ferric hydroxide from ferrous sulphate? Write equations for the reactions after giving the descriptions of the processes and indicate the colour of the product in each case. (Sheffield Scientific School, U.S.A.)

8. Describe briefly and explain the blast furnace process, giving the purpose of each ingredient of the charge. (Amherst Coll., U.S.A.)

9. What are the chief sources of nickel? How can nickel be obtained free from cobalt? For what purpose does nickel find employment in the arts? By what properties are nickel compounds distinguished from those of cobalt? (Board of Educ.)

10. Whence and by what processes is platinum obtained? What are its physical properties and how is it affected by being alloyed with iridium? Point out briefly the utility for chemical investigation of platinum, glass and india-rubber. (New Zealand Univ.)

11. How is platinum found in nature? Describe methods of obtaining it in a finely divided condition, and give one indication of the use of the metal in an inorganic chemical preparation. (Cape Univ.)

CHAPTER XXXVI

1. Give a careful account of the physical evidence for atomic disintegration of the radio-active elements. Outline the chemistry of three of these. (Durham B.Sc.)

2. Write a critical essay on the radio-active elements. (Inst. of Chem.)

3. What do you understand by *radio-active equilibrium, group displacement law, disintegration constant*, and *half value period*? (Oxford Univ.)

MISCELLANEOUS QUESTIONS

1. Discuss fully and critically the distinctions drawn by chemists between (a) atoms and molecules, (b) compounds and solutions. (Inst. of Chem.)

2. Write a short historical essay on the influence of density determinations on the progress of chemistry. (Inst. of Chem.)

3. State Gay-Lussac's law of gaseous volumes, and describe fully how you would show experimentally that it applies to the combination of carbon monoxide with oxygen to form carbon dioxide. Show how the formula of carbon monoxide may be deduced from the result of the experiment, that of carbon dioxide being known. (Oxford H.S.C.)

4. Outline the experiments and arguments which have led to the adoption of the formula H_2O for water vapour. Describe one of the experiments in detail (assume nothing except Avogadro's Law). Explain briefly why the combining volumes of hydrogen and oxygen are not in the exact ratio of 2 : 1. (Oxford H.S.C.)

5. Describe methods by which the equivalents of three of the following elements might be ascertained : potassium, silicon, fluorine, sulphur. State *one* method by which the atomic weight of each element chosen has been decided. (Cambridge, H.S.C.)

6. Give an account of the experiments and reasoning on which are based the molecular formulae of *two* of the following : hydrogen, carbon monoxide, mercurous chloride. (Cambridge H.S.C.)

7. Assuming Avogadro's Hypothesis give the experimental facts upon which the formula H_2O is assigned to the molecule of water. Write equations to show the action of water upon the following substances : sodium, calcium oxide, anhydrous copper sulphate, sodium peroxide, phosphorus pentoxide. (J.M.B. H.S.C.)

8. Describe fully one experiment in each case for determining (a) the composition of water by weight, (b) the composition of hydrogen chloride by volume. What further evidence would be necessary in each case to arrive at the formulae of these substances ? (J.M.B.H.S.C.)

9. Discuss any two of the following : (a) thermal dissociation, (b) catalysis, (c) limiting densities. (Inst. of Chem.)

10. Explain upon what facts and reasoning the molecular and constitutional formulae are assigned to (a) carbon monoxide, (b) mercurous chloride, (c) sulphuric acid. (Inst. of Chem.)

11. "Mercury has a monatomic molecule, but chlorine is diatomic and ozone is triatomic." State clearly the evidence upon which this statement is based. (Inst. of Chem.)

12. Outline historically the development of our views on the nature of the atom and molecule. (Inst. of Chem.)

13. Examine critically the thesis that the current theory of the atom is founded on the Periodic Classification. (Inst. of Chem.)

14. Give a concise account of the methods available for determining molecular weights. (Inst. of Chem.)

15. Give a critical account of the views which have been held from time to time regarding the state of electrolytes in solution. (Inst. of Chem.)

16. Select one of the following groups of elements and justify the position assigned to it in the Periodic Classification :—(a) iron, cobalt and nickel, (b) sulphur, selenium and tellurium. (Inst. of Chem.)

17. 0·256 grm. of the sulphate of a certain element yielded 0·525 grm. of barium sulphate when it was treated in aqueous solution with excess of barium chloride. The vapour density of the chloride of the element was about 67. Suggest possible values for the atomic weight of the element. What further experiments could be made to confirm the value assigned ? (O. & C.J.B.H.C.)

18. Give examples of salts which crystallize from aqueous solution in (a) the anhydrous, (b) the hydrated condition.

0·547 grm. of the hydrated chloride of a bivalent metal when treated with excess of silver nitrate solution yielded 0·717 grm. of silver chloride ; 0·657 grm. of the hydrated salt on heating yielded 0·333 grm. of the anhydrous chloride. How many molecules of water of crystallization are present in the hydrated salt ? (O. & C.J.B.H.C.)

19. What are the essential features of a catalytic action ? Give *one* example of the catalytic uses of each of four of the following : water, spongy platinum, a cobalt compound, a cuprous compound, nickel. (O. & C.J.B.H.C.)

20. Explain with examples what is understood by four of the following terms: eutectic, vapour pressure, efflorescence, deliquescence, sublimation, supersaturation. (O. & C.J.B.H.C.)

21. How do you account for the following facts ?—

(a) a constant boiling point mixture is produced when solutions of hydrochloric acid are distilled,

(b) the solubility curves of some salts show breaks,

(c) when ammonium chloride is added to a solution of ammonia containing phenolphthalein, the colour of the latter fades and eventually disappears,

(d) washing soda crystals effloresce on exposure to the atmosphere. (Oxford H.S.C.)

22. Show how the degree of dissociation of nitrogen peroxide can be calculated from its vapour density. (Oxford H.S.C.)

23. How do you account for the following facts ?—

(a) the vapour density of ammonium chloride is about a quarter of its molecular weight,

(b) an aqueous solution of ammonium chloride freezes at a lower temperature than a solution of cane sugar of the same molecular concentration,

(c) caustic soda does not precipitate ferrous hydroxide from a solution of potassium ferrocyanide. (Oxford H.S.C.)

24. Calculate the degree of dissociation of the compound XY, whose molecular weight is 100, if its vapour density at 50° C. is 40. (Oxford H.S.C.)

25. Summarize the methods adopted in the extraction of the commoner metals, classifying these and pointing out how they conform to the position of the metals in the Periodic Classification. (Oxford H.S.C.)

26. Calculate the atomic weight of the element X from the following data :—

(a) 0·250 grm. of X when heated in a stream of oxygen produced 0·917 grm. of a gaseous oxide,

(b) 1 litre of this oxide weighed 1·98 grm. at S.T.P.

(c) the vapour density of a compound Y which contains 64·8 per cent. of X is 37.

What conclusion about the molecule of Y can be drawn ? (Oxford, H.S.C.)

27. Describe clearly the meanings of the terms (a) vapour pressure, (b) vapour density, (c) water of crystallization, (d) solubility, (e) supersaturation. (J.M.B.H.S.C.)

28. From a consideration of their chemistry, do you think it reasonable to group the following pairs of elements together : (a) oxygen and sulphur, (b) nitrogen and phosphorus. Give reasons for your conclusions. (J.M.B.H.S.C.)

29. How do you explain *three* of the following phenomena ?—

(a) a solution of sodium carbonate has an alkaline reaction,

(b) calcium carbonate is dissolved by a boiling solution of ammonium chloride,

(c) hydrogen sulphide fails to precipitate cupric sulphide from a solution of a cupric salt containing excess of potassium cyanide,

(d) a solution of antimony or bismuth chloride becomes turbid when diluted with water, but becomes clear again when hydrochloric acid is added. (O. & C.J.B.H.C.)

30. What is meant by the dissociation constant of an acid ? Assuming the law of mass action to be applicable to ionic equilibria, derive an expression con-

necting the degree of ionization of an acid with the concentration of its solution. (O. & C.J.B.H.S.C.)

31. How do you account for the following facts ?—

(a) hydrogen sulphide is displaced from iron sulphide by hydrochloric acid, while the latter, a strong acid, is displaced from a solution of cupric chloride by hydrogen sulphide,

(b) aluminium oxide expels carbon dioxide from fused sodium carbonate, while carbon dioxide precipitated aluminium hydroxide from a solution of sodium aluminate. (Oxford H.S.C.)

32. How are the following facts to be explained ?—

(a) a solution of sodium acetate conducts electricity better than one of acetic acid of the same molecular concentration,

(b) the density of air, which has been freed from oxygen, carbon dioxide and water vapour, undergoes a slight change when the air passes through a porous partition,

(c) tinned iron rusts more quickly than galvanized iron when once the iron itself has been exposed to the atmosphere. (Oxford H.S.C.)

33. State Le Chatelier's Principle, and discuss its application to the large-scale production of sulphuric acid and ammonia. (Cambridge H.S.C.)

34. Explain and illustrate with *two* suitable examples in each case the meanings of the terms : acid, base, amphoteric hydroxide, basicity, basic salt. (J.M.B.H.S.C.)

35. Describe in outline how you would determine the solubility in water of ammonium chloride at the temperature of the laboratory.

The following weights of salt are dissolved by 100 grm. of water at the given temperatures :—

Temp. (° C.)	...	0	50	100
KCl (grm.) ...	...	28	42	56
KClO₃ (grm.)	...	3	19	59

Construct temperature-concentration diagrams approximately to scale, and use them to show how you would best obtain more than 57 grm. of chlorate, and some pure crystals of chloride from a solid mixture containing 59 grm. of chlorate and 14 grm. of chloride (assume ideal experimental conditions). (Cambridge H.S.C.)

36. Write a short description of the following processes :—

(a) the softening of permanently hard water,

(b) the setting of plaster of Paris,

(c) the production of ammonium sulphate from calcium sulphate. (Cambridge H.S.C.)

37. How is barium peroxide prepared ? How would you prepare from it a solution of hydrogen peroxide ?

What reaction occurs between hydrogen peroxide and,

(a) silver oxide,

(b) an alkaline solution of chromium sulphate. (O. & C.J.B.H.C.)

38. Give an account of the consequences in nature which follow from the fact that carbon dioxide forms a weakly acid solution when it dissolves in water. Distinguish between the temporary and permanent hardness of water. How may hard water be softened ? (O. & C.J.B.H.C.)

39. Give an account of the preparation, properties and reactions of ozone and hydrogen peroxide. (Inst. of Chem.)

40. Suggest methods for classifying the oxides of the metals. Discuss the characteristic reactions of the following oxides, explaining to which of your classes each should be assigned : aluminium oxide, barium peroxide, lead dioxide, red lead, and chromium trioxide. (O. & C.J.B.H.C.)

41. Chlorine was originally known as dephlogisticated muriatic acid, and later as oxymuriatic acid. Explain the views which led to the use of these names, and why the former was changed to the latter. Describe experiments to show that the views now held concerning the relationships of chlorine and hydrochloric acid, give a better account of the facts. (Oxford H.S.C.)

42. Describe how, given charged accumulators and any further electrical apparatus necessary, you would :—

(a) prepare ozone from oxygen,

(b) prepare sodium from caustic soda,

(c) bring about the combination of considerable proportions of a mixture of nitrogen and hydrogen to form ammonia. (Oxford H.S.C.)

43. What general methods are available for the preparation of oxides of non-metals ? Describe the preparation of *three* of the following in as pure a state as possible : sulphur trioxide, phosphorus trioxide, nitrogen peroxide, silicon dioxide, iodine pentoxide. (Cambridge H.S.C.)

44. Classify the following substances as oxidizing or reducing agents and by summarizing their reactions, illustrate the meanings of the terms " oxidation " and " reduction " :—hydriodic acid, stannous chloride, potassium permanganate, hydrogen peroxide, hydrogen sulphide, potassium cyanide. (J.M.B.H.S.C.)

45. Write a definition of allotropy and illustrate your answer by reference to sulphur, carbon phosphorus, and oxygen. How could you show experimentally that ozone and oxygen are different forms of the same element ? (J.M.B.H.S.C)

46. Outline the principal methods of manufacture of hydrogen and acetylene. Mention two important uses for each gas. (Cambridge H.S.C.)

47. Write a short account of the cycles of carbon and nitrogen in nature. (Oxford H.S.C.)

48. Describe the preparation and purification of coal gas. What are the by-products of coal-gas manufacture ? State what is implied by the equations :—

$$2CO + O_2 = 2CO_2 + 136000 \text{ calories.}$$
$$N_2 + O_2 = 2NO - 43200 \text{ calories.}$$

(O. & C.J.B.H.C.)

49. What methods are available for the preparation of pure carbon monoxide ? Under what conditions and with what result does carbon monoxide react with (a) nickel, (b) chlorine, (c) sodium hydroxide. (Inst. of Chem.)

50. Describe and explain experiments to illustrate *three* of the following matters :—

(a) the dependence of flame propagation on the composition of the gas air mixture,

(b) the effects of chemical reactions on the conductivity of solutions,

(c) allotropic change in elements,

(d) diffusion in gases and vapours. (Inst. of Chem.)

51. What is the action of concentrated nitric acid, hot and cold, upon (a) yellow phosphorus, (b) iodine, (c) sulphur dioxide, (d) sodium chloride. Outline the chemistry of *two* of the products thus obtained ? (Inst. of Chem.)

52. Give an account of the industrial utilization of common salt. (Inst. of Chem.)

53. Describe how you would prepare a specimen of nitrogen peroxide, and determine its vapour density.

The vapour density of nitrogen peroxide at 70° C., and atmospheric pressure is 27·7 (H = 1). Calculate the percentage dissociation of the gas. (O. & C.J.B.H.C.)

54. How are the cyanides and ferrocyanides of the alkali metals prepared ? What are the important reactions of either of these classes of compounds ? (O. & C.J.B.H.C.)

55. Compare and contrast the action of concentrated nitric acid upon metals with that of concentrated sulphuric acid, and discuss whether their activity is due to their acid or oxidizing properties. (Cambridge H.S.C.)

56. Describe briefly how the following substances may be prepared : potassium chlorate, cuprous iodide, iodic acid, phosgene. (J.M.B.H.S.C.)

57. Describe fully the chemical reactions involved in the preparation of iodine from Chile saltpetre. Describe and explain what happens when iodine is treated with the following substances : nitric acid, potassium hydroxide solution, iron filings, mercury. (J.M.B.H.S.C.)

58. Describe with brief outlines of the practical details how you would obtain

one constituent from any *four* of the following mixtures in a state of fair purity :—

(*a*) ammonium chloride and sodium chloride,
(*b*) nitric acid and sulphuric acid,
(*c*) lead chloride and lead sulphate,
(*d*) carbon monoxide and carbon dioxide,
(*e*) chlorine and hydrogen chloride.

(Cambridge H.S.C.)

59. Write a short account of the contact process for the manufacture of sulphuric acid. Why is this acid so frequently used in the preparation of other acids ? Mention *three* acids which can so be prepared. Give *two* examples of cases in which concentrated sulphuric acid could not be used in the preparation of an acid from its salts. (Oxford H.S.C.)

60. Describe and explain how sulphur dioxide can be oxidized. What happens when sulphur dioxide reacts with : chlorine water, ferric chloride solution, hydrogen sulphide solution. (O. & C.J.B.H.C.)

61. Describe and explain as far as possible the action of heat on each of the following substances :—sulphur, mercuric chloride, iodine, ammonium chloride. (O. & C.J.B.H.C.)

62. How would you distinguish chemically between :—

(*a*) bromine and nitrogen peroxide,
(*b*) sodium nitrate and sodium nitrite,
(*c*) cuprous and cupric oxides,
(*d*) sodium sulphide and sodium sulphate.

(O. & C.J.B.H.C.)

63. Describe *two* methods of preparing chlorine in the laboratory. How does chlorine react with :—

(*a*) a solution of ferrous sulphate,
(*b*) a cold solution of sodium hydroxide,
(*c*) phosphorus. (O. & C.J.B.H.C.)

64. Give an account of one of the following subjects :—

(*a*) the discovery of the inert gases and their importance in chemical theory
(*b*) fluorine and its compounds,
(*c*) the colloidal state. (Inst. of Chem.)

65. Describe the effect of heat on each of the following salts : ammonium nitrate, potassium nitrate, lead nitrate, ferrous sulphate, zinc carbonate, and sodium bicarbonate. (O. & C.J.B.H.C.)

66. Describe the preparation of *three* of the following by the electrolysis of sodium chloride : sodium, chlorine, sodium hydroxide, sodium hypochlorite. Describe in each case how the necessary conditions are obtained. (O. & C.J.B.H.C.)

67. Describe the preparation and uses of sodium, sodium hydroxide and sodium silicate. (O. & C.J.B.H.C.)

68. Give an account of the differences and similarities between copper, silver and mercury, and their respective oxides and chlorides. (Oxford H.S.C.)

69. Describe briefly *one* laboratory method for making each of *three* of the following : cuprous chloride, nitric oxide, sodium hydrogen sulphate, aluminium chloride. Describe how you would estimate the percentage purity of your product in *one* case. (O. & C.J.B.H.C.)

70. Give an account of the preparation and uses of *three* of the following : calcium carbide, calcium superphosphate, calcium sulphate, calcium cyanamide. (O. & C.J.B.H.C.)

71. You are given mixtures of :

(*a*) magnesium sulphate and calcium sulphate,
(*b*) potassium chlorate and potassium chloride.

How would you obtain specimens of each constituent of each mixture ? (J.M.B.H.S.C.)

72. Compare the properties of the alkali metals, sodium and potassium and

their principal compounds, with those of the alkaline earth metals, magnesium and calcium and their corresponding compounds. (Oxford H.S.C.)

73. Briefly describe the preparation of the anhydrous chlorides of mercury, tin and iron, from their respective metals. (Oxford H.S.C.)

74. Name the chief ores of zinc and lead, and describe the extraction of one of these metals. How is zinc used in the desilverization of lead ? Describe and explain what happens when (a) a piece of commercial zinc, (b) a piece of amalgamated zinc, is placed in dilute sulphuric acid. (Oxford H.S.C.)

75. Contrast the general chemical behaviour of copper with that of zinc. (O. & C.J.B.H.C.)

76. Outline the technical production of either (a) sodium carbonate by the Solvay process, or (b) ammonia by the Haber process, and discuss as fully as possible the theoretical principles involved. (Inst. of Chem.)

77. Discuss one of the following subjects :—
(a) the hydrides of silicon and boron,
(b) allotropy,
(c) the historical development of methods of liquefaction of gases. (Inst. of Chem.)

78. From what important mineral are thorium and cerium compounds now obtained ? Where does the mineral occur, and how is it treated for the extraction of thorium and cerium nitrates ? Why are thorium and cerium salts of value industrially ? (Inst. of Chem.)

79. Give an account of the chemistry of *two* of the following :—
(a) the smelting and purification of lead,
(b) the manufacture of water gas,
(c) the softening of water.   (Cambridge H.S.C.)

80. Describe the lead accumulator, and give an account of the chemical reactions which take place during charge and discharge. (Cambridge H.S.C.)

81. The periodic table suggests chemical similarity between
(a) tin and lead,
(b) magnesium and zinc.
Discuss the chemical similarity or dissimilarity between the two metals in each case, limiting your answer to the consideration of *four* chemical reactions of the metals and their compounds. (Cambridge H.S.C.)

82. Describe briefly laboratory methods of making *three* of the following compounds : lead chloride, sodium phosphate, sodium bicarbonate, potassium chromate, silica. (O. & C.J.B.H.C.)

83. Describe the method of preparation and the physical and chemical properties of any three of the following : sodium thiosulphate, carborundum, sodium silicate, arsine, silicon tetrafluoride. (Inst. of Chem.)

84. Outline the chief points of similarity and dissimilarity in three of the following pairs of elements :—
(a) thallium and lead,
(b) molybdenum and uranium,
(c) nitrogen and phosphorus,
(d) boron and silicon.   (Inst. of Chem.)

85. Indicate the chief resemblances and differences in each of the following pairs of elements :—
(a) boron, silicon,
(b) sulphur, selenium,
(c) nickel, copper,
(d) fluorine, chlorine.   (Inst. of Chem.)

86. Describe the sources and methods of extraction and purification employed for *two* of the following :—
(a) bismuth,
(b) beryllium,
(c) boron.   (Inst. of Chem.)

87. Give an account of the chemistry of *either* selenium *or* thallium. (Inst. of Chem.)

88. Select one of the following groups of elements and justify the position assigned to the group as a whole in the periodic table :—

      (*a*) phosphorus, arsenic, antimony, bismuth,

      (*b*) magnesium, zinc, cadmium, mercury.   (Inst. of Chem.)

89. How would you recognize and identify in the laboratory :—

      (*a*) ferric chloride,

      (*b*) phosphorus pentoxide,

      (*c*) sodium sulphite,

      (*d*) lead dioxide.   (O. & C.J.B.H.C.)

90. How is white phosphorus produced on the large scale ? In what respect does the allotropy of white and red phosphorus differ from that of rhombic and monoclinic sulphur ? What changes occur when,

    (*a*) each form of phosphorus is warmed with a solution of sodium hydroxide,

    (*b*) a slow stream of chlorine is passed through white phosphorus melted under water,

    (*c*) when the red form is heated with nitric acid ?   (Oxford H.S.C.)

91. Phosphorus falls between nitrogen and arsenic in the fifth group of the Periodic Classification ; and between silicon and sulphur in the second short period. Discuss from the point of view of the Periodic Classification the chemical relationships between phosphorus and the above-named elements. Illustrate your answer by reference to the hydrides, chlorides, oxides, and oxyacids of the elements. (Cambridge H.S.C.)

92. Give a brief account of the production *either* of copper from a concentrated sulphide ore, *or* of pig iron from haematite. As far as possible describe by equations the reactions which take place in the process you select. (Cambridge H.S.C.)

93. Enumerate and define the various classes of salts. Describe how *three* of the following salts are prepared : potassium dichromate, chrome alum, potassium ferrocyanide, potassium persulphate. (Cambridge, H.S.C.)

94. Describe as fully as you can, the preparation of any *three* of the following compounds : ammonium dichromate, ferrous ammonium sulphate, iodic acid, phosphorous acid, silico-methane, sodium pyrosulphate. (Cambridge H.S.C.)

95. How would you distinguish between :—

      (*a*) potassium ferrocyanide, and potassium ferricyanide,

      (*b*) sodium nitrate and sodium nitrite,

      (*c*) mercurous chloride and mercuric chloride ? (O. & C.J.B.H.C.)

96. Describe the preparation and properties and uses of *one* liquid compound of each of the following elements : nickel, sulphur, chromium, silicon. (Inst. of Chem.)

97. Describe the manufacture, properties and uses of three of the following : graphite, potassium permanganate, sodium hexametaphosphate, white lead, sodium cyanide. (Inst. of Chem.)

98. How are tungsten and uranium produced on the large scale from their ores, and what are the chief uses of these elements ? (Inst. of Chem.)

99. Discuss one of the following topics :—

    (*a*) modern views of the structure of matter,

    (*b*) the discovery of radio-activity, and its effect on chemical theory,

    (*c*) positive ray analysis, and its employment in the discovery of radio-active isotopes. (Inst. of Chem.)

The following abbreviations are used above :—

    Cambridge H.S.C. : Cambridge Higher School Certificate.

    J.M.B.H.S.C. : Joint Matriculation Board Higher School Certificate.

    Oxford H.S.C. : Oxford Higher School Certificate.

    O. & C.J.B.H.C. : Oxford and Cambridge Joint Board Higher Certificate.

ANSWERS TO QUESTIONS

CHAPTER II

6. 44·02.   7. 39·93.

CHAPTER IV

3. 59·05, 118·1.   5. 56·23%.   6. 145·57.
7. 16.   9. 19·64 grms.

CHAPTER V

1. (a) 9·01. (b) 12·15.   2. 89·96%.

CHAPTER VI

4. 27. M_2Cl_6.   5. 12.
11. 8·67, 52, 6, MO_3.

CHAPTER VII

3. 32·75.   4. oxygen : air = 1 : 1·054.
5. (1) 6·22 litres. (2) 12·44 litres. (3) 12·44 litres.
6. 29·72 grms. 4·73 litres. $ZnSO_4.7H_2O$. $6H_2O$.
7. Potassium chlorate.   8. MO_3.
9. K, 38 62% ; N, 13·87% ; O, 47·51%.
   H, 2·032% ; S, 32·61% ; O, 65·22%.
   Na, 39·31% ; Cl, 60·69%.
   P, 91·18% ; H, 8·82%.
   Mn, 63·23% ; O, 36·77%.

CHAPTER X

6. N, 64·94% ; O, 35·06%.   11. (a) 24·5°, 36°. (b) 31 grm.
14. 2808·9 gms.   15. 19·73 c.c., 14·77 c.c., 7·72 c.c., 0·28c.c.
16. 5·441 kg.

CHAPTER XI

3. 699·7.   4. 211·4.
7. 146·9.   8. — 0·328°.

CHAPTER XII

1. 0·03764 mhos. 376·4 mhos.
8. 0·0072 grm. oxygen, 0·0283 grm. copper, 0·0971 grm. silver, 0·03195 grm. chlorine.
9. 32·71.   10. 3·195 grm. chlorine, 0·72 grm. oxygen, 2·8314 grm. copper, 9·7092 grm. silver.

CHAPTER XIII

1. 197,000 cal.   3. 1250 cals.,—40,000 cals.
5. 113·0 Cals.   6. 48,000 cals.
7. 1318 K.   8. 87 Cals.
9. (liquid) 54·5 Cals. ; (gaseous) 44·6 Cals.

Chapter XVII

8.　236·2 grm.　　　　9.　(a) 89·6 litres, (b) 44·8 litres, (c) 89ı6 litres.
10.　44·8 litres.　　　　　　　13.　0·204%.

Chapter XIX

8.　(a) 3·73 litres, (b) 2·5 cu. ft., (c) 2·5 cu. ft.
15.　C_2H_2.

Chapter XXVI

4.　(b) 6·05 grm. copper, 3 95 grm. copper oxide.

Chapter XXX

14.　PbO_2.

Chapter XXXIII

7.　79·2,　$CrCl_3$.　　　　　8.　89·3 c.c

Chapter XXXIV

3.　$1 : 1\frac{2}{3} : 1\frac{1}{4}$.

Miscellaneous

17.　26·67.　　　　　18.　$6H_2O$.
24.　25%.　　　　　　26.　12.
53.　66·1%.

INDEX

CG*